# AGRICULTURE

## THE SCIENCE AND PRACTICE OF FARMING

# AGRICULTURE

## THE SCIENCE AND PRACTICE
## OF FARMING

JAMES A. S. WATSON, K.B.

AND

JAMES A. MORE

**ELEVENTH EDITION**

REVISED AND ENLARGED BY

JAMES A. McMILLAN
C.B.E., B.Sc.
*Lately Director of the*
*National Agricultural Advisory Service*

OLIVER & BOYD
EDINBURGH AND LONDON

OLIVER AND BOYD LTD

Tweeddale Court
Edinburgh

39A Welbeck Street
London W. 1

First Published 1924
Eleventh Edition 1962

PRINTED IN GREAT BRITAIN BY
OLIVER AND BOYD LTD., EDINBURGH

# PREFACE TO ELEVENTH EDITION

It is now forty years since this book was planned and the task of writing was begun. My co-author, J. A. More, wrote Parts 1 and 2 while I undertook the remainder.

At the time in question almost nothing had been written, in English, on Farm Organisation and Management, and my treatment of the subject was based on a large work, by Prof. Hugo Werner of the Berlin Agricultural High School, whose course of lectures I had attended in 1908-9. After an exchange of scripts and much discussion and emendation, the first edition went to press, and appeared in 1924. It was kindly received both by teachers and students.

The rapid acceleration of farming progress during these last forty years has necessitated frequent and often drastic revision, and it has been necessary to enlist the assistance of an increasing number of specialists in the various branches of the subject. Those who have helped with the present edition are: W. J. West (Farm Machinery), Drs G. D. H. Bell and J. L. Fyfe (Plant Breeding), C. V. Dadd (Crops), Dr K. L. Blaxter (Animal Nutrition). Drs C. C. Thiel and F. H. Dodd and P. A. Clough (Milk Secretion, Milking and Equipment for Milking), C. T. Riley (Poultry) and W. E. Jones (Farm Organisation and Management).

Having now passed the proverbial three score years and ten, I have felt it necessary to hand over the task of general editor, and have gladly done so to my erst-while pupil, J. A. McMillan who, with a Scottish background and after experience in Yorkshire and the eastern counties of England, like myself ended his official career as Director of the National Agricultural Advisory Service for England and Wales.

James A. S. Watson

# CONTENTS

PART 3

# FARM LIVE STOCK

# PART 4

# FARM ORGANISATION AND MANAGEMENT

# ILLUSTRATIONS
## PLATES

## TEXT FIGURES

# PART 1

# THE SOIL AND ITS MANAGEMENT

# CHAPTER 1

# SOIL FORMATION
# AND NATURAL SOIL TYPES

SOIL is produced from rock by the process of weathering and by the activities of plants, animals and man. Primitive or igneous rocks, formed by the solidification of the magma in the process of the cooling of the earth, consist of aggregates of mineral crystals which are large or small according to the rate at which cooling took place. Each mineral is a chemical compound with specific chemical and physical properties. Igneous rocks are very stable when kept in a dry atmosphere and at constant temperature, but as soon as they are exposed to changing temperatures and alternating wetting and drying, slow processes of disintegration and decomposition set in.

The weathering of a rock is generally due to a combination of physical and chemical actions, but it seems best to consider the two separately.

**Physical Weathering.**—Firstly are processes that result in physical breakdown, *i.e.* those producing much the same result as if the solid rock had been blasted and the fragments ground in a hammer mill.

1. When a bare rock surface is exposed to direct sunlight it heats up rapidly and, when the sun sets, cools again very fast. Under desert conditions the daily range of temperature at the exposed surface has been known to exceed 100° F. Since the different minerals that make up a rock have different coefficients of expansion, and since the surface may become very hot while the interior is still cool (or *vice versa*), it will be clear that great internal stresses must be set up and that the rock will split and ultimately crumble.

2. Under moist temperate conditions the chief disintegrating force is that of freezing water. All rocks are more or less porous, and most have joints and bedding-planes through which rain gradually seeps. As is well known, ice occupies more space than the water from which it has been formed, and the expansion pressure is very high; at −1° C. it amounts to about 1500 lb. per sq. in. It will thus be clear why rocks, exposed to rain and to alternate freezing and thawing, must break up. If the disintegration of building stone is to be prevented the surface must be waterproofed.

3. A great part of Britain (about as far south as the Thames Valley) was covered during one or other of the glacial periods by a

heavy cap of ice. Now when a great weight of ice rests upon a land surface the lowest layer is liquefied by the pressure from above, and the whole mass begins to slide almost imperceptibly downhill. The moving ice carries with it boulders, gravel and sand, which grind and erode the rock surfaces lying below. Thus is produced a mass of broken material which is deposited where the ice melts. This material, called glacial drift, covers large areas throughout the cool temperate regions. Its actual nature depends on the character of the parent rock, sandstones giving rise to glacial sands or gravels, while fine-grained rocks yield a mass of soft mud containing large and small stones which is called " till," or " boulder clay," in the better and more restricted sense.

4. Under desert conditions rock surfaces are eroded by the action of wind-blown sand.

5. In wet and hilly regions the streams, by rolling stones and gravel along their courses, grind down the larger into smaller particles. A similar action is produced by tidal and wave movements along sea coasts.

**Chemical Weathering.**—In order to understand the chemical changes that occur in weathering we must know something of the chemical composition of the primitive crystalline rocks that form the greater part of the earth's crust. In some places such rocks form the surface layers and thus, by primary weathering, give rise to the local soils. In other places they are covered by strata of sedimentary rocks—sandstones, limestones and shales—which have been derived by previous weathering from crystalline rocks. These sedimentary rocks give rise to soils by secondary weathering. In either case the mineral matter of the soil traces back ultimately to the minerals found in the crystalline rocks.

Of these minerals the most abundant are the *felspars*, which are double silicates of alumina with potash or soda or lime or some combination of the last three. Orthoclase felspar, for example, has the formula $K_2O$, $Al_2O_3$, $6SiO_2$. It has been estimated that the felspars, as a group, constitute some 55 or 60 per cent. of the earth's crust. Felspars in general, and more especially those containing lime, weather readily.

Next in order of abundance is the group of complex silicates of iron with lime and magnesia—*hornblende, augite, olivine*—which constitute about one sixth, by weight, of the earth's crust. They are the main source of the iron compounds which occur largely in most soils.

Third, making up about an eighth of the total weight of the earth's crust, is *quartz*, which is the crystalline form of silica ($SiO_2$). It occurs in quite large crystals in the coarser grained igneous rocks (such as many granites) but in other cases as scarcely visible particles. It is colourless when pure, very hard, and extremely resistant to chemical change. It should be noted in passing that secondary forms of silica occur in sedimentary rocks, the flints in chalk being the most familiar.

The *micas* (3·5 per cent.) are complex silicates of potash, or of potash and soda, with alumina and a small amount of ferrous iron. They differ from the felspars in having a flaky instead of a granular structure and in being much more resistant to chemical change.

*Calcium carbonate* occurs only sparingly in crystalline rocks, in the form of calcite or Iceland Spar. Most of the lime that occurs naturally in soils derived from igneous rocks comes not from this source but from the breakdown of the felspars and the hornblende-augite group of minerals. Marble, limestone and chalk are all secondary rocks made up of the skeletons of molluscs, protozoa and other aquatic animals.

Of minerals occurring in relatively small amount the most important are the forms of *apatite*, which are double salts of lime with phosphate and some other acid radical, *e.g.* carbonate, chloride. The apatites are the ultimate source of the phosphate of soils.

As already mentioned, the most resistant to chemical change among all the rock-forming minerals is quartz. It is only very slightly soluble in pure water and little more so in water containing carbonic or other acid. In general the quartz originally present in the native rock remains in the mature soil as grains of sand.

The most important chemical change that occurs in the whole group of rock silicates *e.g.* felspars, is *hydrolysis*. This is brought about by the very slow action of rain water, which of course contains a small amount of carbonic acid. The process is complicated and is not fully understood. Broadly, however, the alkalis and alkaline earths (soda, potash, lime and magnesia) are split off as hydroxides and go into solution in the soil water as bicarbonates. Under wet climates and with free drainage of the material, the soda, lime and magnesia are rapidly washed out and reach the sea, but the potash, as will be more fully explained later (p. 22), is much less completely removed. Under dry conditions some of these bases, especially soda, form various soluble salts which remain as such in the resulting soils, but the bulk of the lime is precipitated in a layer situated in the zone to which rain ordinarily penetrates. This calcium carbonate layer is characteristic of the soils of the drier regions.

Under wet tropical conditions the silicic acid, which is the other product of hydrolysis, is also largely washed out so that the main end products of silicate weathering are hydrated alumina and hydrated iron oxide—generally spoken of together as sesquioxides. More commonly the main residues are hydrated silicates of alumina and iron, with other still more complex substances. It will be obvious from the nature of the process that the weathering of the silicates will give rise to very finely divided material. This constitutes the *clay fraction* of the soil on which many of its important properties depend. The other chemical change of importance is the oxidation of ferrous to ferric compounds.

It is the various hydrated ferric oxides that impart to soils the common reddish and orange colours. If air is excluded from the weathered material, by lack of free drainage, this oxidation does not take place, and the soil colour is then usually a bluish grey.

It should be noted that the weathering of soils is helped to some extent by the action of living organisms. For instance tree roots penetrate any fissures that may occur in the rocks that they encounter and help in the process of disintegration. Again, the fine roots of plants excrete carbonic and other acids, which increase the solvent power of soil water. The carbonic acid content of soil water is further greatly increased through the decay, both within the soil and on the soil surface, of plant remains. Important also is the action of earthworms which occur in all except lime-deficient and waterlogged soils, and which pass great quantities of soil through their bodies and turn it over to the action of the weather; by their constant burrowing they increase the permeability of the weathering material to air and water, and they cause some actual breakdown of particles by the rubbing action that takes place in their gizzards. The addition of organic matter to the mineral soil, through the growth and death of animals and plants, is a very important part of the final process of soil formation and is discussed below.

**Secondary Weathering.**—In the case of sedimentary rocks the type of weathering will vary according to their character. Sedimentary rocks are formed from previously weathered material that has been carried away by wind or water, generally re-assorted in the process and often cemented together. In the ordinary process of denudation of a mountainous region the fast flowing streams roll away stones of considerable size and carry gravel, sand, silt and fine mud in suspension as well as lime and other substances in solution. As the velocity of the running water declines the coarser material falls first, and if, in process of time, it is recemented, the resulting rock will be a conglomerate or " pudding stone." There will follow, in order, materials that go to form coarse grained and fine grained sandstones, and those that will produce shales or mudstones. Finally, far out at sea, the calcium will be extracted by marine animals to form their skeletons, and these will accumulate to form chalk or limestone.

If a coarse grained sandstone is cemented by calcium carbonate the immediate result of the weathering will be the removal in solution of the lime as bicarbonate, with the production of a coarse sand, but this may be altered by further weathering. In the case of chalk, the bulk of the material is removed in solution, leaving behind such other constituents as pieces of flint and quantities of fine clay. Naturally in the case of soil material that has been repeatedly weathered, such as that derived from the tertiary strata of the lower Thames Valley, the main constituents will be the end products—quartz sand and the hydrated silicates of alumina and iron; at the other extreme, the boulder clays of Aberdeenshire, derived from granite, give soils containing many fragments of scarcely altered felspar and mica.

**Sedentary and Transported Soils.**—It is worth noting that the parent material of a given soil may or may not be derived from the underlying rock. We have already seen that a great part of Britain was glaciated, and it will readily be understood that the moving ice not only ground down the rocky material that it encountered but also moved this over greater or lesser distances.   In some cases, indeed, the glacial material is derived from local rock, but in other cases the deposit has come from a considerable distance.   Again, we have many alluvial soils, such as valley gravels laid down by the fast-flowing rivers of glacial times, brick earths and silts laid down along the lower reaches of these rivers or on shelving coasts, and the estuarine muds that produced the Scottish Carses.   In the larger land-masses dust carried by the wind from desert regions, and dropped in areas of moderate rainfall, have produced deep deposits of *loess*, which is the parent material of many fertile soils—*e.g.* in China and the United States.   Apart from long-distance transport there is the more limited movement of material downhill.   In sloping fields, especially such as have been long under cultivation, the soil at the lower end is often derived from rock lying farther up.

**Soil Humus.**—The weathered products of rock do not constitute a soil.   Over a very wide range of temperature and moisture conditions plants establish themselves very soon after weathering begins, and the mineral material thus becomes mixed with plant remains.   These remains, in process of decay, form an addition to the products of rock weathering. Moreover the decay of organic matter is caused by the activity of vast numbers of micro-organisms—bacteria, moulds and other fungi and protozoa.   Soil is therefore a mixture of organic and inorganic material containing a large and complex population of living things.

Where conditions prevent the complete oxidation of plant remains, dead material may accumulate until a position is reached where the greater part of the soil material is in fact organic matter.   This happens wherever air is excluded by the constant presence of water.   If the said water contains little in the way of bases the vegetation is restricted to mosses, certain rushes and other particular species of plants, and the material produced is known as *peat*.   A different type of material—" *Black Fen* "—is produced where reeds, sedges, and other aquatic vegetation grow and decay in lime rich water.   A third type accumulates under dry conditions where the soil is highly acid, the reason being that the organisms which cause oxidation and decay are very inactive in a highly acid medium.   The material then produced is best called *raw humus*. With the presence together of air, moisture and lime is produced the substance known as *mild humus*.   This complex substance, though it is constantly wasting by decay and whose amount can be maintained only by the addition of more plant remains, has an important influence on the structure and the fertility of the soil. Briefly a mixture of inorganic material with mild humus tends readily to form a granular mass of porous " crumbs," the individual crumbs being spongy and therefore capable of holding a good amount of water, but being separated by interconnecting spaces which admit air to the mass. Since the presence of both air and moisture in the soil is necessary to the growth of most crop plants, it follows that the production and maintenance of a good " crumb structure " in the soil is an important aim of the farmer. It should be noted that certain combinations of mineral particles are capable by themselves of being brought into good structural condition, while others are not. The agricultural or horticultural value of a soil may depend largely on maintaining a balance between the organic and inorganic constituents, and the amount of humus that is required varies with the type of mineral matter.

To exercise its proper influence in the soil the humus must be mixed with the inorganic material. Obviously if land is cultivated this admixture will be achieved. In land that is not cultivated the mixing is carried out, under temperate climatic conditions, mainly by earthworms, whose numbers and activity are closely dependent on the presence of lime in the soil.

**Natural Soil Types.**—It will be clear that the general character of a soil will depend to a considerable extent, and for a considerable period after weathering has taken place, on the nature of the parent material. Thus a coarse grained sandstone will generally produce a sandy soil, and a stratum of shale a heavy soil. Most British soils, since they date only from the last glacial period, are relatively young and the influence of the parent material on the soil characteristics is marked. On the other hand, in level areas, situated in warm regions where glaciation did not occur, the soils are very old, and their nature depends less upon that of the parent rock and more upon the type of weathering that has occurred and the type of the natural vegetation. It is therefore possible to base a useful classification of the world's soils on the various types of climatic conditions under which they have been formed. While it is impossible in this work to give an account of all the main world types, it is nevertheless worth illustrating the principles of classification by describing and explaining a number of examples.

We have already seen that the four most abundant products of weathering are: (1) the strong bases (lime, soda, potash and magnesia); (2) silica; (3) the hydrated oxides of alumina and iron (generally called the sesquioxides); and (4) the clay minerals, *i.e.* the hydrated silicates of aluminium and iron and related substances. We have seen that, by hydrolysis and other processes, the strong bases are quickly broken away from their original combinations but that the subsequent fate of three of these (lime, soda and magnesia) depends mainly on the amount of rain that passes through the soil. Where, as in Britain, the total rainfall substantially exceeds the total evaporation it will be obvious that, if the soil is freely drained, the bases will be rapidly leached out and carried away in the drainage water.   One consequence is that the organic acids which are produced by the decay of plant remains will not be neutralised.   Moreover the clay minerals, which behave as acid radicals will, in the absence of bases, combine with hydrogen and so come to behave like weak acids. The soils will thus all tend to be acid.   Three types are recognized, *viz. Podzols, Grey-Brown Podzolic Soils*, and *Brown Earths*.   The second, being intermediate between the other two, need not be specially described.

**Podzols** are produced where leaching is very heavy.   As would be expected, they occur in our wettest areas.   But they are also found in relatively dry districts where the parent materials have little capacity to retain moisture, *i.e.* coarse sands or gravels.   The natural vegetation is coniferous forest.   When this is felled the trees are replaced by heaths, bracken, gorse, wire-grass and other highly acid-tolerant species.   Again, on account of the high acidity, earthworms are generally absent, with the result that the pine needles or other plant debris decay only very slowly, and form a clearly defined surface layer of raw humus.   The relatively strong organic acids derived from the decay of this material not only remove any remaining strong bases from the top layer of mineral soil but also dissolve and carry down the sesquioxides.   Thus is produced a layer of bleached material often resembling silver sand.   Below this is a layer of precipitated humic material and, still lower, a horizon containing a heavy deposit of sesquioxides and generally brown, orange or yellowish in colour.   In some cases the sesquioxide layer is cemented into something resembling a coarse grained paving stone, which is called " iron pan." Underneath the sesquioxide layer is a horizon of parent material.   It will readily be understood that the unimproved podzol is of little or no value except for such purposes as heath gardening, azalea growing or coniferous forest.   Methods of improvement are described in Ch. 3 (p. 51).

**Brown Earth Soils,** whether by reason of lower rainfall, higher evaporation or more retentive parent material, are less heavily leached than podzols.   They are not rich in bases and contain no free calcium carbonate, but they are not extremely acid.   The natural vegetation is deciduous forest or scrub.   The leaf mould which covers the surface is a mild humus and, since earthworms are usually present in numbers, the humus derived from the leaf fall is rather intimately mixed with the general body of the soil. There is no leaching of the sesquioxides and therefore no separation into the pale upper and deeply coloured lower layers that characterise the podzols. In general, however, there has been some downwash of the finer particles, so that the subsoil has a heavier texture than the top soil.   Brown earth soils, with moderate applications of lime and phosphate, are easily convertible into good pasture land.   Many of them require only a little improvement in drainage to make them suitable for the general run of arable crops, but some are too heavy for all-round arable farming.

Not all British soils that happen to be freely drained are deficient in bases generally or in lime. It is true that lime deficiency can occur even in soils that overlie chalk or limestone, but this is normal only where the configuration is flat. On slopes the downward slip of the soil is generally sufficient to bring lime into the upper layers. Again, in many of our soils that are derived from glacial deposits the original supplies of bases are as yet far from being exhausted. Even where no calcium carbonate is present, enough lime is set free by the weathering of felspars and other minerals to keep the base-status satisfactory. Some of our valley gravels, again, contain a proportion of limestone chips. Shallow soils on the chalk and limestone formations can be kept " sweet " by occasional deep ploughings. But though these exceptions are important it is still true that a very large proportion of British farm land can be kept fertile only by repeated applications of lime.

**Peat and Fen Soils.**—Where rainfall exceeds evaporation and where drainage is not sufficient to remove the surplus, the soil becomes water-logged, oxygen is excluded, and the process of soil formation follows an entirely different course. It has already been said that the rate of decay of organic matter is dependent on the supply of bases as well as of air. But whatever the position in regard to bases, the decay of organic matter takes a different course according to the supply of free oxygen. Under anaerobic conditions change still takes place; there is considerable formation of marsh gas and carbon dioxide, which escape. But the remaining carbon compounds remain as a brown or black mass and, after the first few years, change becomes extremely slow. Where lime is lacking the final product is peat. Typical peats are formed from the sphagnum moss and other plants that grow in sour-water bogs. Peat bogs " grow " because the annual addition of fresh vegetable remains, small as this is, exceeds the annual loss by decomposition. The final product is, of course, very acid and contains only a small amount of mineral matter. Peats can be made productive of ordinary crops only by drastic and costly treatments, which are described in Ch. 3 (p. 50).

Where an area is waterlogged with hard water from rivers or springs, as in many lowland marshes, it supports a different type of vegetation— reeds, sedges and the larger rushes. There is a relatively large annual addition of vegetable matter, which contains a considerable amount of mineral substances such as lime, potash and phosphate. The resulting soil, properly known as black fen ("muck soil" in U.S.A. and Canada), while it has certain defects (see p. 29) is much more useful raw material for agriculture than peat. Naturally, in both cases the first operation must be artificial drainage.

**Gley Soils.**[1]—Many fields that lie reasonably dry in normal summers are often waterlogged or even flooded in winter. Such land can be used for summer pasturage or as hay meadow, but the herbage consists of

---

[1] " Gleying " is a term used to describe the processes that cause the reduction of ferric oxide and also the formation of a thin glaze on the sides of the fissures.

tussock grass and other unnutritious grasses, rushes, sedges and water-loving herbs such as meadow-sweet.  Where the herbage is neither grazed nor mown, alders and willows tend to establish themselves and the herbaceous plants may gradually be suppressed.  The cause of the inadequate drainage may be the impervious nature of the parent material, *e.g.* the Oxford, Kimmeridge, Gault, Lias or Wealden Clays that cover a large area in Midland and South-eastern England.  But similar conditions occur in flats and hollows where the permanent water table lies too high and approaches or reaches the surface from time to time.

The roots of ordinary crop plants do not penetrate far into stagnant subsoil water, since this contains no free oxygen.  Hence the black top soil, which contains abundant humus, is shallow.  The deeper subsoil which is permanently waterlogged is of a uniform bluish grey colour caused by the presence of ferrous compounds.  Between the black top layer and the bluish grey subsoil is a mottled layer of grey and red orange, the mottling being due to the alternation between aerobic and anaerobic conditions, with alternate oxidation and reduction of the iron compounds to the ferric and ferrous states.  Since the mottled zone represents the range of fluctuation of the water table, valuable information on drainage conditions can be obtained by examining the soil profile even when the soil is at its driest.

Gley soils in their natural condition are of low value.  Autumn sown crops are frequently drowned out in winter and suitable conditions for spring sowing are not obtained until the season is too far advanced. The better grasses and clovers fail to compete with the indigenous vegetation, which latter is of low nutritive value.  Again, the better grassland plants suffer from summer drought; their deeper roots are killed by winter waterlogging, and new root growth is not rapid enough to follow the water table as it sinks in summer.  When artificially drained some gley soils become extremely fertile; many reclaimed lowland marshes, where the parent material is a rich alluvial silt, are among the best of our arable areas.  Where, on the other hand, the parent material is a very tenacious clay, the land is of limited value even when the necessary and costly drainage works have been carried out.

A range of soil types very different from those with which we are familiar in Britain is produced in areas where all the rain that falls is again evaporated.  Here no leaching occurs, so that the resulting soils are extremely rich in bases.  One of the best known is the *Black Earth* (Tshernozem), which covers a large part of the Ukraine and some part of the Prairie Provinces of Canada.  The conditions are too dry for any kind of natural tree growth, and the vegetation is a short or medium growth of grass—" prairie " or " steppe."  The grass dries up and becomes dormant during the dry midsummer period.  The top two or three feet of soil is a dark brown or black earth containing a considerable amount—10 or 12 per cent.—of humus, with a clearly marked crumb structure.  The great depth of the top soil is explained by the fact that the grass roots penetrate very deeply in search of water. Near the bottom of the black humic layer, or just below it, is a clearly marked horizon with a high content of calcium carbonate, marking the depth to which rain water ordinarily penetrates. Black-earth soils have immense reserves of mineral nutrients, and, since the decay of organic matter is stopped during a great part of the year by frost or drought, there is also a large reserve of humus, which liberates a considerable amount of nitrogen during the moist warm period of early summer. The crops grown are those with low water requirements, particularly spring wheat, barley and linseed. Yields are closely dependent upon spring rain. Summer fallows are taken at frequent intervals, commonly every third year, in order to store up the season's rainfall. Where the parent material is clay or silt, crop yields are relatively steady, but wherever this is sandy, yields are erratic and there is risk of wind erosion.

In most of the drier regions of the world patches of saline or alkaline soil occur. Most of these occupy hollows in which seepage water accumulates, during wet periods or at the time of the spring thaw, and is later evaporated. Such patches, owing to the high accumulation of sodium salts (chloride or sometimes carbonate), are sterile.

As an example of a soil produced under the other extreme of climate we may mention the laterite soil that is formed under very wet tropical conditions beneath a growth of evergreen tropical forest. Leaching is very heavy, so that not only are the strong bases removed but also the silicic acid set free by the hydrolysis of silicates. Laterites, owing to their high sesquioxide content and relatively low content of true clay, have a less markedly acid reaction than temperate soils of correspondingly low base-content. The organic matter added to the surface by the leaf fall is very rapidly decomposed, partly because of the warm humid conditions and partly through the activity of termites. The lack of humus and the high content of ferric oxide account for their characteristic red colour. Owing to the intensity of the weathering processes laterites, where they occur on level sites, are of immense depth. The texture is generally friable and granular rather than clayey. The luxuriance of the natural vegetation gives a very false impression of the fertility of the soil. The fact is that, under natural conditions, the very small reserves of plant food are very rapidly turned over. When shallow rooting annual crops are substituted for trees, and where fertilizers are not used, the productivity of the soil declines very rapidly.

## CONSTITUTION AND GENERAL PROPERTIES OF SOILS

**Soil and Subsoil.**—We have seen that natural soils that have been long undisturbed are composed of rather clearly defined layers or " horizons." Soil scientists distinguish three main horizons—*viz.* the uppermost (A), from which material has been removed by leaching; the second (B), in which has been deposited some of the material removed from (A); and a third (C), which consists of the parent material, *e.g.* the partly disintegrated rock. These main horizons are divided as required by the character of the soil in question; for instance, a typical podzol, such as has been described above, would be divided as follows:—

$A_0$, Raw humus layer.

$A_1$, Mineral soil containing dark-coloured humus.

$A_2$, Mineral soil bleached by removal of sesquioxides.

$B_1$, Dark-coloured layer containing deposited humus.

$B_2$, Yellow or rusty layer containing the precipitated sesquioxides.

C, Parent material.

It will be easily understood that such a natural structure, developed during centuries, will be completely destroyed when the soil is repeatedly cultivated, and even by a single ploughing. On the other hand a new structure develops under tillage in which there is a more or less sharp distinction between the top soil (or soil proper) and the subsoil. The most obvious distinction is in colour, the change taking place in arable land at about the usual depth of ploughing and in grass at the limit of penetration of the mass of grass roots. The top soil is dark because of its high content of decaying vegetable matter (humus) while the subsoil varies from reddish or yellowish to a pale grey tint. Another usual difference is that the top soil is coarser grained than the subsoil, the difference being caused by the washing down of a proportion of the finer clay and silt particles; but in fertile limey soils this tendency is counteracted by the action of earthworms, which produce, by their casts, a continuous top-dressing of fine soil brought up from below. In general, again, the top soil will be richer in nitrogen and phosphate than the subsoil, since manures and fertilizers are largely held in the former; but the subsoil may frequently contain more potash. Counts of micro-organisms show, as would be expected, much higher numbers in the top soil than in the subsoil.

**Soil Particles**.—Typical soils (excepting peats and black fen types) are composed largely of particles and fragments of mineral matter. We must remember that these particles are not by any means all free, one from another—indeed it is obvious that they are often bound together to form clods or crumbs. Nevertheless the character of a soil depends very much upon the sizes of the ultimate particles of which it is composed. If, by suitable means, we break up the clods and crumbs of a soil, pick off the stones and remove the small gravel by means of a 2 mm. sieve, the remaining fine material may be sorted out into size groups. The largest may be separated by sieving but the remainder are separated by sedimentation. The size groups as now distinguished by soil scientists in most countries are:—

|  | Diameter |
|---|---|
| Coarse sand | 2·0 to 0·2 mm. |
| Fine sand | 0·2 to 0·02 mm. |
| Silt | 0·02 to 0·002 mm. |
| Clay | less than 0·002 mm. |

The wide variation in mechanical make up that is encountered among British soils may be illustrated by the following mechanical analyses.[1]

Percentage Composition

|  | Heavy Loam, Caernarvon | Medium Loam, Monmouth | Light Loam, Caernarvon | Coarse Sand, Cheshire |
|---|---|---|---|---|
| Coarse sand | 8·3 | 9·3 | 21·0 | 52·0 |
| Fine sand | 17·8 | 43·9 | 44·7 | 32·4 |
| Silt | 34·0 | 23·4 | 16·0 | 7·0 |
| Clay | 39·9 | 23·4 | 18·3 | 8·6 |

An important distinction is to be drawn between sand and silt on the one hand and clay on the other. The coarser fractions in general form the " skeleton " of the soil. They generally consist of clearly defined particles without colloidal properties—i.e. they do not imbibe water and swell or become plastic when wet, nor bind together into hard clods as they dry. They do not enter into combination with the soil bases. Only rarely do we find any highly reactive material in the form of large particles, and then generally in those classed as silt.

**Clay.**—Apart from humus, which is discussed below, the clay fraction very largely determines both the physical and chemical characteristics of the soil. Some of the properties of clay arise from the enormous area of surface presented by a material that is so minutely divided; the total surface area of the particles in a cubic foot of clay runs to several acres. Again, clay possesses certain of the properties that we associate with colloids such as gelatine. When a small lump of dry clay is wetted it swells by absorbing water; when the water is dried out the clay again contracts. This explains the familiar fact that clay soils open up wide and deep cracks as they dry out in summer. Clay becomes plastic if it is moved when wet, can be kneaded into any shape and retains this shape on drying. The clods that are formed when a clay soil dries may be so hard that they cannot be broken with ordinary implements.

It should be noted that clays with a high ratio of silica to sesquioxides have more pronounced colloidal properties than such as are found in the

[1] From A. D. Hall, *The Soil*, Fifth Edition, by G. W. Robinson, 1945.

tropics, in which the proportion of sesquioxide is high and that of silica low.

Colloids when dispersed in water are in what is called the " sol " condition, and when the particles aggregate together they form a " gel." If a drop of turbid clay water be examined under a high power microscope it will be seen that the particles are in rapid " Brownian " motion, but if a drop of acid is added the particles move together to form little clots. The formation of these clots is called flocculation, and their redispersal is called deflocculation.    Something like this occurs under field conditions.    Thus if clay remains long wet, and especially if it is disturbed when there is enough moisture to make it plastic, it is deflocculated and cannot then be crumbled.    Exposure to frost and thaw, with the addition of lime, acids or neutral salts, all tend to bring about the desirable condition of flocculation; but alkalis cause deflocculation, and salts, such as sodium chloride or nitrate of soda, by yielding free alkali on hydrolysis, are therefore harmful.    The alkali residues that accumulate after frequent applications of nitrate of soda produce a very sticky condition in the soil, and an even more marked effect, which may take years to clear up, is produced when a clay soil is flooded with sea water.    The point is that the clay particle behaves as a weak acid radical which can enter into combination with bases such as sodium and calcium or hydrogen.    Thus we can speak of " calcium clay " which readily forms crumbs and " sodium clay " which has a very high capacity to take up water and then forms a sticky and impervious mass.    This cannot be brought into condition suitable for plant growth except by such means as the application of gypsum and exposure to leaching.    The presence of a large proportion of " hydrogen clay " implies an acid reaction, a condition that is unfavourable to the growth of most plants (see p. 22).    The important property of clay and other colloids of absorbing and retaining potash, ammonia and other ions is dealt with later (p. 22).

The power of crumb formation by clay soils is very important in relation to the growth of crops.  So long as the clay particles are aggregated into crumbs the soil behaves as if it were composed of quite coarse particles. Water percolates freely through the relatively large spaces, and air is drawn in as the water escapes below; but water is held in considerable quantity within the crumbs themselves.    Crumb formation on heavy soils, besides being greatly facilitated by the addition of lime, is also aided by the presence of humus.    A few years ago research was directed to the use of certain synthetic plastics, which it was hoped might act as soil conditioners and improve crumb structure.    Their beneficial effects were found to be of short duration and they were too costly for use by the farmer.

**Humus.**—All soils contain a greater or smaller proportion of complex organic substances, derived from plant roots and other plant and animal remains, which are in process of conversion into simpler substances.    This organic matter may be roughly divided into (1) material in which decomposition has not yet proceeded far, which retains its cell structure and which may be called fresh organic matter, and (2) the dark coloured mixture of partly decomposed material and decomposition products to which the term humus properly belongs.

Fresh organic matter has an important influence on the texture of the soil. When added to heavy clay it improves aeration and drainage so that its effects, in moderate quantity, are beneficial; when added in quantity to sandy soils it tends to increase their porosity, which is already too great for the best results. Until its decomposition has gone some way its presence therefore tends to accentuate the ill effects of drought.

True humus, which consists of the colloidal residue of organic matter that has been attacked and partly decomposed by bacteria and fungi, has far-reaching effects on soil texture and fertility. Whenever it is present in considerable quantity it imparts its black or dark-brown colour to the soil, and since dark coloured materials absorb more of the sun's heat than light coloured ones, its presence tends to raise the soil temperature. Moreover, in well aerated soils humus is constantly undergoing oxidation, with liberation of simple compounds of nitrogen which can be taken up by plant roots. Most important is the fact that humus has many of the properties of mineral colloids—it increases the soil's power of retaining moisture and it absorbs and holds plant nutrient substances.

When organic matter is added to light soils the resulting humus tends to bind the mineral particles into crumbs which absorb and hold water like miniature sponges. Like clay, humus can give cohesion to soils that would otherwise fall into their constituent particles; but unlike clay, it does not give the soil plastic properties nor does it set to a hard consistency on drying. If lime be also present, humus aids flocculation of the clay colloids and promotes improved texture; but if lime is absent, humus will rather add to the stickiness of a clay soil.

It has already been noted that raw humus in the absence of lime imparts to the soil a strongly acid reaction which is unfavourable to the growth of most higher plants. It should also be pointed out that the presence in the soil of both oxygen and lime, which are essential to the healthy growth of most crop plants, tends to promote bacterial action and thus causes the oxidation and disappearance of humus. Hence if a soil is to be productive a relatively high rate of loss of humus is inevitable, and repeated additions of organic matter are necessary if the humus content is to be maintained at a high level. The level to be aimed at depends on a number of factors, such as the nature of the mineral fraction of the soil, the local climate and the types of crops intended to be grown. The means of maintaining the humus content include the use of farmyard manure and composts and the ploughing in of crop residues, grass swards and green manuring crops.

**Pore-space and Density.**—It is obvious that a soil, consisting of particles of solid matter, must contain a considerable amount of pore-space. The amount is indicated by comparing the " apparent density " of an air-dry soil with the true specific gravity of its particles. Neglecting such soils as contain much organic matter, which are relatively light, common figures for apparent density run from about 1·1 to 1·5 (or say 70 to 95 lb. per cu. ft.) compared with a true specific gravity of the particles of about 2·6.

The following figures[1] give the apparent density, weight per cubic foot, and percentage pore space of a number of soils. The last column shows the total weight of top soil (*i.e.* of the top 9 in.) in tons per acre.

|  | Apparent Density | Weight, Lb. per Cubic Foot | Percentage Pore Space | Top Soil per Acre, Tons |
|---|---|---|---|---|
| Heavy clay | 1·062 | 66·4 | 57·0 | 963 |
| Light loam | 1·222 | 76·4 | 51·0 | 1107 |
| Light sand | 1·266 | 79·2 | 49·0 | 1143 |
| Sandy peat | 0·782 | 49·0 | 68·5 | 705 |

In a soil composed of particles of varying size, the pore space may be less than in one of more uniform particle size, since the smaller particles fit into the spaces that occur between the larger. The pore space will depend on the arrangement of the particles; indeed it can be shown mathematically that, with spherical particles, the pore space may vary between a minimum of 25·95 per cent. and a maximum of 47·64 per cent. according to the mode of arrangement. It is a well known fact that when we dig a hole the excavated soil may be considerably more or less than the amount required to refill; in other words, it is rarely that the soil can be disturbed and re-packed without alteration of the pore space in one direction or the other.

It will be seen that, in the first three soils in the table above, the pore space is in inverse proportion to the size of the particle. This is a usual finding, one explanation being that, whereas the weight of an individual coarse sand particle is sufficient to ensure fairly close packing, that of the small clay or humus particle is not sufficient. Another explanation is that heavy soils have a marked tendency to form aggregates or clods, with spaces not only between the individual particles but also between the aggregates.

**Soil Structure.**—Coarse sandy soils show very little cohesion even when wet, and as they dry fall into their constituent particles. Water percolates quickly down their pores and carries down in solution not only nitrates but also considerable amounts of potash. The addition of organic matter binds together the particles but its effect is short lived because, under the

[1] From A. D. Hall, *The Soil*, Fifth Edition, by G. W. Robinson, 1945.

highly aerobic conditions that prevail, humus is quickly destroyed by oxidation.

Again, a soil composed mainly of sand and silt, with little clay, fails to form stable aggregates so that, for example, an autumn seed bed is broken down and closely packed by the winter rains; on drying in the following spring a surface crust may form, aeration of the soil is restricted, and root development is therefore impeded. The farmer expresses the difficulty by saying that such a soil will not " hold its clod."

The other extreme may be illustrated by a heavy clay soil, under pasture, in time of drought. Its high colloid content gives the soil great cohesion and causes it to shrink both vertically and laterally, resulting in wide cracks, widely spaced. Rain, when it comes, flows down these cracks to the subsoil, failing to wet the root zone, so that the grass makes a very slow recovery.

Where, however, colloidal material is present in moderate amount, and more particularly where there is a good supply of humus as well as colloidal clay, the skilful cultivator can produce any one of a variety of different structures; for example, he can have his land, during the winter, in unbroken furrow, and so ensure that the winter rain will penetrate easily to the subsoil; he can have the land in " summer clod," *i.e.* in hard lumps that dry out so completely that enclosed pieces of plant tissue are killed by desiccation; or again, he can have a seed bed of any desired degree of fineness with, as is often to be desired, the coarser clods above and the finer crumbs below.

Unless there is a variety of materials in the various soil horizons (in which case they can be mixed by deep ploughing) the cost of achieving a worth while change in the soil texture is usually prohibitive. Exceptionally, however, this is possible by claying, marling or warping (see pp. 50, 52 and 67).

Soils that have enough colloidal material to give a clearly defined structure are usually plastic within a certain range of moisture content. Above a given water content soil will form a liquid; below this level, and down to the lower limit of plasticity, the soil " pastes " and does not crumble when it is worked. The *plasticity number* of a soil is the difference between the moisture contents at the upper and lower levels of plasticity —*e.g.* if a soil begins to show the properties of a liquid at 55 per cent. moisture, and shows signs of crumbling when worked (or stirred with the foot) at 35 per cent. moisture, its plasticity number will be 20. Generally speaking, heavy and markedly plastic clays have plasticity numbers over 20, and feebly plastic soils have numbers below 10. Many useful soils fall within the 10 to 20 range.

A soil may quite properly be forked over or turned over by means of a suitable plough, when it is considerably above the lower plastic limit. Indeed, if it is specially desired to avoid crumbling, ploughing is best done under such conditions. But any rubbing, scraping or squeezing action, such as that produced by harrowing or rolling, must be avoided until the moisture has fallen below this limit, otherwise the soil will " paste " and " puddle " instead of crumbling.

**Soil Moisture.**—Since poor crops are more often due to unsatisfactory moisture conditions in the soil than to any other single cause it is necessary to consider the subject of soil moisture in some detail. The soil may be supplied with water by irrigation, by springs, by seepage from higher ground, or it may draw moisture from a shallow water table. Again, some moisture is received by condensation of water vapour from the atmosphere. Generally speaking, the only important source of supply is rain or snow.

Some of the facts about the behaviour of water in soil may be illustrated by simple laboratory experiments. We may, for instance, take four glass cylinders, with perforated bottoms, and fill each with different grades of particles such as medium and fine gravel, coarse and fine sand. If the bottoms of the cylinders are closed and water is poured in from above until it reaches the top, the amount of water added will measure the pore space in each case. If now the bottoms are opened water will begin to flow out, most quickly from the coarse gravel and most slowly from the fine sand. But it will be found that not all the water that was poured in will have drained out even after several days. If the drainage water from each cylinder is measured, the quantity retained in each case can be found. This will be greatest in the case of the fine sand and least in the coarse gravel. The difference is partly to be accounted for by the larger surface area to be wetted in the case of the finer material, but partly also by the fact that small soil pores, like fine capillary tubes, exercise a stronger hold on water than large pores or wide tubes.

If we refill the cylinders with dry material and, instead of wetting them from above, stand them in shallow water, we find that there is some upward movement of water in each case; in other words, the force of surface or capillary attraction can not only hold water against the force of gravity but can also move water upwards. In the case of the coarsest material the movement is practically instantaneous and very small, whereas in the finest the movement, while ultimately going a long way, will be relatively slow to begin with and will become progressively slower with increasing distance. There has been a good deal of dispute on the question as to how far the requirements of plants can be met by water that is raised by capillary action from the water table below. In very fine grained material the distance is very great, but it seems that beyond a height of more than two or three feet the rate of movement is so slow that the quantity moved in a period of drought must be negligible.

From what has been said earlier it will be clear that a quantity of gravel or sand cannot be regarded as a true large scale model of the soil. Natural soils contain not only crystalline particles but also particles of colloidal clay and humus, and others of hydrated ferric oxide, which all imbibe water and swell in the process, as does a piece of wetted gelatine. In ordinary soils, under field conditions, the greater part of the soil water is so held, *i.e.* as " imbibitional " moisture. If the colloids are " puddled " or dispersed they block up the pore spaces between the mineral particles so that water ceases to move at all. Imbibitional moisture, as would be expected, is very strongly held against the force of gravity, but if it be present in large amount, some can be drawn off by plant roots.

Thus far we have seen that water occurs in the soil in three forms, *viz.* (*a*) *imbibitional*, (*b*) *capillary*, which is held, by surface attraction, as a thin film surrounding the particles and as a filling of the finer pores, and (*c*) *gravitational*, which is in process of percolating downwards under the force of gravity. A fourth is *hygroscopic* moisture, which must shortly be discussed. If an oven dried soil is exposed to ordinary air it absorbs moisture and increases in weight by an amount that depends on the humidity of the air, the temperature and the nature of the soil itself. Quartz sand takes up only a trace of hygroscopic moisture, which is held as a film of molecular thickness on the surface. Colloidal material, like humus and clay, as well as ferric oxide, are by contrast highly hygroscopic. A peaty or highly sesquioxidal soil may collect as much as 20 per cent. of its own weight of moisture from a not very humid atmosphere.

As has already been pointed out, not all of the water present in soil is capable of being drawn upon by the roots of plants. The moisture content at which a particular soil ceases to yield up water to the plant is termed its *wilting coefficient*. The actual point varies in the case of individual plant species but is fairly uniform as between the ordinary crops. Wilting begins before the water content of the soil has reached the hygroscopic limit—*i.e.* there is some moisture, in addition to hygroscopic moisture, that is not available. The following figures by Heinrich illustrate the point:—

| | Water per cent of Weight of Dry Soil | |
| | --- | --- |
| | Hygroscopic | At Wilting Point |
| Coarse sand | 1·15 | 1·50 |
| Sandy garden soil | 3·0 | 4·6 |
| Fine sand with humus | 3·98 | 6·2 |
| Sandy loam | 5·74 | 7·8 |
| Chalky loam | 5·2 | 9·8 |
| Peat | 42·3 | 49·7 |

It will be seen that, for the middle range of soils, the second figure is about 50 per cent. higher than the first. A scientific measure of the wetness of the soil has been devised and is expressed in terms of a $pF$ scale. Two soils of the same $pF$ are in moisture equilibrium if placed in contact—*i.e.* neither draws moisture from the other. If one were a peat and the other a sand their actual moisture contents would be very different, but each would yield up moisture to a growing plant with the same degree of ease.

Despite a great deal of research on soil moisture problems many questions are still controversial, and there is a considerable amount of conflict in regard to certain matters between scientific hypothesis on the one hand and, on the other, traditional practices and the beliefs on which these are based. Thus the farmer likes to horse-hoe his roots as soon as he can see the rows, whether or not there are weeds to be killed. He believes that, by producing a mulch of dry, loose surface soil, he protects the lower soil from loss of moisture by evaporation. Gardeners are even more insistent upon the benefits of hoeing in dry weather. Scientific experiments, on the other hand, suggest that, unless there is a water table quite near to the surface, the upward movement of water, and therefore the loss by evaporation, will be negligible whether or not the surface is hoed. It would, however, seem that there is a real foundation for the belief in the efficacy of hoeing under certain circumstances. If the soil surface is allowed to form a crust, gaseous exchange between the soil and the atmosphere must be impeded and the carbon-dioxide content of the soil air may rise to a level that restricts root activity. In such a case the plants would in fact suffer from drought. Again, some farmers and gardeners roll in or " tread in " small seeds in the belief that moisture will rise in the firmly packed soil and wet the seeds sooner than would otherwise happen; but again, scientific experiments throw doubt on the efficacy of consolidation as a means of bringing up soil moisture. It will, however, be obvious that a firm seed bed is required, under relatively dry soil conditions, in order to ensure contact between the seed coat and the moisture film that surrounds the soil particles. The evidence from scientifically controlled experiments is to the effect that tillage operations beyond those necessary (a) to allow rain to penetrate the soil, (b) to assure germination of seeds and the establishment of seedlings (c) to break a surface crust and (d) to kill weeds, are so much waste of effort.

**Soil Temperature.**—The usefulness of a soil is greatly influenced by its mean, maximum and minimum temperatures. Most of the heat received by the soil comes from the sun, but it also has its temperature raised by conduction from the warm interior of the earth and by oxidation of organic matter. On the other hand, heat is continually being lost by radiation into space and dissipated by the evaporation of moisture. Now the amount of solar heat received by any soil depends on its latitude and elevation, being greatest near the equator where the heat rays are most concentrated and at low elevations where dense and moist air bring about a maximum of heat retention. The aspect of the soil is also important because land facing the sun receives a greater concentration of heat rays, and in the Northern Hemisphere the soil temperature is always highest on land sloping to the south. Colour, too, has an influence on heat absorbing power. Light-coloured soils reflect much of the energy of the sun back into space, so that dark soils are always warmer. Again, the amount of heat necessary to raise the temperature of dry soil by a given amount is less than that required to elevate the temperature of a similar quantity of water to the same degree; in other words, the specific heat of soil is less than that of water. It follows that when heat rays fall on a mixture of soil and water, the greater the quantity of moisture present the less will be the rise in temperature. Thus peaty or clay soils, with their high water content, are cold and late. Again, the greatest amount of evaporation goes on in wet soils, and as water absorbs a great deal of heat in its change from the liquid to the gaseous state, soils having much moisture will be kept considerably cooler than those that are well drained and have an open texture.

It is worth noting that root activity and growth in many crop species can proceed when the soil temperature is still too low to permit of humification and nitrification. This explains the common occurrence in spring of symptoms of nitrogen starvation (especially a pale yellowish colour) in winter corn and grass. The condition tends to be most acute when a slow spring follows a wet winter. The remedy is, of course, to apply nitrogen in immediately available form.

The local incidence of frost is important, especially for frost sensitive crops such as fruit, early potatoes and certain vegetables; the temperature of the lower air rather than that of the soil is the more critical.

In a general way soil and air temperatures decrease with increasing altitude. Locally, the severest frosts occur in hollows and valley bottoms. In extreme cases a particular area has a traditional reputation as a " frost pocket." In other cases, where only frost hardy crops have been grown in the past, the position is realized only after fruit trees or other susceptible plants have been established.

The occurrence of damage by night frosts to crops in hollows, when the adjoining slopes escape, is explained as follows: the frosts are the result of excessive radiation, which occurs on still nights of clear skies. The soil surface cools rapidly and, in turn, chills the air lying immediately above. The cold air thus produced is relatively dense, and therefore flows down slopes and accumulates in " pools," which have often a clearly defined and almost level surface. The avoidance of sites with poor " air drainage " is thus very important in the case of crops that are susceptible to frost damage. In some cases air drainage may be improved—for example, by the removal of tall hedges or belts of woodland. In other cases the stream of cold air, moving down a slope, may be diverted from the area immediately below by interposing a tall hedge or a belt of trees which would conduct the air, at a lesser pace, into an area where it would do less harm—for example, a valley bottom that is under pasture.

**Absorption.**—Any salt, acid or base dissolved in water dissociates more or less to give positively charged ions or cations and negatively charged ions or anions. In the case of salts the cations are metals and the anions acid radicals; with acids the cations are hydrogen and the anions are acid radicals; with bases the cations are metals and the anions hydroxyl (OH) groups. The ammonium radicle ($NH_4$) behaves like a metallic ion.

The analyses of drainage waters show that the cations calcium, magnesium and sodium, and the anions nitrate, sulphate, chloride and bicarbonate are lost in large quantities from the soil. On the other hand, only a small amount of potassium and mere traces of ammonium and phosphate appear in the drainage. The soil particles, particularly the mineral and organic colloids, possess absorptive properties; that is to say, they can hold, by virtue of their large surface and electrical charges, various cations including hydrogen. When such particles come in contact with a solution, part of their absorbed cations are replaced by cations from the solution. Consequently, the addition of such salts as ammonium sulphate or potassium chloride to a soil will result in the absorption of ammonium or potassium ions and the displacement of calcium and other cations. The displaced ions come into solution and may be lost in the drainage water. In normal soils the ammonium ion is converted rapidly by micro-organisms into nitrate (see p. 35), and an application of sulphate of ammonia may thus produce a concentration of both nitrate and sulphate ion in the drainage. If a growing crop is present, however, the nitrate is likely to be taken up by the plant roots. Anions are not " absorbed " by the soil. The reason why only traces of phosphate are found in drainage water is that phosphate is precipitated as a sparingly soluble calcium compound or, in the case of an acid soil, as an insoluble iron or aluminium compound. The other anions, such as chloride and sulphate, form soluble salts with cations of the soil solution.

**Soil Reaction.**—When the absorptive capacity of the soil is satisfied by metallic cations the soil is said to be *saturated*, but when a proportion of the absorbed cations consists of hydrogen the soil is said to be *un-saturated*. The degree of unsaturation, which may be regarded as the absorbed hydrogen ions expressed as a percentage of the total absorbed cations, is a most important characteristic of the soil. As a rule soils like our own, which have developed under cool humid conditions, are more or less unsaturated because of their long exposure to leaching. This is due to the fact that water percolating downwards to the drains contains carbonic acid, " humic " acids from decomposing organic matter and small amounts of sulphuric and nitric acids from rain and organic sources, and that the hydrogen ions of these acids tend to displace the metallic cations of the soil complexes. The loss of lime from a calcium rich soil may be from 2 to 5 cwt. per acre per annum and much more in those industrial areas where the rain is polluted with sulphur fumes. In course of time a soil may become so unsaturated as to show all the characteristics of " sourness." Once a high degree of acidity has been developed, however, soils retain their small amounts of calcium very firmly.

Unsaturated colloidal particles behave like weak acids, for although they are almost insoluble in water, they are able to dissociate to a sufficient extent to provide free hydrogen ions in solution. Now there are two distinct aspects of soil acidity: the first, which may be termed the *intensity* of acidity, is the concentration of hydrogen ions in solution and is measured in terms of *p*H[1]; the second, termed the *quantity* of acidity, is the whole of the absorbed hydrogen ions, which, although not completely dissociated, are capable of being displaced by metallic cations. These two measures of acidity do not necessarily bear any relationship to each other. The former is active and affects the suitability of the soil for plant growth; the latter is, in a sense, potential rather than active. The remedy for both is to apply lime so that the calcium may displace part of the absorbed hydrogen and so reduce the degree of unsaturation and decrease the acidity.

The greatest degree of acidity met with in natural soils is about *p*H 4. Greater extremes are known, but are generally due to the presence of strong mineral acids—generally sulphuric acid which may be brought down in considerable quantity by rain in areas near to steel works and factories. Alkalinity above *p*H 8·5 is generally due to the presence of sodium carbonate (black alkali), which occurs only in the soils of semi-arid or desert regions. Few British soils are more alkaline than *p*H 7·5, a figure that implies a high content of lime.

The *p*H of a soil may be roughly measured by a colour test carried out in the field. Thus the B.D.H. standard mixed indicator when mixed with the soil solution gives a colour ranging from blue (*p*H 7·5) through green and yellow to red (*p*H 4). A colour chart enables the colour of this solution to be matched to the nearest tint on the scale, and the *p*H for each tint is given. The results of such tests, while useful, should not be used as a basis for recommendation in regard to the quantity of lime that the soil requires.

Many experiments and observations have been made in order to determine the *p*H range best suited for various field crops and the values at

---

[1] Any aqueous solution of a salt or an acid or a base contains hydrogen and hydroxyl (OH) ions, and the product of the concentration of hydrogen ions ($C_H$) and the concentration of hydroxyl ions ($C_{OH}$) is always equal to $10^{-14}$ gram ions per litre at $20°$ C. In pure water with a neutral action,

$$C_H + C_{OH} = 10^{-7}, \text{ or, } 0·0000001.$$
$$pH = -\log C_H = 7.$$

In an acid solution $C_H$ is greater than $C_{OH}$, that is, the *p*H is less than 7; in an alkaline solution $C_H$ is less than $C_{OH}$, *i.e.* the *p*H is greater than 7. The *p*H scale therefore runs from 0 to 14; from 7 down we get increasing acidity and from 7 up we get increasing alkalinity. The *p*H values for normal arable soils in this country generally lie between 5·5 and 7·7, but acid peats may have a *p*H value as low as 3·5 and alkaline soils in semi-arid regions may have values of above 9. It has been suggested that soils might be grouped according to their *p*H values as follows: up to 5, very acid soils; 5 to 6, acid soils; 6 to 7, slightly acid soils; 7 to 7·5, slightly alkaline soils; 7·5 and upwards, alkaline soils.

which crops fail.[1]  Although the $p$H of the soil is merely an index of other properties and may fluctuate considerably with changing conditions, such figures may nevertheless be of practical value for the district in which they were obtained.  A comparison of figures secured in different parts of the country, however, shows that there is not sufficient agreement to warrant their general use.

The failure of crops on " sour " land may be due not directly to acidity but to indirect influences.  Thus the acidity may become sufficient to bring iron and aluminium into solution, and these may prove toxic to plants or may precipitate all the available phosphate.  Again, a very acid soil may possess such a high ratio of absorbed hydrogen to calcium as to cause plants to suffer from calcium starvation, and so on.

There is also a relationship between rainfall and the effect on crops of soil acidity.  This effect is relatively severe in areas of low rainfall, and failures may occur, in dry years, on land that crops well in wet seasons.

The *quantity of acidity,* or total amount of unsaturation, is measured by the amount of calcium or other base which is required to make the soil saturated.  In practice this is not determined directly, the " lime-requirement " being estimated by observing the amount of calcium which is absorbed by the soil under certain standard laboratory conditions. Usually the sample of soil is treated with a solution of a calcium salt and the amount of calcium absorbed from the solution is determined.  A better method is to add increasing quantities of lime-water to different portions of the soil and observe the effects of these additions on the $p$H value.  In this way it is possible to calculate how much lime is required to bring the soil to any particular $p$H.

It is quite possible to have soils of the same $p$H value but possessing different " lime-requirements," and *vice versa.*  This is on account of the differences in the quantity and nature of their colloidal materials.  For instance, let us suppose that a given soil has a $p$H of 4·5 and a " lime-requirement " of 6 tons per acre.  If the soil is mixed with an equal quantity of chemically inert substance, such as quartz sand, the $p$H will remain at the old figure, whereas the " lime-requirement " would work out at only 3 tons per acre.

As already mentioned, the unsaturated colloidal material acts as a weak acid; it therefore possesses a buffer action and prevents a rapid change in the $p$H value on the addition of acid or alkali.  Consequently, a soil possessing large amount of colloidal material may require a large application of lime to bring its $p$H value towards neutrality.  Such a soil may

---

[1] Morley Davies gives the following as the critical $p$H values at which crops fail:—

| | | | | |
|---|---|---|---|---|
| Alsike clover  . | . | . | 5·6 | Swedes and cabbage  . | 4·9 |
| Red clover  . | . | . | 5·5 | Kale  . | . | . | 4·5 |
| Sugar-beet, mangolds, and | | | | Ryegrass  . | . | . | 4·3 |
| barley  . | . | . | 5·3 | Oats  . | . | . | 4·2 |
| Wheat  . | . | . | . | 5·1 | Potatoes  . | . | . | 4·0 |

nevertheless be in less serious need of lime than a sandy soil which, although having a much higher degree of unsaturation, actually shows a smaller " lime-requirement " owing to its smaller total of colloidal material and absorbed hydrogen. The quantity of lime that should be applied must also depend on the crop that is to be grown, and its estimation in practice demands a careful study of all the conditions in each case. Actually, the principal crops of our northern and wetter districts all do best on soils that are somewhat acid; some fail on alkaline soils.

There are soil advisory services which deal with soil samples and among other functions issue recommendations regarding " lime-require-ments." For this purpose the $p$H is measured electrometrically and a measure is made of the amounts of calcium hydroxide required to change the $p$H to suitable values such as 6 or 6·5 or even 7, according to the crops grown. These quantities are then converted into hundredweights of lime per acre.

The following figures illustrate clearly the varying effects of soil acidity

| Year | Crop | Yield per Acre | |
|------|------|---------|------------|
| | | Chalked | Not Chalked |
| 1931 | Potatoes (tons) . | 12·0 | 10·6 |
| 1935 | Wheat (cwt.) . . | 39·3 | 31·2 |
| 1936 | Sugar-beet (tons) . | 13·4 | 1·6 |
| 1938 | Peas (cwt.) . | 40·4 | 13·3 |
| 1941 | Oats (cwt.) . . | 46·9 | 49·6 |
| 1942 | Lupins (cwt.) . | 17·1 | 17·1 |
| 1943 | Wheat (cwt.) . | 34·8 | 16·3 |

as between different crops. They refer to yields on the limed and unlimed portions of a field of originally acid sandy land ($p$H 4·8) at Tunstall in Suffolk. Half the field was chalked at the rate of 5 tons per acre in 1927 and no further lime was applied.

The unlimed plot, presumably, became progressively more acid in the period between 1927 and 1943.

## FARM SOILS AND THEIR CHARACTERISTICS

In most soils the largest group of constituents is mineral particles falling within the four groups defined on page 13, *viz.* coarse sand, fine sand, silt and clay. Moreover, the great majority of soils contain con-siderable amounts of all four fractions. The particular blend may give a texture ranging from extremely " heavy " to very " light." The terms commonly employed are heavy clay, clay, strong or heavy loam, medium loam, light or sandy loam, sand and " blowing sand." The farmer's " heavy clay," however, may contain a considerable quantity of one or more of the coarser fractions, and even a " blowing sand " will usually contain some clay or silt.

Occasionally the preponderance of the silt fraction produces characteristics different from those associated with the mixture of size groups that constitutes an ordinary loam, and the term " silt loam " is then used.    Very occasionally, too, we find soils (generally derived from a mixture of two distinct alluvial deposits) in which the coarse sand and clay fractions preponderate, while particles of the intermediate groups are very few.    In this case the behaviour is different from that of an ordinary loam, and the term " sandy clay " is sometimes used.

Occasionally the proportion of stones is large enough to influence the behaviour of the soil.    The term " brash " or " stone brash " is commonly used to describe soils on the oolitic limestone whose stoniness is their oustanding characteristic.    Again, where the proportion of gravel, or the presence of a gravelly subsoil, affects the soil's capacity to withstand an ordinary drought, terms like " light gravelly loam " may be usefully applied.    Gravelly soils are often described as " hot " or " burning."

Next, the proportion of organic matter may be so high as to require mention.    In this case terms like " peaty loam " or " sandy peat " are used.    " Black-top land " is a term used in Scotland with the same implication.

Again, the lime-content may be so high as to affect the soil's characteristics.    " Marl " and " clay marl " are terms generally used.

Finally, whenever the soil overlies rock, the depth at which the rock lies is a material point.

Naturally a full description of a soil, covering its depth, mechanical analysis, structure, reaction and humus-content, is valuable.    It should also be mentioned that a soil survey of parts of this country has been made and in these areas it is sufficient to indicate that a particular soil belongs to a named soil series whose description has been published.    But the local farmer's description of a given soil may convey a great deal if his terminology is understood.    Descriptions like " thin sticky brash," " cold boulder clay," " hot and hungry gravel," or " good honest loam " convey the essential information in each case.    The following notes deal with the agricultural uses and characteristics of the main classes.

**Clay soils** contain more than 20 per cent. of clay and a correspondingly high proportion of other fine soil particles; their texture prevents the free movement of air and water; indeed, they possess to some extent most of the qualities of pure clay.    They must not be worked when they are in a wet condition since they become puddled and impervious to water, dry into rock-like clods which cannot be reduced to the fineness required for a seed bed, and are rendered useless for the rest of the season.    If the clay land is under grass it cannot be stocked in wet weather as treading " poaches " the surface, prevents the passage of air and moisture and greatly deteriorates the herbage.    It is therefore advisable to avoid deflocculation or puddling by every possible means.    On the other hand, flocculation of clay brings about an aggregation of its particles.    This gives it more of the texture of a coarse grained mass with all the advantages of larger interspaces for the passage of air and the percolation of water. The clay-land farmer can best improve the condition of his soil by the liberal use of lime and of farmyard manure, the periodical ploughing-in of a grass sward, and by ploughing early in the season so that the furrows are exposed to frost and weathering before an attempt is made to prepare a tilth; and, of course, it is of the utmost importance never to work such land until it has attained a certain degree of dryness. When clays are caused to expand by the temperature dropping to near freezing point, the lateral pressure is liable to cause the extrusion of stones and roots.

On the whole, clay soils are rich, and when well handled in suitable seasons they are capable of growing splendid crops; but they tend to dry very slowly and are difficult to drain, their coldness and wetness make them late, and their tenacity causes them to be difficult and costly to work. Moderately heavy soils are highly drought resistant, but very heavy clays, especially when under grass, are less satisfactory from this point of view. A good deal of the winter rain may run off, and in time of drought the clay cracks, with serious damage to the plant roots. Moreover, once the soil has cracked the subsequent rain runs down the fissures, and the mass of the top soil may remain dry for the rest of the season. Plants growing on clay tend to develop less fibrous and fewer roots than plants on light soil. Owing to their coldness and lack of air, clay soils tend to accumulate organic matter, and dressings of farmyard manure are very lasting. Most clays have very large natural reserves of potash but may be poor in phosphates and sometimes in lime. The physical qualities of clays are obviously modified when they contain a good proportion of gravel and stones, which lower the specific heat, improve drainage and make the soil earlier and easier to work. Because of high labour costs, a great deal of our heavy land which was largely used for grain growing up till the seventies of last century was converted to grass when grain prices fell and wages rose. Considerable areas have, however, been brought back into cultivation since 1939. The introduction of leys makes them much more tractable and productive. Typical clay-land crops are wheat, mangels, cabbages and beans.

**Clay loams** are intermediate in type between heavy clays and loamy soils.

**Loams** contain from 8 to 15 per cent. of clay and may be considered the best all-round type of agricultural soil, capable of growing any crop. Their texture is such that they have most of the advantages of both clays and sands yet none of their serious disadvantages. Owing to their high content of sand they are free working, well aerated, easily drained, and respond well to organic manures which soon decompose and become available for plant food; and their clay fraction gives them a sufficiently fine texture to enable them to withstand considerable periods of drought. Like clays, loams cannot be worked when they are in a wet condition, but as they drain freely and warm up early in spring they are in fit condition for tillage over much longer periods.

**Sandy loams** share the characteristics of the loams and the sands. They are not naturally rich but are very early, easily worked, easily drained and respond to heavy dressings of manure. They are greatly favoured by market gardeners who can afford to manure heavily and to water if necessary.

**Sandy soils** contain only about 5 per cent. of clay and are therefore composed of relatively large particles which make them open in texture and easily drained, but at the same time cause them to dry out rapidly during periods of drought. As sandy soils are so largely made up of practically indestructible fragments of mineral matter they are extremely poor in plant foodstuffs and are often short of potash, phosphates and lime; yet they promote such extensive root development that the response of crops to phosphatic fertilizers is often less than would be expected from their analysis. Under certain conditions sands accumulate organic matter, because in the absence of lime the decomposition of plant debris cannot proceed, and a surface layer of raw humus may be formed; but under normal field conditions, where liming has taken place, they are so well aerated that dung and plant remains decompose very rapidly. Sands are therefore generally called " hungry " soils. Because of their low water holding powers and their consequently low specific heat they warm up rapidly in spring and enable early sowing to take place. The dry conditions also cause crops to come quickly to maturity, and if the yields are rather small the quality of the produce is usually good. There is little risk of puddling these soils and so they may be cultivated during all seasons; hence they are very suitable for forms of continuous cropping and market gardening. For this purpose they require liberal manuring. Sandy soils are useless when they overlie hard-pan, rock or gravel, for these subsoils make the water conditions impossible for agriculture; they are best when they rest on a subsoil of good water holding capacity and when they receive a liberal and well distributed rainfall. Where rainfall is adequate it is possible to bring sands into cultivation by marling, or by claying and liming, combined with heavy manuring, but this will be profitable only where supplies of clay or marl are available locally. By the use of organic fertilizers such as farmyard manure, by green manuring, by consolidating with heavy rollers and the treading of sheep, the texture and water-retaining power of sandy soils are greatly improved and their fertility is enhanced. Because of their lack of tenacity and the ease with which implements work in them, sands are known as " light " soils. When they contain a high proportion of gravel or stones they are correspondingly less fertile and more liable to " burn " in dry weather. The crops best suited to light and sandy land are rye, barley, turnips, carrots, potatoes and lucerne.

**Peaty soils** are of different kinds in this country, their worth depending to a great extent on the proportions of organic and mineral matter in their composition. Taking the extreme case of a deposit of peat or a peat bog, one finds that the soil and subsoil are composed of an accumulation of plant debris, such accumulation only taking place under waterlogged conditions where the absence of lime and air prevents normal decomposition. The plant remains are not, however, absolutely preserved, but are converted into true peat by certain organisms which work in the absence of air. Such soils are practically pure organic matter, and compared to other soils are very nitrogenous. But so long as a bog remains in its natural condition it is useless for agriculture, and it is only by the expenditure of a large amount of capital that it can be made suitable for cropping. In the reclamation of a peat bog the first step is to dig large open drains to carry off the water and to allow the land to settle, aerate and dry; thereafter it may be made fertile by liberal dressings of sand or clay—which may be obtained in excavating the drainage channels—and of lime, phosphate and potash. Some areas have been successfully reclaimed by the application of city refuse. This means that to get a bog into cropping condition the soil has, in effect, to be manufactured, and only a high level of agricultural prices can make this economic.

Another kind of peaty or black-mould soil is found in parts of the Fen country, where it was formed in marshy river estuaries by a certain amount of silt and the debris of reeds and estuarine vegetation. Originally very light and liable to blow, some areas of this soil are still in this condition, but others were given cohesion by top-dressing with the clay that underlies a large part of the area. Although black fen soils consist largely of humus they contain a fair proportion of mineral matter including lime. As much of the fen land has been reclaimed by draining in recent times, the decomposition of the organic fraction, though proceeding actively, is still far from complete, and the soil is still enormously rich in organic matter and nitrogen. Black fen soils have a friable, dry, and sooty appearance and texture; they respond well to dressings of superphosphate, but for many years after their reclamation may be injured rather than improved by applications of farmyard manure and nitrogenous compounds. Even old fens give low responses to farmyard manure.

As mentioned above, organic matter may accumulate on sands because of the shortage of lime. Even on heavy land plant debris may tend to gather. Many old grasslands have matted turves many inches in thickness composed of dead but only slightly decayed plant remains. The reason for this accumulation of " mat " is the absence of the normal bacterial flora and of earthworms. Even if ploughed under, the mat, unless the acidity is neutralised, decays very slowly and the land remains infertile.

Suitable first crops for acid, peaty soils are oats, rye and potatoes. After liming and fertilizing a wide variety of crops can be successfully grown, including sugar beet, celery and mustard.

**Calcareous soils** contain from 5 to 50 per cent. of carbonate of lime. Soils of this type, as one might expect, are most common on the chalk and limestone formations where they are formed *in situ* by the action of weathering; but calcareous clays or marls, are common as subsoils in many parts. As lime is gradually removed by percolating water, it follows that in course of time a change to an ordinary mineral soil takes place. For this reason it is possible to find a soil overlying chalk in need of liming.

Chalky soils, in winter, become soft and sticky and some types puff up under the influence of frost, so that autumn-sown corn is liable to lose its root hold. If their clay content is considerable, as it commonly is, they bake into quite hard clods, which, however, crumble very quickly on re-wetting. In general they produce good crops of barley, spring wheat, sugar beet, roots, clover, sainfoin and lucerne. The deeper soils also grow good crops of winter wheat and certain others with lower chalk contents grow useful crops of potatoes and vegetables.

# PLANT LIFE AND SOIL FERTILITY

MANY widely different types of plants are cultivated. Bacteria are important in dairy manufacture; yeasts are used in the fermentation industries and in baking; many fungi, notably the common mushroom, are grown for food; and coniferous species produce a large proporton of the world's timber. The farmer's crops, however, all belong to the class of flowering plants or angiosperms.

Apart from four exceptional groups, flowering plants obtain their needs of minerals and of nitrogen from simple salts in watery solution, *i.e.* in the form of ions of calcium, potassium, ammonium, sulphate, phosphate and nitrate. They synthesise carbohydrate, which is the primary organic compound, from carbon dioxide mostly obtained from the atmosphere, and from water taken up mainly by the roots. The source of energy for the process of carbon assimilation (photosynthesis) is sunlight.

One group of exceptions is parasitic plants such as dodder and broomrape; a second includes insectivorous species which secure their nitrogen compounds by trapping small animals; a third includes the heaths, azaleas, the beech and several other trees which, through symbiosis with root fungi (mycorrhiza), are able to assimilate organic compounds, including compounds of nitrogen and phosphorus. The fourth, and much the most important group, includes most species of the order *Leguminosae*, which, by symbiosis with root-nodule bacteria, are able to assimilate free nitrogen and thus can be independent of a supply of nitrate or ammonium salts in the soil solution.

It would be out of place here to attempt to give even an outline of plant physiology, but it seems necessary to set out some of the facts that are important to the farmer.

**Seed and Germination.**—Ripe seeds are extremely resistant to both heat and cold. Some can survive the temperature of liquid hydrogen, and some can bear, for a period, that of boiling water. Moreover, their respiration rate is so low that many can remain viable for many months in the absence of free oxygen. By contrast the vegetative parts of plants that are used for propagation—such as tubers and bulbs—are much more sensitive to heat and cold, and are dependent for survival upon a supply of free oxygen. Potato tubers, for example, are killed by a few degrees of frost, by heating to comparatively low temperatures and, in perhaps two or three days, by submersion in oxygen-free water or in waterlogged soil.

The seeds of certain species will germinate even before they are " harvest ripe," *i.e.* before the stage at which they separate easily from the mother plant. Others remain dormant for periods of months or even years after they have been shed. In certain cases (of so-called false dormancy) the explanation is to be found in the fact that the seed coat is impermeable to water. Most clovers produce a proportion of " hard " seeds which do not germinate until the seed coat has been broken, either by decay or by artificial treatment. In other cases it may be that the seed coat is impermeable to gases, so that, for so long as it remains intact, there will be a build-up, round the embryo, of carbon dioxide. In other cases (true or physiological dormancy) there is no known physical explanation. Dormancy is important in relation to the control of certain weeds and also to the treatment of malting barley.

Apart from dormancy in either of these senses, it is a familiar fact that seeds of different species germinate at different rates. Beet, mangels and carrots germinate slowly, cereals and crucifers very fast. Part of the explanation is that in the former group there is a coating of corky material that delays the absorption of water. In many cases germination can be speeded up by wetting the seed before sowing, though care is necessary; thus carrot seed will bear immersion in water for a day or two, whereas runner beans are drowned in a few hours. Mangel and beet seed may be wetted by sprinkling and turning over but should not be steeped.

Seed, for safe storage, must be kept dry. In many cases mould growth and heating will occur, especially in large bulks, if the moisture content exceeds about 16 to 18 per cent.

The environmental conditions for germination include a sufficiency of moisture, a sufficient concentration of oxygen, a relatively low concentration of carbon-dioxide and a temperature within a certain range. The optimum temperature is in most cases about 65° to 75° F. Minimum temperatures (permitting only very slow germination) vary as between species; that for rye is about 36° F., for wheat, barley and beet about 40° F., and for maize about 48° F. A high concentration of carbon-dioxide, even if oxygen is present in normal amount, may slow down or even prevent germination. In the case of white mustard 3 or 4 per cent. of carbon-dioxide is sufficient to prevent the process. This may largely explain the fact that weed seeds, buried more than a few inches deep in the soil, may lie dormant for many years; but it may also be that in certain cases the absence of light is the main explanation. Some species germinate best in total darkness, while others fail to germinate at all.

The length of time that seed will remain viable varies greatly from one species to another. Onion seed deteriorates so rapidly, even under good conditions of storage, that what is sown must be of the previous year's harvest. Wheat falls off, both in percentage germination and in germinative vigour, very slowly during the first three years and then much more rapidly. Seedsmen generally carry over, each year, quantities of root, clover and grass seeds as an insurance against a poor harvest, and " yearling " seed of these plants gives quite satisfactory results. In the case of clover (because successive bad harvests occur rather frequently) two-year-old seed is often used, with quite good results. The seeds of many common weeds survive in the soil for long periods, in some cases for several decades.

**Seedlings.**—The seedling plant at first lives and grows by drawing upon the reserves of food material in the seed; not until its shoot has reached the light and has turned green can it begin to be independent. The point is important in relation to the depth at which seed should be sown. Small seeds, such as those of white clover, must be sown at small depth (generally less than an inch), otherwise their food reserves will be exhausted before the shoot can reach the surface. At the other extreme beans may be planted as deep as 4 to 6 in. In this connection it must be borne in mind that the material sown is not necessarily true seed. The " seed " of sugar beet or mangel is in fact a cluster containing usually two or three true seeds, which are very small, embedded in a piece of corky tissue.

Once germination has well begun the developing embryo requires a continuous supply of water. Wheat or turnip seed that has " chitted " will die if the soil dries out. Established seedlings of most species will also die in the absence of sufficient moisture to enable them to continue growth. Those of the grasses, exceptionally, can survive in a shrivelled state for many months, recommencing growth after rain. Hence the farmer must sometimes wait until well into the autumn before he can decide whether or not he has secured a satisfactory establishment of grasses sown in spring.

Germinating seeds and young seedlings are exposed to many risks, for instance, insect or bird or rabbit damage, seed-borne or soil-borne disease, and inability to draw from the soil enough nutrients to keep them growing after they have exhausted their reserves. As might be expected, the elements required in largest amounts at the " weaning " stage are nitrogen and phosphate, which are major constituents of protoplasm. An adequate supply of these nutrients in the near vicinity of the seed is therefore important. Another factor is competition by other plants, including weeds, for light, moisture and nutrients. It is easy to understand the loss of seedlings of slow growing crops—for example, beet or carrots—exposed to the competition of fast growing weeds; in other cases there is no such simple explanation of the failure of seedlings to become established. Sometimes such failure is clearly a result of some form of competition; for instance, meadow fescue establishes well when sown as the only grass in a mixture, or with timothy as a companion plant, but gives a very low establishment when sown with ryegrass. Even in the absence of such competition there are marked differences between species. In one experiment carried out at the Welsh Plant Breeding Station, under uniform

B

conditions, the numbers of seedlings established, per hundred viable seeds sown, were:—

Italian ryegrass . . . . . 52·1
Perennial ryegrass . . . . . 44·1
Meadow foxtail . . . . . 9·6
Smooth-stalked meadow grass . . . 2·2

As might be expected, the proportion of casualties among seedlings varies with weather and soil conditions, and allowance must be made for this factor. For example, common seed rates for wheat vary from about two bushels in early October to perhaps three and a half in December. But here again there are wide differences between species. The following experimental results (expressed as numbers of established seedlings per hundred viable seeds sown) illustrate these differences:—

| Date of Sowing | Perennial Ryegrass | Cocksfoot | Wild White Clover |
|---|---|---|---|
| March to May | 78·1 | 48·8 | 55·1 |
| May to August | 65·0 | 48·4 | 42·1 |
| August to September | 80·9 | 49·1 | 13·0 |
| September to October | 69·9 | 18·9 | 2·7 |

The striking difference between the grasses and the clovers is no doubt related to the fact that grass seedlings are frost hardy whereas clover seedlings are not.

**Plant Development.**—The development of the plant through its various growth phases (tillering or branching, flowering and ripening) is governed partly by temperature and moisture conditions but partly also by light, in particular by length of day. Plants of biennial habit and " winter annuals " (e.g. winter wheat) do not pass out of the vegetative phase until they have been subjected to cold. Thus winter wheat, sown in southern England in April, will usually fail to come into ear in the same season but may do so if there happens to be a May frost. Again, beet, mangels and carrots, which are normally biennial, may " bolt " or run to seed in their first year if they encounter frost at a particular stage of growth, but the propensity to bolt varies from strain to strain. The biennial habit of winter wheat or of sugar beet can be broken down by chilling the sprouting seed, the process known as " vernalization."

In regard to their reactions to frost, plants are sometimes classified as " winter hardy " and " frost tender," but there is in fact no sharp line of differentiation. The winter varieties of rye are more frost hardy than those of wheat, and these in turn are more frost hardy than winter oats or wild oats, but any or all of these may be destroyed under specially severe conditions. Moreover, there is variation between different areas in this country. Many weeds—for example, charlock—which in this country are generally regarded as spring annuals and whose seedlings, established in autumn, are commonly winter killed, may often survive the winter in Cornwall or South West Wales.

Among plants that are more or less winter hardy the effect of frost varies according to the conditions under which it occurs. When the soil is frozen, and when therefore the roots cannot take up moisture, survival depends largely on the plant's ability to retain enough moisture. Hence drying winds may be the immediate cause of death. Again, resistance has been shown to vary with the sugar content of the cell sap, so that plants are more resistant after a spell of bright weather than after a period of dull conditions.

A covering of snow provides protection from drying winds and at the same time admits a fair amount of light.

Sometimes winter killing is due to throwing out of the plants, caused by the expansion and contraction of the soil that occurs during spells of alternating frost and thaw. Some soils, especially those of high organic content, " heave " markedly.

It is a familiar fact that plants which have abundant space tend to branch freely while overcrowded plants do not. The tillering (branching from the base) of cereals is also controlled by light, so that a thin plant of wheat often fills out in spring. Flowering is largely controlled by length of day, or rather by length of night. Most of the plants of high latitudes are summer flowering or " long day," i.e. they flower when the hours of darkness are reduced to four, six or eight. In warm-temperate and sub-tropical regions the plants are mostly " short day," i.e. they flower in response to a period of ten or more hours of darkness. The habit of the plant can be broken by subjecting it to quite a short period of illumination in the middle of the night, or, conversely, by shading it in the morning or evening. Certain species—for example, such annual weeds as speedwell and chickweed—are " ever flowering," i.e flowering is not controlled by the hours of darkness. This new knowledge is now being used extensively under conditions where it is possible to control the length of day and night, e.g. in glasshouses for the production of chrysanthemums throughout the year.

**Plant Nutrients.**—Apart from carbon, hydrogen and oxygen, which are obtained from air and water, the essential elements required by plants in substantial quantities are nitrogen, phosphorus, potassium, calcium, magnesium and sulphur. The remaining essential elements, commonly known as minor elements, are iron, manganese, boron, copper, zinc and molybdenum. A few others—sodium, silicon, chlorine, aluminium and nickel—are " beneficial " to particular species. Sodium, for example, is highly beneficial to sugar beet, mangels and fodder beet.

*Nitrogen* is a constituent of all proteins and of protoplasm. With the exceptions mentioned earlier (p. 31), nitrogen is mostly absorbed in the form of nitrate. Rice and other semi-aquatic plants take up their nitrogen mainly in the form of the ammonium ion, and most other species will readily absorb and assimilate the element in this form. But under well aerated conditions the oxidation of ammonia to nitrate proceeds so rapidly in the soil that little ammonia is present, as such, at any given time. Soils under old grass, being much less well aerated than those in cultivation, often contain substantial amounts of nitrogen in ammonium form.

Soil humus acts as a reservoir of nitrogen, usually containing about one part of the element to ten parts of carbon. But nitrogen in organic form is not available to ordinary crop plants, and the release of nitrogen from humus, in the form of ammonia, is, under cool conditions, usually too slow to provide for the full requirements of crops. On the other hand, fresh nitrogen-rich organic matter, such as cake-fed farmyard manure or a clover-rich sod, may under summer temperatures release nitrogen too rapidly, with the consequence of over-luxuriant growth and, in the case of cereals, lodging of the plants.

The common symptoms of nitrogen deficiency are narrow leaves and an unhealthy pale green colour. Excess of nitrogen is indicated by broad dark green leaves, lush growth and increased susceptibility to frost damage. These effects are most marked when an over-supply of nitrogen is accompanied by a deficiency of potash (see further pp. 75-80).

*Phosphorus* is a constituent of one group of proteins and of protoplasm. It is largely transferred to the seed in the process of ripening, so that grain or pulse has a high content while straw contains very little. Phosphate is a constituent of animal bone and of milk, so that all forms of agricultural production, excepting only the fattening of mature animals, result in a drain upon the stock of phosphate in the soil. The quantity of phosphate present in many soils would be sufficient to provide for the needs of great numbers of successive crops, but much of the total amount is in unavailable form and a large proportion of what is applied as fertilizer reverts to an insoluble condition. Phosphate deficiency is indicated by poor early growth, weak and delayed tillering, a dull bluish green colour of foliage, poor seed formation and late ripening. Laboratory tests provide useful information on the amount of available phosphate in soil (see p. 69).

*Potassium* is taken up in large quantity and plays an important role in relation to the efficiency of the leaf tissue in carbon assimilation. In general, sandy and peaty soils are relatively poor in potash while most clays are rich. But, as in the case of phosphate, the greater part of the soil stock is in unavailable forms. Soil analysis provides useful information on the content of available potash. As might be expected, the crops that yield large amounts of carbohydrate material—sugar beet, mangels and potatoes—have the highest requirements. The drain of potash from the farm as a whole depends largely on the quantities of potatoes, sugar beet, green vegetables, hay and straw that are sold. Animal products contain almost none, and grains and seeds very little.

*Calcium* occurs largely in the leaf and stem and mostly remains there as the plant matures. The common legumes (except lupins) are particularly rich in the element. Actual calcium deficiency in crops is rare, though cases have occurred, particularly in potatoes growing in extremely acid soils. The principal use of lime is in the control of soil reaction (see p. 22). The calcium content and the calcium/phosphate ratio of grassland herbage are important in relation to animal nutrition.

*Magnesium* is a constituent of chlorophyll and also plays a part in connection with the movement of phosphate within the plant. Magnesium deficiency is not uncommon and occurs both in crops under glass and in the open. It can be aggravated by unbalanced fertilizer treatment. On farm land where deficiency symptoms are liable to develop, the use of dolomitic (magnesium) lime is often recommended instead of the usual liming materials. Most low-grade potash salts contain magnesium.

*Sulphur* is a constituent of certain amino acids, many proteins and protoplasm. It is absorbed in the form of the sulphate ion. It would seem that up till the middle of last century a good many British soils were deficient in the element, for there are many authentic accounts of responses to applications of gypsum. Sulphur deficiency is known to occur in other countries, but the long continued use in British agriculture of super-phosphate and sulphate of ammonia has resulted in the build-up of large reserves in most of our soils.

*Manganese* is required by all plants, but some suffer much more than others from the degrees of deficiency that commonly occur. Deficiency causes a pathological condition in the leaves known as " grey speck " in oats, " speckled yellows " in beet and mangels and " marsh spot " in peas. Deficiency is most likely to occur in soils rich in bases ($p$H over 6·5), especially where the content of organic matter is high. Many cases have been related to excessive applications of lime. Affected crops can be cured by spraying with a dilute solution of manganese sulphate or through the use of fertilizers containing manganese.

*Boron* appears to be essential, in greater or less amount, to all plants. Deficiency shows up as " heart-rot " in sugar beet, " brown-heart " or " raan " in swedes and " browning " in cauliflower. As in the case of manganese the use of excessive dressings of lime renders the soil reserves of boron unavailable; another point is that cases are most frequent on land that has rarely received dung. Boron compounds are rather readily leached from the land, and hence sandy soils are most prone to deficiency. Affected crops can be quickly revived by spraying with borax. In some countries deficiency is so common that a small amount of borax is incorporated in fertilizers for the more susceptible crops.

*Copper* deficiency is confined mainly to newly reclaimed peat and fen soils and certain limited areas of grassland. In Holland the condition is known as " reclamation disease."

*Zinc* deficiency is of great importance in certain parts of the world, notably in parts of Australia and the United States. Until recently it was thought to be of no importance in Europe, but definite response to applications has occurred on certain marshland soils in Kent.

*Molybdenum* was first recognized as being of importance by Australian workers who discovered that its deficiency was the cause of widespread failures of clover, the primary symptom being the failure of the plants to form root nodules. In other species the function of the element is related to nitrate metabolism; plants supplied with nitrogen in the form of the ammonium ion do not seem to require molybdenum. The only clear case of deficiency disease in Britain, at the time of writing, was " whiptail " in cauliflowers.

The minor element requirements of animals are different from those of plants. The only deficiency conditions common in Britain are of cobalt, copper and magnesium.

*Plant Growth Substances* or Plant Hormones are akin in their action to the internal secretions (hormones) of animals, *i.e.* they regulate metabolism and growth. At the time of their discovery it was thought that related materials, either produced artificially or extracted from urine, might stimulate growth or increase the overall efficiency of the plant. In fact, all that growth substances do is to influence the direction of development; for instance, they induce the plant to throw more than the normal amount of energy into the production of roots. In practice, synthetically produced materials are used to stimulate the production of roots by plant cuttings, to induce tomatoes to set without fertilization and to prevent the premature drop of fruits. Their most important use is as selective weed killers, which use is based upon the fact that, at any given level of concentration, they have greater or less effect in the way of disorganising the metabolism of different species at different stages of growth (see pp. 121-123).

## WATER REQUIREMENTS OF CROPS

As the plant passes out of the seedling stage and increases its leaf area, its water requirements rise progressively up till the time when the leaf system reaches its full expanse. At the same time, however, the root system develops and ranges ever more widely, so that the plant's capacity to withstand drought commonly increases.

The amount of water transpired, per ton of dry matter produced, varies from four or five hundred tons in the case of cereals to more than eight hundred tons for the grasses. Hence plants producing 3 tons of dry matter per acre may transpire anything from 1200 to 2500 tons of water, equivalent to 12 to 25 in. of rain. The south-eastern half of England is too dry, on average, to permit of full yields of the general run of farm crops, and yields can be increased substantially by irrigation.

Drought resistance depends partly on the efficiency of the leaf in controlling transpiration and partly on the range of the root system and the level of root activity. To some extent these things are characteristic of the particular species or variety—for instance, wheat is more drought-resistant than oats, and sugar beet than swedes; but soil conditions are of obvious importance—for instance, a shallow soil over rock or gravel will have a low total capacity for water, sloping land may fail to absorb all the rain that falls, and sandy soils drain very freely, while heavy clays may be so poorly aerated that root activity is depressed. Moreover, the development of the root system is influenced by the supply of plant nutrients, especially of phosphate. The immediate effects of drought are to induce the closing of the stomata and later, the wilting of the leaves. In some cases—for example, in certain grasses—the leaves respond by folding up. Prolonged drought sometimes results in shedding of leaves, sometimes in the dying back of parts of the blades, and in extreme cases the shrivelling up and premature death of the whole plant. Under dry conditions the vegetative parts of the plant are reduced more seriously than the seed or grain; for example, a cereal, when grown with ample moisture, will yield very much more straw but not much more grain than it will produce in a moderately dry season.

**Soil Air.**—As will be explained later, the biological processes by which some soil nutrients are made available depend upon an adequate supply of oxygen and are checked, even in the presence of free oxygen, by any considerable concentration of carbon dioxide. Moreover, the plant roots must be able to respire. Thus the rate of gaseous exchange between the soil and the atmosphere is important. Lack of aeration may be due to waterlogging or to too close a soil texture, but it may also result from the formation of a surface crust or " cap." This is very apt to occur, in cases where the crumb structure is unstable, when heavy rain is followed by drying winds. Root activity is impeded by concentrations of carbon-dioxide in excess of about 1 per cent. Soil aeration is important in another respect, namely, because the decay of organic matter, in the absence of free oxygen, gives rise to poisonous substances, notably to sulphuretted hydrogen.

**Soil Temperature.**—Air temperature is, of course, important in relation to rate of growth. Plants native to cool-temperate areas generally grow best at about 80° F., while carbon assimilation generally ceases below 40° to 42° F.

In clear, sunny weather the upper layer of a bare soil rises to a temperature much above that of the air. Conversely, on clear nights there is often ground frost, while the temperature, 2 or 3 ft. above ground, remains several degrees above freezing point. A blanket of vegetation makes a marked difference to the temperature of the soil, keeping it cool by day and warm by night.   As might be expected, too, bare soil warms up in spring faster than does pasture land.   The point is important, since, even under British climatic conditions, the temperature of the upper soil layer may become too high for full root activity.   Horticulturists employ mulches of straw to minimise the variation as between day and night soil temperatures.   Soil under closely grazed or closely mown herbage shows a relatively high amount of variation, and root action may be greatly restricted by overheating of the soil during hot sunny weather.   Species show different degrees of tolerance, ryegrass being particularly prone to a degree of " summer dormancy " that cannot fully be explained as due to drought.

## SOIL ORGANISMS

It is possible to grow normal healthy plants in a sterile aerated solution of nutrient salts, and there is no reason to suppose that the nutritive value of the produce, for animal or man, is in any way inferior to that grown under ordinary conditions.   Certain glass-house crops, including tomatoes and some flowers, are grown commercially in water culture, though in practice there is no need to keep the solution sterile.   The method—if care is taken to maintain a suitable concentration of the various nutrients and to keep the solution well aerated—has certain advantages over soil culture; in particular, it avoids trouble with soil-borne diseases and pests.

The farmer, however, works with a material that is inhabited by great numbers of living organisms—earthworms, nematodes, insects and protozoa, green algæ, fungi and bacteria—some beneficial and others harmful, and he can control the situation only imperfectly, and by more or less indirect methods.   It is therefore necessary to have some under-standing of the complex population of the soil and of the biological processes that go on in it.

**Earthworms** constitute the major fraction, by weight, of the animal population of the soil.   There are many species, some six or seven of which are common in British soils.   Their food is organic matter, either fresh or partly decomposed, and all obtain a proportion of it by foraging on the surface.   All species are intolerant of drought and require a reasonably well aerated soil.   Hence shallow and sandy soils on the one hand, and heavy clays on the other, contain relatively small numbers.   The population also varies with the supply of organic matter, so that fertile soils, producing large crops that leave large residues, contain greater numbers than poor land.   Again, earthworm populations are higher in grassland than under arable conditions.   Most species, including all the larger ones, require a continuous supply of calcium for the digestive processes, and their absence from very acid soils (below about $p$H 4·5) is very striking.   Earthworms perform the function of mixing organic matter with the soil, and thus prevent the formation of a layer of surface litter in forest, or of a " mat " of dead plant material on grassland, both of which are characteristic of acid conditions. Earthworms improve soil conditions by promoting aeration and drainage and the power of the soil to absorb rain or irrigation water.

Some species—indeed the majority of those found in Britain—leave their castings on the surface. These consist of an intimate mixture of soil particles and organic matter, well saturated with calcium, and thus constituting a top dressing of loamy material that has an excellent physical structure. The dead bodies of worms are quickly attacked by soil bacteria and yield up nitrogen and other nutrients in readily available form.

Despite all this there is no convincing evidence of any marked overall effect of earthworms on soil fertility as measured by crop yields. In any case, it is only under exceptional circumstances that the natural methods of dispersal fail to provide the nucleus of a worm population, which quickly builds up if conditions are suitable. Some farmers, in the process of reclaiming salt marsh, inoculate the land by scattering about pieces of turf from an old established pasture, in the probably well founded hope that worm activity promotes drainage.

**Other Soil Animals.**—Under tropical conditions termites (white ants) play the major role in the initial breakdown of organic matter. Under temperate conditions the groups (apart from earthworms) mainly concerned are millepedes, springtails, slugs and nematodes (eelworms). The first three groups, however, attack living plants as well as dead material, and certain parasitic species of nematodes, such as the potato root eelworm, are among the most destructive of crop pests.

Protozoa are present in all soils but, since counts are extremely difficult to make, there is no very accurate information on the conditions that affect their numbers. Most of the common types feed largely on bacteria, and since a high level of bacterial activity is an important factor in soil fertility, it was formerly thought that protozoa were harmful. It has, however, been shown that certain forms of bacterial activity, especially nitrogen fixation, proceed faster in the presence than in the absence of protozoa.

**The Soil Flora.**—Turning from animals to plants, *green algæ*, which are single-celled plants containing chlorophyll, are present in most soils in great numbers, and those living on the surface and in the upper soil layer, carry on the process of photosynthesis and thus make some small contribution to the stock of organic matter. They also assist in binding the soil particles into crumbs and, under swamp conditions (*e.g.* in rice fields), help to reduce the carbon-dioxide and maintain the oxygen-content of the soil water.

*Actinomycetes*, which are somewhat intermediate in their way of life between bacteria and fungi, consist of thin, thread-like, much branched hyphæ which in some cases break up into spores. They contain no chlorophyll but can make use of a great variety of carbon compounds. A very few species are parasitic on plants or animals. They are most active under warm, dry and well aerated conditions.  It is probable that they have a benificial effect on soil structure.

*Fungi*, as is well known, include many parasitic forms which are responsible for the majority of plant diseases—rust, potato blight, club root and many more.  Most, however, are saprophytic (living entirely on dead organic matter), while others can live either on dead material or on a living host.  They depend upon a supply of free oxygen, but flourish over a very wide *p*H range.  It is fungi rather than bacteria which are responsible for the breakdown of dead plant material under very acid conditions, and the product—*e.g.* under a pine forest or heath, or very acid grassland—is raw humus (mor).  But in farm soils also, fungi play a part in the breakdown of humus, producing materials that are more readily attacked by bacteria than are the remains of the higher plants.

*Bacteria* are by far the most numerous of soil organisms, the numbers in many cases running to hundreds of millions per gram.  None contain chlorophyll but some are able to obtain their requirements of energy from sources other than organic matter, for example, through the oxidation of ammonia or sulphur.  They may be divided into *aerobic* and *anaerobic* forms; the second obtain their oxygen by breaking down oxygen compounds, for example, by reducing carbohydrate to methane.  Some can make use of either free or combined oxygen.  A majority can assimilate nitrogen only in the form of compounds but some few can utilise nitrogen itself.  In general, they grow best in a near neutral medium and are inactive under markedly acid conditions.

## THE NITROGEN CYCLE

It has already been said that the intermediate products of the decay of organic matter, including the remains of the organisms that carry out the process, are of importance in relation to soil structure, and that the nature of these products varies according to conditions—the composition of the original material, the lime status of the soil and the presence or absence of free oxygen.  The main types of intermediate product are peat (waterlogged conditions), raw humus (acid conditions) and mild humus (aerobic and near-neutral conditions).  It has also been said that humus acts as a reservoir of nitrogen, from which the simple compounds —ammonium and nitrate—that alone can be assimilated by most crop plants are released mainly through the activities of soil organisms.

**Nitrification.**—The process by which organic nitrogen is converted into nitrate occurs in three stages.  The organisms which break down organic matter require some nitrogen for the build-up of their own protoplasms, any balance being released as ammonia.  The proportion so released will depend upon the amount of protein, in relation to that of non-nitrogenous organic matter, that the original material contains.  Pure protein supplies about five times as much nitrogen as the organisms require, so that four-fifths will appear as ammonia. At the other extreme, material that is mainly carbohydrate (*e.g.* straw) releases no nitrogen at all, and indeed requires for its breakdown an additional supply of nitrogenous material such as urine or an ammonium salt.

The second stage is the oxidation of the ammonium ion into nitrite; nitrate, the end product, is produced by the further oxidation of nitrite. The conditions required for these latter processes include, of course, a plentiful supply of oxygen, but also adequate supplies of calcium and phosphate and of four minor elements (iron, manganese, zinc and copper) in properly balanced proportions.

The ammonification of nitrogenous organic matter is brought about by a variety of organisms, whereas the oxidation of ammonia is carried out by particular species of bacteria—the first stage by *Nitrosomonas* and the second by *Nitrobacter*.

Nitrification can proceed only in soils that are moist as well as freely aerated and within a temperature range of about 39° to 105° F. with maximum activity at about 85° F. It should be noted that the germination of many seeds and the root activity of many plants can occur at temperatures below the minimum for nitrification; hence crops can suffer from nitrogen starvation in spring even if there is an abundance of nitrogen rich organic matter in the soil; in such circumstances many show marked response to fertilizers containing nitrates.

Nitrites occur in soils in very small amounts because the second stage of oxidation can be much faster than the first, but the proportion of ammonium to nitrate, at any given time, varies with the degree of aeration of the soil. Arable land generally shows a large excess of nitrate, while in grassland soils ammonia nitrogen may be two or three times as high as nitrate.

**Losses of Nitrogen.**—The nitrogen status of a soil at any given time depends on the balance between past gains and losses. Apart from the physical removal of organic material by wind or water (erosion) the losses fall on the inorganic compounds.

Where there is an insufficient supply of free oxygen in the soil, by reason of waterlogging or a very close texture, many bacteria fall back upon oxygen compounds. It has been said earlier that, under such conditions, the reddish ferric compounds are reduced to greenish coloured ferrous compounds, which change is due to the action of soil organisms, chiefly bacteria. Nitrates are another possible source, being reduced to nitrites, ammonia, or even to free nitrogen, the process being known as denitrification. This process, of course, necessitates the presence of relatively fresh organic matter as a source of energy. Another cause of loss is the volatilisation of ammonia which may, for instance, occur in alkaline soils under warm conditions, in which circumstances the formation of ammonia takes place faster than the product can be oxidised to nitrate.

Secondly, nitrates are very easily leached, and the drainage water from land that is in a good state of fertility may contain as much as the equivalent of 1 cwt. per acre per annum of sulphate of ammonia. Other losses that occur are less easy to explain—for instance, under dry prairie conditions, where practically all the rain that falls is evaporated, it has been shown that the annual loss of nitrogen following the breaking up of a virgin sward may, over a period, be about three times as large as the amount removed in the crops.

**Gains of Nitrogen.**—Apart from the application of fertilizers, the most important agent in adding to the stock of soil nitrogen is the leguminous plant living in symbiosis with its appropriate strain of the nodule organism, *Rhizobium.* The legume produces the carbohydrate and the organism synthesises the nitrogen compounds required by the partnership. The organisms in question can be cultivated in artificial media and can survive in the soil, in the absence of the legume partner, for periods of ten years or more; but they do not fix nitrogen except when living symbiotically.

The nodule organism has high requirements of calcium and most strains become inactive at soil reactions more acid than about $pH$ 5. Exceptionally, lupins nodulate freely, and nitrogen fixation proceeds normally in soil that is quite acid. A high phosphate status seems to be required, under all circumstances, for full activity.

The organism exists in many distinguishable strains, each one being more or less effecting in combination with several different genera of legumes, but a particular strain is fully efficient only when associated with a particular genus or a group of closely related genera. The four most important types, under British conditions, are respectively adapted to the following groups of crop plants;—

1. Lucernes and Medics (*Medicago* and *Melilotus*).
2. True Clovers (*Trifolium*).
3. Peas, Field Beans, Vetches, and Vetchlings (*Pisum*, *Vicia*, *Lathyrus*).
4. Lupins and Seradella (*Lupinus* and *Ornithopus*).

This adaptation is not always clear-cut, *i.e.* there are many generalised strains that are more or less effective over a wide range of legume genera. A further complication is that some strains of organisms, while they freely invade the roots of particular species and produce nodules of normal appearance, fail to provide the plant with any substantial amount of nitrogen, *i.e.* they behave as parasites rather than as partners. Moreover, once a particular plant is invaded by an ineffective strain it is immunized against other types which would be effective as nitrogen collectors. Inefficient strains of the clover group are common in the soils of certain upland areas of this country, so that clovers grow weakly and fail to build up nitrogen in the sward.

Like many other groups of bacteria, the nodule organism is subject to attack by several strains of bacteriophage, each phage being restricted to its particular group of bacteria. The presence of such phages has been supposed to account for clover or lucerne " sickness " of particular soils, but this has not been proved.

Annual legumes are ordinarily invaded, and form nodules within a few weeks of the germination of their seeds. In the case of perennial plants infection takes place throughout the growing season, but the nodules are annual growths, being shed in autumn and renewed, by fresh infections, in the following spring. A point of some importance is that infection of the roots is inhibited in a soil with a high concentration of available nitrogen, *i.e.* nitrate or ammonium ions. Hence dressings of nitrogen, intended to give the legume seedlings a quick start, may do more harm than good.

Under certain conditions leguminous plants excrete nitrogen—presumably surplus supplies—from their roots and may thus directly feed companion plants such as grasses. But it seems that the amounts of nitrogen are ordinarily small. In the main the companion plant benefits through the decomposition, in the soil or on its surface, of the residues of the legume—leaves, roots and the annual crop of nodules. These residues, being highly nitrogenous, yield up available nitrogen rapidly; indeed, a very clovery sward may yield so much in the year after ploughing that the first crop grows too luxuriantly. A balanced grass and clover sward decomposes more slowly and has a longer lasting effect.

Again, a mixture of legumes and non-legumes commonly yields a larger total crop than a pure legume. The following results of a Rothampsted experiment illustrate the point:—

|  | Yields per Acre (Lb.) | |
|---|---|---|
|  | Total Dry Matter | Total Nitrogen |
| Oats alone | 4800 | 55·0 |
| Oats and vetches | 5480 | 100·2 |
| Vetches alone | 3200 | 98·0 |

Another point of importance is that the various legume species add widely different amounts to the soil's stock of nitrogen, the herbage species such as clover and lucerne being generally much more efficient than the pulses. Thus in a Cornell (U.S.) experiment various species were grown in a two year rotation with cereals, with the following among other results:—

|  | Nitrogen Harvested (Lb. per Acre) | | Gain or Loss of Soil Nitrogen per Rotation | Yield of Cereal (Cwt. per Acre) |
|---|---|---|---|---|
|  | In Legume | In following Cereal | | |
| Lucerne | 299 | 66 | +122 | 23·2 |
| Red clover | 125 | 51 | +115 | 19·4 |
| Field beans | 103 | 25 | − 20 | 10·6 |

The annual increment of soil nitrogen effected by clovers and lucerne has been estimated in a number of experiments and figures of the order of 100 to 300 lb. nitrogen—equivalent to about 5 to 15 cwt. of sulphate of ammonia—have been recorded.

**Free-living Nitrogen-fixing Organisms.**—Apart from the symbiotic bacteria just discussed, a certain amount of nitrogen is fixed by free-living soil organisms. Thus the genus *Clostridium* is probably important in forest soils, since there is no other known means by which the nitrogen requirements of certain types of forest growth can be met, *i.e.* there are no leguminous shrubs or herbs in the undergrowth. In agricultural soils the several genera of *Azotobacter* are common, and it is an established fact that these can use and fix free nitrogen. The species found in Britain occur only in near neutral or alkaline soils (*p*H above 6). Some blue green algæ and several other groups of bacteria can also grow in the absence of nitrogen compounds. The chemistry of the process is not understood but it is known that neither the blue green algæ nor *Azotobacter* will fix nitrogen in the presence of nitrates or ammonia. Moreover, *Azotobacter* requires for its activity a source of energy in the form of sugar and other simple organic compounds; cellulose and starch cannot be used directly but the organism can live symbiotically with other species that can break down the cellulose and other carbohydrates of straw.

In general there is very little evidence that *Azotobacter* and other free-living organisms are of practical importance under the conditions that prevail in British farm practice, and there is nothing approaching proof that soil inoculation under British conditions, results in any benefit.

## SOIL EROSION AND SOIL CONSERVATION

Under conditions such as prevail in Britain—relatively low evaporation and moderate, well distributed rainfall—the natural processes of erosion are relatively slow. It is true that cultivated soil tends to move slowly down steep slopes, and that occasional rainstorms may result in local damage by surface run off, but in most cases steep slopes are difficult of cultivation and are therefore left in pasture or rough grazing or forest. It is true that our lightest sandy soils, and also certain types of black fen, " blow " when high winds occur during dry spring weather, causing ditches to be filled up and seedling plants to be uprooted. Again, however, the damage is commonly only temporary; but in many parts of the world erosion has assumed disastrous proportions.

Wind erosion is the less serious problem of the two. The most successful of control measures has been the replacement of the mould-board plough by a heavy disc which does not completely bury stubble and trash but merely anchors the material in the soil so that it acts as an efficient wind-break.

The control of soil erosion is based on the principle of inducing the rain to penetrate the soil rather than to run off the surface. This is accomplished, in the case of arable land, by a combination of measures. The first group is designed to maintain a good crumb structure, to the end that the soil will be kept in highly absorbent condition. This object is attained by ploughing in a grass sward at suitable intervals, or by green manuring. The second group aims at keeping the surface covered with living or dead vegetation during the greater part of the year, and especially during the season of heavy rains, growing vegetation protecting the surface from rain splash and forming an efficient brake on the surface movement of water. Thirdly, there are measures designed to intercept the run off; they include contour cropping (whereby the lines of row crops follow the contours) and broad base terracing (a ridge-and-furrow layout again follows the contours). Where such measures are likely to be inadequate the land is best left in pasture or planted to forest.

In areas with marked dry and wet seasons even grasslands may suffer severely. On the one hand, over-grazing during the dry season reduces the plant cover to a point where it no longer acts as an effective brake on surface water so that soil is removed from slopes and deposited on flat areas below. On the other, the daily movement of stock from areas where there is grazable herbage to watering points, and back again, results in the complete destruction of the plants along the routes of travel, and hence the formation of dusty trackways, which rapidly develop into ravines as the loose soil is washed away by rain. The necessary measures of conservation may include a reduction in the head of stock, or alternatively the use of fertilizers to produce more keep; the conservation of fodder against the dry season, so as to avoid over-grazing; and the the provision of water supplies at a number of widely separated points so that, by using these in rotation, the daily movement of the herds may be controlled and the formation of trackways thus avoided.

# CHAPTER 3

# LAND RECLAMATION AND IMPROVEMENT

## RECLAMATION

IN Britain the process of converting virgin land into farms has been going on for some four thousand years. In general the process was slow and piecemeal until about the middle of the eighteenth century because, until then, the rate of increase of population remained slow. Some coastal embankments date back to Roman times, and drainage works on a really vast scale were carried out in the Fens in the period of the Stuarts. The most active period of reclamation was the century from 1760 till 1860, during which time population was growing very rapidly and there was still no considerable supply of grain from the New Countries.

This, however, is not to say that the farm area has been static during the past ninety years. In fact, a good deal of land has been abandoned or allowed to revert to rough grazing during times of agricultural depression, and has had to be brought back into production in periods of emergency. Thus there was a decline in the farm area in the periods 1890-1910, and again between 1925 and 1939, while there were considerable reclamations in 1917-20 and from 1940 onwards.

The following brief notes indicate the principles to be observed in the reclamation of various types of land.

**Tidal Marshes.**—The reclamation of land that is much below mean sea-level necessitates major engineering works. It is essential to build massive sea walls and river banks, and to raise the drainage water from the reclaimed area by pumping. The greatest project of this kind which has so far been attempted is that which will eventually make available for farming the greater part of what was the bed of the Zuider Zee in Holland.

On the other hand, land that is under water only at high spring tides is relatively easy to reclaim. On parts of our coast, particularly round the Wash, silt is gradually being deposited by natural processes, and from time to time a new area reaches a level that makes embankment feasible. The deposition of silt can often be speeded up by planting rice-grass (*Spartina Townsendii*) in the shallow tidal area, and by erecting groynes in the deeper water so as to check the rate of outflow of the tide. When the flats are considered to have reached the desired level, an embankment is made as far out as practicable. Rice-grass is again useful for protecting the seaward side of the bank against erosion by the sea. Main drains are taken through the sea wall by means of large steel pipes, the outer ends of which are provided with sluices which open to release drainage water but are closed by the backward pressure of the sea at high tide. The soil, when first laid dry, is impregnated with salt, and may contain so high a proportion of sodium clay as to be very sticky, impervious and intractable. The lighter silts are quickly leached, provide useful pastures very soon, and in five years or so can grow the full range of arable crops. Heavy land may be treated with gypsum to expel the salt. The maintenance of the sea wall and of the drainage system is costly, but the charges may be more than covered if the land is inherently fertile, as it usually is.

**Restoration of Sea-flooded Land.**—Land lying below high tide level and protected by sea walls will, of course, be flooded if the banks give way. At rare intervals a combination of circumstances puts a very exceptional strain on the sea banks. Thus in 1953 exceptionally strong northerly gales, coinciding with the period of the spring tides and very heavy seas in the southern end of the North Sea, causing large inundations both in Holland and along the English east coast.

The problem of restoration after such inundation is more difficult than the initial reclaimation of salt marsh by reason of the absence of the salt tolerant flora. Arable crops are quickly killed by relatively low concentrations of salt; certain of the common grasses are more tolerant, but these also may be killed.

The first step towards restoration is to re-establish the drainage system with as little trampling and puddling of the soil as is possible so that leaching of the excess salt can begin. This will proceed more quickly during winter.

The major remaining difficulty results from the formation of sodium clay, which is extremely plastic and sticky when wet and which dries into large, hard clods which do not shatter either under the action of frost or after repeated wetting and drying. If a soil containing any considerable amount of sodium clay is worked while in wet condition, its structure will be completely destroyed, so that rain water will fail to percolate through it. The damage to soil structure is much greater under arable conditions (owing to the absence of a root network and the low humus content) than in grassland.

It is thus inadvisable to attempt cultivation in the early stages, and even later the farmer must be content with very shallow working, with harrows or discs, at times when the lower layers are dry. Ploughing, apart from damaging the structure, would aggravate the problem by bringing heavily impregnated soil to the top.

The reconstitution of calcium clay can be expedited by surface applications of gypsum, which is sufficiently soluble to be carried down in percolating rain water. An ordinary winter's rain—say 12 to 15 in.—

will commonly dissolve about a ton of gypsum per acre. Hence a usual procedure is to apply 2 tons per acre and repeat if necessary after an interval of two years.

It is desirable to establish plant growth as soon as possible, even if there is no prospect of immediate profit from the crop, the point being that the plants will remove a certain amount of salt, and by their root action will help to re-establish soil structure. Barley, all things considered, is the best choice among the arable crops. Beet and mangels are indeed somewhat more salt tolerant, but their harvesting can rarely be achieved without harm to the soil. Ryegrass and the fescues are the most suitable herbage plants.

**Black Fen.**—This type of soil has been produced by the decay of reeds and other marsh vegetation under the prevailing anaerobic conditions. The soil is mainly humus but is not necessarily acid, since typical fen vegetation occurs only where the flood waters contain considerable amounts of lime. Patches of acid peat are, however, found here and there interspersed with the non-acid fen. These areas must be limed and may require dressings of copper, manganese and possibly other minor elements. Drainage presents peculiar difficulties because the soil shrinks and decays when the surplus water is removed and air is admitted. This shrinkage not only soon disturbs tile drains, rendering them quite useless, but the whole surface may ultimately fall below the level of any convenient outlet for a main drain. Thus a large part of the black fen area, which was originally drained by gravity, can now be kept dry only by pumping the drainage waters into embanked rivers.

Drainage alone, in the case of the black fen, may produce land of relatively low value, since the soil, when dry, is often a soot like material that is very subject to drifting. Young seedlings may be blown out by the roots, and the wind carried material frequently fills up the open ditches on which the drainage mostly depends. Fortunately a great deal of the English fen country has a substratum of clay at a depth of a few feet, and it is often necessary in any case (*i.e.* in order to get good drainage) to cut deep and wide ditches which run well down into the clay layer. It is thus often feasible to apply a top dressing of clay to the soil and so give it the necessary cohesion. Large areas of the black fen were treated in this way when the original reclamation was carried out, but in some cases, where the vegetable layer was deep, the labour cost was prohibitive. This fact accounts for the occurrence of patches of " blowing fen " interspersed through areas of much better land. The use of modern mechanical excavators and of crawler tractors may in some cases enable the work of claying to be done at an economic cost.

**Peat Bog.**—Where there is no flow of hard water into a marshy area it is obvious that very acid conditions will develop, and that a type of vegetation very different from that of the fen land will occur. In extreme cases this may consist largely of sphagnum and other mosses. Large areas of lowland peat bog, locally known as " mosses," occurred up till the nineteenth century in various of our western districts—*e.g.* Chat Moss in Lancashire and Solway Moss in Dumfriesshire.

There are at least three possible systems of treatment for such areas after the preliminary work of main drainage has been carried out. In Holland, where there were once large expanses of peat overlying glacial sandy loams, the plan was, and still is, to cut off the upper sod, to dig out the peat and sell it as fuel, and to replace the turf on the mineral soil. The barges used for transporting the peat to towns are used to bring back loads of refuse, which is spread on the reclaimed land and ploughed in. Moderate dressings of lime, phosphate and potash, with sometimes applications of other elements (manganese, magnesium, copper, boron) are then enough to produce tolerable soil conditions for such crops as potatoes, rye and oats. Later on, with further applications of lime, a wider range of crops can be grown.

In north Germany, where large areas of sandy material are overlaid by two or three feet of peat, generally of a kind that cannot profitably be worked for fuel, wide and deep trenches are dug, and the large amount of sand so obtained is spread over the undisturbed surface. The shallow mineral soil so obtained can be neutralised and fertilized much more cheaply than the peat substratum, which is later brought up in small instalments by progressively deeper ploughings.

In still other cases—*e.g.* those of the Lancashire mosses—the procedure was to use the peat itself as the basis of the soil, and to apply large quantities of ashes and other city refuse, with lime and bones, to provide the necessary stock of plant food. By these means, and by the gradual oxidation of the peat itself, a fertile soil was ultimately produced; but it must be remembered that the geographical situation of the Lancashire moss areas was specially favourable—*i.e.* the nearby towns were a convenient source of large quantities of the refuse required, and also provided good markets for farm produce.

**Sandy Heath.**—Where the texture of the parent material of a soil is very sandy, an extreme degree of " podsolization " can occur even under comparatively low rainfall; this is because rain so easily percolates the soil. At first the lime and other bases are washed out, so that acid-tolerant plants become dominant, *e.g.* poor grasses, bracken, gorse and heather. The relatively strong acids produced by the decay of such vegetation dissolve out the iron and aluminium oxides, but these are again precipitated in the lower horizon, in certain cases producing a " hard pan." Percolating water even carries down whatever fine particles (silt, fine sand and clay) the parent material may have contained. Thus is produced the characteristic soil profile, consisting of a thin surface layer of very acid humus, a deeper layer of coarse, bleached sand and a relatively heavy subsoil with or without an actual iron pan.

The destruction of the surface vegetation presents little difficulty since this is usually sparse and the surface soil is very loose and light. If an iron pan is present this must be broken up, and it is often the best plan to accomplish this by trench ploughing, using a heavy, single-furrow tractor plough. The partial reversal of the three soil layers is generally advantageous, since the heaviest material is thus brought to the top and the sour organic matter is put out of the way. Ironstone weathers down fairly rapidly when it is brought to the surface.

The next step is to neutralise the acidity, which of course may be done by means of chalk or ground limestone; but the most successful reclamation has been achieved where there were supplies of marl at reasonable depth and within convenient reach of the farm. In the days of cheap labour, marl was sometimes applied at rates of a hundred or more cart loads an acre, which quantity was sufficient not only to provide an ample reserve of lime, but also to increase very notably the water-holding capacity of the soil. In a few areas the practice of marling has continued even under relatively high wage levels, and it may be that new mechanical methods of accomplishing the work will make for its revival. In the great era of heath land reclamation, when large areas in Norfolk Suffolk, Nottingham and other counties were dealt with, the only other major treatment applied was a heavy application of bones. The recipe, in Norfolk, was " deep ploughing, marl and bones." In many cases, however, the land was grossly deficient in potash and, for lack of potash fertilizers, the cropping capacity remained low until the potash content had been raised by years of stock feeding with large amounts of purchased feeding stuffs, and by feeding, on the farm, all the crop produce except cereal grains. Modern reclamation plans take account of possible shortages of minor elements in addition to the almost universal deficiency of potash.

A further point to note is that it takes some time for even a heavy dressing of chalk, marl or other coarse material to become incorporated with the soil, so that it is best either to begin with acid tolerant crops—lupins and rye being specially suitable—or else to apply a second small dressing of lime, along with the seed, by means of a " combine " drill. This ensures a supply of lime to the young seedlings, which might otherwise find themselves in pockets of acid soil. The first crops should be ploughed in as green manures or folded with sheep, in order to build up a supply of mild humus. After a few years of careful and conservative farming, such land can grow useful crops of barley, roots, clover, sugar beet, carrots and also lucerne leys.

**Moorland.**—There is no clear cut distinction between this type and the last; in both cases we are dealing with a heavily leached and therefore very acid and strongly podzolized soil. But the main cause of the condition in the typical sandy heath is the coarse and open texture of the parent material, whereas in the moors of the northern and western uplands the cause is the low rate of evaporation in relation to the amount of rain that falls—*i.e.* even where the original material has been of rather heavy texture there is excessive percolation. A further point of difference is that our typical moorlands occur in areas covered by glacial drift, where boulders may be so abundant as greatly to increase the cost of reclamation, or even make it prohibitive. Again, drainage is frequently necessary for moorland, and this also may add greatly to the expense. On the other hand it is unnecessary to use bulk materials, such as clay or marl, to improve the water holding capacity of the soil. Finally, there is the point that the reclaimed heath will be best used for arable cropping, whereas for moorland areas the long-ley system (*i.e.* a rotation including only occasional cultivated crops alternating with long periods under pasture) is commonly the most appropriate.

The usual sequence of operations is to burn off the natural herbage (heather, wiregrass, molinia grass), to remove visible boulders, and then to plough and cultivate, making use of the various safety devices that are available to avoid breakages. The disc harrow is useful in the preparation of a tilth. A dressing of one or two tons per acre of lime will generally be enough to neutralise the surface layer of soil so far as to enable useful plants to establish themselves. Moorland soils, however, have a marked capacity to fix phosphate in unavailable form, so that rather heavy dressings of mineral phosphate or basic slag must be applied. Half a ton of mineral phosphate or 15 cwt. of basic slag per acre are common amounts. Potash may or may not be required, but a small application of nitrogen fertilizer is essential to start off the first crop, which commonly consists of grass.

In general, land that carries a strong growth of bracken is a much more promising subject for reclamation than such as is under heather, bilberry, nardus or molinia. Bracken generally infests deeper soils that are relatively rich in potash. Bracken land should be ploughed in June, disced repeatedly and sown to rape. Either in the following spring, or after a further " pioneer " crop, the land is sown to ley, preferably without a nurse crop. If fronds of bracken continue to appear these should be destroyed, while still young, by a heavy roller.

It will be obvious that reclaimed moorland will tend to revert to its natural condition unless steps are taken to prevent this. The essential steps are periodic ploughings and applications of lime and phosphates.

**Derelict Clay.**—The wide areas of heavy clay in the Midland counties of England, in Suffolk and Essex and in the Weald of Kent and Sussex, carried a natural vegetation of deciduous trees—oak, ash, alder, willow— according to the local drainage and other conditions. Large areas of the forest were cleared in early times, when more easily cultivated land was still neglected. The reason for this was that heavy soil maintained its cropping capacity, under the old three field system, much better than light. Up till about 1875 wheat production on clay soil still remained profitable, but from that time onwards the clay lands, except in the driest areas, were increasingly laid down or allowed to tumble down, to grass.

Where the drainage system was well maintained, where phosphate was supplied and a good system of grassland management was observed, the pasture remained productive; but on much of the poorer land the cost of these measures was not covered by the returns, and deterioration set in. The state of a typical semi-derelict clay area is as follows. The surface is generally in ridge and furrow, originally laid out in order to provide surface drainage, and the land has been enclosed by hedge and ditch. The ditches, however, have become choked and often overgrown by the adjoining hedges, so that the escape of surface water is no longer possible. This has resulted in the invasion of the sward by water tolerant plants such as rushes and tussock grass, which commonly grow in bands along the furrows. The upper part of the ridges may still produce a tolerably good sward, unless invasion by hawthorn, wild rose and bramble (which is part of the process of reversion), has become widespread. A further point is that the ant population is usually high, and the surface may be closely dotted with ant hills, a foot or more in height and two or three feet in diameter. If the soil has become highly acid there will be a surface " mat " of dead, undecayed herbage, but severe soil acidity and the resultant mat are by no means universal.

The first step in reclamation is to clear the ditches. This may often be done, at relatively small cost, by the use of a mechanical drag line, excavator or other power implement. The use of such a machine may, however, be impossible until hedge cutting has been carried out. Exploration of the excavated ditch will often disclose the ends of tile drains, and these should be cleared and repaired. The next operation is to remove the thorn and scrub. Moderately small bushes may be most easily uprooted by a tractor with attached ropes or chains—e.g. three men may wind their respective ropes round three separate thorn bushes or patches of scrub and the tractor may then pull up the whole simultaneously. Other devices of the bulldozer type, fixed in front of the tractor, may give good results with less man power. Larger trees may be uprooted by various types of winches. The scrub is later collected and burnt. Ant hills, if not very numerous, can be cut up by hand labour, a broad bladed mattock or adze being used. If numerous, they may be cut off by a special implement and afterwards chopped up by a disc harrow. In some cases a heavy disc harrow, used two or three times, will itself do all that is necessary.

If it appears that the land will still be wet, the possibility of mole drainage should be explored before the more expensive tile system is adopted.

Even if a system of under-drainage is installed the ridges should not be immediately levelled because this will put all the former top soil into the furrow and leave barren subsoil exposed along what was the crown of the ridge. It is better to carry out the levelling process by stages, applying at each stage extra fertilizer along the lines of the old crowns. The ploughing of steeply ridged land by multi-furrow tractor ploughs is difficult, and a single-furrow plough is to be preferred. In some cases ploughing has been done at right angles to the ridges and the furrows retained, but a high ridge and furrow layout is a great obstacle to mechanised cultivation. A rather heavy dressing of phosphate is almost invariably necessary to the production of arable crops or a good pasture sward. The soil should be tested for lime and available potash before any decision is made in regard to applying these.

**Downland.**—Chalk down commonly carries a thin soil, but the underlying chalk is so porous that crops do not greatly suffer from drought. The typical herbage is grass, with scattered gorse and hawthorn, but fairly dense scrub may occur. Extreme potash deficiency is common. The scrub may be pulled by tractor and drawchains, swept into windrows and later burnt. It must be remembered that the soil may contain great numbers of seeds of shrubs, so that two or three years of arable cropping should precede re-seeding to grass. There is a tendency for such soils to fix potash, and so it is usually profitable to sow the cereal in a combine drill using a fertilizer relatively high in potash.

## DRAINAGE

The purpose of drainage is to increase the productiveness of agricultural soils by removing the free water which, mainly by excluding air, inhibits the growth and activity of plant roots. The need of drainage in any particular soil is exhibited by a wet and spongy surface, by the presence of rushes, sedges, tussock grass and other inferior herbage, by the stunted and sickly appearance of growing crops, which may be drowned out altogether in the hollows and by the presence of pools of water and of characteristic dark coloured, damp patches on cultivated fields. Wet land may be unable to bear the weight of tractors or stand the carting of roots in winter, and it cannot be stocked for fear of lasting damage to the soil texture. The colour of the subsoil tends to be grey, blue or green instead of red, yellow or brown as in soil that is satisfactorily aerated. As noted in the description of gley soils (p. 9) the zone of fluctuating water table is marked by mottled coloration. Even where the surface shows no sign of wetness a high water table may create conditions that are little better than complete waterlogging.

The improvements brought about by drainage are manifold:—

(1) The soils are more easily and sooner worked in spring. Undrained soils have a high specific heat, are slow to warm up in the spring and, owing to the risk of puddling, cannot be subjected to the acts of tillage until excess water has been removed by evaporation. The improved mechanical condition, higher temperature and earliness induced by drainage allow

of a longer growing season and earlier ripening. As seed time and harvest are earlier, arable crops may be grown instead of grass, and fallowing may be superseded by green cropping. It must be understood, however, that drainage cannot lower the water content below the inherent field capacity of the soil and that, in the case of heavy soils, this is far above the limit at which tillage can be undertaken. The result is that clays lie wet in winter even if there is little rain and become fit to till only after exposure to drying winds.

(2) When the water is carried away from the surface layers of the soil, air enters the pore spaces and plant roots extend downwards. Thus the weathering of a fresh horizon of mineral matter is induced, the crops are able to absorb food from a greater volume of soil, and the produce is improved as regards both quantity and quality. When pasture is drained the poor herbage gradually disappears and is replaced by strong growing natural grasses of superior nutritive value and by white clover. Even in very dry summers drained land gives better results than does undrained, because the plant roots are so much better developed.

(3) The beneficial action of micro-organisms is stimulated and there is consequently a more rapid liberation of plant food; lime and manures act better and more quickly. Certain parasites of live stock, such as liver-flukes and some parasitic worms, are reduced as surface dampness is removed.

(4) The percolation of water to the drains has a washing action on the soil particles, so that poisonous substances, which tend to accumulate under waterlogged conditions, are carried away, and, in the case of a soil rich in alkaline substances, the efflorescence of injurious salts is stopped.

Rivulets and streams form the natural drainage of any catchment area and must necessarily, in the course of time, remove all the rain water that is not utilised by plants or evaporated. In order more rapidly to dispose of rain water, and for other reasons such as the prevention of flooding, river courses may be modified and ditches added to the natural waterways. The construction, cleaning and repair of these channels are generally the tasks of a public board or local authority.

Field drains may be open furrows or ditches or covered pipes. Open drains are less desirable as they occupy an area that might otherwise bear a crop, interfere with the movement of implements and with cultivation, harbour weeds and pests and are costly in upkeep. They are, however, necessary where covered drains would be silted up by tidal or flood waters or choked by tree roots, and also in deep peat or black fen soils, where tiles are liable to be displaced by the irregular shrinkage of the soil. They are also used in certain systems of irrigation and sewage farming. Ditches should be constructed so that they are sufficiently deep and capacious to drain the land they serve; the slope of their sides should be more gradual in friable than in strong soils so that they neither cave in nor slide and their fall should be such that the water causes neither scouring nor silting. In practice, most systems of farm drainage have numerous covered field drains leading to one or two ditches, which in turn flow into a natural waterway.

Sheep or hill drains are narrow and shallow ditches made by digging out the soil to a depth of about a foot, and heaping the excavated material and turf on the lower side; they are dug to ameliorate marshy conditions where under-drainage would be either impossible or uneconomic. They can be made by means of a specially designed plough.

**Principles of Drainage.**—Except under arid conditions (where all the rain that falls is evaporated) there is a certain ground horizon below which water fills the pore space. The upper limit of this zone of saturation forms a plane that is known as the water table. When rain falls upon the ground its fate depends on a number of factors, such as the temperature and humidity of the air, the presence or absence of a crop and the permeability and wetness of the soil. Usually some evaporates or is used by the vegetation, some is held by the soil, and some percolates downwards to the water table or drains away.

Rainfall in Britain is distributed fairly evenly throughout the year but there is far more evaporation in summer than in winter; moreover, plants transpire much water during the growing season. Thus in summer, soils tend to lose water and dry from the surface downwards. During winter, on the other hand, rainfall exceeds evaporation and water accumulates, first satisfying the field capacity of the soil and then causing the water table to rise. In normal seasons, and in all but our wettest areas, the only drains that run in summer are those which are supplied by springs; in autumn they will not run until the " field capacity " of the soil has been satisfied, *i.e.* until the soil contains more water than it can hold against the force of gravity; in winter they are likely to run almost continuously, or at any rate after every fall of rain. Light soils are freely permeable and have a low field capacity, so their drains are the first to run.

The permeability of soil depends on its relative proportions of clay and coarse particles. Pure or fairly pure clay, when puddled, is practically impermeable. At the other extreme, sands and gravels drain with great rapidity. Indeed, on much of our light land the farmer's main problem is to increase the water holding capacity. Most soils are, of course, intermediate in type and even those rich in clay can be made permeable throughout the horizon of tillage by employing lime, organic manure and cultivations to secure an aggregation of the fine soil particles and an improved crumb structure.

Where soil and subsoil are coarse in structure, water gravitates downwards, more or less vertically, from pore space to pore space; but when the subsoil is clay the only channels for downward movement are those left by roots and worms or formed by cracking during periods of drought. In light land the water table rises after rain until it reaches the level of the drains and the water finds a way of escape, but in heavy land the drains are fed from above by way of the few open channels and the lines of weakness in the disturbed soil over the tiles.

The object of drainage is to offer a quick means of escape for water that is doing injury, and the depth and frequency of the drains are arranged to remove the water as effectively as possible yet at a minimum of cost. There is no profit in drainage unless its cost is more than met by the value of the improvement, and only land that is potentially fairly fertile is likely to bear the full cost of thorough tile drainage. State grants are available to cover part of the approved cost.

The distance between the drains is determined by the texture of the soil. Clay soils offer so much resistance to the passage of water that they drain much more slowly than soils which are coarse in texture. Consequently, in order to get rid of surplus water reasonably quickly, it is necessary on clay soils to multiply the avenues of escape. In other words, the drains have to be placed at relatively close intervals. In the case of light soils, where tiles " draw " for a greater distance, it is obviously economical to space the drains more widely.

The depth of the drains has also to do with the rate of percolation. In heavy land, drains will not act with sufficient rapidity unless they are placed comparatively near the surface, say 2 or $2\frac{1}{2}$ ft. Indeed, the water might fail to reach deep drains. On the other hand, drains may be placed at a greater depth in light soils; and because the deeper a drain is placed, provided that it works satisfactorily, the greater its " draw " and the fewer the number of tiles required for a given area, it is economical to place drains as deep as the texture of the soil will permit.

The following are the usual depths and intervals adopted for draining in this country:—

| Soil | Depth in Feet | Interval in Feet |
|------|---------------|------------------|
| Clay | 2  to $2\frac{1}{2}$ | 12 to 20 |
| Medium loam | $2\frac{1}{2}$ ,, 3 | 20 ,, 30 |
| Sandy loam | 3  ,, 4 | 30 ,, 40 |
| Peaty | At least $3\frac{1}{2}$ | 18 ,, 21 |

The drains in peaty soils may be laid 4 to 5 ft. deep to allow for settling and shrinkage of the upper layers, or may be placed even deeper if this would enable the tiles to rest upon a firm bed of mineral material.

In theory, farm drains should run satisfactorily if they have a fall of not less than 1 in 660, but, owing to the difficulty in ensuring perfect grading, it is considered that where possible the minimum in practice should be 1 in 250. The fall should be uniform, and on no account should a change be made from a steep to a less steep grade, because the check in the velocity of the running water will result in a deposition of silt which may choke the drain. If such a change is unavoidable a silt basin should be constructed at the junction of the two grades. A basin of this kind is a shallow well into which the water pours, is checked, and deposits much of its sediment, and from which, at a point slightly below the in-flow, it passes out into the drain with the lesser gradient. The basin is covered to prevent accidents, and the sediment is removed as often as is necessary. A large sewer tile, perforated for the affluent and effluent drains, placed vertically in the ground and covered by a stone slab, forms a cheap basin. In some cases, where there is no alternative, drains have been laid on the level across a field from one ditch to another. On a steep slope an oblique drain is more effective than one running up and down the slope.

Drain tiles should be circular in cross-section with regular ends that can be closely joined; they should be hard and should emit a clear

*Acres Drained by Tile Mains*

| Slope in Feet per 100 Feet | Size of Tiles in Inches | | | | | |
|---|---|---|---|---|---|---|
| | 4 | 5 | 6 | 8 | 10 | 12 |
| 0·2 | 4 | 9 | 14 | 30 | 55 | 90 |
| 0·3 | 6 | 12 | 18 | 37 | 67 | 111 |
| 0·4 | 7 | 14 | 21 | 44 | 79 | 127 |
| 0·5 | 8 | 15 | 23 | 50 | 89 | 142 |
| 0·6 | 9 | 16 | 25 | 54 | 98 | 156 |
| 0·7 | 10 | 17 | 27 | 58 | 106 | 169 |
| 0·8 | 10 | 18 | 29 | 62 | 113 | 181 |
| 0·9 | 11 | 19 | 31 | 65 | 120 | 191 |
| 1·0 | 11 | 20 | 33 | 68 | 126 | 200 |
| 2·0 | 16 | 28 | 46 | 97 | 176 | 280 |
| 3·0 | 18 | 34 | 55 | 118 | 212 | 350 |

ring when struck ; they should be reasonably smooth on the inside and free from cracks that might reduce their strength.

In considering the size of drain tiles it is necessary to divide drains into two classes: (1) Lateral Field Drains; (2) Main and Sub-main Drains.

(1) Tile drains of less than 3 in. diameter were often used in old field drainage work, but are now seldom laid. Experience has shown that there are greater risks of irregular laying and displacement with the smaller diameter tiles, and of more frequent blocking up with silt. Provided 3 in. laterals are suitably spaced with due regard to soil type, they should function satisfactorily up to 250 yd. on a slope of not less than 1 in 250 under climatic conditions in the country. There are risks in laying laterals that are too short, in that if there is insufficient weight of water to flush them out from time to time, they soon become silted up.

(2) Mains and sub-mains are different. Their size should be proportional to the rainfall, and the area and general slope of the land from which they receive drainage, without reference to the arrangement,

number or size of the laterals used in the system. Experiments have been made to ascertain the carrying capacity of pipe lines having different degrees of fall, and from the results it is possible to plan a drainage system capable of removing any quantity of water in a given time. While bigger drains will obviously be needed in wet districts than in dry, their actual size must also depend on the speed with which the water should be removed. If drains are made large enough to carry away the heaviest precipitation as fast as it falls, as in draining a street, the cost will be very high. On the other hand, the removal of the water must be sufficiently expeditious to prevent the water table from rising and remaining in contact with plant roots for long enough to do harm. Actually the soil acts as a buffer between the rain and the drains, and usually allows the water to escape much more slowly than it is received, thus lessening the need for large tiles. In the end the drainage engineer, from his knowledge of the rainfall and other relevant factors, must plan for the removal of a given amount of rain in a given time, say for an inch or a suitable fraction thereof in a day. The figures on the previous page are taken from a leaflet issued by the U.S. Department of Agriculture. They show the relationship between tiles, falls and acreages where $\frac{1}{2}$ in. of rain has to be removed in 24 hours. This rate of removal should be satisfactory for somewhat wetter than average British conditions. In other districts where the removal of $\frac{3}{8}$ in. of rain in 24 hours would be satisfactory, the acres per drain may be increased by one-third; in the driest places the areas may be doubled. On the other hand, in the wettest parts, or where it is important to prevent any rise in the water table, the same drains may be used for three-quarters or even half the stated acreages. In practice it is, of course, frequently necessary to increase the size of the mains as, stage by stage, they are fed by field drains in their passage towards the outfall.

**The Practice of Drainage.**—The first thing to do in drainage practice is to decide on the system that is to be constructed and the location of the drains, and it is often helpful to dig a number of pits so as to observe the nature of the subsoil. A *natural system* is one where a line of tiles with a few branches is laid to drain a small area by following the natural outlets from higher to lower levels, The principal drain follows the chief depression and, where necessary, branches are run up the adjoining hollows. An *intercepting system* is one designed to catch water where it is seeping from a higher to a lower level and to remove it before it can do any harm to the bottom land. For example, a drain may be led across a slope to intercept water that it welling from a line of springs. A *parallel system* consists of a series of parallel field drains discharging into mains, which in turn carry the water away to some natural waterway. In undulating land the main drains usually follow the lowest levels, the sub-mains the lesser hollows, and the laterals are constructed either up or across the slopes according to the gradients. Fig. 1 illustrates simple systems of drainage. In practice, the best layout of the tiles must be decided in the

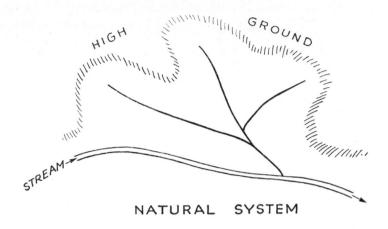

NATURAL SYSTEM

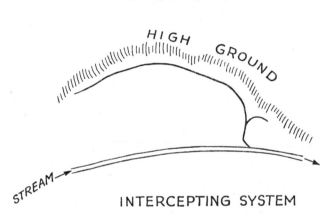

INTERCEPTING SYSTEM

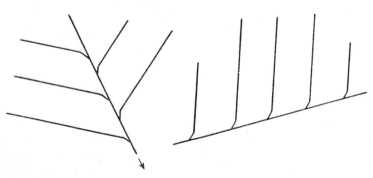

PARALLEL SYSTEMS

FIG. 1.—Arrangement of Drains

field, and this is likely to involve the adoption and modification of several systems.  The line of the main drains should be kept well clear of hedges or trees whose roots might block the tiles, and it is a good plan to keep clear of headlands where much carting is done.  Great care must be taken in choosing an outlet for the main or leading drain.  A clear drop into a ditch or other channel is best.  Actually the difficulty of securing a good discharge point is a frequent obstacle to field drainage.

Having decided on the most suitable system, the next thing is to fix the exact position of the lines of drains.  This may necessitate the use of levelling instruments.  If the fall is very slight or obscure, most farmers would be well advised to call in the assistance of a surveyor, but if a good fall is assured and the system is not too elaborate, one should be able, by the occasional use of rough levelling devices such as boning rods and spirit-levels, to carry out the whole of the work.[1]

When a field of uncertain slope is to be drained it should be divided into squares by driving pegs into the ground.  A level survey should then be made and each peg marked with its own level.  If the position and levels of the pegs are marked on an ordnance survey map of the field, the slope will at once be apparent, and the location of the drains can be made accordingly.  The next thing to do is to put in a series of pegs along the line of each drain to mark the gradient.  For example, suppose a lateral is 10 chains long and the difference between its highest and lowest levels is 3 ft. 4 in. *i.e.* it has a fall on 4 in. per chain.  A peg should be driven into the soil at the top of the slope so that it protrudes 2 ft. above the surface,  and, using a level and staff, another peg is driven at every chain down the slope so that the top of each peg is 4 ins. below the level of the previous peg.  A line along the tops of the pegs will represent the gradient of the drain.

When the location of the drains has been fixed, the drain tiles should be carted on to the land and laid down in convenient rows.  The number of linear yards of tiles per acre is got by dividing 4840 by the proposed interval in yards between the drains.  A 10-yd. interval would give 484 yd. of tiles, and if each tile is 1 ft. long [2] the number required would be 1452, This number, however, must be increased by an allowance for breakages. and sufficient tiles must also be obtained for the mains and sub-mains. On boggy land the tiles  may have to be laid on wooden soles to prevent their displacement, and the depth may have to be 4 or 5 ft. to allow for subsequent shrinkage.

When the drains are to be excavated by hand a cord is stretched on the ground to mark the true line of the trench along which the drainer works with his shovels and ditching spades.  The top of the excavation need not be more than 12 to 14 in. wide, and the trench is narrowed to the

---

[1] For a full explanation of the use of levelling instruments, the reader is advised to consult one of the numerous textbooks on Surveying.

[2] Tiles are ordinarily made from 12 to 15 in. in length.

breadth of the tile at the bottom. Considerable economy may be effected by ploughing out the top layers of the soil, or, better still, by using a mechanical excavator to remove all the material down to the required depth.

Drainage machines differ in construction. Some have bucket or endless chain dredgers, which, when propelled slowly over the ground, dig a trench to the required depth. Another is fitted with an enormous trenching plough and, when drawn by a tractor winch, can open a ditch 27 in. deep; a deeper trench can be made by fitting the machine with a deep excavating unit and going over the ground a second time.

When the trench is completed its bottom must be uniformly graded before the tiles are laid. To do this the drainer makes the bottom of his trench run parallel with the line along the tops of the gradient pegs. The prearranged depth at which the drain is to be placed +2 ft. (the height of the datum gradient peg) will be the depth of the bottom of the drain at any point along the line. Using an ⌐-shaped rod to take sights along the tops of the pegs, the drainer carefully checks the depth of his trench, and, using his drain scoop, levels and grades the bottom until the fall is accurate and uniform. Whenever possible the flow of water should be tested before the tiles are laid.

The next part of the work is to lay the tiles, lowering them into position by means of a tile hook and packing them carefully at the sides. The end of each lateral drain where it enters the main should be curved to form an angle of 30° to 45° with the larger drain, and should point in the direction of flow. Junction tiles undoubtedly give the most satisfactory and accurate jointing. If not available, the top of the lateral should be laid level with the top of the main and a good junction made by chipping the tiles. Where necessary, a little cement can be used to prevent silting at a rough junction.

Great care must be taken in the construction of the discharge point of the main into the natural waterway. Glazed tiles only should be used at this point, as ordinary porous tiles are soon broken to pieces by the action of frost. The last tile should be cemented into a brick or concrete foundation which cannot be undermined by running water, and the end should be covered by a grating to prevent the entrance of vermin.

The trenches may be filled in by means of a spade, a plough or a special soil scraper, stiff clay being left out where possible.

When the work has been completed, a survey of the drainage system should be drawn up and entered on the plan of the field. Such a plan will prove of immense value should it be necessary to trace a choked or displaced drain.

Tile draining is a costly operation, and the number of craftsmen skilled in tile draining is decreasing. The search for a satisfactory mechanical drainer goes on. The more promising developments seem to lie with a machine which draws a mole drain and then lines it with a layer of concrete or other suitable material. One such machine appears promising, and if successful it is estimated that the costs of tile draining might be reduced by some 75 per cent.

## MOLE DRAINAGE

With the exception of permanence, mole drainage has practically all the advantages of ordinary tile drainage, and is far less costly; but it can only be practised on soils which are heavy in texture and free from stones or veins of sand or gravel, and on land with a smooth and regular surface where a good fall is assured; again, the life is short on arable land, especially where heavy implements are used. Under suitable conditions, in soils containing at least 45 per cent. clay and not more than 20 per cent. sand, the drains may last eight years or more; on soils containing rather less clay and more sand their life will be proportionately shorter; on soils with less than 35 per cent. clay and more than 45 per cent. sand the job should not be attempted.

The drainage is performed by dragging a projectile shaped iron " mole " fixed on the end of a strong knife-edged coulter through the soil at a depth varying from 15 to 30 in. The mole is usually about $2\frac{1}{2}$ to $3\frac{1}{2}$ in. in diameter and its passage forms an underground tunnel which serves to remove superfluous water. The walls of the tunnel do not readily collapse and the passage is kept clear by the action of running water. Heavy soils, except for a few surface inches, become practically impermeable, and it has been shown that water reaches the moles almost entirely through the coulter slits.

The construction of mole ploughs varies considerably. The smaller implements, capable of making a $2\frac{1}{4}$ in. drain at a depth of 16 in. have frames rather like ordinary ploughs, guiding handles and very long slades; they can be drawn by an average sized farm tractor. The larger mole drainers have heavy frames mounted on wheels: when pulled by steam tackle of the winding gear type, powerful track-laying tractors or a tractor winch, they can be used to draw a $3\frac{1}{2}$ in. mole at a depth of as much as $2\frac{1}{2}$ ft.

Where shallow draining is being carried out, it is usual to run a mole every 3 yd., but when the depth is over 2 ft. the interval can be increased to 4 or 5 yd. In all cases where the land is laid up in ridges the drains run in the furrow bottoms. Where a very old system of tile drains is beginning to work unsatisfactorily, it is often preferable to proceed with mole drainage at a lesser depth, if the soil is suitable, rather than to carry out costly renovation.

Outfalls and mains for mole drains should be made first so that if the work is interrupted, the system will function as far as it is completed. Heavy rains may do serious damage in silting up mole channels that are drawn before an outlet is provided.

It is preferable to lay tile outfalls and mains for a mole drainage system. Moles drawn from a ditch, even if the outlets are tiled later, or larger moles drawn to act as mains and outfalls are seldom very satisfactory. If good tile outfalls and mains are laid, then mole drains can be drawn over the mains from time to time. This is an operation that is relatively low in cost and can be repeated whenever it is observed that the old moles are not functioning satisfactorily.

# IRRIGATION

The only important natural source of soil water is rain, the amounts supplied in the form of dew and by hygroscopic absorption being negligible. The two main causes of loss are firstly drainage, and secondly transpiration by growing plants. Losses by evaporation from the soil surface are, under British conditions, relatively small. The main factor affecting the rate of transpiration is sunshine. Wind is a minor factor, and in any case total air movement per year shows much less variation from one area to another than rainfall or sunshine. Low rainfall areas are generally sunny, and so the water requirements of plants are higher in low rainfall areas than elsewhere.

In arid regions, where the bulk of the plant's water requirements must be supplied artificially, and where evaporation from the soil surface is considerable, the quality of the irrigation water is important. If its content of soluble salts (especially those of sodium) is high, the accumulation of salt in the soil water may proceed rapidly. Many irrigation schemes have broken down because the soil has salted up. This problem does not arise in Britain, where irrigation in the open is used only to supplement the natural rainfall during the growing season and where the amounts required are ordinarily equivalent to only 2 or 3 in. of rain.

Even in our lowest rainfall areas the soil commonly reaches its field capacity by the end of the year, and further additions, from rain or melted snow, escape after a longer or shorter interval through the drainage system. Field drains commonly continue to run until the spring. Thereafter, on cropped land, the loss of water by transpiration will usually exceed the amount supplied as rain, so that in all but the wettest areas the soil moisture content falls below the field capacity. This loss, however, can go some way before it begins to restrict transpiration and plant growth, the amount of loss that can be tolerated, in soils of medium depth and texture, being equivalent to some 2 or 3 in. of rain. If the soil dries out still more, growth will be checked.

Crops on a shallow, sandy or gravelly soil will suffer sooner and more severely than those on deep heavy loams. Again, as is well known, crop species show varying powers of drought resistance, the main factor being the balance between the depth and range of their root systems and the area of their leaf surface; thus wheat and lucerne are more drought resistant than oats and ryegrass. The date up to which active transpiration

C

continues is another factor. Thus winter oats, because they cease to transpire actively by late June or early July, are less susceptible to drought damage than spring oats, which continue to need moisture for a month longer. Similarly kale, although deep rooted, will suffer from a late summer drought that would not affect barley. In general, plants with a long growing season—sugar beet, main crop potatoes, most leafy vegetables, and especially grasses and clovers—require more water to enable full growth than cereals and late sown annual crops such as turnips.

Some progress has been made in mapping the country from the point of view of the expected response to irrigation of grass together with such long season leafy crops as sugar beet, kale and brassicas. In our driest and sunniest area—that bordering on the lower Thames estuary—substantial response to irrigation would be expected in nine summers out of every ten; and in the south-eastern half of England (the line running from the Humber to South Devon) response would follow in five or more years out of ten.

The earliest systems of irrigation in this country date back to the eighteenth century, when the commonest type was the water meadow, an area of valley bottom land with a brook or stream as a source of supply. The area was laid out in a more or less irregular system of ridge and furrow, with supply channels running along the ridges and open drainage channels along the furrows. Water meadows, under suitable conditions, provided good early grazing and later good yields of hay. But the labour cost of upkeep is very high at present-day wage rates, and the layout prevents the use of modern hay making machinery. Very few remain in operation.

In arid countries, until comparatively recent times, the choice of system was between flooding, sub-surface watering and a method similar in principle to that used in water meadows. Flood irrigation is normal in the cultivation of " swamp " rice. In the sub-surface system the water is led along shallow furrows, with a gentle and even slope running as nearly parallel as may be and at fairly close intervals. The slow-flowing water thus seeps into the lower zone of the soil and spreads laterally from either side of each strip. The system is specially suited to orchards. In recent times spray irrigation has become much more common, and it would seem that under British conditions, where relatively small applications suffice, the spray system is the most appropriate.

Much research and experimental work is under way to determine the most effective and labour saving methods of applying water to crops. A number of instruments is now available to indicate when irrigation is necessary, and automatic watering of glass houses is becoming more common. The reader who wishes to follow these newer developments, particularly in horticulture where it is necessary to be more precise as to time, quantity and quality of water to be given, is referred to the Ministry of Agriculture, Fisheries and Food Bulletin No. 138. Irrigation (second edition) and to other works on horticulture.

Earlier it was generally assumed that only market garden crops could repay the cost of irrigation, except perhaps on land immediately adjacent to rivers. It is now evident that in the drier areas such arable crops as sugar beet, fodder beet, kale, mangels and main-crop potatoes, as well as cabbage, brussels sprouts and other market vegetables that are commonly grown on a farm scale, could profitably be irrigated. Irrigation is also being practised on grass where accessible and cheap sources of water are available.

Irrigation under certain circumstances can have other effects than the mere supply of water. Sewage irrigation results in addition in the supply of plant nutrients, a chalky source of water may help to neutralise soil acidity and early growth in the spring may be stimulated if the water assists in raising the soil temperature.

Some references are made to irrigation practice under certain crops in Part 2.

## WARPING

The practice of warping consists of flooding land with water containing a large load of rich sediment in order to form a new layer of soil, and the source of supply is generally a muddy tidal river. At high tide the lock gates are opened and the water is allowed to rush up channels and to flood the land quickly; the gates are closed and small sluices are opened which allow the water to escape slowly. The check in the velocity of the water brought about in this way causes a deposition of sediment. Near tidal rivers this treatment can be carried out daily, though usually only the larger tides can be used, and in a few years a layer of extraordinarily rich alluvium is laid down. After this the warping is stopped, and the original channels are retained for drainage purposes.

A large area of poor peaty land along the banks of the Humber and lower Trent was warped in the latter part of last century, and some has been done more recently. The area is now under intensive cultivation and produces very heavy crops of potatoes and wheat. The term " warp land " is sometimes applied to natural as well as artificial alluvium.

# CHAPTER 4

# MANURES AND FERTILIZERS

THE fertilizing value of animal excrement, litter and certain waste material has been known from very early times. As recently as last century the only manures used, apart from dung and lime, were substances like bones, ashes, shoddy and soot, but in modern times researches in chemistry and plant physiology have led to the introduction of a great many substances having manurial value, and the classification of fertilizers is now quite complex.

As mentioned before, plants must be able to obtain about a dozen elements if they are to grow healthily. Many of these elements are present in abundance in normal soils, and manuring concerns only the addition of those that are so deficient or so unavailable as to limit plant development. It has been found by trial that the only elements ordinarily required in large amounts to improve fertility are nitrogen, phosphorus, potassium and calcium. Compounds of other elements, *e.g.* boron, manganese, magnesium, zinc, copper may properly be regarded as fertilizers, but several of these are required only in comparatively small areas of this country, and then only in small amounts. The science of manuring deals with the discovery of suitable compounds of plant foods, their specific effects upon plant and animal, and the most profitable methods of applying them.

Manures and fertilizers may be classified as " straight " or " compound " according to whether they supply one only or several of the elements required by plants; or they may be divided into organic and inorganic fertilizers according to their origin. The bulkier organic materials are usually referred to as manures and the more concentrated as fertilizers. The term " artificials " should be avoided since certain fertilizers, like potash salts, nitrate of soda and mineral phosphate are naturally occurring substances.

**Soil Examination and Testing.**—Much work has been done in recent years to develop reliable methods of estimating the " available " nutrients in soils. Though no one method is suitable for all soils in Great Britain, the choice now lies between two or three. There have also been numbers of trials to ascertain if data so obtained can be related to likely crop responses from different soils following the application of fertilizers.

Much wider use is likely to be made in Great Britain of " soil series " as a means of classifying and evaluating soils, as the Soil Survey covers more and more areas. Information is accumulating as to their relative plant food status of differing soils, and the likely responses from applications of fertilizers applied to correct any deficiencies.

These aids to soil assessment can be used with greater confidence where the local conditions are known and information is available on the past history of the land in question and its intended use. Field examination is certainly desirable before the value of taking a soil sample for analysis can be assessed; and if a sample is thought to be necessary, consideration should then be given as to whether a soil or sub-soil sample or both are necessary and at what respective depths they should be taken.

The " lime-requirement " of a soil is estimated as explained on page 23. The determination of " available " phosphate and potash can be carried out by extracting the soil with weak acetic, citric or other acid, or even water. The results are then interpreted by comparison with the analyses of similar soils of known nutrient requirements.

Phosphate and potash contents can be expressed as very low, low, medium low, medium high and high. Normally, marked crop response can be expected from the application of phosphate and/or potash fertilizers if either or both is very low or low, provided there is no other serious limiting factor to crop growth, as for example poor drainage.

## LIME

Calcium is an essential plant nutrient, and lime—*i.e.* calcium carbonate —has highly important secondary effects upon the soil and upon the growth of plants. It improves the texture of the soil by flocculating the clay particles and is particularly beneficial to heavy land. It is the most important base in the soil and it determines the soil's reaction; it has to be employed to counteract the acidity produced by such fertilizers as sulphate of ammonia. The presence of lime is necessary for nitrification, nitrogen fixation and other bacterial activities. Liming old ploughed-up grassland leads to the liberation of a useful supply of nitrogen and perhaps a little phosphoric acid that has been locked up in plant remains. Liming acid land also reduces the tendency for the phosphoric acid of fertilizers to be fixed quickly in an unavailable form. On the other hand, liming may throw out of solution some of the minor elements, particularly manganese and boron, thereby creating a deficiency, and over-liming should therefore be avoided.

A shortage of lime is indicated by the accumulation and slow decay of organic matter, often forming thick springy turfs of unrotted plant debris, by the presence of exceptionally high proportions of certain weeds such as sorrel, spurrey and yellow corn marigold, and by the failure of crops like red clover, barley and sugar beet. Another point is that there are very few earthworms in acid soil.

Chemical methods have been worked out to measure the hydrogen ion concentration and the " lime-requirement " of soils (see pp. 22-25).

These estimations are valuable particularly if used in conjunction with the evidence afforded by the growth of crop plants and weeds on the soil in question.

**Shell and Ground Lime.**—Shell lime is prepared by heating limestone rock to a temperature which reduces the calcium carbonate to calcium oxide or quicklime with the liberation of carbonic acid gas. Its exact composition depends on the purity of the rock, which may be almost pure calcium carbonate. Quicklime is hygroscopic and also takes up carbonic acid from the air. Thus unless the quicklime is freshly prepared it is liable to contain a portion of hydroxide and carbonate.

It was usual to apply shell lime where rather large dressings per acre were required—2 tons or more per acre. The lime was carted out into small heaps placed at regular intervals in the field and after it had been allowed to crumble and " slake " to calcium hydroxide was spread by shovels.

With the advent of mechanical lime spreaders and the extension of contract services for lime spreading, shell lime is now seldom used. Shell lime ground to powder or " slaked " to powder in the form of calcium hydroxide may be spread by fertilizer distributors, but liming is now carried out more commonly with ground limestone or chalk.

**Ground Limestone.**—This is prepared by grinding the naturally occurring rock to a fine powder. It may be slow to act if it is not finely ground and uniformly distributed throughout the soil, but when ground to pass through a sieve with 100 meshes to the inch it has been found to be as effective in sour soil as an equivalent amount of burnt lime. When over 30 per cent. passes this sieve it is fine enough for ordinary purposes. Since $1\frac{3}{4}$ tons of ground limestone are equivalent in effect to 1 ton of shell lime, a heavier application of the former is required. Its advantages as compared with burnt lime are that it can be kept indefinitely without deterioration, that it is much more pleasant to handle and that its use in quantity has no damaging effect on crops; it is also, in many localities, cheaper than burnt or hydrated lime, not only weight for weight, but also unit for unit, calculated in terms of calcium oxide.

Certain limestones contain up to 50 per cent. or more of magnesium carbonate. These can be of especial value on soils having a deficiency of magnesium. Magnesium limestone tends to increase the magnesium content of pastures on acid soils, and may help to reduce the risk of " Grass Staggers ", though by itself it may not prevent the occurrence of that condition.

**Chalk.**—Chalk, where it occurs naturally and can be obtained cheaply, is applied to the soil instead of lime. Some applications of lump chalk are still made where heavier dressings per acre are required, but the bulk of this material is now applied in the ground form frequently direct from contractor's vehicles, equipped with a spreading mechanism.

**Waste Limes.**—Waste limes, usually in the form of finely divided and rather wet calcium carbonate, are obtainable in certain districts from sugar factories and paper mills. They may be used for agricultural purposes in place of ground limestone. They may be so wet and pasty that they have to be heaped and allowed to dry before being spread. Occasionally they contain injurious substances, a point worthy of enquiry before they are used on a large scale.

Marl and shell sand are other calcium-rich substances cheaply obtainable in some places.

## PHOSPHATE FERTILIZERS

Phosphorus is an essential constituent of protoplasm and is necessary for cell division; it is assimilated mostly when the plants are young, and it is largely translocated to the seed during the process of ripening.

Phosphate stimulates root development in young plants, and it is consequently of great value in the case of a crop like turnips, which is shallow rooted and sometimes difficult to start, and on strong clay soils which do not permit of easy penetration and root growth. The tillering of cereals is stimulated by phosphate, and this leads to the development of more ears per plant and a better yield. Another effect of phosphatic manuring is the promotion of early maturity and ripening; indeed its influence in this respect is just a little less marked than that of water scarcity, and in some cases it may shorten the growing period of cereals by ten days. Phosphate has a special value in promoting vigorous growth in leguminous plants, and it is largely used to encourage clover in pastures. Phosphate deficient pastures, particularly in spring, have a characteristic dull, grey green coloration, and there is a marked absence of leguminous plants.

In general, response to phosphate is relatively high in our wetter climates and on our more retentive soils. Indeed, in our drier areas and on light soils, a few cases have been found where the concentration of available phosphate, due to frequent and heavy applications, is harmfully high. This can also occur under glasshouse conditions.

A shortage of phosphate stunts the root system and depresses tillering in cereals; in extreme cases of deficiency, crops may not grow at all.

Most soils contain large reserves of phosphate, for this plant nutrient is firmly retained. Surface applications made on steep slopes and under wet climates may indeed be washed away in surface water, but the amount in drainage water is almost negligible. Phosphatic fertilizers are mostly insoluble in water, and even those that are soluble at the time of application soon revert to an insoluble condition. On neutral or only slightly acid soils the phosphatic fertilizers have a beneficial effect for several years, but on strongly acid soils there is rapid " reversion " to highly insoluble compounds. There is also reversion in cases where the soil contains free lime, but the resulting compounds are less stable. In general, and especially on the more extreme types of soil, frequent applications of relatively small amounts are more effective then large dressings at long intervals (see under **Placement**, p. 84). Land that has received regular dressings of phosphate accumulates a large amount in the top few inches of soil, but, for the reason given above, the crops nevertheless continue to respond to further applications. A few soils are so deficient in available phosphate that animals grazing on the herbage suffer from deficiency and develop bone abnormalities.

In the following text, except where the contrary is stated, the analyses of the phosphate fertilizers are given in terms of phosphoric anhydride ($P_2O_5$), and common usage is followed in designating this " phosphoric acid." Sometimes analyses are given as " phosphate," meaning the equivalent of tricalcium phosphate. The " phosphate " content of a fertilizer can be converted into the phosphoric-acid content by dividing the former by 2·2.

**Bones** are variable in composition, but ordinarily contain about 4 or 5 per cent. nitrogen, 46 per cent. calcium phosphate (22 per cent. $P_2O_5$), 7 per cent. calcium carbonate, 6 to 10 per cent. fat, and 10 per cent. water. Formerly, bones were prepared for application to the land by crushing them into rough lumps in a grinding mill, but they are now usually sent to factories for extraction of their valuable fat and gelatine, and the residues only are converted into fertilizer. The nitrogen and calcium carbonate in bones obviously give the material a value higher than that based on the phosphorus content alone.

**Bone Meal** is prepared from bones that have had their fat extracted; it contains about 21 per cent. phosphoric acid, calculated as $P_2O_5$, and 4 per cent. nitrogen. The gelatinous matter which contains the nitrogen is slow to decompose; indeed the whole of the plant food in the meal is liberated very gradually, but this is considered to be an advantage on light and " hungry " land.

**Steamed bone flour** contains from 27 to 30 per cent. phosphoric acid and about 1 per cent. nitrogen: it is prepared by grinding bones that have had their fat and most of their gelatine extracted, and has a much finer texture than bone meal. The flour is so light that it is best applied in mixture with other fertilizers, and it is often included as a drier in compound manures. It gives good results when applied to light land, and it becomes available at a rate intermediate between those of bone meal and superphosphate.

**Superphosphate.**—This is the most largely used phosphatic fertilizer. It is prepared by treating naturally occurring mineral phosphate with sulphuric acid in order to produce a water soluble acid calcium phosphate. Superphosphate is obtainable as a grey friable powder or in granular form. The common grade contains about 18 per cent. $P_2O_5$ of which all but some $1\frac{1}{2}$ per cent. is water soluble. Superphosphate also contains a considerable amount of calcium sulphate and a small amount of unaltered tricalcic phosphate. When the manure is kept for a considerable period it tends to revert to insoluble phosphate and always reverts when it is applied to the soil; but as it is well distributed before reversion takes place it is the most readily available and quickest acting of the phosphatic fertilizers in soils that contain free calcium carbonate. It is wasteful to use superphosphate on sour soil, because the latter contains soluble iron and aluminium salts which unite with and precipitate the fertilizer in such a stable form that it is practically no longer available for plant nutrition. When superphosphate is first applied to the soil it produces an acid reaction, but, contrary to popular belief, it has no permanent effect in increasing soil acidity.

"Triple" superphosphate is made in two stages: the ground rock phosphate is treated with sulphuric acid in such proportions that phosphoric acid ($H_3PO_4$) and calcium sulphate are formed; the phosphoric acid is then filtered off and reacted with further ground phosphate. The final product, as made in Britain and from which the calcium sulphate has been eliminated, contains 45 per cent. phosphoric acid ($P_2O_5$). Its high concentration gives it an important advantage in areas far remote from phosphate supplies.

**Silico-phosphate** is produced from a mixture of mineral phosphate, soda ash and sand by roasting in a kiln at 1400° C. It contains the equivalent of 33 per cent. of $P_2O_5$—i.e. it is about twice as rich as superphosphate. The greater part of the phosphate is readily available.

**Basic Slag.**—Basic slag is a by-product in the manufacture of steel. The bulk of the iron ore in this country contains a considerable amount of phosphorus, which passes into the pig-iron when the ore is smelted. In order to make the iron into high quality steel the phosphorous must be removed. This removal was first achieved in 1879 by the Bessemer process, in which air or oxygen is blown through the molten iron to which lime has been added. In the consequent oxidation the phosphorus combines with the lime and forms on top of the metal a scum, which is poured off and solidifies. This is basic slag. The various steel making processes produce slags of varying phosphate content, the range being from 7 to 20 per cent. Moreover, a varying proportion of the total phosphate is soluble in 2 per cent. citric acid, and citric solubility is rather closely related to availability of the phosphate to plants. The range in citric solubility is wide—from about 45 to 95 per cent.

A further point is that availability of the phosphate depends on fineness of grinding. This is expressed as the percentage, by weight, of the powder that will pass through a sieve with 10,000 holes per square inch. There is in general very little difference in availability to the plant between water soluble and citric soluble phosphate. On the other hand there is, in many soils, a very marked difference between citric soluble and insoluble phosphate. The vendor of slag is required to state the phosphoric acid content, the fineness of grinding and the amount of phosphoric acid soluble in 2 per cent. citric acid.

The following figures for a number of different slags illustrate the point:—

|   | Total $P_2O_5$ per cent. | Citric Soluble $P_2O_5$ per cent. | Percentage of Citric Soluble in Total $P_2O_5$ |
|---|---|---|---|
| 1 | 18·2 | 15·7 | 86·5 |
| 2 | 15·0 | 13·5 | 90·2 |
| 3 | 12·8 | 10·2 | 80·1 |
| 4 | 10·1 | 5·8 | 58·1 |
| 5 | 9·7 | 8·0 | 82·0 |
| 6 | 7·1 | 6·7 | 93·2 |

Slags also contain lime, equivalent to about half of their weight of calcium and magnesium carbonates as well as certain trace elements, particularly manganese.

The proportion of low soluble slags is now much lower than formerly. The poorer quality slags should be used only in areas of high rainfall and on fairly heavy and rather acid soils. On the other hand, high soluble slag with a high phosphate content is suitable for arable crops and gives beneficial results almost immediately. The combination of phosphoric acid and calcium enables slag often to produce a striking improvement in grassland. This it does by encouraging the growth of clover and indirectly bringing about an accumulation of nitrogen which benefits the other herbage. The best results are obtained when slag is applied to damp, heavy land. On light land and under dry conditions its results may be surpassed by the combined effect of superphosphate and lime.

**Mineral Phosphate.**—Rock phosphates—derived from marine animals or formed by the leaching of bird guano into underlying limestone—vary in purity and hardness. They are found in beds in various parts of the world and form our chief source of phosphoric acid. For example, the following phosphates have been used largely in this country for agricultural purposes:—

South Carolina phosphate containing about 27 per cent. phosphoric acid.
Ephos (Africa)    ,,    ,,    ,, 30  ,,    ,,    ,,
Florida    ,,    ,,    ,, 30  ,,    ,,    ,,
Gafsa (Africa)    ,,    ,,    ,, 26  ,,    ,,    ,,
Nauru (Ocean
      Island)    ,,    ,,    ,, 40  ,,    ,,    ,,
Tunisian    ,,    ,,    ,, 25  ,,    ,,    ,,

It has already been pointed out that rock phosphates are used in the manufacture of superphosphates. Considerable quantities are, however, finely ground and used directly as a fertilizer, particularly for grassland. The fineness of grinding is very important and the best results are obtained when the material is crushed so fine that a large proportion will pass through a screen with 14,400 holes to the square inch (120 mesh sieve). The fertilizer acts more quickly when employed on acid soils and in wet localities, the reason being that the wetness and the acidity cause the insoluble phosphate to become more quickly available. It is best to apply the phosphate some time before it is required to act. It is unlikely that it will have much effect on a crop such as barley, which has a short growing season. Mineral phosphates usually contain from 2 to 12 per cent. of calcium carbonate.

## POTASH FERTILIZERS

Potash is widely distributed and occurs in association with the clay fraction of all soils, but it is often deficient in soils of a sandy nature. Even on rich soils, the potash may not be sufficiently available to supply the needs of crops like potatoes and mangels, which store up large quantities of carbohydrate material, and grass under intensive management. In such cases soluble potash compounds may be profitably applied. The potassium salts commonly used as fertilizers are all highly soluble in water, but the potassium ion enters into firm combination with the soil colloids. In very sandy soils of low humus content, potash is to some extent washed down beyond the reach of the shallower rooting crops, and some appears in the drainage waters. At the other extreme, on chalk soils, some of the applied potash may be fixed in combinations so strong that it is unavailable to plants.

The potash required by plants is very largely assimilated in the early stages of growth, and it remains mostly in the stems and leaves. Potassium is associated with the efficiency of the leaves in carbon fixation, and its action is linked with that of nitrogen in plant development and in the maintenance of a satisfactory balance of carbon and nitrogen in the tissues. Heavy dressings of nitrogen fertilizer with insufficient potash produce large but relatively inefficient leaves and a general " softness " and susceptibility to disease; and cereals tend to lodge. With adequate potash, the plant has a better tone and vigour, an improved capacity for assimilating carbon, and the power of doing well in a cold, dull and unfavourable season when crops getting no potash fail to attain normal yields. It is only by using potash in conjunction with nitrogen that crops like potatoes, sugar beet and mangels can produce the big tonnage per acre that is now common. Plants suffering from potash starvation often develop scorched looking leaves that die prematurely at the tips and edges. Potash differs from both nitrogen and phosphate in distinctly increasing the weight of individual cereal grains, and it is therefore useful in producing a plump, bold sample in a crop like barley.

Potash slightly increases the sugar content of beet; it often brings about a remarkable improvement in clover and other legumes and enables them better to withstand the winter. The too-liberal use of potash may be inadvisable with a crop like early potatoes, because by promoting the vigour of the leaves it may prolong growth and delay the time of lifting.

The potash requirements of plants were formerly met by natural soil reserves and by returning to the land the residues of previous crops or the ashes of wood. Potash fertilizers were little used until the discovery in 1861 of deposits of potash salts in Germany. While Germany remains the largest producer, potash salts are also worked in France, U.S.A., Spain, Poland, Palestine and Russia. A very large deposit exists in the neighbourhood of Whitby in Yorkshire, which is at too great a depth to allow of economic extraction at present. The potassic fertilizers are sold either as refined salts, crude crushed material or as a mixture of crude and refined salts graded to contain a certain percentage of potassium.

The potash fertilizers available in Britain at the time of writing were as follows:—

| | Minimum $K_2O$ | Potassium Chloride | Potassium Sulphate | Sodium Chloride |
|---|---|---|---|---|
| | | | per cent. | |
| Muriate of Potash . . | 60 | 95 | ... | 3 |
| „ „ . . | 50 | 80 | ... | 15 |
| „ „ . . | 40 | 63 | ... | 25 |
| Sulphate of Potash . | 48 | ... | 90 | ... |

As a rule, sulphate of potash is used in manuring potatoes for high quality, for fruit trees and for glasshouse crops. High grade muriate of potash may be used for practically any farm crop, and it is just as effective as the sulphate, except perhaps from the point of view of quality. The lowest of the three grades of muriate (sometimes called potash manure salts) contains 25 per cent. of common salt, which by itself often produces a marked response in crops of mangels and sugar beet. Potash manure salts because of their nature cannot be used as an ingredient of a free running compound, and when used for mangels, sugar beet or grass are normally applied separately.

Sulphate of potash is manufactured by a chemical process and in consequence is rather more costly than the muriates.


## NITROGEN FERTILIZERS

Under British conditions, and indeed in all areas where rainfall is high enough to cause any considerable amount of soil leaching, the supply of available soil nitrogen tends to be the commonest limiting factor in crop growth. It is open to the farmer to ensure supplies by including frequent leguminous crops in his rotation or by growing mixtures of legumes and non-leguminous plants, but even if these are grown, it is usually profitable to make use of nitrogen fertilizers.

The effect of increasing supplies of nitrogen on plant growth is, up to a point, to stimulate the plant as a whole, to promote tillering, to cause a fuller development of stem and leaf and to produce a rich dark green colouration of the foliage. An over-supply, particularly if other plant foods are in short supply, makes the tissues very soft and liable to attacks of pests and disease, reduces their resistance to frost and so weakens cereal straw that the crop is easily laid. The liability to disease which may be brought about by excessive doses of nitrogen is believed to be mitigated by using potash fertilizers, which increase the efficiency of the leaf for carbon assimilation and maintain a better nitrogen-carbon balance in the plant as a whole. Heavy dressings of nitrogen may be better split if it seems that conditions are likely to cause leaching or over-luxuriant growth. The stimulation of vegetative growth by nitrogen retards ripening in cereals and may result in difficulties in late districts. In a crop like turnips the large leaf development is of no value unless there is a corresponding growth of root, hence the importance of an adequate supply of phosphate. In crops like cabbages and kale a luxuriant growth is an advantage provided the plants remain healthy. An over-abundant application of nitrogen may so increase the nitrogen content of barley as to injure the malting quality of the grain; it also tends to lower the sugar content of beet and the dry matter content of root crops.

If the supply of nitrogen for the plant is deficient, the effect is seen in a general stunting of growth, and in consequence reduced yields of crop, for in such cases the amount of other nutrients taken from the soil and air depends on the quantity of nitrogen available. In addition, a yellowish or reddish green colour develops in the leaves and there may even be a certain amount of withering.

Points of some importance in the choice of nitrogen fertilizers are their respective effects on the lime content of the soil, their rate of availability and the liability to loss by leaching.

**Sulphate of Ammonia.**—In the combustion of naturally occurring carbonaceous compounds a considerable quantity of ammonia is produced from the nitrogenous matter which is always present, and in the manufacture of coal gas, the distillation of shale and the heating of blast furnaces, the ammonia is removed by passing the gases through sulphuric acid, sulphate of ammonia being formed. A very large quantity is also made synthetically by fixing atmospheric nitrogen.

The fertilizer is sold with a guarantee to contain not less than 20·6 per cent. nitrogen, but it usually contains 21 per cent. It is in the form of small elongated crystals which may be white, greyish or yellowish in colour. Formerly the salt contained a trace of free acid, which, being deliquescent, caused a certain amount of caking. Most supplies are now

" neutral " and of excellent texture and keeping quality. Sulphate of ammonia must not be mixed with basic substances such as lime or basic slag, otherwise ammonia will be given off.

Although this fertilizer is soluble, the ammonium radical is firmly retained by the soil and it is not until nitrification has taken place that the nitrogen is liable to be lost in the drainage. Sulphate of ammonia may therefore be applied to land some short time before the crop is in a position to absorb it, for even under favourable circumstances it may be a week or more before nitrates are produced. In fact the fertilizer is often applied with the seed, or it may be given in small amounts to autumn-sown crops because, since cold weather reduces the speed of nitrification, the plants are able to absorb the nitrates as they are formed. As it is retained for some time near the surface of the soil it is more suitable than nitrate for shallow rooted crops like turnips and barley.

The acid portion of sulphate of ammonia is washed to the drains in combination with calcium, and this results in loss of lime at the rate of about a hundredweight of calcium carbonate for every hundredweight of sulphate of ammonia applied. It should therefore be used with caution on soils that are poor in lime.

Sulphate of ammonia mixes well with superphosphate and the higher grade potash fertilizers. It is still widely used in compound fertilizers.

**Nitrate of Soda.**—The world's great natural supply of nitrate of soda occurs in beds of soluble nitrates which owe their existence to the rainless climate of the district of Northern Chile in which they occur. The rock salts are mined and nitrate of soda is obtained in a fairly pure state by solution and recrystallisation. A synthetic nitrate of soda has also been produced on a commercial scale.

The fertilizer was until recently sold with a guarantee of not less than 95 per cent. of sodium nitrate or 15·5 per cent. nitrogen, but a granulated form containing 16 per cent. nitrogen is now generally available. The older form was that of rough crystals which varied somewhat in colour, but in the new material the white crystals are partly aggregated into granules and the texture is superior. The manure is deliquescent and, if stored in ordinary bags in a moist atmosphere, becomes damp and tends to cake or get lumpy. Supplies are now usually marketed in treated bags which do much to protect the salt from dampness.

As nitrate of soda does not undergo any change before it can be assimilated, it is one of the quickest manures to act on the crop and will give results in weather too cold for the nitrification of sulphate of ammonia. It is soon washed down into the soil and so favours plants of a deep rooting habit. It may to a small extent " scorch " a delicate crop by plasmolysing the tissues when it is first broadcast. It should therefore not be applied when the crop is wet with dew.

Nitrate of soda is not fixed by the soil and is very easily washed to the drains and lost; it should therefore never be applied unless a growing crop is present to absorb it immediately. The sodium radical interacts with clay and humus in the soil and liberates a certain quantity of potash which becomes available for plant food; this gives it a particular value for potash loving crops. Its continued use on heavy soils leads to the formation of a sodium clay which does not flocculate and which gives the soil a sticky texture. The sodium base has some effect in conserving lime, 1 ton of the fertilizer being in this respect equivalent to 5 cwt. of calcium carbonate.

**Nitrate of Lime.**—This is a synthetic nitrogen fertilizer prepared from the nitrogen of the air. In the manufacturing process atmospheric nitrogen is oxidised to nitric acid by the use of powerful electric arcs, the acid is neutralised by limestone, and the fertilizer is obtained from the solution by crystallisation.

As nitrate of lime is completely soluble it can at once be taken up by the crop and is valuable as a top dressing. As it is in the form of a soluble calcium salt it is often used on soils that are poor in lime, and for certain crops under these conditions it may be expected to give better results than sulphate of ammonia. Its power of absorbing moisture from the air may be advantageous in allowing it to go into solution and penetrate the soil during periods of drought.

Nitrate of lime is not fixed by the soil and should be used only as a dressing for growing crops. An application of 1 ton of the fertilizer has approximately the same influence in correcting soil acidity as has $3\frac{1}{2}$ cwt. of calcium carbonate.

**Cyanamide.**—This is a synthetic fertilizer prepared by heating calcium carbide in a current of pure nitrogen. It is generally made in countries where cheap hydro-electric power is available.

The commercial material contains calcium cyanamide equivalent to 20·6 per cent. of nitrogen, together with carbon and various calcium compounds.

Nitrate of lime and cyanamide, though still manufactured and used in certain countries, are not available in Britain at the time of writing, and it seems unlikely, in view of the development in the home manufacture of other materials, that imports will be resumed.

**Nitro-chalk.**—This is a granular mixture of ammonium nitrate and calcium carbonate. There are two types one containing 21 per cent. and the other 15·5 per cent. nitrogen. The ammonium nitrate has the effect of depleting the lime in the soil, but the calcium carbonate, helps to make good this loss, so that the net result of using the fertilizer is to leave the soil reaction unaffected. Nitro-chalk is an entirely satisfactory and safe source of nitrogen; it has an excellent texture for handling and sowing.

**Nitra-Shell.**—This is a granular nitrogenous fertilizer containing 23 per cent. nitrogen and 31 per cent. calcium carbonate. The nitrogen is present in the form of ammonium nitrate. The fertilizer is evenly granulated. Like nitro-chalk it has excellent texture for handling and sowing, and is suitable as a top dressing for all agricultural and horticultural crops.

**Ammonium nitrate,** which is prepared synthetically, contains 35 per cent. of nitrogen and is therefore highly concentrated. As a fertilizer it is used in mixture because the pure salt is very deliquescent and there is some risk of causing fires.

**Other Nitrogenous Fertilizers.**—Urea in its commercial form contains 46 per cent. of nitrogen and is therefore extremely concentrated and has an advantage where transportation costs are high; its nitrogen is as efficient as that in sulphate of ammonia, but it cannot be mixed with superphosphate and under some conditions it is deliquescent. Resin like polymers of urea, produced by treatment with formalin, are being increasingly used in the United States. They have the advantage that they release ammonia gradually over a considerable period and are used in cases where shoddy and hoof and horn were formerly preferred.

**Ammonium chloride** contains 26 per cent. of nitrogen. It has been used on the Continent and has been tried in this country; on the whole it is as satisfactory as the sulphate.

In the United States, anhydrous ammonia is now being used on a commercial scale as a fertilizer. It has the advantage of very high concentration (82 per cent. N) and ease of distribution. A hundred gallon tank (containing 410 lb. of nitrogen) may be mounted on a tractor or implement and the ammonia released through high pressure hose lines behind coulters. The ammonia must be placed at least 4 in. deep if loss by volatilisation is to be avoided.

In this country trials have been made with the *gas liquor* which is a watery solution of ammonia, containing a variable amount of impurity. The liquor is dilute and therefore costly to transport or store, and at the time of writing it would seem to have only a limited and local value.

## MINOR ELEMENTS

Manganese deficiency affects chiefly sugar beet, mangels, potatoes, oats, wheat, peas and kale. The commonest cases are those in which soils of high organic matter content have been limed more heavily than necessary, the neutralisation of the acid condition tending to throw the soil manganese out of solution. The symptoms depend on the crop: mangels and sugar beet show blotching and necrosis of the foliage, curling of the leaf margins and a greatly reduced yield; oats exhibit spotting and striping of the leaves in the early stages, and in severe cases the crop may have disappeared by June; in potatoes dark brown spots appear alongside the leaf veins; peas develop corky patches within the actual seed. To correct manganese deficiency, 20 to 50 lb. of manganese sulphate per acre may be applied as a fertilizer. Crops showing the need for immediate treatment can be saved by spraying with 10 lb. of sulphate per acre dissolved in 100 to 150 gal. of water.

Boron deficiency affects a number of crops, particularly sugar beet, mangels and brassicas. The symptom in beet and mangels is a discolouration of the leaves and petioles, which later shrivel away as the disease descends and rots the crown. In turnips and swedes the tissues within the bulb break down and rot, the condition being known as Raan or Brown Heart. The preventive is to apply 14 to 20 lb. of borax per acre mixed with fertilizer or any convenient material that will provide sufficient bulk for even distribution.

Magnesium deficiency has been observed on a wide range of crops including potatoes, sugar beet and brassicas. A yellowing of the foliage usually occurs, and is to be expected as magnesium is a normal constituent of chlorophyll. The remedy is to apply magnesian limestone or, if quick results are required, magnesium sulphate.

Minerals are of great importance in animal nutrition (see Part 3, Chapter 18). In this respect there are minor elements which, when deficient or in excess, have no apparent influence on the herbage, but nevertheless profoundly affect the health of the grazing stock. To take but two examples, sheep may pine on certain grasslands for lack of cobalt and, on the " Teart " pastures of Somerset, cattle scour because of an excess of molybdenum.

## COMPOUND FERTILIZERS

The term compound is used for fertilizers that contain more than one plant food. The greater part of the fertilizers now used in Great Britain is in the form of compounds (about two thirds, estimated in terms of plant foods). Fertilizer manufacturers have carried out a good deal of research and many field experiments as a preliminary to the production of reliable, granular and easily handled compounds. The more recent tendency has been to make compounds rather more concentrated in plant foods with a view to cutting down transport and handling costs; and study is now proceeding on the special qualities of fertilizers desirable in bulk handling.

Most compound fertilizers contain nitrogen, phosphate and potash, but others contain only two of these plant foods.

There is a very wide variation in the ratios of the three more common plant foods in the very many different compounds now on the market. But it would seem that in future there will be a trend towards a reasonable number of compounds to cover the more important crop and grass requirements. The National Agricultural Advisory Service of England and Wales has made a first move in this direction by defining eight ratios of compounds (one at two concentrations of plant foods), which it believes from its experience and experiments cover the more common fertilizer requirements. This first list is given below. It should be noted that the list is not exhaustive, that it does not cover exceptional requirements and that it is subject to change in the light of new knowledge and developments. Some changes may indeed be made before this edition is in print.

| Class of Fertilizer | Per cent. | | | Ratios |
|---|---|---|---|---|
| | N | $P_2O_5$ | $K_2O$ | |
| N, $P_2O_5$ & $K_2O$ | 10 | 10 | 15 | 1 : 1 : 1½ |
| | 12 | 12 | 18 | 1 : 1 : 1½ |
| | 6 | 15 | 15 | 1 : 2½ : 2½ |
| | 9 | 6 | 18 | 1½ : 1 : 3 |
| | 12 | 8 | 8 | 1½ : 1 : 1 |
| | 8 | 12 | 8 | 1 : 1½ : 1 |
| N & $P_2O_5$ | 9 | 18 | — | 1 : 2 : — |
| N & $K_2O$ | 16 | — | 16 | 1 : — : 1 |
| $P_2O_5$ & $K_2O$ | — | 10 | 20 | — : 1 : 2 |

There are still many conditions under which " straight " fertilizers are preferred, for example, a phosphate fertilizer on grass or to correct a serious deficiency of one plant food. A high proportion of the nitrogen fertilizers are also used as " straights " for top dressing crops. It seems that there is likely to be a continuing demand for " straights " for such purposes, and for a further improvement in their storage properties.

The swing towards compounds, however, has been steady over the past twenty to thirty years. It started with the demand from the arable areas for fertilizers that would " run well " in combine drills and not " bridge ". Lack of suitable accommodation to store " straight " fertilizers, difficulties in keeping them in condition before and after mixing and the rising cost of labour have also all tended towards the the use of bought compounds with higher plant food contents, *i.e.* more concentrated.

The cost of plant foods is usually higher in compounds than in equivalent " straight " fertilizers, even when full allowance is made for the cost of mixing, but the condition and storage properties of most compounds are better. It is useful to be able, from time to time, to check up on the relative costs of " straights " in a mixture and in bought compounds. An example of a method of doing so is set out on page 94.

## MIXING FERTILIZERS

When fertilizers are home mixed, it is important to ensure that the mixing will not result in a loss of plant foods or a mixture so out of condition as to be difficult to apply. The following precautions should be taken:—

1. Materials containing active lime (slag and cyanamide) should not be mixed with dung, guano, or ammonium salts (sulphate of ammonia and nitro-chalk), otherwise ammonia will be lost.

2. Dissolved phosphate such as superphosphate should not be mixed with manures containing lime or calcium carbonate, which would cause the soluble phosphate to revert to an insoluble form.

3. Nitrates should not be mixed with substances containing free acid, *e.g.* acid sulphate of ammonia or badly made superphosphate, because the acid will cause a loss of nitrogen. Fortunately, samples of " acid " fertilizers are now rare.

4. The effect of the ingredients on the physical condition of the compound must also be taken into account. Soluble salts attract moisture from the air and have to be mixed with a drier in order to secure a sufficiently friable condition for sowing. For example, sulphate of ammonia and superphosphate when mixed together will cake unless a drier is added. Again, there are substances—*e.g.* nitrate of lime—that can be mixed only if sowing is to follow immediately.

For good mixing, the fertilizers, in the proper proportions, should be put down layer upon layer on a suitable floor. The flat topped heap made in this way should then be shovelled over by starting at one end and cutting vertically downwards through the different ingredients. This turning may be repeated until the material is sufficiently well mixed, and it is also well worth while to pass the mixture through a riddle in order to remove lumps, which are then easily broken down. A good riddle for this kind of work is the type of screen employed by builders for riddling sand and gravel. This screen is propped up at an angle and the material is thrown against it so that the small particles pass through and the lumps roll back to the feet of the operator.

Farm mixed compound fertilizers are generally made up of sulphate of ammonia, superphosphate, and one or other of the higher grade potash fertilizers, together with a small amount of a drier such as steamed bone-flour. Even carefully selected materials of this sort tend to cake slightly after they are mixed, thereby causing some difficulty when the manure is being sown. This trouble can be overcome if the fertilizer is mixed and sown on the same day, or, if this is not convenient, the manure can be riddled once more after the caking is completed, when it will be found that it will retain its fine texture.

## APPLICATION OF FERTILIZERS

Fertilizers are generally broadcast on the land before a crop is sown, placed in definite relationship to seed or tubers or used as top dressings on growing crops.

In broadcasting and top dressing the aim is to apply the fertilizer at the appropriate rate as evenly as possible. This appears to be a simple operation, but there is still a need for more study and experiment to produce distributors that do these jobs efficiently, that can be cleaned easily and are resistant to the corroding effects of fertilizers.

**The Placement of Fertilizers.**—There is abundant evidence that the effectiveness of a fertilizer depends on how it is placed in the soil in relation to the crop plants. If fertilizers are spread uniformly over the surface and the crop is grown in rows fairly wide apart, it may be quite late in the season before the crop roots can reach part of the fertilized ground. Meanwhile, nutrients may be utilized by weeds and there is a risk of the nitrates being leached away. A further difficulty is that phosphoric acid and potash may be held so firmly by the soil that, when applied as top dressings, they may remain above the normal root zone of the crop and prove quite ineffective. Finally, when a dressing of phosphate is intimately mixed with the whole mass of soil a large proportion is fixed in unavailable form. Potash may be similarly fixed, though rarely to the same extent. There is less fixation if the fertilizer is placed in pockets or narrow bands.

Since the various nutrients present different problems it is well to discuss each separately and then to consider how best to apply mixed or general fertilizers.

The chief problem in the case of phosphate is, as already said, that of fixation, *i.e.* the formation, with the sesquioxides and clay minerals, of highly insoluble compounds. The extent of these reactions may be indicated by the fact that, even in the case of extremely phosphate deficient soils, it is unusual for more than a quarter of the phosphate applied to be recovered in the three or four crops following the application. In some cases the recovery drops as low as 10 or 15 per cent. An obvious method of reducing fixation is to avoid mixing the phosphate with the general body of the soil, or at least to delay such admixture for as long as possible. This can be done by sowing the fertilizer in narrow bands within the root range of the plant. Another consideration is that all plants, if they are to make full growth, must have an abundant supply of phosphate while they are still in the seedling stage. This suggests that the bands of phosphate should be near the seed. Thirdly, no phosphate fertilizers are so highly soluble as to produce solutions concentrated enough to damage seedlings unless, indeed, large amounts of soluble compounds including phosphate are used; thus there is no objection to a placement in close proximity to (or even in contact with) the seed. Normal dressings can be applied to cereals in this way and smaller amounts to roots and clover. Fourthly, superphosphate, which is the commonest fertilizer in the phosphate group, has some value as a deterrent against wireworm and possibly other insect pests. The simplest way of producing the desired placement in the case of corn crops is to mix a granular form of phosphate with the seed or to use a combine drill which delivers seed and fertilizer into the ground together. Experiments have shown a marked advantage in favour of this method as compared with the older one of broadcasting the superphosphate and harrowing it into the soil. The average of all trials in which there was a clear response to phosphate was that $1\frac{1}{2}$ cwt. applied by the combine drill was as effective as 3 cwt. broadcast. Experiments and observations indicate the same kind of results with drilled grass and clover mixtures. In this connection it is worthy of note that the earliest form of phosphate fertilizer was roughly broken bones, and that applications in this form produced much longer lasting responses than dressings of modern materials dispersed through and intimately mixed with the soil.

Potassium compounds readily enter into combination with the clay minerals and in some cases—notably in soils overlying chalk—are fixed in unavailable forms. On the other hand, where the soil has a very small amount of colloidal material (*i.e.* is very sandy), losses of potash by leaching are not negligible. Moreover, in most cases there is a downward movement of potash from the soil to the subsoil, faster or slower according to the soil's clay content. It would thus appear that no one type of placement can be ideal for all soils. On the one hand, a surface application to a heavy soil may fail to penetrate to the zone of plant roots soon enough to be of benefit to the crop; experiments with surface applications to apple orchards on heavy land have, in fact, shown that the response may be delayed for several years. On the other hand, potash ploughed into a light soil, if it is neither used by the first crop nor brought up again by still deeper ploughing, may in effect be lost. There is one other consideration, viz., that all potash salts are highly soluble so that there is a risk of damage to seedlings, by over-concentration of the soil solution, if large amounts of potash fertilizer are placed near the seed. This danger will, of course, be greatest under dry conditions. Impure potash fertilizers such as Kainit and " potash salts " are (partly because they must be used in larger quantities and partly because of their content of common salt) much more likely to cause damage than the purer forms. Experience shows that it is safe to apply moderate quantities of the purer forms of potash, close to the seed of both autumn and spring sown cereals, provided that the soil is reasonably moist at the time of sowing. If the soil is very dry germination may be delayed, or the germinating seed may be killed. Damage may be done to potato sprouts when large amounts of potash salts are sown in the drills.

It has been pointed out that nitrate of soda, nitrate of lime, nitro-chalk and nitra-Shell should normally be used as top dressings to established crops. This is because nitrates are very readily washed through the soil and lost. In the case of widely spaced plants like cabbage and brussels sprouts in the early stages (*i.e.* before the roots have spread through the soil) there is considerable economy in putting a pinch of any of these fertilizers near each individual plant rather than broadcasting over the surface.

The ammonium radical is firmly held by the soil but in growing weather nitrification is rapid, and the resulting nitrate rapidly diffuses through the soil. Clearly, then, the effect of placement of the common nitrogen fertilizers must be very short lived. But in the case of crops sown in rows the plants will get more benefit, and the weeds less, if the fertilizer is placed near the lines of plants. Sulphate of ammonia, like the salts of potash, is highly soluble and equally liable to cause damage to seedlings or to the sprouts of potatoes, if it is applied in the immediate neighbourhood of the plants and if the soil is dry. Compound and concentrated fertilizers containing ammonium salts can be safely applied, in reasonable amounts, along with the seed of cereals if the soil is fairly moist. This method is inapplicable in the case of roots and sugar beet, partly because the seedlings are more susceptible to damage and partly because the normal dressing gives a much higher amount of fertilizer per foot of drill. Placement is beneficial in the case of peas, but the fertilizer must be placed out of direct contact with the seed, and a special type of drill is required to achieve this. In the case of potatoes, satisfactory results are obtained by broadcasting the fertilizer over the ridges before planting. This method gives much better results than broadcasting before setting ridges.

To sum up, we may say that phosphate, when used alone, should if possible be sown either with the seed or in narrow bands near the seed. Compound or concentrated general fertilizers may be sown with cereal seed, though the amount must be restricted if the soil is dry. The same remark may probably apply to drilled grass and clover seeds, though the amounts must be smaller. In the case of other crops grown from seed, the fertilizer must not be in actual contact with the seed, but should preferably be placed close to the latter—e.g. in bands 2 or 3 in. on either side and 1 or 2 in. below.

## ORGANIC MANURES

**Farmyard Manure.**—Farmyard manure is a valued all-round soil improver. It does not enter into competition with the common fertilizers but should be used in conjunction with them. Its value is greater than can be assessed by the consideration of its content of plant nutrients. Not only does it supply to a greater or less extent all the plant foods that are likely to be deficient in agricultural land, but it improves the texture and tilth of the soil. It also increases its capacity to hold water and to retain soluble nutrients that would otherwise be washed down beyond the root range of crop life. It has been estimated that the total amount produced in Britain annually exceeds 40 million tons.

While this total quantity is large, it is sufficient to provide an ordinary dressing—12 tons per acre—only at intervals of over seven years to the total acreage of farm land.

Farmyard manure consists of a mixture of litter and the excreta of different kinds of stock. In its fresh condition it is therefore made up of straw, fæcal matter that has resisted the action of digestion and urine, which is a solution of substances that have been absorbed from the food into the blood and finally excreted from the system. Urine contains about half of the nitrogen and most of the potash voided by the animal; it is the richest, most quickly available and most easily lost portion of the manure. The solid portion of the manure contains the other half of the nitrogen, which is in a form slow to decompose, and most of the phosphoric acid and lime of the food. The composition of " made " farmyard manure is very variable, but on an average 1 ton contains some 12 lb. of nitrogen, 5 lb. of phosphoric acid, and 12 lb. of potash. This is equivalent to about $\frac{1}{2}$ cwt. of sulphate of ammonia, $\frac{1}{3}$ cwt. of superphosphate, and $\frac{1}{5}$ cwt. of muriate of potash, but so much of the fertilizing material, particularly the nitrogen, is locked up in slowly available forms or is lost in storage and handling. In consequence its value in plant nutrition is probably no higher than half the equivalent quantity of ordinary fertilizer. Again, its content of phosphoric acid is too low to give it the right " balance " for average conditions; on the other hand, practically all the potash contained in the animal's food is excreted in the urine and, if the latter is preserved, dung has a considerable value on account of its potash content. The quality is influenced by a number of factors which are considered in some detail below:—

1. *The Food of the Stock.*—With ruminants and horses on ordinary rations, about half of the dry matter fed is returned in the manure, the remaining portion being built up into the animal's tissues or destroyed by respiration and fermentation in the production of heat and other forms of energy. The proportion will, of course, vary according to the type of ration fed. Thus the proportion of dry matter that is returned in the farmyard manure is nearly 60 per cent. for coarse straw, about 45 per cent. for average hay, and only 15 to 20 per cent. for roots and cereals and low fibre oil cakes. With pigs and poultry, which are ordinarily fed on more highly digestible foods, the proportion of dry matter that reappears in the manure is less. As the oil and starch contents of the food have no influence on the value of the manure, only the nitrogen and ash in the animal's diet require consideration. Oil-cakes and leguminous foods are rich in all the valuable manurial constituents and, because of their high nitrogen content, produce manure that ferments readily and becomes quickly available when applied to the soil; cereal grains and hay produce manure of average richness, while turnips and straw give rise to a manure that is somewhat poor in quality and ferments and becomes available but slowly.

2. *The Litter.*—The chief value of litter is its power of absorbing

moisture and volatile decomposition products. The ordinary cereal straws form the most common litter of the farm: they should be used unsparingly if loss of urine and ammonia is to be reduced. They decompose readily in the field with the liberation of plant foodstuffs. A ton of straw will generally soak enough moisture and retain enough fæcal matter to form from 4 to 6 tons of fresh manure. Moss litter is superior to straw in its power of absorption, but is slow to decay and less suitable for improving the texture of heavy land. When bracken is available it forms excellent litter, for although it does not last as well as straw it is richer in potash. Sawdust and shavings are less satisfactory since they decay in the soil very slowly.

3. *The Age of the Animals.*—Young growing animals absorb a great deal of the nitrogen and ash of their food to build up muscle and bone, and may return less than half to the manure heap in their excrement. On the other hand, when well grown animals are being fattened their live weight increase consists largely of fat, which contains no manurial substance and is therefore formed without loss to the manure. Indeed, fattening bullocks may remove less than 5 per cent. of the nitrogen and ash from their food.

4. *The Kind of Animal.*—Horses produce manure of a dry nature; it is called " hot," as it ferments rapidly and does not last long. It should be well mixed with litter or other manure, as it tends to lose its nitrogen quickly in the form of ammonia. Cows' manure is of a very watery nature it is " cold," *i.e.* decomposes very slowly. The manure obtained from cows may be likened to that of young stock, because in the production of milk and the development of the unborn calf a great deal of nitrogen and mineral matter is extracted from the food and never finds its way to the manure heap. Cows produce a great bulk of urine and, as litter is seldom available in large quantities on a dairy farm, it may be worth while to construct a tank for the preservation of the fluid, which can be removed periodically and distributed over the pastures. The excrement of bullocks is superior to that of cows, the best being obtained from fattening beasts. The manure of pigs resembles cow dung in being cold and slow to ferment, while sheep's excrement is concentrated and rots freely.

5. *The Method of Making and Storing.*—It is generally impracticable and often undesirable to manure crops with fresh excrement and litter. The manure has usually to be stored for considerable periods, and during this time it rots until it has the desirable texture of " made " manure, losing much of its carbonaceous matter by fermentation and oxidation. Unfortunately, these changes are in practice always accompanied by the loss of a considerable portion of the most active and valuable nitrogenous substance of the urine. Although this cannot be obviated without using far more litter than is ordinarily available, it is to the interest of the farmer to reduce the loss to a minimum.

What is the nature of the decomposition which goes on in the manure heap? The most obvious change is the alteration of the straw into brown structureless humus. This decomposition is due to the action of bacteria under mixed aerobic and anaerobic conditions, and results in the loss of at least 20 per cent. of the dry matter of the manure. The loss of non-nitrogenous organic matter is of little importance, but the loss of nitrogen is serious and extremely costly. Manure contains the nitrogen of the straw, the nitrogen of the fæces which has resisted the process of digestion and the soluble nitrogenous compounds of the liquid excrement. Investigations have shown that it is the nitrogen of the urine only that is liable to be lost. When urea ferments it is converted into ammonium carbonate, which in turn may decompose with the liberation of ammonia and even of free nitrogen. Now it has been shown that litter is capable of " fixing " a certain proportion of this ammonia in a stable non-ammoniacal form, but cannot fix more than about 0·7 part of nitrogen per 100 of dry straw. A further quantity of ammonia is retained by physical means when the manure is in a well-preserved, moist condition, but it can be washed out by percolating water and is entirely lost when the manure is dried. It would seem, then, that the ammoniacal nitrogen is so liable to be lost in the carting and spreading of the manure that it is desirable to have as much as possible in the stable state. This can be brought about by using sufficient litter to fix the whole of the nitrogenous matter of the urine, but manure so made has the disadvantage of being very slow to yield its nitrogen to plants.

Farmyard manure that has been " made " may contain a bigger percentage of nitrogen than before rotting took place, but it will normally have a smaller total of nitrogen than was present in the original mass. Up to a point it is desirable that carbonaceous material should be broken down, for, as has been shown in Chapter 2, fresh straw added to the soil so stimulates certain bacteria that they assimilate the nitrates from their surroundings and may thus cause temporary infertility. Rotting has the further advantage that the accompanying heating destroys weed seeds. After a moderate degree of rotting has taken place, however, further loss of dry matter merely reduces the bulk of cellular material that is so useful in the mechanical retention of ammoniacal nitrogen, and leaves less material to improve the texture and water holding capacity of the soil.

Losses may be reduced in the following ways:—

1. Anaerobic conditions should be induced as far as possible by keeping the manure heap moist and well compacted. This is best attained by keeping the animals in boxes or yards, allowing the manure to accumulate beneath them, and adding fresh litter daily so that the animals rest on a dry surface. Thus the air is excluded, the heap is moistened by liquid excrement, and the evaporation of ammonia is reduced to a minimum.

2. Where rain water percolates through the heap it washes out much of the potash and some of the soluble nitrogen compounds; therefore, at least in areas of high rainfall, the manure should be stored under a

roof.   Under other conditions, as where manure is being kept in deep heaps that are liable to dry to a considerable depth below the surface, wetting by rain will keep the surface moist and reduce the loss of nitrogen. In stock yards, when insufficient litter is employed to absorb the urine, an impervious bottom will prevent the escape of liquid to the subsoil or drains.

3.   Where an excessive amount of urine is produced, as is the case in dairy herds, special tanks should be constructed into which the liquid excrement may be led by a system of drains and from which washing water can be excluded.   The tanks may be emptied from time to time and their contents distributed over pastures or young corn crops.   Where the urine has been diluted with washing water, as in many cowsheds, the labour cost of handling the liquid may be greater than its value.   Drainage can, however, be so arranged as to collect the valuable liquid and allow the very dilute washing water to run to waste.   A thousand gallons of liquid manure are equivalent to about 3 cwt. of kainit and 100 lb. of sulphate of ammonia.

**The Application of Farmyard Manure.**—The maximum value is obtained when it is carted to the fields as soon as it is made, and ploughed in; but this is practicable only at certain seasons of the year.   Under ordinary conditions dung must necessarily be accumulated for a considerable time.   Local climate and the availability of labour often determined the best policy, but the wider use of manure spreaders in recent years has helped to speed up the application of manure and to ensure that it is spread under more favourable conditions.

Generally the greater bulk of manure is formed and stored during winter and is available for application either for spring crops or in autumn.   Under drier conditions autumn applications for ploughing-in may be better; in wetter areas it may be applied for ploughing-in in spring or in the ridges prepared for root crops.

The liquid manure accumulated in tanks during the feeding period gives good results when applied either periodically throughout the growing season to rotation grasses or as a top dressing to cereal crops in the spring.   If it is too strong, and especially if the soil is dry, it is inclined to " burn " the herbage and may have to be diluted. A preliminary trial should be made on a small scale, and if no ill effects follow, the tanks may be emptied forthwith.   A good deal of ammonia may be lost if the liquid is applied in hot, dry weather.

**Straw and other Composts.**—Straw in cattle yards and dung heaps breaks down readily because urine provides the water, nitrogen and salts needed by the bacteria that oxidise the carbon compounds.   Straw thrown out in a heap will not readily decay because, although it may be wetted by rain, it contains insufficient nitrogen and salts to be a suitable medium for active fermentation.   However, straw or other similar material can be broken down by the addition of water, nitrogenous salts, and basic material (to check the accumulation of acids), which make the mixture as a whole a suitable one for the action of cellulose destroying organisms. Special reagents sold by various firms may be used; alternatively a mixture of $\frac{3}{4}$ cwt. each of sulphate of ammonia and ground limestone, and $\frac{1}{4}$ cwt. of superphosphate, may be applied per ton of dry straw. This will, in the presence of sufficient added water, cause rotting to take place and yield a product which closely resembles farmyard manure, and which has approximately equal fertilizing value. About 800 gal. of water are needed per ton of straw, and a difficulty is that, to begin with, the straw will not absorb this quantity, so that watering has to be repeated at intervals. Compost has sometimes been made by placing the straw heap so that it is watered by rainfall, building up layer by layer as the previous material has been sufficiently wetted and adding the necessary material to promote rotting. But since it takes 3 or 4 in. of rain to wet sufficiently a 1 ft. layer of tramped straw, the process is very slow. It may be practicable to sweep wet straw to a compost heap in the field.

In making a straw compost heap the base should be calculated at the rate of about 40 sq. ft. per ton of straw. The height of the mass will then be about 7 ft. when built, and about 3ft. after settling. Each ton of straw will produce about 2 tons (or 4 cub. yd.) of compost.

Urine and nitrogenous fertilizers can also be used to help rot down composts of waste organic materials. Straw, road scrapings, scourings from ditches, turf and leaves, may be built into heaps with alternate layers of earth and turned over once or twice until sufficiently decomposed to be suitable as manure. The inclusion of fish, blood and other animal matter will greatly enrich the compost. Market garden waste, such as weeds and unmarketable greenstuff, makes excellent compost. Naturally, it does not require much, if any, wetting, and only small quantities of nitrogen and other salts are required to promote rotting, the amount varying with the proportion of stemmy and lignified matter in the refuse.

Composting is expensive in labour and the more common practice now is to plough in straw before it is rotted. Where this is done, it is advisable to apply $\frac{1}{2}$ cwt. per acre of sulphate of ammonia, in addition to that normally required by the following crop, to ensure that temporary infertility is not induced through its fixing all the available nitrates. The timing of the operation is of some importance, e.g. the ploughing-in of too much dry straw in spring on a light soil may leave the soil too open for effective crop growth.

**Poultry Manure.**—The output of manure from poultry can be computed on the basis that the fresh manure is approximately equal in weight to the dry food consumed by the birds. In the case of a laying hen this will be about $\frac{1}{4}$ lb. per day. If the fowls are on range, about half the droppings will be got in the houses. The fresh material contains approximately 35 per cent. dry matter, 2 per cent. nitrogen, 1 per cent, phosphoric acid, and 0·5 per cent. potash. When the manure is air-dried the percentage of dry matter is raised to 85 or 90, and there is a corresponding increase in the plant nutrients, except nitrogen, some of which is lost in the process of drying. While the above figures apply to average samples of poultry manure, the quality of course depends on whether the birds are growing, fattening or laying. Again, the manurial value may be reduced owing to the presence of chaff, sand or other material which has been used as litter in the houses. The manure is quickly available and should be handled with care to prevent loss of nitrogen.

**Guano.**—The original guano, consisting of an accumulation of the droppings, feathers and remains of sea birds, was obtained from a number of rainless islands off the coast of Peru. It contained about 12 per cent. nitrogen, 10 per cent. phosphoric acid, and 3 per cent. potash, all of which were readily available as plant food. Many other guanos have since been imported, but they are nearly all poorer in nitrogen than the original substance.

Phosphatic guano has originated like ordinary guano, but in a rainy climate. It has been washed almost completely free of nitrogen, and some samples are practically pure calcium phosphate.

Equalised guano is a naturally occurring low grade guano made up to contain a given percentage of nitrogen by the addition of sulphate of ammonia.

Fish guano is not a true guano, but is prepared from fish offal by extracting the valuable oil and grinding up the dried residue. Its composition varies, but an average analysis is 9 per cent. nitrogen, 7 per cent. phosphoric acid, and 0·6 per cent. potash.

All the guanos are thoroughly reliable and useful manures, though they may be rather expenisve in comparison with simple manurial salts. Slow acting organic manures of this kind may produce better results than quick acting soluble substances on the lighter soils for certain horticultural crops.

**Shoddy.**—This is a waste material—produced in the manufacture of woollens—which is very variable in quality and may contain from 3 to 15 per cent. of nitrogen according to the proportion between actual wool and such practically worthless constituents as cotton and cellulose fibres. It is largely used in hop gardens and to some extent also for soft fruit. Common dressings are at rates of 1 or 2 tons per acre. It is, as would be expected, relatively slow-acting.

**Soot.**—Soot contains normally about 4 per cent. of nitrogen in the form of sulphate of ammonia, but may contain considerably more. It is quick to act in the soil and is largely used as a spring dressing for vegetable crops, about 25 bushels, equivalent to 1¼ cwt. of sulphate of ammonia, being applied to the acre. Its dark colour improves the temperature of the soil, and it may be useful in checking the activities of slugs. Its chief disadvantage is its dirtiness.

**Seaweed.**—Seaweed has been used for generations along the coastal districts of Great Britain and Ireland for improving the fertility of the land. Different species of weed have different values, but a ton of average mixed material contains 9 lb. of nitrogen, 25 lb. of potash, and 2 lb. of phosphoric acid. It is thus about as valuable as farmyard manure, but is richer in potash and poorer in phosphate. In certain parts the seaweed is specially cut and harvested, but along most rocky coasts it is carried ashore by undercurrents during stormy weather in autumn and winter. Seaweed is particularly useful for potatoes, and is largely used in the early potato districts of Ayrshire, Cornwall and the Channel Islands. It may be applied at the rate of 20 to 30 tons per acre.

**Other Organic Manures.**—A very large number of waste organic substances such as dried blood, hair, ground hoofs and horns, rape cake and damaged oil-cakes and spent hops, are used for manurial purposes. The value of these materials depends on their content of plant nutrients, and in the case of a tough substance like horn, on the fineness of grinding. The relatively slow production of nitrates from manures in this class is often an advantage on light land and in certain branches of horticulture.

Town refuse can be obtained in certain districts; it is very variable in composition and is on the whole less valuable than farmyard manure; it is sometimes used with the main object of improving the texture of heavy land. It should be valued on the basis of its analysis. It is also possible to obtain standardised and pulverised products from which tins, crockery, and other rubbish have been removed. Sewage sludges are also variable in composition, and since the dry matter content is always low, only the richer types are worth the cost of transportation and distribution. It may be composted with straw or with town refuse.

**Green Manuring.**—Green manuring consists of growing a crop and ploughing it in for its manurial value. As a rule only catch crops—*e.g.* white mustard, white turnips, trefoil and Italian ryegrass—are grown for this purpose, and the system is seldom practised except where it is necessary to improve the water holding power of a light, hungry soil, or where, on rich land, there is a risk of loss of nitrates between the harvesting of one crop and the sowing of the next.

In light soils green manures decay with great rapidity, particularly when the plant grown for the purpose is a legume or where from other causes the nitrogen-content is high. It is therefore important that the soil should be occupied by plant roots soon after the material is ploughed in.

## FERTILIZER UNITS AND VALUES

In the days when most fertilizers were applied to the soil as " straights " or simple mixtures of " straights," it was usual to express a crop's requirements as so many hundredweights per acre of each " straight " or of the mixture. Now compound fertilizers of different concentrations are in much more common use and the variety of " straights " has increased; and the older methods of describing a crop's requirements are of limited value.

Opinion is now swinging to a method of expressing a particular requirement in terms of units of plant food per acre. It has certain advantages, including ease of calculation and of comparing the relative value of different fertilizers. This is the method which is described here, as it is likely to be adopted generally in the near future.

A plant food unit is ·01 cwt. or 1·12 lb. of that plant food i.e. of N, $P_2O_5$ or $K_2O$. In 1 cwt. of a compound consisting of 8 per cent. N. 12 per cent. $P_2O_5$ and 8 per cent. $K_2O$, there are thus 8 units of N, 12 of $P_2O_5$ and 8 of $K_2O$. If the ratios of plant foods in the above compound is thought suitable for a particular crop and the recommendation is 32 units per acre of N, 48 units per acre of $P_2O_5$ and 32 units per acre of $K_2O$, then the rate of application of the compound is 4 cwt. per acre. Or, for example, it is decided to apply 2 cwt. per acre of sulphate of ammonia (21 per cent. N), this is equivalent to 42 units per acre of N.

The use of plant food units is also an advantage relative to certain regulations made under the Fertilizers and Feeding Stuffs Act, 1926, which require the seller of a fertilizer to inform the buyer of the percentages of plant foods it contains. So the percentage of plant food in a fertilizer e.g. 18 per cent. $P_2O_5$, is the same figure as the number of units of $P_2O_5$ in 1 cwt. i.e. 18.

The plant food unit can also be used to compare the relative value of fertilizers. Let us assume that the cost of sulphate ammonia (21 per cent. N) is £21 per ton; superphosphate (18 per cent $P_2O_5$) £13, 15s. per ton and muriate of potash (60 per cent $K_2O$) £20 per ton. The cost of 1 cwt. of each is then 21/-, 13/9 and 20/- respectively (£ per ton= shillings per cwt.) The cost of a unit of plant food in each is obtained by dividing the per cent. of plant food in the fertilizer into the price per cwt. And so:

|  | Price per cwt. | Per cent. of plant food | Cost per unit of plant food |
| --- | --- | --- | --- |
| Sulphate of ammonia | 21/- | 21 | 1/- |
| Superphosphate | 13/9 | 18 | 9d. |
| Muriate of potash | 20/- | 60 | 4d. |

Now use the cost per unit of the three plant foods to estimate the value of the compound in question. Let us take the one mentioned above, then the estimated value is:

|  | No. of plant food units per cwt. | Calculated cost per unit of plant food. | Estimated cost per cwt. |
| --- | --- | --- | --- |
| N | 8 | 1/- | 8/- |
| $P_2O_5$ | 12 | 9d. | 9/- |
| $K_2O$ | 8 | 4d. | 2/8 |
|  |  |  | Total 19/8 |

Now compare the estimated cost per cwt. with the price per cwt. at which the compound is sold. One can then consider whether the difference is reasonable to cover the extra costs in buying " straights ", storing and mixing and whether the home mixed fertilizer could be distributed satisfactorily.

Different " straight " fertilizers and different compounds of somewhat similar properties can also be compared in the same way to give a guide as to those of better value in terms of unit costs of plant food.

## RESIDUAL VALUES OF MANURES AND FERTILIZERS

The residual values of fertilizers and feeding stuffs are taken into account when compensating an outgoing tenant for improvements. In the case of fertilizers these values are determined from their actual content of plant nutrients, taking account of the costs of the nutrients in the three principal fertilizers, sulphate of ammonia, superphosphate and muriate of potash.

When dealing with the residual values of fertilizers applied during the last year of a tenancy, account must be taken of the duration of the effects, for while some nutrients will be completely exhausted in a single season others, according to their form, may become so slowly available that their beneficial action extends over two or more years. Allowances for these differences in availability are made as follows:—

Inorganic nitrogen fertilizers e.g. sulphate of ammonia, nitrate of soda, and dried blood—no allowance.

Organic nitrogen in animal and vegetable residues such as bones, hoofs, meat and bone meal and cake meal—allow one-half the manurial value after one growing season and one-quarter after two.

Phosphoric acid soluble in water, or (in basic slag) in standard citric acid solution—allow two-thirds the value after one growing season, one-third after two and one-sixth after three.

Phosphoric acid in bone products (other than dissolved bones)—allow one-half, one-quarter, and one-eighth the value after one, two and three growing seasons respectively.

Phosphoric acid insoluble in water or citric acid solution—allow one-third of the value after one crop, one-sixth after two, and one-twelfth after three crops.

Potash in potash fertilizers—allow one-half the value after one growing season and one-quarter after two.

In the case of lime, compensation is estimated on an eight-year principle, that is, one-eighth of the cost should be subtracted each year after application.

It is also necessary to value the nitrogen, phosphoric acid and potash in the residues of feeding stuffs purchased during the last years of a tenancy.

If no losses took place between feeding the cakes and meals and applying the farmyard manure, the valuation could be made in just the same way as for fertilizers. But stock remove varying amounts of nitrogen and phosphoric acid for growth and milk production, and what remains in the farmyard manure is subject to further loss according to how it is handled; indeed where urine is wasted and the solids are subject to excessive fermentation and exposure, very little potash and available nitrogen may be left.

Tables of Residual Values are published by the Ministry of Agriculture, Fisheries and Food. They gave a suitable basis for determining compensation, but no formula can deal with every possible contingency, and in the last resort the valuer must use his own judgment.

# CHAPTER 5

# IMPLEMENTS AND CULTIVATION

## PLOUGHS AND THEIR CONSTRUCTION

THE earliest form of plough was simply an enlarged hoe which stirred the soil as it was dragged along. This type of implement, which may be regarded as a single tined cultivator, is still widely used in India and other Eastern countries. A crude mould-board plough came into use in Europe in pre-Roman times, but it was not until the eighteenth century that ploughs approaching the modern type were invented. Modern ploughs vary considerably in detailed construction but in all, the essential features are the beam, the plough body and the coulter (Fig. 2).

**The Mould-board Plough**—The plough body consists of a frame, sometimes called the " frog," to which are attached the share, mould-board, slade and the side cap, " cheek " or landslide. The coulter makes the vertical cut in the soil; the share makes the horizontal cut; the mould-board or breast moves the soil sideways and at the same time inverts it; the side cap receives the side thrust due to the turning of the furrow slice; and the slade takes the weight of the plough and of the furrow slice. The horizontal cut is not the full width of the furrow slice, for enough soil must be left uncut to steady the slice so that the mould-board may invert it and not merely push it into the open furrow.

The draught of the plough is due to the resistance of the earth to the two cutting edges, the energy required to lift the soil and invert it, and lastly, the friction of the plough parts against the soil surfaces. If the plough is properly hitched there will be little or no friction against the side cap, the pressure on the slade will largely depend on the weight of soil resting on the mould-board, and most of the friction will be due to the size and length of the breast. In all cases friction is greatly reduced when the plough surfaces are highly polished.

**The Mould-board or Breast.**—The mould-board may be made of cast iron, but in most modern ploughs it is constructed of soft-centred or soft-backed steel. A steel breast has a wearing surface of high carbon metal which is extremely hard and takes on such a high polish that the draught is minimised. High carbon steel alone, however, is too brittle to be satisfactory, and has to be backed with low carbon metal which is tough and strong and resistant to fracture. For average conditions and for soils which are more or less free from sharp and hard grit, steel mould-boards scour better than other types, but they do not wear as well as chilled cast iron.

D

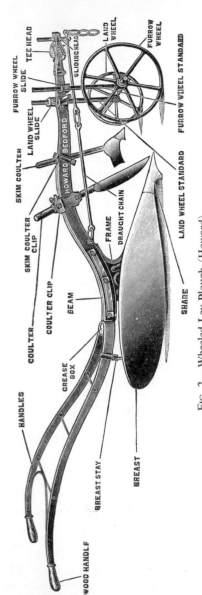

FIG. 2.—Wheeled Ley Plough (Howard)

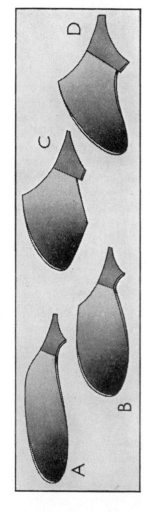

FIG. 3.—Plough Breasts

A. Ley; B. General Purpose; C. Semi-digger; D. Digger

The four main types of plough body, in the order of decreasing length and increasing depth of mould-board, are: ley, general purpose, semi-digger and digger (see Fig. 3). The ley and general purpose bodies have a mould-board with a very gradual curve and a slightly convex surface; the digger body mould-board is short and abrupt with a pronounced concave surface; and the semi-digger is intermediate between the full digger and general purpose, the mould-board having a slightly concave surface. These differences in length and curvature determine the degree of pulverisation of the soil (Plate 1) and the relationship between furrow width and depth. The extent to which the furrow is broken is affected by the speed of working—the higher the speed the more broken the furrow. The ley and general purpose bodies are suitable for shallow ploughing only, the maximum depth being about two thirds of the furrow width. They turn an unbroken furrow slice and press each slice firmly against the previous one, thus " setting-up " the furrows so that they are exposed to the full action of the weather. The work of the semi-digger and digger mould-boards differs from the work of the ley and general purpose bodies in that the furrow slices are not pressed against each other. The soil is caused to rise up the mould-board and fall over in a broken and pulverised condition, the degree of pulverisation being greater with the digger body than with the semi-digger, so that the soil is worked into a mould in addition to being inverted. The semi-digger body will plough a furrow slightly more than 2 in. deep for every 3 in. of width; and the digger body will plough a furrow as deep as it is wide, or even deeper. The digger body is therefore essential for deep ploughing. The forward edge of the deep digger mould-board is subject to rapid wear and may carry a removable shin. Digging ploughs are used extensively for cross ploughing land that has been exposed to the action of frost throughout the winter, and for ordinary spring ploughing, because the broken furrow slice assists greatly in the preparation of the seed bed. The digger body is not always satisfactory for ploughing grassland, particularly on the heavier types of land, because it does not effectively bury the sod. The semi-digger body, on the other hand, will deal with almost all types and conditions of soil, and is gradually becoming recognised as the most widely adaptable type, especially for tractor work.

**The Share.**—Shares are very subject to wear in certain soils. For example, on dry, hard flinty land a day's ploughing can cause one to be worn to the point of requiring renewal or repair, whereas on soft fen land the same part may last two seasons. Shares for the older types of plough were almost always made of wrought iron but at the present time most shares for horse ploughs and small tractor ploughs are made of chilled cast iron. Cast iron cannot be hammered into shape; if sharpening is necessary it has to be done on a grindstone, and when wear has gone too far, renewal of the part becomes necessary. These shares wear well, but their failure to withstand shocks makes them unsuitable for ploughing land containing large stones, especially if the plough is tractor drawn.   Under these conditions cast steel shares are preferable.   Steel shares wear well in land containing little abrasive material.   When they lose their edge they may be sharpened by heating, hammering the metal out to the desired shape and retempering;   this can be done only once or twice, after which replacement becomes necessary.   Shares are obtainable which have the bottom layer of metal hardened.   When they are in use the cutting edges are maintained by the more rapid wear of the softer upper portions and sharpening is unnecessary.   Deep digger bodies frequently have three piece shares of which the point and wing can be renewed as they become worn.

Bar-point shares have been devised for land that is very hard and stony. The principle of the device is to replace the point of the share with the chisel-pointed end of a long solid bar which can be advanced, turned or reversed in a few seconds to make good the wear.   Some are spring-loaded to absorb the shock caused by hitting fast obstructions.   The very advanced point that it is possible to obtain is particularly useful for getting into hard ground.   Bar-point shares can be fitted only to those bodies designed to take them.

**The Coulter.**—The coulter for making the vertical cut in the soil ahead of the plough body is either a knife or a disc.   The knife coulter, like the share, may be made of steel or wrought iron, and has to be sharpened or renewed when it becomes inefficient through wear.   It is clamped to the beam of the plough and has a backward and forward adjustment.   The coulter stem may be round so that the blade can be given a " set " towards the land if necessary, or the same object can be achieved with a flat stem by the use of iron wedges.   For ordinary work the point of the coulter is set forward so that its leading edge points towards the point of the share and makes an angle of about 35° with the vertical, with the tip of the coulter about $1\frac{1}{2}$ in. from the share.   When an absolutely unbroken furrow slice is required the coulter is advanced considerably.   The disc coulter is a freely revolving circular disc with a cutting edge.   It is usually carried on a cranked round stalk clamped to the beam of the plough.   Raising or lowering the stalk in the clamp increases or decreases the clearance between the disc and the share; moving the clamp along the plough beam varies the position of the disc relative to the share point;   and turning the stalk in the clamp adjusts the position of the disc relative to the landslide of the body.   The correct setting of a disc coulter is determined by the conditions under which it has to work, but three general rules can be laid down.   Firstly, it must not be too deep.   On hard ground a deep coulter takes some of the weight of the plough, prevents penetration and causes excessive wear on the coulter bearings.   It should be set just deep enough to leave a clean furrow wall.   Secondly, it should run slightly to the land side of the plough body. Too little clearance between the disc and the side cap produces a broken

PLATE 1

1. High-cut Crested Furrows

2. Rectangular Furrows

3. Broken Furrows

4. Inverted Furrows

STYLES OF PLOUGHING

*Farmer and Stockbreeder*

PLATE 2

*A.* THREE-FURROW TRACTOR PLOUGH (RANSOMES)

*B.* MOUNTED ONE-WAY PLOUGH (*S.K.W.*)

furrow wall, and too much clearance gives the work a poor appearance and may allow the plough to crab. Thirdly, for normal work the coulter should be set over the point of the share; but in hard ground it should be moved back behind the point to assist penetration. The plain disc coulter is not suitable for ploughing-in long material such as straw left by the combine harvester. The straw, being so tough that the coulter cannot cut through it, collects in front of the coulter and prevents it from revolving. This trouble is largely overcome if the edge of the disc is wavy: the wavy edge keeps the disc turning.

The skim coulter is used in addition to the knife or disc coulter for ploughing in herbage and dung. It skims off that corner of the furrow slice against the ordinary coulter and thereby prevents any vegetation from protruding between the turned furrow slices. A skim coulter should be set sufficiently far forward on the plough beam to allow it to pare off the shoulder of the furrow before the furrow is lifted; it should throw the paring into the furrow bottom; and it should not be set too deep. When used in conjunction with a disc coulter the point of the skim is set close to the disc so that surface vegetation and small stones cannot wedge between the two. Skims cannot always be set to do good work on rough ground because of the considerable variations in their depth of working. Under these conditions surface vegetation can be buried satisfactorily if the disc coulter is tilted so that the top of the disc leans towards the ploughed land.

**Multiple Ploughs.**—The multiple ploughs in common use in this country are constructed for tractors and turn from two to six furrows at once. A three-furrow model is shown in Plate 2, *A*. The plough bodies and their associated coulters are attached to two or more parallel beams and spaced so that each in turn inverts its furrow slice into the preceding furrow. The distance apart of the beams, which determines the furrow width, may be adjustable. The bodies are built on the same lines as the body of a single furrow horse plough; but the bodies, except the rear one, have no slades and either very reduced side caps or none at all. Provision is usually made for adjusting the pitch of the individual bodies. The plough is carried on land and furrow wheels in front, with generally a small wheel at the rear running in the open furrow. The land and furrow wheels are on cranked axles through which, by means of screws or by levers working in quadrants, the depth of ploughing is controlled and the plough is kept level. The rear wheel may or may not be adjustable for height. The hitch, which is flexible in a vertical direction and rigid horizontally, usually consists of three members: the hake bar attached to the beams, a drawbar running forward from the hake bar to the tractor, and a cross piece between the hake bar and the drawbar. The three members thus form a triangle. A wide range of adjustment is provided in the hitch so that the drawbar never slopes downwards from the plough to the tractor and so that the line of draught of the plough is brought as near as possible in line with the centre of power. A lever and quadrant or a screw adjustment is often incorporated in the hitch to enable the plough to be moved towards or away from the land and thereby increase or decrease the width of the front furrow.

Tractor ploughs are subjected to much greater shocks than horse ploughs, because, unlike the horse, the tractor does not stop when the plough hits an obstruction, and to prevent damage to the plough a safety device such as a wooden shear peg or a spring-loaded draw hook is put in the drawbar. All conventional tractor ploughs have a self-lift actuated by the cleated land wheel. The lift is either of the rack and pinion type, the pinion being attached to the wheel, or of the drum type, incorporating a clutch. A pull on a cord brings the rack down on to the pinion or engages the clutch, and as the land wheels rotate the cranked axles raise the plough out of the ground. When the plough is lifted completely the rack flies away from the pinion and the clutch disengages. A second pull on the cord drops the plough into work. On the larger tractor ploughs the self-lift also causes the rear portion of the plough frame to move up the pillar carrying the rear wheel.

Some tractor ploughs can be reduced in size by removing a body. For instance, a three-furrow plough can be converted to a two-furrow by removing the centre body and putting the rear body forward into its position.

The cost of ploughing an acre is increased if a tractor capable of pulling a six-furrow plough is used with a smaller plough. It is therefore desirable to give a tractor the largest plough it can pull. In practice, however, a very wide plough cannot do good work on rough land on which one furrow is liable to be too deep while another is too shallow. On rough surfaces it may be better to hitch two of the smaller multiple ploughs together, the larger plough being placed in front of the smaller, and so secure a measure of flexibility rather than attempt to operate a single implement carrying the same total number of bodies.

**Mounted Ploughs.**—There has been a marked tendency in recent years to mount a wide range of cultivating tools on the tractor rather than to trail them behind, the object being to make the outfit more manœuvrable and to simplify the construction of the implements. The method of attaching the implement to the tractor is important. Unless the implement can be put on and taken off the tractor quickly and easily, much time may be lost in changing from one job to another. The " three point suspension " method enables one man to couple a tractor to a mounted plough just as quickly as to a conventional trailer plough. Generally, the depth of ploughing is controlled by adjustable land wheels, but with the Ferguson system the hydraulic lift on the tractor is also used to control depth. At any given setting of the lever operating the lift the draught of the plough remains constant. On uniform ground the ploughing depth does not vary, but if the plough passes from soft to hard ground it will be raised unless the lift lever is adjusted to permit the draught of the plough to increase. An experienced operator, by careful manipulation of the lift lever, can plough at a uniform depth even in variable land. The plough is kept level by a screw adjustment incorporated in one of the lifting arms attached to a lower link in the " suspension." Front furrow width is controlled either by turning a cranked cross bar by means of which the plough is attached to the lower links or by moving the beams along a straight crossbar.

**" One-way " Ploughs.**—Ploughs of this type are constructed with the object of enabling the plough to work backwards and forwards, turning all the furrow slices in one direction. With one-way ploughing marking out is not necessary, there are no ridges or finishes, idle travel on the headland is reduced to a minimum, and land can be ploughed as it is cleared—a great help when land is being folded with sheep or when strips of land in a field are cleared at different times, as often occurs in market gardening. One-way ploughs have right hand and left hand bodies arranged so that it is possible to change from one to the other on the headland. The turnabout plough has the right hand and left hand bodies mounted opposite each other on the same beam. When the plough is turned on the headland the beam rotates through 180° and brings the other set of bodies into the working position. Mounted and trailed one-way tractor ploughs are illustrated in Plate 2, *A* and Plate 3, *B* respectively.

**Special Ploughs.**—Deep digging ploughs are used for ploughing up to 16 to 18 in. deep. The frame of the plough is very heavy and the distance between the point of the share and the beam is much greater than with the more usual type of plough. They are usually of the trailer type but the Wilmot " Turnall " is bolted direct to the tractor and has only a rear wheel, the depth being controlled by varying the pitch on the share. An ordinary wheeled tractor can pull a single furrow deep digging plough; a track-laying tractor is necessary for the larger sizes.

The " Grub Breaker " plough (Plate 3, *B*) has been used in the reclamation of derelict land. It can plough a flat furrow up to 26 in. wide and 12 to 16 in. deep; and the knife coulter placed against the share point enables it to work in rocky land. Another type of plough which can be used on rough land containing tree roots and rocks is the Australian Stump Jump. The bodies on this are mounted so that when one meets an obstacle it rises over it and then falls back into work.

**Disc Ploughs.**—These implements are used to some extent for tractor ploughing. They work on a different principle, employing rotating discs to cut and turn the furrows. The discs are 24 to 28 in. in diameter and usually four or five in number; they are mounted on stub beams which are clamped to the heavy main beam of the plough and the spacing for width of cut is adjustable. The discs are fitted with scrapers which keep them free from sticky soil. Some of the advantages of disc ploughs are: they can be used on hard soils where mould-board ploughs cannot penetrate and will not scour; their rolling action prevents breakages where the soil contains large stones, stumps or tree roots, and, moreover, reduces the wear on the working parts.   On the other hand, under average conditions, mould-board ploughs pulverise the soil better, leave fewer clods and cover surface growth and rubbish more completely.   Stump jump disc ploughs are also made.

Disc implements known as harrow ploughs, one-way discs, or polydiscs (Plate 4, *A*), are made to perform operations intermediate in character between the work of disc ploughs and that of disc harrows. A seed box is sometimes attached to the polydisc so that cultivating and seeding can be done in one operation.

**The Subsoiler.**—Subsoiling consists of stirring up the soil to a greater depth than is reached by ordinary ploughing.   It differs from deep ploughing in that it does not bring the subsoil to the surface but leaves it broken and aerated *in situ*.   Subsoiling is adopted in preference to deep ploughing where it is undesirable to bring the subsoil to the surface. Subsoiling is absolutely necessary where a plough pan has been formed or where an iron pan has been developed by a precipitation of iron salts a few inches below the surface.   Even on ordinary soils it may be advisable to practise subsoiling in preparation for tap-rooted crops like sugar beet, carrots and parsnips.

The essential feature of a subsoiler is a large digging tine strong enough to break up the soil below ploughing depth.   The horse-drawn subsoiler follows an ordinary plough and tears up the bottom of the open furrow.   The digging tine may replace the front body of a two-furrow plough; on some heavy tractor ploughs a tine may be fixed behind each body.   The special tractor subsoiler is a two wheeled stoutly constructed frame to which the subsoiling tine is attached.   A self-lift raises the implement out of work.

**Ridging and Potato Ploughs.**—The ridging body is of the double mould-board type with a renewable point instead of a share.   Ridging ploughs are used in conjunction with a marker to form ridges for root crops and also for earthing up potatoes.   The marker is set according to the row width and makes a mark on the land down which the point of the ridging body is driven on the return bout.   Each time the plough is turned on the headland the marker is swung from one side to the other.   Substitution of a potato raising body for the ridging body converts the ridging plough into a potato lifter.   The lifting body has a broad, flat share behind which is a series of prongs which slope upwards and outwards.   The share is pulled beneath the row and as the whole body of the ridge passes over the prongs partial separation of potatoes from soil is effected.   Some of the potatoes may be buried and picking may be difficult, but the potato plough is probably less damaging to the tubers than any other form of lifter. Ridging bodies and potato ploughs can be attached to tractor toolbars (Plate 4, *B*).   Three ridging bodies or one or two lifting ploughs are usual.

PLATE 3

*A.* Two-furrow " Turnabout " Plough (Bawden)

*B.* " Grub-breaker " Plough (Massey Harris)

PLATE 4

*A.* Polydisc Plough

*B.* Forward-mounted Tool Bar arranged for splitting Potato Ridges (Hudson)

PLATE 5

*A.* Heavy Tractor Cultivator (Ransomes)

*B.* Rotary Cultivator (Rotavator)

PLATE 6

*A.* STEERAGE TRACTOR-HOE (MILLER)

*B.* ROW-CROP TRACTOR WITH REAR-MOUNTED HOES

If there is only a single plough it is often attached to one end of the tool-bar with a harrow leaf on the other end, so that as the plough is raising one row, the last but one row lifted is harrowed. If there are two ploughs they are fixed to the ends of the toolbar to lift every other row. The tractor potato plough is much larger than the horse version, and the extra speed obtainable with the tractor improves the performance of the plough as a lifter.

**Beet Ploughs.**—Before sugar beet can be pulled they have to be loosened by special beet lifting bodies. The bodies are either built into horse drawn ploughs or are attached to tractor toolbars. There are two types of body, the single- and double-arm. In the single-arm a flat steel plate carries at its base a small share which runs under the row and loosens the beets. Right and left hand single arm bodies are made so that when they are mounted on a tractor toolbar they push the loosened rows together in pairs. In the double arm or bow legged type, a single row plough has a share running on each side of the row. This type, which is not often used on tractor toolbars, loosens the beets but does not displace them.

## PLOUGHING

The most suitable depth of ploughing depends to such an extent on the nature of the soil that no hard and fast rules can be laid down in regard to it, and every farmer must determine the most suitable depth for his own land. Deep cultivation creates a deeper root bed for the crop and, by bringing a greater volume of soil under the influences of weathering and aeration, tends to increase fertility; occasional deep ploughing also improves the drainage of heavy land. An average depth in many districts is about 6 or 7 in., the range being from 4 or 5 in. in the case of spring sown barley to perhaps 8 or 9 in. in preparation for potatoes or roots. In some limestone regions 5 or 6 in. represents the maximum possible. At the other extreme, on deep stoneless silt land, occasional ploughing to 15 or 18 in. or sometimes more, is done by tractor ploughs or by steam tackle. No matter what the most suitable depth of ploughing may be, it is advisable to vary it slightly from year to year in order to prevent the consolidation of any particular stratum with the formation of a " pan."

Experiments on the effects of deep ploughing, under the auspices of Rothamsted, have been in progress since 1946. The trials cover a wide variety of soils in various parts of England. In general it can be said that deep ploughing (12 to 15 in.) has in no case done serious harm. It should be noted, however, that extra doses of nitrogen and phosphate have been given to make good the deficiency of the material brought to the surface. This material is usually richer in potash than the former top soil. Only in a few cases has there been a definitely beneficial effect, as measured by crop yields.

Most British ploughs are made to turn furrows up to 10 or 12 in. wide.

Large tractor ploughs have even wider furrows than this, and special single furrow ploughs, *e.g.* the Grub Breaker, may produce furrows up to 26 in. wide. The furrow width of single furrow ploughs can be varied easily, but there is a practical limit to the width because a plough cannot invert a furrow that is wider than that for which it is designed; it will simply raise the soil and allow it to fall back again.

The first operation in the ploughing of a field is the marking off of the headland, and the second is the marking out of the " lands." Marking out is usually done by ploughing a shallow single furrow. The headland is marked off by turning a furrow slice parallel to the boundaries of the field, usually round the whole field, though for horse ploughing it may follow three sides only, and in a rectangular field two headlands may suffice. The width of the headland may vary from 5 yd. in horse ploughing up to 11 yd. with tractor outfits. The " lands " are marked out parallel to one side of the field, generally the longest. The size of a " land " in ordinary arable practice is 22, 24 or up to 48 yd., the greater distances being used in tractor work, but on heavy land which tends to be waterlogged they may be of 5 or 6 yd. or in some cases even less, in order to introduce a large number of open furrows which serve as shallow drains.

The ridges, set up around the single shallow furrows marking out the " lands," are kept as flat as possible and the plough is brought to the required depth gradually. The method of setting ridges depends on the custom of the locality and on whether the field is ley or stubble. For details of the various methods and for information on plough setting reference should be made to " Tractor Ploughing," published by Her Majesty's Stationery Office for the Ministry of Agriculture, Fisheries and Food.

Ploughing in " lands " is necessary with ordinary ploughs to avoid excessive idle travel and the making of sharp turns on the headland. " Lands " are not necessary with one-way ploughs. An alternative method of tractor ploughing which avoids waste of time in turning is to go round and round the field. This may be done by turning the furrows towards the boundary and continuing until the remaining small patch in the middle of the field can be ploughed as a " land " by turning on the ploughed land at its ends. As this method leaves very rough diagonals (where the plough changes direction), these may be marked off as headlands beforehand and ploughed afterwards. If the ploughing is started in the middle there is no need for diagonal headlands, but, at any rate on the first occasion, it is a more complicated business to fix on the right place to start.

## CULTIVATORS

Cultivators are used to break up land that has lain in the furrow throughout the winter, to level land that has been tracked by the carting off of roots, for summer fallowing, stubble breaking, and the inter-row cultivation of various crops such as potatoes, vegetable crops and fruit trees and bushes. Much of their work is heavy and they have therefore to be stoutly built. Cultivators vary considerably in detailed design but all are built on the same general principles—a toolbar to which are attached a number, usually nine or eleven or more rarely thirteen, straight or curved, rigid or spring-mounted tines. The tines are arranged in rows, *i.e.* they are staggered, to obtain the maximum clearance between adjacent tines and thereby allow rubbish to pass between them without causing blockages. The lower ends of the tines carry detachable steel points. The type of point most frequently used for general cultivating is a double ended, narrow and reversible point, but broader points are available for shallower work. Horse and tractor trailer cultivators usually have two land wheels but many tractor-mounted cultivators have only small depth regulating wheels and some may not have wheels, the depth being controlled by the tractor's hydraulic mechanism.

**The Tractor Cultivator** (Plate 5, *A*).—Tractor cultivators are heavier and more stoutly constructed than horse cultivators because they have to withstand much greater strains and stresses. Depth control is usually by a screw adjustment operating through the cranked axles of the land wheels, although on a few makes it is by levers and quadrants. A self-lift of the rack and pinion type, brought into action through a trip cord pulled by the tractor driver, raises the tines out of work. The Ransomes' Equitine cultivator is an interesting type because the tines can swing in their mountings and are joined together by flexible chains and levers. When a tine hits an obstruction it swings backwards, passes over the obstruction, and is then pulled back into work by the forces acting on the other tines and transmitted to it through the connecting chains. On another type of general purpose cultivator (the Ferguson) coiled tension springs hold the tines in work but allow them to rise if they hit an obstruction.

**Rotary Cultivators.**—These are machines provided with power-driven blades or tines that break the soil into more or less fine, loose fragments, thus producing in one or more operations a tilth suitable for a seed bed. The tines are mounted on horizontal or vertical axes that fit behind a tractor, the whole forming a self-contained, self-propelled unit (see Plate 5, *B*); but in some makes the cultivator is a separate attachment that is pulled by an ordinary agricultural tractor and actuated from the power take-off. The size of rotary cultivators varies from a small " walking " machine designed for garden and orchard work, through a range requiring medium tractor power, to the very powerful Gyrotiller which can cultivate to a depth of 18 in. and even clear land of scrub.

As compared with ploughs and ordinary cultivators, rotary cultivators have the disadvantages of being unable to bury turf, trash or manure, and of producing in some soils a tilth that is too fluffy for good planting and one that is liable to cap after rain. Rotary machines are, of course, quite unsuitable for use in winter when land is wet and easily puddled. On the other hand they are excellent for forming a surface mulch and for destroying small weeds as required in the cultivation of an orchard.

**Hoes.**—Crops, usually root crops, grown in rows on the flat and on ridges, are hoed to kill weeds. With a multiple row hoe the number of rows hoed at once is either equal to or an exact sub-multiple of the number of coulters in the drill. This is necessary for accurate close hoeing because, in drilling the seed, the outer coulter of the drill cannot, in practice, be run exactly parallel to the previous row. The hoe blades and sometimes depth regulating wheels are attached to a tool frame consisting of two or more parallel bars. The hoe blades are staggered on the frame so that cut weeds and stones do not jam between them and they are sometimes mounted in such a way that they rise and fall with irregularities in the surface of the ground. Individual hoes or groups of hoes may be so mounted, with a spring in each mounting to keep the hoes in work. Spring-loaded hoes work well under most conditions but when the ground is hard they may not be so efficient as hoes mounted on rigid stalks. When the toolbar is used as a steerage hoe it is equipped with a pair of handles, by means of which an operator guides the implement through the crop and also with a seat if it is attached to a tractor. In the horse steerage hoe the tool frame is connected to a two-wheeled fore-carriage but in the tractor steerage hoe there is no fore-carriage and the tool frame is attached directly to the rear of the tractor (Plate 6, *A*). The connection between the tool frame and the fore-carriage or tractor is flexible so that the tool frame can be moved from side to side to keep the hoe blades in the correct position on the rows.

One-man tractor hoeing outfits have the tool frames fitted in one of three positions on the tractor—on the rear (Plate 6, *B*), beneath the sump between the front and rear wheels and forward of the front wheels. When the tool frame is in the last two positions it is usual to have an additional rear tool bar equipped with tines to take out the tractor wheel marks. Much closer work is possible with the forward and underslung hoes than with the rear hoe because the operator can see the work he is doing.

**The Drill Horse Hoe.**—Drill or ridge horse hoes, harrows, cultivators, scufflers and grubbers are implements designed for cultivating crops grown on ridges, usually one row at a time. The simplest hoe has a narrow frame with handles at the rear, and in front a small wheel, adjustable for height, for controlling the depth of working. The cultivating tools are attached to the frame. The expanding type of horse hoe (shown in Fig. 4) consists of a frame, the side members of which are hinged in front and can be fixed to give any desired width of cut by means of a set screw; it is kept in balance by means of its handles, and its depth of working is controlled by moving the wheel up or down in its socket. Horse hoes vary in size and weight; heavy two-horse implements are made which allow of deep work, and, on the other hand, light five tine hoes can be obtained suitable for market gardens. Tractor-mounted cultivators, rear and underslung with the tines arranged in three groups of three each to deal with three rows at once, are used extensively for drill work (see Plate 6, *B*).

The wide range of hoe blades manufactured to suit all purposes fall into two well defined groups: A hoes and L or side hoes. A hoes are used for cultivating the centres of the rows, whilst L hoes are run close to the plants. If the row width is so great that a pair of L hoes do not completely cover the row, A and L hoes are used together; but on narrower row widths A hoes are used when the plants are either so small that close hoeing is impossible, or so large that only the centre of the row

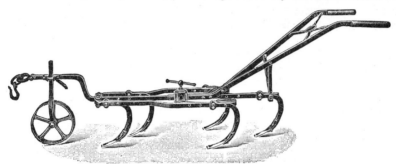

FIG. 4.—Expanding horse-hoe

need be cultivated. On the other hand L hoes are essential for close hoeing. Small power-driven rotary cultivators, capable of working in rows as narrow as 12 in., are sometimes used in place of hoe blades. They are shielded to prevent soil being thrown on to the crop. A pair of dished discs set at an angle to each other and straddling the plants is frequently used for the cultivation of roots grown on the flat and on the ridge. They pull soil away from the plants and thereby facilitate singling. On ridge root crops in wet districts, cutting the weeds with hoe blades does not always kill them, and the only effective control is to use discs to smother them.

**Gapping and Thinning Machines.**—The ordinary horse hoe is used for gapping root crops grown on the flat by driving it across the rows. The Kent and Dixie gappers (Plate 7, *A*) are examples of special along-the-row gapping machines; models are available for both flat and ridge work. Gapping is successful only if the stand is uniform. The width of land left uncut (*i.e.* the size of the bunch) is adjusted to suit the stand, and the distance apart of the bunches is varied on the Kent and Dixie machines by altering the speed of rotation of the gapping knives relative to the forward speed. Two or more of the Dixie units may be mounted on a tractor toolbar.

Thinning machines are used to reduce the number of plants in a braird. They are non-selective in action and a uniform, but not necessarily thick, braird is essential for satisfactory results. There are two types of machine. In one the thinner head consists of a vertical flat disc carrying radial tines (Plate 7, *B*). The disc faces along the row being thinned and as the machine moves forward, it revolves and the tines remove plants from the row. The number of tines on the disc, the length of the small blade at the extremity of each tine and the speed of rotation of the head relative to forward speed determine the proportion of plants removed from the row. The number and arrangement of the tines on the disc is determined by the braird. The braird is assessed by placing a 100 in. long stick against a row of plants and noting the number of inches that have plants opposite them. The number is usually referred to as " plant-inches " or in the case of sugar beet as " beet-inches." This is repeated at several places over the field to get a reliable estimate of the " stand " and then by referring to a table supplied with the machine the number and size of the tines required to reduce this " stand " to leave a given number of " plant-inches " can be ascertained. In the second type of thinning machine the thinner head has one or two vertical tines terminating in blades which oscillate from side to side across the row as the machine travels forward. Here again the braird and the reduction in " stand " required determine the size of blade to be used. Thinning may be done in one operation but if the braird is good two operations may be possible. For example, with the rotary thinner the first operation may be done with eight tines, each tine carrying a $1\frac{3}{4}$ in. blade and the disc making an eighth of a revolution for each $3\frac{1}{2}$ in. of forward travel. Thus half of the plants are removed. The second operation may be done with smaller blades on 16 tines. This reduces the " stand " further, the actual reduction depending on the size of the blade. The thinning heads are sometimes fitted with straight spring steel tines for the removal of weed seedlings from an established braird.

## HARROWS

**The Zigzag Harrow.**—Zigzag harrows (Fig. 5 and Plate 8, *A*) of the ordinary type have fixed vertical tines, and are constructed in many different sizes and weights. The lightest type, which, however, may have a track as wide as 18 ft., is used for covering grass seeds, and consists of a light framework with very short iron teeth. The heavier makes have iron frames and longer tines, so that they have a greater penetration in hard land; their track is 7 ft. 6 in. to 9 ft., and all but the heaviest models can be drawn by two horses. For tractor work the same types of harrow are employed, but the sets may be 20 to 30 ft. wide, and may be equipped with a lift which, on engaging a trip clutch, raises and lowers the harrows during forward travel, thus allowing any accumulation of rubbish to drop from the tines. Alternatively three harrow leaves are mounted on the back of the tractor and are raised and lowered on the power lift. The side leaves are raised into the vertical position to reduce the overall width for transport.

An improvement on the ordinary harrow is an implement fitted with hinged teeth, the angle of which is controllable by means of a tilting

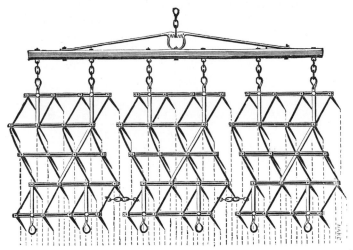

Fig. 5.—Zigzag Harrow (Sellar)

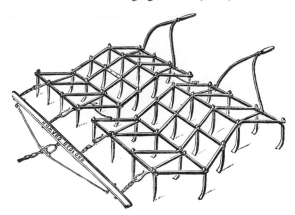

Fig. 6.—Drag Harrow (Howard)

lever. Such an arrangement allows of a forward setting of the tines, which enables the implement to work to a greater depth if the land is hard, and of a backward setting, to avoid clogging of the teeth when the surface is strewn with weeds.

**The Drag Harrow.**—Fig. 6 illustrates an ordinary type of drag harrow. An implement of this kind has usually a 6 ft. track, and is intermediate in its action between a harrow and a cultivator.  The long tines with their forward curve penetrate a considerable way into the soil and create a fairly deep tilth.  This harrow is very largely used for dragging out creeping weeds like couch grass, and it is fitted with handles so that it may be raised and freed from rubbish from time to time.

**The Saddle Back Harrow.**—Saddle back harrows are used for pulling down potato ridges.  As the name implies, each harrow leaf is shaped to fit the ridge so that the straight tines disturb the weeds at the base as well as on the top of the ridge.  Each harrow section is divided longitudinally into two, and the halves are hinged together, thus enabling the shape to

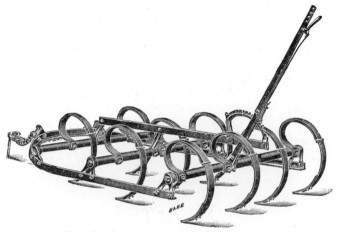

Fig. 7.—Spring-toothed Harrow (Sellar)

be adjusted for high sharp-pointed and low flat ridges.  Saddle back harrows consisting of only two sections are normally horse drawn.  Plate 8, *B* shows four sections attached to a direct mounted rear toolbar.

**Spring-toothed Harrows** (Fig. 7) have an action somewhat similar to that of drags, but the angle of the spring tines can be instantly altered to suit the condition of the land or, when used for weed dragging, to free the implement from trash.  They are sometimes mounted on the back of a tractor.

**The Chain Harrow.**—Chain harrows, constructed of link pieces which may or may not carry small tines, are completely flexible.  They are most largely used for spreading droppings, mole-hills and, on grassland, but they may be employed for harrowing down potato drills and rolling together the weeds that have been dragged out of fallows.  Some models have knife tines on one side and ordinary straight tines on the other, or tines may be present on one side only.  A flexible harrow has a better rubbing effect than an ordinary harrow and under some conditions may be superior for producing a surface tilth.

**Weeders.**—The tractor-mounted weeder consists of a very wide frame which carries a large number of light curved spring steel tines. The tines are staggered on the frame to prevent choking with stones or clods of earth. The implement is pulled over the land at fairly high speeds with the tips of the tines just penetrating the surface. It is used on young crops such as sugar beet, potatoes, peas and corn, to remove weed seedlings without damaging the crop.

**The Disc Harrow.**—This implement, which is illustrated in Plate 9, *A*, is probably the most efficient type of harrow for pulverising and loosening the surface soil. Not only is it used for the creation of a tilth on ordinary arable land, but it may be worked on grassland to cut up the surface and promote aeration, or in preparation for manuring and renovation. No other harrow can work so well on soddy land, since the rolling action of the discs precludes all possibility of clogging or of pulling up turf or buried rubbish. Moreover, the implement exerts more compression than a tined harrow on the lower horizon of the soil. It is therefore very valuable for obliterating the air spaces that tend to cause trouble when tough old swards are ploughed, and for producing a firm seed bed on any land that tends to lie hollow. Finally, the discs have a slight digging and soil turning action, and may be used for the destruction of weeds that have got beyond the control of ordinary harrows; but discs should not be used on couch infested land.

The modern disc harrow is designed for tractor work and consists of two double gangs of dished discs. The discs of the first two gangs move the soil away from the centre of the implement and the rear discs move the soil in the opposite direction. The angle that the discs make with the line of draught is easily adjustable. This adjustment is sometimes made through the lift mechanism on the tractor. The depth of working is determined by the angle of the gangs to the line of draught, the curvature of the discs, and the weight of the harrow. Weight pans are usually provided to take added weights when it is necessary to get extra penetration. Small wheels, with a simple jacking arrangement attached, are used for transporting disc harrows on hard roads. One wheel is put on each gang. Small sets of discs may be tractor-mounted, in which case they are raised clear of the ground on the lift for turning on the headlands and for transport. Smaller two-gang disc harrows are sometimes used with horses.

Tractor mounted off-set disc harrows, consisting of two single gangs in tandem, are used for orchard cultivation where, because of overhanging branches, it is impossible to get the tractor close to the tree trunks. Side draught, due to the off-set position, is eliminated by angling the two sets in opposite directions.

**The Pitch Pole Harrow** is a dual purpose implement which takes the place of a drag harrow for arable land and also acts as a grassland renovator. It possesses double-ended tines, and a knife-edged pattern is employed when the harrow is used for tearing old turf and aerating pasture.  If the knives gather trash they can be cleared by allowing them to revolve or " pitch pole."  Three wheels are provided for transport; the depth is set by hand levers and the pitching action is controlled by means of a cord to the trip lever.  Tractor-mounted models are now available.

**The Cultarrow** is a tractor mounted tool in which the two transverse members carrying the tines have a reciprocating motion across the direction of forward travel.  Power for the motion is obtained from the tractor power take-off.  The Cultarrow has a greater effect on tilth than ordinary tined harrows and has been found very useful for harrowing out potatoes behind the pickers.

**The Float and Scrubber.**—The float is a tool used in the preparation of seed beds for roots grown " on the flat " to remove abrupt irregularities in the surface of the soil which may affect the functioning of seeder units and hoeing outfits.  It is usually made by the local blacksmith and consists of two skids to which are attached several cross members spaced at about 12 to 15 in. apart.  As it is drawn over the ground it scrapes soil from the high spots and drops it in the depressions.  The scrubber is mainly a clod crusher with slight levelling action.  It is very heavy and can take several forms.  In one, it consists of several over lapping timber planks (like very heavy weather boarding) that are dragged over the ground.  The edges in contact with the soil may be iron shod.

## ROLLERS

Rollers vary in diameter, width, weight, shape and the materials of which they are constructed; they are manufactured to suit all ordinary and special purposes.  The most common rollers are constructed of iron, in the form of cylinders mounted on a long axle, the division into sections allowing of more easy turning at the headlands.  Sometimes a single cylinder watertight barrel is used, which can have its weight increased by the addition of water, the quantity being determined according to the nature of the work to be done.  The heaviest iron clod crushers are Cambridge (Plate 9, *B*) and Crosskill rollers, the former being built up of heavy ribbed and the latter of heavy toothed sections.  This construction reduces the bearing surface on the ground and so increases the pressure on clods.  Small rollers for a single horse are fitted with shafts, but large two and three horse sizes have a framework and one or two wheels to support the hitching gear.  When rollers of the latter type are used on hilly farms they must be fitted with brakes in order to avoid serious accidents.  When it is desired to increase the weight of a light roller, iron cart axles and heavy stones may be securely fastened to the framework.  Special diabolo-shaped rollers are made for rolling turnip drills.  These are particularly useful in producing the consolidation necessary to bring about the germination of the seed in a dry spring.  Tractor rollers are often made up in sets of three sections, each set covering a width of 20 ft. or more. For transport along roads and through gateways the three sections are pulled in tandem. It is worthy of note that the effectiveness of rolling is decreased if the implements are driven fast.

A furrow-press is a special type of roller used immediately after ploughing in order to secure a firm bottom for the seed bed. Furrow-presses are popular in certain areas, especially where wheat normally follows clover or other leys. The essentials are a frame, with shafts or hitch bar, mounted on an axle which is supported on the near or land side by an ordinary wheel but on the off side carries a number of heavy press wheels with wedge shaped rims which bear into the furrow grooves. The presses are adjustable for width of furrow. A horse implement has two presses, but in the case of a tractor, which pulls the press immediately behind its plough, the presses correspond in number to the plough bodies.

### SPRAYERS AND DUSTERS (See Plate 10)

Many and various substances are employed for the control of insect and fungoid pests and for the destruction of weeds. Only small quantities of the chemicals are required, and to obtain uniform distribution they are usually applied either as dilute solutions or as finely divided dusts. Many of the chemicals are corrosive and those parts of the machines which come into contact with them are made of special alloys. In most machines the liquid is converted into spray by forcing it through specially designed nozzles; on others the process is effected by feeding a thin stream of the liquid into a strong air blast. Many types of spraying machines are in use, varying from small hand-operated knapsack appliances to large horse or tractor drawn or tractor-mounted units with mechanical pumps. In some the liquid container is airtight and a pump is employed to force out the spray by means of air pressure; in others the liquid itself is pumped, but an air cylinder and a pressure release valve are interposed to equalise the pressure before it reaches the nozzles. Agricultural spraying machines generally work at low to moderate pressures—about 30 to 150 lb. per sq. in.—but in horticulture much higher pressures—as high as 400 to 500 lb. per sq. in. or more—are employed.

When the area to be sprayed is not large, a barrel to hold the liquid may be placed in a farm cart or tractor trailer while the spraybar, carrying the nozzles and hand pump, is clamped on to the back of the vehicle; a man in the cart works the pump. It is more usual, however, to employ a sprayer with a tank capacity of 50 to 150 gal., and provided with a pump which may be driven from the axle, by a small petrol engine or from the tractor power take-off. The power-operated pump may also be used for filling the machine, thus saving a great deal of time on the headland. Such machines have an effective spraying width of about 5 yd. and, allowing time for filling, spray about 2½ acres an hour. Different types of spraybar can be attached to the machines. For spraying weeds in corn all the nozzles are at the same level and face downwards, whereas for spraying potatoes against blight some of the nozzles are on pendants and direct the spray upwards on to the under surface of the foliage. The use of dilute solutions demands an adequate supply of water and means that a great deal of time is spent in preparing the solution and filling the sprayer. These difficulties have been overcome by the introduction of low-volume sprayers, which are machines capable of applying small quantities per acre of concentrated liquid which may be a true solution or a fine suspension. As the amount of liquid needed per acre is small these sprayers may be tractor-mounted. Some sprayers can be used for both high and low volume spraying by regulating the pressure and fitting appropriate nozzles.

Dusting is not always so reliable as spraying, but it can be done much more quickly and with less labour. The most commonly used duster is a very simple machine (Plate 10, *B*). The powder is fed into a fan and is blown on to the crop. Quantities as low as 10 lb. per acre can be applied with a satisfactory degree of uniformity. Small hand-operated dusters are available, but for field work, especially on potatoes, large eleven and thirteen row machines, capable of dusting 7 acres an hour, are used. The fan may be driven from the axle of the machine or it may be power operated from a small auxiliary engine or from the tractor power take-off. Tractor-mounted dusters include machines on which the exhaust gases of the tractor distribute the dust.

Fumigation is employed for the control of certain pests. The chemical is vaporised by mixing it with hot gases and is then released under a very large sheet trailed over the growing crop. These specialised machines are in the hands of contractors.

Aircraft are being increasingly employed in the new countries for spraying and dusting. The small size of the fields in many parts of Britain presents difficulties but, in spite of these, aerial spraying has been adopted on a limited scale for the control of potato blight and of weeds. Great care has to be taken because of the danger of spray drift affecting other farm crops. If and when a satisfactory herbicide is developed for the control of bracken it is possible that it will be applied from the air especially to those areas inaccessible to normal farm tractors. Aerial spraying is also used in the control of pests in forests.

# CHAPTER 6

## TILLAGE—WEED CONTROL

THE final objectives of tillage operations are, on the one hand, to produce in the soil a physical state favourable to the establishment and growth of crop plants, and, on the other, to control weeds so far as to prevent them from competing seriously with the cultivated plants for soil moisture, light and plant nutrients.

Some particular tillage operations aim directly at one or other of these objects. For instance, the spring cultivation of an autumn ploughed ley for a crop of oats may have as its one aim to produce a suitable seed bed— a zone of fine, crumbly soil in which to place the seed and, below this, a well compacted layer in which the plants will obtain a firm roothold and a supply of moisture. Again the inter-row cultivation of a root crop aims at destroying the weeds which would otherwise smother the slower growing crop plants.

In other cases the objective is a long term one. For instance, when land is ploughed in autumn in preparation for a root crop it is hoped that a condition is being created in which the soil will benefit from winter weathering—i.e. will remain sufficiently open to allow rain to penetrate easily into the subsoil and will be fully exposed to the action of frost. In autumn ploughing, however, the stubble of the preceding corn crop is being buried and the opportunity is taken of incorporating with the soil a dressing of dung for certain crops.

As regards weed control, there are certain indirect measures, such as the proper design of rotations and the use of smother crops which are discussed in Part 4, as aspects of farm organisation. Weeds of grassland are dealt with later (pp. 383-384). Direct measures of controlling weeds in arable land are considered here.

A few of the methods that are still employed to-day are of great antiquity. One is *fallowing*—i.e. the devotion of a growing season, in whole or in part, to the destruction of weeds, the land carrying no crop while the process is being carried out. In this country to-day fallowing consists simply of a series of tillage operations, designed to cause annual weeds to germinate so that the seedlings are killed in the next operation. Alternatively, perennial weed rootstocks or rhizomes are killed by baking in the clod, weather permitting. In many primitive systems of farming the burning of the weed vegetation is part of the process of cleaning. The operation of *paring and burning*—" Devonshiring "—survived in parts of this country until after the middle of last century. The other old method is the hand pulling, hoeing up, chopping or spudding of weeds in the growing crop.

The first important innovation was the introduction of drill or horse hoeing husbandry, made possible by the invention of the drill about 1730, but becoming widespread only from about 1800. Much later still, in 1896, came the discovery that a solution of copper sulphate, of suitable strength, would kill certain broad leaved weeds (notably yellow charlock) while causing relatively little damage to cereal plants in the early stages of growth. To-day there is a considerable choice of chemical weed killers, including some that are highly selective in their action as between one species and another. Thus to-day, in dealing with weeds, it is possible to combine measures such as rotational cropping with tillage operations and the use of chemical herbicides.

## COMMON WEEDS [1]

Almost any native or introduced plant may be found as a weed—*i.e.* growing where it is not wanted and competing with the cultivated crop for light, water and plant food. Crop plants themselves must be regarded as weeds if they grow where not intended. Thus ground keeper potatoes can be quite troublesome in fields of roots, and brown mustard, formerly cultivated in East Anglia, could become about as noxious as its relative charlock. Again, plants of one variety of potato, growing in a seed crop of another variety, must be treated as weeds. Such are commonly called rogues. A complete list of British weeds would include some hundreds of species, but the number that cause really serious trouble in any given area and under any particular system of cropping is usually small. Some few, like the couch grasses, docks and the field or creeping thistle, are very widely distributed, but otherwise the weed flora is closely related to the soil and climatic conditions and the cropping system. For instance, in the heavy land arable districts of the midland and eastern counties, where winter wheat is the predominant cereal, the characteristically abundant species are wild oats (the native *Avena fatua* and the introduced *A. ludoviciana*), slender foxtail or black-grass (*Alopecurus mysuroides*), corn buttercup (*Ranunculus arvensis*), shepherd's needle (*Scandix pecten-veneris*), *Agrostis* couch and water grass and, less generally, the wild onion or crow garlic (*Allium vineale*). By contrast, on fertile loam soils in eastern Scotland, where spring sown oats and barley predominate, the major problems are presented by yellow charlock, wild mustard (*Sinapis arvensis*) and couch (*Agropyrum repens*), while on light and lime deficient land in the same area spurrey (*Spergula arvensis*) is the most aggressive species.

---

[1] Students who do not know the common weeds mentioned in this text should consult an illustrated British Flora such as that of Bentham and Hooker or of Clapham, Tutin and Warburg. Illustrations of common weed seedlings may be found in Ministry of Agriculture, Fisheries and Food Bulletin No. 179, Seedlings of Common Weeds.

Again, in the intensively manured market garden area of Bedfordshire, on the Greensand formation, the chief trouble is caused by quick growing annuals such as chickweed (*Stellaria media*), the mayweeds and chamomiles (*Anthemis* and *Matricarea* spp.), fat hen or goosefoot (*Chenopodium album*) and the annual or small nettle (*Urtica urens*).

From the farmer's point of view the most useful classification of weeds is according to habit of growth and method of reproduction.

The *Ephemerals*, so called because they grow from seed, flower and shed their seed all in a matter of weeks, form a fairly distinct group. Most are of low growth or of sprawling habit so that they cannot compete seriously with a quick growing and vigorous cereal crop. On the other hand, they compete strongly with, and may smother, crops like carrots and onions which are slow to become established. The ephemerals are therefore the most important group in market gardening. One or two, notably ivy leafed speedwell (*Veronica hederaefolia*), which are frost hardy as seedlings, can be troublesome in winter corn during the early spring. Otherwise in farming they cause most concern in sugar beet and roots. Examples are the chickweeds (*Stellaria* and *Cerastium* spp.), shepherd's purse (*Capsella bursa-pastoris*), the speedwells (*Veronica* sp.), groundsel (*Senecio vulgaris*) and annual meadow grass (*Poa annua*).

The *Annuals*, which produce only one generation a year, may usefully be divided into those whose seedlings are frost hardy and those others whose seedlings are killed in the average British winter. The first find a favourable environment in winter cereals, shedding their seed before the grain is ripe. These include, besides the wild oat, slender foxtail or black grass and corn buttercup already mentioned, poppies (*Papaver* sp.) and cornflower (*Centaurea cyanus*).

Annuals whose seedlings are not frost hardy, and which therefore are rarely troublesome in winter grain, include yellow charlock and its less widespread but less easily controlled relative white charlock or runch or wild radish (*Raphanus raphanistrum*); mayweeds and chamomiles, goosefoot or fat hen (*Chenopodium album*), and the related oraches (*Atriplex* spp.), fumitory (*Fumaria officinalis*), redshank or willow weed (*Polygonum persicaria*); knot-grass (*P. aviculare*) and bearbine, climbing buckwheat, or black bindweed (*P. convolvulus*); cleavers (*Galium aparine*); annual sow thistle (*Sonchus oleraceus*); spurrey; corn marigold, generally on acid soils (*Chrysanthemum segetum*); annual nettle; hemp nettle, frequently on peat fen, (*Galeopsis tetrahit*) and others of less widespread distribution.

A further useful distinction may be made, as among the annuals, according to the length of the period of dormancy of the seeds. Given suitable conditions, the seeds of chickweed, for example, will germinate as soon as they are shed, whereas those of charlock, wild oat, black-grass and poppy have to undergo a process of after-ripening, which may last for several months, before they can be induced to germinate. Still others, shed in summer, refuse to germinate until the following spring; these include fat hen, knot-grass (*P. aviculare*), mayweed and corn marigold. Sometimes even a minor difference may be important. Thus in the south midlands the seeds of black grass can often be induced to germinate by October, so that the seedlings can be destroyed in the process of sowing wheat; whereas wild oats, even of the winter species, will rarely do so, more usually springing up some time after the wheat is sown.

*Biennial Weeds* such as spear thistle (*Carduus lanceolatus*), wild carrot (*Daucus carota*), and ragwort[1] (*Senecio jacobaea*), are unimportant in arable crops since any plants that gain a footing will ordinarily be destroyed by ordinary tillage operations in their first year, *i.e.* before they have reached the flowering stage.

The *Perennials* that infest arable land are almost exclusively those with underground stems. The only important exception is the dock (*Rumex* sp.), which, although a tap rooted plant, has the rather uncommon capacity (shared with the dandelion) of producing adventitious buds from the upper portions of root. The most common are probably couch (*Agropyrum repens*) and *Agrostis* species. Others, like coltsfoot (*Tussilago farfara*) and horsetail (*Equiselum arvense*) are widely distributed but tend to occur in patches in some fields, often those poorly drained. Plants with surface runners, such as silverweed (*Potentilla anserina*) and creeping buttercup (*Ranunculus repens*), are generally destroyed by good ploughing at a reasonable depth, especially if drainage is good.

The feasibility of destroying underground stolons depends largely upon the depth at which these are found. Thus *Agrostis* " twitch " usually runs at a depth of about 2 or 3 in. and couch grass at 3 to 4 in., *i.e.* well within the normal plough depth even on thin soils. Those of the creeping or field thistle occupy an intermediate position, and it is often necessary to plough at more than the normal depth or to subsoil, in order to reach them. Those of the bindweeds (*Convolvulus* spp.) and coltsfoot (*Tussilago farfara*) are quite beyond the reach of ordinary implements.

Two noxious species have bulbous underground stems. The one, bulbous tall oat grass, known also as onion couch (*Arrhenatherum avenaceum*), has storage organs like strings of miniature onions which can be dragged out of the ground without much breakage if the soil be first very thoroughly loosened. The other, wild onion (*Allium vineale*), which has a bulb like a small tulip with attached bulbils, cannot be dragged out by any implement.

## WEED CONTROL WITH CHEMICALS

While it remains as true as ever that the basis of clean farming should be a sound rotation and good cultivations, the rapid development since the

---

[1] Ragwort sometimes behaves as a perennial, and does so normally if the flowering stems, which appear in the second year, are cut down.

PLATE 7

*A.* GAPPING MACHINE (DIXIE)

*B.* DOWN-THE-ROW THINNER

PLATE 8

*A.* MULTIPLE HARROW AND HITCH

*B.* MOUNTED SADDLE-BACK HARROWS

PLATE 9

*A.* Tandem Disc Harrow (Steel)

*B.* Cambridge Rollers and Hitch

PLATE 10

*A.* TRACTOR-DRAWN SPRAYER (BARCLAY, ROSS AND HUTCHISON)

*B.* AGRO SPRAYER (RANSOMES)

war of a range of selective weed killing chemicals has put into the farmer's hands a very powerful tool. The use of chemicals for weed control dates back many years to the time when copper sulphate, a constituent of the Bordeaux mixture used in vineyards, was found to kill some of the weeds present between the vines. For many years prior to the last war, copper sulphate, kainit, and later copper chloride, sulphuric acid and a number of other materials were occasionally used for the control of weeds in cereal crops. Sodium chlorate and arsenic compounds were also used for gravel paths and patches of land where all vegetation was intended to be killed. In the middle 1930's experiments were being carried out with DNOC,[1] but it was not until 1942 that Templeman discovered MCPA[2] at the same time that 2.4-D [3] was being discovered in America. These growth regulating herbicides were being used commercially by 1946, and by 1960 over $3\frac{1}{2}$ million acres were sprayed in Great Britain for weed control, much of it with these materials. This research and rapid development has now made it possible to control a range of weed species in a large number of the crops grown in this country.

**Classification of Materials.**—The scope of chemical weed control has widened to such an extent that it is more than ever necessary to have some understanding of the way in which the different types of chemicals act on plants. This is, in fact, an understanding of the factors on which selectivity and toxicity depend, and it should enable one to group many of these substances in a logical manner according to their manner of action and use.

It is necessary to distinguish between those chemicals which are *non-selective* in their action and those which are *selective* as between different plant species or groups. Selectivity is usually a matter of degree: it is seldom complete in the sense of killing one species and leaving another entirely unaffected. One may then group the chemicals according to whether they are applied pre-planting, pre-emergence or post-emergence, and again according to whether the material is applied to the soil or to the foliage. In the latter event the chemical may be contact acting or translocated.

Non-selective herbicides may act entirely upon the leaves—some oils are toxic in this way—and kill all tissues with which they come in contact. These are called contact herbicides. Alternatively, the chemical may act through the root system, killing those plants which absorb sufficient of it. The relatively insoluble compounds of arsenic and boron act in this latter way. The soluble sodium arsenite is also a non-selective herbicide but can act through the leaf, as well as later through the roots if a sufficient amount is used. Applied in sufficient quantity to the soil, arsenic can act as a permanent soil sterilant, preventing the growth of

---

[1] Dinitro-ortho-cresol.
[2] 2-methyl-4-chloro-phenoxy-acetic acid.
[3] 2-4-dichloro-phenoxy-acetic acid.

plants for many years. This sense of the word " sterilisation " should not be confused with others; for example, the term is also applied to the effect of steam or chemicals upon the soil microflora.

Sodium chlorate can act non-selectively as a temporary soil sterilant: temporary because it is broken down in the soil in a period of six to twelve months. Sprayed as a solution on to plants, chlorate can, however, show some selectivity, the degree depending on how much of the spray solution is retained on the leaf. A waxy grass leaf will shed most of the spray, whereas a flat and hairy leaf will retain more of the liquid.

Selective action in a herbicide is a feature of great value to the farmer and market gardener; in this context it means no more than that one species (the crop) is affected little or not at all, while another (the weed) is damaged or killed.

A herbicide may act also in a selective manner when applied as a pre-emergence contact treatment, i.e. the weed is treated before the crop seedlings emerge. A number of contact herbicides can be used in this way provided they have no harmful residual effect upon the crop seedlings emerging later on. Perhaps the most familiar example is the sulphuric acid pre-emergent treatment of onions. However, a number of materials, including some tar acids and light oils, penta-chlor-phenol and even dinoseb, can act in a similar manner. Pre-emergence application of a soil acting or residual herbicide may also be made for certain crops. Thus, simazine may be applied after the sowing of beans or of maize for the control of a range of annual weeds. Pre-sowing application of di-allate in barley or of propham in peas may be used for the control of wild oats. Provided conditions are suitable, the weeds which continue for some weeks to germinate near the soil surface will be killed while the crop seedlings, emerging from a greater depth, will be unharmed. This principle is well established, and its application to crops in this country is steadily extending at the present time.

Selectivity is more commonly manifest to-day in the spraying of cereals, peas and grassland, when both crop and weed receive some of the spray (or dust) containing the herbicide. In this case selectivity between crop and weed will depend on one or more, and usually several, of the following factors:—

(a) differential retention of herbicide on the plant.
(b) degree of penetration into the leaf or other aerial parts.
(c) translocation within the plant.
(d) physiological effect at the site of action.

Retention of the material will obviously depend on such factors as shape and position of the leaf (broad and flat, or narrow and upright), the hairiness of the leaf and the nature of its surface (waxy or otherwise). If the herbicide is retained on the leaf surface, a variable amount may penetrate into the tissue through the cuticle or stomata.

Having penetrated into a leaf, the chemical may or may not affect the rest of the plant, this depending on whether it is translocated within the plant.

Finally, the chemical may have no effect upon the species even though it is absorbed (*i.e.* it is non-toxic to that species), or it may have an effect upon some aspect of the plant's metabolism with a consequent damaging effect on growth. The site of action may be the cells of the leaf, the respiratory system or some other part of the plant's system. The precise manner in which many of the herbicides act upon plants is still actively engaging many research workers. It will only be through an understanding of these processes that new chemicals and new techniques will be evolved.

Table 1 groups a range of herbicides according to their manner of use and effect.

TABLE 1

### NON-SELECTIVE HERBICIDE APPLICATIONS

| Applied to foliage | | Applied to soil |
|---|---|---|
| Contact | Translocated | Residual |
| mineral oils, often fortified with DNOC, penta-chlor-phenol, cresylic acids | sodium chlorate diquat amino-triazole | borates monuron (CMU) simazine sodium chlorate |

### SELECTIVE HERBICIDE APPLICATIONS

| | Applied to foliage of weed | | Applied to soil (residual acting) |
|---|---|---|---|
| | Contact | Translocated | |
| pre-sowing (of crop) | cresylic acids diquat sulphuric acid penta-chlor-phenol (but more often used as below) | amino-triazole dalapon | propham chlor-propham simazine TCA di-allate |
| pre-emergence (of crop) | cresylic acids diquat sulphuric acid penta-chlor-phenol | | chlor-propham dinoseb diuron and fenuron penta-chlor-phenol monuron (CMU) simazine atrazine |
| post-emergence of crop) | DNOC dinoseb certain mineral oils sodium monochlor-acetate sodium nitrate sulphuric acid | MCPA, MCPB 2.4-D, 2.4-DB mecoprop (CMPP) dichlorprop (2.4-DP) 2.3.6-TBA, 2.4.5-T barban | propham chlor-propham 2.4-DES diuron and fenuron monuron (CMU) simazine |

**The More Important Chemicals.**—There are so many substances with known herbicidal effects that only a small proportion can here be listed, mainly those already in common use. Full instructions regarding the field use of the materials can be obtained from books or instruction manuals devoted to this subject. The chief reference book is the Weed Control Handbook (Blackwell Scientific Publications Ltd.)

(a) NON-SELECTIVE.—*Oils.*—Many of the unsaturated and aromatic hydrocarbons are toxic to plants when applied to the foliage. These include some of the lighter petroleum fractions (diesel or gas oil and some paraffins) and many of the tar oil fractions. These or other less toxic but equally penetrating oils may be fortified with such materials as penta-chlor-phenol or DNOC to increase their effect upon the plant. The oil spreads over the leaves and assists penetration of the toxic fortifying chemical, thus preventing the (selective) principle of differential retention from operating; hence the spray becomes virtually non-selective in its action. Oils seldom have any lasting effect upon the soil or on the subsequent growth of plants when used in the usual modest quantities—less than about 100 gal. per acre.

*Arsenic.*—Arsenic compounds are not only poisonous to humans but, when present in the soil in sufficient amount, can prevent the growth of plants for a considerable length of time, possibly many years. Frequently of low solubility, the compounds become fixed in the soil and are then removed only very slowly. The period of sterility will depend on the quantity of arsenic used, the soil type and the rainfall. There are only slight variations in susceptibility between plant species. Rates of up to 6 cwt. per acre of arsenic trioxide ($As_2O_3$) or the equivalent in other compounds have been used for soil sterilisation. The soluble sodium arsenite—once widely used for potato haulm destruction—may be partly absorbed through the leaves, but will also act through the roots if it is applied in sufficient amount. The arsenite will decompose in the soil fairly quickly and can then cause some degree of sterilisation. Arsenic weed killers have been withdrawn from the home market due to their toxicity to humans.

*Boron.*—Borax is chiefly known in British farming as being necessary, on some soils, as a plant nutrient. It is seldom used as a herbicide. In sufficient quantity, however, it can act in a manner very similar to arsenic, being highly toxic to plants. An application as low as 30 lb. per acre to a non-sensitive crop such as sugar beet has been known to cause toxic symptoms during the following year in a boron sensitive crop such as potatoes. In America borax is sometimes used for soil sterilisation at rates of up to 6 cwt. per acre. It is preferred by some, because it is safer to handle than arsenic and has none of the fire hazard associated with sodium chlorate.

*Sodium Chlorate.*—At times sodium chlorate has been relatively cheap and easy to obtain and it has been used in a variety of ways. Used in

PLATE 11

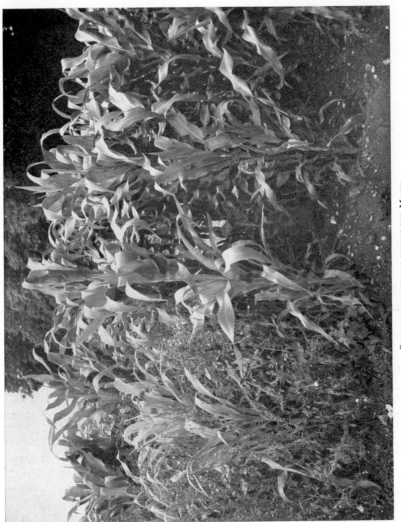

SIMANIZE-APPLIED PRE-SOWING FOR MAIZE
Untreated, *left*—treated, *right*

PLATE 12

BARBAN—CONTROL OF WILD OATS IN WHEAT

Treated, *left*—Untreated, *right*

preference to the less soluble ammonium and potassium chlorates for weed killing and potato haulm destruction, sodium chlorate has one great drawback—it is extremely inflammable when dry: in fact, a serious explosion can be caused if a keg of chlorate is exposed to sufficient heat or to a flame. Sprayed foliage and clothing, wetted with chlorate solution and afterwards dried, can be very inflammable. Because of this, non-inflammable formulations, such as Atlacide, have been developed. These usually consist of a mixture of sodium chlorate and a hygroscopic agent such as calcium chloride. Sodium chlorate has been used in the past as a selective herbicide in grassland at rates of 50 to 70 lb. per acre in 100 gal. of water (5 to 7 per cent. solution). The degree of selectivity, however, is not great, and some scorch damage to the grass is often experienced. As a temporary soil sterilant for the eradication of patches of perennial weeds such as couch and nettles, rates of 3 to 5 cwt. per acre [1] have been used, the precise amount depending on soil type, rainfall and the effect desired. This is applied dry to the soil surface during the spring or early summer. In normal conditions the treated area can carry a crop after the next winter's rains have removed the last traces of the chemical. Sodium chlorate can be absorbed by both the leaves and roots of plants.

*Monuron* or *CMU* (*p*-chloro-phenyl-dimethyl-urea).—Research has shown that some compounds of the group known as substituted ureas, of which monuron is one, have considerable phyto-toxic properties. Nearly insoluble in water and in most organic solvents, monuron is toxic at very low rates per acre to most plants. Since it is only slightly soluble and breaks down in the soil fairly slowly, it has considerable value as a temporary soil sterilant. At suitable rates it may also be used as a selective pre-emergence material, but is being succeeded by simazine and atrazine for this purpose. Diuron and fenuron are also of the substituted urea group of compounds and are used as pre-emergence selective herbicides.

*Simazine.*—This is one of the least soluble of a group of herbicides known as triazine compounds. Used at 20 to 40 lb. per acre, simazine will kill all weeds for two or three years. It is used on some crops as a selective herbicide at rates of 1 to 2 lb. per acre (Plate 11). Atrazine is rather more soluble but otherwise basically similar to simazine.

(*b*) SELECTIVE.—*Oils.*—Although many oils are non-selective in their action, a few fractions have been found to have valuable selective properties. These are the " white spirits " which are used for the control of seedling weeds in umbelliferous crops such as carrots, parsley and parsnips. Certain paraffin fuel fractions, such as are used for tractors, may have similar selective properties, and with certain precautions can be used in this way. Rates are between 40 and 80 gal. per acre, depending on crop, weed and weather conditions. The oil must not be mixed with water

[1] Equal to 1 to 1·6 oz. per sq. yd.

or spreaders or emulsifiers since its selective properties would be destroyed if this were done.

*Copper Salts.*—Copper sulphate is no longer used for weed control since more efficient and less corrosive materials are available. Copper chloride was a rather more effective herbicide for use in cereals but was relatively expensive. These copper salts are extremely corrosive to the metal parts of most spraying machines, even more so than sulphuric acid.

*Sodium nitrate.*—This may be used for spraying such easily controlled weeds as charlock seedlings in sugar beet and mangel crops. Rates employed are of the order of 250 to 300 lb. in 150 gal of water per acre. The treatment is variable in its effect according to weather and other factors and is not widely used.

*Sulphuric Acid.*—Despite the dangerous nature of this chemical, if allowed to come into contact with the skin or with clothing, it is still favoured by some as being one of the most efficient in checking the growth of a winter proud wheat crop. It is relatively cheap and kills a very wide range of annual weeds. Its use is limited not only by the fact that it is dangerous to handle but also by the fact that special machines are needed. Sulphuric acid is available commercially as BOV (Brown Oil of Vitriol), which contains approximately 70 per cent. of the pure acid. BOV, since it has no residual toxic effect, may also be used as a pre-emergence herbicide. It is rendered harmless within about an hour, following chemical reaction with the soil or the plant tissue. Rates of application range from 10 to 16 gal. per acre, and it may be applied either diluted with water or, in some circumstances, undiluted.

*The Dinitro Compounds.*—The two important members of this group are DNOC (di-nitro-ortho-cresol) and dinoseb [1] (di-nitro-ortho-secondary butyl-phenol). Although poisonous to human and animal life, these herbicides have been widely used. DNOC is usually used in cereals either as a suspension of the free acid or activated with sulphate of ammonia. The acid is relatively insoluble in water and is therefore used as a suspension; the salts are rather more soluble. DNOC should be used only in spraying machines equipped with thorough agitation to keep the material mixed; it is not used as a dust. Although the range of weeds controlled is not so wide as with sulphuric acid, DNOC controls a rather wider range than the growth regulating herbicides MCPA and 2.4-D. Dinoseb, developed after DNOC, is used widely on peas, to some extent on lucerne, and to a small extent on beans and seedling clovers. The insoluble ammonium salt is formulated in an organic solvent so that it can be mixed with water for application as a solution to the crop. An amine formulation is widely used also. Broadly, a similar range of weeds is controlled to that controlled with DNOC. Both DNOC and dinoseb act as contact herbicides, affecting the cells of the leaf

[1] Formerly known as DNBP.

and growing point and causing a complete collapse. They are not translocated and hence are of value in the control of annual weeds only. A uniform cover is essential, and for this reason both are applied at high volume rates, at least 60 gal. and, usually, 80 to 100 gal. per acre. Normal rates are 6 lb. per acre for DNOC and $1\frac{3}{4}$ to 2 lb. per acre for dinoseb. Rates of dinoseb are usually varied with the growth of the crop and the temperature conditions—the higher the temperature, the lower the safe rate.

Both DNOC and dinoseb are yellow staining compounds and are highly toxic if absorbed into the human body. Recognised precautions must be observed in their use.

*Growth regulating Herbicides.*—These include:

MCPA   2-methyl-4-chloro-phenoxy acetic acid
MCPB   2-methyl-4-chloro-phenoxy butyric acid
2.4-D   2.4-dichloro-phenoxy acetic acid
2.4-DB   2.4-dichloro-phenoxy butyric acid
mecoprop (CMPP)   2. methyl-4-chloro-phenoxy proprionic acid
dichlorprop (2.4-DP)   2.4-dichloro-phenoxy proprionic acid
2.3.6-TBA   2.3.6-trichlor benzoic acid
2.4.5-T   2.4.5-trichlor-phenoxy acetic acid

Fundamental research into the function of substances, which control the growth processes of plants, achieved most valuable practical results in the development of these herbicides. They are not " hormones " in the proper sense and are best described as " growth regulating substances." Depending for their action first on absorption by leaves or roots, they can be translocated and may have an effect upon the plant metabolism. Because they act in this way, they can be used to control a considerable range of perennial weeds as well as susceptible annuals. Furthermore, they may be applied in low volume (5 to 20 gal. per acre) as well as at high volume rates. This is possible because of their manner of action, since it is unnecessary to secure full coverage but only to ensure that sufficient herbicide is absorbed through the leaf or some other part of the plant. Some formulations may be applied in the form of dusts. Rates vary according to the crop, the weed and the precise formulation, but are generally between $\frac{1}{2}$ and 2 lb. per acre of the active ingredient, this being usually measured in terms of the " acid equivalent."

MCPA and 2.4-D are widely used on cereals and grassland. Precautions have to be taken with their use on cereals, since, if applied at too early a stage of growth, they may cause disorders in the later growth of the cereal. Annual weeds are most easily controlled by treatment at an early stage of growth; the younger the seedling, the better the control. Perennials are generally best treated at a later stage of development, usually at the flower bud stage.

The forms in which these herbicides are available commercially are as follows. The precise formulation for marketing can vary in each case:—

MCPA—Sodium, potassium or amine salt, frequently as 25 per cent. w/v liquid concentrate, but also 1 or 2 per cent. dusts.

2.4-D—

(a) Amine salts, readily soluble in water; very commonly used.

(b) Esters, insoluble in water but supplied in oil, with an emulsifier, for mixture with water.

2.4.5-T, used either alone or mixed with 2.4-D, is valuable for the control of certain woody weed species. Thus it has been used for the control of scrub growth along rights of way. It is commonly formulated as an ester.

MCPB and 2.4-DB are not in themselves herbicides. However, certain plants can convert them after absorption into MCPA and 2.4-D respectively. Clover and certain related species cannot do this, so these materials may be used, for instance, on undersown cereals. The number of weed species controlled is rather less than is the case with MCPA and 2.4-D.

Mecoprop, dichlorprop and 2.3.6-TBA have been developed since the introduction of MCPA and 2.4-D. They kill a rather wider range of weeds including cleavers, mayweed and some of the polygonum species. 2.3.6-TBA is usually sold in mixture with MCPA.

All these herbicides remain active in the soil for some time before they are broken down by specific soil bacteria. In normal conditions this period is six to eight weeks for MCPA and four to six weeks for 2.4-D. Susceptible crops should not be sown before this period has elapsed.

*Other Materials.*—Propham (iso-propyl-*n*-phenyl-carbamate), or IPC as it is sometimes called, is in fact a growth regulating substance but is excluded from the list above since it functions in a very different manner. Whereas MCPA and 2.4-D are toxic to broad leaved plants and less so to the cereals and grasses, propham acts more nearly in the opposite fashion, being, in particular, toxic to seedling grasses. Chlor-propham is a somewhat similar chemical.

Two chemicals for the control, principally of wild oats, are di-allate and barban. The former is for pre-sowing application; the latter is used post-emergence (Plate 12). Di-allate and barban are related chemically and belong to the same group as propham.

TCA (trichloracetic acid). All the chlorinated acetic acids are phyto-toxic in some degree; for instance, the mono chlor derivative (sodium mono chlor acetate) has been used as a defoliant and is a contact acting herbicide. TCA is the most toxic and is usually sold as the sodium salt, a white cyrstalline substance which goes yellow on exposure to damp.

TCA is especially toxic to grasses and is used to some extent for the control of couch and allied weed species. It is mainly root absorbed and, therefore, for maximum effect, needs to be worked into the upper layer of the soil. Its selectivity is not such as to allow its use in the presence of broad leaved crop plants, but in certain circumstances such crops can be sown before the full residual effect of the TCA has been dissipated from the soil. It is usual to combine the application of TCA with subsequent cultivations.

Dalapon is a related compound (sodium 2.2-dichlor-propionate) but is leaf absorbed as well as root absorbed. It is used for the control of perennial grasses.

Penta-chlor-phenol—known also as PCP—is usually available as the sodium salt. This chemical is toxic to a wide range of plants, and in some ways to man. Its main use is in pre-emergence weed control. Since it is very stable its toxicity persists in the soil until it is leached out.

Cyanamide. This chemical has been used on the Continent for many years as a combined nitrogenous fertilizer and herbicide for cereal crops. In Britain the use of the material has never developed on a considerable scale, nor does it appear likely to do so.

**Use on Crops.**—The range of crops which may be treated with one or more of the many herbicides is now extensive. Likewise, the weeds affected or killed are very many. Full details as to the treatment of crops would cover many pages and would not remain up to date for very long. New herbicides are continually being introduced. The reader is referred to the following for field recommendations:—

Weed Control Handbook issued by the British Weed Control Council (Blackwell Scientific Publications Ltd).
Ministry of Agriculture, Fisheries and Food,
Bulletin No. 182 " Use of the Farm Sprayer."
Advisory Leaflet No. 315 " Choosing Selective Weed Killers for Cereals."
Advisory Leaflet No. 346 " Selective Weed Control in Cereals."

*Precautions.*—Stress has already been laid on the fact that with most weed and crop associations the selectivity between the two is often a matter of relative toxicity at the rates used; in other words, selectivity is not absolute. If selectivity were complete the problem in the field would be much simpler than it is.

Many crops can be damaged by a comparatively small overdose. The damage, in the case of DNOC and dinoseb, takes the form of excessive scorch. A too early or too late application of MCPA, 2.4-D or certain other growth regulating herbicides to cereals can cause deformed growth, and affect seed formation in various ways. Again, normal cultivations near the time of spraying may injure a crop sufficiently to allow entry of excessive amounts of herbicide into the leaf, with possibly harmful consequences. The weather conditions and the state of growth of the

E

crop, whether rapid growing or not, may also determine the effect of the herbicide. Disease of the crop may render it more easily affected by the treatment. All these factors have to be considered in the application of herbicides in the field.

Some of the chemicals are dangerous to handle, and in such cases operators must have careful instruction and close supervision.

*Weed Species.*—The choice of a particular herbicide for a particular purpose will depend firstly on the crop and secondly on the particular weeds present. The various post-emergence herbicides differ in the range of weed species which they can control. Sulphuric acid controls the widest range of annuals; DNOC probably comes next, followed in turn by mecoprop, dichlorprop and 2.3.6-TBA/MCPA mixtures. Then comes MCPA and 2.4-D followed by MCPB and 2.4-DB.

A weed killer will be chosen according to whether it may safely be used on the particular crop and to its ability to control as many as possible of the weeds that are present.

There is some evidence from America that the regular use of a single type of herbicide may lead to the evolution of strains of weeds which are resistant to the material in question. Cases quoted have included Johnson grass (*Sorghum halepense*) under treatment with TCA, and Creeping Thistle (*Circium arvense*) with 2.4-D. It is commonly believed that the use, in rotation, of two or more herbicides may avoid this danger, provided, of course, that the alternatives adequately control the weed flora as a whole.

## CLEANING OPERATIONS

It will be evident that the rapid development in the control of weeds by chemical herbicides, both before and after a crop is sown, is exerting a marked change in the cultivation methods of cleaning land. Bare fallowing and the cleaning of land are described in the following pages, as they were carried out before the control of annual and perennial weeds became possible by selective herbicides. In practice to-day the cleaning of land is often effected more expeditiously and at less cost by the use of appropriate herbicides as an aid to any cleaning cultivations that may be necessary to prepare or maintain soil tilth.

*The Bare Fallow* has the primary object of cleaning the land, but it is usually carried out in such a way as to prepare a seed bed for an autumn sown crop, generally wheat. The bare fallow area in Britain is declining progressively with the development of other methods of weed control. Fallowing is, however, still a practice on arable clay land in the hotter and drier parts of England. The following description applies to these particular conditions.

The general plan is to keep the soil, during the earlier part of the growing season, in large clods which are turned over at intervals so that they may dry out thoroughly. The stolons of couch grass, water grass and other weeds of similar growth form are fairly easily killed by desiccation, and even the roots of docks, although they are more resistant to drying, are killed under favourable conditions. Later on, usually after midsummer, the clods crumble under the influence of repeated wetting and drying. If necessary the process is assisted by stirring the land when the clods are moist. A fairly fine tilth is thus produced in which weed seeds germinate freely, and the resulting seedlings are buried by a final ploughing.

The first ploughing should be delayed until the season of frost is over—*i.e.* until April. Frost occurring after the land had been ploughed would so mellow down the furrow slices that these would shatter when moved. Ploughing should be done when the land is fairly wet, and a long mould-board plough should be used so that the furrows may be turned with a minimum of breakage. This first ploughing should be as deep as any other in the rotation.

As soon as the greater part of the furrow slice has dried out, the land should be either cross ploughed or else deeply cultivated across the direction of the furrows. Steam tackle was at one time used for cultivating, but the task can be equally well done by a powerful crawler tractor. The plough has the advantage that it undercuts practically the whole area, thus severing any weeds such as thistles and bindweed that have their runners below the plough depth; this cutting below the surface helps to exhaust the food stores in the root stocks and thus to weaken the plants. If few such weeds are present the cultivator will serve the purpose equally well. The land will now be, as it should be, in a very rough state, *i.e.* with clods three or four times as large as bricks.

The clods are moved perhaps twice more, by cultivator, during June and July, choosing, as far as possible, hot drying weather for the operation. By harvest time, in an average year, the clods will generally have crumbled to a tilth. If this has not happened, and if it is certain that the twitch is dead (as can be determined by its shrunken and brittle condition), the breakdown may be hastened by drag harrowing after a good shower.

If all has gone well a good crop of annual weeds will have sprung up by the time cereal harvest is over, when they are destroyed by ploughing them under. Ploughing is to be preferred to cultivating at this stage; partly because the weeds are better put out of the way, but also because cultivating will tend to make a tilth that is too fine for winter wheat, whereas the plough puts the fine mould underneath and brings some clods to the surface. A second growth of annual weeds may spring up, but these will be automatically destroyed in the course of wheat sowing.

It will be obvious that a bare fallow will sometimes fail to do all that is intended. This will happen especially if May and June are wet. In some cases the risk of failure may be reduced by stubble cleaning (see p. 133) in the autumn preceding the fallow.

Fallowing produces some indirect effects that are not fully understood. For example, when parts of the continuous wheat field at Rothamsted are summer fallowed, the yield on the continuously unmanured plot jumps from something like 13 to about 30 bushels. The effect lasts only one season. No doubt the constant aeration during the fallow stimulates the action of soil organisms and makes available a good deal of soil nitrogen. This is in keeping with the fact that wheat following fallow on fertile soil is often winter proud and runs too much to straw. On poor clay land, however, wheat after fallow usually yields better than after another crop, not excluding clover or beans. Another useful effect of fallowing is a marked reduction of the wireworm population of the land, especially if rooks are plentiful in the area. On the other hand, attacks of wheat bulb fly (see p. 217) are rather common in the succeeding crop.

Light or loamy land that is fairly heavily infested with perennial weeds can generally be cleaned by other and less costly methods than fallowing —*e.g.* by taking a crop of potatoes, planted if necessary as late as May, or by the process of spring cleaning in preparation for a late-sown crop of turnips, swedes or kale. In extreme cases a bare fallow may be made, but naturally the technique must be different, for the reason that light land will not hold its clod—unless, indeed, it is bound together by a close network of couch. In the driest districts good results may be obtained by the simple expedient of repeated ploughings, turning the soil over whenever any considerable number of green shoots is to be seen. This process will obviously dispose of large numbers of weed seeds as well as of perennials.

*The Bastard Fallow* differs from the bare fallow in that operations start later, generally in June. It may be taken after a clover or other ley has been mown, or after an autumn sown silage crop has been harvested. It is effective, even in dry years, only in areas where there is a long growing season as well as a low rainfall. A frequent initial difficulty is that a heavy soil, in June, may be too hard to be ploughed, and the chance of a sufficient spell of dry weather after June is relatively small. However, the production of a good clover aftermath in the drier parts of the country is comparatively rare, so that the sacrifice of income, by breaking up the hay stubble, is not a very serious matter. On thin soils such as those of the oölitic limestone and the Wolds, where wheat is taken after seeds, there is a further reason in favour of the bastard fallow in those cases where ryegrass is included in the seeds mixture. This is that ryegrass harbours frit fly, which may destroy the young wheat (see p. 228).

The procedure in bastard fallowing is essentially the same as that described for a full fallow, except that the work must be completed in a shorter time. Failures to get a complete kill of twitch are rather frequent.

**Cleaning Light Land.**—The usual procedure in dealing with light or loamy land that is infested with couch is to drag the stolons out of the soil. The first operation is to plough with a digger type implement, going no deeper than is necessary to get underneath the stolons. The depth required is usually about 4 in., but the furrow bottoms should be examined for runners that may lie deeper, and, if any considerable numbers are being missed, the depth should be increased. The land, after having a little time to dry, should next be crossed with a cultivator or drag harrow, running to the full depth of the furrow slice, which is thus broken. Some couch will be brought to the surface in the process. After the stirred land has dried, or preferably after it has been moistened by rain and again dried, a drag or other heavy harrow is used to shake the couch free of soil, when it is rolled up by a light zigzag or chain harrow and is either burnt in small heaps or is carted off to a compost heap. The land should then be examined and the whole process repeated if necessary. In extreme cases a third repetition may be required. In the case of onion couch, care must be taken to get the soil very loose before dragging is attempted, otherwise the clumps will break up in the process. The further loosening is best secured by cross ploughing.

The operation described may be done either in the spring—e.g. in preparation for a crop of roots, kale or rape—or alternatively in the latter part of summer—e.g. after a silage crop or once cut clover.

It is worth noting that on specially deep soils this laborious business may be avoided altogether by the simple expedient of trench ploughing with a single furrow tractor plough fitted with a wide skim coulter. The object is to turn the top 4 in. of soil into the bottom of a deep furrow and to cover this with 6 or 8 in. of clean soil from underneath. The following crop should, of course, be roots, kale or potatoes, since some couch will probably struggle to the surface; but the amount will rarely be more than can be dealt with in the course of routine row crop cultivations.

**Stubble Cleaning.**—In this process, as ordinarily understood, no serious attempt is made to deal with perennial weeds. It is true that light land that has carried a crop of winter oats, and may be cleared by early August, can be dealt with by the process last described. More usually stubbles are not cleared till September, by which date, even in the drier areas, the chance of a sufficient spell of dry weather is too small to encourage the attempt to get couch out of the soil. The object of the operation now to be described is to induce the germination of weed seeds that have been shed before or during harvest. Incidentally, shed grains, which might give rise to rogues in a succeeding grain crop, are dealt with at the same time. If the seeds can be induced to sprout, the seedlings will be killed and buried by the normal operation of late autumn or winter ploughing.

What was said earlier (p. 32) about the dormancy or after ripening of weed seeds must, however, be borne in mind. If stubble cleaning operations are carried out in September some seeds will germinate as soon as rain falls, while others will lie dormant until October or November, and still others until the spring. But again it must be remembered that if the previous season has been an early one many of the seeds will have been shed some considerable time before harvest. In general, if the intention is to plough the land in October for winter corn, stubble cleaning will fail in regard to many particular species. On the other hand, if ploughing can be left over till late November or December good results may be expected.

The actual process is simple. All that is required is to disturb the soil to a depth of about 2 in. The Kentish broadshare was specially designed for the purpose, but almost equally good results can be obtained, if the soil is reasonably moist, by a tractor-drawn cultivator fitted with wide-cutting shares. If the land is dry and hard, a disc harrowing, repeated if necessary, will generally achieve the object.

## PREPARATION OF SEED BEDS

The seeds of our farm crops vary greatly in size, from beans at the one extreme to wild white clover and the meadow grasses at the other. A rather common misconception exists in regard to mangels and sugar beet; the material ordinarily sown consists of clusters of several fruits, and the actual seeds are very small.

Large seeds may be sown at considerable depths and therefore in soil which will generally be moist. On the other hand, the smallest may fail to push up to the surface if they are buried 1 in. deep; hence there is, at the ordinary seasons of sowing, a considerable risk that these will fail to find sufficient moisture for germination.

The moisture for germination, in the absence of water that is percolating through the soil, must come either from the thin film that surrounds the mineral particles (capillary moisture) or from that which is held in jelly like form by the soil colloids (imbibitional water). It will readily be understood that a seed, in order to take up the moisture that is available in these forms, must be in close, all round contact with the soil crumbs. Obviously a small seed cannot be in general contact with large clods. Hence it is a general rule that the size of the seed bed crumb must be closely related to the size of the seed; and again it is a rule that the drier the soil in the zone of the seed the more firmly must the seed bed be compressed. The fact that the best take of clover is often to be found on the headlands of a field illustrates the importance of compaction.

Seeds, however, may be sown in autumn, spring or summer, and therefore under very different moisture conditions; hence, quite apart from the size of seed and the particular requirements of the crop, autumn, spring and summer tilths should differ in structure. At the one extreme, wheat may be sown in November when the soil is quite wet—too wet for a drill to run clean. Spring cereals are usually sown about as soon as the lower soil is dry enough to carry tractors and implements without damage, and when, therefore, there is plenty of moisture at the depth of 2 or 3 in. at which the seed is sown; here, however, the farmer must think of the later moisture requirements of the young seedlings, which may be imperilled if the tilth is rough. At the other extreme, land that has been repeatedly worked in a dry May is likely to be so dry that a very fine and very firm tilth is required to ensure germination.

**Autumn Seed Beds.**—Many grasses are quite frost hardy in the seedling stage and might be sown in autumn but for the fact that their hardiness is not shared by the clovers. In British practice, autumn sowing is restricted to frost hardy varieties of beans, vetches and the four cereals.

In order to arrive at the principles of autumn seed bed preparation, we may consider separately the various hazards to which the plants are exposed between seed time (say October) and the following April, when active spring growth ordinarily begins.

The first danger is throwing out—*i.e.* loss of roothold. This is caused by the heaving of the soil, while it is wet, under the influence of alternating frost and thaw. Soils of high humus content are most apt to heave, and sandy soils least so. In order to minimise the risk of throwing out, the zone of soil below the seed should be firm. The farmer tests for " hollowness " by pressing on the soil with his heel. Again, wireworms are more destructive of winter than of spring grain (because the former has to meet both an autumn and a spring attack), and damage from wireworms is minimised by compaction of the layer in which they work.

Next, autumn sown corn may be winter killed, and one frequent cause is the drying out of the plants by wind during periods when the soil is frozen and when, therefore, no moisture is available to the roots. A smooth surface, such as would be produced by rolling, would obviously give maximum exposure to wind, whereas a rough surface with sizeable clods provides a considerable amount of shelter. Again, if a fine surface tilth is prepared in autumn, the soil, if it contains much clay or silt, will be puddled by rain, and, in the absence of subsequent frost, will dry out in spring with a hard cap. A continuous crust may reduce soil aeration and hence root activity, and prevent the effective harrowing of the surface in spring (which may be required in order to destroy weeds), or the preparation of a satisfactory tilth for undersown seeds. No harm will come to the cereal if many of the surface clods at the time of sowing are as large as cricket balls and half bricks, so long as there is a layer of reasonably fine crumb around the seed.

The necessary firm bottom may be obtained (*a*) by ploughing the land several weeks before seed time, so that the furrow may settle down, providing what is called a stale furrow; (*b*) by furrow pressing, which is desirable in some cases where the wheat follows a ley; and (*c*) in cases where ploughing is done late—*e.g.* after potatoes or sugar beet—by setting the plough to a slight depth—say 4 in. Repeated harrowings would, of course, consolidate the lower layers, but would in many cases do so at the expense of producing too fine a surface tilth.

If the surface is to be kept rough and cloddy it will be obvious that the use of any form of roller should be avoided, and that the use of harrows should be restricted to the minimum required to produce the small amount of crumb that is required. Heavy harrows with a small number of teeth (semi-drags) produce the desired amount of compression with a relatively small clod breaking effect, the harrowing, of course, being repeated until there is a tolerable amount of crumb. The desired arrangement (of clods above the crumb) is automatically brought about by harrowing because, when the mixture is disturbed, the smaller material slips down between the larger. In a typical case three strokes with the harrows will produce a suitable tilth. If the furrow slices are tough a disc harrow will prove very helpful.

The surface clods, with a normal amount of winter frost, will be well weathered by the spring and, on harrowing, will break down into a fine mould.

**Seed Beds for Spring Grain.**—The chief weather hazard to spring cereals, apart from a wet harvest, is drought in May and June; this has little or no effect on autumn sown crops, which are by that time deeply rooted. In order as far as possible to ensure a supply of moisture to the plants at the time in question the seed bed must be made firm and rather fine. In general this condition will be most readily obtained, on the heavier sorts of soil, if the land can be ploughed, with an unbroken furrow, before Christmas. If this can be done the farmer may hope that frost will do most of the work of seed bed preparation. Land in old grass, or in two or three year old ley, should be ploughed early even if the soil is light, since it takes time for the turf to decay and for contact to be established between the furrow slice and the subsoil. If ploughing has been late, a heavy disc should be used (as well as the harrow) in working up a tilth, in order to eliminate the spaces under the furrows. If the cereal crop is to follow sugar beet or an early carted crop of roots, ploughing may still be done in time to take advantage of the action of frost. The chief difficulty occurs after late roots, especially if carting has taken place under wet conditions. In this last case the soil will have been puddled in places and the wheel marks and trackways will show up on the ploughed land as lines of intractable clods. In most such cases it will be desirable to run along the trackways with a disc harrow—perhaps two or three times—and then to disc the whole field. Apart from its use as a clod cutting tool the disc has a marked compressing effect on the soil, which is especially desirable if the soil is liable to become puffy.

In a great many cases harrowing alone will suffice to produce the required tilth, but on land where two or three strokes would be enough for winter wheat, more may normally be required for spring corn. On

PLATE 13

*A*. Tractor-mounted Broadcaster (MacLean)

*B*. " Alfalfa " Drill (International)

PLATE 14

*A.* TRACTOR DRILLING

*B.* DRILL SEEDING MECHANISM—CUP-FEED

PLATE 15

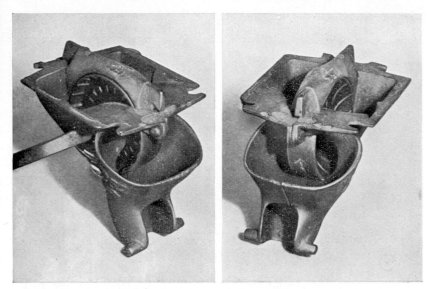

*A.* DRILL SEEDING MECHANISM—INTERNAL FORCE-FEED

*B.* DRILL SEEDING MECHANISM—EXTERNAL FORCE-FEED

PLATE 16

*A.* TRACTOR-MOUNTED SEEDING UNITS

*B.* COMBINE DRILL, SEED AND FERTILIZER HOPPERS (MASSEY HARRIS)

ploughed-up grassland the first double stroke should be done in the direction of the furrows, otherwise the slices may be pulled apart or inverted.

After drilling, the surface is smoothed by a light harrowing and is afterwards rolled, either at once or at any time (except when the first shoots are very turgid and tender), until the young plants are 2 or 3 in. high. At one time repeated heavy rolling was the only known method of mitigating wireworm damage, but a much better preventive is now available—*viz.* seed dressing with B.H.C. dust. The consolidating action of even a heavy roller does not extend much below 3 or 4 in., and compression below that level must be secured by means of harrows or discs.

As regards the particular requirements of the different cereals, the only important point is that barley, especially if sown rather late, requires a finer and firmer bed than the others. The reason is that irregular germination of oats or of spring wheat is no very serious matter, whereas if some grains of barley fall among clods and fail to germinate until rain falls, the crop at harvest time will contain green ears, and the sample will be unsuitable for malting. Apart from this point, some barley growers cross plough their land, with a shallow furrow, as part of the tilth making process. This is a sound procedure in cases where beet tops or turnip tops have been ploughed in, since these must be well distributed through the soil in order to produce a uniform crop. Otherwise there seems to be no clear evidence that a second ploughing is beneficial.

One temptation to be resisted, especially in a late spring, is that of starting operations before the lower soil is sufficiently dry to carry the horses or tractors. The top 2 or 3 in. may be in condition to crumble readily under the harrows while the lower soil is still so wet that it puddles under pressure. A little experience will enable anyone to judge, by the depth of the horse's hoofmarks or of the tractor wheel marks, whether damage is being done. A field rarely dries out uniformly, and it often happens that some parts will be workable when others are still too wet below.

When land has been used for spring folding, and operations therefore start very late, the soil may be so dry that special precautions are necessary to ensure germination. This is best done by dealing with the field piecemeal—*i.e.* ploughing, discing, harrowing and drilling in quick succession, even to the extent of completing each portion in a single day.

**Seed Beds for Small Seeds.**—Grass and clover seeds, when undersown in a spring cereal (which is the commonest practice), present no very difficult problems in the cooler and moister parts of the country. The usual procedure is to broadcast the seed, harrow with a light zigzag or chain tooth harrow, and roll. This may be done soon after sowing the corn, or alternatively after the cereal is up, and firmly enough rooted to bear harrowing. In the drier parts of the country, where risk or failure will establish quite well if there is an inch or so of rather rough material on the surface, whereas charlock requires a fine surface mould. This explains the fact that charlock tends to be most abundant in years when spring frosts have produced a mealy soil condition. By contrast, the condition that is ideal for roots and grass seeds is favourable to the establishment of all annuals.

One method of destroying seedlings is to prepare a tilth and wait until the weed seeds have germinated before drilling the crop and giving the final harrowing. It is unnecessary to wait for the weeds to emerge; indeed the best " kill " may often be obtained before this stage. The ideal time is when a scraping of the soil shows up large numbers of the white thread-like shoots of germinating seeds. Naturally the delay in the sowing of the crop—perhaps for a fortnight after the land has been made ready—may be disadvantageous to the yield and may delay ripening to an undesirable extent.

Certain crops, notably carrots, but also sugar beet and mangels, are slower to emerge than most common weeds. If the weeds happen to be abundant the task of weeding by hand labour will be very laborious and the cost may be prohibitive. In such cases there may be an opportunity—necessarily a fleeting one—for pre-emergence spraying.

The next method is based upon the fact that certain crop plants, in the earlier stages of growth, have a stronger roothold than the general run of annual weeds. This statement indeed does not apply in particular cases—e.g. the wild oat and corn buttercup are often, by the spring, about as strongly rooted as the autumn sown cereal in which they occur—but crops of wheat, rye, oats, peas and beans will usually withstand, without serious damage, a sequence of harrowings that will kill seedling charlock, runch, spurrey and many other species. Barley is rather more susceptible to damage, so that harrowing, though by no means impracticable, must be done with special discretion.

Spring cultivation—harrowing and rolling—is a normal procedure in the case of winter wheat. It is true that experiments have failed to show many cases of significant benefit to the crop itself. But harrowing should be done whenever there is a considerable infestation of annuals such as speedwell, poppies and chickweed. Occasionally the land may be so puffy (loose) that harrowing would uproot many of the wheat plants, in which case rolling should be done first, and the harrowing postponed for a week or two in order to permit the wheat to improve its roothold.

In the case of spring sown cereals (as has already been mentioned in connection with undersowing), the harrowing must either be done before sprouting is far advanced or else delayed until the roothold is strong. The earlier stage will generally be too soon to kill many weeds. The land should be inspected after each successive stroke of the harrows, the operation being stopped as soon as the desired result has been obtained, and before any excessive number of the crop plants has been uprooted. It is worth noting, however, that autumn sown wheat, in spring, may be over thick, in which case some degree of thinning will be desirable. The harrows should not follow the direction taken by the drill since in that case a considerable run of plants might be uprooted by a single tine. In the case of beans, breakage of the stems, rather than uprooting, is what must be feared. Hence the harrowing should be done before the stems are tall enough to be broken. Naturally, in some cases the crop will be too far advanced before the soil is dry enough to be harrowed.

The use of weed killers on cereal crops has already been discussed. A very large acreage of cereals is now treated with chemical herbicides, and on many farms this treatment has become a standard practice in cereal growing. Time of spraying is important. If carried out too early, malformation of the ears may result.

Undersown crops present a special problem on account of the risk of damage to the clover, but a few of the newer herbicides are now used effectively and without damage to the undersown seeds.

## ROW CROP CULTIVATION

Horse hoeing husbandry was first advocated by Jethro Tull before the middle of the eighteenth century—*i.e.* before the time when roots and potatoes began to be grown as farm crops. It is perhaps worth noting that Tull's system was largely based on a misconception. He believed that the roots of a plant took up minute solid particles of soil, and that these constituted its food. He therefore argued that crops would grow better if the soil were very thoroughly broken down, and pointed out that this could best be achieved by continuing the process of cultivation during the earlier stages of crop growth. In order to extend the period during which cultivation would be practicable, Tull advocated the sowing of crops in widely spaced rows between which a horse, drawing the horse hoe that he invented, could walk without damage to the plants. Such spacing was found to be practicable in the case of beans, but in that of cereals it involved a considerable sacrifice of yield. Intertillage of cereals, therefore, came to be restricted to the early period of growth—*i.e.* the period during which the plants are not susceptible to serious damage by treading. This limited application of the system to the cereals became normal in parts of the eastern counties, particularly on heavy soils that were unsuited to roots and potatoes. Horse hoeing of wheat in particular was the normal practice in these areas until the eighties of last century, when the fall in wheat prices tended to make the practice uneconomic. After that time it steadily declined and it is now very rare. On the other hand, beans and peas are still, in many cases, grown on the system that Tull advocated.

The principal row crops of to-day—turnips, swedes, mangels, cabbage, sugar beet and potatoes have all been introduced or brought into field cultivation since Tull's time. The broadcast cultivation of turnips, involving as it did very laborious hand weeding, was largely abandoned in the early part of the nineteenth century.

It is, of course, obvious that the control of weeds in the earlier stages of development of a crop must be a great advantage to the crop itself. Moreover, in the long run, weed control must be achieved by one means or another, and the use of row crops does away with the need for the bare fallow and makes for increased overall production. Whether surface cultivation of land that is carrying a crop has beneficial effects other than the killing of weeds has been a controversial question. The common belief among farmers, and especially among gardeners, is that the maintenance of a surface mulch (a blanket of loose soil) checks evaporation and thus tends to maintain the moisture content of the layer (say the second 2 in.) upon which the young seedling relies for its water supply. It must indeed be said that few farmers do more intercultivation than is required for weed control, but the same statement cannot be made about gardeners; the latter usually endeavour to maintain a summer mulch whether or not any considerable numbers of weeds appear. " The hoe is better than the watering-can " expresses the widely accepted opinion. The upward capillary movement of water is so slow that the amount conserved by hoeing must be negligible. The beneficial effects may, however, be explained as being due to improved soil aeration.

Annual weeds may be killed by cutting them in the region of the hypocotyl—*i.e.* the part of the shoot below the seed leaves. It should, however, be noted that in some species the seed leaves do not emerge above ground. Alternatively they may, in dry weather, be killed by being uprooted; but here it must be remembered that the chance of their taking root again is considerable unless the roots are shaken free from soil. To be fully successful, any sort of hoeing operation should be done when both the air and the surface of the soil are dry. " A wet hoe is better than no hoe," but much less effective than a dry one.

Again, the purpose of hoeing will be defeated if the undercutting of the surface is done at too great a depth. In this case the shallower roots of the weeds will not be greatly disturbed, and will continue to supply the plant with some moisture until new roots can be formed. The optimum depth at which hoe blades should run is usually about 1 in.

As regards stoloniferous weeds the effectiveness of hoeing will depend on the depth at which the stolons lie. Some may be dragged to the surface, and may gradually die from desiccation, but the bulk will usually lie too deep to be reached, in which case all that hoeing accomplishes is to exhaust the food reserves of the plant by cutting off the aerial shoots before these have begun to replenish the underground store. This process of replenishment begins in some species, such as bindweed, within a fortnight of the appearance of leaves, while in others—*e.g.* the field thistle —several weeks elapse before it starts. Naturally the growth of the aerial shoots of deeply rooted perennials, unlike the germination of seeds, is independent of the supply of moisture in the surface layer of the soil, so that the perennials may require attention in spells of dry weather when seedlings are causing no concern.

One of the principles in hoeing is to avoid, as far as possible, damage to the roots of the crop plant. The root system of the young seedling is, of course, small, and its early direction is downwards to secure water, rather than outwards to collect nutrients. In the early stages, therefore, the hoe blades may safely be set to pass very close to the plants, whereas later on a greater interval must be allowed. Again, and especially with shallow rooting species like turnips, the later hoeings should be very shallow. Another point is that in its early stages the roothold of the young plant may be disturbed by sideways movement of the soil. This is especially likely to happen if the surface is crusted or capped, an effect that is readily produced by heavy rain falling upon a fine and close tilth. To some extent such capping can be prevented by a light harrowing after the surface has been rolled and before germination has begun. Again, tractor hoes may be fitted with revolving discs to make a clean cut on both sides of the row, and thus to prevent the sideways movement of the soil from extending to the plants. Discs are also helpful in cases where the weeds have grown to some size, and when, without their use, the hoe might throw uprooted weeds on to the crop.

**Horse and Tractor Hoeing.**—The object of using horse and tractor drawn implements is to enable the greatest possible amount of ground to be cut by mechanical means and thus to reduce hand work to a minimum. The maximum possibilities are realised when the crop is planted on the square—*e.g.* by marking off the land in two directions, preferably at right angles, and setting the plants at the intersections of the lines. The same pattern may be obtained by cross blocking—*i.e.* by double drilling (the second time at right angles to the first)—and by hoeing in both directions, leaving a patch of ground some 4 or 5 in. square at each intersection of the drills. Planting on the square works very well with crops that require to be widely spaced—*e.g.* cabbages and brussels sprouts, which can be set respectively 2 and 3 ft. apart each way. But it is scarcely practicable to work tractor hoes, even when the tractors have special narrow tyred wheels, between rows that are less than 14 in. apart; and 14 in. square may give a plant population that is too low for maximum yield. The normal practice, therefore, is to drill in one direction, to work the ground between the rows by horse or tractor, and to rely on hand labour for dealing with the narrow strips that remain.

At one time the single row horse hoe, drawn by one horse and guided by a man walking behind, was the standard type in many districts. This implied, for a crop sown in 27 in. drills, about three man hours and three

horse hours per acre. This type was later replaced by a two horse cultivator with suitable shares so arranged as to deal with three rows. This
reduced the labour cost to little more than one man hour per acre. A
further marked reduction can obviously be realised through the tractor,
partly because of its greater rate of travel and partly because of the greater
width of the implement that can be drawn. It will, however, be obvious
that special precautions are necessary if a multiple row tool is to do satisfactory work. Thus if the ground is uneven it is very difficult to ensure
that all the shares will run at the optimum depth, and also, if the drills
are not exactly parallel, close work cannot be achieved without the risk
of uprooting some crop plants. This difficulty is not surmounted by
providing independent steerage for the hoe. For close work in crops that
are sown on the flat, the hoe should be either the same width as the drill
with which the crop has been sown or alternatively a simple fraction
of that width. Similarly a three row cultivator will do good work in a
crop grown on the ridge, for which the ridges have been made by a three
row machine, but it will do bad work if a two row ridger has been used
and has not been skilfully driven.

Work in root crops is generally confined to shallow hoeing, though
roots sown on ridges may be slightly ridged up again as the last operation.
The summer cultivation of potatoes is a more complicated affair, which
is fully described in the chapter on this crop.

**Hand Hoeing.**—The flat or Dutch or push hoe is used for inter-row
cultivation where the intervals are too narrow to enable the work to be
done by horse or tractor tools. The ordinary hoe, which is alternatively
pushed and drawn, is obviously more suitable for work along the rows,
especially if the crop is on ridges. In hoeing, properly so called, and
whether or not one of its objects is the singling or setting out of the crop
plants, it is important to cut the whole of the area that has been left
undisturbed by the horse or tractor implements. The point is that, apart
from such weeds as are visible, a good many more may not have emerged
at the time hoeing is done. It is true that at a late stage in row crop work
it may be desirable to go through the crop in order to chop out occasional
thistles and other individual weeds. This, however, is essentially a different
operation and it must always be made clear to the workers concerned
which of the two is intended.

**Other Hand Operations in Weed Control.**—There are still particular
occasions, apart from the hand hoeing of row crops, when manual labour
may be profitably devoted to the destruction of individual weed plants.
Thus the farmer should keep watch for the first appearance of specially
obnoxious species like the wild onion, hoary pepperwort (*Cardaria draba*)
or onion couch, and have these forked out of the ground. Again, workers
may usefully be sent through crops of corn to pull docks, the operation
being most satisfactorily carried out when the soil is too wet for summer
cultivation. Odd plants of charlock or of fat hen in root crops during

late summer may be profitably hand pulled in order to prevent their seeding. In this connection it should be noted that many species, including especially the dock, can ripen a large amount of seed even if pulled at the beginning of flowering; these should be carried to the end of the field and thrown into heaps to rot. Finally, hedgerows and roadsides may contain species that are capable of spreading on to adjoining fields, and such should be mown before they reach the flowering stage.

# CHAPTER 7

# SOWING, HARVESTING AND BARN MACHINERY

## THE SOWING OF SEED AND THE SPREADING OF MANURES

SEED may be sown by broadcasting, dibbling, drilling or ploughing-in. The most suitable method for each of the farm plants is considered under the heading of " Crops." Drilling (including space drilling and mechanical dibbling) is the most modern method, and under normal conditions the most economical. Land must be in fairly dry condition before drills can be worked satisfactorily, and in late seasons and on heavy land an earlier seeding may sometimes be possible by broadcasting. A higher seed rate may be necessary when broadcasting is practised, and horse hoeing is seldom possible in a crop seeded in this way, but the land is more completely covered by the crop and a greater smothering effect is secured. In drilling, it is advisable to sow the headlands first; otherwise they become so heavily trampled that regular planting is impossible.

**Broadcast Sowers.**—Different types of broadcasting machines are available for scattering different kinds of seed. On some hill farms cereals are broadcast by hand from a sowing sheet or hopper, machines being used for the distribution of grass and small seeds only; elsewhere hand sowing has been all but abandoned, mechanical distribution being the rule. A small hand-operated device for broadcasting seeds is the fiddle, which consists of a small hopper for carrying the seed, a horizontal rotating disc and a bow, the string of which is looped round the disc spindle. As the man walks across the field with the fiddle hanging from his shoulders he moves the bow from side to side, thus causing the disc to spin rapidly and spread the seed as it falls from the hopper. The fiddle is only suitable for small acreages, but large machines built on the same principle, with the disc driven mechanically or hydraulically are available, for broadcasting fertilizer as well as seed. The common type of broadcast machine consists of a wheeled and shafted framework carrying a long seed hopper mounted at right-angles to the line of draught. The seed hopper may be mounted on the front of a tractor or on a Cambridge roller. The seed delivery apparatus, which may be in the form of brushes, cups or pinion wheels, is mounted on a shaft which rotates in the bottom of the hopper and passes the seed out and on to the ground through delivery holes or ports. The ports, which are placed at short intervals across the machine, can be adjusted to various sizes according to the type of seed and the weight that is required per acre. Plate 13, *A* illustrates a tractor drawn model.

**Drills.**—The modern corn drill (Plates 14 to 16) has a large capacity hopper mounted on a frame carried on two wheels; a seeding mechanism, driven from one or both of the land wheels, to feed out the seed; coulter tubes to take the seed to ground level; and coulters which cut grooves in the soil to receive the seed. The drill, if horse drawn, may be fitted with a fore-carriage, which necessitates an extra man for working but enables the drill to be steered accurately. The wheels on the fore-carriage are adjusted so that when one is held in the track made by the appropriate main wheel on the previous bout, the distance between the two rows sown by the outside coulter is uniform and equal to the row width. Drills without a fore-carriage are usually run " wheel to wheel," but many American drills have the land wheels one row width from the outside coulters, and have to be driven so that the land wheel runs on the outside row of the previous bout.

There are three main types of seeding mechanism: cup feed, external force feed and internal force feed. The cup feed (Plate 14, *B*) consists of a series of discs on a long shaft extending the full width of the drill and forming the seed-barrel. A cog wheel on one end of the shaft is connected through a chain of gears with the land wheel. Near the periphery of each disc are a number of cups on short arms standing out at right angles from the surface of the disc. The cups may be on one side of the disc only, in which case they feed one coulter, or they may be on both sides to feed two coulters. Each arm may carry a large cup on one side and a small one on the other. The alternative cup is brought into use by reversing the seed-barrel. The seed-barrel is carried in the feed compartment, which is behind and slightly below the seed box. Shutters in the rear wall of the seed box allow seed to flow to the cups. As the seed-barrel revolves the cups pick up seed and drop it into the coulter tubes. Seed rate is adjusted by fitting different sized cogs to the end of the spindle, thus varying the speed of rotation of the barrel. The cup feed is very adaptable. It will sow any type of seed provided the cups are of appropriate sizes, and it does not damage the seed. It is, however, affected by rough and sloping ground and some seed is always left in the drill after the cups have ceased to pick up. A tilting lever is provided on the seed box to counteract the effect of sloping ground.

Both the external and the internal force feed mechanisms are placed in the bottom of the seed box and they can therefore sow all the seed in the box. The external force feed (Plate 15, *B*) is a series of fluted rollers mounted on a square shaft. The seed rate is determined by the amount of roller exposed to the seed. The internal force feed (Plate 15, *A*) consists of small dished discs on a square shaft. The surface of the disc is corrugated. The discs are usually double-sided, one side having a shallow dish to deal with the small seeds, and the other a deeper dish for larger seeds. The rate is adjusted by varying the speed of rotation of the discs. As the force feed mechanisms revolve they draw seed from the seed box and deliver it to the coulter tubes. They are unaffected by sloping or uneven ground, but they cannot deal with as wide a variety of seeds as the cup feed; they tend to crack very large seeds and often cannot be adjusted to sow small quantities of the smaller sorts. The coulter tubes are made of flexible steel ribbon, of telescopic steel cylinders or of rubber. The Suffolk is still a common type of coulter fitted to British drills, but single and double disc coulters are becoming more popular. The latter penetrate the soil better than the Suffolk coulter, do not clog with surface trash, and help to improve the tilth of the seed bed. The coulters are staggered to give the maximum amount of clearance between them. A lever is provided for raising and lowering the coulters and for putting the seeding mechanism in and out of gear. The same lever may also be used to exert pressure on the coulters, through springs or a press bar, where it is necessary to assist penetration. Small weights hung on the coulters have the same effect.

Makers provide directions for setting their machines for different sizes of seed and rates of sowing, but the delivery rate can be checked by putting bags on the coulters, which are kept clear of the ground, and driving the drill for a measured distance. Many drills are fitted with meters which show the acreage that has been covered and so enable the rate of sowing to be checked from time to time. On some machines the coulters have a certain range of lateral adjustment which allows of the drills being made at any required distances apart, and for drilling roots on the flat some of the coulters may be removed and their delivery ports shut off. For example, a thirteen coulter drill with 7 in. between coulters can be converted into a five-row root drill with 21 in. rows.

Large drills for tractor haulage have a separate lift for each half of the machine, an arrangement which not only enables the coulters to be lifted for turning but also allows one half to be used alone, in order to avoid excessive overlapping when finishing a field. However, a set of three 7 or 8 ft. drills may be preferred to one large drill for tractor work as the total sowing width is more than that of a single large drill, and the three narrow machines follow uneven ground better than does a single wide one. Drills can also be got with a fertilizing attachment consisting of a second hopper to hold the manure, and a distributing mechanism, usually of the star wheel type, which feeds the material directly into the grain coulter tubes. Occasionally there may be separate grain and fertilizer coulter tubes. Combine drilling obviously saves an operation and puts the fertilizer just where it is needed (see Fertilizer Placement, p. 84). With wheat and barley a granular manure may be mixed with the seed and thus sown with an ordinary drill, 1 cwt. of fertilizer representing about $1\frac{1}{2}$ bushels in the setting of the machine. Under very dry conditions, however, even moderate dressings of certain fertilizers may be harmful.

Most corn drills have their coulters 6 or 7 in. apart, but machines with other settings can be obtained.

A recent development is the attachment of the drill to a tractor's three point implement suspension in such a way that when the lift is put in the up position the coulters are raised and the seeding mechanism is put out of gear, while the main weight of the drill is still carried on its land wheels. The complete outfit is short, very manœuvrable, and has the great advantage, over other tractor drills fitted with automatic lifts, that the coulters can be raised while the outfit is stationary.

The " International " alfalfa drill, with twenty disc coulters at 4 in. spacing and with a miniature internal double-run force feed, is designed for sowing lucerne, but will handle grass seed mixtures satisfactorily (Plate 13, B). The John Deere grass seed drill is similar, except that it has a miniature external force feed. The narrow spacing of the coulters enables the young grass to cover the ground quickly. The sod-seeder used for rejuvenating pastures and for the improvement of hill grazings has a seed box containing a distributing mechanism mounted on a stout frame that has coulters capable of cutting a slit in the grass sward to receive the grass and clover seeds.

**Root Drills.**—Root drills are built on the same general lines as the cup feed corn drill but are much lighter. Some have an arrangement by means of which it is possible to steer the bar carrying the coulters independently of the drill chassis. Another seeding mechanism is the brush feed which pushes the seeds through a round hole in a plate fixed near the bottom of the seed box. The plate has a series of holes of different sizes, one of which is chosen according to the kind of seed and the required seed rate. The coulters on root drills are sometimes equipped with light harrow teeth to pull soil over the seed, and with light single wheel rollers to consolidate the soil. The rollers may rise and fall independently of the coulters or they may be rigidly attached to the latter in order to regulate the depth of sowing. The slutherum drill has small, light mould-boards which throw a miniature ridge over the seed. This ridge is harrowed down, just prior to the emergence of the crop, in order to kill weed seedlings.

Some root drills consist of a number of independent self-contained seeder units mounted on a common frame, which is often a tractor toolbar (Plate 16, A). The mounting is such that the individual seeders follow uneven ground surfaces. Each unit has a seed box, a seeding mechanism, and a coulter which is followed by tines, and a single wheel roller for covering in the seed, and it may be preceded by a land wheel. There is no coulter tube: the seed falls straight from the seed box into the coulter. The seeding mechanism, which is driven by one of the land wheels, may be cup, brush or agitator feed. Precision drills sow individual seeds at pre-determined intervals along the row. The two commonest seeding mechanisms are a rotor with cells on its circumference and a perforated rubber belt. The cells on the rotor are large enough to take a single seed and therefore separate rotors are required for different sized seeds. The distribution of the cells on the circumference of the rotor and the speed of rotation of the rotor relative to forward speed determine the actual spacing of the seeds along the row. Compared with the rotor the perforated rubber belt is simple and inexpensive although it requires more frequent replacement. The rubber belt seeder may be fitted with a system of lights which warn the operator if a unit ceases to function properly. Closely graded seed is essential for all precision seeders. Single-row seeder units are used to sow small plots, particularly market garden crops, and they are usually pushed by hand.

FIG. 8.—Root Drill (Jack)

Small seed boxes, one to each row and each containing a separate seeding mechanism, may replace the single large seed hopper on the common root drill. All the seeding mechanisms are connected by a shaft driven from one or both of the land wheels. The American corn and cotton planters are of this type; their seeding mechanism is a revolving plate, with holes near its periphery, placed in the bottom of the seed box. As the plate revolves each hole picks up a group of seeds and carries them round to the coulter tube. Separate fertilizer boxes are also provided for each row. The fertilizer is conducted to the ground in its own tube and goes into the same coulter as the seed, but the coulter is so designed that the seed and fertilizer do not become intimately mixed. This type of drill, as well as the lighter models of the common root drill, is sometimes attached to the tractor's power lift, so that it may be lifted clear of the ground for turning on headlands and for transport.

The special type of drill designed for sowing root crop on ridges, and illustrated in Fig. 8, has separate seed boxes for each row, but here the land wheels are replaced by moulded rollers, which, as well as providing the drive for the seeding mechanisms, keep the implement on top of the ridges and consolidate the ground in front of the coulters. Flat rollers can be obtained for fitting behind the coulters to counteract their loosening effect. Drills of this type, sometimes to sow four rows at once, are also mounted on tractors. Some machines of this type are fitted up so that they can deposit water, liquid manure or artificial fertilizer with the seed.

**Manure Distributors.**—Machines in great variety are available for the distribution of artificial fertilizers; for large applications these are more economical than hand distribution, and they are certainly more conducive to the comfort of the operator. Some of the more important distributing mechanisms are: rapidly revolving horizontal discs; slotted reciprocating plates forming the base of the fertilizer hopper; a plain roller rotating in the bottom of the hopper and carrying the fertilizer through a slot; an endless chain dragging scrapers along the floor of the hopper and forcing fertilizer through slots; a slowly moving canvas belt in the bottom of the hopper which carries the fertilizer to a revolving brush outside; a series of slowly rotating " soup plates " below the hopper which take the fertilizer to rapidly rotating flickers; and star wheels rotating in the bottom of the hopper and pushing the fertilizer through slots. One of the mechanisms, illustrated in Plate 16, *B,* is the star wheel mechanism used in the fertilizer hoppers of combined grain and fertilizer drills.

To facilitate loading and rapid spreading the broadcasting machine may be fixed behind a cart or trailer drawn by a tractor. A man in the cart, which carries a load of fertilizer, fills up the hopper as the outfit goes along. Another type consists of a hopper that is fixed to, and carried on, the rear of a lorry, the mechanism being driven by gearing from the lorry wheels.

Special fertilizer distributors, some of which are tractor-mounted, are constructed with two or three spouts for depositing fertilizers in the bottoms of potato and turnip ridges. Some standard distributors can be adapted for the same purpose by fitting baffles below the distributing mechanism.

Manure distributors must be very thoroughly cleaned after use, since most fertilizers are somewhat deliquescent and cause rapid corrosion of the metal parts.

Moderate dressings of ground lime and ground limestone may be spread by manure distributors. Special lime spreading appliances, suitable for contractors and designed to apply the lime at rates up to 2 tons or more per acre, have been introduced in recent years and are now used on an extensive scale (Plate 17). Some are built on lorry chassis, so that when working within easy reach of the lime works they can cart the lime and spread it without any additional handling. The lorry body is replaced by a large capacity hopper, in the bottom of which is a conveyor to carry the lime back to the spreading mechanism on the rear.  One type of distributing mechanism consists of three rapidly rotating impellers placed across the machine.  The central one spreads the lime beneath the vehicle, and the lateral ones drive the lime outwards beneath a wind shroud.  The impellers are driven by direct coupled electric motors.  The width of spread is about 30 ft.  Another type of spreading mechanism is a revolving horizontal disc having a width of spread of about 20 ft.  Other machines are designed to be drawn by tractor and driven from the tractor power take-off or by a hydraulic motor connected to the tractor's hydraulic system.

Attachments are available for converting some of the trailer types of farmyard manure spreaders for lime (Plate 17, *B*).  The back axle type of distributor is made by attaching a disc to the shortened propeller shaft of the back axle of a car or lorry.  The back axle is rotated through 90° so that the shaft is upright.  As the machine is pulled forward the disc is driven at high speed by the wheels acting through the differential. Lime is allowed to fall on to the disc from a hopper or is shovelled on to it from the towing lorry or tractor-drawn trailer.

**Farmyard Manure Spreaders** (Plate 18, *A*) are made in the form of low two- or four-wheeled trailers with false creeping bottoms that carry the load towards the shredders and spreading rotors normally placed at the rear of the trailer although in one model they are at the front.  The floor conveyor and the spreading mechanism are driven either through suitable gearing from the land wheels or through the tractor power take-off.  The time taken to spread a load (about 1 ton), at the rate of 14 tons per acre, is about five minutes.  A spreader may be very handy if it can be kept beside a ramp and filled as dung accumulates, each load being taken away and spread as soon as the spreader is full.  This may be possible on certain farms, at least at certain seasons, but the distribution of unfermented dung is often undesirable.  Machines may have difficulty in dealing with long dung, but mechanical distribution is very easy if the bedding straw has been chaffed.  On a large arable farm three machines would be required to complete a set for economical working, and their cost may prove excessive.  Spreading by hand can sometimes be done when no other productive work is available.

The spreader illustrated in Plate 18, *B*, works on small field heaps set out as for hand spreading.  It is tractor-drawn and power take-off driven.  As it is drawn over the heaps a high speed rotor, running at ground level, disintegrates and spreads the dung.  The machine can also be used for spreading coarse lime—*e.g.* shell sand or waste lime products, set out in small field heaps.

Liquid manure is usually transported in a tank mounted on a cart frame, and is distributed by allowing the liquid to flow into a perforated tray or a grooved spreader which is placed across the back of the machine. The Continental method of transporting liquid manure through irrigation

PLATE 17

*A.* MARKJOHN LIME SPREADER

*B.* ATKINSON LIME SPREADER

PLATE 18

*A.* FARMYARD MANURE SPREADER (FAIRMILE)

*B.* DUNG SPREADER (WILD-THWAITES)

PLATE 19

*A*. Tractor-mounted Fore-end Loader (Horndraulic)

*B*. Grab-type Dung Loader (Ransomes and Rapier)

PLATE 20

*A*. Tractor Mower (Bamford)

*B*. One-man Pick-up Baler (International)

lines and spreading it by "rain guns " specially constructed for the purpose
has been recently introduced into Britain and its use is likely to increase
in association with the keeping of stock on slatted floors.

**Farmyard Manure Loaders.**—Obviously a power-driven device for
loading farmyard manure on to carts or spreaders would save a great deal
of heavy work. It is desirable that the manure should be moved in
such a way that it will not be unduly difficult to spread. In fact, much
progress has been made in developing machines for this purpose.
Several different principles are used; some machines are worked by
the farm tractor and other have their own engines. A small two-man
outfit consists of a motorised winch and elevator and a fork attached
to the wire rope on the winch. The elevator and motor stand at a
convenient place for delivering the farmyard manure into a cart or
trailer. One man pulls the wire off the winch until he can push the
fork into the heap of manure, and the second man controls the clutch
on the winch. The loaded fork is pulled to the base of the elevator,
on to which it discharges its load. This loader can be used to
clean out loose boxes and other buildings which cannot be entered by a
tractor, and with the help of a snatch block can move the manure round
corners. Tractors with front and rear-end loaders, which are raised and
lowered hydraulically, are used as manure loaders (Plate 19, *A*). They
require room to manœuvre and are sometimes handicapped by wheel
spin on the floors of the yards. Another type of loader (Plate 19, *B*)
takes the form of a crane and grab.

The Mechanical Byre Cleaner is a conveyor belt running in the manure-
channel. The manure and litter are raked on to the belt, which is then
pulled along the gutter by being made to wrap itself round a revolving
shaft, and the manure falls off the belt into a waiting vehicle. The empty
belt is pulled back into the gutter and remains in this position until
further manure has to be removed.

## THE CUTTING OF CROPS

Except for very small acreages or for badly laid cereals, the scythe
and reaping hook are seldom used in the cutting of crops. They have been
almost entirely superseded by the mower for cutting hay and forage crops,
and by the binder and combine harvester for harvesting cereals and beans.
Special methods have to be adopted for certain crops. If peas are cut
with a mower it is necessary to move each swath to one side as it is cut
so as to make a clear path for the mower on the next bout. The peas may
be moved over by hand, or a side-delivery rake may be used. A special
pea cutter is also available (see p. 160). Flax, because of its long and
valuable fibre, is usually pulled by hand or by machine.

If neatness is aimed at and labour is available, the scythe may be used
to open roads round the fields so that the horses, tractor or implements

may not crush down any of the crop, but this is neither necessary nor of much advantage as a preliminary to mowing. It is, of course, quite unnecessary in the case of a self-propelled combine, because in this case the cutter bar is in front.

The use of a high-speed mower produces the most thorough cutting and leaves the shortest stubble. Such a machine can usually deal with a lodged crop. The most effective implement for dealing with laid and tangled crops is, however, a combine harvester equipped with a pick-up reel. A good upstanding crop can be cut round and round with any harvester, but when strong winds have given the corn a pronounced lean

Fig. 9.—Horse-drawn Mower

in one direction, cutting two ways or even one way only, against the bend, may be necessary. Every farmer uses his own discretion in the choice of machines, and, by reason of its economy in time and money, uses the binder or combine for cereals whenever feasible.

**The Mower.**—The land-wheel driven mower (Fig. 9) consists of a framework mounted on two wheels, suitable gearing to transmit the power from the wheels to the cutting apparatus and a cutter bar containing a reciprocating knife. The gearing, which may be taken from one or both wheels, is high speed, and the bearings are ball, roller or plain, according to their positions. A dog clutch is provided to put the mechanism in motion and is disengaged for convenience in travelling. The cutter bar may be either on the nearside or the offside of the machine; its usual width is 4½ or 5 ft.

The cutting apparatus consists of a long bar furnished with projecting fingers, the function of which is to hold the herbage while it is being cut by the knife, and to prevent the knife from entering the ground and being damaged. The fingers are slotted horizontally to allow of the insertion of the knife and its movement to and fro. A " twin finger " cutter bar will enable a machine to deal successfully with short grass. The knife consists of triangular steel knife sections riveted to a steel bar. The rivets are easily punched out, and new sections can be inserted when the old ones are worn or damaged. The knife is retained in position by steel clips and moves over hardened steel wearing plates, which reduce friction in a piece of mechanism that is difficult to lubricate. At the end of the cutter bar is an adjustable swath board which rolls the cut herbage to one side in the form of a swath, and leaves a clear track behind the machine. A very small wheel is placed behind the swath board to take the weight of the cutter bar. A tilting lever attached to the bar allows of very close cutting when the ground is smooth, and of elevation of the fingers when stones or unevenness of surface render close cutting undesirable. The whole of the bar is hinged and can be moved into an upright position for travelling. Providing a small engine, to drive the mechanism of a two-horse mower, enables one horse to pull the machine.

Modern tractor trailer mowers have their control levers pointing forward so that they are within easy reach of the tractor driver. The mechanism of the mower may be driven from the power take-off of the tractor. The great advantage of this system is that, as the knife does not depend on the traction of the ground wheels for its operation, a 6 or 7 ft. cut can be made. With the tractor going much faster than horses the rate of cutting is very high. A safety clutch is incorporated in the power shaft so that in the event of a stone or other foreign body fouling the cutter bar the clutch slips and no damage is done. Sometimes a trailer mower is hitched so as to cut behind the tractor mower, and the two cutters overtake an enormous acreage in the day. Mowers mounted on the tractor, either on the rear or between the front and rear wheels, and driven from the power take-off are now available (Plate 20, A). The rear attached model may be wheelless or may have trailing castor wheels. The cutter bar of mounted mowers usually has a " break-back " action. This means that if the cutter bar hits an obstruction it swings back and at the same time disconnects the drive from the power take-off to the knife, thereby reducing the risk of damage. Reversing the tractor is normally sufficient to bring the cutter bar back into the working position. A tractor-mounted mower in which the cutting mechanism consists of three side-by-side rapidly rotating horizontal rectangular plates with renewable knife sections at the corners, has been developed particularly for topping pastures, cutting weeds and mowing grass that it is not necessary to collect. The plates are driven by V belts. This mower has now been built into a forage harvester.

A windrower can be attached to the cutter bar of a mower to roll the swath into a compact windrow for easy loading and to leave a clear space for the tractor or horses and the machine on the next round.  The wind-rower consists of a number of spring steel slats trailing behind the cutter bar.  The length of the slats increases with their distance from the swath board and their free ends are in the form of a spiral.  In the swinging windrower some of the longer slats are pivoted to reduce drag when turning (Plate 24, *A*).

An important matter in the maintenance of mowers is to ensure that the cutter bar is kept at right angles to the line of draught.  Any backward lag of the cutter bar automatically throws the knife out of register with the fingers, and thus makes for very bad work.

**The Binder.**—The modern reaper and binder (Fig. 10) is the outcome of many years of patient investigation and experiment, and no single man can claim the honour of being its originator.

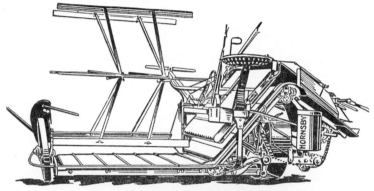

FIG. 10.—Combination Binder (Hornsby)

The frame of the machine is made almost entirely of steel and is well braced, so that it is both light and strong.  The main wheel (commonly known as the bull wheel) is carried in the frame.  A steel platform strengthened by crossbars is riveted to the frame, and is supported at its free end by means of a grain wheel.  The cutter bar is situated in front of the platform, its structure and action being similar to those of the mower.  In order to prevent the grain wheel from running over a portion of the corn, a wedge shaped divider is fixed in front of the grain wheel; this not only prevents the standing crop from being damaged but also tends to raise fallen shoots so that they are cut more readily.  Special dividers are sometimes used for laid crops.  These may be large and torpedo shaped, projecting well ahead of the cutter bar; they may be ordinary dividers through which a vertical cutter bar, with a reciprocating knife driven from the standard knife, projects and they may be rotating corkscrew dividers mounted above the ordinary dividers.  Another divider is placed at the elevator end of the platform, but it only comes into action when the machine is filled to the utmost.  A tilting lever is provided to regulate the height of the cutter bar. Sometimes grain lifters are clamped to some of the fingers of the cutter bar to facilitate the cutting of a lying crop.

The reel, which is caused to rotate by means of gearing, is adjustable by hand levers, both vertically and horizontally, and can therefore be placed in whatever position is best suited to the length of the crop and the direction in which it may be leaning. Its action is to bend the straw slightly towards the knife so that it may fall naturally on the platform as soon as it is cut. Special pick-up reels are available for dealing with laid crops and they are a great improvement on the standard reel.

As soon as the corn falls on the platform it is received by the bottom canvas and is carried towards the two elevating canvases, which raise the material to the deck of the machine. The canvases are all adjustable, and should be kept just tight enough to prevent slipping on the driving pulleys. Special looseners are usually fitted, which enable the canvases to be slackened in a few seconds when the machine is being left overnight. The leather straps and buckles normally used for fastening canvases are sometimes replaced by a self-adjusting elastic lace which is threaded, criss-cross fashion, through leather loops on the ends of the canvas. This fastening helps to prevent tearing of the canvases when crops are damp. Rubberised canvases, since they are unaffected by moisture, are superior to those that have generally been used.

As soon as the corn reaches the deck it is acted upon by the packers and butters, which jointly compact the material into a sheaf and carry it to the knotter. The sheaf is compacted against a vertical lever which, when a sufficient weight of material has gathered, gives way and engages the binding gear. A curved and threaded needle arm carries the twine round the sheaf and leaves it in the grasp of the knotter, which ties and cuts the twine; the sheaf is then kicked off the deck by a set of three levers.

The principal adjustments which may be carried out on the deck are those which regulate the size of the sheaf and the position of the band. To regulate the distance of the band from the butt of the sheaf, a lever is employed which alters the position of the whole of the deck, together with the knotting mechanism, relatively to the elevating canvases and the butter, and it is thus possible to tie every sheaf in the centre, no matter what the length of the straw may be. To regulate the size of the sheaf, the compression and trip levers have a range of adjustment, and the tightness of the twine can be controlled by varying the compression of the spring actuating the trip lever.

The difficulty of moving a binder through narrow field gates or along roads is overcome by providing it with removable wheels for travelling purposes. These wheels are fixed on the front and rear of the frame, the main and grain wheels are elevated out of the way, the drawbar is shifted into a position at the extremity of the platform, and the machine is ready for transportation.

The mechanism of all horse-drawn and the early tractor-drawn binders is driven from the main wheel which has therefore to be made very strong because it also carries most of the weight and is subjected to severe strains especially when moving off from a standing position. For the same reason the machine should never be put in gear while it is moving. Wheel-driven binders, which have a cutting width of 5 to 7 ft., must be kept going at a fair pace if good cutting is to be secured. Any clogging of the knife or other working part acts as a brake on the driving wheel and may cause slip if the ground is soft. Slip stops the cutting and the knife instantly chokes. These difficulties are eliminated when the binding mechanism has a drive that is independent of the traction of the big wheel. A small motor may be fitted to the binder to serve this purpose.

Tractor binders are generally more strongly constructed to withstand heavier work at higher speeds. When they are driven from the tractor power take-off, they may have a cutting width of 7 to 8 ft. or even more and their wheels, which only take the weight, may be rubber tyred. They have a safety clutch which slips if the knife should jam. Power binders have the advantage of speedy cutting and of being able to work on wet or hilly land and in heavy or laid crops where trailer binders would fail. There is now a semi-mounted, power take-off driven tractor binder. It does not have a bull wheel and the platform wheel is replaced by a skid. The front of the binder is attached to the tractor's three point implement suspension and at the rear there are two castor wheels. The control levers point forward so that they can be operated from the tractor seat. This is a one-man outfit and even on sloping ground is very manœuvrable and easily controlled, because the tractor and binder behave as a single implement.

**Care of Mowers and Reapers.**—For long life and satisfactory working it is of the utmost importance that careful attention should be paid to the lubrication of the moving parts. Most makes have grease cups, or nipples for grease gun lubrication, fitted to all the important bearings, but there are also minor bearings that require regular and frequent oiling in order to avoid excessive draught and rapid wear of the parts.

Knives of the ordinary type should be sharpened at least twice a day when the machines are in use, and more frequently on stony land. Spares should be kept so that sharp knives can be fitted as required. Hardened steel knives, which cut a big acreage without need of sharpening, are sometimes used, but they cannot be sharpened with a file and they are easily broken by stones.

Canvases should be slackened off after each day's work, and the machine covered over to protect the parts from rain or dew.

When the season's work is over the machines should be thoroughly cleaned, overhauled, and worn parts renewed; greasy oil holes should be washed out with paraffin, and all bearings should be left oiled. Parts that are liable to rust may be painted over with a mixture of paraffin and thick oil; the paraffin carries the oil into all the interstices of the mechanism, and when it evaporates leaves the parts coated with a thin protective film. The canvases should be removed and if necessary sent to the saddler to have all rents repaired and broken slats renewed, and afterwards stored in a dry place.

With regard to the problem which presents itself to the farmer as to which make of machine he should buy, there is, in fact, little to choose between modern equipment turned out by reputable makers. A good plan is to purchase from a local agent who carries a full stock of spare parts. The availability of spare parts is of the utmost importance in the case of a breakdown, as delay may bring the harvesting operations to a standstill. Where several machines are bought they should be of the same make so that their parts are interchangeable, and the farmer can afford to keep a few useful spares himself.

**Green Crop Harvesters.**—Green crop harvesters are used on grass, seeds, silage mixtures, kale and maize. The crops may be cut by a mower and then picked up by a buckrake or a green crop loader. The buckrake is similar to a hay sweep, but generally has more closely spaced and shorter tines. It is attached to the tractor with a power lift or may be a special fitting for a tractor fore-end loader. Green crop loaders are often very similar to hay loaders: in fact, there are dual purpose machines suitable for both jobs (Plate 21, *B*). On some machines the elevating mechanism may also pick up the swath, but others have a tined pick-up cylinder which lifts the swath off the ground and delivers it to the elevating mechanism. The standard binder, preferably power-driven, is suitable for cutting silage mixtures, the sheaves of green material being easier to handle than a swath. Loading of green sheaves is heavy manual work, but it can be done by some green crop loaders. A machine similar to a binder, except that it has no deck or knotter mechanism but has the elevating canvases extended to a height suitable for delivering into a trailer, is used for cutting and loading lucerne. It will also deal with other similar crops. Another cutter loader is the Wilder Cutlift. It has a twin finger-cutter bar with an elevator which delivers into a trailer drawn behind. It is often used for cutting and loading short grass for drying and can be used for other crops.

Forage harvesters not only cut the crops but feed them through a chopping or lacerating device before loading them into trailers. The cutting device is usually a conventional reciprocating knife with triangular knife sections. Gang mowers have a number of barrels carrying spirally arranged knives. The Silorator-Hayter harvester has a cutting device consisting of two high speed rotary horizontal plates to which are attached triangular knife sections. The chopping is done by a flywheel cutter (like a chaff cutter), or by a cylindrical cutter like the barrel of a lawn mower. There are two types of lacerating device. In one a long cylinder, carrying radial knife-like projections and revolving at high speed, works in conjunction with a stationary concave with similar projections. In the other a fan-like rotor beats the green material against a toothed ring which partly surrounds it. The treated material is then either blown into a trailer by fan blades mounted on the flywheel or, in the case of the lacerating machines, by the wind set up by the fast moving cylinder and rotor, or it is elevated by canvases. Flail-type forage harvesters, (Plate 21, *A*) which have been adopted on a large scale during recent years, have a horizontal rotor with a large number of swinging hammers. The rotor revolves at high speed and the hammers both cut and chop the crop. On some forage harvesters the cutter bar can be removed and a pick-up cylinder or a row crop attachment fitted. The pick-up lifts swaths of green material cut by a mower. The row crop attachment was designed for harvesting maize, but it has been used successfully to harvest both thinned and unthinned marrowstem kale. Some harvesters with a cutter bar will handle broadcast kale. Forage harvesters, especially those with a blower, should be pulled and driven by a tractor having a reserve of power, because if the speed of the engine is pulled down by a heavy crop there is a risk of blockages either in the chopper or in the pipe leading from the blower.

**Pea Cutters.**—The Leverton pea cutter is a tractor-mounted tool consisting of large torpedo shaped dividers placed in front of the tractor wheels to part the drill rows and make paths for the wheels, and three large V shaped cutting blades mounted on a rear toolbar. The blades cut through the pea stems just below ground level and leave the cut crop standing almost in the growing position. The crop is collected by hand or by a pick-up loader. The windrower or swather used for harvesting corn can also be used for peas. Green peas for quick freezing and canning are usually carried to a stationary viner which is a machine for threshing the peas and separating the peas from the vines. Machines for combining green peas have come on the market in recent years but they are not yet in common use. They are in effect mobile viners and, although they have a satisfactory output, the sample they produce is not quite so clean as that obtained from the conventional stationary viner.

**Flax Pullers.**—On the Boby machine the flax is gripped between a flat rubber belt and a large diameter revolving drum, and is thus uprooted. There are two pullers, one set just behind the other, and rotating in opposite directions. As the drums revolve they grip and pull the flax and carry it upwards. The belts, as they leave the drums at the top, release the flax, which is then carried to a tying mechanism like that of a binder. The machine is drawn and driven by a tractor. Two operators are required—the tractor driver and a man on the machine to see that tidy sheaves are produced and that all the flax is pulled.

## THRESHING

Threshing is the process of removing grain from its straw and chaff, freeing it from impurities and fitting it for the market. Machines designed for threshing vary greatly in size and capacity for work. As a rule, the

PLATE 21

*A.* Flail-type Forage Harvester (Lundell)

*B.* Green-crop Loader

PLATE 22

*A.* P.T.O. Combine Harvester (Claas)

*B.* Self-propelled Combine Harvester (Massey Ferguson)

output of a machine is proportional to the size of its drum, which may be from 2 ft. to 4ft. 6 in. wide.

The ordinary English portable thresher has a 4ft. 6 in. drum, 22 in. in diameter, which revolves at a speed of about 1000 revolutions per minute, and is capable of threshing a maximum of 36 cwt. of wheat or oats or 40 cwt. of barley per hour. Such a machine has to be driven by an engine capable of developing about 20 brake horse power. While British threshers differ in certain details, they are all constructed on the same general plan. Fig. 11 illustrates a section of a Foster thresher, and Fig. 12 shows a transverse section of a Ransomes model.

The all steel American thresher is so designed that it can be operated with fewer men than the British thresher. It is invariably fitted with a self feeder, comprising band cutters and feeding elevators which spread the cut sheaves so that the straw is fed evenly over the full width of the drum. The drum and concave are of the peg type, rows of pegs on the drum alternating with similar rows on the concave. The drum is often used at much higher speeds than the British beater bar type. Because of its construction and the speed at which it is driven the peg drum breaks the straw much more than the British drum. Straw shakers, sieves and wind are used to effect the separation of grain from straw and chaff. Only one dressing shoe, corresponding to the first dressing shoe on the British thresher, is employed. The incompletely threshed heads from this shoe are returned to the drum, the light bits of straw and chaff are blown into the stacker along with the bulk of the straw as it comes off the shakers, and the cleaned grain falls into an auger conveyor which takes it to one side of the machine. The grain is then elevated to either a weighing off apparatus or chutes which deliver it in bulk into grain wagons. The straw and chaff are dealt with by the straw stacker. The stacker may be a simple elevator or a pneumatic conveyor capable of blowing the straw into a heap well clear of the thresher or into buildings convenient for feeding it to stock.

**The Operation of Threshing.**—The corn is fed into the top of the machine by hand after the sheaf bands have been cut, or is placed on a mechanical feeder. The self feeder (not illustrated) is usually constructed in the form of an endless travelling canvas carrier, which is fitted with a device for shaking out the sheaves by tedding and oscillation, and may or may not be fitted with a band cutter. The object of self feeders is, of course, to economise on labour; and most makers fit them as extras. When the corn enters the machine it falls between the revolving drum and the concave, and the grain is knocked out of the ears. The mixed material passes on to the shakers, where the grain and chaff are thoroughly shaken out, while the straw is passed out at the end of the machine; it may be allowed to fall on the ground, or it may be received by an elevator and transported to the stack; or a trusser may be fitted which automatically ties the straw into bunches with either single or double strings; or a

F

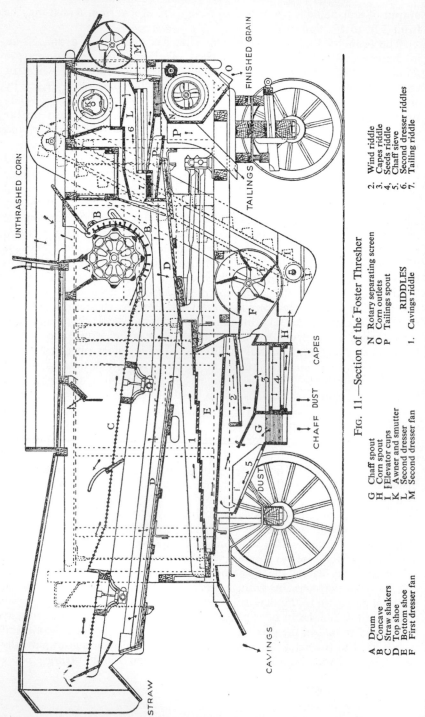

UNTHRASHED CORN

FINISHED GRAIN

TAILINGS

STRAW

CAVINGS

DUST

CHAFF   DUST

CAPES

FIG. 11.—Section of the Foster Thresher

A  Drum
B  Concave
C  Straw shakers
D  Top shoe
E  Bottom shoe
F  First dresser fan

G  Chaff spout
H  Corn spout
I  Elevator cups
K  Awner and smutter
L  Second dresser
M  Second dresser fan

N  Rotary separating screen
O  Corn outlets
P  Tailings spout

RIDDLES

1.  Cavings riddle
2.  Wind riddle
3.  Capes riddle
4.  Seeds riddle
5.  Chaff sieve
6.  Second dresser riddles
7.  Tailing riddle

supplementary baler may be used to compress it into wire bound bales.

Everything that descends through the concave and shakers falls on

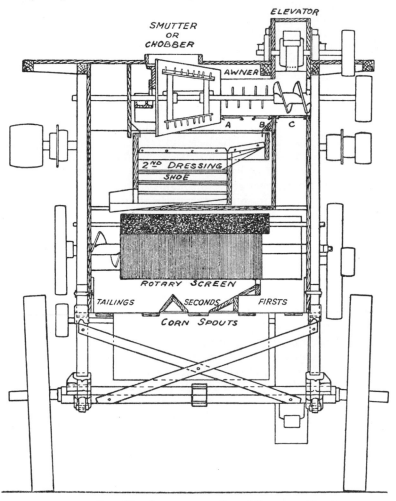

FIG. 12.—Transverse section of Ransomes Thresher

the collecting board or top shoe, which by its oscillation carries the material back to the middle of the machine and allows it to fall on the cavings [1] riddle. The oscillation of this riddle, assisted in some makes by blast, carries the cavings forward and delivers them on the ground below the

[1] The term cavings is applied to the short strawy material that passes through the shakers. It contains leaves, some empty ears and broken pieces of stem.

straw board; but the chaff and grain fall through to the bottom shoe or collecting board, and are again carried to the middle of the machine where they fall through an opening on to the wind riddle, which receives a blast of air from the large blower. This blast removes the chaff from the grain and weed seeds, and either delivers it on the ground or passes it into bags through a special bagging apparatus.

The winnowed grain passes into the first dressing apparatus, which is designed to remove pieces of ear, stones and weed seeds, and then down an oscillating spout into the endless belt and cup grain elevator. The grain may be delivered from the elevator:—

1. Through the awner and smutter, which removes beards and polishes the grain, into the second set of dressing riddles, where it is subjected to a blast of air from the small blower and freed from dust and awns, and then into the rotary screen, which removes weed and thin seeds, sorts the grain into two sizes and delivers the material to the corn spouts.

2. As in 1, but without going through the smutter.

3. To the second dressing apparatus without passing through either the awner or smutter, and thence through the rotary screen into bags.

4. Directly into bags.

**The Practice of Threshing.**—The thresher is provided with two spirit levels, and, if the work is to be satisfactory, these must be placed absolutely level before operations commence. The transmission of power from the engine is by belt, and the driving and driven pulleys must be perfectly aligned if the belt is to be prevented from jumping off. The belt must not be too tight or it will throw undue strain on the bearings, which may heat. All bearings must be kept thoroughly oiled and cleaned. The machine should be gone over after every day's work, and all nuts should be kept properly tight. Should a knock or grinding noise develop during threshing the machine must be stopped at once and the fault remedied, otherwise a serious breakdown may occur. Feeding must be regularly and carefully performed, and any damp material should be fed very slowly: a choked drum resulting from overfeeding throws an enormous strain upon the mechanism and may cause a breakage.

The sample of grain must be examined from time to time to ascertain its condition; the straw should be examined for thoroughness of threshing, and the chaff for the presence of grain. Whenever imperfect work is being done the cause should be ascertained and the fault remedied immediately.

When certain parts of the machine are not in use, for example the awner or the rotary screen, their driving-belts should be removed to reduce wear and save engine power.

**Adjusting the Concave.**—The revolving drum beats the grain out of the ear by striking it against the concave, and it is of the utmost importance that the concave should be adjusted to suit the crop that is being threshed.

If the setting is too wide the straw will pass out of the machine imperfectly freed from grain, while, on the other hand, too close setting produces violent concussion, and a proportion of the grain may be broken or badly bruised, while much of the straw may be broken up into cavings. The usual distance between the drum and the concave for threshing cereals is $1\frac{1}{2}$ in. at the top, $\frac{3}{4}$ in. at the middle and $\frac{3}{8}$ in. at the bottom. A closer setting is generally necessary for damp grain because this is difficult to remove from the straw, but when the corn is dry and brittle a wider setting will give satisfactory results. With regard to the adjusting screws for the concave, it is important that the same number of turns should be given to the nuts on each side of the machine, and adjustment should never take place while the thresher is in motion.

Drums that have been in use for a considerable time become worn in the centre, where most of the corn is usually dropped, and when they are adjusted to give good results in the middle tend to crack the grains which fall towards the sides. Drums in this condition should have their bars renewed or straightened, and the concave must be given similar attention.

**Regulating the Blowers.**—The strength of the blast can be regulated by opening and closing the blower slides. When cleaning out the machine the blasts should be fully opened and the thresher run at full speed, empty, to clear the riddles. The weight of the grain determines the strength of blast required, and adjustment should be made so that all the chaff, awns and dust are blown away and yet no light grain is carried with them.

**Selection of Riddles.**—The object of the riddles is to remove pods, seeds and dirt from the grain, and it is important that suitable riddles should be fixed in the dressing shoes for the particular kind and quality of corn to be threshed. Large grains like oats require larger riddles than wheat, and wheat than rape. When the grain is a little damp larger riddles may be necessary.

In the first dressing apparatus there is an upper (capes or chob) riddle which allows the grain and smaller rubbish to pass through but removes the capes (stones, pieces of stick, broken ears and the like). Machines are provided with a selection of upper riddles to suit grain of different sizes, and the best is the smallest which will not pass the grain out with the capes. For example, $\frac{1}{4}$, $\frac{5}{16}$ or $\frac{3}{8}$ in. mesh may be used for wheat, according to its size, while a $\frac{1}{2}$ or $\frac{5}{8}$ in. may be used for oats. There is also a bottom or seeds riddle which has a $\frac{1}{16}$ or $\frac{3}{32}$ in. mesh; this retains the grain and rubbish of similar size but allows dust and small weed seeds to fall out of the machine; it may be replaced by a blank plate when it tends to choke.

The second dressing apparatus is provided with two riddles, both of which must be changed to suit different types of corn. The upper has generally the same mesh as the capes riddle, and the lower has perforations $\frac{1}{16}$ in. less. The grain passes through both of these, and in so doing is subjected to the blast of the small blower and freed from dust, chaff and broken awns. Material that is too large to pass is usually returned to the first dresser, but may be discharged through a tailings riddle and spout. In the bottom of the shoe there is a fine mesh screen, and there may even be a third blower, to dress the grain further before it reaches the rotary screen.

A complete set of riddles is provided with each machine, and makers' instruction books give full particulars as to their use.

**The Rotary Screen.**—The rotary screen separates the material into tail corn, including weed seeds and seconds, and firsts or head corn; it delivers these to separate bagging spouts. The openings of the screen can be adjusted to suit different kinds of grain or to alter the relative proportions of head corn and seconds.

**The Awner and Smutter.**—These consist of a rotating shaft carrying a number of knives and bars which move in an iron cylinder or wire cage. The grain enters the end of the awner and is gradually worked through the cylinder owing to the set given to the blades, which cut the awns off barley; it next reaches the conical smutter, where beaters further free it from chaff, awns and dust, and polish it. The severity of the treatment in the smutter may be adjusted by sliding the beaters to the larger or smaller end of the conical casing, thereby increasing or decreasing the clearance through which the grain must pass. In most makes, when less drastic treatment is required, the grain may be passed through the awner without going through the smutter.

Wet grain should not be put through the awner or smutter. If broken grain is being delivered, the grain should be examined as it leaves the elevator. If damaged at this point the concave is set too close; if whole at this point the smutter needs adjustment.

**Threshing Wheat.**—When the proper riddles have been inserted wheat may be passed through the whole of the cleaning and sorting apparatus. Bunted wheat must not be put through the awner and smutter, which break up the bunted grains, liberating the spores and so spoiling the whole of the sample. If in a wet or soft condition, wheat may be bruised in the smutter, and should therefore be passed from the elevator direct to the second dresser.

**Threshing Oats.**—The proper riddles, which are larger than those required for wheat, should be fixed, and a blank plate may have to replace the seeds riddle of the first dresser. Oats are seldom passed through the awner and smutter, as their action is likely to break and shell the grain. Occasionally, however, the smutter is adjusted to clip the oats by removing the chaffy ends. Where oats are wanted for feeding the grower's own live stock it is not necessary to carry out the second dressing, so they are sacked direct from the elevator.

**Threshing Barley.**—It is particularly desirable that barley should not be nibbled or broken in threshing, because its value for malting purposes would thereby be greatly reduced. The sample must be carefully examined from time to time, and the concave and smutter adjusted at once if broken grains are being delivered; indeed, good malting barley is not often put through the smutter. The maltster does not object to a sample in which some grains carry parts of their awns.

**Threshing Beans.**—The concussion of the ordinary drum is too great for beans and causes a large proportion of the sample to be broken. For this reason most makers furnish special drums for pulse threshing. For moderate quantities, however, the drum may be made suitable by the removal of every second beater, or a larger pulley may be fitted to reduce the speed of the drum. The upper portion of the concave should be thrown right back and fitted with an iron plate—supplied as an extra by the makers—and the bottom portion should be lowered to about 1 in. from the beaters. Special riddles should be fitted to the first dresser and the beans should be delivered into sacks from the elevator. The feeding of the machine must be done carefully and slowly.

**Threshing Small Seeds.**—Adjustments can be made to the standard thresher to enable it to deal with grass and clover seeds. For most grass seeds a piece of sheet iron is placed over the upper portion of the concave, the drum speed is reduced slightly, a special cavings riddle is fitted, special sieves are put in the first and second dressing shoes, wind blast is very carefully regulated and the rotary screen is closed right up. If the awner and chobber are used they must be set correctly to prevent damage to the seed. The good seed comes out of the tail corn spouts, and the unthreshed heads and other material from the other spouts are put through the machine again. Clover seed is first put through the standard thresher, when the unthreshed heads are collected from the first dressing shoe. A special hulling apparatus, consisting of a concave plate to fit over the ordinary concave and a set of clover riddles, is then fitted and the heads are put through the machine again. A second type of huller dispenses with the double handling of the clover heads. This attachment, consisting of a small drum rotating at high speed in a cylindrical wire screen, is fixed to the top of the thresher. It takes the clover heads from the first dressing shoe, draws the seed and passes it into the second dressing shoe, which has a special clover sieve. Large single purpose hulling machines are available for dealing with large quantities of clover seed. They are normally in the hands of contractors.

The standard thresher can also be converted for threshing linseed and seed crops of brassicas, roots and sugar beet.

## COMBINE HARVESTING

**Harvester threshers** (Plate 22), as their name implies, cut and thresh crops in one operation. They were first developed for harvesting in semi-arid regions where compact eared cereals could stand for long periods in a dead ripe condition without risk of damage by weather, but they are now used extensively in all cereal producing countries, very often on crops specially bred for them.  In humid regions they must be used in conjunction with dryers.  The range of machines is very wide with outputs rising to as much as six tons an hour or more.  The capacity, under British conditions, is greatly affected by the amount of straw the machine has to deal with.  The season's output may be reckoned as so many acres per foot of cutter bar.  Working on average crops, a combine in the south of Britain harvests 30 acres per foot of cut during the season, but in the north, where the combine-day is shorter and the harvest is later, the average is less, 16 to 20 acres per foot.

The mechanism of the small combine is frequently driven from the power take-off of the towing tractor; but on larger combines it is driven either by an auxiliary engine (the tractor being used for towing the machine) or, as on self-propelled combines, by its own large engine.  The cutter bar with the mechanism for conveying the cut corn to the drum is usually called the header.  The smaller combines have a header with a canvas which takes the cut corn straight back from the cutter bar to the drum. On larger machines with offset headers, the canvas operates in the same way as that of a binder platform, taking the crop to one side into an elevator which leads to the drum.  Wide headers on large self-propelled combines have right and left hand canvases which carry the crop on to a centrally disposed, horizontal slat conveyor running back from the knife to a vertical slat conveyor which feeds the crop into the drum.  The canvases may be replaced by augers.  Augers are unaffected by damp straw and have a longer life than canvases; but although they are satisfactory with medium and short straw they are not so efficient with long straw.  The grain is separated and cleaned, and is then conveyed either to a grain tank or to a bagging apparatus; light weed seeds are blown out with the chaff, but the heavier pass through with the grain, from which they are sometimes separated and bagged.  The straw is either left in a swath behind the machine, to be gathered later, if required, by sweep or pick-up baler, or is tied by means of a trussing or bunching attachment. Spreading devices are available to distribute the straw evenly on the stubble in order to facilitate ploughing in.  With a heavy crop the tractor must be driven slowly to enable the thresher to keep pace with the bulk of the incoming material, especially if the header is wide and the machine is set to cut a low stubble.  The labour requirement for a large tractor-drawn combine is a man for the tractor and a man for the control platform of the machine, but when bagging is done at least one more operator has to be carried.  On some of the smaller combines the control levers are so arranged that they can be reached by the tractor driver, when an operator on the platform is not required.  The self-propelled type, when fitted with a grain tank, can be operated by one person.  The grain has, of course, to be driven from the field, and where a tank is employed a truck run in below the grain chute can collect its load in bulk.  If bags are used, they are dropped on the field in batches and have to be picked up later and loaded into wagons. It saves labour to use bags containing not more than 1 cwt. When a long stubble is left the quantity of straw is not large, and on a specialised grain farm it is sometimes left on the ground and ploughed in.

When the crop is not ripe enough for direct combining, or when it contains green and succulent weeds, it is sometimes cut and left in a windrow until the green material has withered and the grain has ripened. The windrowing is done either with a binder with the knotter out of gear (so that the crop falls off the deck in a continuous stream) or with a special windrowing machine which has a reel, a cutter bar, and a platform canvas to deliver the crop to one side. The platform canvas may be in two halves with a space between them. The two canvases deliver the cut crop through this central gap on to the ground. A combine with a pick-up fitted in place of the cutter bar and reel is used to lift the windrows and do the threshing. There is evidence that a cereal dries quicker in the windrow than when bound and stooked. It is important that the swath should be kept off the ground by a moderately long stubble; if the stubble is too long it will buckle and allow the heads of corn to come into contact with the soil. Combining from the windrow is a method often used for harvesting clover seed and linseed.

**Grain Dryers.**—In our climate the moisture content of combined grain is usually too high for the grain to be stored without first being dried artificially. When wheat is regarded as fit to cut with a binder the moisture content of the grain may be over 30 per cent.; when it is to be combined it must be allowed to stand until it is a good deal drier, but unless the moisture content of the grain is less than 16 per cent. it will heat and go mouldy in store. Only in exceptional seasons is grain straight from the combine as dry as this. Several types of farm dryers are on the market. In most, hot air is blown through a thin layer of the grain to take away the surplus moisture, and the grain is then cooled by having cold air forced through it.

Dryers are usually divided into two classes: continuous and batch. A simple continuous dryer has a coke furnace to produce hot air without smoke, a power driven fan to draw air over the fire and blow it through the grain, and a double walled rectangular tower of perforated sheet metal. The space between the inner and outer walls is filled with grain, which falls slowly at a rate determined by the adjustment of the size of the exit at the base of the tower. Hot air is blown into the upper portion of the space between the inner walls and is forced outwards through the layer of grain; and cold air is blown into the lower portion to cool the grain. In the cascade dryer the grain flows over louvres in an inclined floor up through which the drying air is blown. Cooling air is blown up through the grain as it passes over the lower portion of the floor. The three types of batch dryer are the tray, the platform and the ventilated silo. The tray has a perforated floor on which a layer of grain of uniform thickness is spread, and through which hot air is forced upwards. The platform dryer consists of a hollow chamber, the roof of which has a series of openings over which are placed bags of grain usually 100 to 112 lb. in weight (Plate 23, *B*). Warmed air, normally about 25° F. above atmospheric temperature, is blown into the chamber and escapes through the grain. The simplest form of ventilated silo has a perforated or porous floor. In it the temperature of the air is about 10° F. above atmospheric, and drying proceeds gradually from the bottom of the silo upwards. Other forms of silo have air inlet and outlet ducts distributed at different levels, so that drying is faster in these than in the simple silo with a perforated floor. The radial flow ventilated silo has a central cylindrical perforated duct into which the drying air is blown. The air passes radially through the grain and escapes through the wall of the silo. A barn or granary can be converted into a series of silos by erecting suitable partitions, and ventilation may be provided through ducts laid on the floor. Electricity or a furnace fired by coal, coke or oil may be used for heating the drying air; but when only relatively small temperature rises are required—as, for example, in platform dryers and some silos—the waste heat from the engine driving the fan and conveying equipment may be used. In one ventilated silo the drying air has its relative humidity reduced by passing it over silica-gel, which has the power of absorbing moisture quickly. The silica-gel is regenerated by passing over it very hot gases from an oil-fired furnace.

Although in practice it is not difficult to judge when the grain has been dried sufficiently, moisture meters capable of determining the moisture content of grain rapidly are now frequently used. The temperature of the hot air is measured by a thermometer placed where the air duct enters the dryer, and is regulated by allowing more or less cold air to mix with the hot draught from the furnace. If the grain is overheated it will be damaged, and the following temperatures should not be exceeded:—

| Type of Grain | Maximum Temperature |
|---|---|
| Seed corn and malting barley, exceptionally damp (over 24 per cent. moisture) . . . . . . | 110° F. |
| Seed corn and malting barley, moderately dry (under 24 per cent. moisture) . . . . . . | 120° F. |
| Linseed, mustard and other oily seeds . . . | 115° F. |
| Wheat for milling . . . . . . | 150° F. |
| Oats and dredge corn, not for seed . . . . | 180° F. |

Some dryers are equipped with pre-cleaners for removing green stuff, such as fragments of weeds, which would otherwise slow down the drying process. If the green material goes through the dryer it is removed later by winnowing.

What are the advantages and disadvantages of this type of harvesting? There can be no doubt that if the combine is given sufficient acreage to keep overhead charges per acre down to reasonable limits—and this depends largely on the original cost of the machine—the cost of harvesting is greatly reduced, mainly because of the elimination of those operations, such as stooking, carting and stacking, which have a high labour requirement. Once a crop has been combined the grain is no longer liable to damage from unfavourable weather. This advantage is to some extent offset by the fact that a crop has to be left seven to ten days after it is binder-ripe before it is fit for the combine; and during this period losses may occur through the crop going down or through shedding in high winds. The combine will harvest more grain from a laid crop than a binder. The system has several disadvantages. A large combine is costly, and difficult to house and move from field to field. It is heavy, and it may be unsuitable for soft land in wet seasons. Small combines do not have these drawbacks, but neither are they so labour saving as compared with older methods of harvesting. Losses may result when the threshing mechanism is tilted on uneven ground. Machines designed especially for hillside work are made, but they are not in common use in this country. Although it is possible to leave a short stubble and to collect the straw either by sweep or by a pick-up baler, there is usually, in practice, a considerable loss of straw. While this does not matter on a purely grain farm, it is a disadvantage on a mixed farm where bedding is required for stock. Green weeds are not easily dealt with by the machine unless the wind-rowing method is followed. Users of combine harvesters must always have access to drying facilities. Many farmers have their own dryers whilst others rely on the services of contractors or merchants.

## THE STORAGE OF GRAIN

Grain that lies wet will sprout and waste, and damp grain will heat and mould in bulk. Thus, if a particular batch is deemed too moist for bulk storage, it must either be put through a dryer or spread out in a thin layer on a dry floor so that, with the aid of frequent turning and ample ventilation, it will dry naturally; but natural drying will make little or no progress if the weather is cold and wet.

It is sometimes necessary to store damp combined grain for short periods prior to putting it through a dryer. Heating and mould formation are prevented if the grain is kept in a bin with a perforated floor through which cold air can be blown. The upper layers of grain in a ventilated bin tend to collect the moisture driven off the lower layers; it is therefore necessary to turn it at frequent intervals. Turning is facilitated if a number of bins are used so that the storage capacity must be in excess of the bulk of grain. With a series of bins an extensive conveyor system is necessary for handling the grain. The several types of conveyor available include: pneumatic, bucket, scraper, jog-trough, belt and auger. Pneumatic conveyors have many advantages over the more conventional bucket type: their initial cost is comparatively low; a single unit can convey grain in any direction and the conveying duct may include a reasonable number of bends; the fan is the only moving part; the position of the ducts is easily and quickly altered; and the system is self-cleaning. A disadvantage of pneumatic conveying is that it requires slightly more power per ton of grain handled than a bucket elevator and it may give rise to a dust problem.

In some parts of the country farms are provided with large well ventilated granaries in which grain can be kept in bulk until used or marketed. The safe depth for the heaps depends on the moisture content, "raw" material requiring to be more thinly spread than dry. If there seems to be any risk of heating, the grain must be examined frequently and turned at once if any perceptible rise in temperature occurs.

Wheat and oats can be kept in bins if their moisture content is less than 14 per cent., but barley should be a little drier—say 12 per cent. Grain silos are common at the ports and mills where large quantities have to be held, and, in the event of combine harvesting becoming still more common, the provision of similar storage may be required in grain producing districts. Bins and silos have to be strongly constructed, because grain, like a liquid, exerts outward as well as downward pressure (Plate 23, A).

Grain can also be kept in bags, but this is a costly method of storage, and the bags are liable to damage by vermin. Sacks of corn must be protected from ground moisture as well as from rain.

## HAY MAKING MACHINERY

The process of hay making and the use of hay making implements are considered in detail in Part 2 (see Fodder Conservation); in this section it is necessary to give only brief descriptions of a few of the hay making machines in common use.

**The Horse Rake.**—The horse rake is used not only for dragging hay into windrows and raking over hayfields but is employed for raking stubbles after the principal harvesting operations have been completed. The construction of the rake is simple and can clearly be seen in Fig. 13. In the older types of machines the teeth were raised by means of a tilting lever when it became desirable to deposit the load, but in most new makes a self lifting mechanism is incorporated, which, by means of a friction or pawl clutch brought into action by the pressure of a pedal, causes the wheels to raise the teeth and by this means frees the implement of its load. The wheels on the wide tractor rake may be shifted on to secondary axles so that it can be pulled sideways through gateways and along roads.

PLATE 23

*A.* BASE OF VENTILATED GRAIN SILO UNDER CONSTRUCTION: (a) VENTILATING DUCT; (b) PLENUM CHAMBER; AND (c) FOAMED SLAG BLOCK FLOOR

*B.* IN-SACK GRAIN DRYER

PLATE 24

*A.* SWINGING WINDROWER

*B.* PICK-UP BALER ROTOBALER (ALLIS CHAMBERS)

**The Swath Turner.**—The swath turner is employed to turn over the herbage which has been left on the ground by the mower, so that it may receive further exposure to the drying action of air and sun; it does not

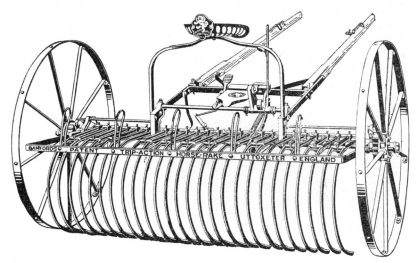

Fig. 13.—Self-acting Horse Rake

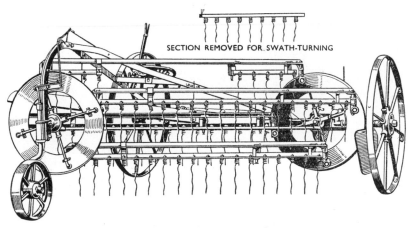

SECTION REMOVED FOR SWATH-TURNING

Fig. 14 —Combination Swath
Turner and Side-delivery Rake (Bamford)

ted the material in any way, and causes a minimum of damage to the brittle tissues. The turner is generally constructed to deal with two swaths. Fig. 14 illustrates a combination machine which, with the centre sections of each rake removed, is a swath turner and, with all the rakes complete, is a side delivery rake putting two or more swaths together to form a windrow. The rotating head type of machine has independent forward and reverse gears to each set of rakes: they can turn the swaths to the right or left, or together so that they form small windrows. The cylinder type has a number of rake bars attached to two end plates. As the machine passes along the swaths with the long axis of the cylinder horizontal and at right angles to the swaths the rake bars revolve and are controlled by a linkage to keep the actual tines approximately vertical. During recent years a new type of turner capable of being operated at high speeds behind

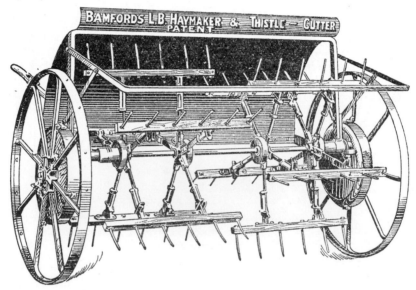

FIG. 15.—Hay Tedder (convertible to Thistle Cutter)

a tractor, has been introduced. It has a number of light wheels mounted obliquely on a frame. The circumference of each wheel carries a large number of small tines. The wheels, which are free to move vertically so that they can adjust themselves for irregularities in the surface of the ground, turn because they are in contact with the ground. All the wheels can be arranged on the frame *in echelon* to rake swaths into windrows or they can be arranged in two gangs for swath turning.

**The Tedder.**—Fig. 15 illustrates a rotary tedder, which is used to ted and scatter the hay over the surface of the field, thus facilitating drying. For very thorough work the machine can be given a forward motion which carries the hay up under the guard and throws it backwards over the axle. For less drastic treatment the motion of the forks is reversed, and the material is tedded backwards without raising it far from the ground.

Other rotary tedders, designed for operation through the tractor power take-off, have tines attached to a horizontal rotor. Some makes of tedders have a kicking action, and spread the hay by means of their oscillating forks. Tedders, used carelessly, damage the herbage considerably and leave it spread uniformly over the ground—a condition that renders it easily damaged by rain. The model illustrated can be converted into a thistle cutter by substituting blades for the forks.

A machine called an aerator, developed primarily for use in harvesting grass and clover seeds, lifts single swaths off the ground and with a very gentle action aerates them. This, like some swath turners and tedders, is driven from the tractor power take-off.

In good weather drying is facilitated by crushing or bruising the crop as soon as it is cut. Crushing is done by passing the swaths between rollers, and bruising by a power take-off driven rotor carrying swinging beaters. Modified flail type forage harvesters can be used for this purpose but they have to be operated with care because if the crop has reached the brittle stage they may cause serious loss of leaf. Crushed and bruised material is difficult to handle in unsettled weather, but in spite of this the practice has been adopted on a limited scale in Britain.

**The Hay Loader.**—The hay loader is a wheeled elevating gear which is attached behind a trailer or lorry. The elevating mechanism consists of forks mounted on rake bars attached to cranked shafts or an endless apron or rake bars taking the hay off a cylindrical pick-up drum. The drive for the mechanism is taken from the wheels, and the hay is raked up, carried to the top of the elevator and dropped on the trailer, where it is trampled and built by one or two men. The machine is useful for ordinary meadow hay, but causes a good deal of breakage and loss in the case of clover, lucerne or leafy young grass and clover mixtures, in all of which materials the leaves become brittle on drying.

A pike or rick making machine consists of a hay loader delivering into a tall, inverted, dome-shaped metal cage. A man or boy in the cage consolidates the hay as it falls from the loader, and when the cage is full it is turned upside down, so that the pike or rick falls to the ground. Doors in the wall of the cage are opened to allow the machine to move away from the hay, which is then dressed down in the normal manner.

**Hay Sweeps.**—Hay sweeps are used to collect hay that is in windrows or cocks and to transport it to where the stack is being built. Early sweeps were horse drawn but, to-day, the general practice is to mount them on the front of tractors and to use the tractor's hydraulic mechanism to raise them clear of the ground when loaded. Sweeps save an immense amount of labour but the large models cannot be taken through gates or along roads and can only be used where the stacks are constructed in the field. Sweeps attached to a fore-end loader can load hay on to trailers. A sweep fixed to the back of a tractor, and capable of being raised clear of the ground, is used for transporting hay pikes and stooks of corn.

Some of the smaller forms of hay-drags or tumblers require one horse only and are tilted to dump their loads.

**The Stacker.**—This is a device introduced from America, which enables a load of hay brought by a sweep to be elevated as a whole on to the stack. In the loading position it has long horizontal and shorter upright tines, and it rests on the ground like a large fork. The fork is anchored and pivoted at its base so that it can be swung from a horizontal to a vertical position. When in use, a load is deposited on the fork by a sweep, and a motor, pulling on a rope that acts through a system of pulleys and levers, swings the load upwards and pitches it on to the stack.

**The Stack Elevator.**—Elevators are constructed in the form of a sloping wooden gangway in the bottom of which are endless chains carrying transverse bars with upstanding teeth, which, when the gear is in motion, carry the hay or corn sheaves from the ground to the top of the stack. Elevators are telescopic, adjustable for height, and are usually worked by means of a horse gear or a small oil engine.

General purpose elevators, suitable for handling a wide range of farm produce, can be used to load bales of hay and straw on to transport vehicles or to lift them on to a stack. The conveying mechanism is usually a series of slats attached to two chains which carry the bales up a metal bed. The delivery height is adjustable.

**The Horse Fork.**—This is a form of crane used to raise hay from the ground or from a wagon to the stack. Special forks are required for seizing the hay, and these may be either in the form of a double harpoon or a four tined grapple, which works on the principle of ice-tongs. The fork works best when the hay is brought to the stack in wagons or by means of rick lifters and is thus well consolidated. The fork full of hay is either raised by a horse pulling on a rope or by a power driven hoist and when the fork has been swung over the stack the hay is released by pulling on a rope.

**Pick-up Baler** (Plates 20, *B* and 24, *B*). The modern pick-up baler is a one-man outfit that collects hay from the windrow, compresses it into a bale and automatically ties two bands of twine round the bale. Some of these balers are of the ram type which produce neat compact bales; others are press balers which produce loosely tied bales. The Rotobaler, in contrast with other machines, produces a " swiss-roll " type of bale which is prevented from unrolling by several coils of binder twine. The twine is not tied: one end is trapped in the bale and the other is pushed into the bale by hand after it leaves the machine.

Normally the bales are dropped on to the ground but this makes collection difficult because they are scattered over the field. Various collecting devices can be attached to the rear of the baler, the simplest being a sledge on which a man stacks the bales as they leave the baling chamber. The small stacks are pushed off the sledge on to the ground with the machine continuing in work. The bales may be arranged on a wooden pallet which is put on the ground when it has been fully loaded. Another device, which does not require an extra man to operate it, is a light metal cage mounted on skids. One make of pick-up baler has an ejector mechanism that throws the bales from the baling chamber into a following high sided trailer.

Special machines are available for collecting bales that have been left scattered over the field. These are usually tractor-mounted machines although some may be attached to the side of a trailer being driven from the trailer's wheels. Ordinary bale elevators are used to load bales from the small stacks left by a sledge or special attachments to a fore-end loader can be used to lift the whole stack of bales and put it on a trailer. Alternatively one tractor equipped with front and rear sweeps can collect and transport two stacks of bales at once.

## POTATO MACHINERY

**Potato Digger.**—The rotary digger or spinner (Plate 25, *A*) is provided with a very strong share which is dragged under the potato drill and completely loosens the soil and the tubers. The share is followed, in a fork action machine, by a reel of revolving digging forks, kept in a vertical position by means of a link motion system, which throw the whole of the soil and crop at right angles across the track and leave the potatoes on the surface. In the older type the reel carries rigid forks projecting radially from a centre boss. There are two types of screen that may be fitted to facilitate gathering. One, a flat open mesh screen, hangs vertically to one side of the reel to prevent the tubers being thrown too far. The other is a cage like structure in the shape of a truncated cone, open at both ends and with a wall of steel rods. The cone rolls along the ground with its end of larger diameter near the reel. The potato ridge is thrown into the cone by the spinner. Loose soil falls through the wall of the cone while the potatoes, together with stones and clods of similar size, roll out of the end of the cone and are left in a narrow band on the ground. Another type of spinner digger has a reel of vertical tines revolving about a vertical shaft with an auxiliary (the spider) reel at the side to help separate haulm and weeds from the potatoes. This type has a stirring effect on the drill and is more gentle in action than the previous one. Tractor-drawn spinners may be driven from their land wheels or from the tractor power take-off. Direct attached power-driven spinners are also available for tractor work.

It is seldom that a potato digger works unsatisfactorily, but if the potato tops are heavy and green it may be necessary to pulverise them or to destroy them chemically, to prevent persistent clogging of the share and also to prevent them from hindering the pickers. Again, when the share is worn it may be difficult to get the machine to work to its full depth, and many of the tubers may be sliced or left buried. This trouble is most common in dry seasons when the land is hard. The remedy is to have a new point fitted to the share.

The elevator digger (Plate 25, *B*) is used on the lighter types of soil. It is usually a one-row machine, although two-row machines are available, drawn by a tractor, or mounted on it, and driven from the tractor power take-off. The machine consists of a scoop which is pushed under the ridge, and which delivers the soil and the tubers on to a moving endless apron built up of steel rods. This is agitated as it travels backwards so that the soil passes through to the ground. The tubers fall off the rear of the apron in a narrow row. On light land the elevator digger is superior to the spinner in that a higher proportion of the potatoes are exposed so that they may be more easily and more completely gathered. On heavier land, particularly under wet conditions, the elevator type is less efficient than the spinner because the agitated web is unable to get rid of the soil and this passes on to the ground with the potatoes. Light abrasive soils, on which the elevator type is most efficient, cause rapid wear to the apron, rollers and agitators. A large deflector can be fitted on the rear of the digger to move the potatoes to one side so that the machine can lift the next row before the previous one has been gathered. The same result is achieved at greater expense by fitting a cross conveyor on the rear. Picking and bagging platforms are sometimes attached to elevator diggers to allow up to six persons to separate the potatoes from the soil, haulm, weeds and stones as they come off the digger. Two-row diggers have been recently introduced. It is claimed that a picker will handle more potatoes behind the two-row machine than behind the one row.

The shaker digger has a pair of reciprocating grids set one behind the other instead of the elevator apron. The grids are not subject to the same amount of wear as the elevator apron and are less expensive.

**Potato Harvester.**—A complete potato harvester lifts the crop, frees it from soil, stones, haulm and weeds and elevates and delivers the potatoes undamaged into bags or vehicles. The complete mechanical separation of potatoes from stones and clods of similar shape and size, at an economical speed under actual field conditions and without damage to the potatoes, had not been achieved at the time of writing. The cleaning mechanisms found on existing harvesters—the agitated rod link web, a revolving horizontal spider taking the drill from a disc-type share, a revolving drum, and a pair of rotating discs with radial projections, one behind the other on an inclined chassis—sift the contents of the potato drill so that only material over a certain size is retained on the machines (Plate 26, *A* and *B*). This material is a mixture of potatoes and extraneous matter, the final separation of which has to be done manually. Devices recently incorporated in existing British harvesters work on the principle that when potatoes and stones are dropped on to an inclined surface, which may be a turntable or a special type of conveyor, most of the potatoes roll off while most of the stones stay on; these reduce the labour required for the final separation. A Swedish mechanical separator has a series of spaced rubber strips, kept under tension, in reciprocating frames. The stones fall through the strips, leaving the potatoes behind. With many types of harvesters haulm disposal is a difficult problem. Haulm pluverisers, consisting of high speed rotors carrying metal blades or rubber flails, have been developed. They precede the harvesters and break the haulm into very small pieces, if it has not already been destroyed by a desicant.

**Potato Planter** (Plate 27, *A*).—Many types of machine have been devised for potato planting. Some have been very elaborate, aiming not only at setting the tubers but also at forming and splitting the ridges in one operation. Others have been so simple that they were little more than light wheeled frameworks from which the sets were dropped down spouts by the operators.

The spacing of the sets is usually done mechanically by either hand fed or fully automatic devices. The commonest type of hand fed mechanism is a series of cups on an endless belt which delivers the potatoes into the furrow. Other types include:—

1. A wheel with a channel section rim divided into compartments by transverse metal sheets. One potato is placed in each compartment. The wheel may be large, in which case it revolves through being in contact with the ground, or may be small and driven from the land wheels.

2. A wheel revolving on a horizontal platform in which is an opening above a chute leading to the furrow. The potatoes are placed between the spokes of the wheel, and as the wheel revolves they fall down the chute.

3. A series of cups hinged on radial projections from a horizontal turntable, and held up by a stationary circular platform which is incomplete at a point above the furrow. When the cups reach this point they swing down and drop the potatoes into the furrow.

4. On the Packman planter the cups are carried on arms radiating from a central hub. Mounted eccentrically with the hub, and carrying pins that engage with the radial arms, is a circular guide the purpose of which is to bring the cups close together at the feeding position and to space the cups at ground level so as to give the required setting distance.

The most popular automatic device consists of an endless chain which carries cups up through the potatoes in a hopper. Each cup picks up a potato and conveys it down a chute into the furrow. This mechanism works reasonably well with closely graded seed, but with irregular seed the number of misses and doubles is high. To prevent misses some planters are equipped with a hand filled reserve tray which automatically releases a potato into any empty cup.

Another automatic device consists of a series of spiked radial arms. As the arms revolve through a trough situated below the potato hopper they impale potatoes, carry them round and release them into the furrow.

Both hand fed and automatic spacing devices can be adjusted to give various spacing distances, usually by putting sprockets or gears of differing sizes in the drive from the land wheels.

Most American planters are fitted with distributors for the accurate placement of fertilizer in relation to the position of the seed. Some British planters also have fertilizer distributors but accurate placement is not always attempted although with the Packman various fertilizer patterns are possible, including a ring of fertilizer round each set. When placing fertilizer care has to be taken that the concentration is not so high as to damage the sprouts.

Planters may work on the flat or on previously ridged land. For planting on the flat, one and two row machines can be used only if later inter-row cultivations are to be done one row at a time; a three-row planter

FIG. 16.—Potato Sorter (Cooch)

is necessary if a three row toolbar is to be used for the subsequent cultivation. On the other hand, one, two or three row planters can be used on previously ridged land, and can be followed by three row cultivators provided that the ridges have been made accurately—preferably with a three row ridger.

Some potato planters are mounted on the back of the tractor; the spacing mechanism is driven from the tractor power take-off and the whole machine is raised and lowered on the power lift.

**Potato Sorter.**—Before the introduction of the mechanical sorter, potatoes were separated into various sizes by passing them over hand riddles, which are still used to some extent in conjunction with light iron frames.

A modern sorter, such as that illustrated in Fig. 16, separates the material into ware, seed, chats and dirt by passing it over oscillating grids and riddles. The two main riddles are removable and are supplied in many different sizes. The most common mesh for a top riddle, which removes the ware from the rest, is from $1\frac{5}{8}$ to $2\frac{1}{4}$ in., and that of the bottom

PLATE 25

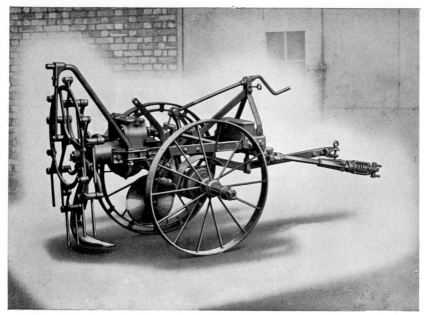

*A.* Fork-action Potato Digger (Ransomes)

*B.* Elevator-type Potato Digger

PLATE 26

*A.* Potato Harvester, Elevator Type, Front view, showing Side Loader (Johnson)

*B.* Potato Harvester—Bagging Model (Massey Ferguson)

riddle, which removes the seed from the chats and dirt, 1¼ in. A conveyor is provided which carries the ware to the bagging apparatus and is long enough to allow one or two operators to look over the tubers as they pass and to remove all that are malformed, damaged or affected by disease. The power is transmitted from the hand crank to the oscillating riddles and conveyor by means of a chain and counter shaft, but many of the larger machines are ordinarily equipped with a small internal combustion engine, the complete assembly being mounted on wheels to facilitate movement. The wires of the riddles may be covered with rubber to avoid damaging the potatoes. Another type of sorter has a rotating cylindrical riddle. The wall of the cylinder constitutes the riddles and is made of removable sections. As potatoes pass through the cylinder chats fall through the first section and seed through the second, while ware passes out at the end. The machine may be hand or power driven. Sorters should be as low as possible to facilitate filling and they must be easily portable as they have to be moved frequently in the course of a day's work. Some large sorters have a special feeding elevator which reaches from ground level to the riddles. The quantity of potatoes that can be dressed in a day depends very much on the presence or absence of disease and sprouts, and, of course, on the size of the machine; the larger power operated farm machines may dress from 12 to 18 tons a day. The large sorters sometimes used in potato storage houses have a higher capacity.

Another type of sorter consists of a series of specially constructed rubber rollers. Each roller is made up of several diabolo shaped sections mounted on a common shaft. Two or more of these rollers placed side by side form a series of holes the size of which can be regulated by moving the rollers either closer together or farther apart. Each machine has two sizes of diabolo shaped sections—one for removing chats and the other for seed. All the rollers turn in the same direction and move the potatoes along as they do the grading. Chat and seed conveyors project laterally from beneath the grader, while the ware conveyor projects in line with the grader. All conveyors are rubber belts. The extensive use of rubber in this type of sorter means that the potatoes being dressed do not come into contact with any metal components and the risk of damage is thereby reduced.

## TRANSPLANTERS AND ROOT HARVESTERS

**Transplanters.**—Machines have been designed to plant cabbages, cauliflowers and other species that can be raised in a seed bed for transplanting purposes. The machines are usually tractor drawn, because only with a tractor is it possible to get that slow steady pull which allows the operators to work rhythmically. They are provided with trays or boxes to hold the supply of plants, seats for the operators who feed the tilted so that the leading edge only is in the ground; it may be a two bladed horizontal rotor or a U-shaped blade that oscillates from side to side as the machine moves forward. On the rear of the machine there are deflectors that put two rows of harvested bulbs in a windrow. The machines are capable of good work but the performance, especially the topping, may be adversely affected by bulbs that are out of line or are not standing upright.

Turnip harvesters are topping and tailing machines that have a cleaning mechanism and an elevator to deliver the roots into trailers. The topping unit may work on a row in advance of the one being lifted. Maincrop carrots are sometimes harvested with the elevator potato digger and occasionally with the complete potato harvester embodying the elevator principle. The carrots have to be grown in row widths suitable for the machine.

## BARN MACHINERY

**Chaff Cutters.**—Chaff cutters are made in almost all sizes, from small hand machines to large power cutters which are capable of dealing with material as fast as a worker can pitch. The chief working parts are a large flywheel, which has steel cutting knives fixed to its spokes, a self feeding arrangement to carry the hay or straw to the knives, a change-speed gear which allows the material to be cut into different lengths and a clutch to put the mechanism in and out of gear. Cutters are sometimes used in conjunction with threshing machines, receiving the straw from the shakers, cutting it and delivering it into bags. Large power chaffers are usually fitted with an apparatus which frees the material from dust.

**Grinding Machines.**—Grinding mills should be capable of producing any degree of fineness, from broken beans to cereal flour. In a modern plate machine the process begins by passing the material through the cracking cones, which produce fragments that are easily ground between the revolving grinding plates. These plates are held together by the pressure of a spring, the compression of which can be varied, according to the fineness of the meal required, by the adjustment of a screw. Should a piece of stone or metal get into the machine the spring will yield and prevent the plates from being scored or damaged. A roller mill does not grind the material but simply rolls it out flat, and is most largely used in the production of crushed oats for feeding stock.

A hammer mill can be used not only to deal with grain but also to pulverise materials as dissimilar as hay and chalk; it can produce " Sussex oats." As compared with a plate mill it works on quite a different principle : it has a high speed rotor which carries swinging or fixed hardened steel hammers that break the grain or other material by impact only. The exit for the ground material is a screen placed just outside the hammers. Screens of various sizes can be used to determine the fineness of the issuing material, which is blown into a collecting cyclone from which it can be bagged off. Hammer mills are expensive and, compared with grinding and crushing mills, have a high power requirement.

Small mills, powered by electric motors and used in conjunction with a suitable arrangement of bins for holding whole grain and meal, are often included in systems with automatic control. A time switch starts the electric motor, possibly during off-peak periods to take advantage of a cheap electricity supply, and, when all the grain has passed through the mill, the motor is automatically switched off. Automatic control and the absence of any need for constant supervision enable small hammer mills to be used over long periods to produce the same quantity of meal as large mills over much shorter periods.

**Food Mixers.**—There are two types of food mixer: vertical and horizontal. The vertical is cylindrical with a tapering conical base. A central auger mixes the ingredients by lifting them from the conical section and distributing them over the surface of the meal in the cylindrical portion. Filling of the mixer is done either from the top or via a small hopper at the bottom of the auger whilst emptying is through a chute at the base of the conical section. The horizontal mixer consists of a trough in which an agitator revolves. It is suitable for mixing wet mash.

**Root Cleaners and Cutters.**—A root cleaner is designed to remove the adhering earth from mangels, turnips and other similar types of roots. It is usually built in the form of a revolving sparred drum. As the roots pass through this drum they are agitated and scraped, and the dirt falls between the spars to the ground below. The drum can be elevated or depressed at one end by means of a screw, and consequently the speed with which the roots pass through, and the thoroughness of their treatment, can be varied according to their condition. Portable cleaners equipped with a large intake hopper and a delivery elevator capable of loading on to road haulage vehicles are used for sugar beet. They are usually powered by small engines. Cutters are made in several different forms, and may either slice the roots or cut them into fingers of various lengths, the work being performed by slicer knives or finger piece cutting discs. Turnip cutters may be fitted to carts and can be used for automatically cutting and distributing roots on grassland.

**Cake Breakers.**—Oilcake as received on the farm may be in the form of long flat cakes, which must be broken up before being fed to stock; the size of the fragments has to be varied for different kinds of animals. A simple cake breaking machine soon pays for its cost in economy of time. The essential parts of a breaker are a framework, two toothed rollers connected up to the driving apparatus by suitable gearing, and an adjusting arrangement whereby the rollers can be set to produce material of any desired degree of fineness. This implement is becoming less necessary with the growing tendency of feeding stuff firms to supply concentrates in the form of cubes or nuts.

**Winnowers.**—The farm winnower is used mainly for dressing seed corn and malting barley. Combine harvested grain is usually dressed by a more elaborate dressing machine worked in conjunction with the dryer. Milling grain as it comes from the ordinary thresher is normally well enough dressed for sale. The winnower is a series of reciprocating sieves on to which an air blast from a fan is directed. The wind blast removes the lighter grains and the sieves remove small and shrivelled grain and weed seeds. The severity of the dressing is varied by adjusting the wind blast and the screen sizes. In aspirating machines, which have sieves too, a vertical air-stream, operating in a " leg," lifts light impurities and small grain and carries them to a disposal point. The strength of the air-stream is capable of fine adjustment to suit the type of material to be removed from the bulk.

Seed merchants use dressing machines much more elaborate than the farm winnower for removing those weed seeds which are very similar in size to the grain or seed in which they occur.

**Seed Dusters.**—Most seed merchants dust their seed corn with an organic mercury dust before sending it out. There are occasions, however, when a farmer wishes to use his own seed and has the dusting to do himself. An old end-over-end butter churn is satisfactory for treating small quantities; the grain and an appropriate amount of powder are put in the churn and the handle is turned for some minutes. For the treatment of larger quantities it is advisable to use one of the special machines designed for the purpose. The simplest is the Cascade, in which there are no moving parts. The grain and powder are allowed to fall down through the machine, and the grain, when it reaches the bottom, is covered with a film of dust. Larger machines usually have a slightly tilted revolving cylinder into which the grain and dust are fed continuously from hoppers.

**Cutter Blowers.**—The cutter blower is used in silage making to chop the green material and blow it into a silo. Most machines are similar to a chaff cutter with the addition of a fan and ducting to take away the chopped material. Two types of cutting mechanism are employed—the flywheel type and the cylindrical type, which last is similar in principle to a lawn mower. The fan blades are attached to the flywheel, but with the cylindrical type the cutter and fan are usually quite separate, with independent drives. It is advisable to have a tractor with a considerable reserve of power to drive the machine in order to eliminate the risk of blockages in the ducting leading into the silo. In some small cutter blowers the fan is replaced by an ordinary elevator. The machine may be equipped with an attachment to feed molasses into the cut material. Lacerating and shredding machines, sometimes with and sometimes without special fans, are used to put green crops into tower and pit silos (see p. 394).

Where chopped material is delivered from a forage harvester a simple blower is used to convey the chopped material into the silo. Such machines have a feed trough into which the loads of greenstuff from the forage harvester are tipped. A slatted chain or an auger conveyor feeds the greenstuff into a fan which blows it up the ducting.

**Grass Dryers.**—When grass in contact with air is neither losing nor gaining moisture a state of equilibrium exists between the moisture in the grass and the water vapour in the air. The amount of water vapour in air is usually expressed in terms of relative humidity, *i.e.* the ratio of the water vapour it contains to the amount required to saturate it. If the relative humidity of air is reduced below the equilibrium point, moisture will pass from the grass to the air; and if the air is continually renewed the grass will get progressively drier until it approaches a moisture content that would be in equilibrium with the air. This is the principle of all dryers, whether for grain or for grass. The relative humidity of air can be reduced by removing moisture chemically, *e.g.* by silica-gel, by refrigeration or merely by raising its temperature. The amount of water vapour required to saturate a given volume of air increases rapidly with temperature; hence the usual commercial method of drying grass is to treat it with air whose relative humidity has been reduced by heating. Oil and coke furnaces are normally employed or electricity may be used. Drying of grass takes place in two stages. In the first the rapid evaporation of the water from the surface of the grass keeps it cool. In the second, moisture has to diffuse through the grass tissues to the surface before it can be evaporated, and the drying rate therefore falls. Where high drying temperatures are used in the first stage the grass will escape damage provided there are means of removing it as soon as it has lost its surface moisture. The means must be selective, because leafy material passes through the first stage more quickly than stemmy material. The second stage drying must be done at comparatively low temperatures. But the whole drying process must be done at low enough temperatures to obviate risk of scorching. The temperature of the inlet gases in low temperature dryers is 220° to 300° F. In high temperature drying it may be 1000° F. or more. The amount of water to be evaporated from grass samples with initial moisture contents of 80, 70, 60 and 50 per cent., for each ton of finished material with 8 per cent. moisture content, are respectively 3·6, 2·1, 1·3, and 0·8 tons. Preliminary wilting of the grass thus greatly increases the capacity of a dryer. There are, however, practical difficulties in the way of wilting. The chief of these is the difficulty of getting a uniformly wilted product. Grass is usually dried down to a moisture content of 10 per cent. for baling and 7 to 8 per cent. for grinding in a hammer mill. By drying down to 10 per cent. for baling the risk of damp patches (with the critical moisture content of 15 per cent.) is negligible. On standing, dried grass comes into equilibrium with the atmosphere, when its moisture content may be about 15 per cent., at which level it keeps satisfactorily. At any much higher moisture content mould will develop.

**Tray Dryers.**—A tray dryer has one or several trays with perforated floors on which the grass is placed and through which air, at about 300° F., is blown upwards. In the simple one tray dryer the air, after passing through the grass, escapes into the atmosphere, *i.e.* there is no recirculation. This limits the efficiency of the dryer. (The efficiency of a dryer is usually given as the fuel consumption in British Thermal Units per lb. of water evaporated.) The chief advantages of this type are its relatively low initial cost and the simplicity of its operation. In multi-tray dryers there is recirculation of unsaturated drying air. The air that has passed through the almost dry grass is collected by a metal hood over the tray, is then passed through another tray containing fresh wet grass, and is only then allowed to escape to the atmosphere. A dryer may have four trays side by side which are used together in pairs—while one pair holds grass that is being dried the other pair is being charged. Of the pair being dried, the inner one has grass in the final stages of drying and the outer one wet grass. A hood over the inner tray collects the drying air after it has passed through the grass and mixes it with hot air from the furnace. Air passing through the outer tray escapes. When drying is complete in the inner tray of one pair the hood is moved over the inner tray of the other. The dried grass is removed and the partly dried material in the outer tray is teased out and transferred to the inner tray. Fresh grass is put in the outer tray. While this is being done the other two trays are being dried. The Fewster tray dryer has six trays which together form a hexagon which can be revolved, so that each tray in turn receives the drying air direct from the furnace. Four of the six contain grass being dried, that next to the furnace containing material in the final stages. Air passing through this is collected and passed downwards through the adjacent tray and finally upwards through the next two, which contain wet grass. Of the remaining two trays, one is being emptied of dried material and the other is being charged with wet. Tray dryers are dual purpose—they can be used for grass and grain.

**Conveyor Dryers.**—In conveyor dryers hot air is blown through a thin layer of grass as it is carried through a drying chamber. The dryers are so designed that unsaturated air leaving the almost dried grass is re-used on the wetter. In single conveyor dryers this is achieved by having the drying chamber divided into sections, and by mixing the exhaust air from the dry section with fresh inlet gases before forcing it through grass in the wet section. At least two hot air fans are thus required. In multi-conveyor dryers the conveyors are arranged one above the other. Wet grass is fed on to the top conveyor. Partially dried grass falls from the end of this on to the lower conveyor, which travels in the opposite direction, and this process may be repeated with additional conveyors. The drying gases are blown through the grass from below, and the speed of the conveyors is so adjusted that when the grass falls off the lowest conveyor it is dry. With conveyor dryers great care has to be exercised in order to get the material evenly spread on the conveyors. Self feeders have been designed for this purpose.

**High Temperature Dryers.**—For tray and conveyor drying, grass is generally handled in the long state. For high temperature dryers it has to be chopped. Here the drying takes place in two or three stages. In the first, which is done either in a tower or in a revolving drum, extremely high temperatures are used. The chopped grass is fed into the stream of hot gases at the base of the tower or at the inlet of the drum. There are baffles in the drum to prevent the material from being blown straight through, and there are vanes on the inner surface to lift the grass and drop it across the flow of the gases. Evaporation of moisture (which, however, takes place more quickly from the leaves than from the stems) is so rapid that the temperature of the grass remains low. As soon as the grass particles reach a certain moisture content, and before they attain a high temperature, they pass automatically from the tower and drum into cyclones. Leaf material leaves the hot gas stream before stem. The second and third stages take place in revolving drums. As the grass passes through the drums longitudinally it comes into contact with transverse streams of hot gases. In succeeding stages the temperature is progressively reduced until, in the final one, it is similar to that of low temperature dryers. Recirculation of drying gases may be employed in the second and third stages. At all stages the grass particles leave the hot gases as soon as they become dry enough and before they are scorched. High temperature dryers are new to this country. They are said to have a higher efficiency than low temperature types, but their operation requires greater skill and they are generally more expensive.

## TRACTORS AND THEIR EQUIPMENT

Tractors occupy an important place on the farm as a source of power, and on most British farms they, together with motor trucks or trailers, have entirely displaced horses for farm work. An advantage of tractor power over horse is that the tractor can be used continuously for heavy work whenever soil and climatic conditions make the operations most effective. In addition to pulling implements like ploughs and cultivators, a tractor may be used with implements for bush and hedge clearing, ditch filling and land levelling. Small tools for these purposes may be operated by farmers themselves, but the larger and more specialised, such as bulldozers and angledozers, which require powerful track laying tractors, are usually in the hands of contractors. A tractor may be provided with a power take-off to enable its engine to actuate the machine it is drawing. Thus a tractor can pull a binder and at the same time drive the binding mechanism. In this way the main wheel of the binder is relieved of the drive, wheel slip on soft land is prevented, and the speed of cutting and binding is no longer dependent on the rate of forward travel. The power take-off can also be used to work the knife of a mowing machine, the self-lift mechanism of a toolbar, a winch or some other drive. The winch may be mounted on the tractor or may be a separate trailed machine. Winches are extremely useful for manœuvring large machines—e.g. threshers—into awkward places, for pulling implements through patches of land on which the tractor wheels cannot get a grip, and for exerting a very heavy pull at a low travelling speed as is required with some drainage equipment. Most tractors are fitted with pulleys for belt work, and when properly governed they can be used to drive machines such as threshers and balers.

Small " walking " tractors of from 1 to 10 horse-power, fitted with single or twin cylinder petrol engines, may be used for garden and orchard work. Most are provided with handles, like those of a plough, on which the controls are mounted and by which the machines are guided. They can be fitted with a plough body, cultivator tines or other fittings to perform a variety of operations. The Ransomes tractor is a small track-layer driven from a seat, for which there is a range of miniature equipment including plough and tool bar.

Tractors may have spark ignition or compression ignition engines. The former run on petrol or start on petrol and run on vaporising oil whilst compression ignition engines run on diesel oil. A very high proportion of the British tractors being made to-day are fitted with compression ignition engines. Farm tractors may be divided into two groups: wheeled and track-laying. Wheeled tractors may be further subdivided into standard and row crop types. The nominal horse power attached to different makes is often misleading, but as a rule a machine of the lighter type, which develops about 10 horse power at the drawbar and 20 horse power on the belt, can draw a two furrow plough at fair speed on average land or a three furrow plough on light land, and can drive the usual farm threshing gear. A 20 drawbar horse-power outfit, dealing with four or five furrows, can plough 1 acre of medium land to a depth of 6 to 8 in. in one hour.

Fitting half-tracks to a wheeled tractor, i.e. replacing the rear wheels by tracks, gives the tractor a drawbar pull equal to that of a track-layer fitted with an engine of similar power. The half track tractor, however, is not so manœuvrable as the track-layer.

Most wheeled tractors are driven through their rear wheels only. A small number of four-wheel-drive tractors is in use: many of these are converted two-wheel-drive models. For pushing on with operations in spring, for cleaning stubbles after harvest, and for ploughing many classes of land, two-wheel-drive tractors are usually quite satisfactory. When the engine of the tractor drives all four wheels the risk of slip is very largely eliminated; indeed the grip is almost as good as in the case of track-laying machines. A recently introduced four-wheel-drive tractor is the tandem tractor. This is made up of two wheeled tractors with their front axles removed and linked together to form an articulated one-man outfit. Hydraulic power steering and the turn table incorporated in the linkage between the two units give an easily controlled manœuvrable tractor capable of high drawbar pulls.

Most modern tractors are fitted with pneumatic tyred wheels. Such a tractor, compared with one equipped with steel wheels and spade lugs, is more versatile in that it can be used for work that involves both field and road operations and, under many conditions, is more efficient in transmitting power. On the other hand, pneumatics may have insufficient adhesion for certain heavy jobs; on juicy clover or any wet surface they may even be unable to transmit light power. The adhesion of pneumatic tyres is improved by keeping them at the lowest inflation pressure recommended by the manufacturers, by adding weight to the back axle, by using girdles or adjustable strakes and by running in the highest gear possible. The back axle weight is increased either by attaching cast iron blocks to the steel wheel centres, or by filling the tyres with water to which calcium chloride has been added to prevent freezing in cold weather. Girdles are similar to but much larger than the skid chains fitted to car and lorry tyres. Adjustable strakes are steel paddles or bars attached to the centre of the wheel in such a way that when they are required they can be extended to stand proud of the rubber tyres, and again retracted when not required. Cage wheels may be bolted to the outside of pneumatic tyred wheels to prevent tracking on seed beds.

Standard wheeled tractors are used for general farm work and do not have those special features associated with row crop tractors. Row crop tractors can be used for all ordinary purposes, but in addition they are specially designed for working in root and other row crops. They are given a high ground clearance so that they ride over growing plants; their front and rear wheels are adjustable so that the track can be set for rows of different widths; their rear wheels are equipped with independent brakes to facilitate turning on the headlands; they may have a chassis on which to fit various toolbars to carry implements such as ridgers, hoes and cultivators, and they have a power lift to raise and lower the implements. The power lift may be mechanical or hydraulic. The extreme type of row crop tractor, which is not common in this country, has three wheels and very high clearance and may be very streamlined to give the driver an unobstructed view of the crop in front of him.

Toolbars are of three types: mounted on the rear of the tractor; underslung, *i.e.* underneath, between front and rear wheels; and forward, *i.e.* in front of the tractor. The rear toolbar is usually better than the forward or underslung types for such operations as ridging or cultivation of potatoes, where it would be a disadvantage to run over the work; but for the close side hoeing of turnips the rear toolbar is at a disadvantage because it is behind the driver, and because it swings over to the right if the tractor is steered to the left and *vice versa*, so that it may cut out some plants before the tractor straightens up again.  Certain rear toolbars can be converted into steerage hoes.  The forward toolbar is easiest to handle for splitting back potato ridges (see Plate 4, *B*), especially if it is fitted with diabolo shaped rollers to run on the ridges.  This is because all the tractor wheels are behind the covering in bodies and therefore run in furrows, whereas with the other two types of toolbar some or all of the tractor wheels have to be kept on top of ridges—a difficult operation, especially if the ridges are pointed or if the work is on a side land.

For any row crop operation on bare ground a marker is used to make a line on the soil down which the front tractor wheel is driven on the next bout.  A convenient formula for setting a marker is as follows: if the front wheel track is less than the distance between the outside cultivating units (*e.g.* ridging bodies or seeders) the distance of the marker from the outside unit is equal to the row width plus the distance between the front wheel and the outside unit.  If the outside units are inside the front wheel track the distance of the marker from the outside unit is the row width less the distance between the outside unit and the front wheel.  It is sometimes difficult to drive the front wheel of a tricycle type tractor down a mark.  To overcome this difficulty sighting markers are fitted on to each side of the front of the tractor.  These markers are treated as front wheels when setting the true markers, and in work are driven above the marks made by the true markers.  Correctly set markers give accurate joins between successive bouts.  (Markers can be set in the same way for a tractor pulling a corn drill.)

Track-laying tractors or crawlers have the great advantage that they take a powerful grip without exerting much pressure on the soil;  indeed their pressure per square inch is much less than the treading of a horse.  They can be used for heavy loads on almost any class of land.  They are considerably more economical in fuel than are wheel machines, but their greater initial cost and their maintenance, particularly that of the tracks, may outweigh this advantage.  The crawler is, however, the more efficient type of tractor and, moreover, can go on the land earlier after rain and so can work a greater number of days per year.

The cost of running a tractor is almost as high when it is running light as when it is fully loaded.  When the machine is used to its full capacity it can perform operations at a lower cost than can horses, but it is wasteful to use it for jobs that make no great demand upon its power.  Moreover, unless there is automatic control of the cooling, under-loading makes for cold running with consequent oil dilution and excessive cylinder wear.  It is rarely possible to offset the disadvantage of a light load by running the tractor at a high speed.  Many farm operations with existing implements have to be done at speeds not greatly in excess of that of a walking horse, and therefore to take advantage of a tractor special large implements should be employed or, alternatively, the load should be made up by hitching implements in tandem.  A set of harrows, for instance, can

PLATE 27

*A.* Potato Planter (Packman)

*B.* Transplanter with Ritchie Easy-feed Attachment

PLATE 28

*A.* Turnip Topper and Tailer (Fordoun)

*B.* Turnip Harvester (Reekie)

often be hitched to a tractor corn drill. When this is done, and the drill is being run wheel to wheel, the harrows should be hitched in such a way that they swing from one side of the drill to the other when turning on the headland and do not obliterate the outside wheel-mark as the outfit goes across the field. If the corn drill has a marker, the harrows can cover the full width of the drill. Harrows can also be hitched behind a set of tandem disc harrows. Instead of hitching two different types of implements in tandem, two or three identical implements, such as three corn drills or three manure distributors, are often used in echelon behind a single tractor. Where three are used it is usual for the central implement to be hitched ahead of the two lateral ones. Most row crop cultivations do not impose a heavy draught, and they can be performed most economically by machines of relatively low power.

## TRANSPORT

Transport is a very important and time consuming operation on the farm. The introduction of the pneumatic tyre for farm equipment has had a profound effect on farm transport. Replacing the iron shod wooden wheels of the horse drawn cart by pneumatic tyres reduced the draught by as much as 40 per cent. The rubber tyred tractor equipped with a rubber tyred trailer can haul heavier loads at much higher speeds, especially along metalled roads, than were possible with horse drawn vehicles. Consequently tractors and trailers are quickly replacing the horse and cart and the horse and waggon. In fact, many farms, especially those in arable districts, rely entirely on tractors for transport and, under such circumstances, the wheeled tractor may spend up to half of its working life transporting crops and food for live stock about the farm. The range of tractor trailers now available is just as wide or even wider than the range of horse drawn vehicles. The standard two wheeled tractor trailer, with or without tipping equipment and high sides, can be regarded as the tractor equivalent of the horse drawn cart. It is usually made front heavy so that part of the weight of the load is thrown on to the tractor drawbar. This might give rise to hitching difficulties if it were not for the fact that a jack or a small castor wheel, adjustable for height, is incorporated in the drawbar. When the tractor is unhitched from a loaded trailer the jack or wheel is let down so that it takes the weight off the tractor, and the trailer drawbar is then at the correct height for coupling up again. Also, because the trailer is front heavy, tipping is done mechanically either by a hand operated tipping gear similar to that used on lorries or, on those trailers equipped with the necessary telescopic drawbar, by withdrawing a pin from the drawbar and reversing the tractor. There are trailers with hydraulic tipping mechanisms worked off the hydraulic system of the tractor. Some trailers are made to tip sideways and are very useful for carting potatoes to the clamp.

G

In some parts of the country low bogies, equipped with flat tipping platforms, are employed for moving ricks of hay from the field to the stack. They are fitted with winding gear, manually operated or driven from the tractor power take-off, to enable the ricks to be pulled straight on to the tipped platforms. Several types of self unloading trailers, driven from the power take-off of the tractor, are available. For unloading green material, e.g. in zero grazing and for discharging into a silage pit, a chain and slat conveyor may be placed on the floor of the trailer, or the actual floor of the trailer may be a rubberised conveyor. There may be a transverse conveyor on the front or rear of the trailer, sometimes associated with various types of rotor working on the face of the load as it is conveyed along the trailer, to deliver the material to the side into feeding troughs. Trailers for handling potatoes in bulk have a hopper shaped body along the base of which is a narrow conveyor which is gradually exposed as the trailer is emptied. There are also special trailers for transporting grain in bulk from combine harvesters.

Some progress has been made in designing tracks for heavy trailers to enable them to deal better with heavy loads on soft land. Trailers equipped with axles driven from the tractor power take-off, in effect making four-wheel-drive outfits, are capable of carrying heavy loads under conditions where a tractor and standard trailer could not operate but, so far, probably because of their relatively high initial cost and, until recently, because of the difficulty of matching the gearing of the trailer axle with the tractor gears, they are not common. Low loading trailers equipped with skids and hand operated winches are used for transporting implements including steel wheeled and track-laying tractors. Such are equipped with pneumatic tyres which, on the largest trailers, can carry loads up to 10 tons. A fuel trailer is useful when a tractor is working a long distance from the farm buildings. It may have a 120 to 200 gal. fuel tank, a semi-rotary pump to put the fuel into the tractor, a lock-up box in which oil, grease and spares (such as ploughshares) can be kept, and sometimes a platform on which the tractor driver can put his bicycle or motor cycle when moving from one field to another.

The Opperman Motocart is a self-propelled three wheeled vehicle suitable for light farm transport. The air cooled engine is built into the centre of the large front wheel by which the vehicle is steered. Also suitable for carrying light loads, *e.g.* a few bags of seed corn or milk churns, is the transport box mounted on the back of a tractor.

Many farmers now keep one or more motor trucks for road haulage and for some jobs on the farm. Such vehicles may be used as lorries or may be fitted with the usual drop sides and tail board to take bulky produce; they may be provided with high sides for transporting cattle or with double decks to provide maximum accommodation for sheep; they may also be fitted as horse boxes. Light trailers, strong enough to carry one horse or one beast, are frequently used behind high power motor cars.

# PART 2

# CROPS

# CHAPTER 8

# CROP VARIETIES AND PLANT BREEDING

THE Principles of Genetics are outlined in Chapter 17 of Part 3. Meantime it is necessary to an understanding of some aspects of crop husbandry to explain what varieties are, what steps are necessary in particular cases to maintain the purity and health of stocks, and how new varieties are produced.

The term *variety* connotes a group of plants in which the individuals are more nearly alike than those that make up a species or sub-species; the plants belonging to a particular variety may differ, in genetic make up in varying degree. Five main types may be distinguished—*clones, pure lines, open-pollinated varieties, synthetic varieties* and *hybrids*.

1. Where simple vegetative propagation is the method used in the production of the commercial crop—*e.g.* as in the potato, strawberry or blackcurrant—the so-called variety is a *clone, i.e.* it consists of a group obtained by vegetative division and redivision of a single original parent plant. Genetic variations—mutations or " sports "—may indeed occur from time to time; for instance, a potato variety may occasionally produce a tuber with a different colour or texture of the skin, and the variant can be multiplied to provide a new variety. In some species, too, abnormal behaviour of the chromosomes may result in the production of " off types "; for example, some varieties of potato produce a proportion of bolters or wildings or both, and it is essential to the maintenance of the stock that these be eliminated. Again, whereas only a few virus infections are transmitted by the parent to offspring through the true seed, they rarely fail to be transmitted in vegetative propagation. Thus a potato plant infected with leaf roll during the early part of the growing season will pass on the virus to its progeny. Moreover, the infection may be spread from plant to plant in the field either by contact or through the agency of leaf-sucking insects. Hence in the production of seed potatoes it is necessary to remove (a) plants of any different variety, commonly called rogues; (b) bolters and wildings; and (c) plants showing symptoms of virus infection.

Many plants can be vegetatively reproduced by cuttings, layers and pieces of rhizome. But in some cases a cutting produces only a feeble root system. This is true of most kinds of top fruit, and it has long been the practice to graft or bud the scion of the desired variety on to a seedling rootstock of the same or a related species. Thus cultivated varieties of apple were at one time commonly grafted on seedling crab stocks. But the growth habit of the scion is influenced by the rootstock, and seedling

196

crabs show a wide range of variation. It is therefore preferable, where possible, to propagate both stock and scion vegetatively and, in the case of the apple, certain particular types produce stool shoots that root freely. Thus a particular variety, such as Cox's Orange or Bramley's Seedling, budded on Malling IX stock, gives a tree that can be relied upon to grow only to a small size and to come into bearing at a young age.

As already said, new types—vegetative " sports "—occasionally appear in clonal varieties, but these are rare and very seldom of any economic value. New varieties are obtained by raising seedlings, generally produced by hybridisation. Since most clones are highly heterozygous, a wide range of material is produced even when the parent plant has been self-pollinated, but the chances of useful forms are much greater among seedlings that have been produced by cross fertilisation. If a promising type appears among a group of seedlings, this is multiplied vegetatively and the resultant clone is compared with established commercial varieties. Since the characteristics of the new clone will be transmitted to its vegetative offspring, there is no need to fix the type by selection.

2. Many of our annual crop plants—for instance, wheat, barley and oats (but not rye)—are habitually self-fertilising. Repeated reproduction from self-fertilised plants has the effect of " fixing " the plant's heredity— *i.e.* of eliminating variability within progenies. A *pure line* variety—*e.g.* of wheat—is by definition produced by self-fertilisation from a single plant which itself resulted from many generations of self-fertilisation. A *pure line* reproduces its characteristics just about as regularly and fully as a clone—*i.e.* it produces only occasional off-types. Most of these are due either to accidental cross fertilisation with a different variety or to abnormal chromosome behaviour, as in the well known " fatuoid " type of oat (so-called because it somewhat resembles the wild oat.)

In the multiplication of pure-line varieties for the supply of commercial seed no special precautions are ordinarily necessary to obviate the risk of cross pollination. Certification schemes are based on the authenticity of the seed sown, the trueness to type of the growing crop and its freedom from other crop species and from weeds, especially those whose seeds would be difficult to remove by the available seed dressing machines.

New pure-line varieties are produced by artificial cross pollination of, usually, two parental types. Selection is practised in the second and subsequent generations to isolate better combinations of desirable characters, or even forms superior to either parent in a particular character. Selection must be continued until true breeding progenies are obtained. The success of the procedure depends on a suitable choice of parents, the effectiveness of the selection and testing and, quite often, on the occurrence of some rare genetic recombination. Crosses are usually made within the species, but related species can be used if they give fertile offspring (but see also Polyploids).

3. Next we have those plants that are habitually cross fertilised and show a marked loss of vigour if compelled to inbreed. Here belong the brassicas, beets and mangels, maize, rye and most of the grasses and clovers of agricultural importance. Some, including the grasses, maize and rye, are wind pollinated, while the clovers depend on insects. In these crops the three main types of varieties are *open-pollinated, synthetic* and *hybrid*, each representing a different method of achieving improvement by selection and maintaining it.

The simplest method is continual selection, producing an *open-pollinated variety*. Selection may be on an individual plant basis or on a family basis. Ultimately a group of selected plants is grown in isolation from other plants of the same species to produce a small bulk of seed. This will be grown-on for one or more generations, with little or no further selection, to yield commercial seeds. Uniformity and continuity of the variety depend on the skill of the breeder, who must continually reselect the foundation plants on which the variety is based. Inbreeding is avoided or minimised by selecting many foundation plants and ensuring that they are as little related to each other as possible. Most varieties of root crops are produced in this way—varieties within which there is considerable genetic variation.

Some perennial crops, such as grasses, though normally grown from seed, can easily be propagated vegetatively. The breeder can then maintain selected foundation plants, more or less indefinitely, as clones and so make use of the relative constancy of clones to avoid the need for continuous selection. With annual crops this is not usually possible but, if true breeding inbred lines can be produced, it is practicable to base a new variety on a group of inbreds known to give desirable progeny on crossing. A variety based on a group of inbreds or of clones is called a *synthetic variety*; genetically it is very similar to an open-pollinated variety and both types have in the past been called *strains*.

When it is feasible to control pollination on a commercial scale, a breeder may use inbreds to produce a *hybrid* for direct commercial use. The first generation of a cross between two inbred lines is, in principle, as uniform as a clone or a pure line; of course, it does not breed true. This method allows the breeder of cross fertilising crops to achieve the same precision in his selection as the breeder of clonal or self-fertilising crops. If seed produced on inbreds is too expensive for commercial use, because of inbreeding depression, some precision has to be sacrificed; commercial seed is then produced on hybrids. The pollinator may be a selected inbred line, producing a three way cross (AB × C) or, more usually, another hybrid is used, to make a double cross (AB × CD).

The most notable success achieved by this procedure has been with maize. The maize plant bears male and female inflorescences separately on the same plant, so that if two lines are grown in alternate rows and the male flowers (tassels) are removed from the one, the detasselled plants will be pollinated exclusively by the other. Maize breeders achieved by this method improvements not previously possible and " hybrid corn " has now virtually replaced the former open-pollinated varieties in the U.S.A.

The principle involved in the production of hybrid maize is obviously difficult to apply in practice to the general run of crop plants. Hybrid tomato seed is produced commercially, the cross pollination being effected by hand. Hybrid onion seed can also be produced by selecting as the female parent a male sterile clone—*i.e.* a type that can be reproduced vegetatively by bulbils.

The production of new hybrid varieties involves a long continued process of self-pollination, some ten generations of selfing being commonly required to obtain a pure line—*i.e.* a completely homozygous group. A number of inbred lines having been produced, the numerous possible combinations must be made and tested for their commercial usefulness, the various pure lines being maintained permanently.

Seed inspection schemes for the cross fertilised crops are based on the authenticity of the seed sown and on the suitability of the site on which the commercial seed is to be produced; for instance, the proposed site for certified S 143 cocksfoot must be examined in relation to the possibility of cross pollination from plants in adjacent hay fields, pastures or hedgerows; and a field of pasture to be harvested for wild white clover should not be adjacent to another containing a different type of white clover. In each case the growing crop must be inspected for trueness to type and for the absence of weeds and of certain crop species, whose seeds would be difficult to separate from those of the crop itself. There are no certification schemes for root crops, but there is a voluntary zoning scheme for seed crops of sugar beet, mangels, fodder beet and red beet, to help growers to minimise the risk of accidental crossing between varieties of different types.

*Polyploids.*—The simplest situation with regard to chromosome number is that the number ($n$) in pollen grains and ova is the basic number ($x$) and that in the fertilised egg is double or *diploid* ($2n = 2x$). By treatment with the drug colchicine it is relatively easy to double the chromosome number and so obtain plants with $2n = 4x$, producing pollen and ova with $n = 2x$ chromosomes. Such plants are called *tetraploids* and in general plants with higher multiples than two of the basic number are called *polyploids*. An example of a practical application is provided by sugar beet, in which polyploid varieties have been produced and have had some commercial success, mainly because of higher sugar content. In producing commercial seed, a mixture of diploid and tetraploid seed is sown and the produce is a mixture of diploid, triploid and tetraploid. The proportions in the mixture sown are adjusted to give the maximum of triploids, which are superior to diploids and tetraploids in this case; triploids ($2n = 3x$) cannot, of course, reproduce themselves.

Polyploids of this type, in which the plant whose chromosomes were doubled was not a hybrid between distinct species, are called *autopolyploids*. This is believed to be the situation with potatoes and with some herbage crops (*e.g.* lucerne, sainfoin, cocksfoot); in other herbage crops *e.g.* red and alsike clovers) which are normally diploid, breeders have produced autotetraploid varieties, so far without much commercial success.

When a hybrid between distinct species undergoes chromosome doubling, the result is a different kind of polyploid, an *allopolyploid*. In an *allotetraploid*, for instance, the four sets of chromosomes comprise two from one species and two from the other. At meiosis, pairing is mainly between sets of similar origin. An allotetraploid is much more fertile than the diploid hybrid from which it is derived, the latter being often almost completely sterile. Many species of plants, both wild and cultivated, are allopolyploids, *e.g.* wheat, oats, swedes and white clover among our crop species. Hundreds of allopolyploids have been produced experimentally, two well known examples being wheat × rye and radish × cabbage; here the crosses were made between different genera. So far, no artificial allopolyploids have had any significant commercial success but plant breeders make use of them in further breeding work.

**Variety Testing.**—Farmers are the final arbiters of the merits of new varieties. They are assisted in their choice of variety by the results of officially sponsored variety trials and by recommendations made on the basis of these results.

The trials are conducted at several sites, considered to represent the different agricultural regions, and for not less than three seasons at each site. In each season the trials are replicated to allow statistical assessment of the significance of the results. Standard varieties are included as controls. Data are recorded on yield, earliness, resistance to diseases, to pests and to lodging, in fact on any attribute that bears on the value of the variety to the farmer. Information is also obtained on the quality of the produce.

In deciding which varieties to recommend all these data have to be considered and account taken of the undesirability of recommending too many varieties (*e.g.* maltsters like to make up large bulks of one variety). Sometimes the decision is easy, but more often it is difficult, the choice depending on the relative weight given to different attributes.

Where open-pollinated varieties are concerned, a final decision cannot be reached, because the relative merits of the products of different breeders may change, *e.g.* with sugar beet. In any case, the work of variety testing is unending, because new varieties of all crops are continually coming forward.

# CHAPTER 9

# THE CEREALS

## WHEAT

THE cultivation of wheat was begun in prehistoric times and the cereal was greatly valued by the ancient Persians, Greeks and Egyptians. Cultivated wheats seem to have originated by the accidental hybridization of certain species of wild grasses, and the varieties now grown have been evolved by the selection of subsequent mutations and by hybridization, either accidental or artificial. Wheat was introduced to Britain by Neolithic settlers about 2400 B.C.

Wheat, since it is the favourite cereal for the production of bread, is the basic carbohydrate food of Western peoples. In Asia, on the other hand, the main food grains are rice and various millets. Wheat grain is frequently fed as such to poultry. Otherwise it is ground to flour, the milling by-products being fed to farm animals. Each grain of wheat consists of an embryo plant in close contact with an ample store of starchy and nitrogenous food material, the whole being surrounded by a pericarp or coat, which goes to form the miller's bran. Flour consists of the most digestible portion of the food store and is obtained by subjecting the grains to a milling process. The admirable qualities of wheaten flour depend largely upon the nature of the nitrogenous portion, which is in the form of gluten. When the flour is prepared for the baking process some of the starch is converted into sugar, which in turn is broken up by the action of the yeast, with the formation of carbon dioxide gas, whereby the dough is puffed up into a spongy mass. The so-called " strong " wheats have a high gluten content, and the dough produced is of a tough, rubbery nature that prevents the escape of gas and produces a light, well risen, even-textured loaf. The diastatic power of wheat, *i.e.* its capacity for producing sugar, is also important, and sometimes bakers have to blend malt extract with flour of poor diastatic quality. Other things being equal, the best flour from the baker's point of view is the one that yields the largest number of loaves per sack.

**Milling of Wheat.**—Before milling takes place the wheats are blended, so that the flour produced will be of the desired strength for baking purposes. In modern flour milling the wheat is first of all subjected to a very thorough cleaning process. Not only does this remove weed seeds and foreign matter that would injure the quality of the flour, but also gets rid of stones, pieces of iron and scraps of material that would be likely to injure the delicate machinery used in the milling process. The milling proper is done by passing the grain between a series of rollers of increasing fineness and closeness of setting, so that the berries are cracked and the endosperm or floury portion is liberated with the least possible breaking up of the dark coloured bran. At each stage the material issuing from the rollers is sorted out, by means of sifting machines and fans, into materials of different grades and degrees of fineness. When home grown wheat is milled for flour of " white " standard, about 68 per cent. of the grain is recovered as flour, but the best imported wheats, subjected to the same process, yield up to 74 per cent. flour. The final products of the milling process are: (1) flours and semolinas of different grades; (2) wheat germs; (3) middlings, sharps, thirds, pollards or weatings, which may or may not be separated into " fine " and " coarse " grades; and (4) bran, which again may be separated into " broad " and " medium." Higher rates of extraction, such as 80 or 85 per cent., give rise to flours of a lighter or darker shade of greyish brown. These, owing to the inclusion of part of the germ and more of the aleurone layer, have a much better vitamin content (vitamin B) than the ordinary white flour. When the rate of extraction is raised above 85 per cent. the flour necessarily contains more of the fibrous outer layer of the grain, and is therefore less digestible. Methods of milling devised during the war, and based on analysis of the various parts of the wheat berry, aimed at retaining the vitamins as far as possible while eliminating as much as possible of the bran. It is possible by these methods to get a flour which is almost white and which yet contains practically all the valuable nutrients of the grain, the extraction rate being about 83 per cent. In many countries a flour of wheat and rye is the standard material for baking.

**Quality of Wheat.**—Wheat is valued according to its suitability for milling on the one hand, and the suitability of the flour produced for bread or biscuit making on the other.

A good milling wheat should mill easily and yield the largest possible proportion of flour and a correspondingly small proportion of milling offals. Quality is also indicated by the thinness of the bran and the largeness of the wheat grains, large grains having a relatively smaller surface than small grains, and consequently a smaller proportion of bran. It is essential that the wheat should be in a sound condition, free from odours and indications of heating; it should also contain a minimum of weed and other foreign seeds. The wheat should be hard, as hardness indicates the presence of a minimum proportion of water.

Wheats of good quality for bread making have a horny or flinty appearance and an absence of flouriness when the grain is examined in cross-section, and they possess a high protein content. Yet the converse is not true, as wheat may have a hard translucent endosperm, and yet not be " strong." " Weak " wheats are usually soft, starchy and opaque; but a weak wheat can be given a " strong " look by nitrogenous manuring and early cutting. Actually the rapid ripening that takes place in dry, hot countries favours the development of strong wheat, whereas in this country the moist atmosphere and slow ripening are conducive to the development of soft grain. While some wheats may require favourable conditions to produce grain of good baking quality, the fact that strength can be inherited independently of everything else means that the choice of the variety is the most important factor in the production of strong flour. It should be noted that whereas " strength " is required in wheat for bread making, some " weak " wheats give the class of flour required for most sorts of biscuits and many kinds of cakes. Other varieties that are not particularly good either for bread or biscuit making find a market as poultry food.

If wheat is being bought for seed purposes it should be plump, with a smooth, well filled skin, and show every indication of having attained maturity at harvesting; it should bear no signs of weathering, overdrying or heating in the stack, should be free from bunt and should be as free as possible from weed seeds, a condition of much greater importance in seed wheat than in a sample for milling. The seed should have a high germinating capacity, and in case of doubt an official test should be procured. The Seeds Act requires that all wheat sold as seed should give a germination of at least 90 per cent.

The best wheat from the farmer's point of view is not necessarily that of the highest baking quality. In a free market the higher prices will ordinarily be obtained for samples of better baking quality, but much British wheat is used for biscuit manufacture; and in the production of baking flour it is usual to blend the " weaker " home-produced types with " strong " imported grain. Yield of straw may sometimes be important—*e.g.* to the potato grower or the dairy farmer; otherwise the shorter strawed varieties are commonly preferred on account of their adaptation to modern husbandry methods. The individual farmer should choose varieties suited to the soil and climatic conditions of his farm and resistant to the diseases locally prevalent. On rich or highly manured land resistance to lodging is of obvious importance.

**Choice of Variety.**—Wheat, in common with many other species of cereals, is practically always self-fertilised. Under ordinary conditions each sort breeds true, and strains developed from individual plants, selected for their apparent merit, are ordinarily the same as the produce from unselected parents. How, then, have the dozens of varieties of wheat come into existence? Some, no doubt, have been developed from rare cases of mutation or of cross fertilisation under natural conditions. The great majority of our wheats, however, have been produced by artificial cross-fertilization of pre-existing distinct varieties, with selection from among the diverse types that appear in the progeny.

The official testing of varieties of wheat, and of many other crops, is carried out in England and Wales by the National Institute of Agricultural

Botany and the National Agricultural Advisory Service; in Scotland by the Department and Colleges of Agriculture and in Northern Ireland by the Ministry of Agriculture.

Lists of " recommended " varieties are published annually for both winter and spring wheat[1]. These are regularly revised so as to include new varieties of proven worth.

Only a relatively small proportion of new commercial varieties become officially approved or recommended in this way. The problem of choice for the farmer need not therefore be as difficult as it sometimes seems to be. His problem is to choose a variety which will give as high a financial return as possible, and will suit the conditions of the farm. This includes an assessment of the soil fertility, liability to certain diseases and the demand for straw on the farm.

A variety must have a high yield potential for the particular area and soil type. The straw must be strong so as to prevent lodging before harvest. Some farmers will prefer rather longer straw which is suitable for thatching, others will want a high yield of straw for use as litter. However, length of straw is usually, but not always, correlated with resistance to lodging. Some wheats have a thick walled, others a thin walled, straw. This also is often related to the ability of a variety to remain upright in spite of heavy grain yield, storm and wind.

Many of the higher yielding wheats are of indifferent baking quality and some of poor milling quality also. This is unfortunate, and the farmer has to judge whether the highest yield will more than offset a rather higher price for his produce when coupled with the lower yield from a " quality " variety . The farmer's choice in practice is usually governed by considerations of yield potential, straw length and disease resistance, rather than by considerations of processing quality.

A cause of loss with some varieties can arise from the premature " sprouting " or germination of the nearly ripe grain in the ear before harvesting. This can occur in very wet harvests and when harvesting has been delayed by catchy weather. It is a curious fact that the tendency to sprouting is correlated with grain colour, white varieties being more prone than red. Chaff colour is not related in this way.

A few varieties are rather liable to " shatter " when fully ripe; that is, to lose their grain when disturbed by wind while awaiting the combine harvester. Varieties are not likely to be officially recommended if this tendency is a feature of any new variety.

Susceptibility to disease is of obvious importance (see pp. 214-216). The most troublesome include Loose Smut, Yellow Rust and Powdery Mildew. There are marked differences between varieties in their susceptibility to these diseases. There is a practical control for Loose Smut (the hot water treatment of the seed) but not for the others. A disease which

---

[1] National Institute of Agricultural Botany, Huntingdon Road, Cambridge. Leaflet No. 8 " Winter Wheats "; Leaflet No. 9 " Spring Wheats ".

PLATE 29

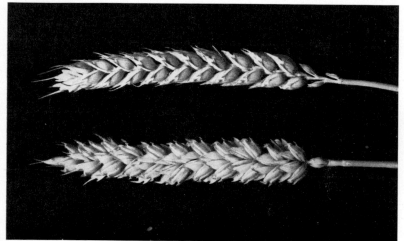

*A.* Cappelle Desprez

*B.* Hybrid 46

*National Institute of Agricultural Botany*

PLATE 30

SPRING WHEAT

*B.* KOGA II

*A.* JUFY I

is important in some seasons in the south west of the country on spring wheat is Black Rust. A variety susceptible to this disease is most unlikely to gain any popularity in that part of the country.

Some varieties of winter wheat show a tolerance to the soil borne disease Eyespot. This can be of considerable importance in those parts of the country where intensive cereal rotations are practised. This tolerance shows itself as an ability of the variety to yield well and to remain standing where other varieties would lodge and yield poorly. The disease, however, can still be found on the plant, hence it is not so much resistant to the disease as tolerant.

There do not appear to be differences between varieties in their susceptibility to other soil borne diseases such as Take All and Brown Foot rots.

Winter hardiness is of obvious importance in the winter varieties. This is not a simple matter of frost resistance, for certain varieties, that may be highly frost hardy, can suffer severely under typical British winter conditions—*i.e.* wet soil with alternating frost and thaw.

Varieties differ in their relative maturity. Some come to harvest earlier than others. This factor can be important in certain areas and it provides a means of spreading the harvest on farms growing a very large wheat acreage.

Some varieties permit later sowing than others. A varying degree of vernalisation by cold temperature in the late winter or early spring is necessary in order to cause the production of ear primordia by true winter varieties. Many varieties of Scandinavian and German origin require longer and colder periods than do some of, say, French origin. Certain wheat varieties will need to be sown not later than Christmas time in order to produce a normally eared crop. Others can be sown as late as mid-February. There are a few wheat varieties which can be regarded as dual purpose in Britain: that is, they are true spring varieties in that they do not require this period of cold treatment in order to produce ears. At the same time they are sufficiently hardy to survive the average winter conditions (Plates 29 and 30).

Late sowing of a true winter variety will almost always lead to a lower yield than would sowing at the normal time. There comes a time in late winter when it will pay to sow a true spring variety rather than a winter one. Local circumstances must determine when this will be. It should be remembered that a winter variety sown at the proper time in autumn will usually yield about 15-20 per cent. more than the best spring variety.

## The cultivation of Wheat

**Soil and Climate.**—Wheat thrives in subtropical, warm temperate and cool temperate regions. It is grown in this country as far north as Ross-shire, and is cultivated more or less extensively in all the eastern and thin to produce a full crop will generally give a high proportion of grain to straw. A thin seeding, however, has the disadvantage of allowing weeds to develop and spread, and a thin crop is slow to ripen. While the seed rate should provide for average conditions, the ultimate stand is largely determined by the mortality in winter and the degree of tillering. Fortunately, minor mistakes in the rate of seeding have less effect than might be expected, because when too little seed is used the plants produce more tillers and more grains per ear, whereas if too much is employed the wheat produces fewer tillers and fewer grains per ear.

The average seed-rate of $2\frac{1}{4}$ bushels per acre, given full germination, produces a stand of about thirty seedlings per square foot. The loss of plants that occurs in the winter naturally varies widely according to weather conditions, but the average is high. However, a spring stand of eight plants per square foot is capable of producing a full crop. Thin stands may be mended by drilling an appropriate amount of seed of a spring variety.

If wheat is sown in spring it is usually drilled early in March or in February. Earlier seeding than this may be attempted if the condition of the land permits, but it should be remembered that the ravages of rooks and other grain devouring birds become particularly severe at a time of the year when food is scarce, and it is possible that these may remove much of the seed that is sown.

The method of preparing an autumn seed bed will depend on the preceding crop. If wheat is to be taken after a fallow, the last fallowing operations should be designed to leave a fairly firm bottom and a rough surface mould. If the land is ploughed, only a shallow furrow slice should be turned over, and the use of the cultivator should then be sufficient to leave the soil in a fit condition for the corn drill. The soil should on no account be worked fine, as overworking before the winter rains may bring about the formation of a surface " cap ", leading to surface waterlogging. This will prevent free aeration of the soil. The ideal is a layer composed of fine crumb and small clods in the zone in which the seed will lie, with a surface covering of clods, including some as large as a man's fist.

When wheat is taken after potatoes, which leave the soil in an open, friable condition, a seed bed can often be prepared by the use of culti-vators and drags. If the land is ploughed, either after potatoes or after roots eaten off by sheep, a shallow ploughing will usually give the best results. Wheat grows poorly where there is a subsoil " pan," or where the subsoil becomes waterlogged in winter. Deeper ploughing or subsoil-ing, when the soil is dry, may remedy either condition.

When wheat is grown after a crop of seeds the preparation of the ground is relatively simple, the wheat being drilled across the furrows, with only a small amount of preliminary harrowing or sometimes no previous cultivation. If the crop is to be sown on freshly ploughed ley a furrow press should be used to consolidate the seed bed, but it is often better to plough earlier and so obtain a measure of natural consolidation.

**Manuring of Wheat.**—Wheat has a long period of growth and a deep rooting habit, and as far as phosphate and potash are concerned can sometimes be grown, if the land be in good condition, on the residues of previous crops and manuring. Commonly, some phosphate, and on light or chalk soil potash also, is applied at seed time, preferably by combine drill. In most cases, with the possible exceptions of wheat taken after a strong leguminous crop or after a clovery turf that will decompose rapidly, the application of between $1\frac{1}{2}$ and $3\frac{1}{2}$ cwt. (30-70 units N) of sulphate of ammonia or other nitrogenous fertilizer in spring produces a marked improvement and a profitable return; indeed it is becoming customary to apply nitrogen up to the limit that will cause lodging. On very light land even more than $3\frac{1}{2}$ cwt. per acre of sulphate of ammonia may be applied, usually split between two dates of application. A shortage of nitrogen is frequently exhibited by a yellowing of the crop about the time when active spring growth is commencing, *i.e.* in late April or early May. Experiments have shown that the time of applying the nitrogen is important. A February application stimulates tillering and greatly helps a thin crop, but when given to a thick crop it causes an undesirable development of straw. To improve the grain yield of a normal crop without increasing the straw, the nitrogenous fertilizer should be applied early in May. With modern short strawed winter wheats, the risk of lodging due to increasing the straw weight is not great. As a consequence top dressing is frequently carried out during late March or early April. Under some systems of farming the seeds land is top dressed with farmyard manure before it is ploughed for wheat, when no dressing of fertilizers should be necessary.

Sulphate of ammonia is most commonly employed as the form of top dressing. However, a quicker effect may be obtained by using a nitrate form such as Nitro-chalk, Nitra-Shell or the more expensive nitrate of soda.

If wheat is taken after another corn crop, or after potatoes on land that is light and in poor heart, and particularly for late sown wheat, it may be desirable to apply $\frac{1}{2}$-$\frac{3}{4}$ cwt. of sulphate of ammonia with super phosphate—or an equivalent amount of compound fertilizer—with the seed in autumn, followed by a top dressing in April or very early May. The quantity of superphosphate that will give a profitable return depends mainly, of course, on the soil reserves and to some extent on the district, for it has been shown that all crops respond more to phosphate in the north and where the rainfall is heavy. If $1\frac{1}{2}$ cwt. (30 units $P_2O_5$) per acre suits central and northern England, 1 cwt. will probably be enough for the drier south and east, whereas between 2 and 3 cwt. (40-60 units $P_2O_5$) may be optimal in the wetter west and in Scotland. Another point is that the quantity of phosphate may be reduced considerably where it is put in with the seed instead of being scattered on the surface (see Place-ment of Fertilizers).

Where wheat is grown in rotation with crops such as potatoes, beet or mangels, which normally receive dressings of potash and farmyard manure, it will not as a rule respond to potash manures. But on light land or where the soil is known to be deficient in available potash, it may be worth giving wheat a dressing of the order of 1 cwt. per acre of muriate or its equivalent.

The manuring of spring wheat follows rather similar lines to that for feeding barley. A seed bed application may be given of $2\frac{1}{2}$-3 cwt. per acre sulphate of ammonia (50-60 units N), $1\frac{1}{2}$ of superphosphate (30 units $P_2O_5$), and on light soils $\frac{1}{2}$-$\frac{3}{4}$ of muriate of potash (30-45 units $K_2O$), or the equivalent in the form of a compound. This may be best combined drilled as compound. It is seldom of benefit to withhold any of the nitrogen for top dressing.

**After-cultivation.**—In spring, wheat is usually subjected to a fairly severe harrowing in order to break down clods, which readily fall to pieces after the winter frosts, and to tear up the surface " cap " that has been formed by the beating action of rain. The harrowing also drags out some surface weeds, especially straggling weeds like speedwell, and is considered to have a beneficial action in separating the plants and causing them to tiller. Should the crop be thick it may be harrowed both ways, but if it be thin it is safer to harrow in the direction of the drills only. If the land be dirty with annual weeds, and the crop can stand fairly rough treatment, the harrowing may be repeated a number of times. The operation that follows the harrowing is usually a heavy rolling to consolidate the soil about the roots of the plants. Rolling across the run of the drills with a Cambridge roller used to be practised to check the ravages of wireworms. But where wireworm damage is feared, the best practice is to apply a BHC or other wireworm dust either to the seed or to the seed-bed (see p. 217). Where the soil is very loose and " hollow " in spring, and where the plant is not over thick, rolling should precede harrowing, otherwise the harrows will drag out too many plants. Horse-hoeing, which was of undoubted service in keeping the land clean, used to be practised widely. The same result may be obtained with a tractor hoe, fitted with A blades of suitable width, but hoeing is not often practised today, except occasionally in the control of wild oats. The width of the hoe must match that of the drill which has been used, *i.e.* should cover either the same or half the number of rows. To make this practicable the distance between the drill coulters must be somewhat greater than normal, *viz.* 8 or 9 in., and a steerage type of hoe (see p. 108) must be used. Hand hoeing, the common method of cleaning adopted in the past for the suppression of strong growing weeds, like thistles and docks, is rarely practised to-day, the objective generally being attainable by the use of selective weed-killers. Generally, spring cultivation is now limited to the minimum to break surface " caps " or obtain consolidation.

If the land is in good heart and the winter has been mild, wheat may become " winter proud," that is, it may be so much overgrown by the spring that it tends to become too heavy, and is likely to lodge before harvest. Wheat in this condition can be checked by turning on sheep or cattle and allowing the animals to graze it down fairly closely, but grazing must not be continued after the middle of April. Stock should be put on only in dry weather, and then only for limited periods. Where stock cannot be had to graze down the crop, sulphuric acid spray may be used to obtain the same effect, or the wheat may be " flagged," *i.e.* the top leaf may be cut off.

**Harvesting.**—If wheat is cut before its time the yield of grain is reduced and much of the food material of the plant is retained in the straw; the sample is also poor in quality, as the grains are shrunken and small, and particularly unsuitable for seed purposes. When a crop is cut too late the sample is bold, well filled and of excellent appearance, but the bran may be too thick to give the best yield of flour in the milling process; this condition, however, is ideal if the grain is to be used for sowing. The chief disadvantage of late cutting is the liability of the grain to shake out of the ear, both before and during harvesting operations. Some varieties are more liable to this shattering at harvest than others. When the straw, which loses its green colour from the base upwards, has assumed a distinct yellow tinge below the ear, it is time to examine the ripeness of the grain with a view to harvesting. The grains should be rubbed out of a few average ears, and their condition determined by pressing them between the thumb nails; they will probably be soft, but, if they exude no milky juice, the crop may be considered ripe enough to be cut by the binder, when the final stage of ripening will take place in the stook. If a milky fluid can be expressed from the seed the crop should be left for a few days; but when the grains have matured beyond this stage, cutting should commence. When wheat is to be cut with a " combine," it will need to be left for about a week after the stage indicated, and experience has shown that with most modern varieties this does not involve much risk of loss through shaking.

Before cutting with the binder some farmers " open roads " round the field with a scythe, so that a way is made for the machine to move without destroying any of the crop. However, where labour is scarce the binder may be driven straight into the crop without causing very serious loss. In this case the " back swath " or outside bout, which is pressed down by the passage of the machine, is left until the rest of the field has been reaped, by which time many of the flattened stalks will have risen far enough to let the knife get under them. The back swath is, of course, cut in the opposite direction from the rest of the field. With the self-propelled combine, which has the knife in front, the problem does not arise. Most of the corn crops of the country are now cut with the combine harvester, but neither the normal combine nor the binder are completely satisfactory unless the crop is standing well. Should the wheat be leaning in one direction, so that the machine travelling in that direction simply pushes the straw farther over, and either does not cut it or leaves too long a stubble, the machine should be used to cut one way—against the direction of lean—and then driven back to the starting-point with the mechanism out of gear. The pick-up reel available for the combine is a great advance on the traditional pattern for dealing with lodged crops, and laid crops of wheat are now seldom harvested by manual labour. If patches were badly laid (see p. 242) in all directions they used to be cut with the scythe or hook and bound by hand; a good scythe man and two binders were capable of clearing about an acre per day, which is a laborious and costly business when it is considered that a combine can perform very much more than this amount of work in an hour. Cutting with the binder should not take place if the crop is wet with rain or dew, as not only do the canvases tend to shrink and jam, but the excess of moisture in the tightly bound sheaf causes undue delay in drying. Combine harvesters also require the crop to be in dry condition and, if possible, free from juicy weeds. If the latter are present in quantity they tend to clog the threshing mechanism. In this case the crop may be cut and left in windrows and afterwards picked up and threshed by a combine with a pick-up attachment.

Grain harvested by combine will frequently need artificial drying before it can be stored. Wheat more often than barley will need such drying. The grain may come off the combine at anything up to 23 per cent. moisture (exceptionally moist). It will need to be dried to 16 per cent. moisture for bulk storage, or to 15 per cent. for long term storage. The operation of combine harvesters and grain driers is dealt with in Part 1.

**Stooking and Carting.**—After the crop has been bound the sheaves are arranged so that they may dry as quickly as possible, and at the same time be able to withstand a spell of inclement weather. This is done by setting them up in shocks or stooks, each stook consisting of ten or twelve sheaves, half on one side and half on the other, arranged as far as possible in rows running north and south so that each side obtains equal benefit from the sun. Pains should be taken to plant the sheaves with their oblique butts firmly on the ground, and their heads in close contact, or the whole erection is likely to topple over in a slight wind and much labour will be required for resetting. Daily resetting of the stooks is essential during periods of mild and wet weather if the quality of the grain is to be preserved. If the crop is undersown, the stooks must not be allowed to stand long enough to damage the underlying grasses and clovers.

As a rule the crop is ready for carrying in from four to fourteen days after cutting. This period is required for the proper drying of the straw, because if too much sap is present when the crop is stacked heating and moulding will ensue and the germination will be spoiled. In order to ascertain when the crop is ready to carry, a few straws should be taken from the middle of the sheaf and examined at the nodes. When these have become hard, shrunken and concave in outline, it may be taken that the straw is sufficiently dry. When too much sap is present the nodes are soft, juicy and convex.

In certain seasons the crop may be dry enough to be threshed out of the field, meaning direct from the stook, using a stationary thresher or a combine harvester, the sheaves being pitched into the latter machine as it moves about the field.

If the crop is to be stacked, care should be taken to examine the straw in all parts of the field, as a portion of the crop in a hollow or sheltered situation may still retain too much moisture when all the rest of the corn is fit to carry. A rattling or crackling of the straw when it is being carried, and a certain looseness of the sheaf within the twine, indicate that the crop is in excellent order for stacking. When once the crop is dried, a shower of rain should not be allowed to hinder the carrying operations, as the surface moisture will do no harm; in this respect wheat is more easily managed than the other cereals.

The method of carrying the crop depends on the local custom, the type of trailer or cart employed, the style of stacking and the number of hands available for the different operations. A simple and economical method is to employ one man as builder of the stack, one man to fork the crop in the field, and two or three trailers or single horse carts (the number depending on the distance between the field and the stackyard) to drive in the crop, each driver building and pitching his own load. But if the stack is large the builder will need an assistant.

Different types of stack are built in different districts. In the north it is customary to build stacks small and round; in the south they are sometimes made very large, and are, as a rule, rectangular in shape. Whichever method is employed, it is wise to lay out the stackyard with great care, always bearing in mind the possibility of pitching directly from the stacks on to the platform of the thresher, the accessibility of the first varieties to be threshed and the reservation of the outside and exposed positions for crops that have been secured before they were in a proper condition. Building in the bays of a Dutch barn saves time by avoiding the delay that occurs when " topping out " stacks; in addition, no thatching is required.

When completed stacks have settled, and when sufficient time has elapsed to ensure that there is no possibility of heating, they should be thatched with sound wheat or rye straw, and the thatch well secured with ropes or strings and pegs. The appearance of the stacks will be greatly improved if the outside is pared or trimmed to remove all loose straw and the protruding " tail " ends of the sheaves. This also saves a small amount of corn that otherwise would be eaten by birds or damaged by weather.

(For threshing, see Part 1.: Threshing, Combine Harvesting.)

**Yield.**—The average yield of wheat in Britain is over 20 cwt. (4½ qr. of 504 lb. per qr.) to the statute acre. Crops of 35 to 40 cwt. (8 to 9 qr.) are, however, grown on good land, and yields of over 60 cwt. have been recorded. The highest authenticated British yield is 70½ cwt. The total weight of straw is about one and a half times that of grain; that is, the total produce is 40 per cent. grain and 60 per cent. straw. The proportion however, varies within rather wide limits and is notably lower, as would be expected in the short strawed varieties. The weight of harvested straw depends of course on the height at which the crop is cut. The bushel weight of the grain averages 63 lb.

## Fungoid Diseases

**Bunt.**—A casual examination of the ear of an affected plant does not reveal the presence of this disease, but when the grains are removed and broken they are found to consist of a mass of black spores, giving off a strong fishy odour. When threshing takes place the affected grains burst, discolour the healthy wheat and impart to the whole an objectionable odour. In this way not only is the yield of grain diminished but its value per cwt. is greatly reduced. If wheat is sown with spores of the fungus adhering to the grain, the seeds and spores germinate together and the fungus finds its way into the reproductive shoot, finally destroying every grain in the ear.

The disease can be prevented by dressing the seed with a suitable fungicide. At one time solutions of copper sulphate or formaldehyde were used. For many years dry dust preparations of organo-mercury compounds have been used. These are now giving way to specially formulated liquid dressings of rather similar chemical nature. The dry dressings are used at the rate of from 1 to 2 oz. per bushel, but good dry seed is not injured by rather larger doses. The success of the treatment depends on the complete spreading of the powder over the surface of the grain, and mixing should therefore be done in a machine or revolving container. An old butter churn will serve as a mixer, but some special machines have an eccentric motion which makes their action very thorough. While most machines have to be emptied after each batch has been mixed, there are mixers constructed on a continuous flow principle; that is, the grain and disinfectant are fed in continuously and emerge in a well mixed stream. As the dusts are irritating to the nose and lungs, masks should be employed by workers who have to handle large batches of material, and the treatment should preferably be in closed containers.

Though the dry dressings could be applied, with care, on the farm, they were usually applied by the merchant from whom the seed was purchased. The newer liquid dressings need special equipment for their safe application. This is a specialist, not a farm, operation.

These fungicide dressings may be combined with insecticidal dressings in the control of wireworms and wheat bulb fly.

**Loose Smut.**—This fungus attacks the developing ears in such a way as to destroy the flowers completely, and also the pales and glumes (chaff). The whole head of the plant becomes covered with a black mass of spores. It is not possible to prevent the recurrence of the disease by dusting infected grain, as the mycelium of the fungus is present inside the apparently healthy seed. Although the fungus can be killed by immersing the seed for ten minutes in water at 128° F., this treatment is difficult to carry out in practice, and the best way to avoid further attacks is to obtain seed from an unaffected crop. The hot water treatment is seldom used except for the maintenance of breeder's seed stock free from this disease.

**Yellow Rust.**—This is a very common disease of wheat in this country. Affected plants can be recognised by the bright yellow spots on the leaves and chaff: these spots represent patches of leaf surface through which the spore-bearing organs of the fungus have burst, and the yellow powder issuing from the ruptures consists of spores. The grain of rusted plants does not fill properly, but remains small and shrunken like wheat that has been cut prematurely or has been grown in a district too late for it to ripen.

There is no known preventive measure that gives absolute immunity from rust attacks, but there are varieties of wheat that exhibit a much greater power of resistance than others. There are several strains of yellow rust fungus. Some varieties are susceptible to more of these strains, others to relatively few.

**Brown Rust.**—While yellow rust may be found on wheat at all times from early spring to harvest, and even on young plants in autumn, brown rust is first seen about the middle of June when the grain is beginning to fill. The fungus destroys the foliage and prevents the ears from developing properly. Wheats which resist yellow rust do not necessarily withstand the attacks of this species; but there is reason to believe that should brown rust become more prevalent, resistant wheats could be produced. At present brown rust is not very widely distributed.

**Black Rust.**—This is the well-known wheat rust of America and India which for a long time was believed not to exist in this country but is now found in some seasons in the south-west and south. In this rust the spots do not occur on the leaves but on the stem (it is sometimes called stem rust), and the spores are of a very dark, almost black, colour. The black rust fungus has a second host, namely the common barberry, on which it passes part of its life cycle. If the wheat of a district becomes affected with the disease, the barberry bushes should either be removed—a measure that has met with great success in U.S.A.—or varieties of wheat should be found that are resistant to the fungus.

**Take-all.**—This is a disease of wheat and barley—oats are relatively immune—which causes the plants to die early and produce typical " white-heads " with little or no grain in the ear.  The fungus attacks the root system, producing a black felt like mycelium over them; by harvest-time the straw also becomes blackened at the base.  The fungi remain on the stubble and in winter or early spring produce spores which are capable of reproducing the disease in young wheat plants.  This disease is most prevalent on soils that are low in organic matter and high in lime, and is likely to be serious only where wheat and barley are grown year after year, or in very close rotation, on the same ground.  The worst outbreaks are in wheat that follows either barley or wheat.  Oats are scarcely affected. The remedy is to adopt a system of cropping that will starve the fungus out.   In this respect it should be noted that couch-grass, Yorkshire fog and bent-grass all perpetuate the fungus, but the disease is usually found to decline under a ryegrass and clover ley.  Where wheat is to follow wheat it is a good practice to burn over the stubble of the first crop.  The damage is greatest under conditions of low fertility, so that the liberal use of fertilizers, particularly of nitrogen, is to be recommended when there is reason to fear an attack.  The Take-all disease is discussed in Advisory Leaflet No. 304 (Ministry of Agriculture, Fisheries and Food).

**Eye-spot** is caused by the fungus *Cercosporella*.  In serious cases the fungus, which attacks the base of the stem, causes the lodging of the whole crop.  The only effective preventive measure is again the adoption of a suitable rotation.  In some respects the problem of eye-spot is different from that of Take-all.  Firstly, its incidence is greater on heavy than on light land.  Secondly, susceptible crops (wheat and barley) must be kept off heavily infected land for at least two seasons and for three if, during the first of these, there was any considerable amount of self-sown wheat or barley.  Thirdly, the common grasses do not act as host plants for the fungus, so that the first crop after old turf is usually very clean.  In this case a second crop of wheat can be taken with safety.  The disease rarely causes heavy damage except to winter wheat.  Certain varieties are less affected by this disease than are others.  The Eye-spot disease is discussed in Advisory Leaflet No. 321 (Ministry of Agriculture, Fisheries and Food).

**Powdery Mildew** caused by the fungus *Erysiphe graminis* affects not only wheat but other cereals and many grasses.  It is usually to be found on wheat towards harvest time, but serious damage is caused only from an early attack.  These early attacks occur mostly when a dry spring follows a mild winter.  Excessive use of nitrogen fertilizers makes the crop susceptible to attack.  Varieties vary in degree of susceptibility.

### Insects and Other Pests

**Wireworm.**—These are the larvae of several species of click beetles which formerly caused enormous damage in both farm and garden. Among major farm crops those which suffer most severe damage are wheat, oats and potatoes. Barley, perhaps because it is often sown in late spring and therefore quickly grows beyond the seedling stage, is less liable to disastrous damage. Beans and flax are highly resistant.

Wireworm population tends to increase while land is under grass and to diminish under continued arable cropping. Damage to grass sward is not very noticeable even when very large numbers are present, because established plants can quickly repair root damage. On the other hand a wheat seedling is killed if the lower part of the stem is eaten through just below ground level, which is the usual form of attack.

Entomologists have evolved a technique for estimating the number of wireworms per acre, and are able to predict the chances of success or failure of a given crop. For example, with a population of 750,000 it would till lately have been unwise in most areas to attempt winter wheat or spring oats; but barley, sown rather late on a very well prepared seed bed, would have quite a fair chance of success. Beans or flax would be quite safe.

The situation has been radically changed since the introduction of BHC—the gamma isomer of benzine hexachloride and of Aldrin. The application of these materials, either to the seed bed or to the seed itself, which can be done at very moderate cost, is a cheap insurance against loss. Seed-bed treatment should be preferred to seed dressing in cases where infestation is really heavy. The material heptachlor is also used for this purpose as a seed dressing. The Advisory Leaflet No. 199 (Ministry of Agriculture, Fisheries and Food) *Wireworm* should be consulted for further information.

The following insects are also injurious to wheat and other cereals: **the wheat bulb fly**, which, because the fly lays its eggs on bare ground from July throughout August, is worst when the crop is taken after a fallow but attacks can also follow after potatoes and peas; **the frit fly** (see p. 228), **the gout fly**, **the Hessian fly**, and **the wheat midge**. All are difficult to suppress, and may cause serious damage.

Early sowing is particularly helpful in cases where bulb fly seems likely to cause trouble. Seed dressings have also been developed which are of value when sowing of wheat has to be delayed. These are similar to those used against wireworms but are of a more concentrated nature. With certain of these there is a risk of causing deaths of wild birds if they are able to consume sufficient of the dressed grain; and at the time of writing certain measures were being taken to reduce that risk. For fuller particulars of treatment and remedial measures the reader is referred to the Ministry of Agriculture, Fisheries and Food leaflets [1] or to works on Entomology.

Slugs may become so numerous that they cause damage to wheat; they can also cause serious losses in other crops. They may be poisoned by applying to each acre $\frac{1}{2}$ lb. of metaldehyde mixed with 25 lb. of bran [1]

---

[1] Advisory Leaflets : No. 110 " Frit Fly " ; No. 177 " Wheat Bulb Fly " and No. 115 " Slugs and Snails."

Cutworms or surface caterpillars, the larvae of a number of species of moth, eat through the stems of wheat, and eat the stems and leaves and hollow the roots of other crops. They may be poisoned with Paris green as in the case of " leather jackets " (see p. 228).

## OATS

The oat is the most extensively cultivated cereal in this country, and is grown in every county and under widely different conditions of soil and climate. The total area of oats grown is, however, rather less than it was ten or twenty years ago. On many farms the area of oats has been replaced by barley (for feeding) and on others has decreased markedly. While not as resistant to winter cold as wheat and barley, oats are much more successful than these cereals in wet districts. The varieties now cultivated in Britain nearly all belong to the species *Avena sativa*. Some of the varieties grown in hot countries are derivatives of another wild species named *Avena sterilis*. Varieties of *Avena strigosa* are still to be found in late and cold districts such as Shetland and in the upland parts of Wales. The spring wild oat, *Avena fatua*, is a worthless annual weed which infests the corn crops in many localities where winter-sown cereals are very frequently grown. The winter wild oat, *Avena ludoviciana*, introduced about 1930, is another troublesome weed.

In the economy of the farm the oat crop fulfils a dual purpose: it is a producer of feeding grain and at the same time supplies straw that is superior to all other cereal straws in palatability and nutritive value, and is often used to replace hay in winter feeding of stock, especially in the north of the country. Crushed oats are used in the feeding of sows and fattening pigs, but if the grain is to be used as a feed for very young pigs it should be employed in moderation, because its fibre content is rather high, and it should be finely ground. The feeding of new oats is sometimes attended by a certain amount of danger, and old oats, or at least such as have been matured in a well settled stack, are to be preferred in stock dietary. Those responsible for the feeding of racehorses are usually most particular in this respect. Large quantities of oats are, of course, used for human consumption in the form of rolled oats and oatmeal.

**Milling of Oats.**—In the manufacture of oatmeal the first process is to screen the oats thoroughly in order to remove impurities. The grain is then heated in a kiln until its moisture content, which is normally about 13 per cent., is reduced to about $2\frac{1}{2}$ per cent. Shelling is next carried out by passing the oats between revolving horizontal stones which rub the husks away from the kernels. The material issuing from the stones is then treated to remove the dust and the husks, while the kernels or groats, after a special scouring to remove the external fibrous layer, pass to a stone mill for grinding. The ground oats are sorted through sieves into meals of various grades of fineness such as round, medium cut and fine cut oatmeals. The yield from 100 lb. of oats is about 60 lb. oatmeal, 17 lb. husks, and 9 lb. of dusts and residues from the sorting screens; the remaining weight is lost in the process of cleaning and drying. The oat husks are of practically no value for feeding but are used as litter for poultry, by brewers as a mechanical aid to the draining of their mash, and as packing. The oat dusts and screenings may be used in mixture with other foods for stock.

Rolled oats are prepared by rolling out and drying the kernels after they have been softened with steam.

**Quality of Oats.**—High quality oats are plump and well filled; they have a minimum of husk and a high bushel weight. Varieties differ in their grain shape and length. Many of the shorter types appear plumper than the long-grained types, but may have a higher husk percentage. In British grown samples the percentage of husk, by weight, varies between extremes of about 22 and 28 per cent., and bushel weights for unclipped grain run from about 37 to 48 lb. for samples in good dry condition. The highest bushel weights and lowest proportions of husk are obtained when the crop ripens slowly in cool weather. The colour should be bright and there should be no indication of heating or sprouting; there should be no shelled grains, weed seeds or other impurities. Oats grown in the cooler and wetter parts of Britain seem to have a higher proportion of oil and protein in their composition, and this may account for the acknowledged superiority of Scottish oats for milling purposes.

The best oat straw is fine and grass like, and has a higher nutritive value than poor hay, but some varieties are so coarse in the stem and leaf that they are not only innutritious, but also unpalatable. In order to secure the best fodder one of the noted straw-producing oats should be grown, or the crop can be cut before it is ripe so as to stop the transference of nutrients from the straw to the grain and check the lignification of the cellulose which occurs in the later stages of ripening. The proportions of grain and straw differ in different oats, and as a rule those varieties which give a high proportion of their yield in the form of straw also produce straw of fine quality.

In aiming at the greatest profit per acre the farmer looks for a variety that produces a high yield; but he has also to select, according to the needs of his stock or the demand of the market, either a variety that will give him an abundance of good fodder for home consumption or one that will yield a maximum of corn for sale. Unfortunately these qualities are somewhat antagonistic and cannot fully be combined in a single variety.

As mentioned above, the oat crop is grown under a wide range of conditions. At times it is grown on land that is fat with the residues of heavy manuring, when there is a great risk that the crop will be laid and will suffer heavy loss. To reduce this risk to a minimum, a variety should be grown that is either short or very strong in the straw. On the other hand, the sort of oats that will yield best under good conditions of soil and climate may give poor results when sown in an elevated or late locality —either because the plants are not sufficiently hardy, or because they take so long to mature that the crop cannot be ripened or got into sufficiently dry condition for stacking in the normal season. Earliness is specially important in late districts, where the crop is to be undersown with grass and clover.

The capacity of the variety for tiller formation is important because of its influence on the amount of seed that is required. Under adverse conditions a proportion of the seed fails to produce plants, even though it has been chemically dressed and consequently the poorer the land the greater the need for a thick seeding or, on the other hand, a good tillering variety. Our largest grained oats have the poorest tillering capacity, and on poor soil or at high elevations the cost of seeding these varieties is a disadvantage. Where the stand is poor not only will the yield be diminished but ripening will be uneven and greatly delayed.

If oats are being grown for home consumption it is immaterial whether the natural colour of the grain be white, yellow, grey or black. Yellow oats are often popular in late districts where the rainfall is heavy, because under these conditions white oats tend to acquire a dull colour, while slight weathering can hardly be detected in yellow grained varieties. Few black or grey varieties are cultivated today.

**Varieties.**—The number of oat varieties in cultivation is still large, and since the crop is grown under a very wide range of environmental conditions, from the poorest to the most fertile soils, from Shetland in the north to Kent and Devon in the south, and under annual rainfalls of 20 to perhaps 70 in., it will be obvious that a wide choice of types is desirable. At high elevations in Scotland and in Wales even the earliest varieties do not reach full maturity, and the crop is commonly fed to livestock in the form of oat sheaves. Moreover, in the moister areas generally, oat straw has a high feeding value, and the farmer therefore thinks in terms of total yield rather than of grain only. Under such conditions leafy and small-grained types of *Avena sativa* and very occasionally of *Avena strigosa* are cultivated.

In the drier areas the straw becomes highly lignified and is hence of little value as fodder. Under such conditions the farmer's main consideration is the yield and quality of the grain.

There is a fairly sharp distinction between true winter varieties (which are normally sown in October and are usually ripe for harvest before the end of July) and the spring varieties, for which seed time ranges from late February to the middle of April and which ripen from early August to late September, or even as late as October in the extreme north.

**Winter Oats.**—These are sufficiently frost hardy to survive average winters throughout the south-eastern half of England except, of course, in elevated districts; they can also be grown without serious risks in areas

PLATE 31

Oats

B. BLENDA

A. POWYS

*National Institute of Agricultural Botany*

near to the seaboard farther north.   No winter oat so far produced is
as frost resistant as the general run of winter wheats; in the south Midlands, where loss of wheat by frost is very rare, even the hardiest winter
oats are very occasionally winter killed.   The winter oat seedling has a
characteristic prostrate habit of growth and the shoots do not assume an
erect habit until active growth commences in the spring.   Most varieties
tiller very freely so that a relatively small seed rate is sufficient to produce
a full crop.   Since the plants are usually well rooted by the time when
drought is liable to occur, winter oats give higher yields than spring
varieties in the drier districts.   Moreover, they are much more resistant
than spring oats to attacks of frit fly, which can be a major cause of damage
to spring varieties in the south-eastern half of the country.   The point
is that autumn-sown plants have passed the susceptible stage of growth
by May, which is the egg laying season of the fly.   A difficulty in growing
winter oats in districts where the practice is uncommon is that the crops
become attractive to sparrows and other small birds before the general
run of cereals have reached this stage.   The damage is greatest in the
neighbourhood of towns, but even in country districts birds tend to flock
to winter oat fields.   Winter oat varieties do not require a cold period for
verualisation in the same way as a true winter wheat does.

The choice of a winter variety lies between the highest yield and
moderate to long straw on the one hand, to a lower yield but with the
strongest straw on the other.   S.147 is a good example of the former type;
S.172 is the winter oat with the strongest straw.   There are certain intermediate types such as Powys.   All these varieties have been bred at the
Welsh Plant Breeding Station.   Current recommendations on varieties
given in the National Institute of Agricultural Botany's Leaflet No. 13
*Oats* (Plate 31).

**Spring Oats.**—Until recent years very many " special " varieties of oats
were cultivated in the upland and colder regions where even oats are at
some disadvantage as a tillage crop.   Varieties such as S.171 (Ceirch
Llwyd Cwrta) and S.75 (Ceirch Llwyd) were grown and still are but to
a very limited extent.   The latter is a pure line selection of the old Bristle
pointed oat (Avena strigosa) while the former is a hybrid of the latter
species with Avena brevis.   These oats are extremely hardy and are
suited only to home consumption.   Varieties such as Black Tartarian,
Sandy and Bell were once extensively grown under somewhat less extreme
conditions.   The variety Potato is also still grown to a limited extent.   It
has high quality grain and long fine straw of high feeding value, but its
yield and resistance to lodging is surpassed by many of the modern varieties.
Oats grown in the upland districts are always at a disadvantage.   It is
by no means certain that they will ripen in anything but a favourable
season.   Many crops are cut green, preserved and fed in the sheaf.   Therefore, the maintenance and replacement of seed stocks in such areas present
considerable problems.   Farmers like to be self supporting and indeed

The oats and peas or oats and vetches may be mixed and sown together, the quantity of oats being from two to four times that of the pulse; but if oats and beans are grown for threshing some prefer to sow the beans about three weeks before the oats, as the former take longer to ripen. Recent experiments confirm the traditional view that the total yield from such mixed crops is greater than that which would be obtained (from the same acreage) with separate sowings of the components. A mixture of oats with one or other of the legumes is a convenient way of producing feed grains with a tolerably high protein content.

It is found that the oat crop benefits more often from a change of seed than do the other cereals. If badly ripened seed is used the yield is inferior, and it is therefore necessary, on poor farms and in late districts, to obtain fresh seed from time to time from a locality where the crop attains perfect development and maturity. In a late district it is common for seed to be renewed from an early district at least every three years, and even on good land a change may produce beneficial results. It is very probable, however, that the need for change of seed in certain districts is due to the incidence of seed-borne diseases, which can now be checked by seed disinfection (see p. 227.

A common problem on rich land is how to manage the crop to prevent lodging. Experience has shown that the risk is reduced by selecting a strong-strawed early maturing variety, by using plump and well grown seed, by early sowing and the use of a comparatively light seeding, and by using fertilizers to balance the soil nutrients and so promote early ripening.

In areas where winter oats are grown it is usual to sow a week or two earlier than winter wheat. Late sown winter oats often give poor yields, but may be preferable to spring crops in areas prone to spring droughts and frit fly attacks.

**Manuring.**—While the oat crop is capable of producing a fair yield on very poor soil, it nevertheless responds to liberal manuring, and it is common to treat it with nitrogenous, phosphatic, and under certain circumstances, potassic dressings. A suitable treatment for spring oats is to give 1 to 3 cwt. of superphosphate (20-60 units $P_2O_5$) according to local conditions (see manuring of wheat), up to 2 cwt. of sulphate of ammonia (40 units N) at seed time, and if the soil is light, an addition of 2 cwt. of kainit (30-40 units $K_2O$) applied a month or so before sowing. The commoner practice is to use a compound fertilizer having a nutrient balance suited to the particular soil conditions. This will often be combine drilled with the seed. Winter oats may receive a dressing of phosphate and possibly of potash (especially on high land) in the seed bed, as for wheats. The nitrogen will be applied in the spring as a top dressing, up to about 2 cwt. per acre (say 40 units N.) being used according to the nature of the soil. The limit up to which fertilizer can be profitably applied is determined by the liability of the crop to lodge when it becomes too luxuriant, and a short, strong strawed variety can be given a much heavier dressing than one having long and slender stems.

On good soils that are in high condition, first class crops of oats can be grown without the application of any manure; but if the soil is in particularly rich condition (e.g. after ley) and there is a danger of the crop becoming laid, it may be advisable to apply 2 cwt. of superphosphate (40 units $P_2O_5$) to hasten ripening and 2 cwt. of kainit (30-40 units $K_2O$) to balance the other nutrients. If oats follow another straw crop a liberal dressing of fertilizers will certainly be required unless the first crop was taken after a very rich old pasture. As a rule farmyard manure does not give good results when used for this cereal, as it encourages over development of the vegetative parts, delays ripening and decreases the yield of grain. If oats are suffering from the attacks of frit fly, stem eelworm or " leather jacket," the application of a quick acting nitrogenous fertilizer to hasten the growth of the young plants over the critical stage should never be overlooked, even if the soil is in good enough heart to warrant the expectation of a good crop without manuring.

**After-cultivation.**—The oat crop is usually rolled, either immediately after sowing or when plants are a few inches high, in order to consolidate the soil about the plant roots. It should be noted, however, that the harrowing of oats is considered to be distinctly risky in some parts of the country, though it may be practised in others when the crop is thick enough to stand it. Spraying with a suitable weed killer is usually carried out to control weed infestation (see p. 127).

**Harvesting.**—The degree of maturity that the crop should be allowed to attain depends on the use to which it is to be put. Where a high value is placed on the straw for feeding purposes the crop is cut early—when there is just a shade of yellow over the field—because at this time the food materials have not all passed out of the leaves and shoots, and the stem has not become woody. Early cutting, of course, interferes with the development of the grain, but it seems that the maximum feeding value, of grain and straw together, is reached some time before the crop is dead ripe. The time to cut, where grain is the main object, is when the crop has changed to a yellow colour and about a week before it is absolutely ripe. The grain will then be able to mature in the stook and there is little risk of corn being lost in the harvesting operations. If cutting is delayed until the crop is dead ripe, shaking may cause heavy loss with some varieties, before the grain is safely secured in the stacks. In this respect the crop is rather less suitable than the other cereals for combine harvesting as it cannot be left so long after binder ripeness. However in low rainfall areas, combining is common, the grain being artificially dried if necessary. In cool and moist districts relatively early cutting is the rule, because the translocation of foodstuffs from the straw to the grain will go on in the stook; in dry, hot areas the plants shrivel very rapidly after cutting.

The oat crop is more liable to ferment and heat in the stack than are

H

the other cereals, and great care should be taken to ensure that it is thoroughly dry before carrying operations are commenced.  Before it is in a fit condition to lead, the crop should stand in the stook for about a fortnight, though winter oats, ripening in the hot weather of late July, may be ready in a week.  The condition of the crop should be determined from time to time by examination of the juicy leaf insertions and the weeds in the base of the sheaves.  Should rain, other than the slightest of showers, occur while the crop is being carried, it is advisable to discontinue the work until the crop has dried.  Less care need be taken, however, if very small stacks are being built, or if the stackyard is in a position well exposed to wind.

In the wetter and upland districts oat stacks are frequently built small say six cartloads of sheaves, equivalent to perhaps 12 qr. of grain—and they may be constructed round wooden tripods or hollow frames, which may communicate with the outside air by means of another frame placed in a horizontal position during the building operations.  In this way cold air enters at the bottom of the stack and passes upwards and out through the sheaves, drying the corn and preventing heating.  Another plan is to build the stacks small and over field or roadside walls, thus preventing undue consolidation and promoting aeration.  In some districts the danger of overheating is so great that wire and timber drying racks, roofed with sheet iron, are erected, and into these the sheaves are packed and left until they are in a condition that allows them to be stacked with safety.  Another way of securing the crop in a wet district is to build the sheaves into "huts" around metal tripods.  These "huts" take the place of stooks in the field, but since they are very much larger the sheaves may best be brought to a given site by means of a sweep; they are built with three ventilating shafts to ensure aeration, and in them the crop is practically safe from the effects of bad weather.  When a stack does over-heat it begins to lose shape and bend over towards its weakest side, and vapour may be seen issuing from its top.  Such a state of affairs can only be corrected by pulling down the stack and re-setting the sheaves in stooks, or by rebuilding the contents into smaller ventilated stacks.

The stacks are thatched when they have settled, and threshing takes place from time to time throughout the season according to the requirements of the stock and the condition of the market.  As threshed straw tends to go stale and is then less palatable, it is customary in some feeding districts to thresh frequently so as always to have fodder that cattle will eat with relish.

**Yield.**—The average weight of a bushel of oats is 42 lb., and the grain was formerly sold by the quarter of 336 lb.  The average British yield is between 19 and 20 cwt. of grain per acre; 26 cwt. might be considered a satisfactory crop on land of medium quality, and crops of 40 and even 50 cwt. are occasionally recorded.  The yield of straw depends on the nature of the variety grown and on the rainfall.  Grain-producing varieties when grown under moderately moist conditions yield about 40 per cent. grain or one and a half times as much straw as corn.

## Fungoid Diseases

**Smut.**—Oats are attacked by two species of smut, one covered and the other loose, but in practice they are difficult to distinguish and their differences are unimportant.

When plants are affected by the disease the reproductive shoots issue from their sheaths covered with a mass of black fungus spores, though in other respects the plants appear to be perfectly healthy. The spores, which are those of the fungus feeding on the nutrients provided by the plant for the development of the grain, are carried by wind and rain to healthy grain and lie dormant until the following year. When the grain is sown they become active and produce a mycelium which enters the young plant, finds its way to the ear, and produces towards the end of the season a fresh crop of spores.

Smut can be checked by treating the seed with a seed disinfectant, as for bunt in wheat.

**Leaf-stripe.**—This disease, which is sometimes called yellow leaf, used used to be widespread, and in some parts of the country it was formerly the most destructive disease affecting oats; it was worst on spring crops that were sown early. The mycelium of the fungus is carried on the seed, and a striking feature of the disease is that, while affected seed may show a very high germination capacity in the laboratory, it fails to establish the expected number of plants in the field. An examination following on a partial failure reveals that much of the seed has germinated but that the shoots have wandered in the soil and have been unable to push above ground. The name *pre-emergence blight* is often used to describe this condition. Of the affected plants that succeed in breaking through and establishing themselves, quite a number show the first symptoms of " stripe," namely lightish spots on the leaves which gradually elongate until they form distinct yellowish or brownish stripes. Some plants succumb before reaching the four-leaf stage. Later on, when the oats have reached the flowering stage, stripes may again be observed on the upper leaves.

A sure prevention for this disease is to treat the seed with a suitable organo-mercuric material, as for smut of oats and bunt of wheat; and where this is done as a matter of routine the disease virtually disappears. Seed rates above 4 bushels ($1\frac{1}{2}$ cwt.) of treated seed are rarely required for a full stand.

**Grey speck** " disease " is due to manganese deficiency. It occurs mainly on alkaline peaty soils or on soils of high organic matter content after excessive dressings of lime. Spraying should be carried out at the first sign of the symptoms. This should consist of 8 lb. of manganese sulphate, in 25 to 100 gal. of water per acre, with the addition of a wetting agent. If, as sometimes happens, the check to the crop has allowed a weed infestation to develop, spraying with a selective weed killer may follow.

### Insects and Other Pests

" **Leather Jackets.**"—These are the larval forms of species of crane-flies, popularly known as " daddy-long-legs." They attack all farm plants, but cause more apparent damage to oats taken after old grass than to any other crop. The adult flies appear from June to about the end of September and lay their eggs on grassland, preferring that which is rough and moist. The larvae feed till the following spring before passing into the pupal stage, and during this time they not only attack plant roots but they come to the surface at nights and gnaw through the leaves and stems. The loss is usually most severe in a backward spring when the crop cannot grow away from the attack, and the damage may be accentuated by birds pulling the plants out of the ground in search of the larvae.

Practical measures to combat the " leather jackets " are to stimulate the affected cereal with a top dressing of quick acting nitrogenous fertilizer and to destroy the larvae by means of poison baits.

If " leather jackets " only are present, the bait is made up with a dispensible DDT (20 per cent.) or gamma-BHC (50 per cent.). If slugs are present Paris green (containing arsenic) is used.

To prepare poison bait for 1 acre, mix 1 lb. of Paris green, DDT or BHC with 30 lb of bran or thirds and 2 gal. of water, to which a little treacle may be added. The material should be sufficiently moist to cause the poison to adhere, yet dry enough for convenience in sowing. The mixture should be broadcast over the affected crop, and it is found that the best results are got when this is done on a moist, warm night. See also Ministry of Agriculture, Fisheries and Food Advisory Leaflet No. 179, *Leather jackets.*

**Frit Fly.**—The larvæ of this fly cause damage to all cereal crops and grasses, but in this country the oat crop is the greatest sufferer. The frit fly population seems to be subject to cyclical changes; a gradual rise occurs over several years, culminating in a few years of heavy damage, and is followed by a rather sharp fall and a few more years during which there is relatively little trouble. Early in the season the maggots do damage by feeding on the young plants inside the shoots; the upper leaves of injured shoots turn yellow and later wither away. A close inspection shows that the central shoots and one or two of the first tillers are yellow and badly developed, while a few of the youngest tillers and the outer leaves are healthy and green. The maggots, which are $\frac{1}{8}$ in. long, can be found in the hearts of the stunted stems, and a few pupæ may be found behind the outer leaf sheaths.

The first brood of flies appears in April and May, and egg laying takes place shortly afterwards. The females prefer to lay on young plants— those that have not passed the four-leaf stage—and will avoid crops that are strong and in a forward condition. It is advisable, therefore, in districts where the fly is a serious pest, to sow the oats early in March or even, in southern England, in the latter part of February, and to manure them liberally so that they may be strong and well established before the egg laying season commences. Winter oats suffer much less from the spring attack than spring sown-crops.

A second generation of flies lay their eggs on the developing ears and the larvæ feed on the immature grain, causing considerable loss. A third generation lay eggs on grasses, particularly ryegrass, but the damage to the grass itself is inconsiderable. Serious damage may also occur in autumn-sown cereals following a ryegrass ley, the larvæ moving from the grass shoots, after ploughing has taken place, to the corn seedlings. The most certain preventive is to plough out the ley before August—*i.e.* before the egg laying period of the third generation flies.

Partial prevention of attack may be obtained by spraying the crop with DDT emulsion or other suitable insecticides. Similarly some improvement in the condition of a damaged crop can be produced by the use of insecticides (see Ministry of Agriculture, Fisheries and Food Advisory Leaflet No. 110, *Frit Fly*).

**The Stem Eelworm.**—Nematode worms attack many field and garden plants, the chief farm crops affected being oats and potatoes. An oat plant parasitized by the eelworm suffers in much the same way as one attacked by frit fly, but if the stem base be examined it will be found to be swollen or " tulip rooted." As the eelworms are only $\frac{1}{25}$ in. in length their presence should be confirmed by the use of a magnifying glass. Autumn sowing gives the pest more opportunity to cause damage. The old winter varieties, such as Grey Winter were, highly resistant, but some of the new sorts, especially S. 147, are rather susceptible. Eelworm and frit fly attacks frequently occur simultaneously, and where the frit larvæ are discovered the other parasites are apt to be overlooked.

The chief preventive measure is to allow longer intervals between successive crops of oats. (See also Ministry of Agriculture, Fisheries and Food Advisory Leaflet No. 178, *Stem and Bulb Eelworms of Cereals and other crops.*)

**Cereal Root Eelworm.**—This cyst forming species can damage all cereals, but attacks are generally most severe in oats. The young stages attach themselves to the root system and later form cysts which can be seen with a strong hand lens. The life-history is similar to those of the potato and beet species. (See also Ministry of Agriculture, Fisheries and Food Advisory Leaflet No. 421, *Cereal Root Eelworm*).

**Wireworm** is dealt with under Wheat (p. 000). (See also Ministry of Agriculture, Fisheries and Food Advisory Leaflet No. 199, *Wireworm*.)

## BARLEY

Barley has been cultivated from time immemorial, and is believed to be derived from wild grasses native to northern Africa and western Asia. It is widely grown in all subtropical and temperate countries, and large areas are devoted to its cultivation in many parts of the British Isles. It is used for human food and is an important bread cereal in some parts of Europe. In this country barley flour is little used in normal times, but pot and pearl barley are in considerable demand for culinary purposes. An interesting feature in the composition of barley is the nature of its protein matter, which is quite different from the gluten of wheat and goes into solution when boiled in water; this extract, known as barley water, is largely used as a nitrogenous food for infants and invalids. For the feeding of farm stock, barley and its by-products have a very high value. The husk-content of the grain is much lower than that of oats, and this makes the cereal unsurpassed for the feeding of pigs; but it should always be crushed or soaked before use as it is extremely hard, and the animals are apt to swallow it without sufficient mastication. The straw is soft and friable and makes poor litter; it is usually cut when the grain is dead ripe and then contains little material of feeding value; but if it is cut early it approaches oat straw in quality and is at all times superior to wheat straw for feeding purposes. A proportion of the best barley, however, is used for malting, and its degree of suitability for this purpose influences the market value of the crop, the straw being strictly a by-product.

Before the 1939-45 war nearly a half of the home grown crop was used for malting. Production since then has expanded very much and only about 25 per cent. of the crop is so used today. The requirement for malting is a little under one million tons annually.

**Malting of Barley.**—Barley is used largely for malting because of its high percentage of starch. The object of the process is to bring about certain changes that enable the starch to be converted into sugar. When barley is placed in a suitable environment of air, moisture and temperature, a number of ferments or enzymes are produced which convert the material of the endosperm into soluble substances suitable for transference to the embryo for the nourishment of the growing stem and roots. The chief enzyme produced is diastase, which converts starch into sugar, but protein- and cellulose-dissolving ferments are also formed. Maltsters take advantage of this natural process to obtain fermentable sugars from the contents of the grain. The first stage in the conversion of barley into malt is to soak the grain in water for two or three days, so that it may absorb enough moisture to activate its latent life; then it is spread out on the malting floor to encourage its germination. Its temperature is carefully controlled and it is turned over for aeration from time to time for about twelve days, by which time the rootlets have developed and the plumule has grown to about two-thirds of the length of the grain. The sprouted seeds are then removed to a kiln and thoroughly dried; they are then dressed to remove the dry rootlets, which are placed on the market under the name of malt coombs, and the finished malt is ready for marketing or storage.

When the malt is used for brewing it is crushed and mashed in water, and the ferment diastase once more becomes active and much of the remaining starch is brought into solution as sugar. The residue of the grain, consisting of the insoluble carbohydrate and protein materials, is removed and marketed under the name of brewers' wet grains, or, to reduce its weight and facilitate transportation, it may be desiccated and placed on the market as dry grains. A quarter of barley (448 lb.) will produce about 336 lb. of malt, which should yield 80 to 100 lb. of soluble material or brewers' extract.

**Quality of Barley.**—The quality of barley for malting purposes is related to the yield and quality of extract from a given weight of the grain. As the amount of the extract depends on the carbohydrate content, and varies inversely with the proportion of oil and protein, the best samples possess a maximum of starchy material and show the least possible flintiness: the grain should be plump and the skin fine and wrinkled. Actually a nitrogen content of above 1.6 per cent. on the dry matter (equivalent to 10 per cent. of protein) so detracts from the value of the grain that much barley is now bought subject to a nitrogen test. The colour of the barley is also important, as dark coloured grains can be used only in the production of dark coloured beers and stouts, while for pale ale a bright colour is necessary; and as light barleys are somewhat scarce they always command a higher price. Red ends to the grain indicate that the crop was cut before it was ripe. As barley has to be germinated and a solution of extract prepared from the malt, it is essential that it should be in a sound, mature condition with a high germination capacity. It should be carefully dressed so that it contains no broken or damaged grains and no foreign matter. If the crop is severely treated in threshing, owing to the concave being set too close to the drum, the grains are frequently broken or skinned. Broken grains die and form a medium for mould growth, but they can be removed by modern machinery. Grain that is skinned or that has the skin loosened, however, is very objectionable, as these conditions lead to abnormal absorption of moisture during malting. The threshing, then, should be carefully performed and the grain well screened if it is to realise a good price. It is almost needless to state that any heating and weathering that detract from the appearance and odour of the sample will have a serious influence on the marketability of the crop. Barley varieties should be kept strictly pure, because in the malting process it is essential to have a uniform sample; it has been found that different sorts of barley do not germinate at the same rates and have to receive different treatments; mixed samples are difficult to malt and never produce satisfactory results.

From the farmer's point of view a variety must produce quantity as well as quality; but most of the best sorts in wide cultivation are not only capable of producing good yields but of securing the highest awards at the brewers' exhibitions. It is a fallacy that quality can only be obtained when the crop is cultivated on impoverished soil that has a restricting action on the growth and yield.

In some of the Scandinavian varieties, some of which are notably high yielding with very strong straw, the quality, from the point of view of the British maltster, is less satisfactory.

**Varieties of Barley.**—The races of barley that are cultivated are: (1) six-row barley; (2) bere or four-row barley; and (3) two-row barley.

The barley ear has three spikelets at each node and the groups of spikelets are arranged alternately on opposite sides of the rachis or main stem. In the six-row and four-row varieties all the spikelets produce grains. In the two-row varieties the central spikelet only produces a grain, the side florets producing only stamens.

It is probable that the six-row race of barley is a very ancient one. In the varieties cultivated many years ago the straw was short and strong and the ears very compact; the grain was irregularly shaped, poorly filled, and, when grown in our climate, poor in colour, and generally unsatisfactory for brewing purposes. The race was extremely hardy and was sometimes grown as a catch crop, being sown in autumn and cut for soiling purposes in spring, or it might be folded for stock. Much of the barley that is imported, whether for feeding or malting, from California, North Africa and Persia, belongs to the six-row type. *Prefect*, a six-row variety bred by Dr. Bell at Cambridge, was introduced in 1944. It was not widely adopted and has gone out of cultivation. It stood well and resembled most six-row varieties in having fewer ears per plant than is the case with two-row barleys, but it had a greater number of grains per head.

Bere or four-row barley has all the florets fertile but only two regular rows of grains, the remaining four rows being irregularly placed on the lax ear in such a way as to give it the appearance of having four rows only. The race is still cultivated but to a small extent under the severe climatic conditions of north-west Scotland and northern Europe. The grain has the inferior malting qualities of the six-row type; it is used as a food for stock and to some extent in the manufacture of alcohol, but it is not good enough for brewing. Bere may be autumn sown and used as a catch crop for spring fodder, either alone or in a mixture with other autumn sown species.

The two-row barleys are by far the most widely cultivated in Britain, and are the sorts used in the best barley growing districts for the production of grain of the finest malting quality. These barleys may be broadly

PLATE 32

BARLEY

*B.* RIKA

*A.* PROCTOR

*National Institute of Agricultural Botany*

divided into winter and spring types, the former requiring vernalisation by cold temperature as with winter wheat before they can form ears.

True winter barleys are little cultivated in comparison to spring types and only one variety, Pioneer, is currently recommended (but see the latest National Institute of Agricultural Botany Leaflet, No. 10, *Barley*). In the milder parts of the country, especially near the coast in the South-East and South, a considerable area of one or other of the spring sorts of barley is sown during the late autumn or winter. In very hard winters this may be frost damaged and may need re-sowing in the spring.

For many years during the last century the spring barley crop was represented by the famous Spratt, Archer and Chevalier types. The renowned Goldthorpe was first introduced in 1889. Between the two wars the most important varieties were Spratt-Archer and Plumage-Archer, both excellent varieties which were a great improvement on what had been used before and greatly prized for malting purposes. The history of the development of the barley crop over the last century is a fascinating one. The reader is referred to two excellent books on the subject by E. S. Beavan and H. Hunter respectively.[1]

Just before the 1939 war, certain of the Scandinavian barley varieties, notably Kenia, began to be cultivated. While of high yield and stiff straw, these introductions found favour with but few of our maltsters. Newer varieties from the continent, especially from Scandinavia, have continued to be of value for the production of feeding grain. Their stiff straw and high yield make such varieties particularly suited for cultivation on rich land where a malting sample is unlikely to be produced.

In 1953, Proctor (Kenia × Plumage-Archer) was first introduced. Its high yield, moderately stiff straw and good malting quality quickly made it a most popular variety. At the time of writing over 75 per cent. of all barley grown in England is the Proctor variety (Plate 32).

Mildew is one of the common fungus diseases of barley which can cause a considerable loss of yield in seasons which favour this disease. The plant breeder has now been able to incorporate mildew resistance into commercial useful barley varieties. The first commercial introduction into Britain of a mildew resistant variety was in 1960: this marks another milestone in the development of improved barley varieties.

Currently recommended varieties are listed in the National Institute of Agricultural Botany Leaflet No. 10, *Barley*.

## The Cultivation of Barley

**Soil and Climate.**—Barley can be grown under a wide range of soil and climatic conditions, the only frequent cause of failure being soil acidity; but all conditions do not give equally good barley for

[1] E. S. Beavan, *Barley*, Duckworth 1947.
 H. Hunter, *The Barley Crop*, Crosby Lockwood 1952.

malting purposes. The crop for malting is cultivated most largely in the better parts of the country, and the finest samples are obtained from a limited number of districts. Probably the best barley is grown in Norfolk, Suffolk and Cambridgeshire, but there are a number of belts in different parts, mostly bordering on the sea coast, that give almost equal results in yield and quality. Of these the best known are Fife, East Lothian and Berwickshire in Scotland, and in England, East Yorks, Lincolnshire, the southern chalk belt and Taunton Vale in Somerset. Small areas in South Devon have also produced prize malting samples. In Britain, then, the barley districts are the eastern and southern counties, which are the regions of maximum sunshine and moderate rainfall. Considering the temperature of these districts during the growing season, it is found that where the rainfall is almost constant, as along the east coast, the cooler the temperature the greater the yield. Although the barley districts are relatively dry, the biggest yields are obtained when the rainfall is above average, but not excessive; in very wet seasons the yield is reduced, and rain during ripening and harvest time injures the quality. A high rainfall in June, followed by a dry July and August, produces excellent results; but if sowing is delayed by wet weather both yield and quality will suffer, for late sowing brings about an increase in the nitrogen-content of the grain. Seasons that are hot and dry throughout produce pinched, hard and inferior samples. The best soils are light calcareous loams, and no great depth is required. These may be naturally poor, provided that fertilizers are used generously. In past times the chief means to the maintenance of the fertility of typical barley land was the folding of sheep receiving oilcake or other high-protein concentrate. With the decline of sheep folding, barley growers now rely mainly on fertilizers. In East Anglia, however, where barley and sugar beet are now the main light land crops, the sugar beet tops, either folded off or ploughed in, play a part of some importance. The type of light gravelly soil that " burns " is unsatisfactory, since prematurely ripened grain is unsuitable for malting. Probably the best barley is grown on the Chalk, Tertiary and Recent deposits, and it is seldom that a good sample is obtained from heavy or high conditioned soil that is suitable for wheat, or from peaty soil. In dry seasons, however, good yields and good samples are obtained from medium and strong loams. It is essential that the soil should not be acid, otherwise barley will not thrive; indeed, it may die out entirely.

Some years after the last war both the acreage of barley and the area where the crop was cultivated began to expand. Barley is now grown more extensively than ever before and this has resulted in some reduction in the area sown to oats. The increased production is of course used for feeding purposes. Higher yields from modern barley varieties than from oats are possible in many areas, even in the west, and the crop will generally stand better.

**Place in Rotation.**—On the lightest soils, barley commonly follows crops such as roots and kale, but on heavier land it usually succeeds a cereal, normally wheat.  On thin, light soil sheep-folding leaves the upper layer impregnated with manure, consolidated by the treading of the animals, and in excellent condition for the cereal crop that is to follow. In good districts where the land is in high condition the feeding-off of a root crop is likely to leave the soil too rich, when the succeeding barley will be liable to lodge, and the grain will be nitrogenous and dark in colour.  If barley has to be grown under these conditions a strong strawed variety should be selected, yield not quality being the objective.

Probably the finest samples of barley are grown not after roots but after another straw crop.  In this way the first crop removes the excessive richness, and the barley, feeding upon a controlled quantity of soil nitrates, tends to be of a more starchy nature and of better colour;  the sample is also more even because the inequalities of manuring produced by the sheep feeding are mostly removed by the first crop.  With efficient weed control and with adequate dressings of properly balanced fertilizers, several successive crops of barley can be grown with success.

**Preparation and Seeding.**—The nature of the preparation depends on the condition of the soil;  but on land that tends to become poached by the treading of sheep or the carting of roots it is desirable to plough early, so that the furrows are exposed to frost and thaw and the detrimental effect of the puddling is removed.  On light land, where the texture is not injured by sheep, ploughing can be performed any time before it is necessary to prepare the ground for sowing.  Barley is generally believed to do best on a very fine and moderately deep seed bed, and this should be prepared by dragging, harrowing and rolling as often as is necessary.  It is in the driest areas that the greatest attention must be given to seed bed preparation.  A rough tilth or an uneven depth of sowing may result in delayed germination of some of the seed, and the resulting crop, containing a proportion of unripe ears, will yield an unsatisfactory sample for malting. On light land in dry areas excessive or ill timed cultivation may lead to drying out of the seed bed with the consequence of patchy germination. The grain is drilled at the rate of 1 to $1\frac{1}{2}$ cwt. (2 to 3 bushels) per acre in England, and $1\frac{1}{4}$ to 2 cwt. ($2\frac{1}{2}$ to 4 bushels) in Scotland.  The drills should not be more than 7 in. apart, otherwise there is a risk of an increase in the nitrogen content of the crop.  When the drilling is completed the field is given a harrowing and finally rolled.

Barley has a shorter period of growth than the other cereals, and in a late season crops can be obtained from seed put in as late as May.  Nevertheless the best crops and the finest samples are got when seeding takes place in early March, or even in late January or February on light land in coastal areas where there is little risk of frost damage;  indeed, it is best to sow as soon as a satisfactory tilth can be secured, provided there is no risk of the growth being subsequently checked by severe frost. When winter barley is grown, it is sown in the same manner as wheat.

In parts of East Anglia many farmers sow part of their barley area with ordinary spring varieties, in October or December. October sowing permits the crop to be established before the winter, but liable to all the winter frosts. December sowing results in the crop emerging sometimes during February generally. Whilst " on the seed ", the seedling is rather more frost hardy than it is when weaned. In the milder parts of the country the severe weather will often be over before the latter stage is reached. November sowings are less likely to prove successful. If the winter turns out to be severe, the plants may not survive, but in a normal season they do well and produce an early crop, usually of excellent quality and good yield.

**Manuring.**—When barley is grown on land in high condition, especially where a root crop has been folded off such land, it is seldom necessary to apply any fertilizer. In other circumstances it is usual to apply fertilizer, usually in the form of a compound for convenience.

Barley requires adequate amounts of phosphate and of potash but the amount of nitrogen will depend on whether the crop is intended for malting or for the highest yield irrespective of malting quality. It will also depend on the nature of the preceding crop.

It is usual to apply between $1\frac{1}{2}$ and $2\frac{1}{2}$ cwt. per acre of superphosphate (30-50 units $P_2O_5$) depending on whether the soil is deficient in this element or not. It is usual to apply rather more phosphate in the wetter north and west of the country than in the east and south.

Adequate potash is especially necessary for malting barley on naturally potash deficient land. Between $\frac{1}{2}$-$\frac{2}{3}$ cwt. per acre of muriate of potash is a usual dressing (30-40 units $K_2O$). This may be increased to $\frac{3}{4}$ cwt. or 50 units where the soil is very deficient in potash.

The amount of nitrogen to use will vary from nothing on good land after, say, a clovery ley to $3\frac{1}{2}$ cwt. per acre of sulphate of ammonia (70 units N) for a stiff strawed variety for feeding, grown as a second cereal in the south east part of the country.

In arable farming systems barley for malting as a first cereal may receive from nil-$1\frac{1}{2}$ cwt. sulphate of ammonia or equivalent nitrate fertilizer. As a second cereal it may receive $1\frac{1}{2}$-$2\frac{1}{2}$ cwt. per acre (30-50 units N). For feeding quality these quantities may be increased by 1 cwt. (20 units N).

Moderate amounts of fertilizer nitrogen do not necessarily cause an increase in the proportion of nitrogen in the grain; in fact, the reverse is the case in most circumstances on typical light barley soils.

It usually pays to combine drill the phosphate and potash, and on good seed beds on medium and heavy land all the nitrogen as well. Damage to germination may occur if all the fertilizer, especially heavy rates of nitrogen are combine drilled into light or dry seed beds. In any event the nitrogen should all be put into the seed bed. Delayed application of nitrogen is likely to increase the proportion of nitrogen in the grain, so lowering the malting quality.

Farmyard manure is unsuitable for barley because of its high nitrogen content and the difficulty in securing its uniform distribution.

**After-cultivation.**—The cultivations carried out between seeding and harvesting barley are very similar to those for the other cereals. The land is usually rolled when the plants are a few inches high, and a harrowing may be given to loosen the surface tilth if necessary and to suppress annual weeds. Spraying for weed control is commonly practised. Correct timing of the spraying is important and depends on the particular weed-killer being used (see p. 127). Weed competition can seriously affect both yield and quality.

**Harvesting.**—Barley is allowed to become dead ripe before it is cut. When this state of maturity has been reached, the ears tend to bend over (some varieties more than others), the individual grains are hard, with pale yellow wrinkled skins, and the straw is practically dry. If the crop is cut too soon an uneven sample results, and the maltster is unable to obtain that uniformity of germination so necessary to the production of high class malt. It is interesting to reflect that at one time much barley was cut with a scythe or mower and " made " in the same way as hay. It was exposed in the swath and turned from time to time so as to benefit by the bleaching action of the sun, and finally carried and stacked in the loose state. With the advent of the binder and the rise in cost of labour, the crop began to be cut and bound in the usual way, with no serious detriment to the quality. Some barley, especially in the west and north on small farms, is still harvested by binder. The majority, however, is combined. Direct threshing by combine harvester eliminates the risk of sprouting or discoloration in the stook, but there is rather more risk of loss of ears in the field if high winds precede harvest. Close control of temperature is necessary in the artificial drying of barleys for malting. In the early days of combining many samples were seriously damaged through the use of poor types of tray dryers which did not permit of proper temperature control. With a modern flow dryer and strictad herence to the maximum temperature indicated by the table on page 170, no damage whatever need occur.

If the barley has been harvested by binder and good weather follows, the crop is generally ready for carting out of the shock in about a week, but during periods of wet weather carting is greatly delayed. The straw is of a soft nature and holds rain readily, and the grain, which is unprotected by chaff, becomes dark coloured and poor in appearance. When the crop has been used to nurse clover seeds the bottoms of the sheaves frequently contain an abundance of soft green herbage, and the drying period in the stook is thus greatly prolonged.

Barley is stacked in the usual way, and if it is secured in a dry, sound condition its colour generally improves very considerably before threshing takes place. If, however, the corn is badly secured or in a wet condition, it changes in the stack to a dark inferior colour and in bad cases becomes mouldy. It seldom comes out of the stack having the same quality as when it was put in: it either improves or deteriorates.

**Yield.**—The weight of a bushel of barley varies a great deal. A good sample should weight 56 lb., although prize winning barleys are heavier. The bushel weight is indicative of the plumpness and fullness of the grains, light weights being got when these are thin and contain a high proportion of husk. The average yield is about 21 cwt. to the acre, and about the same weight of straw. The yield of grain may often reach or exceed 40 cwt. under good conditions, and crops of 60 cwt. and more have been recorded. The British average yield is second only to that of Denmark.

## Fungoid Diseases

**Loose Smut.**—Barley suffers from the attacks of a fungus which causes symptoms similar to those of Loose Smut of wheat. The ear emerges covered with the black spores of the disease in place of grain. It cannot be controlled by dressing the seed with the normal chemical dressings. Some varieties are more liable to this disease than others.

If a stock of barley becomes seriously infected it should not be used again for seed purposes. A hot water steep treatment is used by some merchants in order to maintain clean nuclear stocks.

**Covered Smut.**—In this disease the ears issuing from their sheaths are not covered with sooty powder, but the grains, though held together by the skin, contain a mass of black spores enclosed by the thin adherent chaff. The grains remain whole until threshing takes place, when the concussion breaks them up and the spores are liberated. Not only do the spores infest healthy barley grains, but they discolour the whole sample and reduce the market value of the crop.

The transmission of covered smut to the next crop can be prevented by dressing with a seed disinfectant, as in the treatment of wheat for the prevention of bunt.

**Leaf-stripe.**—This disease, produced by the attack of *Helminthosporium gramineum*, causes the leaves of the young plants to wither and die off, and an examination reveals longitudinal dark coloured stripes on the laminæ. Affected plants produce blind ears and the loss is therefore much greater than is occasioned by the reduced assimilating surface. Another species, known as *Helminthosporium teres*, produces spots on the leaves, the condition being known as net blotch; the disease does not occur regularly throughout the crop, but in isolated patches; it does not cause blindness.

Leaf-stripe can be controlled by the mercuric dust methods of seed disinfection already described.

**Mildew.**—Barley can be considerably affected by powdery mildew in some seasons. There is no direct counter for the disease. Certain varieties, however, are resistant.

## Insect Pests

**The Gout Fly (Ribbon-footed Corn Fly)** is a pest that can cause considerable damage to barley and also to wheat. The flies lay their eggs on the plants, and when the larvæ hatch out they eat their way into the stem below the ear while it is enshrouded by its surrounding leaves. They eat a groove down the axis to the first node. which is so characteristic that it is quite sufficient to confirm the nature of the attack. The plants become stunted and " gouted " in appearance and fail to produce grain.

As egg-laying takes place in May and June, and again in September, either autumn or spring sown plants may be attacked. In districts where the fly is troublesome it is therefore advisable to sow winter wheat and barley late, and the spring crops should be put in early so that they will be well established before egg laying commences. If a crop is obviously suffering badly from an attack it may be stimulated into producing a certain amount of grain, which may pay for the labour of harvesting, by giving it a quick-acting nitrogenous dressing; but where the ears are practically all grainless it should be fed off by sheep. See also Ministry of Agriculture, Fisheries and Food Advisory Leaflet, No. 174, *Gout Fly*.

**Cereal Eelworm.**—Barley may be attacked by this nematode but is rather less susceptible than is the oat crop. Avoiding cereal cropping, especially with oats is the normal method of reducing an infestation; and barley should not be taken for two or three years. See Ministry of Agriculture, Fisheries and Food Advisory Leaflet, No. 421, *Cereal Root Eelworm*.

**Wireworm** may also attack barley but control can be achieved by using a suitable dual purpose seed dressing, containing both insecticide and fungicide.

## RYE

It is probable that our cultivated varieties of rye were obtained originally from a wild perennial species found in eastern Europe and Asia Minor. Rye is used to a considerable extent as a bread cereal in parts of N. Europe, and resembles wheat in having grain easily separated from the chaff in threshing, and in yielding corresponding offals on milling. In this country it is cultivated as a forage crop, and also for its grain and straw. Rye straw is longer, stronger, and wears better than the straw of wheat. It is therefore valued for thatching and packing. Rye bread is little used in this country, much of the grain produced is used for the manufacture of a form of rye biscuit.

**Varieties.**—At one time the rye grown in this country was of a " native English type ". While some of these stocks were suitable for sowing in the spring, the majority were winter types. Greatly improved grain varieties were introduced from the Continent, principally from Scandinavia and Germany just before and again after the last war.  The older English stocks then became less easy to obtain and of doubtful value, often being mixed in type or misnamed continental varieties.

In general the English type was more leafy and suited to forage production while the continental types were both stronger and shorter in the straw and produced considerably higher grain yields.  For many years the variety King II was grown.  This gave way to Petkins Short Straw which gave higher yields and had stronger straw.  Today there is an increasing demand for forage rye for early spring grazing and special varieties principally from the Continent are becoming available for this purpose.  (See N.I.A.B. Leaflet No. 12 *Rye* for current recommended varieties).

Rye is normally a cross-pollinated diploid plant but tetraploid forms have been introduced commercially.  These two types should not be grown in close proximity to each other since the diploid pollen can cause the flowers of the tetraploid plants to fail to form grain.

## Cultivation of Rye

**Soil and Climate.**—Rye is a drought resistant plant which thrives under a great variety of conditions; it is productive upon almost any class of soil and very resistant to acid conditions.  When grown for grain on good soil it is usually less profitable than the other cereals, and its cultivation is therefore confined to districts of poor, dry, light land that produce inferior wheat and oats.  It also succeeds on peaty soils and on the poorer sorts of black fen.  This does not mean that rye does best on poor soils: it does best on good loams, which, however, yield more profit under other crops.  It has the additional advantages that in late districts it enables an early start to be made with the harvest, and that it is considerably more winter hardy than wheat.  When rye is grown on good land it is mostly cultivated for forage purposes, and it is, on account of its earliness, extremely valuable for feeding off or for soiling.  The plant must be consumed at the right stage, for it very soon becomes fibrous and unpalatable.

**Place in Rotation.**—When rye is grown for seed it takes the place of any of the other cereals in the rotation, and is usually taken after roots or clover.  When grown as a catch crop, as it often is, it frequently follows another white crop, is sown in the early autumn for feeding off in the spring before the ryegrass leys are ready for grazing, and may be followed by roots or kale.

**Preparation and Sowing.**—The seed bed is prepared as for wheat, and the grain is drilled in the usual way.  From 1 to $1\frac{1}{2}$ cwt. (say 2 to 3 bushels) is required to sow an acre, and seeding should take place from two to three weeks before wheat sowing commences.

**Manuring.**—The old native types of rye are rather unresponsive to fertilizers and prone to lodge; but the new varieties may be treated about as generously as oats without risk of lodging. Short strawed varieties such as King II have been shown to respond well to spring applications of nitrogen, and quantities up to 3 cwt. (60 units N.) per acre of ammonium sulphate have been used with profit. Except on good land it is usual to apply 1 to 2 cwt. superphosphate (20 to 40 units $P_2O_5$) and often potash as well. About $\frac{1}{2}$ to $\frac{3}{4}$ cwt. per acre (30 to 45 units $K_2O$) of muriate of potash would be an appropriate dressing on light potash deficient land. In many instances a suitable phosphate-potash compound would be combine drilled.

**Harvesting.**—Cutting takes place about a fortnight before wheat harvest commences, which is about the beginning of August in medium early districts. The crop may be harvested by combine in the usual way or cut by binder. In the latter event, the crop is bound and stooked in the usual way and, as the straw contains very little sap, carrying can take place a week or so after cutting. When high quality rye straw is required for special purposes it may be cut before the ear has filled, then dried and used: this avoids the threshing process which damages the stems considerably. Where it is grown as a forage crop it must be cut early—before it shoots—as towards the end of its growing period it becomes hard, dry and unpalatable.

**Yield.**—The average weight of a bushel of rye is about 58 lb., but much depends on the variety, the winter sorts weighing up better. Common yields are 16 to 20 cwt. (4 to 5 qr.) of grain and 30 cwt. or more of straw per acre. Yields of grain of over 30 cwt. may be obtained on good land.

## DREDGE CORN

The term *dredge corn* is sometimes applied to mixtures of cereals and pulse crops—*e.g.* oats with beans, peas or vetches or all three (see p. 223). It is also used for a mixture of oats and barley, which is common in Cornwall and occasionally grown elsewhere. It is cultivated for the production of feed corn and on average may produce a rather higher yield, from a given acreage, than would be obtained from the two species cultivated separately. Care is necessary in the choice of varieties so that the two components may ripen together.

The corn is sown at the usual time for spring cereals, at the average rate of 4 bushels per acre, the proportion of oats being half, two-thirds or three-quarters according to the local soil and climatic conditions and the use to which the crop is to be put. It is manured and harvested like other cereals. The yield will vary according to the type of soil, but a normal crop should give between 20 and 30 cwt. of grain per acre. Yields over 2 tons may be secured on occasion.

## LODGING IN CEREALS

All cereals and hay crops are subject to lodging. Apart from the attack of the eye-spot fungus, which has already been discussed (p. 216), lodging may be caused by over luxuriant or ill balanced development, by rainstorms or by a combination of those causes. The effect of lodging on the yield and quality of the crop depends on the stage of development at which it occurs. Rain and wind may cause a winter proud crop to lodge when the straw is still growing and is therefore still capable, by bending at the nodes, of restoring the ears to an upright position, and in such a case there is no serious damage except to any under-sown seeds. Lodging at a later stage, when the straw has lost its power of growth, has much more serious results, because the ears do not mature satisfactorily when lying on the ground, and even if the crop can be harvested, there is a loss of yield and a high proportion of shrunken grains; moreover the condition is often rendered worse by the development of second growth— that is, by the growth of new shoots from the bases of the fallen stems. Lodging at the end of the season when the grian is almost full and mature may have little if any effect on the yield; indeed the lodged crops often outyield the standing crops in the same district, but the subsequent difficulties in harvesting may adversely affect the quality of the grain.

Lodging is generally caused by wind and rain, and the varieties most affected are those which are characteristically weak in the straw—usually because the diameter of the culm is small in proportion to its length— or are lacking in root development. In the former case knuckling over generally occurs at the lower internodes; in the latter the plant may be partly uprooted so that it topples over at the ground. Certain fungi attack the base of the stems and make them unable to bear the weight of the ears. Again, repeated pressure of the elements may bend the straw right over without any breakage taking place.

The use of too much seed on rich land may cause lodging. In this case the lower parts of the plants are so dense and shaded that they become drawn and weakened and unable to withstand wind and rain or support a heavy ear. It is noteworthy that excessive seeding may be due to the use of small sized seed at normal sowing rates. On rich land it is helpful to adopt wider spacing between the rows of grain.

Poverty of a particular nutrient may weaken the plants and produce lodging, but there is no evidence that the straw is strengthened by applications of potash and phosphate in addition to what is required to make a balanced fertilizer. A reasonable amount of nitrogen fertilizer, by promoting the vigour and well being of the plant, will reduce the risk of lodging, and it is only where excessive amounts of nitrogen are used that the straw is weakened, ripening is delayed and liability to lodging is increased. Of course, even strong strawed cereals, seeded correctly and given the correct manuring, are likely to go down when grown after clover rich pastures in a wet year.   Obviously the better plan here is to grow not cereals but potatoes, roots or kale in the first season.

When a cereal crop has " swung " it can generally be harvested with a binder cutting one way;  but if the condition is rather bad, corn lifters may have to be fitted to the cutter bar.   The combine harvester, fitted with a special pick-up mechanism, can harvest crops that are beyond the capacity of the binder.   When too badly laid for machine cutting, the harvesting may be carried out with the scythe, which is handy for dealing with patches of corn that are lodged in all directions.   For the worst cases, where straw and ears are practically flat on the ground, the reaping hook has the advantage of enabling the straw to be eased or pulled up with the point before it is cut with the blade.   But under present conditions wherever the acreage of cereals is large in relation to the number of workers, it is seldom practicable to do much, if any, harvesting by hand.

# CHAPTER 10

# THE POTATO

THE potato (*Solanum tuberosum*) was introduced from South America in the sixteenth century, but in those early days it was regarded rather as a curiosity than as an article of commerce, and it was not until about two centuries later that it was cultivated to any extent on a field scale. The potato has been one of the most important food crops in the earlier history of the British Isles. For an examination of this the reader is referred to *The History and Social Influence of the Potato* by R. N. Salaman, Cambridge University Press, 1949.

As a source of human food the potato is the most valuable crop grown in this country; it is relatively cheap, and its dietetic value is considerably higher than was for a long time supposed. As a food for stock, especially pigs, it is very valuable and gives a high production in terms of energy per acre—about twice as much as a cereal. In this country, however, only diseased or damaged or unmarketable potatoes are used for stock feeding in substantial amounts. Boiled potatoes will develop acidity and ensile quite satisfactorily if they are packed tightly in a pit, tank or other suitable container. The silage can be used for pigs and poultry when fresh potatoes are not available.

The potato crop has, however, a number of disadvantages. Its bulky nature makes it costly to handle and market, and for this reason large-scale production has in the past tended to concentrate in areas not too far from cities. Again, even where a ready market was at hand, the large number of workers required for timely planting and harvesting restricted cultivation (on a large scale) to districts where casual labour was available. Mechanical planters are now widely used and on suitable soils complete harvesters work satisfactorily. The labour required by this crop has been greatly reduced by these developments. The crop was formerly very speculative, the yield being variable and the demand very inelastic, so that in years of high yield the market was glutted and prices fell to an unprofitable level. Both average yield and prices are still variable but an assured market for sound ware is provided by the Potato Marketing Board, though the grower cannot always sell at the time of his choice.

**Quality of Potatoes.**—The farmer, of course, requires a variety that will produce the greatest possible yield per acre, but he must also consider the buyer's point of view or his crop will not meet with a ready sale. Apart from yield, the most important points are keeping quality and resistance to disease. Potatoes have to be stored for considerable periods, and it is disastrous if a large proportion decays or deteriorates in the clamp or store. Not only should the variety be capable of resisting disease and decay in storage, but it should withstand the effects of the many and serious pests that beset it in the field, the most devastating of which are blight, wart disease and the virus or degeneration diseases. No varieties in general cultivation are immune from blight, though many are resistant in greater or less degree. Attempts have been made by hybridisation with certain wild species of *Solanum* to create commercial varieties with immunity to all the common strains of the fungus, but so far without success. As regards wart disease, it is fortunate that many completely immune varieties have been produced, so that it is possible to grow healthy crops on land that is heavily infested with the disease. For general economy it is also advisable to obtain varieties that develop their tubers at a suitable depth below the surface; if they protrude above the soil they become greened by the light and are then difficult to sell, while if too deep they are difficult to harvest and, apart from the numbers that are sliced and damaged, many may be left in the ground to become a source of trouble in the following crops. The potato is an important cleaning crop in the rotation of many farms, and a variety that develops a large amount of surface growth and leafage is most efficient as a smotherer of weeds, and most likely to leave the soil in a clean condition. There are varieties that cannot satisfactorily be cut for seed as they do not grow well from cut sets, while at the other extreme there are potatoes that give excellent yields when cut to a single eye. The use of cut seed is rarely practised in this country.

From the point of view of the consumer the cooking quality of the variety is most important. In Britain, white fleshed sorts that become meally on boiling are generally the most popular for the ordinary domestic trade. On the Continent yellow fleshed potatoes possessing a waxy texture are preferred. Varieties that produce either very large or very small tubers are not in demand, and varieties that are irregular in shape or deep in the eye, and are consequently difficult to peel without occasioning considerable loss, are never popular. The colour of the skin varies through a wide range—purple, red, pink, red-eyed, russet and white all being common, but colour does not matter much when the other qualities of the variety are satisfactory. The shape may be round, oval or kidney, but this is of little importance in the domestic trade provided the tubers are regular. For the chipping trade, which absorbs an enormous tonnage, the potato should make a firm chip that turns golden brown on frying and stays firm. Quality for processing will depend on both variety and storage conditions. Very low temperatures during storage will lead to an increase of reducing sugars which causes chips or crisps to fry dark brown. Potatoes for mechanical peeling should also be without sunken eyes and of regular shape—preferably round—so that they can be peeled without undue waste. Blemished tubers that require hand trimming are greatly disliked.

Apart from varietal differences, eating quality appears to be determined more by the soil and climate than by manuring. Quality is best in dry districts and in dry years, dryness and warmth having the most beneficial effect towards the end of the growing season. For good quality the potatoes must be fully mature, and poor quality may result when the growing season is interrupted by blight or early frost. Loam and light soils give better quality than those that are heavy or peaty. The quality after corn is likely to be better than after newly ploughed ley.

**Varieties.**—A considerable number of different kinds of potatoes are now on the market. In years past potato varieties tended to be rather short lived, but many sorts popular to-day —Majestic and King Edward, for example—have been in cultivation for many decades. One reason is that new varieties have been subjected to increasingly severe tests and another is that certification schemes for seed crops do much to control virus infection. A variety consists, strictly speaking, of a great number of parts of the same individual mother plant, and the old view was that degeneration was the inevitable consequence of the old age of this plant or, in other words, the result of continued vegetative reproduction. It is, however, now certain that degeneration is, in the main, not a loss of constitutional vigour but is due to the accumulation in the stock of virus diseases (see p. 272).

When new varieties are being raised the chief objects kept in view are the production of a good yield, resistance or immunity to disease, good shape and colour with good keeping and cooking qualities. The commonest way to raise new sorts used to be to sow the seed from a self set potato berry. In the case of organised plant breeding, crosses are made between selected parents by emasculating the plant on which the berries are to be grown and impregnating the stigmatic surface with pollen from the other parent. When the berry has matured, the seeds, which may number two or three hundred, are sown. The seedlings which develop exhibit many forms and characters differing from the parent types. The great majority are as a rule inferior or unsuitable: some develop long stolons and few tubers; most are poor croppers and many are quite useless because of their irregular shape and unattractive appearance; only a few are of sufficient merit to justify their propagation until they can be given a fair trial on a field scale. A number of experimenters are using certain wild species of potatoes for crossing purposes, with the object of imparting hardiness and disease resisting capacity to our cultivated sorts, and it is likely that a much wider range of varieties will become available in the future.

The different varieties of potatoes are generally classified according to their earliness. There is a gradation from the extreme sorts to the very late maincrops, but (although there are no real dividing lines) potatoes are classed as Earlies, Second Earlies and Maincrops. Sometimes such terms Early Maincrop and Early Second Early, are also used.

The comparative popularity of the numerous varieties under cultivation can perhaps best be deduced from Tables 2 and 3. It can be seen that the majority of the area is taken up by relatively few varieties: Arran Pilot and Home Guard in the case of earlies, and with maincrops by Majestic, King Edward and Kerr's Pink, the latter almost wholly in Scotland. In spite of the introduction of new varieties, none has challenged the popularity of these few which were introduced many years ago.

Descriptions of the morphological characters of varieties grown in this country will be found in *Seed Potatoes* issued by the Dept. of Agriculture for Scotland. Varieties currently recommended for use in England and Wales are listed and described in the National Institute of Agricultural Botany Leaflet No. 3, *Potatoes*.

Descriptions of three of the most popular maincrop varieties are given below:

*Summary of Acreages of Groups*

|  | England and Wales | Scotland | Total | Percentage |
|---|---|---|---|---|
| First Earlies . . | 125,000 | 31,700 | 156,700 | 18 |
| Second Earlies . . | 10,000 | 7,100 | 17,100 | 2 |
| Maincrop . . | 566,000 | 153,000 | 719,000 | 80 |
| Total . | 701,000 | 191,800 | 892,800 | 100 |

*Majestic.*[1]—Tuber: kidney (pear-shaped to long oval); skin white; eyes shallow; flesh white; sprouts faint pink; second growth takes the form of cracking.

Foliage: haulm of medium height, spreading; less rigid than that of British Queen. Leaf and leaflets flat, open and smooth, ashy green; stalks of young leaves with a pink tinge, the colour extending into the midribs; terminal leaflets oval; secondary leaflets fairly numerous, small.

Flower: creamy white, profuse, sometimes with a purplish tinge on the back of the petals; anthers orange; flower stalk long, slightly bronzed; buds dark with green tips.

This variety is immune from wart disease but is susceptible to blackleg, leaf roll and the three common viruses; its tubers are susceptible to blight. It is an early maincrop and is notable because of its heavy cropping capacity. On good land the tubers may be large and coarse; the texture is generally waxy. The seed is often unsatisfactory when cut.

*King Edward VII.*—Tuber: kidney (oval to pear-shaped); skin white, more or less splashed with pink; characteristically smooth on surface; eyes shallow; flesh white; sprouts pink.

[1] Immune from wart disease.

Foliage: haulm erect, tall, branching, tops crowded; stems with a pink tinge; leaves medium green and glossy; leaflets with waved margins, the younger leaflets on top being very small, narrow, numerous, and twisted forward, the last pair fitting round the terminal; secondaries fairly numerous and small.

Flower: red-purple, but seldom formed; buds pink; sepals fairly long; flower stalks short.

The variety is an early maincrop. It is not immune from wart disease and is susceptible to blackleg, leaf roll and virus Y; it is virtually immune from viruses A and X, and mosaic diseases are very uncommon; all the plants carry another virus (para crinkle) which is unimportant. Bolters and wildings are common. Because of its good eating quality and its suitability for the chip trade it is in great demand in many markets and commands a higher price than most other sorts. It does not do well on light dry land—indeed it requires good land and the drills should not be too wide; it does not respond as well as some sorts to extra heavy manuring.

*Red King* is a self-coloured variant of King Edward.

*Kerr's Pink.*[1]—Tuber: round, pink, dented at heel; eyes usually medium but sometimes deep; flesh white; sprouts pink.

Foliage: haulm tall and branching; very vigorous; stem strong, tinged pink.

Flower white and freely formed.

Kerr's Pink is immune from wart disease and virtually immune from virus A. Susceptible to virus Y, but does not suffer severely. Susceptible to blackleg and leaf roll. Tubers susceptible to blight. A heavy cropper of excellent cooking quality and popular in Scottish markets. It keeps exceptionally well, but is rather prone to second growth.

**Selection of Seed.**—As mentioned above, the use of seed tubers with a minimum infection with the virus diseases is important. If an appreciable proportion of the crop is infected by certain of the more virulent of these diseases, the yield will be reduced, often seriously. Some varieties will become infected more readily than others, but most will be useless for seed if grown on in the main ware growing areas for more than one year unless special steps are taken to limit the spread of virus (see below).

In order to maintain healthy stocks of seed for use in the ware growing areas of the country, it is usual to propagate in those parts free or nearly free of the leaf sucking insects, such as aphids, which spread the disease. Thus much of the seed potatoes are grown in Scotland, Ireland and the higher lying parts of north and west England and Wales. The insect chiefly responsible for the spread of virus infection is the peach potato aphid, *Mysus persicae*, commonly called the green fly.

In the case of early varieties many English growers use once-grown seed for the bulk of their planting, since this produces an earlier crop than Scottish seed.

---

[1] Immune from wart disease.

In the northern and elevated districts, where there are few disease spreading insects, it is possible to maintain the vigour of a potato stock by roguing out any plants which show signs of virus disease (see p. 272). But where stocks are badly affected it is generally more profitable to purchase a small amount of really first class stock seed and to propagate it at least a quarter of a mile away from other varieties—say in the middle of a turnip field—so that it will not readily be contaminated. The tubers should be set close together in narrow drills so that a large number of small potatoes may be obtained as seed for the selling crop in the following year.

On all farms where there is a sale for seed potatoes the crops should be rogued during the growing period so that the produce may be certified with regard to purity and health. Early harvesting is desirable, since this prevents late infections from reaching the tubers. Burning off the tops with sulphuric acid or other chemical has the same effect. Special machines for haulm destruction are available.

The useful life of a potato stock may be extended when grown on in the ware producing areas (where the peach potato aphid is often numerous) by careful use of certain insecticides. Frequent application of DDT or of one of the systematic insecticides will limit the spread of viruses X and Y within the treated crop by killing the aphids. Stocks have been maintained with a low virus content for several years by this means when combined with careful roguing.

Approximately two thirds of the ware crops in England and Wales are grown from certified seed, the majority of the balance are planted with once-grown seed.

Government Agricultural Departments have schemes for the official inspection of potato crops during the growing season and the issuing of appropriate seed certificates. The standards that have been adopted in the various parts of the British Isles are approximately the same and alter from time to time in a minor degree. The Scottish standards and designations are as follows:—

|  | Varieties immune from wart disease | Varieties not immune from wart disease |
|---|---|---|
| Designation . . | S.S.[1] (Scot.[2]) | S.S. (Scot.) N.I. |
| Standard . . | 99·95 per cent. pure and true of type and not more than 0·25 per cent. of virus diseases and wildings, including not more than four plants per acre leaf roll, severe mosaic and wildings, and from which all bolters have been removed. | |

[1] Stock seed.
[2] The source of the seed is indicated in the brackets: (Scot.)=Scotland; (E.)= England; (W.)=Wales; (Nor. Ir.)=Northern Ireland; (Eire)=Eire.

| Designation . . | A (Scot.) | A (Scot.) N.I. |
|---|---|---|
| Standard . . | Purity of not less than 99·5 per cent., not more than 1 per cent. virus diseases and wildings, of which not more than 0·5 per cent. may be leaf roll, severe mosaic and wildings. | |
| Designation . . | H (Scot.) | H (Scot.) N.I. |
| Standard . . | Purity of not less than 99·5 per cent. and not more than 3 per cent. of leaf roll, severe mosaic and wildings. | |

There are also certain special grades of seed which are normally retained for seed production purposes in the country of origin. This class of seed is far too valuable for use in the growing of ware crops.

V.T.—Virus tested and issued only in Scotland.

F.S.—Foundation seed, also issued only in Scotland.

S.S.S.—Special Stock Seed, issued only in N. Ireland.

Uncertified seed potatoes may also be sold, and there are special designations within the group:—

Uncertified (English once-grown) and Uncertified (Welsh once-grown) refer to material from crops that have not themselves been certified but have been produced directly from Certified (S.S., A, or H) seed.

Uncertified (English) and Uncertified (Scottish), include any other potatoes sold for seed. Uncertified stocks must, however, be 97 per cent. true to name.

All potato seed must have the size specified at the time. This is ordinarily such as will pass through a $2\frac{1}{4}$ or 2 in. mesh and over a $1\frac{1}{4}$ in.

The southern grower who intends to sell his crop entirely as ware may expect quite satisfactory results from seed that has an H certificate and indeed it may be uneconomic to pay the higher price that S.S. seed commands. Even where H seed is derived from a crop showing the maximum permissible infection (3 per cent.), it is very unlikely that the proportion of infected tubers will be greater than three times this amount —say 9 per cent. Where the infected plants are below 10 per cent. there is no appreciable reduction in yield, a finding that may be explained by the fact that two healthy plants, growing on either side of a diseased one, benefit by the absence of competition. Where, however, the stock in question is intended to provide seed again for a second season, the reduction in yield from the once grown seed may be serious. It follows that a higher grade than H should be purchased if the intention is to plant the produce again.

The size of the seed is a matter of considerable importance, not only with regard to economy in planting but also with a view to the size and number of the tubers that develop in the crop. Before potatoes are

TABLE 2

## POTATO ACREAGE BY VARIETY PLANTED BY REGISTERED PRODUCERS IN 1961

(Data by permission of the Potato Marketing Board)

| | ENGLAND | WALES | ENGLAND AND WALES | SCOTLAND | GREAT BRITAIN |
|---|---|---|---|---|---|
| *First Early* | | | | | |
| Arran Pilot | 39,918 | 3,801 | 43,719 | 7,376 | 51,095 |
| Duke of York | 2,518 | 4 | 2,522 | 1,034 | 3,556 |
| Eclipse | 456 | 5 | 461 | 250 | 711 |
| Epicure | 619 | 7 | 626 | 9,611 | 10,237 |
| Home Guard | 10,847 | 3,221 | 14,068 | 2,781 | 16,849 |
| May Queen | 98 | — | 98 | 9 | 107 |
| Ninetyfold | 539 | 4 | 543 | 12 | 555 |
| Sharpe's Express | 144 | 53 | 197 | 393 | 590 |
| Ulster Chieftain | 5,471 | 76 | 5,547 | 435 | 5,982 |
| Ulster Premier | 4,709 | 987 | 5,696 | 303 | 5,999 |
| Ulster Prince | 8,419 | 111 | 8,530 | 398 | 8,928 |
| Other Varieties | 1,452 | 131 | 1,583 | 358 | 1,941 |
| TOTAL FIRST EARLY | 75,190 | 8,400 | 83,590 | 22,960 | 106,550 |
| | | | | | |
| *Second Early* | | | | | |
| British Queen | 1,076 | 23 | 1,099 | 188 | 1,287 |
| Craigs Royal | 15,532 | 1,548 | 17,080 | 4,382 | 21,462 |
| Great Scot | 1,282 | 6 | 1,288 | 608 | 1,896 |
| Royal Kidney | 53 | — | 53 | 788 | 841 |
| Ulster Dale | 1,266 | 34 | 1,300 | 16 | 1,316 |
| Ulster Ensign | 51 | 7 | 58 | — | 58 |
| Other Varieties | 1,530 | 82 | 1,612 | 1,058 | 2,670 |
| TOTAL SECOND EARLY | 20,790 | 1,700 | 22,490 | 7,040 | 29,530 |
| | | | | | |
| *Maincrop* | | | | | |
| Arran Banner | 1,436 | 330 | 1,766 | 249 | 2,015 |
| Arran Chief | 117 | 5 | 122 | 165 | 287 |
| Arran Consul | 1,248 | 21 | 1,269 | 797 | 2,066 |
| Arran Peak | 4,509 | 45 | 4,554 | 212 | 4,766 |
| Bintje (Muizen) | 885 | — | 885 | 154 | 1,039 |
| Conference | 322 | — | 322 | 77 | 399 |
| Doon Star | 884 | 5 | 889 | 131 | 1,020 |
| Dr. McIntosh | 13,869 | 213 | 14,082 | 1,364 | 15,446 |
| Dunbar Standard | 1,414 | 110 | 1,524 | 134 | 1,658 |
| Gladstone | 250 | 73 | 323 | 26 | 349 |
| Golden Wonder | 22 | 5 | 27 | 4,266 | 4,293 |
| *Carry forward* | 24,956 | 806 | 25,743 | 7,575 | 33,338 |

|  | ENGLAND | WALES | ENGLAND AND WALES | SCOTLAND | GREAT BRITAIN |
|---|---|---|---|---|---|
| *Brought forward* | 24,956 | 806 | 25,743 | 7,575 | 33,338 |
| Kerr's Pink | 390 | 44 | 434 | 20,307 | 20,741 |
| Redskin | 10,117 | 35 | 10,152 | 18,806 | 28,958 |
| King Edward VII | 95,697 | 250 | 95,947 | 13,130 | 109,077 |
| Red King | 8,310 | 101 | 8,411 | 1,195 | 9,606 |
| Majestic | 206,031 | 3,188 | 209,219 | 30,879 | 240,098 |
| Record | 6,023 | 7 | 6,030 | 1,688 | 7,718 |
| Stormont Dawn | 285 | — | 285 | 18 | 303 |
| Ulster Beacon | 420 | 6 | 426 | 1 | 427 |
| Ulster Supreme | 1,414 | 92 | 1,506 | 4 | 1,510 |
| Ulster Torch | 962 | 14 | 976 | 54 | 1,030 |
| Up-to-Date | 131 | 1 | 132 | 684 | 816 |
| Other Varieties | 1,724 | 95 | 1,819 | 629 | 2,448 |
| TOTAL MAINCROP | 356,460 | 4,640 | 361,100 | 94,970 | 456,070 |
| TOTAL ALL VARIETIES | 452,440 | 14,740 | 467,180 | 124,970 | 592,150 |

NOTE: The total area for 1961 in Great Britain was approximately 100,000 acres less than for 1960

TABLE 3

## PROPORTION OF THE TOTAL POTATO ACREAGE IN ENGLAND AND WALES PLANTED WITH THE LEADING VARIETIES

(Data by permission of the Potato Marketing Board)

As % of Total Acreage

| VARIETY | 1957 | 1958 | 1959 | 1960 | 1961 |
|---|---|---|---|---|---|
| *First Early* | 16·9 | 14·1 | 14·9 | 16·9 | 17·9 |
| Arran Pilot | 8·9 | 6·9 | 7·5 | 8·9 | 9·4 |
| Duke of York | 0·7 | 0·5 | 0·5 | 0·5 | 0·6 |
| Home Guard | 2·7 | 2·6 | 2·7 | 3·3 | 3·0 |
| Ulster Chieftain | 1·4 | 1·2 | 1·1 | 1·0 | 1·2 |
| Ulster Premier | 0·8 | 0·8 | 0·8 | 0·9 | 1·2 |
| Ulster Prince | 1·1 | 1·1 | 1·3 | 1·3 | 1·8 |
| *Second Early* | 2·8 | 2·1 | 2·4 | 3·4 | 4·8 |
| Craigs Royal | 2·3 | 1·6 | 1·8 | 2·7 | 3·7 |
| *Maincrop* | 80·3 | 83·8 | 82·7 | 79·7 | 77·3 |
| Arran Banner | 1·4 | 1·3 | 1·2 | 0·7 | 0·4 |
| Arran Peak | 2·0 | 1·7 | 1·6 | 1·3 | 1·0 |
| Dr. McIntosh | 3·2 | 3·2 | 3·1 | 3·1 | 3·0 |
| Redskin | 2·5 | 2·6 | 2·6 | 2·2 | 2·2 |
| King Edward (incl. Red King) | 26·8 | 25·7 | 20·2 | 20·3 | 22·3 |
| Majestic | 40·9 | 44·9 | 49·1 | 47·9 | 44·8 |
| Record | 0·7 | 1·0 | 1·2 | 1·1 | 1·3 |

marketed it is customary to sort the crop into three grades—namely, ware, which is sold for culinary purposes; seed, which is reserved for planting; and chats, which are usually fed, along with damaged tubers, to stock. The ware is removed from the rest by passing the tubers over a $1\frac{5}{8}, 1\frac{3}{4}, 1\frac{7}{8}$, 2 or $2\frac{1}{4}$ in. riddle,[1] and another riddle of about $1\frac{1}{4}$ in. mesh is used to remove the chats from the seed. It is obvious that the larger the mesh of the first riddle the greater will be the proportion of seed sized tubers and the smaller the amount of ware. The shape of the variety must obviously be taken into account; kidney varieties of a given weight will pass through a sieve that would hold back round tubers of the same volume. Growers who can obtain a better price for seed than for ware naturally endeavour to sell as much of their crop as possible for seed purposes, and they use a first riddle with as large a mesh as the buyers will tolerate. On the other hand, those who purchase the seed can make a given tonnage plant a much larger area when the tubers are small, and they therefore endeavour to obtain seed that has passed through a riddle with a relatively small mesh. In practice the size of the dressing riddle is therefore determined by the relationship between supply and demand, or by regulations based upon these factors. In some rare cases a new and valuable variety can be sold for seed purposes as grown. The weight required to plant an acre will obviously depend upon the average size of the sets and their spacing. The latter may range from about 22 by 10 in. to 30 by 18 in. For example, with 2-oz. sets planted in 27-in. drills at intervals of 15 in., the requirement would be about 17 cwt. per acre. Experiments have shown that, assuming Scottish or Irish seed to cost in England twice the price obtained for the produce, the most economical size of set is one weighing about 2 oz., i.e. about the size of an average hen's egg.

What effect has the size of the set on the number of tubers produced by the plant? Large sets tend to produce several stems and a large number of tubers which, under ordinary conditions of spacing, cannot grow to any great size owing to the competition of neighbouring plants. This is, of course, an advantage if the object is to produce a crop with the maximum possible proportion of seed size or small ware tubers. On the other hand, when small or cuts sets are planted, a limited number of stems are produced and the young tubers tend to be few in number but large in size, thus yielding a crop in which ware sized potatoes predominate. Actually the heaviest yields of ware are usually secured by planting sets that run about seven to the pound.

With regard to the yield per acre, large seed potatoes on the whole braird quicker and produce a heavier crop than small: this is due to the extra food content of the large sets enabling the plants to attain a better

---

[1] The Potato Marketing Board has power to prescribe the minimum size of mesh over which ware potatoes must pass. The power is used to reduce the quantity of potatoes coming on the market at times when the supply is likely to prove excessive.

development. But with very large sets the cost of the extra weight of seed required for planting may not be met by the improvement in yield. Where seed is scarce or of high value, chats or thirds, as they are sometimes called, may be used provided they are of sound healthy stock.

Examination of experimental results over some twenty years has led to the following conclusions:—

1. Increase in seed rate results in increased yields. The increase is substantial up to a rate of 15 to 20 cwt. per acre, and falls off gradually until, at rates of 40 cwt. and over, the increase in yield only just equals the increase in seed weight.

2. It appears to make little difference whether the seed rate is increased by closer planting or by the use of larger sets—*i.e.* the optimum weight of seed is almost the same for large and small sets. Hence there is substantial loss of yield if small sets (chats) are planted at normal intervals: they should be planted more closely if a normal sized crop is required.

3. The most profitable seed rate will depend on the relationship between the cost per ton of the seed and the price per ton obtained from the crop. In general the most profitable seed rate, with Scottish or Northern Irish seed, will thus be lower than that with material grown on the farm or in the area where it is to be planted. At the prices prevailing at the time of writing the most profitable rate for Certified A seed was 15 to 17 cwt. per acre, whereas with the farmer's own once grown seed it would be at least 20 cwt.

4. A crop planted with a high seed rate will produce smaller (and more) ware potatoes than a crop of the same variety, planted with a low seed rate. Some control of the size grading of the ware sample can therefore be exercised by altering the seed rate or planting distance.

It is found that when potatoes are cut they can be planted immediately with safety, whereas if the cut sets are exposed for even a short time to drying conditions, organisms are liable to infect the tissues and cause the sets to rot; but if the newly cut surfaces are allowed to heal in a fairly warm and not too dry atmosphere, the risk of decay is greatly reduced. Some varieties that are soft fleshed—*e.g.* Majestic and Arran Pilot— have to be cut and stored with particular care if rotting is to be avoided. In fact such varieties are rarely if ever cut. Cut potatoes, if they are to be stored for a considerable time, should be prepared in such a way that the cut from the rose end is not quite taken to the heel. The tuber will then appear to remain whole but the cut portions may be pulled apart easily at the time of planting. In this way healing of the cut surface will be satisfactory.

**Sprouting the Seed.**—The practice of sprouting, chitting or boxing the seed tubers is by no means new. There are references to the benefits of producing this pre-planting growth dating back 150 years or so. It is only since the 1920's that the practice has become of importance as a part of potato husbandry (see Plate 34, *A*).

The objective is to produce sprouts about $\frac{3}{4}$ in. long, firm, well greened and with a tuft of leaves at the tip. There should also be young root buds (primordia) on the slightly swollen base of the sprout. Sprouts longer than $\frac{3}{4}$ in. are not necessarily a disadvantage in field performance but are liable to be damaged in the planting process if longer than about $1\frac{1}{2}$ in. or 2 in.

The purpose of sprouting the seed is to bring forward the date at which tuber formation and growth takes place. It also will advance the date of emergence of the crop. By advancing the time of tuber growth there will be heavier crop produced at an earlier date than when unsprouted seed is used. For this reason the practice is almost universal in the husbandry of the early potato crop. During seasons of early haulm death due to Potato Blight (see p. 270) or of late planting the yield increase due to this practice can be considerable—up to 4 or 5 tons per acre. In seasons of long growth, say into late September, the yield increase may be negligible if planting was carried out at the normal time. The *average* response in yield from sprouted seed in the King Edward variety grown in the Eastern Counties is about 2 tons per acre.

One may summarise briefly the benefits of using sprouted seed as follows:—

(*a*) earlier tuber formation, hence

(*b*) longer period for tuber growth during the weeks of maximum sunlight, June and July.

(*c*) higher yield in seasons when haulm is killed early by potato blight.

(*d*) greater flexibility in planting date. Delay does not lead to such great reductions in yield—hence opportunity to plant under really good conditions on land which cannot be prepared for planting by the normal time.

(*e*) reduction of yield by the planting of diseased tubers (*i.e.* Dry Rot, blighted tubers, Skin Spot), is avoided. Such tubers may not sprout normally and are therefore not planted.

Sprouting is carried out by placing the seed in shallow boxes or trays The best results are got when this is done immediately after lifting, but it is worth doing even as late as a month or two before planting. Different sizes of boxes are used, the larger being less costly per ton of seed but rather more difficult to handle at planting time; the small sizes have cross spars and can be conveniently carried by a single worker. When the boxes have been filled they must be stored in a suitable building where they will receive adequate light and good ventilation, and where there is no risk of the temperature falling below freezing point. In Lincolnshire growers have for many years used large glass houses, provided with simple heating apparatus for use in the coldest weather, in which they sprout the whole of their seed. The houses are very occasionally used in summer for other crops, generally tomatoes but this seldom is very convenient. It is inadvisable to keep the buildings at a high temperature; but during periods of severe cold and threatened frost the heat should be turned on to avoid any risk of the potatoes being damaged. The optimum temperature range before sprouting commences, to avoid both chilling and sprouting, is 36° to 40 ° F. The boxes are stacked in tiers so as to economize space, but they must be arranged so that all the sets are exposed to a certain minimum amount of light. When potatoes are sprouted in the dark the shoots are long, thin and weak, and when handling takes place before planting, the stems tend to be broken off, thus diminishing the food reserves of the tuber and causing a loss of time before new shoots develop. Nevertheless sets that have long shoots do well if they are carefully handled. There is a wrong belief that long sprouts should be broken off at planting time; it has been demonstrated that this usually leads to a diminution of the crop. The most desirable sprouts, which develop when the tubers are exposed to plenty of light, are short—not less than $\frac{3}{4}$ in and not exceeding 2 in.—strong and well greened; they are not easily broken and develop rapidly when the sets are planted.

Seed potatoes may also be sprouted by placing the trays in barns or other buildings with adequate ventilation and protection from frost. Light is supplied by special fluorescent lighting units. The chief advantages of this method lie in cheapness relative to a new glass house, and a rather better control of temperature.

Details of the various types and construction of buildings for sprouting potatoes are given in Ministry of Agriculture, Fisheries and Food, Fixed Equipment for the farm, leaflet No. 48 *Potato Chitting House*. The management of the chitting or sprouting process is discussed in an advisory leaflet No. 504.

### Cultivation of Potatoes

**Soil and Climate.**—The most suitable soil for potatoes is a light deep loam or alluvium, but the crop does well on black top or peaty land. The potato is one of the few farm plants that tolerate a rather acid condition of the soil, but the yield suffers where there is an extreme deficiency of calcium. Except in cases where very acid moorland or bog is being reclaimed, liming shortly before planting should be avoided, since the yield is reduced rather than increased and there is risk of inducing common scab (see p. 268). When grown on peaty land potatoes can produce a heavy yield; but the quality is somewhat poor, and on the English market they command a price below the average. The finest quality is obtained from the loams of the Old Red Sandstone formation, which produce potatoes that do not darken after boiling but remain pure white. Potatoes do badly on heavy soils and under wet conditions, and farms situated on such land seldom produce the crop at a profit. It is, however, true that the crop has recently spread on to soils that formerly were considered too heavy; particularly in the drier areas of East Anglia. The development is largely due to the possibilities, opened up by the heavy crawler tractor, of deep ploughing in early autumn and thorough cultivation in the spring. The main remaining difficulty is lifting, and it is necessary to select varieties that mature soon after the cereal harvest when the land in most years is still dry. Naturally there is a risk that, in wet autumns, lifting may be difficult or even impossible.

As potatoes are cultivated on a field and garden scale from the dry east coast to the heavy rainfall districts of Ireland, it may be concluded that they thrive under our whole range of climatic conditions; but in very wet seasons the liability to blight is much accentuated, and there is the difficulty of securing the crop from the water sodden soil. Warm, light land districts especially bordering on the sea coasts are ideal for the production of early varieties, because the sets can be planted as early as February without fear of destruction of the young plants by late frosts. The best potato soil is one that admits of liberal manuring; it does not require to be naturally rich. Some areas devoted to the cultivation of early potatoes have a northern or western exposure, while land lying to the south or east in the same districts is considered unsuitable. This is because occasional late frosts are inevitable, but where the plants are gradually thawed, as when exposed to the north, they are not injured. On the other hand, where rapid thaw is produced by direct insolation, the leaves are stricken to the ground. Frost does not necessarily kill the plants, but in having to replace the lost foliage the potatoes receive a serious setback.

The most favourable seasons are those of moderate rainfall: in rainy seasons the temperature is too low for optimum growth and, as mentioned above, the incidence of blight tends to be high; in dry summers the yield is greatly limited by the water supply. The best eating quality is generally obtained when the last phase of the growing season is fairly dry, as it is then that the tubers are formed with the lowest moisture content. On the other hand, any premature check in the deposition of starch in the tissues—as when the foilage is destroyed by frost or blight—results in a watery potato of poor eating quality. Second growth, which is most common when rain comes after a dry summer, seriously reduces the quality of the crop. It takes various forms such as unsightly cracking, especially in Majestic, prolongation of the tuber and " glassy end ", knobbiness (known as " dolls ") and the formation of runners and secondary tubers.

**Place in Rotation.**—Potatoes are usually taken between two straw crops so that the rotation receives a maximum of benefit from the cleaning of the land. On some of the best potato soils, potatoes have in the past been cultivated year after year but in many cases this practice has resulted in the infestation of the soil with potato root eelworm, a very serious pest. It is rarely safe to crop potatoes regularly more often than once every

I

five years; certainly four years is the closest rotation which should ever be considered. The early sorts may be followed by a quick growing catch crop of mustard, rape, white turnips, ryegrass or by winter crops such as broccoli or cabbage. Potatoes do exceptionally well after old grass and, if the land has been rendered very rich through a long period of grazing with heavily fed stock, are a safer crop than oats or wheat. The decaying sod provides the humus that is so necessary for high yields, and on a system of farming where the farmyard manure supply is somewhat short, it is always advisable to grow a portion of the potato crop in this place in the rotation. Before deciding to plant potatoes after old turf it is desirable to have an estimate of the wireworm population. With a very heavy infestation potatoes should either be avoided or a preplanting soil treatment of aldrin applied. In some places potatoes are grown after peas or vetches or after red clover, the aftermath being preferably ploughed in as green manure.

**Preparation and Planting.**—As the potato crop often receives a dressing of manure, the management of the cultivations will depend very largely on the time of the year when this is applied. Ploughing for potatoes should be completed before the winter and is usually to the full depth of working soil. When this has been done, the land, as early as it becomes workable, is worked into a deep, loose tilth. Potatoes will grow satisfactorily in a good tilth even though there are some clods present. However, the presence of clods will interfere with the fully mechanised harvesting of the crop where this is practised. Clods in the ridge will generally remain throughout the season and add to the work of separating them from potatoes on the picking table of the harvesting machine. In these circumstances the production of a clod free tilth is important. Repeated crossing of the land with cultivators and harrows should be avoided, especially if the subsoil be still wet, as this leads to undesirable treading and consolidation. If, therefore, it is clear that a good deal of tillage will be necessary it may be better to replough. In dry areas the less working of the soil the better: less moisture will be lost. On the heavier soils re-ploughing may not be possible unless there is ample frost mould to turn over. When the crop is taken after a tough old ley the preparation is frequently much more difficult, as the sods take a long time to decompose and tend to work to the surface during the cultivating and ridging operations. Under such circumstances the disc harrow is a valuable implement. In deep soils this difficulty can be more completely overcome by double ploughing. For this purpose two ploughs are required: the first skims off the whole of the sod and turns it into the bottom of the furrow: the second plough, following in the same furrow, cuts about 6 in. deeper and throws its furrow slice on top of the turf. Many soils are too shallow to allow of such deep cultivation, but can be worked according to the same principle, though on a smaller scale, by fitting each plough with an efficient skim coulter to bury the turf.

For planting by hand the land is then drawn into ridges by means of a double mould-board plough or a furrow opener that is capable of forming two, three or four ridges at a time, though an ordinary plough can also be used. When the manure is applied in spring it is spread between the ridges at the same time as the fertilizer is broadcast over the ridges, and the potato " seed " is placed directly on the manure. This method of application gives very good results, as the manure decomposes immediately round the plant roots; but the carting and spreading are slow and laborious at a time of the year when much other work has to be performed.

While many crops are still set by hand, hand assisted or semi-automatic potato planting machines are very widely used. These soon repay their cost in economy of labour and the speed with which the operation of planting can be completed. Machines have the further advantage, in the drier parts of the country, that their use conserves soil moisture by reason of the speed at which the operation is carried out. While most of the mechanical planters do good work with ordinary seed they are not all suitable for planting sprouted potatoes, as they may break off too many of the shoots. These machines can, of course, be set to drop the tubers at any desired intervals (see Plate 33, A).

In planting by hand or by a machine that does not cover the sets, the ridges have to be split back. This is normally done by tractor, with front mounted ridging bodies, the tractor wheels following in the furrows. With trailed equipment special precautions are necessary to avoid running over the sets. If a horse drawn ridging plough is used, the near side horse should be trained to walk on top of the ridge. It is important, with mechanical planting, that a two-row planter should be used in conjunction with two-row cultivators, a three-row planter with a three-row cultivator and similarly in four row work.

The time of planting depends upon the district and the variety that is being grown, the risk of early planting being in proportion to the liability of the district to late frosts. At the one extreme, in small frost free pockets on the Cornish coast, earlies may be planted about Christmas. February or early March is usual in the general run of coastal areas where first earlies are grown. Early April is the time for setting maincrops—the earlier the better—so long as the land is in fit condition. In the average season every week's delay after 10th April results in a loss of about half a ton per acre in the yield. Moreover, the response to dung and fertilizers (especially potash) is much reduced by late planting. This is illustrated by a five-year series of experiments at Rothamsted which gave the following average yields (tons per acre):—

|  | Planted 14th April | Planted 30th May |
|---|---|---|
| No manure . . . . . . | 7·1 | 6·0 |
| Farmyard manure only . . . . | 11·2 | 8·5 |
| Potash only . . . . . . | 10·1 | 7·0 |
| Farmyard manure and potash . . . | 12·8 | 8·4 |

It is a matter of prime importance that the land should be sufficiently dry and in good working order at planting time, as a crop set in cold wet soil seldom develops satisfactorily.

The distance between the potato drills should be varied according to local circumstances and the requirements of the crop. When potatoes are grown for the early market, and their growing period is too short to allow them to benefit by abundant space, it is usual to have the drills comparatively close together (about 22 in.) and to set the tubers about 1 ft. apart. For exceptionally early marketing even closer intervals should be adopted. Maincrop potatoes, however, because of their long growing period, require more room to develop, and it is usual to place them in

TABLE 4

RELATION OF NUMBERS OF SEED TUBERS PER CWT.
TO SEED RATE PER ACRE

| Width of Drill | Distance between sets | Plants per Acre | Seed rate of sets averaging[1] | | | | |
|---|---|---|---|---|---|---|---|
| | | | 1200 | 900 | 700 | 600 | 500 |
| | | | | (per cwt. of seed) | | | |
| in. | in. | | | | | | |
| 27 | 12 | 19,360 | 16 | 22 | 27 | 32 | — |
| 27 | 15 | 15,488 | 13 | 17 | 22 | 26 | 30 |
| 27 | 18 | 12,907 | 11 | 14 | 18 | 22 | 25 |
| 27 | 21 | 11,063 | — | 12 | 15 | 18 | 22 |
| 28 | 12 | 18,669 | 16 | 21 | 26 | 31 | — |
| 28 | 15 | 14,935 | 13 | 17 | 21 | 25 | 29 |
| 28 | 18 | 12,446 | 10 | 14 | 17 | 21 | 24 |
| 28 | 21 | 10,668 | — | 12 | 15 | 18 | 21 |

[1] The figures are rounded off to nearest whole number.

27 or 28 in. drills and to set them at intervals of 15 to 20 in., depending on variety and the size of ware sample required. Where the land is very rich and the potatoes tend to attain an excessive size, or where it is desired to obtain a large proportion of seed, the tubers may be set at lesser intervals.

The table above sets out the seed rate in relation to the size of the sets and the spacing.

The depth of the drills is varied according to whether the land is dunged on the flat or in the drill, more depth being required in the latter case. At least 2 in. of soil cover should be given; deep planting implies a cover of about 6 in. of soil. It is advisable that early planted maincrops and indeed all crops in districts that are liable to late frosts, should be deeply set so that the sprouts may receive adequate protection during the early stages of growth; they can be brought nearer the surface by harrowing down the ridges when the danger of frost is past. Earlies planted in a relatively frost free area will be planted shallowly so that they emerge quickly.

**Manuring.**—The basis of potato manuring should be a dressing of good farmyard manure where this is available in sufficient quantity, and the only occasions when this may be neglected are when the crop is taken after a rich old pasture, where seaweed is available, where green manuring has been carried out or on certain organic soils such as the black fen. The amount of dung applied usually varies from 10 to 12 tons per acre. Best results are usually got by applying a limited amount of farmyard manure supplemented by fertilizer. In many coastal districts seaweed is used for potatoes and produces very good results. Ton for ton it is slightly better than farmyard manure, its superiority being due to its higher potash content. The potato crop is responsive to all major nutrients, nitrogen, phosphate and potash, normally applied as fertilizer.

The amounts of these nutrients needed by a maincrop under ordinary conditions, where farmyard manure is not being applied, are as follows:—

$$
\left. \begin{array}{l} 100 \text{ units N} \\ 100 \text{ units } P_2O_5 \\ 150 \text{ units } K_2O \end{array} \right\} \text{ or } \left\{ \begin{array}{l} 5 \text{ cwt. Sulphate of Ammonia} \\ 5 \text{ cwt. Superphosphate} \\ 3 \text{ cwt. (50\%) Muriate of Potash} \end{array} \right.
$$

*Potato manuring on fen peats*

| Type of Peat | Soil Organic Matter % | N | Units per acre P$_2$O$_5$ | K$_2$O |
|---|---|---|---|---|
| Loamy Peat | 43+ | 100 | 150 | 200 |
| Peaty Loam | 31–43 | 120 | 180 | 180 |
| Skirt or Org. Loam | 10–28 | 120 | 180 | 50–120 |

If a compound fertilizer is being applied the nutrient ratio should be 1:1:1½ for these normal conditions. For instance 8½ cwt. of a 12:12:18 compound will supply the correct amount of plant food.

If the phosphate and/or potash status of the soil is either high or low the amounts of these nutrients, and hence the type of compound, may be varied. The amount of phosphate may be reduced to 50 units P$_2$O$_5$ where soil reserves are high on analysis. Where potash is low, the amount of potash may be increased to 200 units K$_2$O.

Where farmyard manure is used the amounts of fertilizer applied may be reduced by about one third.

The response of potatoes on fen peats to fertilizer varies according to the type of peat. The heavier the peat the greater the response to phosphate; the lighter the peat the greater the response to potash. In general nitrogen will produce rather less response than on mineral soils.

The manuring of early potatoes is slightly different. A little more nitrogen may be used, up to 120 units N. Rather less potash is given since too much may delay the bulking up of the crop. The amount will vary from 60 to 100 units of $K_2O$ according to soil type. Farmyard manure (or seaweed in some areas) will be applied wherever possible.

On some soils, those of an alkaline reaction and organic nature, potatoes are liable to show symptoms of a deficiency of manganese. This may be corrected by spraying the foliage during mid-late June with a solution of 8 lb. manganese sulphate in 25 gallons water with a wetter. In severe cases two such applications may be needed.

Correct fertilizer placement is highly important, not only to achieve the maximum yield response but also to avoid scorch damage to the young shoots and roots from the considerable amounts of fertilizer normally applied. When hand planting, the fertilizer should be broadcast over the ridges before planting. When planting by a machine which works from the flat the fertilizer should be worked into the top 4 inches of soil before planting. Machines which both plant and apply fertilizer in one operation should apply the fertilizer in bands to the side and below the position of the seed tubers.

The majority of potato fertilizers contain potash as the muriate (chloride). Some growers prefer to use sulphate of potash. The experimental evidence indicates that the yield response will be the same to equivalent amounts of the two forms of potash, but that the dry matter content (specific gravity) of the crop grown from sulphate is often higher. If this is represented by a higher price for the crop, the extra expense of the sulphate of potash may be justified.

**After-cultivation.**—Probably no crop receives more cultivation than the potato, because from the covering of the sets until the plants meet across the drills there is an opportunity to improve the tilth and systematically to destroy weeds. The sequence of operations depends on local custom and the available implements; it should also be determined by the time of planting, the rate of growth and the importance of weed destruction. A common method of working potatoes in the north is, after planting, to leave the drills for two or three weeks until the weeds begin to appear, then to harrow them down with saddle back or chain harrows and, almost at once, to run them up again with a ridging plough. This moves the soil without actually exposing the tubers, thereby killing the weeds and encouraging more to grow, yet it does not leave the sprouting sets for long near the surface and incompletely protected against frost. The next operation, performed when the risk of frost is reduced but before the sprouts are too long, is to harrow the drills down again. This harrowing should be timed so that it leaves the tops of the shoots just below the surface. The field is then left until all the plants are through the ground and showing the rows quite distinctly. At this stage, before the potato roots have spread far enough to suffer damage, a tractor mounted cultivator is often used to stir the soil deeply. The traditional practice was to give one hand hoeing and, later on, a further walk through to chop out any weeds that later appeared or might have been missed. To-day many of the best growers in the drier parts of the country dispense with handwork altogether. Alternate harrowing down and ridging up are continued until some time after the plants have emerged, even up to the point when this results in the breaking off of an occasional sprout. Inter-row cultivations are continued until the tops are widely spread. Earthing up should be done first before the crop meets between the rows and when the soil is rather damp so that it packs properly. Even after the potatoes have been earthed up, hand pulling of any remaining weeds may be carried out if labour is available. If part of the crop is intended for seed, it is necessary to go through the field when plants are in flower and to remove all rogues, so that the purity of the variety can be guaranteed. Bolters, wildings and plants affected with virus diseases should be removed at the same time.

The need to produce a clod free tilth for making up the final ridge when a harvester is to be used is important. Methods of inter-row cultivation are changing. Deep tining between the rows will often bring up clods from unweathered soil below. Instead, rapid and shallow working with special hoe type blades or with special rotary hoes may be carried out.

The chemical control of weeds in potato crops is not current practice. It is true that numbers of growers use MCPA without apparent harm, but critical experiments, so far as they go, suggest that there may be some loss of yield. Only if a crop appears likely to be smothered should resort be had to MCPA. Certain new residual acting herbicides show promise of successful use in the potato crop. This would avoid the need for the many post-planting cultivations aimed largely at weed control. The introduction of such techniques will demand a re-consideration of many of the traditional cultivations carried out on the crop.

**Irrigation.**—The potato crop is one of the most sensitive to moisture conditions. Ample water at the time of tuber swelling has a very marked effect on final yield, and often on quality.

Irrigation of the maincrop varieties should normally commence when the young tubers have reached the size of the small finger nail—provided of course that there is a moisture deficit in the soil (see p. 65). Irrigation should cease at the end of August or 10 to 14 days before lifting, which ever is the earlier.

Early potatoes will benefit from planned watering from the time of emergence. Under irrigation the date and rate of tuber swelling will be brought forward.

Potato Blight may spread more rapidly in an irrigated crop but is unlikely to strike the crop any sooner

**Spraying.**—Perhaps the greatest loss sustained by potato growers is due to the ravages of blight. Protective spraying is the only practical control measure. Potatoes grown in the south and west suffer more from the disease than those cultivated in the drier eastern counties, but in a wet season the ravages of blight are very severe and the whole country suffers. There are, of course, districts where blight is so seldom serious that it may not pay to spray every season on the chance of protecting the crop in a disease year. Most intensive growers of susceptible varieties such as King Edward, however, find that regular spraying is well worth while.

The losses from blight will depend on the stage of growth the crop has reached when the haulm is killed. A loss of leaf to the extent of 75 per cent. is considered to be the stage at which tuber growth virtually ceases. It is estimated that if this stage is reached by mid-August, then the yield loss will be about 25 per cent. If it is not reached until mid-September, the loss will be about 10 to 15 per cent.

At best, protection of the haulm with a suitable fungicide can only prolong the life of the crop by about 2 weeks, or 3 weeks exceptionally, if the weather is particularly favourable to the epidemic spread of the disease.

The timing of the spray or dust fungicide will depend on the area of the country concerned and on previous local experience. An outline of the control measures of the chemicals used will be found at the end of this section, on p. 270.

Spraying or dusting will be carried out from the end of June onwards depending on the locality. This will be at a time when the crop has usually met in the row. Damage to the haulm by the machines can be serious. And the ridges themselves may be compressed by the passage of heavy wheels which can also cause a loss in yield. Experiments have shown that this yield loss can be as high as $2\frac{1}{2}$ tons per acre *in the wheeling rows*. Care in the choice of machine and the way it is used can reduce this loss to nil. In suitable fields the fungicide may also be applied by aircraft with good results.

There are important differences between varieties in their susceptibility to blight. Some, like Majestic, are resistant in both haulm and tuber, others like King Edward are susceptible. A few varieties are resistant in the haulm but very susceptible to blight in the tuber.

**Lifting Potatoes.**—Maincrop potatoes are lifted when the foliage has died off and the growing season has come to an end. At this time, too, the skins of the tubers are thickened by a deposit of corky tissue, and they suffer much less through mechanical injury and keep better than when they are lifted early in the season. The time of lifting varies according to the season and the locality, but most crops are secured between the middle of September and the first week in November. The tubers are brought to the surface by a potato plough, a spinner or an elevator digger, to be picked up by hand. Mechanical harvesters are suitable for use on the kinder soils only and where there are few stones. The plough is probably less injurious to the crop, but it does not scatter the tubers well, is slow and many are left covered by soil; the " spinner " type of digger, on the other hand, may slice and bruise a few tubers, but it greatly facilitates gathering—an operation which at best is laborious and expensive. The elevator type of digger, which works satisfactorily only on lighter soils, causes very little damage and leaves the tubers well exposed in a narrow band and even more convenient for gathering.

In late districts the crop must, in many years, be lifted long before the haulms would have died down naturally, otherwise frost damage would be very probable. Moreover, haulm destruction may be very important in relation to the prevention of blight infection of the tubers (see p. 271). Again, where the crops are being grown for seed, it is often necessary to bring growth to a stop when the tubers have reached the desirable seed size.

Some harvesters will not work satisfactorily unless the haulm has been destroyed. On a small scale the tops may be mown with a scythe. The large scale grower has a choice of several methods. The most effective is to spray with 18 to 20 gal. per acre of undiluted commercial sulphuric acid (B.O.V.) or with about 15 gal. of this to 100 gal. of water. This is normally a task for contractors, since a special type of machine must be used and special precautions observed. Almost as effective is an application of 25 to 30 gal. per acre of a tar-oil fraction which is known commercially as T.O.F. 54. A low volume sprayer is required. There are a number of different types of haulm desiccant on the market. For example, the chemical known as Diquat is effective, easy to apply and safe to handle. No other method however is as rapid or efficient as sulphuric acid.

Another method is to use a special machine which disintegrates the tops by beating them with steel or rubber flails.

The potatoes, having been left on the surface of the ground will be picked up by the gangs of women or men, often paid on a piece work basis. They may be picked into mesh baskets or aprons and transferred into bags, tipped direct into carts or trailers or into stillage boxes placed in the field. These will then be transferred to the clamp site or grave, or taken direct to an indoor store. Great economy of labour can be achieved by the careful organisation of this work. For example, a picking gang of 10 to 12 women working a $5\frac{1}{2}$ hour day with two tractor drivers, one each for the spinner and the transport of stillage boxes, can lift 2 to $2\frac{1}{2}$ acres per day, a total of 20 to 30 tons of potatoes.

The mechanical harvester will usually deliver direct into trailers but models with a bagging attachment (for direct sale of the bags) are available.

Except in specially favourable localities—the Cornish and Pembroke coastal areas—lifting of early potatoes commences in June, long before the tubers are hardened or the foliage has ceased to function. On very small areas such as the Cornish cliff fields, where extreme earliness can be achieved the crop may be raised by hand, using a three or four flat pronged digging graip or fork.  When this is done a gatherer works with each digger, and not only lifts the potatoes but, using two containers, separates them into saleable and undersized tubers.  An average daily output is about 2 tons per fork.  The potatoes are then packed, preferably into barrels or chip baskets, which are more protective than bags, and sent straight from the field to the market.  Owing to the greater cost of hand lifting and the difficulty in getting the large squads of experienced workers that are required, this method of lifting is practised as a rule only with the very first earlies that command a high price and are too immature for machine digging.  The majority of earlies are lifted in the same way as maincrops.

After the preliminary gathering has been completed the field is given a good harrowing to bring to the surface any tubers that have been missed or overlaid by soil; they are then collected and removed in the usual way. Chain harrows are very good for rolling up the haulm, which can be heaped and burned when sufficiently dry.

**Storing Potatoes.**—The crop is secured as it is lifted by putting it into a pit or clamp, or by storing it in a shed or special potato store. The principles of clamping are the same throughout the country, the construction being designed to protect the potatoes from frost and rain and at the same time to allow a certain amount of ventilation.  The clamp which is made as long as is necessary, and generally from 4 to 6 ft. wide, is commenced by excavating the soil to the depth of a few inches, or simply by levelling the surface of a piece of land that has a good natural drainage and is adjacent to a cart track.  It is important to choose a well drained site since a few days' immersion is enough to kill the tubers.  The tubers keep best in narrow pits, but these are more expensive in straw and in labour.  The common dimensions take from 10 to 20 cwt. per yard run. The potatoes are tipped on to the pit bottom, dressed up as steeply as possible, and immediately covered with good wheat straw to a depth of nearly a foot.  The straw should be kept as straight as possible, so as to shed rain.  Soft straw, such as barley, may be used along the ridge.  The straw is then covered to within a foot of the top of the clamp with about 2 in. of soil, so that there is ample ventilation to allow the heat, produced by fermentation and respiration, to escape.  Some heating due to these causes is quite normal, but in the presence of sufficient moisture and the absence of ventilation the bacteria may become so active that the temperature rushes up, the potatoes are literally cooked, and the clamp collapses. The risk of this is greatly increased if a considerable proportion of the tubers is bruised, cut, frosted or affected by blight or other fungoid disease. Such samples should be marketed at the earliest possible opportunity. Alternatively they may be dressed before pitting, the unsound material being fed to pigs or cattle.  It may also be cooked and ensiled for later use. After a few weeks, however, when the free moisture in the clamp has decreased, and the respiration of the tubers has become less active, the clamp should be earthed up a second time so that there is a covering of about 6 or 8 in. of soil to protect the contents from frost. This earthing up may be done quite soon if the crop has been pitted in dry condition. Where wet pitting has been unavoidable the earthing up should be delayed as long as seems safe so that the excess of moisture may be driven off by the heat of fermentation, but even at this stage bunches of straw should be allowed to protrude at intervals along the apex to allow a certain amount of aeration. If the pit runs east and west extra cover should be given to the north side (see Plate 33, *B*).

Where the grower has quantities of surplus straw a labour saving method of storage is to build walls, two bales high and about 6 to 8 ft. apart, packing loose straw between the bales to make the walls wind proof. The potatoes are placed between the walls and piled up to a ridge in the middle. The top is covered with a layer of loose straw and is finally thatched.

A considerable proportion of the maincrop in this country is now stored in large specially built or adapted sheds, some of which cover an area of 100 by 45 ft. and have doorways which allow the entry of carts or trailers. In these buildings sound mature tubers can be stored to a depth of 10 to 12 ft. Straw is spread over the surface to prevent greening and as a protection from frost. Special ventilation arrangements prevent overheating of the potatoes. The volume/weight relation for potatoes is 54 to 56 cu. ft. per ton. In winter the crop can be dressed by power driven machines, the workers being protected from inclement weather and provided with artificial light when necessary (see Plate 34, *B*).

Potato under storage is described in Bulletin No. 173 and less fully in Fixed Equipment of the Farm leaflet No. 24, both entitled *Bulk Storage of Potatoes in Buildings*, Ministry of Agriculture, Fisheries and Food.

In order that the crop may keep well it is important that the tubers be stored in as dry a state as possible; moisture encourages bacterial and mould growth which produce rapid deterioration. Harrowings, which consist largely of inferior and damaged potatoes, should be stored separately and used up as early as possible.

An inevitable weight loss, due to respiration, goes on while potatoes are in store. This may reach 3 to 5 per cent. by weight in March. If disease is known to be present, the tubers should be inspected every two or three weeks so that they can be sold and despatched at once if they are found to be deteriorating rapidly.

When potatoes are held over until the spring considerable loss of weight and of food value results from sprouting. There are now chemical means of preventing sprouting while in store, thus reducing the weight loss and improving quality. It is also very much easier to riddle unsprouted potatoes. The chemicals which may be used for this include nonyl alcohol vapour, maleic hydrazide and mixtures of CIPC and IPC.[1]

Marketing potatoes consists of grading them as outlined in a previous section (see p. 253), picking them over to remove diseases or broken tubers, and either weighing and bagging them or carting them in bulk to wharf or railway wagon. With earlies, however, the soft skins may make it desirable to market the first lots in rigid containers.

Large quantities of potatoes are now washed before sale, partially dried and marketed, ready weighed in polythene or other perforated bags. The increased cost of this will range between £6 and £12 per ton depending on circumstances.

When potatoes are ensiled they should first be steamed (boiling adds too much water) until they are soft, then mashed by treading into a small silo or a trench lined with waterproof paper. The mash packs too closely to admit much air, and topping with earth is an additional precaution against wastage.

**Yield.**—An average crop of potatoes will yield about 8 tons per acre, but 16 tons and over may be got in good districts. Under irrigation yields of over 20 tons and up to 25 are occasionally achieved. When ordinary riddles are used for dressing, about 7 and 25 per cent. of the crop may be sorted into chats and seed respectively, but the proportions actually vary very greatly.

## Potato Diseases

The following is a broad grouping of the common potato diseases together with notes according to their importance.

*A.* Diseases affecting the tuber only, and that superficially:—

(*a*) **Common or Brown Scab** (*Streptomyces scabies*).—The scabbing gives the potatoes a very unsightly appearance, but has little effect on the yield. Tubers badly affected about the eyes should not be used for seed. The attacks are rarely troublesome where the $p$H of the soil is 5·6 or less; they are worst on sharp soils and after liming, because these conditions promote a rapid loss of humus and cause the fungus, which can live saprophytically on decaying organic matter, to pursue a parasitic existence. The disease is usually worse in dry seasons. Some control has been demonstrated using penta-chlor-nitro-benzene (PCNB) but at present this is not regarded as economic. Where the suppression of the disease is secured by allowing the soil to remain slightly acid, there may be considerable difficulty in growing successfully such crops as barley, sugar beet and red clover. In such a case it is necessary to make a detailed survey of the soil reaction of the individual field and to adjust the application of lime from place to place according to local variations. The aim should be to get the reaction uniform at about $p$H 5·6. The lime should

---

[1] CIPC or chlorpropham-isopropyl-N-3-chlorophenyl carbamate.
IPC or propham-isopropyl-N-phenyl-carbamate.

of course be applied as long as possible before potatoes are to be grown. In the United States, varieties showing a high degree of resistance to scab have been introduced into commerce.

(*b*) **Powdery or Corky Scab** (*Spongospora subterranae*).—This form of scab may be indistinguishable from common scab and in its mild form does practically no harm. Where potatoes are repeatedly grown on the same ground, however, the attack may be so severe as to form a canker not readily distinguishable from wart disease and render the affected tubers useless. To control the disease, plant unaffected seed and do not grow the crop frequently on the same land.

*B.* Diseases which cause the tuber to rot:—

(*a*) **Sprain and Internal Rust Spot.**—These conditions are most prevalent in dry seasons on light soils; they are not perpetuated through the planting of affected seed but are probably related to soil conditions. Sprain, which is also called spraing, takes the form of concentric rings of dead tissue within the tuber and may show as raised arcs beneath the skin. The other disease takes the form of flecks of dead tissue which are revealed when the tuber is cut; there are no external symptoms. Both conditions render the affected tubers unfit for the table.

(*b*) **Dry Rot** (*Fusarium caeruleum*).—This fungus does most damage to the seed of early varieties in boxes during the storage period. The affected tubers shrivel and become dry and wood like; they should be removed and burned. The trouble is rarely severe in pitted potatoes but may develop a few weeks after the pit has been opened and its contents aerated; consequently it may break out in consignments of seed that looked quite normal at the time of shipping. Since *Fusarium* is essentially a wound fungus the disease is most likely to spread when the potatoes have been bruised through careless handling. It may be controlled by disinfecting the seed immediately after lifting. Dry powders, such as Fusarex, are most convenient for this purpose.

(*c*) **Gangrene.**—This disease is caused by *Phoma sp.* and, like dry rot, it develops in storage. An affected tuber develops pits or cavities which are lined with mycelium. Control as for dry rot.

(*d*) **Wart Disease** (*Synchytrium endobioticum*).—This disease came into prominence about the beginning of the present century because of the increasing area of the land affected, the loss occasioned by its ravages and the methods established for its suppression. The fungus produces wart like excrescences at the eyes of the tubers and on the basal shoots of the plants. The outgrowths are at first white but later become dark brown in colour, and vary from the size of a pea to a warty mass that envelops the whole tuber. The disease is propagated from year to year by spores that are liberated in the soil, and as the organism is capable of existing in a latent state for many years, it is practically ineradicable.

Fortunately the existence of immune varieties, makes the growing of healthy crops on badly infected soil possible, but if any other kinds are cultivated, there is no possibility of starving out the fungus and of getting the land clean. For this reason the Departments of Agriculture have found it necessary to define certain disease areas in which only varieties that have been proved immune may be planted.

C. Diseases which attack the foliage but not the tubers:—

(a) **Stalk Disease** (*Sclerotinia sclerotiorum*) occurs in the west of Ireland, particularly where potatoes are grown repeatedly on the same land.

(b) **Botrytis Disease** (*Botrytis cinerea*) rarely does serious damage.

D. Diseases which attack the whole plant and destroy both haulms and tubers:—

(a) **Blackleg** (*Pectobacterium casotovorum var. atrosepticum*).—By the middle of June affected plants may be detected by their yellowish colour. The base of the stem is blackened and decayed and the stalks are easily pulled away. Later in the season the young tubers become more or less affected, especially at the heel end. Decay continues and spreads during storage, and if slightly diseased tubers are planted they give rise to diseased plants. Blackleg may be kept in check by planting only healthy seed, and it may pay to dig and destroy affected plants. It has been observed that certain varieties are rather susceptible to the disease, these include: Kerr's Pink, British Queen, Great Scot, King Edward VII, Majestic, Duke of York, Epicure and Eclipse.

(b) **Potato Disease or " Blight "** (*Phytophthora infestans*).—This is the worst scourge of the potato crop; not only does the fungus attack the foliage of the plant and cause it to decay and die off prematurely, but the disease finds its way through the soil to the tubers, which develop dark coloured sunken areas on the surface and brown rot below the skin. The disease extends until the whole tuber has suffered a dry rot, but secondary organisms may later on convert this into a wet rot. Affected potatoes have to be discarded as soon as they are lifted, and spores of the fungus, present on seemingly unaffected tubers at lifting time, cause the potatoes to become diseased during the period of storage. As far as is known the disease is chiefly carried from one season to the next in the tuber and the first spores come from the foliage of affected plants. There may be less than one plant per 500 acres of potatoes, but this is sufficient to carry on the disease. The earliest infection is often found in the sites of the previous year's clamps. Systematic destruction of plants growing on such places should always be carried out.

The outward manifestation of the disease on growing potatoes is a browning and dying-off of a portion of the leaf tissue, and if the under-surface of an affected lamina is examined the presence of the spore bearing conidia can be observed round the dead tissue. The affection starts in June, July or August, and is most severe during periods of warm, damp and misty weather,[1] which facilitates the germination of the reproductive spores on healthy plants and thus enables the disease to propagate rapidly (see Plate 35).

As mentioned earlier (p. 264), the only effective preventive measure is to treat the plants with a fungicidal spray. The protectant sprays or dusts used are usually based on copper either as the oxychloride or as cuprous oxide. The oldest and still the best spray is Bordeaux mixture, made up by mixing copper sulphate with quicklime in the proportion of 2 to 1 by weight and the correct amount of water. Burgundy mixture, using washing soda, sodium carbonate, in the proportion of 4 to 5 is an alternative. Such materials are a trouble to mix up correctly, are corrosive to most spraying machines and therefore are seldom used. The copper sulphate or bluestone, has to be altered into an insoluble form which will stick to the foliage; if copper sulphate were used it would scorch the foliage very seriously.

Newer organic fungicides for this purpose are based on zinc or manganese thio-carbamates (zizeb or maneb) and quite non toxic to foliage, but in general are not quite so long lasting in their protectant properties.

The disease can be prevented to some extent by a very careful selection of seed, taking care to exclude all sets that exhibit the minutest trace of infection: this inspection, of course, can best be performed when the seed is sprouting in boxes. Infected tubers often sprout earlier and produce rather spindly sprouts. None of the established varieties can resist attack, but the degree of resistance to haulm and/or tuber infection varies widely and in some varieties is quite high. In all cases thorough earthing up of the rows is helpful, because a good layer of soil filters the percolating rain and prevents the spores, washed off the foliage, from reaching the tubers.

It is now known that there are several distinct strains of the blight fungus, but one or other of the wild species of *Solanum* possesses complete immunity to most if not all of them. It was hoped that plant breeders would be able to produce a completely immune variety. So far this has not proved possible since strains of the fungus have arisen to which the new varieties proved susceptible in haulm or tuber. Increased resistance to blight would seem a goal more likely to be attained.

The haulm of potatoes is usually killed chemically or mechanically (see p. 265) before lifting. This is in order to prevent the infection of the tubers during harvesting operations by contact with any blight spores on the still living haulm. Once all the haulm is dead, the blight on it will die also.

[1] Not less than 48 hours with a minimum temperature of 50° F. and relative humidity of 75% are known as Beaumont periods, called after the research worker who showed that these were critical for the epidemic spread of Blight.

*E.* Disease affecting the whole plant but not destroying the tubers:—

**Verticillium Wilt** (*Verticillium albo-atrum*).—This fungus more or less blocks up the water channels in the plant, thereby causing the leaves to become limp or to wilt. The haulms die prematurely and the development of the tubers is checked. The fungus passes into the young potatoes through the underground stems, and if such potatoes are planted they will give rise to a diseased crop. The remedy is to buy in healthy seed.

*F.* Diseases which affect the whole plant but do not cause decay:—

**Virus Diseases.**—It was formerly believed that potato stocks underwent a natural process of degeneration, and that, no matter how good the variety might be for a few years, it would ultimately have to be discarded owing to old age. It is now known, however, that deterioration is brought about by virus diseases such as Leaf Roll and Mosaic. Virus X is transmitted from affected to neighbouring plants by contact—*i.e.* by the rubbing together of the foliage. The others that are responsible for mosaic and also that of leaf roll are transmitted by insect vectors. The insect mainly responsible is the green-fly, *Myzus persicae*. In late spring or early summer the winged forms migrate to potato fields and carry the infection with them. The spread of virus disease thus depends largely on the aphid population, which varies greatly from one district to another. There are large areas in Scotland and Northern Ireland and smaller ones in England and Wales where the aphid population is generally small and where, therefore, with due precautions, infection can be kept at a low level. There is, however, a considerable year to year variation in numbers of aphids. In some particular upland areas and in certain of the Scottish Western Isles aphids seem to be absent. A stock suffering slightly from the effects of one virus may have its condition greatly worsened through infection by one or more other viruses. The diseases are perpetuated through the tubers and there is no chance of recovery; indeed it is quite normal for the number of diseased plants to be trebled from year to year. The effect on the yield depends on the severity of the attack, and the susceptibility of the variety, but it is not unusual for leaf roll, mild mosaic and severe mosaic to cause reductions of the order of from 40 to over 90, 20 to 40, and 40 to 75 per cent. respectively. When both leaf roll and severe mosaic affect a plant, the result is devastating. In some cases the symptoms of virus infection, apart from a decline in yield, are so slight as to be imperceptible to the eye. In certain cases, too, infection with any one of two viruses may have but little effect; yet when the one is superimposed on the other the effect on the plant may be very severe.

Leaf roll is caused by a single virus which in the year of infection may produce no visible symptoms or, if introduced early enough, may cause a condition known as *Primary Leaf Roll* that is characterised by slight curling and stiffening of some of the leaves. In the following year plants from affected tubers develop *Secondary Leaf Roll*, which takes the form

PLATE 33

*A.* CROXTON POTATO PLANTER AT WORK
*Farmer and Stockbreeder*

*B.* CLAMPING POTATOES, USING A CLAMP FORMER AND A STILLAGE BOX FOR TRANSPORT
*The Farmer's Weekly*

PLATE 34

B. Loading Potatoes into store

A. Sprouting Seed Potatoes using artificial light

*The Farmer's Weekly*

PLATE 35

*A.* POTATO BLIGHT ON LEAF AND IN TUBER

*B.* BLIGHT ON TUBER

*C.* DRY ROT

PLATE 36

*A.* HEALTHY PLANT         POTATO WITH LEAF ROLL

*B.* HEALTHY PLANT         POTATO AFFECTED BY MOSAIC

of a hardening of the leaves, an upward and inward rolling of the leaf margins and a general stiffening and stunting of the haulms. The visible symptoms arise from damage to and blocking of the phloem tissue and consequent interference with the transfer of starch from the leaves to the tubers. No known species of *Solanum*, whether cultivated or wild, appears to be immune.

Mosaic in its various forms is caused principally by three viruses, designated X, Y and A, which invade the plant singly or in different combinations. *Negligible Mottle* is usually caused by mild strains of X or by A. In *Mild Mosaic*, which is normally caused by virus X but also occasionally by A in combination with mild strains of X, there is a mottling of the leaves in shades of light and dark green or even yellow and green, but no wrinkling of the leaves or reduction in their size. In *Rugose* or *Severe Mosaic*, caused by the combination of A with severer strains of X, or by Y alone or in combintation with A or X, mottling is also present but is accompanied by a wrinkling or distortion of the leaves and a dwarfing of the whole plant. In extreme forms, as for instance in Majestic, the affected leaves die prematurely and hang by a thin thread to the stem. This condition has been called *Leaf-drop Streak*, but it is due to the same causes as typical rugose mosaic. With virus diseases the degree of severity actually ranges from a mottling so slight that it can barely be noticed, through increasingly diseased conditions, to the most marked mottling, distortion and stunting of the plants (see Plate 36).

Apart from infection with virus disease, potatoes may develop degenerate forms which have been termed respectively bolters and wildings. A bolter possesses abnormally tall, open and vigorous foliage and usually has a very free flowering habit; it is late in maturing. A wilding has an abnormally bushy habit of growth and develops an exceptionally large number of thin branches; it produces a very large number of small tubers. Both the bolter and wilding conditions are now believed to be due to chromosome abnormalities and are perpetuated through the tubers, so that the only means of eliminating either is by thoroughly roguing the seed crop (see p. 263).

## Pests

Potatoes are not much parasitised by insects, but are attacked to some extent by the Death's Head moth, and in other countries, the Colorado beetle. Aphids, leather jackets, wireworms and slugs are, of course, destructive.

**Aphids.**—The peach-potato aphid or green fly (*Mysus persicae*), winter on brassicas and in summer migrate to the potato crop. The insects transmit virus diseases and in a warm, dry season may become so numerous that they destroy the foliage; but cold and wet weather retards their increase. Aphids may be controlled by spraying with a suitable systemic insecticide.

**Colorado Beetle.**—There have been several outbreaks of the pest in southern England. The standard method of control is to add DDT to the copper dust or spray, employed as a preventive for blight. In some cases, however, the beetles become numerous before the ordinary time for spraying against blight, in which case a special application of insecticide becomes necessary.

**Root Eelworm.**—When potatoes are grown year after year on the same ground they may be seriously attacked by the Potato Root Eelworm (*Heterochera rostochiensis*). Once established in the soil, the parasites spread from year to year in ever widening circles, and the yield of the attacked crop is reduced to quite an unremunerative level. Diseased patches may be detected by the stunted growth and sickly colour of the foliage and the withering of the lower leaves, which gives the heads of the plants a tufted appearance. Examination of the roots confirms the nature of the attack, for there can be found the bodies of the females, in all stages of development, protruding from the cortex. At first the bodies are white and pear-shaped, but after fertilisation they swell up and change into brown resting cysts, each containing 250 to 300 eggs or larvae, and having the appearance of poppy seed. The cysts are loosely attached to the roots and break off when the crop is lifted; they remain dormant in the soil until potatoes are again planted. Soon after the growth of the next crop begins, the larvae hatch and bore into the potato roots, thereby damaging the tissues, interfering with the water supply of the plant and reproducing the symptoms of the disease. An important aspect of the disease is that its presence greatly depreciates the value of the land.

The initial infection of clean ground is most likely to be brought about by introducing the cysts in purchased seed. It has been shown that some land has been infected through the barrels used for marketing early crops, and also by the purchase of cabbage or other plants grown on infected soil. If containers have been used for infected potatoes, the soil and rubbish in them is full of cysts, and if this material is emptied out on another field the disease will obviously be introduced. Early potatoes suffer less than maincrops because the crop is lifted while a large proportion of the cysts are still immature. The only certain method of avoiding the risk from this disease is to grow potatoes no more often than once in five, or at most four years. To reduce an infection may require a period of up to 8 or 10 years without the host crop.

The eggs of the eelworm normally remain dormant in the soil until potatoes are planted, and it has been shown that hatching is induced by a substance secreted by the potato roots. Research is at present being directed to determine the nature of this secretion, and to discover some chemical that might have the same effect. If hatching could be induced in the absence of a potato crop the larvæ would quickly die and complete control would be secured. Another approach is to apply some material which would mask the effect of the substance that induces hatching.

Mustard oil has been shown to have some slight effect of this kind. Soil sterilisation is, of course, effective against soil nematodes and is employed in the case of glass house soils. Fumigation is a possibility with small areas, and the dichlorpropanes (including that sold as D.D.) are the most effective compounds for the purpose. Field experiments with D.D. have shown that the material has a beneficial effect, but the cost is high. So far it is only in Jersey (where potatoes and tomato crops are grown in succession each year) that the treatment has been used commercially. Other materials also have similar properties but are not economic on a field scale at present.

A possible long term solution is the production of commercial varieties with an immune wild species (*Solanum andigenum*) as one of the parents.

Wild species of *Solanum* (the nightshades) are sometimes found to be slightly infected. The only other crop host is the tomato.

Another species, the potato tuber eelworm, is widely distributed but of comparatively small economic importance.

**Wireworms** can damage potatoes by riddling the tubers with holes and in bad cases rendering them unsaleable. This may be avoided by using the insecticide aldrin in the seedbed. Potato fertilizer incorporating aldrin may be purchased for this purpose.

**Slugs** may damage potatoes, by burrowing into the tubers at the end of the growing season. This pest is seldom a problem on coarse soils, but in some seasons is quite serious on the fine silts especially. There is no control 'at present.

*References.*—The following publications of the Ministry of Agriculture, Fisheries and Food may be of value for reference.

Bulletin No. 94—Potatoes.

Bulletin No. 24—Bulk Storage of Potatoes in Buildings.

Fixed Equipment for the Farm Leaflet No. 48—Potato Chitting Houses.

Advisory Leaflets

No.   5   Common Scab of the Potato
    71   Colorado Beetle
    99   Powdery Scab of Potatoes
  107   Black Leg of Potatoes
  115   Slugs and Snails
  139   Potato Virus Diseases
  150   Millepedes and Centipedes
  160   Swift Moths
  179   Leatherjackets
  199   Wireworms
  218   Dry Rot of Potatoes

# CHAPTER 11

# THE ROOT CROPS

## TURNIPS AND SWEDES

TURNIPS and swedes are biennial plants belonging to the cruciferous genus *Brassica*: they are termed " roots," but the fleshy portions are in fact enlarged hypocotyls and contain but little true root tissues. Their habit is to store up large quantities of food material in the first year of their growth and to develop their reproductive parts and to ripen their seed in the second season. The species that do not develop swollen hypocotyls are known as rapes, and are grown for seed production and for soiling or folding.

Turnips and swedes form our most widely cultivated root crop, principally suited to the more humid regions of the north and west. It is commonly but wrongly believed that the turnip was brought to Britain about the time of the origination of the Norfolk rotation, and that it is therefore a comparatively recent introduction; in reality it was cultivated in gardens at a much earlier period. During the early days of field culti-vation turnips were sown broadcast, but about the end of the eighteenth century drilling on ridges began to be common. About thirty years later a new sort, possessing distinct characteristics, was introduced from the Continent and called a Swede or Swede turnip, after the country of its origin. The term " turnip " is often used to refer to both groups since they are basically similar from the husbandry point of view. Turnips and swedes increased rapidly in popularity as soon as the system of drill cultivation had been established, as up to that time the only means of bringing foul land back to a state of cleanliness and fertility was to turn it over to bare fallow. Turnips grown in drills, however, permitted cleaning operations and avoided the waste and expense due to the want of a crop. Demanding a considerable amount of hand labour, the crop has been declining in area. Recent techniques of mechanisation show promise of greatly cheapening production and reducing labour demand; in consequence the acreage is now tending to increase in some areas.

Root crops are grown with the primary object of producing winter food for stock, and differ from potatoes in being almost universally consumed on the holding, thus conserving the soil fertility. They also, as mentioned above, form a most important cleaning crop in a great many rotations. The food value of turnips is high—not weight for weight with

their keeping quality and frost resisting power are very low. One of their greatest advantages is that they will crop well even when sown late. Two well known varieties of this class are Greystone and White Globe.

2. *Soft Yellows* are intermediate in quality between whites and yellows, and contain 8½ to 9 per cent. dry matter. Fosterton's Hybrid and Early Sheep Fold are of this type.

3. *Hardy Yellow Turnips*, of which the Aberdeen Yellow is the best known, are about as good as swedes in keeping quality and feeding value; they contain approximately 10½ per cent. dry matter, and are very hardy and frost resistant. The Bruce variety, which is highly resistant to " finger and toe " disease, belongs to this group.

## Cultivation

**Soil and Climate.**—Turnips and swedes are the typical roots of Scotland, Ireland and the north and west of England; but they were formerly largely grown on the poor, thin soils of the chalk and oölite regions. The crop, like oats, attains its highest perfection in cool and fairly moist climates; when grown under dry conditions the yield is very low. Turnips thrive better than mangels in an absence of sunshine, and their shallow root systems render them liable to be dried out in districts of low rainfall.

The acreage of both turnips and swedes in the south-eastern half of England has greatly declined in the last twenty-five or more years. This is in part a result of the cultivation of sugar beet and the availability of the beet tops for stock feed, in part a reflection of the high labour requirements of the crop and in part due to the greater use of fertilizers and the lesser emphasis on the need for folded sheep and yarded cattle as means of maintaining soil fertility. The crop is more liable to mildew in the drier parts of the country.

The most suitable soils are those of the lighter class, but the crop may be grown on the heavier soils if a fine seed bed can be produced.

**Place in Rotation.**—In most cases roots form the chief cleaning crop of the rotation, the cleaning operations commencing before seed time and going on throughout the period of growth. As is to be expected then, roots are taken between two straw crops, but they cannot easily be taken before autumn sown wheat, since it is difficult to get them off the land in time. The frequency with which turnip crops may recur on the same ground depends largely on the risk of " finger and toe " disease, but the interval is rarely less than four years, and may be seven or more in districts where the soil is poor in lime and the disease is more insidious.

**Preparation and Sowing.**—The soil for turnips receives a more complete and thorough preparation than is the case for most other crops in the rotation. This is possible because turnips are sown comparatively late and at a time when most of the labour of the farm is freed from the other spring operations, and is necessary because of the very fine tilth required for germination and growth.  The land must also be cleaned of weeds which would compete with the struggling plants in their young stages, and it is usual to drag out and burn any twitch or other perennial weeds.  As in the management of the potato crop, the sequence of operations varies according as the farmyard manure is applied in autumn or in spring. When spring manuring is intended the land is ploughed as deeply as possible in autumn to bury the surface weeds, to facilitate aeration and drainage and to allow the soil to benefit by the action of frost.  In spring it may be desirable to plough again, but if there is a danger of losing the frost mould and bringing up clods, this will have to be done early enough to secure a further period of weathering.  On foul land more than one spring ploughing may be given, each being followed by a dragging to fetch the weeds to the surface, so that they can be rolled up with chain harrows, collected and removed to a compost heap or burned. The fine mould for the seed bed is normally prepared by a series of cultivations, harrowings and rollings.

Two important points should always be borne in mind when preparing turnip land: the first is the danger of over-cultivation, resulting in the drying out of the surface layers and a consequent failure of the seeds to germinate;  the second is the importance of seizing every opportunity to gain the required tilth with a minimum of operations, which is best done by taking advantage of every fall of rain to work the clods when they are most easily broken, *i.e.* when they are in a half-wet, half-dry condition. When the desired tilth has been obtained, the land is, in many of the wetter districts, ridged as for potatoes but in row widths of 18 in to 27 in., well rotted manure is spread in the furrows, the fertilizers are broadcast, the ridges are split to cover the manures, and the land is ready for seeding.  Growing on ridges may assist in surface drainage in areas of high rainfall.  Elsewhere there is little point in it provided cultivations are carried out correctly.

Where turnips are grown in the dry districts of England they are sown on the flat, in drills 18 to 20 in. apart, because it is held that the extra surface exposed when ridges are made allows the soil to become so dry that the crop cannot thrive.  Many authorities recommend that wherever the annual rainfall is less than 24 in., or where the soil is specially liable to dry out, this method should be followed.

The modern techniques which show signs of revolutionising the production of this crop are chemical weed control, the use of the precision drill and of low seed rates.  The down-the-row thinner may be used if normal seed rates are used and it is desired to reduce the time taken to thin the crop by hand.  The aim is to reduce hand work to a minimum or cut it out altogether, and to reduce the number of cultivations needed.

The weed killer is applied to the seed bed shortly after sowing and keeps the crop clean during the critical early weeks of growth, giving it a start over the weeds.  At present, contact pre-emergence weedkillers like

P.C.P. or cresylic acid are used but new chemicals with a lasting residual effect may be introduced.

As a rule swedes are sown between the beginning and the end of May, and turnips about a fortnight later; but on thin soils in hot, dry districts, such as the chalk and oölite regions in the south of England, where mildew is apt seriously to affect the early sown crops, seeding does not commence until the last week of June. The incidence of mildew is an important deterrent to turnip and swede growing in the drier areas. In some localities turnips and swedes are often regarded as a half crop, foul land being fallowed throughout May and June and the seed sown in July. The roots in such a case are naturally small, but they resist frost well and are useful for sheep feeding in late winter. On the other hand, swede sowing may occasionally commence in April. Crops that are sown too early tend to bolt, turnips being worse than swedes in this respect. If singling is to be carried out by hand, it is advisable to allow short intervals between the sowings, and to sow only a few acres at a time, so that the whole area will not reach the singling stage simultaneously.

The traditional seed rate is 3 lb. per acre for turnips and 4 lb. per acre for swedes. Where a really good tilth has been prepared, very thin sowing of $\frac{1}{2}$ to $\frac{3}{4}$ lb. per acre, allows the plants to grow quickly and makes them easy to thin, if any thinning is necessary. The seed or the seedlings may be treated with a suitable insecticide for protection against the turnip fly. A relatively heavy seeding may be used on heavy land or where sowing is abnormally early. In the former case the unsuitable nature of the tilth will lead to diminished germination, and in the latter a high mortality among the seedlings must be expected.

Traditionally, the machines used for ridge sowing take two drills at a time, and are fitted with rollers to pack the soil about the seed and to enable the rootlets easily to get their water supply; but many light land farmers like to follow up the drill with a light roller so as further to increase this consolidation. The machines used for drilling on the flat sow four rows at a time, and are of the cup feed type. Many farmers now use precision drill units for turnip and swede sowing either on the ridge or on the flat.

**Manuring.**—Swedes and turnips are particularly responsive to phosphate and relatively high amounts have been used. While the crop is also responsive to nitrogen, care should be taken to restrict the amount in wet areas, where mildew is especially feared and where frost hardiness in the crop should not be lowered.

Farmyard manure is also of considerable benefit and may be applied as previously described in the autumn. If it is found necessary to manure in the drills in spring, the dung should be short and well rotted so that it will not interfere with the supply of soil water. If the only available manure is long and unrotted, it should be turned over so that it may ferment and break down, even though a loss of nitrogen is occasioned thereby.

Normal conditions require the following average dressings of nutrients:

| | | |
|---|---|---|
| Nitrogen | 80 units N approx. | 4 cwt. sulphate of ammonia |
| Phosphate | 80 units $P_2O_5$ approx. | 4 cwt. superphosphate |
| Potash | 80 units $K_2O$ approx. | 1⅓ cwt. muriate of potash |

Where soil analysis indicates low levels of phosphate or potash, the dressings may be increased to 100 units respectively. In wet areas the dressing of nitrogen may be halved.

Where farmyard manure is being applied the fertilizer dressings may be reduced by one half.

These crops respond to the placement of fertilizer, especially to placed phosphate. They are relatively short season crops and a good quick start is of great benefit. When grown on the ridge, the fertilizer should be broadcast on the flat before ridging. It will then lie in the ridge, under the young seedlings, where it is most needed. When the crop is grown on the flat a side band placement drill should be used if available. In no circumstances should the fertilizer be placed in contact with the small seed.

Swedes and turnips seldom if ever require a top dressing of nitrogen if the correct seed bed fertilizers have been used.

**Subsequent Cultivations.**—Usually the first implement that is used when the plants have appeared through the ground is a side hoe, which pares down the ridges to some extent and greatly facilitates the task of singling; but a scuffler may also be used for this purpose. In an average season the plants are in rough leaf about three weeks after sowing and then the sooner they are singled the better. The usual distance to which turnips are singled is 9 in., but it may be anything from 6 to 12 in., depending on the fertility of the soil and the habit of growth of the variety. Singling is usually carried out with a hand hoe, but in some districts where small acreages are grown it is performed entirely by hand, or the hoe may be used only to give a preliminary bunching.

If a chemical weedkiller has been used in conjunction with a very low seed rate, it will not be necessary to hoe until some time later when the effect of the weedkiller has disappeared. In fact hoeing would destroy the effect of a residual acting weedkiller which has to remain on the soil surface to achieve its effect. If the low seed rate has been correctly judged, no singling will be done. Some unevenness in spacing and hence size of roots is acceptable in return for the great saving in hand labour.

If normal seed rates have been used, a down-the-row thinner can reduce the braird to a predetermined density so as greatly to ease the final hand singling.

When singling is over, the plants are kept free from weeds, and the soil well aerated, by hand hoeing and by a series of drill cultivations, until the foliage is so large that it is liable to be damaged. Sometimes the crop is lightly ridged up before it is left, in order to assist surface drainage; but on light soil it is questionable if the operation has any advantage.

**Lifting Turnips and Swedes.**—In a mild season some varieties of roots go on growing right up to New Year, but when the outer leaves fall away the crop may be considered mature and may be removed when it is required. At this stage or a little earlier, the dry matter yield is at its maximum, for thereafter the leaves fail to make good the losses due to respiration. Turnips are usually pulled by hand. They may be fed together with their leaves as long as the latter are green and fresh, but unless they come out of the ground very free from dirt the roots are struck off with a turnip knife. Later in the season when the tops are partly decayed, or when the turnips are to be stored in bulk, the crop is both topped and tailed. The lifter deals with two drills at a time and leaves the produce of four drills in one row so as to provide passage for a trailer or cart and facilitate loading. Turnips can also be topped, tailed and lifted by means of a special root lifter. The implement may do the job rather roughly but it is a useful standby when hand labour is short. White turnips, which are usually grown in small quantities only, are generally fed with their tops to animals on the grass in September, or they may be fed off with sheep. Yellow turnips are ready for use in October and swedes about the end of November. From November onwards it is the custom in most districts to remove the turnips from the land and store them for winter feeding; but they may be treated in any of the following ways:—

1. In mild districts, and where the crop is grown near the sea, the hardier sorts of swedes and even of turnips may stand out all winter and be removed when required. They may also be allowed to stand out in poor districts where the roots are small and hard and are hence not liable to injury by frost.

2. The turnips may be left growing in the fields and fed off as they stand on the ground. When one part of the crop is folded and the remainder is carted off, it is worth removing the roots from strips at regular intervals over the field. This ensures that the droppings of the sheep consuming the remaining roots will be distributed evenly over the ground.

3. They may be stored in small clamps, containing about four to six loads each, which are distributed over the turnip field or on a stubble, and roughly covered to protect them until they are sliced for sheep feeding in the winter months.

4. Turnips or swedes, especially the latter, may be protected in the field by ploughing them in. This is done by ploughing out a furrow, lifting two rows and placing the roots in the bottom, and then ploughing the soil back to give them a good covering. Roots stored in this way probably keep better than when they are preserved in any other manner; but when they are ploughed out for use a good deal of time may be required to clean them.

5. The most usual method of storing, however, is to cart the roots to

a suitable spot in the vicinity of the feeding sheds and place them in long, broad clamps, well covered with straw to protect them from frost.

In all cases where the bulk of the crop is allowed to remain in the fields during winter, it is necessary to keep a supply in the farm buildings which will be sufficient for the wants of the animals during any ordinary spell of hard weather.

**Yield.**—The average yield of turnips for the whole country is about 16 tons per acre; but in the typical turnip districts of the north 20 to 25 tons can easily be grown, and, on the other hand, 10 to 12 tons is an average crop on some thin soils.

## Growing Turnip Seed

Instead of purchasing turnip seed it is an easy matter to grow all that is required for use on the farm. To do this, good, solid, shapely mother-roots, which are entirely free from disease, should be selected and transplanted to a sheltered spot, giving each plant about a square yard of ground, so that they will remain in good condition throughout the winter. The site should be as far as possible and at least four hundred yards from any garden or waste ground where other brassicas might flower at the same time as the turnips and thus cause cross fertilisation. Shooting takes place early in the following season, and it is helpful to remove some of the small top branches so that every chance is given for the production of good, large seed. The ripening seed may have to be protected from birds by means of netting on a suitable framework. The shoots should be cut as soon as they are ripe and stored in an airy shed until they are dry and brittle. When threshing has taken place the seed should be passed over a riddle and the small specimens discarded, as it has been shown that the largest seeds produce the biggest and most robust plants.

The ordinary routine adopted by seedsmen is to sow, in late summer or early autumn, stock seed obtained from selected bulbs, the early sowing causing the resulting crop to run to seed in the following year. Commercial crops thus represent the second generation from the selected plant. Commercial seed is grown chiefly in the eastern and south-eastern counties of England. Often, an insecticide treatment against the pollen beetle and/or the swede seed weevil are necessary in such areas. Average yields are about 8 cwt. for turnips and 6 cwt. for swedes, but the seasonal variation is extremely wide.

## Fungoid Diseases

**Finger and Toe.**—This disease is due to the attack of a slime fungus which finds its way into the growing root tissue from the soil. At first the affected plant is unthrifty in appearance and its leaves are somewhat wilted. An examination of the root reveals the chief characteristic of the disease—the presence of malformations of " club roots " due to the stimulating action of the fungus which multiplies rapidly within the cells. The root is stunted and small and afterwards decays.

The longevity of the fungus makes it difficult to deal with; but it is found to be most persistent on land that is definitely acid, although not confined to such soils. An ordinary degree of acidity can be remedied by applying 30 cwt. to 2 tons of slaked lime per acre, or rather more of chalk or limestone, the influence of such dressings on the activity of the organism being most marked when they are applied in the autumn six or eighteen months before the turnips are to be sown. Such a dressing, if in excess of soil need, may immobilise the boron in the soil and so induce the condition known as heart-rot, brown-heart or raan, which is due to boron deficiency. It can be prevented by making a small application of borax (see p. 81). When it is practicable to lengthen the rotation or to put the worst infected fields down to grass for a period, the fungus is either eradicated or its activity greatly reduced. Only it must be remembered that the land will be re-infected if diseased roots are thrown out on the grass for feeding. A point that should never be overlooked when turnips have to be grown on badly infected soil is the selection of varieties that are resistant to the disease. It is possible to obtain varieties—e.g. The Bruce turnip and the Wilhelmsburger swede—that are affected only to a slight degree. It is, of course, recommended that cruciferous weeds should be suppressed, and the dung containing the remains of diseased roots should not be used for turnips; but these precautions are difficult to carry out in practice.

**Turnip Mildew.**—A number of species of leaf mildew attack the leaves of turnips and other cruciferous plants, the greatest damage being sustained in the southern counties, where the growth of the crop is apt to be retarded by hot and dry weather.

In southern districts turnips are sown a month later than in other places, because they are then found to suffer less than when early sowing has brought about a considerable development of foliage by the time the hottest and driest season is reached. If seedling turnips are found to be affected they should be singled at once, so that each plant may have room to develop and the competition for the available soil moisture may be reduced.

**Other Diseases.**—Crown and Root Rots (*B. caratovorus*) and Dry Rot (*Phoma lingam*) are other diseases which greatly affect the proportion of useable roots in the crop. At present the only way to deal with them is to secure varieties that have some resistance to their attack.

### Insect Pests

**The Turnip Fly** (flea-beetles).—These insects are readily recognised by the swift and long jumps that they make when disturbed. The beetle is only about $\frac{1}{10}$ in. long, and the commonest species is readily recognisable by the broad yellow band running down each wing cover, but other species are respectively bluish black and black all over. The period of greatest activity is from about late April to mid-May, but this varies somewhat with the locality and the season. The eggs are laid from May to July in the soil near a host plant, and five or six weeks later, after the larvæ have fed and pupated, the adults emerge. The young beetles are active until September and hibernate in sheltered places over winter; they do not lay their eggs until the following summer. Thus there is only one generation per year, but two generations may co-exist for a time in late summer. The damage is caused not by the larvæ but by the adult beetles which attack the delicate seed leaves of the turnips and related species as soon as or even before they are through the ground. In a season when growth is slow the plants may be eaten off altogether. When the plants have reached the rough leaf stage, they may be considered safe, but it used sometimes to be necessary to sow the crop several times before it could establish itself.

Control can be effected by dusting the seedlings (or the surface of the ground before the seedlings break through) with a suitable material. Derris, nicotine and nicotine sulphate were formerly among the most effective materials, but dusts containing D.D.T. or B.H.C. are much better, mainly because they remain effective over a much longer period. Special seed dressings containing B.H.C. are available which avoids the need for subsequent treatment of the crop. These are cheap and generally effective.

Other insects that attack turnips are surface caterpillars, the silver Y moth, the turnip mud beetle, the turnip gall weevil, the diamond-back moth, the turnip root fly, the swede midge, the mealy cabbage aphid and the peach-potato aphid.

## MANGELS AND FODDER BEET

Mangels are supposed to have been evolved by a long process of careful selection from the wild sea beet, which is still found in many temperate districts. The mangels, (or mangel wursel), which is of German origin, was introduced to this country in 1786 but was little grown until about 1810. It was gradually realised that under southern conditions the crop yields a substantially larger amount of nutrients than turnips or swedes and the acreage has gradually increased at the expense of the other roots. In northern England and in Scotland it is no more productive than swedes, but it is becoming increasingly common to find a small acreage of mangels on northern farms, the object being to have a reliable supply of succulent food in late April and May, by which time swedes generally deteriorate in quality.

The mangel " root " consists of part of the stem immediately below the cotyledons and part of the true root tissue, enlarged and modified as a food reserve. Transverse sections show the concentric ring formation so well known in the garden beet. Like the turnip it is biennial, but by special methods it can be made to produce its seed within twelve months.

Fodder beet is the name given to a range of feeding roots derived from sugar beet alone or from crosses between sugar beet and mangel. Incidentally, sugar beet and mangel are closely related, being derived from the same wild species. The main differences between the two groups are in dry matter content and in the growth form, especially the position of the mature " root " in relation to the soil surface. " Sugar beets for Fodder," as the Danes call the types with the highest dry matter content, closely resemble true sugar beet, while the most widely grown varieties are intermediate, both in growth form and in dry matter content, between the two parents.

Mangels and fodder beet are capable of yielding more dry matter per acre than any other crop of a similar nature, and the greater part of the food material is in the form of sugar. The yield is highly elastic and can be influenced greatly by manuring. Indeed, where conditions are suitable and manuring is understood, crops of over 60 tons of mangels and 35 of fodder beet, containing perhaps 6 tons of dry matter, have been grown.

The rôle of the mangel in the economy of the farm is similar to that of the turnip, but where climate and soil are favourable it is a better yielder. It is less liable to parasitic infestations, is a more certain cropper and keeps better than any cruciferous root. The mangel is superior to the turnip as a food for dairy cows, since it does not taint the milk nor spoil the flavour of the butter. As a food for sheep, however, mangels are not so satisfactory as turnips; although they can be fed safely to ewes after lambing, they tend to produce urinary disorders in male sheep and are unsuitable for tegs. In all cases, however, it is essential that mangels should be properly ripened before they are offered to stock, as immature roots cause the animals to scour badly. Because of their liability to injury by frost, mangels have to be lifted before they are properly ripe. The lifting of the crop is therefore followed by a period of maturation in clamp, and farmers as a general rule do not feed mangels to stock before Christmas. In most cases the leaves are left on the field and returned to the soil as manure, but in years of scarcity, after they have wilted, they can be used in limited quantities for feeding purposes. They are of lower feeding value than sugar beet tops since the latter will have a portion of the root crown attached to it.

Fodder beets have been grown in Britain, on any considerable scale, only since 1949; those of the intermediate type are mostly favoured. Even on the Continent large scale cultivation began only in the thirties.

In regard to production of total dry matter per acre there is little difference between fodder beet and mangels, but fodder beet has a higher proportion of the total carbohydrates in the form of sugar. Fodder beet has the advantage in the lower total weight that has to be handled at harvest. Most important, perhaps, is the fact that pigs, whereas they cannot eat enough mangels to provide a major part of their total energy requirements, can, in the later stages of growth and fattening, get up to half their total needs from fodder beet.

**Varieties.**—Mangels (as distinct from fodder beets) may be classified according as their shape is long, intermediate tankard or globe, and their colour red, orange, gold or yellow, but except in the case of Golden Tankards, which as a group are uniformly high in dry matter and good keeping but low yielding, there is no relationship between the colour or form of the roots and their cropping powers or other economic qualities.

Mangel and fodder beet varieties are best classified, from the point of view of utilisation, according to their average dry matter contents. It happens, too, that growth habit is correlated with dry matter content, the high dry matter fodder beets having the " root " mostly below ground-level, the mangels having it mostly above, and the intermediate types being about half-way between. The usual British classification is:—

|   |   | Dry Matter Content. Per Cent. |
|---|---|---|
| 1. Fodder sugar beet | . . . | 18 to 22 |
| 2. Fodder beet | . . . | 15 „ 18 |
| 3. Mangels (high dry matter) | . . | 11 „ 15 |
| 4. „ (low „ „ ) | . . | 7 „ 11 |

Typical examples of the first group are Hunsballe and Pajbjerg, and of the second Red Otofte and Pajbjerg Rex.

## Cultivation

**Soil and Climate.**—The mangel is the typical root crop of all the heavy classes of land, but it grows best in deep rich loam and is unsatisfactory on shallow and very light soils. Since mangels do best in sunny, dry climates, they occupy the greater part of the fodder root crop area in the southern and eastern counties. Once established they are highly resistant to drought; they do well where heat and drought would check the growth of cruciferous roots. It is in the south midland and south western counties, however, that mangels grow to perfection. In Scotland, the climate is too dull and cold for the best results, and there is an increased tendency for the plants to bolt; but many farmers are now cultivating a small acreage for spring use.

**Place in Rotation.**—Mangels have in the past occupied much the same place in the rotation as the turnip crop, because they facilitate the cleaning of the land in the same way. They cannot be taken after a spring consumed forage crop, as they have to be sown early. Since the carting of so

K

bulky a crop over any considerable distance is a very laborious business there is a strong reason for restricting its cultivation to fields near to the point of consumption. There is, however, the risk of infection of the land with sugar beet eelworm, if cropping with beet or mangels is too frequent (see Sugar Beet Eelworm p. 308). Mangels, since they are rarely cleared till late autumn, and since the heavy carting damages the soil structure, must generally be followed by a spring sown crop.

**Preparation and Sowing.**—The preparation for the crop depends on the soil texture, the preceding crop, the amount of couch or other perennial weeds, and, not least, the pressure of other work. Autumn ploughing should be the aim, but if farmyard manure is to be applied, later ploughing will generally be inevitable. In spring the frost mould should be kept on top—*i.e.* a second ploughing should generally be avoided. In the eastern and southern counties the treatment both for mangels and fodder beet is the same as for sugar beet (see p. 301). In the north the crop is sometimes grown on the ridge, and preparation is closely similar to that required for swedes (see p. 280).

The row width may vary from 20 to nearly 30 in., and there is an obvious advantage in making this the same as that adopted for the other main root crop. The ultimate aim is a plant population of 20,000 to 25,000 per acre for mangels and about 30,000 for fodder beet.

Mangel " seed," like that of sugar beet, is, in fact, a fruit cluster containing two, three or occasionally four true seeds. Seed rates vary, according to the time of sowing and the state of tilth, from about 6 to above 15 lb. per acre. Too thick a plant makes for very laborious singling.

Techniques to reduce the need for hand singling may be used for mangels as for sugar beet. Specially graded and rubbed seed is available for sowing by precision drills. Precisely the same methods are used as for sugar beet (see p. 303).

In the Midlands of England the usual time for mangel sowing is from the second week to the end of April, but the crop may be put in up to the middle of May. In Scotland mangels are sown about the beginning of May. If sown too early a proportion of the crop tends to bolt; if seeding is late, part of the growing season is lost and the yield suffers. Fodder beet is sown at about the same date.

**Manuring.**—Traditionally the most important and widely used manure for mangels is dung. It has been found, however, that dung alone does not supply nitrogen fast enough for the best results, and a moderate dressing, supplemented by artificial fertilizers, will produce a greater yield than an excessive application of farmyard manure. With regard to the mineral fertilizers, mangels are less dependent upon phosphate than are turnips, but require a more liberal supply of potash. All roots of this family respond also to applications of common salt up to 5 cwt. per acre. It was formerly believed that the salt rendered available some of the soil reserves of potash and that the mangels benefited indirectly, but it is now known that sodium can be utilised directly by the crop.  Bearing this in mind, it is worthy of note that kainit, a crude form of potash salts, contains a considerable proportion of common salt, and therefore has a particular value when applied for mangels.  The common salt or kainit is applied some weeks before sowing, so as to prevent delayed germination or injury to the young seedlings.  Ordinarily the fertilizer should be applied immediately before sowing and worked into the seed bed.  It may also be applied by a side band placement drill at sowing,  Where no dung is used half of the nitrogenous fertilizer may be given as a side dressing at singling time in the wetter parts of the country.

The quantities of manure which can be applied profitably depend on the condition of the soil.  On land of good depth and good texture the crop responds to heavy dressings more readily than on poorer or shallow soils.  The optimal dressing of phosphate for mangels, as for other crops, is generally highest in the north and west and least in the south and east.

The general manuring follows closely to that for sugar beet although the rates per acre may not be quite so high since the crop is not such a profitable one.  It is as follows:—

| 100 units N | | 100 units N |
|---|---|---|
| 50 units $P_2O_5$ | or | 50 units $P_2O_5$ |
| 150 units $K_2O$ | | 100 units $K_2O$ |
| (where no salt is used) | | 3 cwt. salt |

Where 10 tons per acre of farmyard manure is used, the fertilizer may be reduced by about one-third.  On soils low in phosphate or in the west and north of the country the phosphate is increased to 100 units $P_2O_5$.

**After-cultivation.**—The growth of mangels being at the outset slower than that of turnips, inter-row hoeing is generally necessary before thinning.  As a rule the crop is ready for thinning about four to six weeks after sowing; but in some districts a preliminary bunching is given, and the plants are afterwards carefully singled.

The tillage operations for the suppression of weeds are the same as for the sugar beet crop, and must be carried out until the leaves meet in the drills, care being taken to prevent any of the weeds from seeding, otherwise much of the cleaning effect of the crop is lost.  Those weed killer techniques used for sugar beet may also normally be used for mangels.

Towards the end of the growing period a proportion of the plants may bolt, or produce their reproductive shoots.  In some seasons the proportion is very small, but in others, especially in the northern districts, bolting is very troublesome.  If this takes place, the shoots draw upon the reserves of food material in the roots and the yield is reduced.  Bolting may be caused by a spell of cold weather at a particular point in the seedling's growth.  Some strains are much less prone to bolt than others.

**Irrigation.**—Mangels and fodder beet are responsive to irrigation in dry seasons. The technique and timing of watering is the same as for sugar beet (see p. 306).

**Securing the Crop.**—Mangels grow well into autumn and it is desirable to give them as long as possible to mature; on the other hand they do not withstand much frost, so they have to be secured before this danger becomes serious. In practice, lifting and clamping usually take place towards the end of October or, in the south, before the end of November. Lifting is generally performed by two workers together, taking two rows apiece, and dropping the mangels in the drill between them when they have cut off the tops. In this way four drills separate every row of topped mangels, and this is ample room for taking through a trailer or cart when carrying takes place. If, however, the roots are not to be carted at once they should be collected into heaps containing about one fifth of a load each and covered over with leaves, since, whereas growing mangels are protected from frost by their tops, bare roots are much more easily destroyed. This practice is also believed to improve the keeping quality, as mangels sweat a little immediately after pulling; if taken directly to the clamp, and especially if they have been pulled before their growth has ceased, they are apt to suffer serious loss through fermentation, heating and decay.

It is important to avoid causing serious damage to the roots. They should not be tailed and, if storage is to be for a long period, it is better not to load them by fork. Injuries are likely to give rise to bacterial decay and the destruction of a proportion of the crop.

Fodder beet, because of its higher dry matter content, is less liable to frost injury than the mangel. The shallower rooting types may sometimes be harvested in the same way as mangels; the deeper rooting varieties generally have to be loosened by means of a beet lifter. Topping of fodder beet may be merely the removal of the leaves or, alternatively, the removal of the crown as well. If the tops are to be fed the latter procedure is best, since the collection of leaves, without the crown, is laborious.

As a rule mangels and fodder beet are stored in clamps in the vicinity of the feeding courts or sheds. In most cases the clamps are made as large as the roots can be conveniently heaped, because, once the first sweat is over, they can be kept in bulk without fear of further fermentation. Buildings that are well thatched can be filled almost to the roof, or clamps may be built against a wall, or between two parallel walls, to a great depth. Nevertheless a good covering of straw is essential, as the outer roots are very easily frosted; and clamps in the open should get a final covering of soil.

**Yield.**—The average yield of mangels is 19 or 20 tons, but crops of 30 tons are not uncommon, while 60 tons is occasionally reached with the low dry matter types in particularly suitable areas such as South Devon. Yields of fodder beet vary with the variety as well as for other reasons. Fifteen tons is a good yield for the high dry matter types.

**Growing Mangels for Seed.**—Most mangel seed is grown in the southern districts, and the system employed enables the crop to be produced within twelve months. The crop must be grown in isolation from sugar beet or red beet crops in order to avoid cross pollination. The seed is sown in a prepared bed about the beginning of August, superphosphate being generally used to promote strong root development. The steckling bed will be sprayed two or three times with a systemic insecticide to control the aphid vectors of virus yellows.

Transplanting can take place early in October. The land on which the plants are to be grown is dunged, ploughed and given artificial fertilizers if these should be necessary; after harrowing it is marked off to allow each plant at the most 1 sq. yd. of ground. Within limits, the higher the plant density the higher the seed yield. The plants or stecklings are then dibbled in. In winter the mangels look rather backward, and severe weather may cause a few blanks that require to be filled from the seed bed. In spring the crop can be given a top dressing of nitrate of soda. Early in the season the plants produce their reproductive shoots, and, when a fair height has been attained, the tips may be cut off to encourage the lower branches to spread. When the first fruits begin to harden and turn brown the crop should be cut, tied into bundles and stooked to dry. When dry, the crop can be stacked or threshed. The yield varies from 10 to over 20 cwt. of seed per acre. The seed of sugar beet can be produced in the same way. Recent experiments with sugar beet for seed suggest that a suitable manuring is about 10 tons of dung, 3 cwt. of common salt a few weeks before planting, 2 cwt. superphosphate (40 units $P_2O_5$) and 1 cwt. muriate of potash (60 units $K_2O$) at planting time, and 2 cwt. of nitrogen fertilizer (say 40 units N) in spring.

**Diseases of Mangels.**—Mangels and fodder beet are liable to attack by the same diseases and pests as sugar beet (see pp. 307-308).

## CARROTS

Our cultivated carrots have been obtained from the wild carrot, which is a common annual or biennial weed, by a process of selection which has fixed a biennial habit and a fleshy root. There are numerous varieties, varying from the small, sweet garden sorts to the large, white fleshed field carrots which are grown exclusively for stock. These are rarely if ever, grown in Britain today, but may be found in cultivation on the Continent. The feeding value and dry matter content is substantially higher than that of swedes or mangels. The yellow varieties are rich in carotene, which is the precursor of vitamin A.

Carrots grow well under all our climatic conditions, but large scale cultivation is almost restricted to two soil types—very deep, sandy loams and the light peats of the fen lands. No attempt should be made to grow field varieties on shallow or stony land, as the crop is certain to be inferior and unprofitable. Crops grown on heavy land are usually unprofitable and are very difficult and costly to harvest.

It is important that deep cultivation should be given in preparing land for carrots, and if there is even the slightest pan it must be broken up by subsoiling. When the deep working has been completed a fine surface tilth should be prepared as for the turnip crop, and the ground must be thoroughly cleaned. The importance of clean land for carrots can hardly be overestimated, as the seedlings are so slow growing and delicate that they cannot compete with weeds. In recent years, however, the culture of the crop has been revolutionised by the introduction of selective oil sprays for weed control. Special oil fractions or even (with suitable precautions) tractor vaporising oil can be used at an early stage of growth (see p. 125). Pre-emergence sprays may also be used (see p. 123).

The seed may be obtained either in its natural state or with its bristles machined off. In the former case it is difficult to sow as the appendages cause the seeds to cling together, and before being put through the seed drill it should be mixed with a large bulk of sand or dry soil. About 4 lb. of seed is sufficient to sow an acre, if the plants are to be singled. But most commercial growers now sow at a rate of $\frac{3}{4}$ to 1 lb. and dispense with singling, which is a very laborious operation. Row widths vary according to district and other circumstances. Seven to 10 in. is sufficient, with relatively wide spacing in the rows, but mechanical cultivation is difficult. A row width of 14 to 18 in. facilitates tractor work. But if the land is free from perennial weeds, and if a selective weed killer is used to deal with annuals, little inter-row cultivation is required. Another plan is to have narrow and wide rows alternately—about 8 and 18 in. respectively. This plan has the advantage that the double rows can be lifted by means of an elevator type of potato digger. The seed must not be placed too deep (1 in. is sufficient) or the plants will fail to come to the surface. The crop may be singled to intervals of 4 to 5 in., but because the chief demand is for a small sized carrot, large areas are now sown thinly and not singled at all.

Some growers treat the crop, so far as fertilizers are concerned, in much the same way as sugar beet, but this treatment is over generous. On land that is in reasonably fertile condition the crop gives little response either to phosphate or nitrogen. Potash, however, will usually produce a response. If dung is used it should be ploughed in deeply in autumn; but it is better to grow carrots in the second year after applying farm manure. Unrotted dung tends to make the carrots fork and reduces their value.

An average fertilizer dressing for normal carrot soils would be:—

| 45 units N | = | $2\frac{1}{4}$ cwt. sulphate of ammonia |
| 45 units $P_2O_5$ | = | $2\frac{1}{4}$ cwt. superphosphate |
| 90 units $K_2O$ | = | $1\frac{1}{2}$ cwt. muriate of potash |

Carrots respond to salt although little is used in practice. If 3 cwt. salt per acre is applied, the potash dressing may be halved.

If farmyard manure is used the quantities of fertilizer listed above may be halved.

Maincrop carrots are sown in April or early May. In the mildest districts crops for the market may be sown in February.

The subsequent cultivations consist of keeping the land thoroughly clean by spraying, tractor hoeing and hand weeding if weeds should get out of hand. The last is very laborious, and every effort should be made to eliminate it. Motorised hoe equipment (see p. 143) is very suitable. In large scale production singling is rarely done. The crop may be irrigated in dry seasons with great benefit to both yield and quality.

Although carrots can stand a certain amount of frost, it is usual to lift and store in October or November those intended for the winter and early spring markets. The lifting is usually done by two workers, one loosening the soil with a fork while the other draws out the roots and twists or cuts off the leaves. The carrots are stored in small clamps built after the fashion of potato pits, and provided with a ventilating shaft of straw to prevent overheating. Many growers, especially in milder areas, take the risk of leaving the crop in the ground, and lift as required for market.

The average yield of mature carrots per acre is about 11 tons. On suitable soils 20 ton crops are not uncommon, and yields of 30 tons have been recorded.

The chief pest of the carrot is the larva of the carrot fly. There are two generations each year and most of the first generation emerge in the latter part of May. They shelter in such places as hedge bottoms and, after mating, lay their eggs in the soil very near to the host plants, which may be attacked any time after the cotyledon stage. The maggots burrow into the roots, so destroying many plants and doing much damage to others. When fully fed the larvæ pupate and produce a second generation of flies during August to October. These in turn give rise to more maggots which tunnel in the root tissues and do great destruction even after the carrots have been lifted and stored. Carrot fly may be controlled by the use of certain insecticides such as aldrin applied either to the seed bed or to the young crop. For details of the currently recommended methods the reader is referred to Ministry of Agriculture, Fisheries and Food Advisory Leaflet No. 68, *Carrot Fly*.

There is also an eelworm parasitic on carrots. Fortunately it is not extensively distributed.

## KOHLRABI

In the kohlrabi that part of the primary stem above the cotyledons thickens and develops into a turnip like food store. This " bulb " grows entirely above the ground, and as it thickens the lower leaves fall away, leaving characteristic broad scars. There are two main classes of varieties, the one being entirely green and the other purplish.

Kohlrabi takes the place of a root crop in the economy of the farm, and can be safely fed to all classes of stock. As a food for cattle it is excellent, being less liable to cause scouring than turnips or swedes. It has a particular value for dairy cows in that it does not taint the milk as do turnips. When fed to sheep it is usually eaten off, and it is more economical than swedes, as only the little thin roots are left in the ground. It may be fed to pigs, and as its nutritive value is much higher than that of the mangel, it has been found that sows having the run of a little grassland can be kept on kohlrabi without the addition of concentrates during the early months of pregnancy. Kohlrabi is used for culinary purposes and is generally prepared like a dish of turnips.

The crop is rarely grown at the present time but may be found occasionally chiefly in Essex, Suffolk and Kent, and mostly on the stiffer class of land. Its requirements are more akin to those of the mangels than to those of the turnip. For this reason kohlrabi is sometimes grown in southern districts where turnips form an uncertain crop.

In growing kohlrabi the land is prepared as for turnips, and sowing takes place in April. The seed is sown on the flat at the rate of 4 lb. to the acre, and the drills are 18 to 24 in. apart. When the plants are sufficiently forward they are singled to intervals of 10 to 12 in. Sometimes the plants are started in a bed and dibbled in by hand in May or June; and because they can be transplanted very successfully, a small bed may be sown in March and the plants used to fill the gaps in mangel crops. Kohlrabi may also be sown at $\frac{3}{4}$ lb. to the acre by means of a precision drill in which case the singling needed will be reduced to a minimum.

In the manuring of the crop it is usual to apply a moderate dressing of dung supplemented by fertilizers, but the plants do not respond to nitrogenous dressings as well as mangels or cabbages. A suitable manuring would be 12 tons farmyard manure, 4 cwt. superphosphate (80 units $P_2O_5$), 3 cwt. kainit (60 units $K_2O$), and $1\frac{1}{2}$ cwt. sulphate of ammonia (30 units N.).

It is usual to feed the crop in the autumn, but if necessary the bulbs can be stored in clamps like turnips. If a hardy variety is selected, however, the plants may be allowed to stand out until well into the winter and lifted as they are required.

**Other Root Crops.**—Considerable acreages of red beet and of parsnips are now grown, in rotation with corn and other ordinary farm crops, in certain areas. For information about these the reader is referred to standard works such as Hoare's *Vegetable Production for Market.*

# CHAPTER 12

# SUGAR BEET

SUGAR BEET is a biennial plant closely related to the mangel and red beet. It differs from the mangel in that its parsnip shaped " root " develops in the ground and only the crown, bearing the leaves, appears above the soil. Sugar beets are white coloured; their average weight is about 1 lb.; they do not bleed like mangels and garden beet when cut; they have a high dry matter content, their sugar content alone amounting to from 13 to more than 20 per cent. of their weight. A typical analysis is:—

| | | | | | | | |
|---|---|---|---|---|---|---|---|
| Sugar | . | . | . | . | . | . | 16·50 per cent. |
| Fibre | . | . | . | . | . | . | 4·70 ,, |
| Proteins | . | . | . | . | . | . | 0·60 ,, |
| Other organic matter | . | . | . | . | . | 1·05 ,, |
| Ash . | . | . | . | . | . | . | 0·75 ,, |
| | | | Total dry matter | . | 23.60 | ,, |

The sugar beet of to-day has been developed from an early type of mangel by breeding and selection, which have been carried out with the primary object of obtaining a maximum yield of sugar per acre. The early work of improvement took place in France and Germany, but beet cultivation has now extended to every country in Europe, to America and to many other temperate countries throughout the world. Although the main object of growing beet is the production of sugar, the by-products —tops and pulp—are important to many growers, especially dairy farmers. In other cases the tops are ploughed in as manure.

Beet tops, whose food value is rather better than that of swedes, can be consumed on the ground by sheep or carted for cattle. On light peaty and it has become a practice to run cattle over the beet fields after harvest, with straw and water as the only supplements. Heavy soils would, in many cases, be damaged by treading, and on light mineral soils there would be a risk that the cattle would ingest harmful amounts of sand. Beet tops have the disadvantage that when fresh they tend to cause violent scouring. This trouble is usually avoided by allowing the leaves to wilt for ten to fourteen days, but if this is not sufficiently effective it may be desirable to feed along with them 0·1 to 0·2 per cent. of ground chalk. Another fault is that when tops are fed in too large quantity to milch cows they may produce a fishy taint in the milk. In any event they should be fed after milking, either fresh or in the form of silage. Fifty six pounds per head per day should be the maximum.

Beet pulp, which is the residue of the roots after the sugar has been extracted, is a very valuable substitute for the ordinary root crops. In the wet state it is of rather poorer feeding value than white turnips, but it is nevertheless the only succulent food given to many continental herds during winter. The dry pulp is sometimes used to absorb molasses, which is another by-product of the factory. In this form it has, like the tops, a tendency to produce a taint in milk. The wet pulp, having a high and variable moisture content, is costly of transportation, and it is therefore used mostly by farmers in the vicinity of the factories; it can be stored in pit silos, either with or without the addition of the tops and leaves, for long periods. Most factories also produce dry pulp in which the moisture content is reduced from about 93 to 11 per cent. The dried pulp is, of course, much less bulky, and it can be sent long distances at relatively small cost; it can be stored in bags for an indefinite period. Some of the dried pulp is processed into solid blocks, which are more convenient and less wasteful than the bagged loose product. When used in moderate quantity, 1 lb. of dried pulp may replace 7 lb. of swedes or mangels, or 10 lb. of soft turnips. It is comparable in energy value with oats, but much lower in protein. If fed in larger quantities, the dry material is generally swelled by soaking it in water before feeding, but soaking is unnecessary provided the animals have access to water.

**The Extraction of Sugar from Beet.**—For the extraction of beet sugar, factories are erected in districts which are likely to be suitable for the cultivation of beet in quantity. The crop is grown for the factories at a contract price per ton of washed beet containing a standard percentage of sugar, and a bonus is given where the sugar content is above this standard or a corresponding deduction is made for a short fall. The work of extraction commences towards the end of September and the last beets are usually disposed of by the middle of January. There are seventeen factories in England and one in Scotland, all under the control of the British Sugar Corporation, which promotes and carries on research on the crop and which has a field staff.

The beet is consigned to the factory as it is required, and on its arrival a representative sample is taken in order to estimate the tare and the sugar content. The tare is the difference in weight between the beet as delivered in a more or less dirty condition and the same beets after washing and, if necessary, dressing; top tare and dirt tare together ordinarily amount to some 14 to 16 per cent. of the gross weight. The sugar content is estimated in the factory laboratory: it generally increases up to the end of October, about which time the crop also reaches its maximum, and thereafter decreases. As the farmer gets nothing for the tare on his consignment but has to pay carriage thereon, it is obviously in his interest to deliver the roots in as clean a condition as possible and properly topped.

In the manufacturing process the beets are first washed and after weighing they pass to the slicing machines, which reduce them to fragments suitable for extraction. The sliced beet then has its sugar extracted by passing it slowly, step by step, up a long sloping cylinder down which hot water is run. Thus the beet slices are first extracted by juice, then, as the sugar is removed, by a solution of decreasing concentration and finally by hot water. The residual pulp is removed and sold, either wet or after desiccation, for stock feeding. The purification of the juice from the extractor is brought about by the addition of lime and the subsequent precipitation of the lime with carbon dioxide. The juice is next evaporated to a syrup and, after further purification, it is concentrated in vacuum pans by boiling at a sufficiently low temperature to prevent caramelisation. When the crystals are sufficiently formed, the material is centrifuged to remove the non-crystallisable matter, which is the by-product known as molasses or treacle. Beet factory waste lime or sludge can be bought at an almost nominal price. It contains nearly 50 per cent. of water and traces of phosphate and other plant nutrients. It is widely used as a source of lime for application to farm land in areas adjoining the factories.

**Quality and Varieties.**—Beet roots should average 1 lb. or a little more in weight, richer soils producing the larger size; the shape should be that of a nicely formed cone without any tendency to forking or fangy growth. There should be no coarseness about the crowns, very little of which should appear above the ground. A well developed leaf system is essential for a good crop, but an over development due to excessive nitrogenous fertilizer is often correlated with lateness, poor root development and reduced sugar content.

A high sugar content is desirable and this is usually more easily obtained by growing a large number of medium sized roots on a given area than by having larger and wider spaced plants. The sugar content, however, must be considered in conjunction with the yield. There are three types of sugar beet varieties but only the first two are normally grown in this country. They are: E strains which produce a high yield but contain a relatively low proportion of sugar, N strains that are medium in yield and sugar-content, and Z strains that give a relatively low yield but contain a high proportion of sugar. Varieties should be selected from the lists offered by the factories and recommended by the National Institute of Agricultural Botany[1], according to the type that is likely to be most profitable under local conditions. A high sugar content is most desirable from the factory owner's point of view, but a larger yield with a lower sugar content may be more profitable to the grower. At one time the Z strains were recommended for wet districts, but since most of the British crop is grown under fairly dry conditions, in practice the E and N types are now used almost exclusively. Where the crop is to be lifted before the roots are fully developed, N types are to be preferred.

[1] N.I.A.B. Leaflet No. 5, *Varieties of Sugar Beet.*

Bolters in crops of sugar beet are not uncommon and if they occur early in the season they are extremely undesirable, as their roots become woody and of little value for sugar extraction. While the proportion of bolters is undoubtedly influenced by the occurrence of a cold spell when the plants are in the three or four leaf stage, and also perhaps by the manuring, bolting is an hereditary characteristic which is more common in certain varieties than in others. The incidence of bolting may be reduced by delaying the date of sowing, but recent experiments have shown conclusively that early sowing makes for higher yields. This is particularly marked in seasons when the crop suffers an attack of virus yellows (see p. 308). Moreover, plant breeders have recently produced a number of bolt resistant strains, which can safely be sown as early as mid-March. Cambro is a notable example, which, however, is outyielded by others if sown at the normal time, *i.e.* April.

For many years one of the most popular and successful varieties has been Klein E (Sharpe's) but others originating from Battle, Johnson, Bush and Hilleshog are widely grown. There are also a number of polyploid varieties in cultivation.

Varieties which produce a single seed (monogerm) instead of the usual seed cluster are coming onto the market.

Beet is an open pollinated species.

## Beet Cultivation

**Soil and Climate.**—The best soil for beet is a deep free working loam, but the crop has been grown quite satisfactorily on well drained soils of practically all types. Light soils have the advantage of being warm in spring and thus enabling the young plants to establish themselves more quickly; they also allow of the crop being lifted in a somewhat cleaner condition, and they do not suffer much damage by puddling during a wet harvest season. On the other hand, clay is less satisfactory because of the difficulty of poaching when lifting the crop. Stony soils are unsatisfactory because they cause the roots to fork and make the full mechanisation of the crop very difficult, and soils that possess a pan are quite unsuitable for growing beet until the pan has been broken up by deep ploughing or subsoiling. Beet cannot be grown profitably on land that requires liming, and it is important to have the lime requirement of the soil estimated before trying to grow the crop. With regard to quality, it is found that the highest sugar content is obtained when the beet is grown on light land and the lowest on peaty soil.

Sugar beet has been tried in most parts of the country. In the colder and wetter districts of the north and west it has not been a very satisfactory crop, for while it has done well in a few favoured places, the yield has too often been too small to be remunerative. On the other hand, many areas in the east, south, west Midlands and especially in East Anglia, are suitable for the cultivation of beet on a large scale. The cultivation of the crop is likely to be profitable only on soils in a fair state of fertility. Owing to the infrequency of hard autumn frosts in Britain, the roots—which withstand 8° of frost when lifted, and more in the ground—do not require elaborate storage precautions; but it is necessary that the roots be protected in really hard weather. Roots left in small heaps in the field, and those on the top and sides of clamps, can be so damaged by frost that sugar extraction at the factory is slowed down and made more difficult. They may also decay after thawing. Field heaps should be covered with a layer of tops, and clamps should be strawed when hard frost threatens.

**Place in Rotation.**—In this country beet generally takes the same place in the rotation as the root or potato crop, *i.e.* between two straw crops, where maximum benefit is obtained from the opportunity of cleaning the land. However, if land is really foul, beet should be avoided, as the cost of hoeing and singling is apt to be prohibitive—unless, perhaps, where the crop is sown in very wide rows. Beet was in the past grown successfully on the same ground for several consecutive years, but in the long run the practice led to the infestation of the soil with beet eelworm. As such an infestation is a very serious matter, successive beet crops should be avoided. British factories now make it a condition of their contracts that beet (or other hosts of the beet eelworm, such as brassicas) shall be grown at intervals of not less than three years, and the *Sugar Beet Eelworm Order*, 1952, imposes other cropping restrictions in certain specified areas.

**Preparation and Sowing.**—In early districts it may be possible to clean the stubbles after harvest, and this should be done whenever it is practicable. In autumn or early winter the farmyard manure, if it is to be used, is spread before ploughing. The ploughing should be as deep as the nature of the soil will permit, and in some cases it may be profitably accompanied by subsoiling; it should be done early so that the furrow slices get the benefit of long exposure to winter frosts. One way ploughing is of advantage since it leaves the land even, without ridges and furrows. Most authorities are against cross ploughing in spring, maintaining that this practice turns down the frost mould and tends to dry the soil, thus hindering the preparation of a fine tilth and involving the risk of an unsatisfactory plant. In spring, harrows should be sufficient to prepare a fine surface mould. This is important for an even braird, leading to a full plant. Care should be taken to avoid pulling up clods of unweathered soil from below by using cultivators. A full germination of the seed depends on an adequate moisture supply, and this is best secured by consolidating the surface soil with rollers both before and after sowing.

Where the singling is to be mechanised a level and even tilth is important. Scrubbers or special levelling tools may be used if necessary.

The yield of the crop depends very largely on the number of beets that can be grown to the acre, and experience has shown that on average

not be done in the ridges. Green manures may be used for beet but they are not so effective as farm manure.

Sugar beet does not respond greatly to phosphate fertilizer except where the phosphate status of the soil is low. Beet does respond to nitrogen, potash and to salt. If salt is applied at 3 to 5 cwt. per acre the response to potash is decreased. The following are average recommended dressings for the crop. In practice the crop is extremely well manured, the amounts of phosphate and potash being varied to meet soil conditions.

*Without farmyard manure and without salt (per acre)*

$$100 \text{ units N} = \text{approx. 5 cwt. sulphate of ammonia}$$
$$50 \text{ units P}_2\text{O}_5 = \text{,,} \quad 2\tfrac{1}{2} \text{ cwt. superphosphate}$$
$$150 \text{ units K}_2\text{O} = \text{,,} \quad 2\tfrac{1}{2} \text{ cwt. muriate of potash}$$

*Without farmyard manure and with salt (per acre)*

100 units N
50 units $P_2O_5$
100 units $K_2O$
3 cwt. salt

*With farmyard manure and salt (per acre)*

10 tons farmyard manure
70 units N
35 units $P_2O_5$
70 units $K_2O$
3 cwt. salt

Instead of using salt, nitrate of soda may be used in the place of sulphate of ammonia at equivalent rates of N, since that will supply the sodium needed. Alternatively, kainit may be used instead of the muriate of potash and salt.

It should, however, be remembered that sodium salts—either as common salt or in kainit—may cause injury to the texture of heavy soils. As is true also of mangels, it is usual to obtain a marked response from common salt even when the potash supply is optimum. In other words sodium, as such, acts as a plant nutrient in the case of beet and mangels.

The fertilizers are applied at seed-time, and there seems to be no advantage, at least in the drier regions where most of the beet crop is grown, in reserving part of the nitrogen for a subsequent top dressing. Care should be taken to avoid the excessive use of nitrogen fertilizers on land that is in a high state of fertility, otherwise the ripening of the crop will be delayed and the sugar content lowered.

The fertilizer should be thoroughly worked into the top 3 or 4 in. of soil during the process of seed bed preparation. Combine drilled fertilizer impedes germination and should never be practiced. The use of a placement drill, putting the fertilizer in bands on either side of the seed (2 in. to the side and 1 in. deeper), saves an operation, and in some circumstances appears to be of benefit to the yield. It is not a common practice however. Common salt if used is applied a few weeks before sowing.

**After-cultivation.**—In from ten to twenty days after sowing, according to the weather conditions, the sugar beet plants should be through the ground and the land may be given its first hoeing. The procedure then will depend on whether the crop is to be hand worked or mechanically thinned.

Hand thinning of the crop is carried out as soon as the beets reach the four leaf stage, and when they are still very small. Early singling is of the utmost importance, because if the plants are allowed to grow unsingled until they become drawn and spindly—especially if weeds are also present —they will not yield satisfactorily; indeed up to a ton of beet per acre can be lost for every week's delay. In order to thin the plants the hoe should be at least 2 in. narrower than the proposed spacing—say an 8 in. hoe for 10 in. intervals—and the work must be done with very great care in order to ensure that the best plants are left, that there are no blanks, and that the ground is thoroughly cleared of weeds. In some countries beet is thinned and the soil is consolidated about the roots of the selected plants by hand, but this practice is declining due to shortage and cost of hand labour. Sometimes bunching is performed as a preliminary to singling, and it has the advantage that it enables the cock beet, which it is desirable to select, to assert itself. Many farmers pay their workers a bonus according to the regularity of the spacing which they achieve in singling. Singling is an expensive operation, since if a man is to make good work he can generally do no more than a quarter or a fifth of an acre per day. After the plants have recovered from singling, the crop is again tractor hoed. This is followed by hand hoeing between the plants and the removal of any doubles that have been left inadvertently at singling. Yet another power hoeing should be possible before there is danger of damaging the leaves. More after cultivation may be given, but if the work is overdone and the roots are damaged, the yield will suffer.

Mechanical thinning may be carried out with the down-the-row thinner. This is best done on crops sown thinly with rubbed seed through a precision drill. A thin *uniform* braird is essential for good results. First it is usual to take the weeder head through; this brushes out many seedling weeds in the rows without harming the crop seedlings. Then the thinning blades (like very small hoes) are fitted to the machine and one or two operations are carried out to remove a large proportion of the seedlings. The speed of the machine, the size and number of hoes per thinning head will depend on the braird density. The braird density has to be counted and must be as uniform as possible if the right number of plants are to remain at the end. The most uniform results will be achieved by thinning only once and finishing by hand.

The complete mechanisation of the crop depends on good weed control as well as the factors already mentioned. There are certain chemical treatments which may be applied before the crop emerges (see p. 123) but so far none is satisfactory in all conditions under which beet is sown. It is likely that there will be considerable development in this field, so permitting a still wider application of full mechanisation.

**Irrigation.**—The sugar beet crop responds greatly to irrigation in dry seasons and especially on light soils. Apart from the occasional use of seed bed watering in dry springs, irrigation may commence sometime after mid June. The main period is July and August. If watering is carried out it is essential that enough is applied each time so as to wet down to 24 in., a dry soil zone will encourage fanginess of the roots. Irrigation in September may decrease the sugar content considerably.

**Harvesting.**—When beets are ripe the outer leaves tend to fall down and the whole of the foliage assumes a shrunken appearance. As the factories require beet from about the end of September, lifting commences at this time, although the beet is not fully ripe and has not developed its maximum sugar content. At the end of October the beet is at about its best, but the consignments despatched to the factories at the end of the year may have undergone some shrinkage. In order to give growers equal advantages in time of delivery, and to keep the factory fully employed throughout the three months' season, dated loading permits are allotted to each grower.

Beet cannot be pulled easily by hand as can turnips and mangels because it is far too deep rooted. Small areas can be dug with a special two pronged beet fork, but whenever a commercial acreage is being grown the crop is harvested either by hand with the aid of a special lifting plough or is harvested mechanically. In one type of plough there are two lifting prongs with digging points so placed that they enter the ground on either side of the row of beets, and as the implement moves forward the roots are caught on either side and wedged upwards clear of the soil. The other common type has one digging share which loosens the beets on one side and passes them upwards so that they are easily withdrawn for hand topping. A large number of mechanical harvesters are available (see pp. 182-183), and well over a half of the total acreage of the crop is lifted by machine. Some machines leave the topped beets for hand loading, others do the whole job and leave heaps of topped beet on the field or at the headland.

In hand lifting, after the plants have been loosened by the beet plough, they are drawn up and knocked together to remove as much as possible of the adhering soil; they are then laid in rows for topping. Topping consists of cutting the beet through at the level of the lowest leaf scar. As previously pointed out, the whole of the top should be removed, because if part is sent to the factory its food value is lost and it will be counted as part of the tare on the consignment.

It is best to harvest the last of the beets in November and to place in clamps that portion of the crop which has to be delivered at a later date. Protection from frost is generally considered to be unnecessary, but some covering is desirable if a spell of severe cold seems imminent. If beet is left in the ground as late as December the land is likely to be very wet and the harvesting operations to be more difficult and costly. Where topping is done as a separate operation, lifting must follow within a day or two, since the sugar content of the roots, left buried in the soil, falls rapidly.

**Yield.**—The average yield of beet has risen greatly since the last war and during the five years prior to 1961 was of the order of 15 tons per acre. Crops of under 10 tons are considered poor and show little profit. Fields of over 20 tons and even 25 tons are not unusual under good conditions and especially under irrigation. The sugar in British grown beets generally runs from 15 to 17 per cent. of the weight of washed roots. The weight of the crowns and tops varies greatly, but a 15 ton crop of sugar beet will yield about 12 tons of crowns and leaves.

## CHICORY

Chicory is grown to a limited extent in the Eastern Counties, the roots being dried, ground and blended for use with coffee. The crop greatly resembles sugar beet in appearance and the cultivation is along very similar lines. It is suited to peat soils and is also grown on the light soils bordering the fen near Lakenheath in Suffolk where there is a factory for the processing of the crop. There is another factory near St. Ives in Hunts.

Chicory is not a host of the Beet Eelworm and therefore may be grown on eelworm sick land.

The crop is grown on contract to one of the two factories.

## SUGAR BEET DISEASES AND PESTS

Sugar beet (and mangels) are attacked in the seedling stage by a number of diseases which are seldom encountered now that the seed is treated with a suitable protectant.

**Wireworm** can be very damaging but beet seedlings can be protected by dressing the seed with one of the insecticidal seed dressings. If wireworm populations are very high the soil may be treated but this is more expensive and troublesome.

**Heart rot** may develop in beet (and mangels) when the plants are suffering from boron deficiency, a condition which is most frequent on light soils of low humus content that have recently been limed. An application of about 20 lb. of borax per acre has been found to prevent the condition developing and also to cure it in its early stages; but it is important to know that large dressings of borax are likely to be toxic. Another deficiency which sometimes occurs is that of manganese, and it is the cause of speckled yellows, not to be confused with virus yellows. Manganese deficiency is liable to occur on alkaline soils of high organic matter, especially some of the peat fens. The symptoms may be cured by spraying with 8 lb. of manganese sulphate in 25 gal. of water plus wetter per acre.

**Virus Yellows** is the most important disease of sugar beet with which we have to contend; it has been known to reduce the sugar yield by 40 per cent. The symptoms are a very marked yellowing of the under-part of the leaf blades, only the larger veins retaining their green colour. The disease is not transmitted through the seed but is carried by aphids— *e.g.* the common peach aphis and the black fly—from infected beet and mangel crops to the healthy plants, over wintering taking place principally in seed crops, in mangel clamps and on escape plants of beet or mangels. Some degree of control of the disease may be effected by growing the seed stecklings in isolation so that vectors cannot carry the virus from them to the commercial root crops, by spraying to destroy the aphids or by producing disease resistant varieties. One should ensure that mangel clamps still in existence after 1st May do not harbour over-wintered aphids.

In the south and eastern beet areas most fields are sprayed once or twice with a systemic insecticide to delay the spread of the virus yellows by the aphid vectors. This treatment seldom prevents the yellows coming in but greatly delays it. In this way large yield responses may be produced in years when aphids are common in beet areas.

The **Sugar Beet Eelworm** has caused immense damage in areas of continental Europe where beet has been grown too frequently on particular fields. The pest has appeared in England, and although it is not yet widespread it is obviously important to keep it under control. As already mentioned, the only insurance is to avoid successive beet crops on particular fields.

There is a Bulletin of the Ministry of Agriculture, Fisheries and Food No. 162, " *Sugar Beet Pests*," another, No. 142, *Sugar Beet Diseases* and a third No. 153 *Sugar Beet Cultivation*, to which the reader is referred for more detailed information.

# CHAPTER 13

# PULSE CROPS AND FLAX

## BEANS

THE common bean (*Vicia faba*) is one of the most ancient of cultivated plants. Although field beans are grown in most parts of Britain it is in the eastern and midland counties of England that they are cultivated to the greatest extent. The bean acreage in this country decreased greatly in the fifty years up till 1939, largely because the crop is suited to the very heaviest land, much of which, during the period in question, was put down to permanent grass; there was, however, a considerable revival during the war, stimulated largely by the shortage of imported feeding stuffs. However, the area cultivated at present is relatively low since the crop is not a very profitable one to grow. It does not compare with cereals in returns per acre, for instance.

As beans are a high protein concentrated food that can be grown in a great many localities, they are of great value for blending with starchy cereal grains in preparing well balanced rations for stock, especially dairy cows. Cracked beans may be fed to horses, calves and sheep, but bean meal is the most useful form for pigs, fattening cattle and dairy cows. Where, as in the north, beans are cut while still somewhat succulent, the straw is nutritious, and when chaffed and mixed with other foods is a valuable addition to the rough fodder of the farm. Beans form a constituent of many arable ensilage mixtures, and produce a very large bulk per acre when thickly sown and heavily manured.

Beans, however, have a number of disadvantages. In hot seasons the crop may be very severely attacked about the beginning of July by the black aphis, and although winter beans are less susceptible than the spring varieties they also are attacked in very bad years. However, the black aphis may be controlled by carefully timed spraying with a systemic insecticide. When the whole crop is covered with aphids its yield is likely to be negligible, and it may be most profitable to make it into silage. Rooks are another common cause of serious damage. Wind frosts may injure the plants in March or April and blacken them to the ground, and beans that are sown early and become proud in autumn may be affected in the same way. May frosts, even if relatively slight, are also very harmful. Frosted crops never recover properly and they leave bare patches of ground which tend to become foul with weeds. A badly damaged crop had better be ploughed in, though if the damage is slight it may be worth while to drill in a few bushels of peas or spring cereal in order to fill up the blanks. The most serious disease is Chocolate Spot, which affects winter beans and is caused by a common grey mould fungus (*Botrytis*) that becomes parasitic in some seasons. The attack takes place between April and July, the symptoms being reddish brown discoloration of the leaves and stems and blighting of the plants. Frost damage and soil deficiencies may predispose the crop to attack, but there is no cure for affected plants. Spring beans are seldom, if ever, attacked.

Beans cannot be grown on the same ground year after year, since they are liable to a disease akin to clover sickness. On the whole, a crop of beans allows the land to become rather dirty, and if drilling is carried out in rows wide enough apart to permit of hoeing, a maximum yield cannot be expected. Recently introduced residual pre-emergence weed killers are likely to make the crop a cleaner one to grow.

In some areas mixed crops of beans and cereals (see p. 223) are preferred to pure crops, and there is some evidence that the mixture yields more than the two constituents grown separately. Moreover, the protein content of the oats seems to be improved when they are grown in association with a legume.

**Varieties.**—The two main types of beans which are generally recognised are the winter and spring varieties. Winter beans, which will grow under relatively poor soil conditions, are sown in autumn and withstand moderate frost; they develop strong lateral branches, and come to maturity much sooner than the spring sorts. Spring varieties resemble winter beans in appearance but are less hardy and do not tiller so well; they are late in ripening, and if not sown early may fail entirely in a dry year. As is the case with wheat, the winter crop, because of its greater productiveness in some areas such as Essex, may be preferred where it will stand the climate; but the climate of Scotland and the north of England is too severe for winter beans. If spring beans are grown, the earlier the seeding the greater and more certain the crop, provided that late frosts do no damage. The Granton Horse Bean and the small seeded Albyn Tick are examples of spring-sown varieties grown in northern localities for many years. In the English bean growing districts many of the strains were known merely as spring beans or winter beans.

Work by the National Institute of Agricultural Botany and others has led to the introduction into wider cultivation of some of the best strains. The Suffolk Red Spring horse bean is an example. The Throws M.S. (mixed strains) is a winter bean developed to benefit from some hybrid vigour. There are also a number of good varieties imported from the Continent.

Tick beans are smaller, rounder and smoother than the common winter and spring horse beans. The Mazagan is a very large flat sided sort, as also is the Dutch Weir bean. Some of the commercial stocks consist of mixtures of types, and since most varieties are largely cross-fertilised in the field—to the extent of about 30 per cent. in the case of winter types—the maintenance of purity of types is difficult.

The National Institute of Agricultural Botany leaflet No. 15, *Field Beans*, lists currently recommended varieties.

## The cultivation of Beans

**Soil and Climate.**—Beans are grown to some extent in most of the arable districts of Britain, but they give much the best results when grown on stiff clay soils, and may even fail on the lighter portions of a field. Probably the very best soils are the chalky boulder clays, as the bean does best where there is plenty of lime; but the crop will not thrive unless the land be well drained. On land rich in humus the yield of grain is often disappointing, though the weight of straw may be very great. When once established on good soil the bean resists drought well, but because of its liability to suffer from frost, the winter varieties are reliable only in the south. The risk of loss in winter is greatest on very wet soils.

**Place in Rotation.**—Beans may take the place of clover in a rotation, as, being legumes, they tend to increase the soil reserves of nitrogen and are an excellent preparation for wheat. They may be grown between two cereal crops, but, as has been said, could not be regarded as a satisfactory cleaning crop, although this is likely to change as weedkillers are increasingly used in this crop. The bean is one of the best crops to grow on broken up grassland, as not only does it crop well on such a soil but it is probably more resistant to wireworm and leather jacket attacks than any other farm crop—flax and linseed only excepted. The introduction since the war of reliable control measures for these pests makes this aspect of beans of lesser importance than hitherto.

**Preparation and Sowing.**—Winter beans should be sown early, and most farmers like to get the operation over before the end of the second week of October. On rich land, September sown beans may develop too strongly before the cold weather sets in and consequently suffer from frost. On the other hand, sowing after the first of November is very risky, and it is better to wait and put in a spring variety. The usual autumn seeding is often at the rate of 3 bushels (of 63 to 66 lb.) per acre, but field experiments have shown that higher rates ($3\frac{1}{2}$ to 4 bushels) commonly give better results. Spring beans must be sown early, and once the beginning of February is reached the sooner the seed is in the ground the better. It is not always possible to get on the land as early as this, but at any rate the beans should be sown before any other spring crop, and a seeding of at least $3\frac{1}{2}$ bushels per acre is necessary. If beans are too thickly sown, or grown in close rows, there is a tendency for the foliage to develop strongly at the expense of the grain yield; indeed, light must be able to reach the lower flowers if the pods are to set. Some farmers prefer new beans for seed; others sow year old seed. It matters little which is used; the choice should be those that have been harvested in the better condition and show the higher germination. As with many other crops, the methods of prepartion and of sowing depend on how the farmyard manure is applied, and, of course, whether autumn sowing is to be adopted. Seeding may be carried out in any of the following ways:—

1. Beans may be sown on the flat in rows between 20-30 in. apart by means of a cup feed or suitable grain drill fitted with special spouts. This may be done either in autumn or in spring. The operations preceding drilling consist of ploughing, cultivating and harrowing until, for spring sown crops, a moderately fine tilth has been secured.

2. One of the cheapest and best methods of sowing is to plough beans in. Under ordinary circumstances a row is ploughed in under every second furrow, though every third furrow may be preferred where tractor cultivations are likely to be required, the furrows being about 10 in. broad but not more than about 4 in. deep. This is done by attaching a small drill or hopper to every second or third plough body, the seeds being deposited in the open furrow and covered over by the next furrow slice. Seed put in in this way is left at a uniform depth and protected from the ravages of birds.

3. Land for spring beans may be deeply ploughed in autumn and left exposed to the weather throughout winter. In early spring the soil is cultivated and harrowed, and drawn up into 26 in. ridges by means of a double mould board plough. Farmyard manure is spread in the bottoms of the drills, and the seed is broadcast, or a special three row bean drill is employed to drop the seed on the top of the manure. The ridges are then split to cover the seed, and harrowed and rolled before the plants come through the ground. Beans grown in this way may be looked upon as a true fallow crop, as the method permits of the thorough cultivation of the soil between the rows. But the suppression of weeds is never so successful as in the case of potatoes, because the smothering power of the crop is much less. This system was common in Berwickshire and Northumberland.

4. In the west of Scotland beans are sometimes broadcast at the rate of about 2½ bushels per acre on the ploughed grassland in February and harrowed in. About three weeks later a late variety of oats is sown at the rate of 2 to 3 bushels per acre on the same land and harrowed in also. The name mashlum is given to this mixed crop; the object of sowing the two species at different dates is to secure that the different plants will be ready for cutting at the same time. After threshing, the beans may be separated from the oats by screening or the mixture may be ground for stock food.

**Manuring.**—Traditional practice is to apply about 10 tons of dung, without fertilizers, in cases where beans follow a cereal, and to give neither dung nor fertilizer where they follow a long ley. It is to potash that beans mostly respond, and the farmyard manure will supply sufficient for the crop's needs. Farmyard manure is often heeded more for the cash root crops, in which event fertilizers will be applied. Nitrogen fertilizers are not used in practice, and in some experiments they have depressed the yield of pulse, a result that may be due to over development of leafage in the early stages of growth. On soils low in phosphate and potash a dressing per acre of 40 units $P_2O_5$, (2 cwt. superphosphate) and 80 units $K_2O$ ($1\frac{1}{3}$ cwt. muriate of potash) may be applied.

Such dressings may be applied to the furrow slice and worked deeply into the seedbed.

There is often considerable advantage to be gained, where the necessary equipment is available, in the placement of fertilizer. The fertilizer bands should be 2 in. away from the seed and 1 in. below it.

**After-cultivation.**—As soon as the land is sufficiently dry in March the beans should be harrowed, except when a residual acting weed killer has been used (see p. 123). This tears out numbers of annual weeds and breaks up the caked surface of the soil so that the air gets access to the plant roots and growth is stimulated. When further drying has taken place, tractor hoeing may be commenced and should be continued throughout the season as often as is practicable. The type of hoe employed will depend on the width between the drills. By far the most thorough cleaning can be carried out when the rows are far enough apart to admit of the use of a single row cultivator. However a row crop tractor with suitable equipment will do good work in narrow drills before the plants become too tall. If the land does tend to become foul when the crop is ripening a thorough scarifying of the stubble after harvest will do much to minimise the ill that has been wrought. When tractor hoeing is no longer possible, hand hoeing can be carried out if labour can be spared. Winter beans, unless the growth is very lush, may with care be safely sprayed with dinoseb weedkiller. It is true that beans are more susceptible to damage than are peas and that with late sown spring beans the risk is too great to be taken. In any case the precise stage of growth is important, and success requires specialist knowledge and experience.

**Harvesting.**—Winter beans are generally ready to cut about the beginning of August, but the spring varieties are very late and are seldom ripe until after the cereal cutting is over. The time of cutting has a very great influence on the feeding value of the straw; when cut in green condition bean straw is very little inferior to good hay, but if allowed to become dead ripe it is not only unpalatable but fibrous and innutritious. Moreover, late cutting gives rise to considerable loss through the beans shelling during harvest. If the crop is taken a little early, the only inconvenience will be a slight delay until it is dry enough to stack. The best way to judge the ripeness is to examine the scar (hilum) on the end of the bean where it is attached to the pod. Individual seeds may be considered ripe when the hilum has turned black; but the pods ripen over a considerable period, the lower ones first. If cutting is delayed until the uppermost pods are ripe the lower are very liable to shell during the cutting and subsequent handling. The usual compromise is to cut when the middle pods are ripe. Earlier cutting, though it may avoid loss by shelling, results in a large proportion of shrivelled seeds.

Cutting is most expeditiously carried out by means of a binder, but some farmers employ the combine harvester with consequent extra risk of shelling out. After cutting by binder, the sheaves are stooked in the usual way and stacked when they are dry. No crop while in the stook will withstand bad weather better than beans. They may be left in the field until the more susceptible white crops have been secured, and suffer no damage if they get a brisk shower while being carried; indeed a shower will help to prevent the pods splitting open and so save loss during forking and carting. Because of the large number of pods exposed on the outside of a bean stack, many farmers carry the thatch right down to the ground in order to provide better protection.

New beans do not form a healthful food for stock and the crop is better left unused until January; moreover they may be too soft to grind. In practically all cases the bean crop is the last on the farm to be threshed, and in some cases the pulse is not fed until it is a year old.

**Yield.**—The bushel weight of beans is 63 to 66 lb., and the yield of a good crop is 30 to 35 cwt. per acre; but it appears that, by contrast with other crops, yields have been tending to fall; the national average for recent years was estimated at only 16 to 17 cwt. The average proportions of pulse and straw are 40 and 60 per cent. respectively, *i.e.* an ordinary crop will produce nearly 1½ tons of roughage.

## PEAS

Peas are very similar in composition to beans, *i.e.* they contain nearly 20 per cent. of digestible protein and have a low fibre content. They are therefore valuable for blending with cereals in the making up of balanced rations for live stock. When intended for animal food, peas may be grown either pure or in mixture with oats, and the mixed crop may be either treated as a grain crop or cut green for soiling, ensilage or hay. Where the mixture is intended to be ripened and harvested by binder the proportion of peas must be kept low—say one part of peas to four or five parts of oats—otherwise the crop may become so tangled as to create great difficulties in harvesting. A mixture with a higher proportion of peas may be treated like threshed dried peas, *i.e.* be cut with a pea harvester, a cutter swather or a mower, and cured in the swath.

**Varieties.**—Dried peas for animal feeding (as compared with garden varieties) are more dwarf in habit and mostly have coloured flowers. Varieties in this group are the Maple (mottled in colour) and the Dun or Partridge, the latter rarely being cultivated today. The Maple is the most important. Marathon Maple is a late, high yielding type, while Minerva is a recent product of the Cambridge Plant Breeding Station. The white and bluish skinned varieties may be used either as human food or for animal feeding, whereas Maples are rarely saleable for the former purpose. On the other hand Maples are the favoured food for racing and other pigeons, and find a limited market, at what is often a profitable price for this purpose. Marrowfats such as Zelka (known also as Harrison's Glory), the Dutch Blue type and other varieties, largely grown for human consumption (threshed dried peas), yield well. Varieties of the Dutch large blue type yield about 20 per cent. more than the marrowfats as a rule.

Peas grown for human food are dealt with in four different ways. Firstly, any of the dwarf garden sorts, excepting the most delicate, can be grown in the field and be picked for market when the pods are still green and the seeds still soft. In many cases it is unprofitable to make more than one picking, and where this plan is followed the plants are pulled up and stripped. Secondly, the crop may be mown and the whole material sent to a factory, either to be canned or to be preserved by quick freezing or the accelerated freeze drying process (A.F.D.). Shelling is done mechanically by a viner and the shelled peas are then graded according to size and preserved by processing. The haulm, which is much more nutritious than that of a ripe crop, may be brought back to the farm and may be fed to stock at once or ensiled. Naturally, canning peas are normally grown on contract, and the canning factory ordinarily supplies seed of the variety stipulated. The varieties used are garden ones and include Thomas Laxton, Lincoln, Kelvedon Wonder, Gregory's Surprise, Dark Skinned Perfection and many others. A dark coloured pea is preferred for freezing. A light coloured pea permits it to be coloured at will and is generally preferred for canning.

Thirdly, the crop may be ripened and threshed, when either of the above mentioned types may be grown. The threshed dried peas may be cleaned, sorted and put up in packets for sale, or alternatively they may be processed in order to soften them and then canned. Either large seeded varieties of the marrowfat type, such as Zelka or Big Ben or small round seeded sorts like the Lincoln Blue, are suitable for this purpose, the former under high fertility conditions and the latter on poorer land. The Dutch large blues—Servo, Rondo and Pauli—are also grown, but are often rated less highly for processing. They are very short strawed, have a shorter flowering season and often yield better than the marrowfats.

In general, varieties that produce long straw are suitable for field cultivation only on poor soils, and very dwarf sorts should be chosen for the richest soils, such as silts and fens.

**Soil Type and Place in Rotation.**—The best all round pea soil is a medium calcareous loam, but dry sandy or gravelly land is required for the production of early picking crops. Maincrop sorts sown in March do quite well on fairly heavy land provided it is well drained. Peas take the same place in the rotation as do Beans. They are an excellent rest crop and preparation for wheat.

**Manuring.**—As regards manuring, farmyard manure and other rich organic materials tend to produce rank growth, even on the poorer soils, and are therefore seldom used. Experiments have shown that the crop responds most markedly to potash, and to phosphate only when the soil shows a marked deficiency. It has been common practice to apply small amounts of nitrogen, but experiments have failed to show that a profitable response is regularly or often obtained on naturally rich soils. Where the preceding crop has been generously fertilized it is unnecessary to apply any fertilizer. In other circumstances a suitable application might be 1 cwt. per acre superphosphate (20 units $P_2O_5$) and 1 cwt. per acre muriate of potash (60 units $K_2O$) or the equivalent in the form of a special pea fertilizer.

Most growers of green picking peas have been accustomed to apply some nitrogen, since this is thought to improve the colour of the pods and to bring the crop a little earlier.

Fertilizers should either be worked deeply (3 to 4 in.) into the seed bed or preferably be sown with a placement machine. The bands should be 2 in. away from the row of seed and a little below the seed level. The normal dressing of fertilizer (about 2 cwt. per acre of the compound mentioned above) will give an extra 2 cwt. of peas if the fertilizer is applied as above rather than broadcast. This, of course, applies to soil on which a response to fertilizer may be expected.

**Sowing.**—For green picking, *i.e.* for direct sale on the vegetable market, it is usual to grow a succession of varieties and also to stagger the dates of sowing. In the drier areas and on light, free draining land the first sowings may be made as early as December or even November, despite the fact that, even in the milder areas, the resulting crop may be winter killed in occasional years. Further sowings are made at intervals till May. Popular varieties for autumn sowing are Meteor and British Lion.

Bulk sowings for the production of dried peas for human food and also of field peas for stock feeding, are generally made in the latter half of March if conditions are suitable, but an earlier opportunity, any time after mid-February, should not be missed. Seed sown under wet conditions in cold soil is very liable to rot, but seed dressings containing TMTD and certain other protectants give good protection. The sowing of peas for vining is staggered as for the green pea market in order to produce a succession for the factory.

Considerable differences are to be seen in the matter of the distance between the rows. The seed can be sown with an ordinary grain drill, *i.e.* with about 7 in. between the coulters. This method precludes inter-row cultivation, and is only to be recommended in cases where it seems that weed control can be secured merely by harrowing in the early stage of growth or where it is proposed to control weeds by selective herbicides. Peas will stand harrowing well, but many experienced growers prefer to grow in drills sufficiently wide apart (about 18 in.) to permit of tractor hoeing. A wide range of annual weeds may be controlled by the careful use of dinoseb (see p. 126). MCPB may also be used but controls a smaller range of weed species.

The seed rate varies from 10 to 18 stones, depending mainly on the size of seed and the row width. The seed bed should be fine and rather firm, a result that is best obtained by autumn ploughing and by cultivating and harrowing in spring. Inoculation of the seed (with nodule forming organisms) is not practiced, but treatment of the seed with TMTD preparations is worth while in the case of early sowings in order to minimise the risk of rotting.

**After-cultivation.**—The land is generally rolled about the time or soon after the seedlings emerge, and if many annuals appear within the following week or two the land may have one or two light harrowings. Spraying with weedkiller may be carried out while the peas are between 4 to 10 in. tall. Thereafter, inter-row cultivation, with horse or tractor hoes, should be repeated as frequently as may be necessary until the plants begin to sprawl across the rows.

**Irrigation.**—Irrigation of peas is not widely practised but can be profitable. Apart from seed bed watering for very late sown crops, it is rarely desirable to apply water before the stage of pod swelling when 1 to $1\frac{1}{2}$ in. may be applied. Too much water, especially too early, may lead to too much haulm growth and extend the flowering period. The latter is almost always a disadvantage.

**Harvesting.**—As already indicated, the harvesting of peas is a peculiar problem because the plants are not only more or less prostrate and entangled but are attached to each other by their tendrils. Moreover the crop must be dealt with before it is fully ripe, since the lower pods will begin to shell while the tops are still green. It should not be left beyond the stage when the lower two-thirds or three-quarters of the plant has turned brown.

As already said, picking peas are generally uprooted and stripped of their pods by hand, the haulm being left on the ground until it is fully dried out and then collected.

Until comparatively recent times canning or processing peas have ordinarily been cut by mower, with pea lifters attached to some of the cutter bar fingers and sometimes with a further special fitment known as a swath mover, *e.g.* the swinging windrower. The Leverton cutter has proved useful on stone free land, but the most satisfactory equipment is the cutter-swather. This machine is useful over a considerable range of crops, including lucerne.

In any case, the cut crop, after some preliminary wilting, is put up in large cocks, or better still, on to hut racks or tripods, the number required being ordinarily twelve to sixteen per acre. The crop can safely remain on hut racks for many weeks and still yield a sound and bright sample. Hut racks are to be preferred to tripods due to the easier entry of air under the stacked crop.

When drying is completed the material from the cocks or hut racks is carted and stacked, the handling being as gentle as is practicable. Alternatively, the crop may be left in windrows to dry and then be combined, the machine being fitted with its pick-up attachment.

From what has been said it will be understood that the cultivation of peas on a commercial scale is restricted to the drier parts of the country. A wet harvest is apt to result in serious difficulty often resulting in very great wastage of peas.

**Yield.**—The national average yield of dry harvested peas varies greatly from year to year according to harvest conditions. It may range from 14 to 18 cwt. per acre. Crops of over 30 cwt. are considered very good.

Peas for vining generally give a more reliable yield from year to year. An average of about 34 cwt. of fresh green peas (after vining) has been produced during recent years. On good soils crops of 50 cwt. and even over 60 cwt. per acre are grown.


## PESTS AND DISEASES

The two most serious pests of peas are the Pea Moth, because it is common, and the Pea Root Eelworm which although rare in this country is a serious threat lest it should become more widely established.

The **Pea Moth** lays its eggs in the crop at about flowering time. The larvæ feed within the developing pods and tunnel into the peas so rendering them useless. Control is by carefully timed spraying with insecticides such as D.D.T. or parathion. (See Ministry of Agriculture, Fisheries and Food Advisory Leaflet No. 334, *Pea Moth* for greater detail.)

**Pea Root Eelworm** behaves similarly in respect of peas, beans and vetches, as does Potato Root Eelworm to potatoes. There is no practical control measure save the growing of the susceptible crops at intervals of not less than five years. This should prevent a build up of the numbers of this nematode should it be introduced on to a farm. Fortunately it is but rarely found. (Ministry of Agriculture, Fisheries and Food Advisory Leaflet No. 462 describes this pest.)

Other pests include Pea and Bean Thrips, Pea and Bean Beetles, Pea, Bean and Clover Weevils. Fuller details are available in Ministry of Agriculture, Fisheries and Food Advisory Leaflets Nos. 170, 126 and 61.

Aphids may cause damage to peas in some seasons. Spraying with a suitable systemic insecticide is the standard method of control.

One of the most troublesome diseases of peas is Downy Mildew. In some seasons this can cause the almost complete loss of individual crops.

It is a disease of moist seasons in contrast to powdery mildew which is often most troublesome in dry seasons. There is no control measure at present for this parasitic disease.

A more complete list and description of pea diseases will be found in the Ministry of Agriculture, Fisheries and Food, Bulletin No. 123, *Diseases of Vegetables*.

## FLAX AND LINSEED

Flax and Linseed are distinct cultivated strains derived from the same original species (*Linum usitatissimum*). Cultivation began very early and flaxen fabrics occur among early prehistoric remains in Egypt. The plant is an annual with slender erect stems and usually blue flowers, but some white flowered varieties of flax occur. The seed is produced in globular fruits or bolls. Flax, having been developed with the object of producing long straight fibre, is taller than linseed—up to 40 in.—and when well grown has few and short branches. It gives a low yield of seed —normally only 3 or 4 cwt. per acre—even when allowed to ripen fully. Linseed is shorter and more widely branching in habit, so that its fibre is of poor quality. The yield of seed from improved varieties, under good growing conditions, may be expected to reach 10 to 12 cwt. per acre, and yields of 20 cwt. have been recorded.

The ripe seed has an oil content of the order of 35 per cent. and about 20 per cent. of digestible protein. Ground linseed is the most nutritious of all common concentrates, with a starch equivalent of about 120. It is laxative and healthful and is useful as a constituent of calf meals and as a conditioner for convalescent animals of all sorts. The ground seed, when soaked in cold water, sometimes develops poisonous qualities, due to a glucoside; it should therefore either be fed dry or else boiled or scalded.

Linseed is generally used for the extraction of oil, the residue being the universally esteemed linseed cake. The oil is a " drying " one, *i.e.* when exposed to the air it oxidises into a dry, elastic, durable film. Previous boiling increases the drying quality. Linseed oil was widely used in the manufacture of oil paints, linoleum and waterproof materials— *e.g.* oilskins, but some of the new synthetic materials are taking its place. Raw linseed oil is in general use as a mild purgative for farm stock, and small quantities may be given to animals that are out of condition or are being prepared for showing. Linseed and its products have a marked tendency to soften the body fat of animals to which they are fed. This is no particular disadvantage in the case of sheep and cattle, but oily fat is very objectionable in a bacon carcass.

Flax fibre is the material from which linen is made, but it is also used for cordage and fire hose and a variety of other purposes. The fibre is the bast tissue which extends throughout the whole length of the stem;

it is very durable and strong. The process of extraction starts with retting, *i.e.* soaking in water. Most retting is now done in artificially heated water, the process being completed in a very much shorter time than was involved in the old process of soaking in pond water. When retting has gone so far that the bast separates readily from the woody tissue, the material is dried, artificial drying being now the rule. The brittle, woody core of the stem is then broken by means of rollers, and the material is finally scutched to remove the broken pieces from the long silky fibre.

The area of linseed and of flax has never been large in this country. A moderate acreage of both were grown during the war, but interest in either crop has since steadily fallen away. The cultivation of flax ceased in about 1958 with the impending closure of the last remaining flax processing factory in Britain. A small area only of linseed continues to be grown. Flax continues to be grown in Ireland and there is a considerable production in parts of the Continent such as in Belgium and the Netherlands.

Both flax and linseed grow on a wide range of soils, but on heavy land it is difficult to obtain the necessary fineness of tilth, and very thin, dry soils are unsuitable, more particularly for the fibre types. The crop has little competitive power, so that the land should be clean. Weeds are particularly objectionable in flax, and any large proportion is likely to result in the crop being unsuitable for processing. The use of weed killers on flax requires special care but is possible. Where flax is to be pulled by machine special care must be taken to level the ridges and fill the open furrows before sowing otherwise the machine cannot operate satisfactorily.

Neither type of plant is a gross feeder, and as a general guide it may be said that the appropriate level of soil fertility is about the same as for the stiffer strawed sorts of barley. Linseed can have rather more nitrogen than flax. The crop is generally grown after corn but on the poorer sorts of land. It does well after a ley.

The plant is practically immune from wireworm attack and is disliked by rabbits. It is attacked by leather jackets and by the linseed flea beetle. It makes a good nurse crop for grass and clover seeds. In preparing the soil the initial ploughing should be fairly deep, but it must be done early if the very firm and fine seed bed, which is necessary for successful establishment, is to be obtained. In spring, rolling and harrowing must be repeated until a turnip tilth has been produced.

The seed should be sown at a depth of $\frac{1}{2}$ in. It may be broadcast and covered by a light harrowing, or it may be drilled. The American alfalfa drill (see p. 149) is very suitable. Failing this an ordinary grain drill, with coulters 6 or 7 in. apart, may be employed, though drilling in two directions is desirable in flax in order to get uniform distribution over the ground. Some drills, however, may not be adjustable to the half seed rate—*viz.* about 40 lb. per acre—that is then required. Rolling is desirable to get proper consolidation, but if the soil is liable to cap or crust the roll should be followed by a light harrow.

The seed rate for flax is relatively high (90 to 112 lb.) since a close stand is desirable to prevent branching; 70 to 80 lb. is usual for linseed. Very early sowing involves the risk of frost damage, but it is a mistaken idea that good crops can be obtained by seeding in May or June. The crop indeed has a short period of growth, but late sowing often results in a severe check by drought. In England late March or the first week of April is probably the optimum time, and in Scotland the second or third week in April. Late sowing, in certain years, results in heavy attack by flea beetle, necessitating treatment with a suitable insecticide.

If any considerable number of tall growing weeds appear in a flax crop they must be hand pulled or spudded. Flax must be pulled (not reaped) in order to obtain the full length of fibre. Pulling machines are reasonably efficient in the hands of experienced workers. Flax must be harvested before it is ripe in the ordinary sense. In general the finest quality of fibre is obtained by pulling at the stage when only the base of the stem has begun to change colour. At this stage the yield of seed is small and much of the seed is immature.

The optimum time for cutting linseed is more difficult to determine, since the bolls ripen, in succession, over a period of several weeks, and the earlier begin to rupture and shed their seeds before the last are filled. Harvesting should commence as soon as the earliest pods are dry and brittle.

Flax is bound in small sheaves which are set up in stooks for a few days or a week. If rain threatens, the sheaves should be built in small cocks, preferably round tripods. In favourable seasons the material may be carted and stacked from the stook. Every endeavour should be made, during handling, to keep the straw straight and undamaged.

Linseed is harvested in the same way as a cereal, but it is more difficult to cut. The bottom of the stem is extremely wiry, and it is well not to attempt to make too close a stubble. The binder knife must be carefully sharpened at short intervals. Sometimes there is a good deal of trouble in adjusting the divider. Threshing may be done with the ordinary type of machine if suitably adapted. Combining is possible, but a special fitting is necessary to crack the bolls, which may otherwise fail to release their seed.

Breeding of flax has been carried out in Northern Ireland and formerly at the Flax Research Unit in Norfolk, now closed.

At one time commercial Argentine seed (Plate Linseed) was commonly grown, but it has been shown that newer Canadian and Swedish varieties are much more productive. The Canadian variety, Royal, is popular among late maturing types, but is outyielded by the Swedish Valuta. For northern and other late districts Dakota and Redwing are early maturing types, the former giving a higher yield.

L

# RAPESEED AND COLESEED

Following the development of rape as an oil seed in Scandinavia during the war years came a slight increase in the British acreage of this crop. Yields are seldom high enough to make the crop a very profitable one.

Cultivation is broadly similar to that of mustard and other brassicas grown for seed.

There are both winter and spring types of both species, swede (or true) rape and turnip rape. The spring varieties are less productive than the winter sorts, which must be sown in late August or very early September. The respective average yields may be about 8 to 10 cwt. in the one case and 16 to 18 cwt. in the other: skilled growers may produce up to about 30 cwt. in good years. Sowing of the spring crops can be left till May if necessary, and can therefore leave time for a partial fallow. Margo and Rapido are good varieties of the winter swede and winter turnip groups respectively. Regina is the best known of the spring swede group, and Nida is the most popular of the spring turnip type. Others are Gute, Black Argentine and Sweet German.

The cultivation of rape as a forage crop is described at page 335.

# CHAPTER 14

# FORAGE CROPS AND SOILAGE[1]

## VETCHES

VETCHES or tares (*Vicia sativa*) are leguminous plants which are very widely cultivated for forage purposes.  A proportion must necessarily be ripened for seed, but practically all the produce so obtained is used for sowing purposes, the grain very rarely being fed, like beans and peas, to stock.  Tares may be grown alone or in mixture with other plants such as beans, oats or rye; they may be soiled, made into silage or hay or folded with sheep or pigs.  The nitrogenous nature of the vetch makes it extremely valuable for feeding to stock, and its proper use reduces the necessity of purchasing expensive cakes and meals; but while it can be fed to all classes of stock with safety it should not be supplied in excessive quantities when in a wet or succulent condition, as it is then very liable to cause bloat.

There are two common varieties, namely winter and spring tares, which differ little in appearance.  There are not any clearly distinct varieties, seed being sold as spring or winter tares.  The winter vetch is hardy, and may be sown in autumn in the midland and southern counties, but it cannot always withstand the more severe winter climate of the north.  Very often both winter and spring sorts are sown, and the dates of seeding so arranged as to produce a supply of green fodder throughout a large part of the summer.  When the crop is cut early for hay or soiling, a certain amount of aftermath develops which is useful for grazing sheep or other stock, and winter tares may be cut in time to allow the farmer to sow a crop of turnips or plant cabbages on the same land.  Spring vetches may be removed in plenty of time to allow of the preparation of the land for wheat, and the crop is sometimes grown for ploughing under as a green manure.

Tares form a useful crop on all classes of land, but attain their greatest perfection on clay soils which are rich in lime.  Their fibrous roots do much to improve the fertility and texture of poor, heavy land.  Being a legume, vetches are a good preparation for wheat.  For soiling purposes vetches may be grown throughout the full range of our climatic conditions, but no attempt should be made to grow seed or to make the herbage into

[1] The term " Soilage " has been in use for many years and implies the same method of crop usage as does zero grazing when applied to grass.  In a general sense the terms are synonymous.

hay except in early districts of low rainfall.  Even in favourable localities ripening and drying are difficult to secure and the seed crop seldom gives complete satisfaction except in dry years.

Vetches may follow a cereal crop in the rotation, and although their habit of growth makes it impossible to suppress weeds by hoeing they produce an excellent smothering effect, and if cut green, leave the land cleaner than either beans or peas.  In Scotland small acreages of tares are often grown to supplement the pastures in the fall of the year, and pieces of land which are not cleared until late in spring—*e.g.* land on which potato pits have been situated—are frequently used for this purpose.

Winter vetches are usually sown in September and October.  The seed may be broadcast at the rate of $2\frac{1}{4}$ cwt. (4 bushels) per acre on the ploughed land and harrowed in, or drilled at the rate of $1\frac{3}{4}$ cwt. (3 bushels) per acre with an ordinary corn drill on a bed that has been prepared by cultivating and harrowing.  It is even possible, by drilling on stubbles which have been broken by cultivators, to avoid the cost of ploughing, but this is satisfactory only on particularly clean land.  Spring tares may be sown in February, March and April, and although later sowings may be carried out there is a risk of the plants being adversely affected by drought, and in all cases of late sowing a heavier seeding is necessary.  Frequently, however, vetches are not sown alone but are grown along with other species.  Owing to the great difficulty of securing seed crops in good condition some farmers sow about $\frac{1}{4}$ bushel per acre along with beans.  These give the tares plenty of support, and the troubles associated with the lodging, moulding and decay of heavy tare crops are altogether avoided.  When threshing has been completed the seed of the two species may be separated by screening.  A good mixed crop, whether for silage, for green fodder or for ripening, may be got by sowing 1 bushel of winter beans, $\frac{3}{4}$ bushel of winter vetches and $1\frac{1}{2}$ bushels of winter oats per acre; but the most suitable proportions are determined by local soil and climatic conditions.

Although vetches are sometimes given light dressings of dung they respond best to phosphate, and potash is necessary on light soil only.  There is little critical evidence on the manurial needs of the crop.  A dressing of 3 to 4 cwt. of high grade slag used to be a common dressing and is all that is needed on heavy land.  Superphosphate at 2 to 3 cwt. (40 to 60 units $P_2O_5$) is an alternative, the rate varying as to whether the soil is phosphate deficient.  On light soil a similar amount of superphosphate and $\frac{3}{4}$ cwt. of muriate of potash (45 units $K_2O$) will probably be more satisfactory.

Winter tares grown either alone or with a cereal may be harrowed and rolled in spring, rolling being more important on soils that puff up under the influence of frost.

The time of cutting vetches will depend on the purpose for which the crop is grown.  If the tares are intended for silage, cutting should take place when the lower pods are nicely filled but still soft. If required, for hay, cutting should be delayed until the plants are a little more mature, because there is a loss of moisture in the ripening process, and up to a certain point this can be more safely effected when the crop is growing than when it is on the ground. If for seed, cutting should take place when the pods are filled and have lost their juiciness and the colour of the foliage is changing to brown. When the crop is a mixed one and the vetches are supported by beans or a cereal, cutting may be performed with an ordinary mower. Cutting is most troublesome when the vetches are grown alone and ripened for seed, as they frequently form a tangled mass which is badly laid. When intended for soiling or ensilage, the green crop is often allowed to wilt for a few hours so that it may lose a proportion of its moisture before being carted. When hay or seed is required, the vetches are put in cocks or on hut racks and treated in the same manner as a crop of peas. As tares are difficult to secure in perfectly dry condition and tend to become mouldy in the stack, it is often worth while to build small stacks round tripods, which permit of a free circulation of air, an elevated situation where there is plenty of wind being chosen. Thatching should be done early as the herbage is very porous and does not run off the wet. The seed is separated by an ordinary thresher and the straw forms an excellent feeding roughage.

A moderately good crop of tares will yield 10 tons of green forage per acre. Green tares weight well, but the moisture content is high, frequently 80 per cent. The bushel weigh of the seed is about 64 lb., and a yield of 14 cwt. is not often exceeded; the yield of threshed straw varies from 20 to 25 cwt. per acre.

## LUCERNE

Lucerne (known in America as alfalfa) is a very valuable leguminous forage plant which is grown largely on the continent of Europe, in North and South America, South Africa, Australia and New Zealand. As a pure crop it is largely restricted to the dry south eastern half of England, but it is used over a wider area, in mixture with grasses, to provide both hay and grazing (see p. 364). Its roots penetrate suitable soils to great depths, rendering it extremely resistant to drought, and tapping sources of food and moisture which are seldom reached by other farm plants. The plant is a true perennial, and when properly manured will continue to produce heavy crops year after year; but it cannot compete with weeds, and when grown on dirty land its productiveness gradually falls off until it has to be ploughed up. Mixtures with grasses are much less liable to weed infestation than pure crops. If, however, the land be properly prepared and the crop well managed, even pure stands will last for six or seven years, and in this time, through the agency of the bacteria in its roots, the crop influences the nitrogen reserves in the soil in such a way that the benefit can still be observed after several years of arable cropping.

rows of 14 to 18 in. with grass, frequently cocksfoot. This is often the practice when it is intended to graze the crop during the winter. Less damage by treading will occur if this wide row system is employed.

In order that it may develop a strong root system lucerne should not be overcut during the first cropping year. Emerging seedlings may be attacked with great loss by a weevil. Early treatment with D.D.T. or B.H.C. preparations is very effective. Weeds in established crops may be controlled by dinoseb dressing, and the same treatment, with special precautions, can be used on seedling stands. 2.4-DB may be used on seedling lucerne but controls a smaller range of weed species than dinoseb.

Lucerne is responsive to phosphate on soils low in this element but it is to potash that the greatest response is shown. Many crops have failed because insufficient potash has been applied to the seed bed regularly during the life of the crop. Normal seed bed dressings of 100 units of $P_2O_5$ (6 cwt. superphosphate) and 200 units $K_2O$ ($3\frac{1}{2}$ cwt. muriate of potash) should be given. On potash deficient soils up to 180 units of $K_2O$ may be given annually: up to 50 units $P_2O_5$ may also be given annually during the growth of the crop.

If the soil is short of lime, appropriate dressings should be applied before any attempt is made to grow this crop. Very often the slow development and the pale colour of lucerne can be traced to the absence of the proper nitrogen fixing bacteria. The old remedy for this was to obtain soil from a field that had grown lucerne well and to scatter it over the crop at the rate of a few hundredweight per acre. The modern treatment is to inoculate the seed with the correct strain of micro-organism,[1] and this should always be done when growing the crop for the first time. In many experiments such inoculation has doubled the yield and at the same time has greatly increased the protein content of the herbage.

In the drier areas of North America a combination of lucerne and smooth brome grass is widely used for three or four years' pastures. Mixtures with cocksfoot, meadow fescue and timothy are used in this country. Such leys require special systems of management, the main point being to avoid over close grazing, which is apt to be fatal to the plants. The balance between lucerne and grass must be decided in relation to the climate, since in the higher rainfall areas most grasses tend to dominate the lucerne. Common mixtures per acre are 12 lb. lucerne with 3 lb. cocksfoot or 5 lb. timothy or 6 lb. meadow fescue, together with $\frac{1}{2}$ lb. of one or other of the persistent types of white clover.

When seed is taken from lucerne it is the second cut that is ripened, harvested and threshed. Cutting should take place when the seeds have hardened; the material is then dried as in making hay, stacked and allowed to stand for some time before being threshed with a clover hulling machine.

[1] Cultures may be obtained from Messrs Allen & Hanburys Ltd.

# SAINFOIN

Sainfoin is a leguminous plant which is of some importance in the sheep districts of the south of England. It may be used for soiling purposes but it is usually grown for hay or grazing. It is often used as a substitute for clover on land where clover sickness is prevalent, and it forms such a healthful food that sainfoin leys are frequently used as pasturage for sick or weakly animals. Sainfoin hay is also in demand for racehorses. It produces stems about 20 in. high, is deep-rooted like lucerne and forms strong rosettes of basal leaves which withstand hard grazing.

There are two distinct types, namely Common and Giant sainfoin. Common sainfoin is a perennial which reaches its maximum development in the second or third year, and is used to sow down leys for up to six years' duration; it differs from Giant in having finer stems, a more prostrate habit of growth, greater persistency and the inability to flower twice per season; it produces a hay or a seed crop per season and the aftermath provides grazing or it may be used for grazing only; it grows more slowly and produces less bulk than the Giant variety and, like lucerne, it has ultimately to be ploughed up, as it becomes very weedy. Giant sainfoin is shorter lived than the Common variety, and is cultivated as a rotation legume for one or two years in place of clover; it establishes itself quickly, produces good bulk and as it flowers early and grows vigorously after cutting, it will produce at least two crops of hay, or a crop of hay and a crop of seed, in a season. Between the Common and Giant types is a range of intermediate strains, one example being Cambridge Common. Selecting seed from a second flowering sort favours the Giant variety, while taking seed from a crop that has stood for several years favours the Common. There are also differences in the strains of Common grown in different parts of the country. The Cotswolds and Hampshire both produce good strains.

Sainfoin is most largely grown on the dry, chalky and limestone soils of the Downs and Cotswolds. As it is deep rooted and drought resistant, it thrives on light land, but it will only grow where the climate is warm, and fails utterly unless the soil is well drained. It is also intolerant of acidity.

The seed of sainfoin is really a fruit which contains a true seed within a light and spiny husk; it is bulky, and owing to its lightness is very difficult to harrow into the soil. However, it is possible to obtain true seeds, which have had their husks removed by milling, and these are more easily handled. The land should be in clean condition before sainfoin is grown, and the crop should be seeded under a nurse crop of barley by broadcasting or drilling at any time from early March to late April. About 56 lb. of milled seed is required per acre, but the seeding has to be increased to 120 lb. when rough seed is used. It is usual to drill the seed in rows about 10 in. apart, and in a direction at right-angles to the rows of barley.

A good manuring per acre is $1\frac{1}{2}$ to 2 cwt. of superphosphate (30 to 40 units $P_2O_5$) and $\frac{3}{4}$ cwt. of muriate of potash (45 units $K_2O$) applied to the nurse crop, which is commonly barley; but where Common sainfoin is down for several years and a crop of hay is removed each season, further dressings of phosphate and potash will be necessary to prevent rapid deterioration. Short dung is sometimes employed, but this can generally be more usefully applied to a root crop.

Although a crop of seed may be taken from sainfoin before it is broken up, the production of seed in the early years of the ley tends to reduce the persistency of the plants. Consequently, good management demands that they should either be kept well grazed or else mown as soon as flowering begins.

When sainfoin is made into hay it is cut at the commencement of flowering, and very carefully handled in order to avoid breaking off the delicate leaves. Turning can be most safely carried out in early morning when there is dew on the herbage: 30 cwt. of hay is about the average yield.

## TRIFOLIUM

Crimson or Scarlet clover, generally known as Trifolium (*Trifolium incarnatum*), is an annual legume which finds a limited but useful place in the agriculture of the south of England for catch cropping purposes. It establishes itself very quickly, and produces a fair bulk of nutritious fodder which may be either grazed or soiled, but it develops practically no second growth. The chief disadvantage of the crop is that it is dangerous food for stock when it is over ripe, for it produces very hairy flowers which may form balls in the intestines and cause death.

Crimson clover is successful only in the warmest English counties as it cannot survive a very cold winter; it thrives on light, firmly compacted soils. Trifolium is almost always grown as a catch crop after a cereal has been harvested or to mend patches in a one-year legume ley, *e.g.* of red clover or trefoil; and it is consumed in the spring in time to leave the land clear for bastard fallowing or the sowing of a late forage or root crop. It cannot be sown under a nurse crop in spring like most other leguminous forage crops, as it will not grow again after being cut at harvest.

Sowing takes place on a stubble which has been worked into a fine surface mould without ploughing. The plant thrives much better on a firm bottom of this kind than on land which has been ploughed. The seed is broadcast at the rate of 20 lb. per acre as early in August as possible, and harrowed in. If there is rain the plants grow quickly and are firmly established before winter sets in. Trifolium is too hairy and fibrous to make satisfactory hay. Some varieties possess white flowers.

The common clovers and also Trefoil are discussed in Chapter 15. Two other species that may be worth mention are Sweet Clover and Serradella. The former is widely grown in North America. It is quick growing and productive, but very woody. Serradella, like the lupins (and unlike most of the legumes), is highly tolerant of acid soil conditions. The early types were of little value under British conditions, but new and improved German or Dutch selections might be worth a trial.

## CABBAGE

The cabbage is a cruciferous forage plant which, along with broccoli, brussels sprouts and many allied species, has been obtained by a long process of selection from the wild cabbage, *Brassica oleracea*. At one time it was one of the more important forage crops cultivated in this country, and was grown in almost all arable farming districts. Fodder cabbage is still grown to a limited extent, more so in the south west than most other areas. The cabbages fed to stock now are frequently those surplus to the vegetable market.

Cabbages may be safely fed to all classes of stock, and being mild in flavour, do not taint milk unless fed in very large quantities; they are useful as green food for pigs and poultry. They may be folded with sheep and are superior to turnips and mangels in feeding value, and if suitable varieties are grown they may be sold for human consumption. A great advantage of the cabbage is that it can safely be fed whether mature or immature. If the stems and basal leaves are left in the ground when the crop is cut, fresh leaves and buds will form and will provide a further supply of food suitable for sheep; on the other hand, the final residue of stems is slow to decay and difficult to dispose of. Cabbages have the disadvantage that they cannot be harvested and stored like roots, and the flat topped varieties are susceptible to a certain amount of decay if left standing for prolonged periods of wet weather. In late summer pasture grass deteriorates greatly in yield and nutritive value, and cabbages may be most usefully employed as a supplementary feed for stock during this period.

**Varieties.**—Cabbage varieties differ in appearance, size, hardiness and the time required for their development. Although cattle cabbages are coarser than the ordinary garden sorts there is no hard and fast distinction between the two types, and garden varieties are frequently grown on a field scale. Cabbage varieties are very numerous, but they may be grouped roughly in the following way:—

1. *Late or Maincrop Varieties.*—These are large cabbages which require a long time to reach full size; indeed, from seeding to cutting they may occupy ground for over a year. The largest, such as Flatpolls and Drumheads for stock feeding, may require a square yard per plant to

allow for their full development. Other kinds, for example, some varieties of Savoys, are grown in 2 to 2½ ft. drills and planted at intervals of up to 2 ft. The seed is sown in a bed during August and the plants are normally left there over winter and planted in April. The time when the cabbages are ready for cutting depends on the district and the variety, but main-crops are primarily intended for late autumn and winter use. When the varieties in this group are sown in March to April for transplanting in May to June they are unable to attain full size and are consequently more closely spaced. They are fit for cutting very late in the following winter.

2. *Autumn sown Early Varieties.*—Early varieties are often sown in July or August and planted out in September with the object of supplying the spring cabbage trade. They may be planted 1 ft. apart in 1 ft. rows. Alternate plants may be removed in March or April and sold as greens, the remainder being cut and sold as soon as they are well hearted. Wider spacing is adopted for crops that are to be marketed later. Suitable sorts for this purpose are Sutton's April, Flowers of Spring, Enfield Market and varieties of the Early Offenham type.

In some districts certain varieties normally sown in spring are sown during August, wintered in the seed bed and transplanted in April. When a hardy early variety such as Winningstadt is treated in this way it may be ready for cutting in July.

3. *Spring sown Varieties.*—These may be sown from March to April and planted out in May and June. Early sorts will be ready for cutting or feeding in August, and may be spaced 1 ft. 6 in. to 2 ft. each way. In order to avoid the set back of transplanting, the earliest varieties may be drilled in 18 in. rows and singled. Sometimes early cabbages are planted in July after a forage crop that has been removed in June or after early potatoes, and for this purpose the seed should be sown in May. The most forward plants will be ready for use in October, and the remainder may stand out until the end of the year. Early Drumheads and Winning-stadts are suitable varieties in this class. Later varieties will be ready for cutting in winter.

There may be considerable differences between similar named varieties but from different seedsmen. Being a cross pollinated species the difficulty of maintaining a fixed type can be considerable.

Although approximate dates of sowing, planting and harvesting certain varieties are mentioned above, it should be remembered that much depends on local conditions, and the custom of the district had better be followed until experience of the crop has been gained. Cabbages are irregular in the time taken to reach their full size, and it is generally most profitable to cut the best plants and allow the smaller ones further time to develop. By using summer, autumn and spring sown varieties of different degrees of earliness it is possible to secure a supply of cabbages all the year round.

## Cultivation

**Soil and Climate.**—The cabbage is a typical heavy land crop and attains its greatest perfection on strong clays that contain plenty of lime. However it grows well on light soils which have been given body by dunging. Light soils are essential for spring cabbages, which attain the necessary development for early marketing only on warm, free draining land. The crop thrives anywhere in Britain and resists drought when once it is well established; but it does not start well unless it gets a good deal of rain, and in a dry climate is less resistant to parasites.

**Place in Rotation.**—Cabbages occupy the same place as roots in the rotation. When planted regularly and wide apart, cabbages offer even greater facilities for cleaning the land than do roots. Planting may be done on the square so as to allow hoeing in two directions, and hand labour is thus reduced to a minimum.

**Preparation and Planting.**—The most important sowings take place in late July and August; too early seeding may result in a proportion of the plants bolting. A piece of good land in a sheltered spot is selected for the bed, and the soil is reduced to a fine tilth by ploughing and harrowing. In order to stimulate the growth of the young plants about 3 cwt. of superphosphate (60 units $P_2O_5$) may be applied, and the seed is put in with a hand drill in close rows at the rate of 20 lb. per acre. The whole should be well harrowed in and then rolled. An acre bed will grow enough cabbages to plant about 20 acres in the field, the exact number of plants required being, of course, determined by the intervals of planting. If the raising of plants cannot conveniently be carried out or the climate is too severe for the plants to withstand the winter, cabbages of suitable size may be purchased from farmers who specialise in this business. Cabbages may be sown with a drill like an ordinary root crop at the rate of about 2 lb. of seed per acre; and although the plants get a later start, and the cost of singling is as much as that of dibbling, some growers in dry districts adopt this practice to avoid the set back of transplanting.

The ground is prepared in exactly the same way as for root crops, and the cabbages may be planted in any of the following ways by hand. Machine planting is now very widely practised.

1. The field may be drawn up into ridges 24 to 30 in. wide in the same manner as when preparing for roots, and the plants dibbled along the ridge tops. When dibbling young cabbages care should be taken not to bend the tap roots, and they should be planted firmly and deeply.

2. On free draining soils which are used for growing spring cabbages the plants may be set along the bottom of shallow furrows which are opened by a double mould-board plough. The object of this is to provide shelter from frosty winds.

3. When cabbages have to be planted in dry spring or summer weather, good results may be got by dibbling the plants into the middle of freshly

turned furrow slices. The object of following the plough closely in this way is to set the plants in the dampest and firmest portions of the soil.

4. Cabbages may be laid by hand along the side of every third furrow slice, so that their roots are covered by the soil turned over by the next plough. This is a quick method, but as the soil is not firmly pressed about the plant roots it is not very satisfactory in dry weather.

5. Cabbages may be planted on the flat after the soil has been ploughed, cultivated, harrowed and rolled. Before this takes place the land must be marked off. A marker can be made by fitting short tines to a suitable framework, but even a seed drill can be used if its coulters are set to the desired intervals. If the marker is taken across the field in two directions, the one at right angles to the other, it becomes possible to space out the plants on the intersecting marks so accurately that hoeing can be carried out in both directions, and very thorough cleaning effected.

Alternatively transplants may be put in with a planting machine (see p. 181). This is a quick and satisfactory method which saves much hand labour.

The seed may also be sown in rows where the crop is to be grown, and singled in the same way as roots. The quantity of seed required is, of course, much increased, and cabbage seed is rather costly. Moreover, the crop occupies the ground for a longer time. On the other hand, the method avoids the risk of failure in transplanting, which is a serious one in the drier areas, especially where the job falls to be done in late May or in June. In almost every case early planting produces a distinct improvement in the yield.

**Manuring.**—As cabbages have a long growing season and are capable of producing an enormous weight of dry matter per acre, they should be manured liberally. Like kale the crop is sometimes said to be a gross feeder, but this must be reckoned as a point in its favour; its capacity for responding to fertilizers fits it for the most intensive types of farming. If available, farmyard manure is the basis of all dressings and may be ploughed in at the rate of from 10 to 15 tons per acre.

With farmyard manure the crop needs about 100 units N, 5 cwt. sulphate of ammonia, 50 units $P_2O_5$, $2\frac{1}{2}$ cwt. superphosphate and 60 units of $K_2O$, 1 cwt. muriate of potash. If farmyard manure is not given, the $P_2O_5$ and $K_2O$ should be increased to 100 units of each. For summer and autumn cabbage the nitrogen may be applied either to the seed bed or partly as top dressing. For spring cabbage, planted or sown in autumn, most of the nitrogen should be applied in spring.

The subsequent management of the crop consists in the usual cleaning operations, and in filling any blanks by means of seedlings, which should have been retained in a bed for this purpose.

Where cabbage root fly is troublesome, 4 per cent. calomel dust or other suitable insecticide should be applied round the stems about the end of April or when setting out the plants at a later date. Alternatively, the transplants may be dipped in an insecticide solution prior to planting. The caterpillars of the white cabbage butterflies may cause serious damage unless control measures are applied in time. A variety of effective sprays and dusts are available including a dust containing 5 per cent. of D.D.T.

**Securing the Crop.**—Many attempts have been made to store cabbages and retain them for late use, but the methods are too costly to be worth consideration and the practice cannot be recommended. The crop is best left in the field until it is needed for stock. Unless the land is wanted immediately the plants should then be cut so that the large bottom leaves remain on the stem. This method of cutting retains a number of buds, which will sprout and provide a very useful bite for sheep if needed later in the season. If decay is to be avoided an endeavour should be made to have a mature crop used up before the end of the year.

On good land maincrop market varieties yield 15 tons and upwards per acre. On the other hand, spring cabbages, cut as small, early greens, may produce only 3 or 4 tons per acre. With fodder varieties 20 tons per acre is often exceeded.

# RAPE

Rape is sometimes grown for its oily seeds (see p. 322), but its main use in this country is for forage purposes and generally as a catch crop. There are two types, botanically closely related to turnips and swedes respectively, but producing no bulb. The swede like type is the one commonly grown in Britain. In the south the crop is liable to suffer from mildew when sown early, and it is most popular in the damp and cool districts of the north and north west. It may be cut for soiling, but is more usually folded with sheep, and for this purpose it may be grown in mixture with Italian ryegrass. It is also sometimes used as a nurse crop for grass seeds where cereals are unsatisfactory for this purpose. In this last case $1\frac{1}{2}$ to $2\frac{1}{2}$ lb. of seed per acre should be used.

The varieties commonly grown for fodder are winter hardy biennials, *i.e.* they flower and set seed in their second season. There are a number of varieties of the ordinary swede-like rape, tall growing early sorts that are not highly frost resistant, later and dwarf varieties and the highly frost resistant rape-kales such as Hungry Gap and Fill Gap which are useful for folding in March and April.

Rape is usually broadcast at the rate of 10 to 12 lb. of seed per acre, but if drilled in rows 10 or 12 in. wide, 3 or 4 lb. less seed will suffice. Sowing may take place at any time from May to about the middle of August, and as the crop is second only to mustard in the rate at which it attains maturity, it may be grown after any crop that has been consumed, or removed in spring or early summer. It is particularly useful if the land cannot be got ready in time to sow turnips.

Under average conditions a yield of 10 tons per acre may be obtained.

## KALE

Kale is now regarded by many farmers as the most valuable of all arable crops for cattle; and it is true that, when properly grown and fully fertilized, it can produce as high a yield of nutrients (starch equivalent and protein) as any other crop species.

Kale belongs to the cabbage tribe, and is for all practical purposes a tall growing cabbage with spreading foliage which forms no heart. As a home grown food for stock it has to be compared with cabbages on the one hand and swedes on the other. While it is susceptible to the cabbage parasites, its open habit of growth, which prevents the lodgment of water, makes it more resistant to winter conditions, and although from January onwards it is apt to suffer loss owing to the withering of leaves, the hardier types may be allowed to stand out until spring in the milder areas. As compared with the swede, which it has largely replaced in many districts, it shows a much greater response to fertilizers, especially to dressings of nitrogen. Moreover, it withstands drought better and makes recovery when rain comes; it is also far more resistant to a number of parasites, including finger and toe disease. Against these advantages over the swede, it cannot be stored except as silage, and when it does stand out it suffers more loss. Some feeders also find that, as the stems may become rather fibrous or woody, the crop as a whole is not as completely eaten as are roots.

Regarding the relative proportions of the different parts of the plant, marrowstem kale has on the average rather more than 50 per cent. of its weight in the stem, 15 to 20 per cent. in the petioles (leaf stalks), and 20 to 30 per cent. in the leaf blades. In quality the leaves are greatly superior to the stem; they contain about twice the protein, three times the ether extract, about as much nitrogen free extract and the greater part of the ash. The petioles are intermediate in composition, often more nearly resembling the stem.

Kale may be soiled for cows, cattle or pigs, or it may be folded with sheep. The practice of folding dairy cows on the growing crop is now common, especially on the lighter sort of land in the milder parts of the country. A single electrically charged wire, carried about 2 ft. 6 in. above ground level, is used to confine the cattle. The daily fold should be a narrow strip, long enough to allow about 3 yd. per cow and wide enough to provide the daily allowance, which is ordinarily some 40 to 50 lb. This amount will be consumed in little more than an hour. Folding is ordinarily done after the morning milking. The preparation of the daily fold can be done in perhaps an eighth of the time that would be required to cut and cart the daily requirement. Kale gains in dry matter up to November, and as pointed out above, it tends to lose both bulk and quality after frost in the latter part of winter. The crop is lifted by cutting through the stems above the woody portion and the plants may be fed whole or chopped. Not only is kale a safe and satisfactory forage crop for milch cows, but the carotene which is present in the leaves gives milk a rich colour and a high vitamin content. Many dairy farmers therefore use kale throughout the winter, 15 to 20 lb. of leafy material per head per day being sufficient to maintain a very fair colour. Kale is given to fattening and other cattle in place of roots, and to pigs as a succulent which is also a source of vitamins and minerals. When kale is used for feeding sheep the best results are likely to be got before it begins to deteriorate, that is, before the end of January. In the south of England, however, it is very common to drill swedes and kale in alternate strips and to use the crop in January and February for flocks during and for some time after lambing. Indeed an elaborate succession of (1) turnips, (2) kale, (3) swedes and kale and (4) swedes alone, is often planned for wintering the sheep, but some farmers use only turnips and the swede and kale mixture. Chopped kale is easy to make into silage without the addition of acid or molasses, but the process entails a very considerable loss of nutrients. It is probably wise, in most districts, to ensile that part of the crop that is not likely to be consumed by Christmas, but opinion is divided on the comparative merits of kale silage on the one hand, and swedes and mangels on the other, for late winter and spring use.

Thousandhead kale and marrowstem kale are the best known varieties, the latter being thicker in the stem, taller and more responsive to rich soil and favourable climate; but grown side by side on poor to average land the two sorts are very similar. Thousandhead is the hardier of the two and is therefore used for late winter keep. The seed is usually sown in April at the rate of 2 to 4 lb. per acre in drills 18 or 20 in. apart. The yield of kale is little affected by singling to about 10 in. Most kale is therefore sown thinly and left unsingled. The precision drill is often used for the sowing of this crop. Kale should be manured in the same way as cabbages and is quite as capable of responding to liberal treatment; indeed a fertilizer such as Nitro-chalk or Nitra Shell, if applied in several dressings, can be used at a rate of 4 to 5 cwt. per acre. Such generous treatment, however, lowers the plant's resistance to frost and should not be applied to crops for late winter use. Drill cultivations can be performed throughout the early part of the growing season, but should be no more than are necessary to check weeds. Deep working between the rows is likely to damage the roots and do more harm than good. There are certain weed killers which may be used in this crop (see p. 126).

While kale is most commonly grown as a row crop, many farmers in the wetter areas sow broadcast, either alone or in mixture with Italian ryegrass. The common practice is to sow in summer for the production of winter grazing. This mixture and also one of rape and ryegrass, are used as pioneer crops in the reclamation of hill land (see p. 380).

In certain seasons, especially when crops of spring cabbage have been destroyed by winter weather, there is a good demand for kale tops in

March and April for human consumption.   In such cases it may be very profitable to pick over a field of late kale before folding with sheep.

The weight of crop per acre, of course, depends on the soil, climate and manuring.   Even on poor land yields of 10 to 12 tons can be got without much difficulty, while under favourable conditions yields of 20 to 30 tons are not uncommon.

## MUSTARD

**White Mustard** [1] is a cruciferous annual which is commonly grown as a catch crop.   It may be used for green manuring or folding with sheep, and it has a high reputation for flushing ewes.   Its most valuable characteristic is its very rapid growth;   on good land it may attain a height of over 2 ft. in less than a couple of months.   It is often grown after a crop of early potatoes, and is useful for conserving the residues of the heavy dressings of manure applied to this crop.

The seed may either be broadcast at the rate of 20 lb. per acre or sown in 12 in. drills at the rate of 15 lb., and seeding may take place at any time between early spring and the month of August.   However, if the crop is to be eaten off it must be consumed before winter, as the plants are not sufficiently hardy to withstand frost.   When mustard is grown for green manuring, and the plants are tall, it is necessary to attach a drag weight and chain to the plough in order to roll the long material under the furrow;   indeed it may also be desirable first to roll the crop according to the scheme of ploughing so that the plants lean in the direction of travel.

White mustard is also grown for its relatively large seeds, which are ground and mixed with the product of brown or black mustard in the manufacture of the ordinary condiment.   There is also a considerable sale of seed for the production of green (seedling) mustard and cress.

**Black Mustard** [2] is not grown for forage, but is cultivated in the Eastern Counties for its seed.   Production is chiefly on contract for the manufacture of condiment.   The common variety is Trowse, which may yield some 9 to 12 cwt. of clean seed per acre.   Black mustard has replaced the older Brown Mustard (*B. nigra*) which was widely grown until about 1952.

**Brassica Vegetable Crops.**—Numbers of farmers, especially in the eastern counties, regularly grow large acreages of brussels sprouts and cauliflower, in rotation with cereals.   In mild districts broccoli is also grown, often following early potatoes.   Information may be obtained in such standard works as *Vegetable Crops for Market* by Hoare (Crosby Lockwood).

[1] *Sinapis alba.*     [2] *Brassica juncea.*

# MAIZE

Maize originated in America and very soon after the discovery of the New World spread very widely throughout Africa, southern Europe and southern Asia. In this country even the earliest varieties have been found to ripen seed only in the warmer years and in the sunniest and hottest districts such as Kent, Essex and Suffolk, but continuous progress in the direction of earlier maturity is being made in the northern United States and Canada, and new strains are being tested in the south of England. The sweet corn varieties are grown on a small scale for table purposes and some of these can produce ripe seed with fair regularity in the south east of England.

In Britain maize is one of the minor forage crops for use in the late summer. For this purpose it should be cut when the grain is well formed but still pasty in consistency. Many of the newer hybrids easily reach this stage of development in the south eastern half of England. The leaves are readily killed by slight frost and the crop is not worth trying in districts where even slight summer frosts are liable to occur. Its greatest value is to dairy farmers in dry areas where pastures often produce little growth during August and September. If it is not required for soiling it can be made into excellent silage.

Maize grows best on warm, fertile loams, but when well manured it produces good crops on light soils, provided that these are of fair depth. Light soils have the advantage of warmth and earliness; on clays it often fails to reach the best stage of maturity.

In the past the most popular variety used to be American White Horse-tooth, which is a vigorous grower but which in England never reaches the best stage of maturity for ensilage. It is essential to procure seed of tested germination, because the grain may often be damaged by frost, before harvest, in the areas where the early varieties are grown.

National Institute of Agricultural Botany Leaflet No. 17 *Maize*, lists currently available variety hybrids and indicates their relative maturity class. Ministry of Agriculture, Fisheries and Food Advisory Leaflet No. 94 deals with the general cultivation of maize.

The crop is generally grown on land that has received a good dressing of farmyard manure, and at seed time it is given about 2 cwt. of sulphate of ammonia (40 units N), 3 cwt. superphosphate (60 units $P_2O_5$), and 1 cwt. muriate of potash (60 units $K_2O$) per acre. A deep seed bed is prepared by harrowing, rolling and cultivating, and in mid-May the seed is drilled in rows from 18 to 24 in. apart, at a depth of about $2\frac{1}{2}$ in., and at the rate of about 45 lb. per acre. The minimum temperature for germination of the seed is higher than that required for the general run of British crop plants, and if sown in cold soil the seed will rot. Dressing the seed with T.M.T.D. dust may prevent this. Special measures are necessary to protect the seed from rooks.

After sowing, the crop may be harrowed to suppress weeds, hoed as often as is necessary or practicable and sometimes hand hoed. If sown thinly there is no need for singling. The maize grows rapidly and a good crop soon checks weeds by shading. Modern practice, using the soil acting weed killers Simazin or Atrazin, saves much work and produces virtually weed free conditions for this crop. After the pre-emergence spray, no further cultivations are carried out.

The crop is cut as required in late August and September, loaded into trailers and driven on to the pastures. Forage harvesters with a special maize attachment are used for cutting in preparation for silage making. The yield varies from under 15 to 30 tons per acre.

## BUCKWHEAT

Buckwheat or brank is a crop of the polygonum family of plants. It is little grown in this country but is capable of rapid growth on most soils, being used for green manure or as a lush food for flushing ewes.

The crop is susceptible to frost injury and is therefore sown late and utilised before autumn frosts threaten. Fertilizers are seldom applied for buckwheat.

The seed rate is 50 to 80 lb. per acre, the seed being drilled shallowly.

Rather fuller information on this crop may be found in Patterson, W. G. R., *Farm Crops*, Vol. IV, Gresham Publishing Co., 1925.

## LUPINS

Lupins are occasionally grown as a green manure crop. Being a legume they enrich the soil with nitrogen, and being tolerant of acid soils, they are sometimes used as a pioneer crop in the reclamation of poor light and acid soil. Blue lupins are used for this purpose, being the most vigorous.

Blue lupins cannot usually be fed due to the presence of a toxic alkaloid. Some strains of yellow flowered lupin (Weiko for instance) do not contain this substance and are grown in parts of the Continent.

Another forage legume tolerant of very acid soils is serradella. This has been grown in the past in this country but is not at present cultivated. Sweet clover (melilot) will grow under moderately acid conditions and may be found occasionally being grown on the Brecklands of East Anglia.

## SOILAGE

Soilage is the practice of feeding animals on cut green forage, referred to as zero grazing when applied to grass. In an extreme case the stock may be kept in confinement throughout the year; more commonly forage crops may be cut and used to supplement the pasturage at the beginning and end of the grass season or in periods of summer drought. The advantage of soiling stock is associated with the greater productiveness in the drier areas of arable crops over grass, and a properly designed soilage system enables a larger head of stock to be carried on a given acreage.

**Advantages of Soilage.**—The advantages of soilage over the ordinary method of keeping stock on mixed arable and grass farms are as follows:—

1. When a plant is kept closely grazed its leaf surfaces are reduced to a minimum and its power of synthesising foodstuffs is diminished to a corresponding degree.   Moreover, frequent defoliation reduces the plant's root system and therefore its power to resist drought.

2. With many farm crops the longevity of a species is opposed to its productiveness, *e.g.* Giant sainfoin is a heavier cropper than the perennial Common variety.   Under arable conditions it is possible to select the most productive species, and the length of life is immaterial provided that one good crop can be obtained, but for permanent pasture the selection of lasting species is essential.

3. The plants are not damaged by being trampled and broken by stock or fouled by manure, and certain parasitic troubles are avoided.

4. In hot weather and during the " fly " season, when so many animals lose condition, stock may be comfortably housed so that they go on producing substantial gains, and there is no falling off in the milk yield of cows.   In wet or cold weather the advantages of protection are equally obvious.

5. It is possible to cultivate a bigger proportion of the land by doing away with such expensive structures as fences and other field boundaries, and the removal of these shelters for weeds and vermin results in bigger and cleaner crops.   There is no need to have watering places all over the farm.

6. With a well arranged sequence of soiling crops the animals receive abundant and suitable fodder all the year round, and neither milk production nor live weight increase is affected by drought or by the reduced feeding value of pasture towards the end of summer.

**Disadvantages of Soilage.**—The merits of soilage as an economic proposition should be compared with its chief disadvantages, which are as follows:—

1. More labour is required not only for feeding the stock but for the intensive arable farming necessary for the reproduction of a sequence of forage crops throughout the year.

2. In order to justify this extra labour a very large head of stock must be carried on the farm, and this requires extra capital and accommodation.

3. The sequence of crops required for feeding the animals necessitates periodical seedings during the greater part of the year, and long periods of wet or dry weather may so seriously interfere with these operations that one or more of the crops is missed and a food shortage may result.

Moreover, when crops are seeded at odd times the ravages of birds can assume a serious aspect, since, when no other sowing is going on in the district, these creatures give the seed their undivided attention.

4. The forage must be cut daily in order to avoid losses through fermentation and moulding, and this is difficult to carry out in bad weather.

5. When crops are grown in close sequence the soil is liable to become very dry, and in localities of low rainfall this results in difficulty in getting the seed to germinate and in diminished yields.

The cutting and carting of green stuff is, of course, laborious, and at modern wage rates is far too costly where hand labour is used. But the forage harvester (see pp. 159-160) can make for economic production. Moreover, the task must sometimes be done when other work is very pressing. Even when pasturage must be supplemented by the produce of arable land the alternative of folding the animals on the growing crop by means of an electric fence (see p. 372) will often be preferable. Provision of green food for indoor pigs, for cattle and sheep that are being prepared for show or sale and for the few remaining town dairy herds, is commonly made in the form of soilage. Otherwise, the practice is now restricted to dairy farms in the dry areas, where pastures are liable to give out during July to September. Common crops for soiling are lucerne or lucerne grass mixtures, clover, mixtures of cereals with peas or vetches (either autumn or spring sown), maize and early sown marrowstem kale and, of course, grass.

Most crops grown for soilage may be ensiled if it happens that they are unwanted at the time they are ready.

CHAPTER 15

# GRASSLAND

It is a point of more than historical interest that most of Britain's grass-lands—including even moorland grazings—are in some degree artificial. The truly natural grasslands of the world—for example, the American and Canadian short-grass prairies—occur in regions that are much drier (taking both rainfall and evaporation into account) than any part of Britain, *i.e.* regions too dry to support forest. Such natural grasslands are of low productivity—chiefly because it is only during short periods each year that the soil is moist enough to support active growth. Typical range country of this kind has a carrying capacity of a breeding cow to every 20 or 30 acres. Such areas, unless the soil is very light or the rainfall very erratic, are much more productive under drought resistant arable crops such as wheat, sorghums and sunflower than under grass. More-over, lucerne, where it can survive the winter, gives much higher yields than the native species. Most of the world's highly productive pastures— for example, the best dairy pastures of New Zealand and the Netherlands, or the fattening pastures of the English Midlands or the Norfolk Broad-lands—have been created out of deciduous forest or out of marsh.

The native vegetation of the well drained lowland areas of this country is deciduous forest, mainly oak-wood,[1] with smaller areas of beech and ash, associated with a " brown-earth " soil. In lowland swamps with black fen or peat soils the typical association is alder carr. In the wetter uplands, with their higher rainfall and highly podzolised acid soils, the natural association is pine-and-birch wood, degenerating with increasing altitude into scrub and petering out at about 2000 ft. into upland moor.

As might be expected, the grasslands that have been established under these several conditions depend for their maintenance upon continuing human action. For instance, if drainage, manuring and liming are neglected, and the land is understocked, a Midland pasture on clay soil will revert to scrub and eventually to oak-wood. Close grazing and mowing are the chief means of preventing the establishment of seedling shrubs and trees, while it is the use of lime and phosphate that prevents

---

[1] Such terms as " oak-wood," " pine-wood," and " alder carr " do not, of course, imply pure stands of the named species but refer to the dominant plant in each case. Thus oak-wood has a " top storey " of oak and other deciduous trees with a " shrub layer " of holly and hawthorn, often some blackberry and bracken, and a ground layer of shade-bearing grasses and other herbs.

the replacement of the better grasses and clovers by heathers and other moorland species.   In either case deterioration is gradual.   Thus a clay pasture, undergrazed and never mown or fertilized, may first be invaded by such shrubs as bramble, wild rose and hawthorn, which are avoided by grazing animals.   Under the protection of such thorny shrubs appear seedlings of ash and other trees, whose seeds are wind-borne.   Later come oak and beech from seeds that are carried by birds, and in the end oak-wood will become re-established.   On highly podzolic soils gorse, broom, ling and bracken will lead the invasion and the " climax " vegetation will be pine-wood.

Although the distinctions are by no means clear cut, grazing lands may be usefully classified into three main groups.   First are the *semi-natural* types whose constituent species have not been sown and whose flora has been little influenced by such major improvements as liming, drainage and the application of fertilizers.   In other words, the only measures of human interference are the control of the grazing animals with perhaps occasional mowing or burning.   The second group are the improved permanent grasslands where, again, the constituent herbage plants have not been sown, but where the composition of the sward has been largely modified, and is maintained, not only by relatively close control of grazing and perhaps mowing, but also by such measures as drainage, the use of lime and fertilizers, the spudding of weeds and perhaps surface cultivation.   Thirdly are *artificial* grasslands or leys, where the herbage consists mainly or largely of plants that have been sown.

**Semi-natural Grasslands**.—Sand dune conditions are unsuitable for tree growth, partly because the seedlings are apt to be smothered by blown sand or to have the soil removed from their roots;  partly because of exposure to wind itself;  and partly also by reason of the very low water holding capacity of the soil.   In " young " dunes the commonest dominant species is marram grass (*Ammophila arenaria*), though occasionally it is sea lyme grass (*Elymus arenarius*).   Marram does not form a continuous sward and is of very low nutritive value.   Older dunes are generally invaded, to a greater or less extent, by sand fescue (*Festuca rubra arenaria*) which is a sward builder and fairly useful feed.   Sand sedge (*Carex arenaria*), which often accompanies the fescue, is also useful.   Among the commoner herbs are the hawkweeds and ragwort, the latter of which is poisonous when eaten in quantity.   Sand-dune grazings, while of low value for most purposes, provide useful wintering for hill sheep.

**Salt Marshes**.—*i.e.* coastal mud-flats that are inundated only at spring tides—provide excellent pasturage upon which stock (especially sheep) fatten quickly.   They are notably healthy and, unlike many fresh water marshes, are free from liver-fluke—for the reason that the second host of this parasite is a fresh-water snail.   In marshes that are closely grazed, sea manna grass (*Glyceria maritima*) usually dominates the areas of heavy silt, with sea fescue (a form of *F. rubra*) on the drier and sandier patches.

Both are highly nutritious. There is usually a variety of other salt-tolerant species, such as sea lavender, sea plantain and thrift, which are readily eaten by sheep. When the spring tides are excluded by embankments the salt-tolerant species quickly give place to the usual good pasture plants, and many ryegrass-clover fattening swards have been produced by this means alone.

**Chalk Downs**, especially where the soil is thin and the grazing has been mainly by sheep, carry a very characteristic close and springy sward. Under hard grazing the two small fescues, *ovina and rubra*, are often co-dominant, but on specially dry sites only the former contributes much to the sward. The little sedge *Carex flacca* is often the next most common species. Other frequent and not unuseful grasses include the common, the downy and the golden oats, the small (diploid) form of timothy (which has yielded the S. 50 pedigree strain), crested-hair-grass (*Koeleria cristata*) and sweet vernal. Common bent, which associates with sheep's fescue in most swards of the dry uplands, is very rare on the chalk. Two weed grasses that intrude when grazing is neglected are erect brome and tor-grass (*Brachypodium pinnatum*); typically the former is dispersed through the sward, while the latter tends to choke out all competitors and to form expanding patches which are conspicuous because of their very coarse leafage and pale yellow-green colour. Among common legumes are bird's-foot trefoil, kidney vetch and horse-shoe vetch (*Hippocrepis comosa*). White clover is abundant or sparse according to the phosphate status of the soil, and spreads rapidly after a dressing of basic slag or other appropriate form of phosphate. There is a striking abundance of miscellaneous herbs which, however, vary from one area to another. Burnet, ribwort, the hawkbits, thyme, rock rose and in places dropwort are very common. Common shrubs are white-thorn and juniper.

Downland pastures, though their productivity is not high, suffer less from drought than might be expected. Moreover, they can carry cattle as well as sheep in winter without hurt to the sward. Unless the soil is excessively thin (as it usually is on the steeper slopes) marked improvement can be achieved by the use of phosphate alone or of phosphate and potash in combination. Moreover, large areas of downland have, in recent years, been profitably converted into arable land. Earlier attempts at reclamation often failed for lack of the heavy dressings of potash that may be required, many of the soils being not only potash deficient but having a marked tendency to fix the element in unavailable forms, so that small applications may produce little or no response.

The thinner soils of the limestone uplands—oölite and mountain limestone—produce semi-natural swards with some resemblance to those of the downs. But since most outcrops of these occur in relatively cool and moist parts of the country, patches of acid soil are more common. Under moderately acid conditions common bent is often co-dominant with sheep's fescue, while more extreme soil acidity is reflected by the presence of such heath species as tormentil and lady's bedstraw (*Galium saxatile*).

**Lowland Sandy Heaths** are exemplified by the Brecklands of Norfolk and Suffolk, and occur in many other areas such as the New Forest, the Bagshot sand district of the Thames Basin and Sherwood Forest. Even under low rainfall conditions coarse sands and gravels become heavily leached and therefore very acid, so that extreme podzolisation, with the formation of " iron pan," is common. The soils are very poor in plant nutrients as well as in lime. Bracken is very common, but grows strongly only on patches of relatively heavy and not extremely acid soil. Common heather (ling) and purple bell-heather (*Erica cinerea*) are co-dominant over wide areas but (by contrast with upland and northern moors) bilberry is rare. The dwarf-gorse (*Ulex minor*) occurs in patches. A saying of the old improvers was " copper under heather, silver under gorse, and gold under bracken." The commonest grasses are bent and wavy hair (*Deschampsia flexuosa*).

As might be expected, the grazing value of typical sandy heath is almost negligible; moreover, ploughing-out and re-seeding, which is a successful method of improvement in the wetter uplands, gives poor results since the better long-lived species of grass are unproductive under the dry conditions. The less poor land has largely been converted to useful arable, and some that was formerly thought to be incapable of economic reclamation is now being successfully farmed on a system whereby lucerne or lucerne-cocksfoot leys are alternated with arable crops such as barley and sugar beet. Afforestation, particularly with Scots Pine, is in many cases the only profitable form of utilisation.

**Mountain Grazings.**—Upland and mountain regions, by reason of their short growing season and their heavily leached and therefore acid soils, have more or less severely limited agricultural potentialities, so that costly improvements—drainage, fencing, liming and the clearing of boulders—are often ruled out on economic grounds. The common choice is between afforestation and extensive sheep farming.

The plant associations found under pastoral conditions depend upon such factors as the type—acidic or basic—of the underlying rocks, the elevation and aspect, the combination of grazing stock (sheep, cattle and hill ponies) and the frequency and severity of burning. Five main associations may be distinguished:—

*Heath* is typically dominated by common heather or ling (*Calluna*), though bilberry and bell heather (*Erica cinerea*) often form large patches. Ling provides useful sheep keep, especially in winter and early spring, but is rarely eaten by cattle. Bilberry is of very little value. The heath association occurs where rainfall is high but drainage fairly good and where the soil is very acid. Many of the plants, including common heather, depend for their nutrition upon a symbiotic root fungus (*Phoma*) which cannot live under alkaline conditions. Moreover, heather cannot survive under continuous close grazing. Bell heather tends to dominate on the driest sites. The heaths are generally interspersed with grasses, the commonest species being wavy hair (*Deschampsia flexuosa*), *Nardus* (mat grass, wire grass or white bent) and *Agrostis*, one or other of which may become dominant when an old stand of heather is destroyed by burning. Heather is " browsed " rather than grazed by sheep—*i.e.* only the tips of the shoots are eaten; these contain a surprising amount of calcium. *Nardus* is the main species on the so-called " white land " of mountain grazings. The name " mat grass " derives from the fact that its rhizomes give rise to a tough mat of raw humus, and the name " wire grass " indicates the character of the leafage. *Nardus* occurs under the same conditions as heather, but colonises much more rapidly from seed; hence, it often succeeds heather when the latter is killed—*e.g.* by burning an old stand in very dry weather. The spring growth of *Nardus* is reasonably nutritious, and the tufts of dead leaves are accessible at times when lowlier herbage is covered with frozen snow. Otherwise the value of " white land " depends largely upon the proportion—never very large—of other species with which the *Nardus* is associated. The commonest of the grasses are sheep's fescue, wavy-hair grass, sweet vernal and, under the better conditions, *Agrostis*. The common herbs of acid uplands are tormentil and bedstraw.

*Flying bent* or purple moor grass or blae grass (*Molinia caerula*) becomes dominant under wet conditions—*e.g.* at the foot of slopes and in depressions—but is not found in deep stagnant bogs; it seems to favour sites where the ground water has a relatively high mineral content.

*Molinia* provides abundant and relatively nutritious grazing in the early summer, and is the main constituent of the hill shepherd's " bog hay." The leaves break off in late summer and are so light that they are easily blown away. The grass therefore provides very little keep during winter.

*Bent-fescue.*—Apart from " flush " land, which is mentioned below, this is the most valuable association found on hill grazings. *Agrostis* tends to dominate the wetter areas and sheep's fescue the drier. Soil requirements are somewhat the same as for heather—*i.e.* a relatively well drained site and a soil reaction about *p*H 4 to 5. But the grasses tolerate close grazing, and hence replace heather in areas where the sheep congregate or which they often traverse. Bent-fescue swards often contain suppressed plants of white clover, and an application of phosphate will often induce change to an *Agrostis*-clover sward.

*Bracken*, although originally a woodland plant, grows most vigorously in full light, and is mainly found on sheltered slopes and in valleys, on land which would otherwise carry an *Agrostis*-fescue sward. It is fully vigorous up to elevations of about 1200 ft., but extends in places up to 1500 ft. and occasionally higher. It will not grow on heavy clay nor on shallow soils overlying rock, nor under boggy conditions. Bracken is rarely grazed by sheep but is eaten by cattle when other herbage is scarce, and continued consumption causes poisoning. Bracken is the principal weed of hill land. Control is discussed later (p. 373).

**Mountain Bog.**—Land that is too wet for *Molinia*, and especially stagnant bog on high plateaus, is usually dominated by cotton sedge or drawmoss (*Eriophorum vaginatum*). This provides valuable feed in early spring before other hill plants have begun to make growth. The leaf bases, which are pulled out by grazing sheep, are rich both in protein and phosphate, a circumstance that may explain the shepherd's belief that drawmoss stimulates milk production in the ewe. The commonest associate is deer sedge (*Scirpus caespitosis*).

**Flush Land.**—It will be readily understood that soil conditions will be markedly changed where water, having percolated through basic parent material, reaches the surface as springs. The sites of such springs on hillsides, are marked by triangular patches, of vivid green the apex being at the point where the spring emerges. If the sward is examined it will usually be found to contain a considerable amount of clover, and a variety of the better grass species. The value of even a small amount of flush land—because of the high protein and mineral content of the herbage—is considerable.

**Improved Permanent Grasslands.**—Some fields of old grass are used solely for grazing, some are mown annually for hay (but are normally grazed in the latter part of the season), while others are grazed in certain seasons and mown in others. There is thus no clear cut division between pastures and meadows. The character of the herbage is, however, considerably influenced by the frequency of mowing.

Most old pastures contain a large number of species of more or less useful grasses, legumes and other herbs, together with numbers of others that can properly be regarded as weeds. Moreover, there is no sharp distinction between the poorest of the " improved " grasslands and such " semi-natural " associations as the downland fescue and the upland fescue-agrostis already described.

The botanical make-up of permanent pasture swards (*i.e.* of swards that are grazed rather than mown) is usually complex, but one or two species are often dominant. The relative proportion of the various species depends on a number of factors—the rainfall and the water-holding capacity of the soil, the elevation and exposure of the site, the lime and phosphate status of the soil, the make-up of the grazing stock (sheep and cattle), and the degree of grazing control. The constituent plants are generally grouped as grasses, legumes and miscellaneous species or " herbs," and each group in turn is divisible into good, middling, poor and worthless.

Among the grasses, ryegrass, cocksfoot, timothy, meadow fescue and meadow foxtail are of first quality. Second grade species, according to the majority view, include rough-stalked and smooth-stalked meadow grass, crested dogstail, golden and tall oat, hard fescue and both common bent (*Agrostis tenuis*) and fiorin (*A. stolonifera*). The third group includes such as are of low productivity, nutritive quality or palatability, but which are eaten by the less fastidious animals—sweet vernal, the small fescues, Yorkshire fog, creeping soft-grass (*Holcus mollis*), downy oat, meadow barley, soft brome and wavy-hair grass. The fourth list of species (that must be regarded as weeds even under the poorest conditions) includes tussock grass, tor grass and erect brome.

By much the most valuable of the legumes is wild white clover. Other useful species are wild red clover, bird's-foot trefoil and kidney vetch. Yellow suckling clover and black medick are less desirable. The only out-and-out weed in this group is rest-harrow.

Among the common herbs that are readily eaten are yarrow, rib-grass and burnet. Among those of little value but not particularly aggressive are daisy, the hawkweeds, dandelion and broad-leaved plantain. Troublesome weeds are the spear and field thistles, docks, the bulbous and creeping buttercups and sheep's sorrel. Poisonous weeds include the widely spread ragwort and the very local but much more deadly autumn crocus (*Colchicum*). The garlics, though non-poisonous, are highly objectionable in dairy pastures because their pungent taste and smell are imparted to the milk of animals that eat them.

In meadows—fields that are frequently mown—the tall-growing species such as tall oat, meadow foxtail, tall fescue, timothy, meadow vetchling, wild red clover and tall umbelliferous herbs, tend to dominate the more prostrate species such as ryegrass and white clover. Excessive soil moisture is reflected in colonies of rush, meadowsweet, reeds and other water-tolerant species. Very wet places may harbour poisonous species, especially water dropwort and other umbellifers. Yellow rattle, which is parasitic on grass roots, is common in south-country meadows, especially on heavy soils.

The majority of improved permanent pastures can be conveniently classified according to the proportion, in the sward, of three species—ryegrass, bent and wild white clover. The associations, in descending order of value, are described as ryegrass-clover, ryegrass-agrostis-clover, agrostis-ryegrass-clover, agrostis-clover and agrostis. Thus top grade fattening pastures, *e.g.* those of the Midlands and of Romney Marsh, are of the first class, ryegrass being dominant, wild white clover sub-dominant, and the association including smaller amounts of cocksfoot, rough-stalked meadow grass and timothy, with only small amounts of bent, Yorkshire fog and other poor quality species. The maintenance of this association depends on a regular supply of soil moisture, a fairly high lime and phosphate status, and a system of management that combines winter rest with full summer stocking. At the other extreme, the agrostis sward is established on rather acid soil, with a low phosphate status, where over-grazing in winter is combined with under-grazing during the growing season. Such land generally carries a " mat " of dead but only slightly decayed herbage, formed from the ungrazed material under acid conditions and in the consequent absence of earthworms. Practicable measures of improvement (short of ploughing out and re-seeding) can improve the botanical composition of the poorer swards, but only to a level that depends upon such factors as the depth of soil and shortness of the growing season.

In some particular areas the foregoing basis of classification is not entirely appropriate. For instance, on chalky soils the small fescues take the place of agrostis, while in most of the north *Holcus* and *Agrostis* tend to be co-dominant in the poorer swards and to be sub-dominant in the better. Indeed, under conditions of extreme acidity in northern industrial districts the poorest pastures are sometimes dominated by creeping soft grass (*Holcus mollis*).

Methods of improvement are discussed later.

**Artificial grasslands or leys.**—These are distinct from the natural types of vegetation in that the land is cultivated, fertilized and prepared to reduce the competition, from grasses, weeds and other indigenous plants in order to give the species to be sown every chance of establishing themselves quickly without competition.

The mixture of seeds sown may be simple or complex and is varied to suit the particular soil and the system of husbandry management to be practised.

## AGRICULTURAL CHARACTERISTICS OF THE MAIN HERBAGE SPECIES

A knowledge of the characteristics of herbage species is essential to the successful establishment and after-management of sown grasslands. Some of the qualities desired in a grass or clover are self-evident—productivity, palatability and nutritive value. Others of importance in particular circumstances are *persistence*, *i.e.* the power to survive and to spread by vegetative methods (tillering); *aggressiveness*, *i.e.* the power to survive the competition of, or to suppress other species; *frost-tolerance* (winter-greenness); *seasonal distribution* of production; *power of recovery* from hard grazing and treading; and *drought resistance*. *Leafiness* is important from two points of view—firstly because the leaf and leaf-base contain a smaller amount of lignified tissue than stem (and are therefore more nutritious), and secondly because a stemmy habit is often associated with high seed production and this in turn with a short life. Again, the capacity of the plant, under appropriate management, to produce a tolerable yield of viable seed is of obvious economic importance. Finally, some of the species that are potentially very valuable are ill-adapted to particular conditions—*e.g.* ryegrass to thin and poor soil under a dry climate.

A further complication arises from the fact that herbage species, like other cultivated plants, show a wide range of genetic variability so that it is possible by continuous selection and other means, to create strains within each species, of rather widely different characteristics—e.g. with varying growth habits and related responses to environmental conditions. Moreover, certain important economic characters are correlated in greater or less degree; for example, pasture strains not only tiller or produce runners freely, and are typically of rather low, spreading habit, but are also late in starting spring growth. Conversely, hay strains are not only tall and upright in habit, but are less inclined to tiller and tend to be early. Differences between strains of the same species may be greater than those between average specimens of different species. Thus ryegrass is early and timothy is late, but an extreme hay type of timothy may be earlier than an extreme pasture type of ryegrass.

Another general point in relation to strains is of practical importance. All the agricultural species are cross-fertilising, the grasses being wind-pollinated and the clovers insect-pollinated. Many individual plants are self-sterile, and those that are self-fertile, when self-fertilised, give a high proportion of worthless progeny. The continued inter-crossing that occurs in the field maintains a greater or lesser range of variability—apart altogether from the possibility of pollination from an outside source, e.g. of plants in an old pasture by pollen from an adjacent ley.

As would be expected, seed harvested from an old pasture yields a large majority of leafy and persistent types. But if a stock obtained from such a source is repeatedly grown for seed, and especially if seed is taken in the first year after sowing (which is convenient in practice), the forms that will be inadvertently selected will be those that run to seed freely and bear seed abundantly; and these are undesirable for many purposes. Many early attempts to propagate indigenous types of ryegrass broke down because of failure to recognise this difficulty. The desirable characters of a strain can be maintained only by returning frequently to a stock of " mother " plants—either to an old pasture or to a " pedigree " stock that is subjected to constant selection. In either case, precautions must be taken against contamination by pollen from outside sources.

**The Ryegrasses.**—As already said, perennial ryegrass is native to Britain, is widely distributed in the better old pastures and is dominant in the best of these. But the seed which first became available in commercial quantities was that of a type which (along with red clover, Dutch white clover and trefoil) had long been cultivated from seed in Flanders. Seed of indigenous types of perennial ryegrass, from old pastures, has been used from time to time, but increasingly in the last twenty years. Also, during this last period, pedigree strains have steadily increased in popularity. The other " artificial grasses " of the old writers were lucerne and sainfoin. Italian ryegrass was introduced in 1831 from Northern Italy, where again it had been long cultivated.

*Italian Ryegrass* is easily distinguishable from typical plants of perennial by its more tufted and upright habit, its broader leaves, rather lighter green colour, longer spike with spikelets more widely spaced and by the presence of an awn on the seed. It is regarded as a sub-species. In general, the plant behaves as a biennial, but when grown under favourable conditions and when closely grazed it may survive longer. Its presence in second- and third-year swards is often to be explained by self-sowing.

Under suitable conditions Italian ryegrass is exceedingly productive. Its requirements in the matter of soil nutrients and moisture are high. It succeeds on relatively poor soils in the wet uplands provided that ample amounts of fertilizers, and particularly of nitrogen, are applied, but it is of less value on thin and light land in the drier areas. It is the principal grass for one-year leys, and is valuable as a catch crop, sown either by itself—*e.g.* after early potatoes—or under-sown in corn with the object of producing autumn and winter grazing. It can be used as a " nurse " (in place of a cereal crop) when sowing down land to long leys, but in this case it is essential, if the perennial grasses and clovers are not to be crowded out, that the new sward be kept closely grazed from the outset. Again, it is often included in mixtures for two or more years' ley in order to increase the yield of herbage during the first year. If the field is to be grazed in the first year this may properly be done, but if hay is taken in the first year the slower-developing species may be overtopped and suppressed. Under average conditions it combines well with broad (early flowering) red clover in one-year mixtures, reaching the hay stage at about the same time; but if the land is very rich, or if a large dressing of nitrogen is applied, it tends to suppress this or any other clover.

Italian ryegrass grows late in autumn, makes growth during short spells of mild weather in winter, and produces grazable herbage or material suitable for drying, earlier than any other grass. When heavily fertilized and irrigated, or when treated with liquid manure, it may be expected to give four cuts in a normal season, with a total yield of 4 or 5 tons per acre of dry matter which is of high nutritive value. The seed is relatively large but light, running about 225,000 per lb. Under good seed bed conditions 8 or 10 lb. per acre will produce a sufficient stand for a crop of hay. Where, however, the objective is the rapid formation of a dense turf—*e.g.* where the improvement of soil structure is the main consideration—seedings of 50 lb. per acre or more are sometimes used. Four to 6 lb. is a suitable amount when the grass is being used as a " nurse." As a " pioneer " crop, in the reclamation of derelict grassland it may be used alone or may be combined with rape or with rape and hardy green turnips. Commercial seed is mainly produced in Northern Ireland and France.

Two improved forms of short-term ryegrass are now available. S. 22, a pedigree strain bred at the Welsh Plant Breeding Station, was introduced in 1951. It is selected mainly for its leafiness and quick growth and is more persistent than the " commercial " forms. It is not only sown for pure swards but also at times to patch thin stands of grass where the aim is to produce bulk quickly for cutting for silage or hay.

New Zealand short-rotation ryegrass (H. 1) is another leafy form, combining the earliness and high productivity of its Italian parent with a good deal of the powers of survival of New Zealand perennial. Under good conditions in the south and west of England and in the absence of severe frosts it may continue in full production for two or three harvest years.

Perennial ryegrass exists in a wide variety of forms which, however, have many characteristics in common. It is, among all the better grasses, the easiest to establish from seed, and the seedlings develop rapidly. This is not an unmixed advantage since the grass competes so strongly in the seedling stage with species of slower development, such as timothy and meadow fescue, that these may be almost completely suppressed. It is more or less evergreen and makes some growth (though less than Italian ryegrass) in mild periods during winter when many other species remain completely dormant. It withstands close grazing during summer, but it is greatly weakened by frequent severe grazing in winter and early spring—so much so that it may, in the succeeding summer, be dominated by other plants—e.g. white clover or agrostis—that lie dormant over winter and commence spring growth relatively late. Conversely, a pasture that is ungrazed in winter and early spring will tend to become ryegrass dominant. Ryegrass grows vigorously in spring and early summer, and again from September until the onset of winter, but it makes relatively little growth during July and August even if soil moisture is abundant. In the drier parts of the country this summer dormancy is especially marked.

The common *commercial* types are early both in commencing spring growth and in throwing up flower heads. They have few barren (non-flowering) shoots and are only weakly tillering. They have a relatively high proportion of stem to leaf and a marked tendency to summer dormancy. Since the seed crops are heavy and easily saved, the seed is ordinarily cheap. Grown for hay under conditions of good or high fertility, commercial perennial is liable to lodge. Persistency varies with conditions: on poor thin soils and in dry areas, especially if it is allowed to reach or pass the hay stage or is over-grazed in winter, it may virtually disappear by the mid-summer of the second harvest year. At the other extreme—on fertile soils, under a moist climate, and with regular grazing—many plants may survive a third or fourth season.

Other " commercial " or " semi-commercial " types are of only local importance. The best known is Devon Eaver, which is remarkably winter green and very early.

Seed of *indigenous ryegrass* is harvested (usually along with wild white clover) either from old pastures or from leys that have been established

M

by sowings from such old pastures. The chief centre of production is Kent. The plants are about mid-way in earliness, tillering capacity and in the proportion of barren tillers, between the extreme forms— " commercial " on the one hand and the pedigree pasture types on the other.

The pedigree strains have been selected for leafiness and persistence and to meet varying conditions and requirements. The best known are Aberystwyth S. 23, S. 24. and S. 101, but certain seed houses offer others.

S. 23 is the most widely used of the three. The foundation stock was selected entirely from very old pastures, mainly in the Midlands, Kent and Lincolnshire, but also from Holland and Wales. It is late-flowering— about three weeks later than typical commercial forms—and has a rather spreading growth habit. It tillers strongly, has many non-flowering shoots and the growth is dense and leafy. Spring growth is slow, but summer dormancy is much less marked than in the commercial forms, while autumn production is very good. The plants remain green during winter, with rather active growth in mild periods. Under reasonably good management the density of its sward prevents the intrusion of bent and other inferior plants, and its persistence under grazing conditions is very striking. As would be expected, seed production is low by com- parison with that of other strains. Though it is the best form of ryegrass for long leys under poor conditions and high rainfall, it responds well to liberal treatment, especially with nitrogen. In long leys it blends well with the smaller types of white clover (wild white and S. 184). For leys of intermediate length, S. 100 or New Zealand white clover is generally chosen as the companion plant, though in this case some care is necessary to avoid the dominance of the clover.

S. 24 represents the other extreme form. The aim in selection has been to combine the good qualities of the Irish and Ayrshire commercial forms—their earliness and capacity to produce a large bulk of hay—with quicker recovery after mowing, a less marked propensity for the aftermath to run to seed, a more leafy habit and some improvement in persistency— though much less than in S. 23. In spring growth it is rather earlier than the commercial type, but it comes into flower a little later. It may thus be used, with advantage, to replace commercial ryegrass in leys for two or three years, especially where hay is to be taken in one or more.

S. 101 is also derived from plants found in old pastures, but in the Midlands and Kent only. It flowers only slightly earlier than S. 23 and the habit of growth is less spreading, with longer and often broader leaf blades. It produces a less dense sward than S. 23 and is less persistent under poor conditions and under close and continuous grazing. On the other hand, it has a more erect habit, and yields a good cut of very leafy hay.

Perennial ryegrass seed is similar in weight to that of Italian (about

250,000 per lb.). Seed rates vary rather widely. S. 23 quickly forms a close sward by tillering; when sown without a nurse and under good seed bed conditions, 8 or 10 lb. per acre, with perhaps 3 or 4 of white clover, will suffice. At the other extreme, with commercial types intended to constitute about two-thirds of the total for a two-year ley, sown in corn under average seed bed conditions, the seed rate is generally of the order of 16 to 20 lb.

**Cocksfoot** readily establishes from seed even in competition with ryegrass; it reaches full productivity almost as soon as perennial ryegrass and outyields the latter on the lighter and shallower sorts of soil and under low rainfall conditions. It is less easy to manage successfully, since it tends to become coarse and tufted when under-grazed. It comes into full growth, in spring, at about the same time as ryegrass, with a rather narrower range between the early and late types. There is, however, a marked contrast between the two species in the seasonality of production. Some types of cocksfoot are moderately winter green, others dying back (" winter burning ") after the first considerable frost. In any case, there is little or no winter growth. On the other hand, few pasture plants except lucerne are so productive during the late summer, when ryegrass is often dormant. The drought resistance of cocksfoot is partly at least to be explained by the deep and strong root-system which it develops. It should, however, be noted that the full development of roots depends upon leniency in grazing at certain times of the year. If the plant is kept closely cropped throughout the early part of the season its root system will be weakened and its drought resisting powers accordingly reduced. Moreover, cocksfoot is capable of laying up, in August-September, a large reserve of food material in its roots and leaf bases, and the vigour of its spring growth depends on the amount of these reserves. The maximum value is thus to be obtained from a cocksfoot dominant ley only by a carefully planned system of utilisation. One such plan is to take the first growth for grazing and to lay up the field in April for a crop of silage, which is taken about the time that the flower-heads appear, *i.e.* ordinarily at the end of May; the aftermath is grazed from perhaps mid-July till late August, and the subsequent growth is allowed to stand over for consumption by out-wintering cattle. It will thus appear that a ryegrass dominant and a cocksfoot dominant ley can be mutually complementary, providing good grazing over a long and continuous period and also yielding a considerable amount of herbage for conservation.

Cocksfoot when too mature is not well liked by stock. The first spring growth and also the young aftermath, is greedily eaten by all classes of stock, but the more mature growth tends to be neglected by animals that have free range and opportunity for choice.

The pedigree strains are exemplified by the well known Aberystwyth series. S. 143 was developed from indigenous plants of an extremely leafy type. It forms broad cushions rather than tufts. It may be regarded as the fellow of S. 23 ryegrass, but departs even further from the average of its species. The leaves are broad and very palatable and there is a profusion of tillers. It is productive and persistent on poor soil and under hard grazing, but comparatively late. It is a poor seed bearer when grown in a sward, but yields well when grown in rows with appropriate fertilizer treatment. It blends very well with the more vigorous types of white clover. S. 37 is tall and erect, but more leafy than Danish and almost as early. Under difficult conditions it is less persistent than he other pedigree strains. It is less prone to get out of hand in a mixed sward. Scotia from the Scottish Society for Research in Plant Breeding is earlier than S. 37 in heading, but otherwise is somewhat similar to it. It is thought to be more suitable for northern districts. S. 26 is the intermediate form, making a persistent sward under grazing conditions but yielding also good crops of leafy hay. It tillers more profusely than S. 37 and much more so than Danish.

Cocksfoot seed is about half the size of ryegrass (about 450,000 per lb.) and, since establishment is relatively good, 6 to 10 lb. per acre will usually suffice to form a cocksfoot dominant sward. A small amount in a complex seeds mixture is apt to result in very tufted plants.

Among the commercial types of cocksfoot, American is unsuited to British conditions, being early but coarse and stemmy, but Danish is used in the north of England and in Scotland as a provider of the early keep.

**Timothy.**—It has long been agreed that timothy is a valuable grass for hay. The hay types thrive best on heavy or peaty land, and a stand, even of the commercial Scottish type, may remain productive and relatively free from intruders for five, seven or even ten years. It has long been the custom in the Scottish carses (alluvial clays), and also on the clay-land dairy farms of Ayrshire, to grow the plant in pure culture, with a little ryegrass and red clover to increase the yield in the first season. With heavy dressings of fertilizer (and especially of nitrogen), yields of 4 tons per acre, in a single cut, are not unusual. Attempts to repeat these results in the clay lands in warmer and drier areas have never fully succeeded.

The value of timothy as a pasture grass has only been recognised in recent years. This is due mainly to the suppressing effects of ryegrass and cocksfoot with which it was often sown. For example, a small amount of timothy was included in standard mixtures for three- or four-year leys (Cockle Park and Craibstone mixtures), but in competition with ryegrass and cocksfoot establishment of the timothy was often poor.

The seasonality of production is unlike that of ryegrass or cocksfoot, since spring growth starts late and the grass reaches the hay stage about three weeks later than ryegrass. The most successful results, in pasture leys, are now secured by sowing it with meadow fescue and the larger forms of white clover.

The most widely used of the timothies are Scottish and Aberystwyth S. 48. The latter is much later-flowering and more freely tillering, more leafy, and also more winter green. It is, moreover, highly resistant to rust, which is a common and serious disease. S. 48 yields heavy crops of hay and yet persists under heavy grazing, except indeed where the soil is very light or very low in organic matter. S. 51, which has a characteristic light-green colour, is also rust resistant. It is essentially a hay type but produces a much better aftermath than the Scottish and other commercial forms. It persists well unless it is closely grazed by sheep. Scotia heads rather earlier and tends to have less winter growth than S. 51.

What has been written does not apply to the S. 50 strain, which may almost be regarded as a separate species. It is genetically distinct, being a diploid form which does not intercross with the other (tetraploid) strains. The foundation stock was raised from " rootings " (portions of the creeping stolon) procured from some of the finest old pastures. S. 50 has a very spreading habit, forming very low grassy cushions which carry few short-flowering stems ending in slender heads. After flowering there is a large production of barren tillers, which trail over the ground and often branch profusely. When trodden into the ground these root at the nodes. This strain, as will be understood, is a poor seed bearer, and the seed is difficult to harvest. It makes a compact lawn like sward which withstands invasion by inferior grasses and other weeds. It has a special value in areas where deterioration of sown swards is specially difficult to prevent.

Timothy seed is very small—about a million to the pound—so that, despite rather poor powers of establishment, seed rates are relatively low. Under favourable seed bed conditions 10 lb. per acre, with a normal amount of clover, will produce a full stand.

**Meadow Fescue** has long been recognized as a productive, persistent and nutritious grass and has gained greatly in popularity in recent years. It was almost invariably included in the highly complex seeds mixtures that were formerly recommended for long duration leys or permanent pasture, but its seedlings were so suppressed by those of ryegrass and cocksfoot that its inclusion under such conditions was of little value. Meadow fescue does, however, flourish in combination with timothy or lucerne or both, or with timothy and white clover. In general, meadow fescue, by contrast with cocksfoot, is most useful on moderately moist and fertile soils. The best of the commercial types is Danish, which is early but not so leafy as might be wished. S. 53 is a late, leafy, free-tillering and persistent type. S. 215 is tall, erect, a few days earlier than Danish, and yields both a heavy crop of hay and a lush and leafy aftermath. The seed of meadow fescue is similar in size and shape to that of perennial ryegrass.

A number of other grasses are occasionally sown under special circumstances. **Tall Fescue** is a strikingly tall and broad leaved sub-species of meadow fescue, is deeper rooted than the latter and grows more vigorously on poor light land. It is generally regarded as too coarse and unpalatable to be included in grazing swards, and its value has yet to be established. **Tall Oat Grass** is commonly grown for hay in France. It is very productive under dry and hot conditions but cannot survive hard grazing or treading. It seems to have no particular place under British conditions. **Meadow Foxtail** is indigenous in British grasslands, is extremely early, is quite productive under moist conditions and grows well under moderate shade. Unfortunately it is very difficult to establish from seed and comes very slowly into full production. Moreover, seed crops suffer severely from attacks of the foxtail midge, so that yields are often very poor.

Among the so-called " Bottom Grasses " the most useful is **Rough-stalked Meadow** which thrives on heavy moist soils, and reproduces so freely that it survives in arable crops to an extent that makes it a weed. In former times, when only commercial types of ryegrass and cocksfoot were available, it was often included in mixtures for the heavier sorts of land with the aim of maintaining a close sward. But with the advent of S. 23 ryegrass, S. 143 cocksfoot and S. 48 timothy, the case for its use is poor. **Smooth-stalked Meadow Grass** (the American Kentucky Blue Grass) is drought-resistant but markedly summer-dormant. It is strongly creeping (stoloniferous) and more prone than rough-stalked to become an arable-land weed. **Crested Dogstail** is widely distributed in old pastures under a variety of conditions. It is winter-green, but produces only a small amount of keep, and it seeds very freely because its wiry flower stalks are neglected by grazing stock. It may occasionally be included in long leys on poor land where the live stock is mainly sheep.

**Broad Red Clover,** which is probably indigenous to southern Europe, has an erect habit of growth and relatively large leaves. It is a biennial that establishes itself quickly and is comparatively early. It may be used as a catch crop and for one-year seeds. Its own short life and the depressing effect it has on wild white clover render it unsuitable as a constituent of mixtures for long duration swards. It is susceptible to " clover-sickness," which is usually due to the fungus *Sclerotinia trifoliorum*, but sometimes to eelworm. Most seed is English grown, but some is also imported from Sweden, Canada, U.S.A., Chile, New Zealand and a number of other countries. Stocks from these various regions show considerable differences in their characteristics. Aberystwyth S. 151 is an early, good cropping strain that persists better than the commercial English type in the second year. There are various local strains—*e.g.* Dorset Marl—which vary in type and in adaptability to local conditions.

Late flowering red clover, sometimes known as single cut cow-grass, differs from the broad red variety in having narrower and more pointed leaves, being more spreading in habit of growth, tillering better and lasting into the second or third year; it is relatively slow to reach its full productiveness and is late in starting spring growth; it produces very little aftermath; it is rather less susceptible to clover-sickness than broad red. Late flowering red clover is an important plant in the first two years of a sward, and, when sown with a species such as perennial ryegrass, contributes largely to the yield of hay and greatly increases the yield of dry matter per acre. It is often included in mixtures that are sown down for more than one year and intended for hay in the first season. In districts where long duration swards are hard to establish it may be omitted from the seed mixture, for although it is not as depressing on wild white clover and the slow growing grasses as is the broad red variety, it nevertheless delays the establishment of these species. Strains and types may be divided into medium, late and very late. Among the former are Essex, Norfolk, Cotswold and Vale of Clwyd; among the extra late are Montgomery, Cornish Marl and S. 123. The latter group are the more persistent and the more reliable under poor conditions.

Red clover grows best on well drained clay loams in a high state of fertility and well supplied with lime. Complete failure is likely if the soil is more acid than $pH$ 5·3. The late flowering sorts are better than the broad-leaved strains for withstanding poor conditions, but even they will fail on sour and water logged soil. Red clover has a deep root system and does not often suffer from drought. Its agricultural value lies in its nitrogenous nature and its power to produce a large bulk of nutritious foliage which may be grazed, soiled, made into hay or utilised for green manuring. On the other hand, owing to its susceptibility to disease, its limited adaptability to soil conditions and perhaps to the use of unsatisfactory, red clover is a somewhat uncertain cropper. It should be grazed lightly after the harvest of the nurse crop to prevent its flowering and thus prolong its life and also as a measure of control against the clover rot *Sclerotinia*.

In the south-east of England red clover is often sown alone, but elsewhere it is more usual to sow it, at the rate of 2 to 8 lb. per acre, in mixture with grass seeds. The seed runs about 230,000 per lb., about the same as that of ryegrass. The usual amount of Late flowering Red in general purpose leys that are to be mown in the first year is 2 lb. Seed rates for a pure stand of Broad Red are usually between 12 and 18 lb.

**Alsike Clover** (*Trifolium hybridum*).—This clover was introduced from the Continent in 1834, and takes its name from a parish in Sweden. Alsike is not a true perennial, but is more lasting than most strains of red clover, and on good soil may continue to grow for three years. Unlike white clover, it has an upright habit of growth and is therefore more suitable for hay than for pasture. It commences growth later and does not produce so much aftermath as broad red. Alsike does best on heavy, damp soils, and since it is fairly resistant to clover-sickness and will grow under conditions that inhibit the development of the red variety, it is sometimes included in mixtures to ensure the presence of a plant should the red clover fail. It is inferior to red clover in producing bulk. In mixtures for long leys the more vigorous strains of white clover are much more useful than alsike.

The seed of alsike, which is largely imported from Canada, is small (about 700,000 per lb.), and when sown with other clovers and grasses, 1 or 1½ lb. per acre should suffice.

**White Clover** (*Trifolium repens*).— Dutch white clover is not a true perennial, though under good soil and climatic conditions it is rather more lasting than alsike. The variety is procumbent in habit, but, unlike wild white clover, its trailing stems do not root freely at the nodes; it is well situated to form the bottom herbage in one-year leys that are intended for pasture, and especially for sheep grazing. As it produces very little top foliage it is almost useless for mowing, but it is highly nutritious. It grows on all types of soil and, being deep rooted, is resistant to drought; it will not grow in the shade. It has now been replaced largely by improved forms of white clover.

New Zealand certified white clover is intermediate in character between Dutch white and wild white. Aberystwyth S. 100 is a highly productive and early strain of somewhat similar type, which in many parts of the country is the standard for leys of intermediate length. Kersey White, which may have originated from the New Zealand type, is a third member of this group. All three forms spread freely by runners. Under good conditions they are more productive than wild white, but are somewhat less persistent under upland conditions and on poor land.

Wild white clover is fairly easily distinguished from the Dutch variety in appearance, being smaller, later in flowering, more actively creeping and rooting freely at the nodes. As it is almost the only useful perennial legume found in many of our pastures it has a great significance from the point of view of nitrogen fixation and the improvement of the soil. It is an indigenous plant and tends to increase where conditions are favourable; it is much more resistant to soil acidity than is red clover and it withstands drought. Wild white clover commences growth somewhat late in the season. Hence, if a pasture is left ungrazed during the spring period (April-May) the clover will tend to be suppressed by early grasses such as cocksfoot and ryegrass. Close grazing on the other hand at this time encourages the clover at the expense of the grasses. It is desirable, therefore, to manage the sward to preserve a balance between the grasses and clover.

The seed of wild white clover is harvested from old pastures,[1] and the various types show considerable differences owing to the varying conditions to which each has become acclimatised. Thus there are more or less distinct types from such places as the Weald, Romney Marsh, Suffolk.

---

[1] The National Certifying Authority for Herbage Seeds (see pages 361-362) approve fields, under its local strains scheme from which the produce may be officially certified. Previously, a scheme was administered by the Ministry of Agriculture.

Hereford and the Cotswolds. There is also an Aberystwyth pedigree wild white S. 184, which is much more uniform in size and vigour than the produce of seed saved from old pastures. The seed of wild white clover is rather costly. Some of the seeds, and sometimes a large proportion, are hard-coated, and may lie dormant in the soil for as long as a year before germinating. Once-grown wild white clover seed is got from a cultivated crop produced by sowing seed from a certified field. The effect of such cultivation is to increase the proportion of free flowering and short lived plants. Twice-grown seed gives a range of types quite markedly different from the original (see p. 351).

The seed of wild white clover runs about 900,000 per lb. and that of Dutch white about 750,000. The other types are intermediate. Usual amounts in mixtures are ½ to 1 lb. of wild white or S. 184, and 1 to 4 lb. of the larger types.

**Trefoil** (*Medicago lupulina*).—This is a legume which has no value for permanent pastures but is useful for short leys on poor, shallow and sandy soils where the better clovers will not grow. It is chiefly used for one-year mixtures, as after fifteen or sixteen months it dies out and allows weeds to develop. It is sown as a substitute for red clover on land that is clover-sick. It is very sensitive to soil acidity.

The seed is relatively large (300,000 per lb.), and normal seed rates for pure stands are around 20 lb. per acre.

**Kidney Vetch** (*Anthyllis vulneraria*).—This is a legume which thrives on poor, light, sandy and chalky soils; it is extremely hardy and resists both cold and drought. It is not truly permanent but may last several seasons, and where red clover will not grow it can be included in mixtures to the extent of 2 or 3 lb. per acre.

**Lucerne** (see p. 325) is frequently grown as a pure stand but is also being increasingly used as a component of special purpose leys (see p. 364).

## HERBAGE SEED PRODUCTION

The production of grass and clover seed is, in many cases, a highly specialised enterprise, and the subject can here be dealt with only in general terms.

Climate is very important in herbage seed production, and indeed limits the districts in this country where grass and clover seed can be grown each year with a good chance of success. Clover seed is normally grown in districts with an annual rainfall of less than 30 in. Grass seed can be produced in districts of higher rainfall, but the bulk is grown in south and east England, where there are better prospects of good weather for harvesting. Good crops, but on a more limited scale, are also grown in Scotland, Northern Ireland and Wales.

Though grass leys that have been sown primarily for grazing or mowing are still used for grass and clover seed production, the great bulk of herbage seeds is now grown from specially sown seed on land selected because of its suitability for seed production.

It is important to use a good authentic stock of seed and to sow it on land in good heart and free from weeds and other plants which would be difficult to separate from the harvested herbage seed. Herbage seed-growing is now finding a place in farm crop rotations and is planned with care.

In 1956 a National Certifying Authority for Herbage Seeds was set up with the primary object of preserving proven strains of herbage plants. This authority has drawn up and now works under rules and regulations for a comprehensive certification scheme, which covers the choice of authentic seed, the pre-inspection of fields on which herbage seed is to be grown, the field inspection of the growing crops and the final testing of the harvested seed. Particulars of the National Scheme for Comprehensive Certification of Herbage Seeds and Herbage Seed Growers leaflets are available from the National Institute of Agricultural Botany, Huntingdon Road, Cambridge. Changes in the regulations and standards of purity are made from time to time, and those who wish to have up to date information on this specialist branch of farming are advised to obtain the latest publications on the subject.

## SEEDS MIXTURES

From the species and strains described it is possible to make up many different combinations; and a great variety of mixtures are recommended by different authorities for different purposes. The considerations which should be kept in mind in compounding the mixtures are as follows:—

1. The intended duration of the ley. It is generally sufficient to distinguish between leys for one year, two years and those for three years or more.

2. The intended use—*i.e.* hay, ensilage, artificial drying, pasture or any combination of these—for example, one year's hay and two years' grazing.

3. The soil and climatic conditions, more particularly the average soil moisture supply during the mid-summer period.

4. In the case of leys for grazing, the predominant type of stock—dairy, store or fattening cattle or sheep.

5. The season of the year for which the ley is intended to provide; for example, two fields of pasture may be intended to be complementary—the one to provide spring and autumn grazing and the other to yield a silage cut and to cover the summer gap.

6. The degree of importance which the farmer attaches to the build-up of soil structure. This varies according to the soil type, and the particular crops that he intends to grow during the two or three years after the ley is broken up.

Management of leys now is regarded as of great importance, regardless of the type of mixture sown. There is now much greater flexibility in the management of leys arising from the introduction of more bred strains of grasses, the more common practice of sowing leys on bare ground for quick establishment and the use of nitrogen fertilizers as well as those containing phosphate and potash. Persistency for the shorter ley is now less important—the aim is to secure the maximum production from the ley over its duration whether that be one, two or, three or more years. Before a ley appreciably declines in productiveness, it is now usual to plough it up for arable or restorative cropping.

**One-year Mixtures.**—Italian ryegrass and broad red clover—one or the other or the two in combination—provide productive one-year swards. On the poorer and lighter soils, and particularly on the chalk, pure clover is generally preferred since it is the better preparation for wheat. On good land that is in high condition, and especially if nitrogen is to be liberally applied, the ryegrass is liable to smother the clover, so that there is little to be gained by including the latter.

The bred strains of Italian ryegrass are now being used more widely. S. 22 is a short-term ryegrass, which, sown alone at 20 to 25 lb. per acre is capable of giving a substantial crop, if suitably treated with fertilizers. The land so sown can be used for grazing, ensilage or hay. Where much grazing is planned and the ley is expected to run into the second year 2 lb. of S. 100 white clover may be added to the seeding of grass.

**Two-year Mixtures.**—The choice of grasses for two-year leys is generally confined to Italian and perennial ryegrass. The clovers worth consideration are broad and late flowering red, alsike, and the stronger growing types of white New Zealand and S. 100.

The choice will rest largely on the intended use of the ley. If a full crop of hay is to be taken in the first year, the early and vigorous Italian ryegrass and broad red clover will tend to suppress the other components of the sward with serious detriment to production in the second year. They reach the hay stage earlier than perennial ryegrass or late flowering red clover. On the other hand, they are the most useful species in the aftermath of the first year. If the sward is to be grazed throughout the first season, or if, in the first year, the field is to be grazed with sheep before being laid up for hay or again, if the first cut is to be taken for silage, the balance of argument is in favour of their inclusion.

For grazing a suitable mixture would be:—

|  | | | lb. per acre |
|---|---|---|---|
| S. 22 Italian ryegrass | . | . | 22 |
| or New Zealand short rotation ryegrass | | | |
| S. 123 red clover | . | . | 3 |
| S. 100 white clover | . | . | 2 |
|  | | | 27 |

**Three to Four Year Mixtures.**—There have been greater changes in the recommendations for three to four year mixtures than in those either for short leys or for more permanent grass. Perennial ryegrass for many years was the dominant ingredient in such mixtures, and it still remains so for general purpose mixtures in many of the moister western areas of this country. But it does not provide for the summer drought gap in the drier areas.

Timothy and meadow fescue have to some extent taken its place. For example, a useful mixture to provide for ensilage, mid-summer grazing and an autumn or early spring bite would be:—

|  | | | | lb. per acre |
|---|---|---|---|---|
| S. 48 timothy | . | . | . | 6 |
| S. 53 meadow fescue | . | . | . | 6 |
| S. 215 meadow fescue | . | . | . | 6 |
| S. 100 white clover | . | . | . | 2 |
|  | | | | — |
|  | | | | 20 |

The use of the above mixture would be more common on a farm where there were a number of fields in leys and where variations in mixtures could be made. On the smaller farm where this is not possible the general purpose mixture is used, and is managed—*i.e.* grazed and fertilized—to meet the requirements of the farmer for grazing and conserved grass for winter use. A mixture of this type would be:—

|  | | | lb. per acre |
|---|---|---|---|
| S. 24 perennial ryegrass | . | . | 6 |
| S. 23 perennial ryegrass | . | . | 6 |
| S. 143 cocksfoot | . | . | 6 |
| S. 48 timothy | . | . | 4 |
| S. 100 white clover | . | . | 2 |
| wild white clover | . | . | 1 |
|  | | | — |
|  | | | 25 |

In the drier areas lucerne proves of great value for the period of the summer drought. Formerly it was sown along with a companion grass, the normal seeding being lucerne 15 lb. per acre, S. 37 cocksfoot 3 lb. per acre. Now it is becoming more common to sow the lucerne and cocksfoot in alternate rows 12 to 14 in. apart—a typical seeding being lucerne 6 lb. per acre, S. 143 cocksfoot 3 lb. per acre. The combination provides a useful cut for silage or hay and good late summer grazing. It can also be used for winter grazing under certain circumstances.

**Long Ley and Permanent Mixtures.**—During last century seed of a large number of grass species became available, and from the eighties onwards highly complex mixtures, containing a dozen or more, with two or three of the clovers (none of them persistent) were commonly recommended. The " discovery " of wild white clover, and its growing use in the early years of this century, was the first major step of progress in the production of improved long term leys. It is interesting to recall that the work of Gilchrist at Cockle Park and of Findlay at Aberdeen, resulted in the elimination of many species which today are widely used under conditions in which they can make a real contribution to grassland productivity, *e.g.* meadow fescue, which failed to compete with other species, and Italian ryegrass and broad red clover, which suppressed the more lasting components of the sward. Both workers were thinking at that time of a sward which would be mown in its first year. By a long process of trial and error the two arrived at similar conclusions, and recommended a mixture that was more complex than that formerly used for short leys but much simpler than the typical " permanent " mixtures of the time. The Cockle Park prescription was 14 lb. perennial ryegrass, 8 lb. cocksfoot, 2 lb. timothy, 2 lb. late-flowering red clover, and 1 lb. wild white clover. Sometimes a pound of rough-stalked meadow grass was added, and the proportion of cocksfoot and timothy might be varied according to climate and soil type. This prescription is still the basis of our modern general purpose long leys, the chief modifications being the partial or complete substitution of indigenous or pedigree strains of grass for the commercial types, the substitution in some cases of S. 100 or other more vigorous strain for the wild white clover.

One difficulty with this mixture is that really good grazing management is difficult to achieve. But if a goodly proportion of the first-year grass is mown for hay there will be little difficulty in dealing with the spring flush, and the aftermath will often be sufficient to compensate for the relatively small seasonal decline in output from the grazed fields during July and August. Moreover, the pressure of stock will ordinarily be relieved in July-August by the sale of fat cattle or of fat or store lambs. There is a risk that over-grazing by ewes in early spring may so weaken the cocksfoot that it fails to perform its function of filling the summer gap. On the other hand, in seasons when keep is very abundant, fattening cattle and lambs become rather selective, and the cocksfoot may get out of hand. If a dairy herd constitutes the bulk of the live stock and the system of strip grazing (see p. 372) is adopted, these difficulties need not arise.

The following may serve as examples of variants of the Cockle Park prescription for the lighter sorts of land. On heavy land timothy would be substituted for part of the cocksfoot:—

| | I<br>Grazed<br>Throughout | II<br>Mown in First<br>Years |
|---|---|---|
| Italian ryegrass . . . . | 4 | ... |
| S. 24 or S. 101 perennial ryegrass | 7 | 8 |
| S. 23 ryegrass . . . . | 7 | 8 |
| Danish cocksfoot . . . | 3 | 3 |
| S. 143 cocksfoot . . . | 3 | 3 |
| broad red clover . . . | 2 | ... |
| late-flowering red clover . . | 1 | 2 |
| S. 100 or New Zealand white clover | 1 | 1 |
| wild or S. 184 white clover . . | 1 | 1 |
| | 29 | 26 |

## ESTABLISHMENT OF SWARDS

Seeds mixtures are normally sown in spring and late summer. Sowing in mid-summer is risky in all but the areas of higher rainfall; and too late sowing in autumn can result in a sward deficiency in clover, as the young plants are not frost hardy.

Sowing without a nurse is recommended where a quick establishment of a sward is required, especially in connection with the establishment of long duration or permanent swards. It has been said that this practice wastes a year, but in fact the young sward will usually produce a substantial amount of grazing within two or three months of sowing, and, if spring sown, will reach full production during July and August, at which time succulent young herbage may be of great value. Again, seed rates may well be reduced in the absence of a nurse crop, because casualties among the seedlings are fewer. Establishment is helped by consolidation of the ground, and hence it is desirable to turn stock on to the land as soon as there is enough growth for them to eat. It is often good practice to sow a short lived and quick growing herbage plant along with the seeds that are intended to form the sward. Such a plant functions as a nurse in a real sense. A bushel of oats, or 5 lb. of Italian ryegrass or 2 or 3 lb. of rape will serve the purpose. Rape is commonly employed where, as in the re-seeding of upland pastures, sowing is often best done in June. The young seeds and rape together will fatten large numbers of lambs.

Annual weeds may, in extreme cases, smother the grass seedlings, but a moderate infestation does no serious harm. Docks and thistles are the most important weeds that infest both ploughland and pastures, but trouble is often encountered with chickweed, red shank and other species. There is also risk of weed competition in direct re-seeding—*i.e.* where the old sward is replaced by a new one without an intervening period of arable cropping. The danger here is that the bent and other poor grasses in the old sward may re-establish and crowd out the seedlings. Under certain conditions this can be prevented by ploughing to a sufficient depth and in such a way as to ensure that the old sod is well covered; but this may be impossible, more particularly on rough upland. In this case a shallow ploughing and a bastard fallow, followed by deeper ploughing after the sod has been killed, may produce the desired result; but a sure method is to introduce a pioneer crop—*e.g.* of rape—before re-seeding. These procedures are discussed later (pp. 380-381).

It is still a common practice to sow under a cereal crop. It has sometimes been suggested that a cereal " nurse " protects the grass and clover seedlings from drought, but the so-called nurse depletes the soil of moisture and its presence increases the risk of failure. In the cooler areas failures from drought are rare, but in the hotter and drier parts of the country they are common. Hence it is in the latter that the case against the nurse is strongest. A second risk is that of lodging of the cereal crop which, if it occurs some time before harvest, may result in the total disappearance of the clovers, and possibly the grasses as well. On land that is in good condition a strong-strawed cereal should be selected, and the taller and leafier varieties of cereal should be avoided, since the heavy shade that these throw weakens the seedlings, especially the clovers. In northern and upland regions still another hazard must be considered: the interval between harvest and the onset of winter may be so short that the seeds fail to get firmly established and may consequently be winter-killed and so it is necessary to select an early ripening variety of cereal. In higher rainfall areas the risk from excessive shading is often more serious than that from drought, and the seed rate of the nurse crop may be reduced to something less than would be employed if the yield of grain were the only consideration.

In certain seasons autumn sown corn can successfully be under-sown in spring, but the practice is now less common. In general, the best cereal nurse is a short- and strong-strawed variety of spring barley, sown at a little less than the normal seed rate. Such a crop throws a relatively light shade and, having a low water up-take, leaves a relatively large amount of soil moisture for the under-sown seeds. There is, however, the risk that the young grasses and clovers may grow too luxuriantly and cause great difficulty at harvest. This indeed usually happens when the late summer is wet and harvest delayed. Broad red clover, being a quick grower and very succulent, is the greatest source of trouble. Another question, the answer to which depends on circumstances, is whether to sow the seeds immediately after the cereal nurse, or to delay for perhaps three weeks, by which time the cereal will be sufficiently well rooted to bear harrowing. If the land is known to contain many annual weed seeds, there is a strong argument for delay, since many of the weed seedlings will be destroyed in the process of harrowing-in the grass seed. Weed destruction by such means is the more to be wished since the common weed-killing sprays may cause damage to the clover seedlings. Again, late sowing reduces the risk, referred to above, of an over luxuriant growth of clover at harvest. On the other hand, and especially in the drier areas, delay in sowing greatly increases the chance of a failure to get a " take."

As has been said, grass and clover seeds require a seed bed that is both fine and firm, conditions that can best be achieved by early ploughing (to permit the land to consolidate and to weather) and by the judicious use of the harrow and roller. Under moist, warm conditions the seeds of grasses will strike even if they are not covered, but clover seeds must be buried. The ideal depth under average conditions is about an inch, but this may be somewhat exceeded in the driest parts of the country.

In cool and moist districts the common practice is to broadcast the seeds, by means of a grass seed barrow or a " fiddle," and to follow with the harrow and roller. With a very fine soil crumb, coverage may be difficult to secure, and under such conditions it is good practice to use a ring roller rather than a flat type for the last operation before sowing; a fair proportion of the seed will then come to rest in the little furrows and be covered by the subsequent harrowing and rolling. A machine composed of two gangs of ring rollers, with a seed hopper discharging between them, gives good results. The alternative to broadcasting, and one which is to be preferred in the drier areas, is to drill. If a special small seed drill (with closely spaced coulters) is not available and a standard drill has to be used, some advantage is gained by drilling in two directions, preferably at an angle of about forty five degrees. This procedure makes for quicker closing of the sward and therefore reduces the chance of serious invasion by weeds.

Under cool and moist conditions grass seeds may be sown at any time from early spring until about the end of August. In cold and wet uplands June is perhaps the best time. If a failure occurs under a nurse crop, a second sowing may be made—without ploughing—on the stubble. Where patches fail owing to lodging of the cereal, the sward can be mended, at the earliest opportunity after the corn harvest, by hand broadcasting and harrowing or raking.

The better grasses, to make vigorous growth in the seedling stage, require a high status of soil nutrients and a neutral or only slightly acid soil reaction. When sown without a nurse, the young plant should be grazed as soon as the plants are tall enough to provide a bite for cattle, since the treading of animals, at times when the land is dry enough to carry them without poaching, is beneficial, but excessively close grazing by sheep may weaken the plants. Seeds sown with a nurse may be grazed lightly in autumn after the corn crop has been cleared, but much depends on the period of growing weather that can be expected; in late districts, where there is only a short interval between harvest and the onset of winter, it may be well to leave the autumn growth untouched. Moreover, severe autumn grazing will so weaken the plants that spring growth will be slow, and the early bite from young seeds is usually more valuable than autumn keep.

Treatment of sown pastures in their first harvest year is also important. In general, the best swards are produced by grazing, but on some types of land the young turf is too " tender " to carry cattle. The main long term objective is to prevent the suppression of the white clover, which is liable to occur if the sward is laid up for hay in its first year, more especially when mowing has to wait for settled weather until the crop has passed the proper hay stage. It may be better to cut for silage, since this can and should be done at an earlier stage of growth. The aftermath should be rather closely grazed, but not up till the very end of the growing season. In general, lenient grazing will encourage the grasses, while continuous hard grazing, by removing the competition of the grasses, will encourage the prostrate white clover.

# MANURING AND MANAGEMENT

**Principles of Grazing Management.**—An understanding of some biological principles and processes is a necessary foundation to good grassland management, and these may be illustrated by reference to a ryegrass-clover sward.

In autumn herbage plants lay up reserves of food material—mainly carbohydrate—in their roots, stolons and leaf bases. The amount of these reserves is dependent upon the amount of active leaf tissue and on the length of time during which conditions (light, temperature and soil moisture) enable photosynthesis to continue. Accordingly, if a sward is grazed hard and continuously during the latter part of the season, and up till the onset of winter, the plants' accumulated reserves will be small and, in consequence, spring growth will be feeble. Again, it should be remembered that the leafage which ryegrass throws up during mild periods in winter is produced mainly at the expense of food reserves. If this winter growth is eaten off, the plants will be further weakened.

Ryegrass commences active spring growth when the soil temperature reaches a figure of about 44° F., but the rate of growth is determined, not only by soil and air temperature and by light, but also by the supply of available soil nitrogen. Under typical British conditions soil nitrates are almost completely leached by winter rains, and the bacterial activity by which the stock is replenished begins only when the soil temperature has risen to about 48° F. There is thus a period, longer or shorter according to the rate at which the soil warms up, during which the production of grazable herbage is dependent upon the application of nitrogen in a readily available form. The production of early bite thus depends on three things, viz.: (1) the presence in the sward of naturally " early " types of grasses such as ryegrass; (2) the resting of the sward in autumn and winter; and (3) the application in February or early March of quick-acting nitrogen fertilizer. A common dressing is 2 cwt. of sulphate of ammonia, Nitro-chalk or Nitra-Shell.

The subsequent effects of such treatment must also be borne in mind; if the ryegrass is forced into early growth and is then severely and continuously grazed, it will be weakened at a time when the white clover is still dormant; and when, later, the clover comes into growth, it will be in a strongly competitive condition and will tend to dominate the sward. The restoration of a good balance can be assisted by lenient grazing in summer or by laying up the field for a cut of silage; but it is inadvisable to treat a given field repeatedly, in successive years, in the way described. It will also be readily understood that if the early growth of ryegrass is not grazed, the balance of the sward will be upset in the opposite sense—*i.e.* the ryegrass will overtop and suppress the clover. Incidentally, the problem of maintaining a balanced sward can be avoided by using a pure grass sward for early bite, Many farmers rely upon

Italian, New Zealand or S. 22 short rotation ryegrass for the purpose, these types making earlier spring growth than any of the strains of perennial grasses.

To turn from the early spring to the main grazing period—say from May till October—it must be recognised that, with a given botanical composition and a given level of fertilizer usage, the nutritive value of the herbage per pound of dry matter and also the total yield of nutrients per acre depend largely upon the system of grazing adopted; but, the maximum yield of nutrients is not fully compatible with maximum nutritive quality. The percentage of protein is highest and that of crude fibre is lowest in the young leaf—*i.e.* at the shortest and earliest stage of growth that will allow the animal to satisfy its appetite. But if grazing is so intense as to maintain a lawn-like condition the leaf area will be kept small, so that carbon assimilation is depressed. This will, in turn, be reflected in feeble root growth and lowered capacity to resist drought. By contrast, the highest yields of nutrients per acre are obtained, in cutting experiments, with two or three cuts per season, the first being made about the time of emergence of the flower heads. Management based upon such considerations is not always practicable, if only because of the excessive waste by soiling and treading that would result. Moreover, animals thrive best when they have a full bite and no more, *i.e.* when they can fill themselves in a short time and yet are not tempted by the abundance of keep to become highly selective. Full bite implies a length of about 5 to 7 in. for mature cattle and less than half this length for lambs.

Deep milking cows and also fattening cattle and sheep require suitable production diets, and pasture management for these groups must aim at the production of highly nutritious herbage even though this will imply some reduction in the output of total nutrients per acre. By contrast, dry cows, two-year-old heifers and store stock can maintain themselves in satisfactory condition on a less nutritious diet, and larger numbers can be carried if the grazing is relatively lenient.

The major difficulties in achieving the desired degree of intensity of grazing arise from the fact that the rate of growth of pasture herbage varies from month to month during the average year, and varies also—especially during the midsummer period—as between one year and another. Variation during the season is at its maximum on the thinner and lighter soils of the drier and warmer (south-eastern) districts and in the low rainfall pockets that occur in the Midlands and elsewhere. Under the least favourable conditions production during the period May-June may amount to 50 or even 60 per cent. of the year's total. In the cooler and moister parts of the country the production curve shows less violent ups and downs, but is never anything like level.

The traditional method of levelling out the seasonal supply of pasturage has been to mow for hay some proportion—up to about half—of the total grass area, and to use the aftermath for grazing; but the hay crop, by reason of its high rate of transpiration at what is ordinarily the driest part of the year, often leaves the soil with very little moisture, so that the growth of aftermath may be delayed until there is a good rain. Moreover, the plants use up, in the formation of their stems and flower heads, a substantial proportion of their carbohydrate reserves, and the extent of this exhaustion is increased if the plants are allowed to set seed—as they will, of course, do whenever mowing is delayed by unsettled weather. All this explains the unreliability of hay aftermaths for the purpose of filling the summer gap in the supply of pasturage. The most certain means to the desired end is to provide a second sward, composed of drought resistant species, as a complement to the ryegrass-clover type, and to mow this for ensilage. At the season in question there is likely to be a fair supply of soil moisture, and the plants will have sufficient food reserves to enable their quick recovery after mowing.

Another important aim of pasture management is to ensure that the herbage will be consumed at the desired stage of growth. The ideal is to allow successive crops to grow undisturbed—*i.e.* to give the sward periods of complete rest—and to harvest each successive crop, by means of grazing animals, quickly and completely. The procedure is thus essentially the same as that of folding sheep on clover.

Traditional systems of grazing management fall short of the ideal in varying degrees, and practical considerations often prevent its attainment. One fact is that different kinds of grazing animals are more or less selective in their feeding habits. Horses are extremely so. From the start of the season they usually concentrate on particular large patches and completely neglect others—upon which they usually dung. They prefer young growth to old and bite very close, so that the final result, where a field is stocked with horses alone, is a mosaic of lawn-like and rough, neglected patches. Sheep are also highly selective, but after another fashion—picking out individual plants, shoots, and leaves, and, in particular, avoiding the flowering stems of the grasses. Sheep pastures must be topped by the mower if the grasses are to be prevented from wasting their energies on seed production. Cows in milk are not very fastidious, but if they are compelled to clear up rough or soiled herbage their milk yields fall—often quite abruptly. Two-year-old store cattle, dry cows and in-calf heifers in the earlier stages of pregnancy can, without suffering harm, play a useful role as scavengers.

Where relatively large groups of stock are allotted to particular fields, with the intention of leaving them for a period of perhaps two or three months, suitable combinations are fattening cattle with a few sheep or, a flock of ewes and lambs with a few store cattle or suckling cows with their calves. If it appears that the farm stock as a whole is inadequate to keep the pastures under control—as will happen in a warm and moist season—some concentration will be required, and a field or two should be laid up, preferably for a silage cut.

A refinement of the system of free range grazing is found in areas that specialise in the grass fattening of cattle, particularly in the Midlands. The store animals are kept during early spring in " holding fields " of relatively poor grass, being given hay if necessary, until the fattening swards commence active growth, which they commonly do in late April or early May. Numbers are adjusted with the object of maintaining control of the growth during the spring flush period. Meanwhile, a reserve of cattle is carried on one or two of the holding fields, the rest being laid up for hay. The usual aim is to have a proportion of the cattle in forward condition at turning-on time, so that these may be sold fat towards the end of the flush season, and thus leave a sufficiency of feed for the remainder. Many graziers also keep a relatively small flock of draft ewes, which go off fat with their lambs soon after midsummer and thus give further relief. Another point is that shade should be provided as a protection against gad flies. The fattening fields are " cleaned up " by lean cattle in autumn, and are either completely rested throughout the winter or carry only a few ewes—rarely more than one per acre.

Another traditional system, for which there is less to be said, is common on small dairy farms. Two enclosures provide for the needs of the milking herd—a relatively small night paddock and a large day pasture. A third field, usually of poorer quality, is allocated to the heifers and dry cows. The remainder of the grassland is used for hay, and the aftermath is expected to fill the summer gap. This plan gives very limited scope for controlled grazing, and the night paddock commonly collects fertility from the day pasture. An improvement of this system which is feasible in many cases, is to divide the grassland—apart from the night paddock where this must be retained as a matter of convenience—into perhaps six or seven enclosures. These are used in rotation, each in turn being grazed first by the milking herd and immediately afterwards by the followers, and then rested for about three or four weeks. During the flush period growth may be controlled by laying up, for a silage cut, any piece that is not needed as pasturage. The scheme makes practicable the use of summer dressings of nitrogen, whereby growth can be stimulated in summer and autumn according to need; and it makes possible the ploughing up and re-seeding of each enclosure in turn.

In general, still better control with a substantially higher output of milk per acre, can be secured by the system of strip grazing, whereby the daily or half daily ration of pasturage is provided by the step by step movement of a fence that consists of a single electrically charged wire, on easily movable and insulated supports. The longer the fence and the narrower the strips the less will be the wastage through soiling and treading. A back fence should preferably be used in order to prevent access by the herd to ground which it has recently traversed. The area provided at each move must, of course, be adjusted, partly by trial and error, to the herd's daily (or half-daily) needs; but with a close sward at the optimum stage for grazing—about 6 in. high—a first approximation might be one-sixtieth of an acre per cow per day.  It is necessary to plan ahead and to mow, possibly for silage, any area that is likely to be unwanted, or that is passing the optimum growth stage for pasturage.  Records show that the gain in output by substituting strip for free range grazing, expressed in terms of milk per acre, is of the order of 20 to 25 per cent.

A strip grazed herd may include dry cows and in-calf heifers, but there are difficulties in applying the system to other classes of stock.  The dairy herd must in any case travel twice daily from shed to pasture, giving four opportunities for watering;  moreover, during " fly weather " the cattle can be kept in the shed, or given access to shade, during the heat of the day.  But the problems of water and shade arise in the case of store or fattening cattle, and sheep are less effectively controlled by any existing type of fence that is easily movable.  It seems however, that the improvement or output, under strip grazing, is of the same order with store and fattening stock as with milch cows.

**Manuring of Pasture.**—Lime is lost from grassland by leaching at much the same rate, other things being equal, as from arable ground;  but the lime status required even for the better sort of grasses and clovers —about $pH$ 5·5 to 6—is lower than that needed by such crops as sugar beet and barley.  Lucerne and sainfoin, among pasture plants, are exceptions, giving optimum results on neutral or slightly alkaline soils.  The symptoms of moderate lime deficiency are less obvious in grasses and clovers than they are in most arable crops, so that soil tests for lime are more often required.  In extreme cases the disappearance of the better species, the presence of sorrel or of *Holcus mollis*, and the formation of a surface " mat " of dead but undecayed material, are sure signs.  The intrusion of the sward by *Agrostis*, which is the commonest form of deterioration, is often due to causes other than acidity—to phosphate deficiency or to over-grazing in winter combined with under-grazing in summer.  The general rule about liming—that frequent and moderate dressings are better than mass applications at longer intervals—applies equally to grass and arable land.

With soil of reasonably good body, and where the grazing stock is composed of store or fattening cattle or sheep, losses of potash are very low, practically the whole amount consumed being returned to the land in the urine.  By contrast, milch cows pass a good deal of urine in the cowshed, or in course of their travels between shed and pasture, with the consequence that most dairy pastures require periodic dressings.  Obviously, also, if grassland is mown for any purpose, without getting dung in exchange, the drain on potash reserves will be large.  Even an occasional cut of hay, unless this is fed back on the land where it has grown, will result in potash depletion.  The species most susceptible to potash deficiency are lucerne and red clover.

Losses of phosphate by true leaching are small, but it may be noted that, on steep slopes and especially where the soil is light or stony, substantial amounts may be carried away in suspension by surface or subsurface water. Growing animals retain substantial amounts of phosphate in their bones, and milch cattle also make considerable demands; a cow producing 500 gal. of milk during the grazing season will deplete the soil of the equivalent of about half a huhdredweight of superphosphate. Full grown fattening animals, on the other hand, excrete practically all the phosphate that they consume.

It has already been pointed out (p. 36) that most British soils have a marked capacity to fix phosphate in unavailable forms, so that a simple balance sheet of gains and losses has often very little meaning. In fact, the only pastures that do not need regular applications are on soils of high phosphate status and low powers of phosphate fixation, and where the land is regularly stocked with mature non-milking stock.

Soil surveys and field experiments show that, despite the relatively high rate of usage during the past decade, much of our poorer grassland is still markedly phosphate deficient. Where such marked deficiencies have to be made good, suitable sources are ground mineral phosphates for the typically rather acid soils of the high rainfall areas, and high-soluble basic slag elsewhere. Where there is no such gross deficiency, and only maintenance applications are required, the evidence is in favour of small dressings at short and regular intervals. In such cases it is often convenient to use either superphosphate alone or a compound fertilizer containing soluble phosphate. Under intensive systems of management phosphate is generally applied in the form of compounds with nitrogen or with both nitrogen and potash.

Practice in regard to nitrogen usage varies very widely; the choice for a particular farm depends largely on economic considerations and individual circumstances. A well balanced clover-grass sward can be self-supporting in regard to nitrogen—i.e. the needs of the grasses can be met, throughout the greater part of the season, by the nitrogen fixed by the clover and later made available either in the form of " stock nitrogen " (mainly urine) or by the decay of clover nodules and leaves. New Zealand workers have shown that, under their very favourable prevailing conditions, the clover in a balanced sward may fix as much as 200 or 300 lb. of nitrogen (equivalent to 10 to 15 cwt. of ammonium sulphate) per acre during the nine or ten months that the plants continue in active growth. But under British conditions the amount fixed is ordinarily much less, and the loss by leaching during our much longer dead season is considerably higher. Nevertheless, with adequate supplies of lime and phosphate (upon which the growth of clover so greatly depends), and with competent grazing management, quite high outputs of live stock products can be attained without resort to nitrogen fertilizers. Overall production is, however, not the sole consideration, especially where, as in the case of a dairy herd, a high level of nutrition must be maintained week by week throughout the year. April grass, grown with the help of applied nitrogen, will necessarily be more expensive than June grass grown without, but is ordinarily much cheaper than the equivalent in the form of hay and concentrates. Again, if growth can be sustained throughout the late summer, and again into the late autumn, a considerable saving of more expensive alternative foodstuffs will be achieved. It is often good business to plan for the early bite on the lines previously discussed (p. 369), to top-dress such fields that are shut up in late May with the object of filling the summer gap and to stimulate the autumn growth of a ryegrass ley by an August application. In other words, nitrogen can be used to increase the amount of grazing at the periods when keep is liable to be short; and if this is done, the greater part of the acreage allotted to the dairy herd will be top dressed at one time or another during the year.

The practice indicated above is rarely applied as a matter of routine where the grazing stock consists of store or fattening cattle or sheep. Store cattle due for turning out in spring, whether or not they are intended for summer fattening, can generally be held, at no very great expense, until the time when an ordinary pasture has produced a good bite; only in years when winter fodder is likely to be short is there a strong case for forcing early growth; and the stocking can often be reduced, by sales, to ease the pressure on the pastures in late summer.

In the case of lowland flocks of breeding sheep there is often a good deal to be gained by applying a February-March top dressing to some part of the pasture, ewes being often short of milk up till the commencement of spring growth.

Many milk producers, especially those whose acreage is small in relation to their available capital, have used fertilizers more liberally than that described above. In such cases it is essential to resort to rotational or strip grazing in order to maintain proper control of the sward. A common programme is to apply, about February, 4 to 5 cwt. of a compound fertilizer, and to follow with two or more applications of nitrogen, providing perhaps 40 to 70 lb. units of nitrogen per acre during the season. Nitro-chalk, Nitra-Shell or nitrate of soda is to be preferred to sulphate of ammonia, the response to the latter being too dependent on rain. Such farmers have generally a strong preference for leys of three or four years' duration, mainly because the clover, being at a disadvantage in competition with the grasses, is often almost completely suppressed in the later years.

Such a combination of treatments—high fertilizer usage with complete grazing control—may be expected, in the cooler and moister areas, to raise the output of milk per acre substantially. In the hotter and drier areas, and especially where the soil is light, the achievement of the full benefit depends on irrigation, which is likely to be economic only under conditions that are not general—e.g. on fields adjoining streams.

**Permanent Grass for Mowing.**—The acreage of meadow hay has in recent years shown a marked fall—less than one half of the acreage in 1939. The level of production from typical old meadows is low, an average yield of little more than 1 ton, providing perhaps 6 to 7 cwt. of starch equivalent and about 1 cwt. protein equivalent per acre. It is true that part of this acreage will have yielded some grazing before being laid up, and also that the aftermath will normally be grazed. But the total yield is so low, as to suggest a look at other methods of using the grass.

Most permanent swards have obvious shortcomings when regarded as sources of hay. They contain a large number of grass species whose flowering times are spread over many weeks, so that there is no particular date when a large majority are at the optimum stage for mowing—*i.e.* the commencement of flowering. Again, some of the earliest flowering species —sweet vernal and Yorkshire fog—are weeds, and these will be ready to shed their seeds before the later-flowering among the good grasses—*e.g.* timothy—are ready to mow. Many weeds that cannot bear close grazing or treading, and therefore cause no trouble in pastures, multiply rapidly in swards that are regularly mown. Again, white clover is the only true perennial among the useful legumes, and wild forms occurring in old swards are so prostrate that they contribute little to the mown swath, and what is reached by the mower knife is largely composed of single leaves that are easily lost in the process of hay making. Obviously, too, any treatment that produces a good growth of grass will result in the suppression of the clover. The argument in favour of young, sown swards is thus stronger for meadows than for pastures.

In particular cases, circumstances virtually dictate mowing year after year. For instance, the small amount of low ground that is attached to the typical mountain sheep farm must serve the double purpose of providing grazing during the " starvation period " in spring and yielding a stock of hay against periods of severe winter weather. Again, there is land which is either liable to flood, or which is dry enough to carry grazing animals only in late summer and autumn. The lack of drinking water for cattle is another common reason for continuous mowing.

The appropriate fertilizer treatment for meadow land will generally be different from that for pasture, even under similar soil and climatic conditions. Unless the hay crop is consumed in the field where it was grown, the taking of successive crops will rapidly deplete reserves of available potash, which depletion does not arise so quickly in the case of pasture. Again, it is not to be expected that, under meadow conditions, wild white clover will persist in sufficiently vigorous condition to provide enough nitrogen for the grasses. In general, then, meadows should have regular dressings of a complete fertilizer, even if a limited quantity of dung is also available.

In cases where the permanent grass area of a farm is fairly uniform, and where water can be provided in every field, the question arises whether it is better to allocate particular fields as meadow and pasture respectively or whether each field should be mown one year and then grazed for a year or more. Both schemes have their advocates. On the one hand the alternate system, with good management, makes possible the maintenance of a reasonable grass-clover balance in the sward, with lower expenditure on nitrogen fertilizers for a given level of production; and alternation results in better weed control. The competition of a tall hay crop, combined with cutting at a critical time, greatly checks the growth of stoloniferous species like field thistle, while the combination of close grazing and treading kills out erect growing species that have no underground stems—*e.g.* yellow rattle. On the other hand, most of the desirable pasture species, which withstand treading and close grazing by reason of their prostrate growth habit, or because their growing points are at or below ground level (notably the indigenous types of ryegrass and white clover), are by no means ideal hay plants; a good deal of their leafage escapes the mower knife, and the short leafy material that is cut is difficult to cure and collect.

Mowing at the silage stage rarely causes serious deterioration of a grazing sward, whereas mowing for hay does a lesser or greater amount of harm according to the growth stage that the plants are allowed to reach. If the maintenance of high quality swards were the sole consideration there would be a case for all surplus grass to be ensiled. This step has, in fact, been taken by some few farmers, but it is not generally practicable. For one thing, if the product has to be hauled a long way—to the farm buildings or perhaps to a hill or mountain grazing—the greater weight of the silage (three times that of hay) is a consideration. A more general difficulty is that of providing the necessary labour and equipment to deal with the whole area that is to be mown before the herbage has passed the proper growth stage for ensilage; and silage is heavier and more difficult to move for feeding.

Where a sward—temporary or permanent—is to be mown every year, the system of fertilizer treatment and management will depend upon the relative importance which the farmer attaches to the yield of hay on the one hand and, on the other, to the amount and quality of autumn, winter or spring grazing. The production of maximum hay yields implies a large usage of fertilizers and leads to the suppression of white clover and the more prostrate types of grasses. The highest yields of hay—up to 4 or 5 tons per acre—are obtained from timothy meadows which, in addition to liberal dressings of mineral fertilizers, are ordinarily given nitrogen equivalent to 3 or 4 cwt. per acre of ammonium sulphate. Any clover sown is quickly suppressed, and the timothy itself produces only a small aftermath. At the other extreme are the enclosed " in bye " grasslands attached to mountain grazings, on which the farmer depends for wintering and often also for the keep of part (or even the whole) of the flock at lambing time in addition to a crop of hay. Here the usual scheme of manuring omits nitrogen fertilizers entirely, but if the stock includes house wintered cattle there will be an occasional dressing of dung. Permanent meadows on lowland farms are generally treated on some intermediate plan. A four year plan might include a dressing of dung the first year, a light dressing of nitrogen the second, a substantial application of balanced fertilizer in the third, and nitrogen alone again in the fourth.

**Seeds Hay.**—The term " seeds " is usually applied to hay that is taken from leys. In some cases it is meant to refer to a crop taken in the first harvest year.

Even when land is sown down with the primary object of producing hay, a certain amount of grazing is usually provided. Grazing in the autumn of the seeding year assists establishment and, where there is a considerable proportion of red clover, reduces the spread of clover rot. The young seeds should be rested over winter, or at least should not be heavily grazed. If hay is to be taken in the first harvest year the question arises whether the spring growth should first be grazed. The answer depends largely on soil and rainfall conditions. On thin, poor soils and in dry areas spring grazing tends to depress the grasses and weaken their root systems, thus making for a too clovery sward and leading to a reduced yield of hay. On good, deep soil in areas of high rainfall it ordinarily does little harm, and may indeed prevent a crop from becoming over-luxuriant and perhaps lodging and rotting at the bottom. The normal practice in dry areas is to " shut up," about Christmas seeds fields that are intended for hay in the following season, whereas in cool upland regions the field may be grazed as late as the beginning of May.

If hay is to be taken in the first harvest year of a ley that is to lie for two or more years, thought must be given to the maintenance of balance in the sward. If a heavy dressing of nitrogen be given, if cutting be delayed beyond the flowering time of the early grasses, and if the aftermath be allowed to grow to a considerable height, the grasses will tend to suppress the white clover, with the consequence that subsequent production will be seriously impaired. The general aim should therefore be to mow early and to stock the aftermath as soon as there is a good bite. Full productivity during the first season is much more fully compatible with the maintenance of sward balance if the first growth is taken for silage. If a ley is sown without a cover crop, it is better to graze lightly some six weeks or so after sowing and not to take a cut in the first year.

It is usual to provide for the initial needs of a ley in regard to lime, phosphate, potash and nitrogen at the time of sowing—the requirements of the grasses and clovers, as well as those of the nurse crop, if any, being met by a single dressing. If the ley is to be grazed in its second and subsequent years after being mown in the first, subsequent fertilizer treatment will be devised to maintain a balance of grasses and clover and to stimulate production.

There is a good general case for grazing a ley in the first year and mowing in the last. One argument is that, since there is no need to maintain botanical balance in the last year, the management may be planned with the sole objective of a heavy hay crop—*i.e.* the field may be rested in spring and given a heavy dressing of nitrogen. Moreover, the resultant sod may be of more value, as a source of soil fertility to the succeeding arable crops, than that produced by grazing. A closely grazed and clovery sod decays very quickly and releases nitrogen rapidly. A grassy sod decays more slowly; and the grasses, if allowed to grow to the hay stage, leave a large mass of fibrous root material that has a long-lasting effect on soil structure.

**Grassland Improvement.**—It has already been explained that it is only under particular conditions of soil and climate, and under systems of management that are not always practicable, that a high level of grassland productivity can be maintained indefinitely. Under most sets of circumstances inferior grasses (bent, dogstail, Yorkshire fog or sheep's fescue) increase at the expense of the better species, miscellaneous weeds increase, and the proportion of clover falls below the optimum.

There are three possible approaches to the problem. The one is to bring the largest possible proportion of the farm under a system of alternate husbandry, thus reducing the area ofi permanent grass. The second is to plough out and directly re-seed such fields as, for one reason or another, are unsuited to arable cropping. The third is to supplement the use of lime and fertilizers and good normal sward management with occasional drastic surface treatment and perhaps to introduce a certain amount of seed. The last of these procedures is the least effective and should be resorted to only where the land is practically unploughable. The subject of the following paragraphs is the improvement of lowland and upland pastures in cases where deterioration has gone far. The improvement of hill and mountain grazings is discussed later.

A major cause of deterioration in many cases is the disrepair of the drainage system, and where this has happened reconditioning must be the first step. The common signs of inadequate drainage are the occurrence of rushes and tussock grass. It may be that a complete new drainage system will be required, but there are many fields where a thorough clearance of the ditches, together with minor repairs to old tile drains, will meet the need. The standard of drainage required for grass is not as high as for arable land, but it must be adequate to permit of a reasonable length of grazing season. The second step must be the correction of any serious lime deficiency, and a lime survey of the land will be desirable, particularly as the lime status may vary widely from point to point. The phosphate and potash requirements should be ascertained at the same time. Extreme phosphate deficiency is common, whereas (except in old hay meadows) serious potash deficiency is rare. If the land is to be ploughed and re-seeded, some part of the lime should preferably be applied before ploughing and the balance after. The clearance of scrub may be necessary before ploughing.

Ploughing may be ruled out by outcrops of rock, by the occurrence of large numbers of boulders or by excessively steep slopes. The quality of the work is important. If possible the sward should be completely buried, since otherwise bent and other poor species will grow and spread before the sown grasses have become established. If complete burial cannot be achieved seeding must be delayed, and discs or a rotary cultivator must be used during the interval to ensure a complete kill of the old herbage. Indeed, where this difficulty is foreseen, it may be best to disc the land two or three times during the first summer of operation and to defer ploughing until a fairly complete kill of the old herbage has been achieved. Normally, ploughing should be carried out in autumn so that the land may have time to consolidate before sowing in the following spring or summer. Phosphate, and potash if necessary, should be applied soon after ploughing.

Preparation of the seed bed in spring should begin with discing, since tined implements are apt to bring up pieces of old turf; and discs produce the better consolidation. A dressing of nitrogen should be given at seed time. Since the treading of grazing stock assists establishment, it is important to include the seed of some fast growing herbage plant which will provide grazing at the earliest possible date. A bushel of oats or about 8 lb. of Italian ryegrass per acre will serve the purpose. In cool upland districts, where sowing is late, rape is frequently used as the nurse producing useful keep for weaned lambs; but if the rape is intended to reach full growth only about 2 or 3 lb. per acre should be sown. Heavier seed rates, unless the land is to be stocked while the plants are still small, may have a depressing effect on the young grasses and more especially on the clovers. In drier lowland areas the seeds should be sown early—March or early April—whereas in cold and wet upland districts June may be the best time.

A special case, common in upland areas, is presented by land that is heavily infested with bracken, when the preparations for re-seeding must be designed to eradicate the weed. Here the time of ploughing is critical, the best being late June. In some cases a catch crop of rape may be grown in the same season, the sowing of the grasses being delayed until the following year. Indeed, where the land is very poor, and has been acid for a long period, it may be well to grow two pioneer crops—first rape and then perhaps broadcast kale and turnips, and to eat these off with sheep in order to achieve the necessary build-up of fertility.

Where ploughing is impracticable the improver must have recourse to surface treatment as a preparation for sowing. Drainage and liming must be carried out if necessary, and fertilizer dressings must be applied. The mechanical treatment required depends largely on the presence or

absence of " mat "—*i.e.* of a surface layer of dead but undecayed vegetation; " mat " is of course, indicative of severe lime deficiency. In the
absence of a " mat " the choice of method depends on the proportions of
good and bad species, and especially on the presence or absence of white
clover. If the botanical composition is reasonably good, satisfactory
results may be expected from the following procedure, viz. (1) the sward
is closely grazed, in autumn, by lean animals; (2) phosphate and potash
are applied in the quantities indicated by the soil analysis; (3) a moderate
dressing of nitrogen is applied in spring and the land is harrowed sufficiently to break the surface, but not so severely as to drag out any considerable number of plants; (4) the field is closely grazed and completely
rested by turns throughout the grazing season and is rested during the
succeeding winter.

Still assuming the absence of " mat," but with a predominance of
poor species, the foregoing plan must be changed in three respects.
Firstly, surface treatment must be more drastic, including generally the
use of a heavy disc in both directions in addition to spike harrows.
Secondly, the appropriate species—including especially wild white clover
—must be introduced; a suitable renovating mixture might include
2 lb. of wild white clover, 5 lb. of indigenous ryegrass, and a few pounds
of some other appropriate species of grass. Thirdly, the seed must be
buried, preferably by means of a chain tooth harrow, and the land must
then be heavily rolled.

The combination of poor species, a thick " mat," and unploughable
land obviously presents a most difficult problem, and quick results cannot
be looked for. Some time before beginning mechanical treatment—a year
or even two—the land should have lime and phosphate according to need.
The next preparatory step is to clean off the top growth, either through
close grazing and treading by lean cattle receiving some supplementary
feed, or alternatively by burning off in late autumn or early spring. The
" mat " is next cut up and moved by repeated discings, if possible in two
or more directions, and its break-up is carried further by means of a
chain-tooth harrow or a rotary cultivator. A catch crop —*e.g.* of rape
and Italian ryegrass—is now sown (in early summer) with a moderate
dressing of nitrogen. When the resulting crop has been fed off, and the
fertility of the land has thus been improved, the land is reworked with
discs and harrows, and is re-seeded in spring or early summer with a
" permanent " mixture, along with a light seeding of oats, Italian ryegrass
or rape to yield grazing as early as may be.

There are a number of circumstances in which it may be better and less
costly to renovate the existing sward than to plough out and re-seed, even
though the latter is possible. For example, in the industrial districts of
Lancashire, where atmospheric pollutionn, a acid soil and a high rainfall
make it a slow and difficult task to establish new grass. Recent work
with sod seeders and new cultivating implements would suggest that in

future there will be an increase in the areas of permanent pasture improved by renovation. The use of newer types of herbicides, to kill off all existing surface vegetation may become a more common first operation in grassland improvement under certain conditions.

**Maintenance and Improvement of Hill and Mountain Grazings.**—At the beginning of this chapter, in the description of types of mountain herbage, it was pointed out that heather is kept in good condition by burning at fairly long intervals, that *Molinia* may have to be burned from time to time, and that *Nardus* remains almost unproductive unless it is burned relatively frequently. The optimum interval between the burnings depends on the condition and rate of growth of the herbage; for example, the rotations adopted for burning heather vary from five to over twenty years. The usual time for the treatment is in March and April, but in some of the wettest parts of the country it is difficult to get a sufficiently dry spell for the heather to burn at all. Sheep thrive better and losses are smaller on grazings that are regularly burnt.

Surface or " sheep " drains are dug on upland pastures, not on the hill as a whole but only on such parts as are likely to benefit. For instance, where a spring is causing a rush covered swamp, a drain may be cut to divert it to the nearest waterway. Sheep drains should be about 20 in. wide at the top, 6 in. at the bottom, and fully 1 ft. deep. The Cuthbertson plough drawn by a crawler tractor, is a very satisfactory tool for making sheep drains; its use effects a great economy as compared with hand labour. Channels are cut to spread as well as to remove moisture. If water that springs from basic rock is distributed over the typical flora of acid soil a very great improvement is effected. The " flushing " is brought about by digging a channel from the spring along the contour and by causing it to fill and overflow so that the water soaks down the slope. Sheep generally graze the flushed area very hard, and this may contribute to the improvement, which consists largely in a reduction of poor species like *Nardus* and blaeberry and in a corresponding increase of useful grasses.

Where uplands are grazed by cattle as well as sheep the pasture is kept in much better condition. This is because the larger animals eat the coarser kind of herbage that, in their absence, would be neglected and would actually spread, and so reduce the area that is useful for sheep.

It will commonly be quite uneconomic to deal with any very large part of a hill or mountain grazing by the methods outlined earlier. Much, however, can be done in certain cases by the treatment of carefully selected areas whether by lime and fertilizer only, by lime, fertilizer and surface treatment, or by the latter combined with re-seeding. In any case, some degree of grazing control is necessary to prevent the extermination of the better species by persistent over-grazing. Even the partial replacement of *Nardus*, *Molinia* or Sheep's fescue by *Agrostis*-clover constitutes a major step of improvement; and this can sometimes be achieved at no very great expense. The crawler tractor, and also special equipment for wheeled tractors, has made possible the ploughing or the roughing up (by discs or pitch-pole harrows) of land that could not have been cultivated by older types of tackle. A major remaining obstacle is the high cost of fencing the many small patches of improvable land, so as to protect the improved swards from being over grazed. In some cases it is possible to concentrate the improved patches in one particular section of the hill, to fence off this section as a whole and to unstock it—*e.g.* in the late summer and autumn—when the flock can be restricted, without suffering harm, to the unimproved land. The control of stock on hill pastures is more fully discussed later (p. 580).

**Control of Weeds.**—The most effective control of weeds in grassland is secured by careful stocking and judicious management. Dwarf weeds, such as daisies and plantains, can be kept in check by fertilizer treatment, which encourages the grasses and clovers to such an extent that the weeds remain stunted. They can also be very completely killed by certain selective weedkillers (see p. 127). Creeping buttercup can be dealt with by the same means. Field thistles should be cut when they are about 6 in. high, and the cutting has to be repeated as frequently as fresh stems appear, so that the plants never flower: selective weedkillers are also effective, though two successive treatments may be required. Yellow rattle can usually be checked by hard grazing in spring, but also succumbs to cutting early in the season. Land that has been badly managed and is overrun with Yorkshire fog, bent and brome can hardly be improved without recourse to ploughing and re-seeding or drastic surface improvements.

Bracken is much the worst weed in many upland pastures and also on grazings of the lowland heather type. The most effective treatment, when conditions permit, is to plough the land in June or early July, to disc at intervals during the remainder of the summer and to re-seed, with the necessary applications of lime and fertilizer, in the following spring. Any fronds that appear among the grass can be broken, while they are still young and brittle, by a heavy roller. Where ploughing is impracticable recourse must be had to cutting either by hand or machine or to repeated crushing with a type of roller which has longitudinal blades to cut or break the fronds. A single cutting in June is helpful in some cases, but not if the bracken is really strong; and it has to be repeated for many successive years. Where cutting of the whole area of infestation is impracticable, it is best to concentrate on the outer fringes of the bracken areas so as to prevent their spreading outwards. Search is now being made for an effective selective weedkiller.

Rushes are very troublesome in areas of high rainfall or poor drainage. They may be reduced either by repeated cutting, by very hard grazing in the young stage or by treatment with selective weedkiller (see p. 127). Ploughing and re-seeding is often ineffective, since the soil of the infested areas usually contains great numbers of buried seeds. Naturally, **thorough** drainage must be the first step in dealing with rush infested land, but this must be followed by dressings of fertilizer to encourage the grasses, by careful adjustment of the grazing stock and by mowing.

Tussock-grass (*Aira cæspitosa*) is also characteristic of wet land; in clay areas where pasture drainage is attained by a ridge and furrow layout the weed is usually confined to the furrow bottoms. Tussock-grass generally dies out after drainage, and on the type of land where it is apt to be troublesome mole drainage is often practicable. Scattered tussocks should be dealt with by hand.

Other plants that can become troublesome unless steps are taken to keep them under control are shrubs such as bramble, briar, whitethorn and gorse. The former three are most troublesome on the clay pastures of the south. Seedling plants are not sufficiently grown to damage a mower until their third year, so that the easiest preventive is to take hay or to run the mower over the pasture at intervals of two or three years. Gorse bushes burn easily in spring, but are rarely completely killed. Regular mowing, where conditions make this possible, is effective. Sheep graze on the young seedlings in winter.

Ragwort, which is a biennial, is generally troublesome only in the absence of sheep, which usually suppress the small seedlings by close grazing. Since it reproduces only by seed, and since seeds stand little chance of establishing plants in a dense sward, the weed can generally be controlled by liberally fertilizing the grass, but this is not effective on really poor sandy soil. Selective weedkillers are effective against established plants, but fresh seedlings may appear at intervals. Spear thistle is best controlled by spudding.

Bent-grass and crested dogstail may tend to occupy too large a proportion of the ground, particularly where sheep have long been grazed alone, and may be checked by hard grazing with cattle or mowing for a few seasons.

# CHAPTER 16

# FODDER CONSERVATION

GRASSLAND herbage and other leafy forages (lucerne, vetches, peas and unripe cereals), can be conserved by any one of three processes.

Haymaking depends in the main on natural drying, the process being speeded up by swath turning, tedding and, in certain cases, by the use of tripods or racks. The curing process may sometimes be finished artificially.

The terms *grass drying* and *green-crop drying* imply the use of artificial heat for the removal of the whole or the greater part of the moisture— *i.e.* the material may be taken to the dryer either immediately from the forage harvester or the newly cut swath, or, alternatively, it may be partially wilted in the field.

The process of *ensilage* may be applied either to freshly mown or to slightly wilted material. It depends on two conditions, (1) the exclusion of air (to prevent moulding and aerobic fermentation) and (2) the development of a lactic-acetic type of fermentation which should proceed to a reaction of about $pH$ 4 to 4·5. When this point is reached anaerobic fermentation comes to a standstill, but it should be remembered that moulds will develop if the silage is exposed to the air for more than a few hours. The process is thus analogous to that of pickling food in vinegar. In the case of highly nitrogenous material the lactic-acetic type of fermentation may be encouraged by the addition of readily fermentable carbohydrate, usually in the form of molasses. Alternatively, mineral acid or a preservative such as sulphur dioxide may be added, but in practice at the time of writing, these are little used.

The choice as between the three methods depends in part on the type of product desired—whether a roughage or a more or less concentrated feeding stuff. Other considerations are (1) the comparative efficiency of the three processes as measured by the percentage loss of nutrients during conservation; (2) the amount of labour involved in processing; (3) the labour required to transport and handle the finished product; (4) the capital cost of the equipment required; and (5) the availability of labour at the time of year when the operation falls to be done—for example, hay making may clash with the early potato harvest, and silage making with sugar beet singling.

N

## HAY MAKING

The rate of natural drying of mown herbage depends on whether it is dry or wet at time of cutting, the temperature and humidity of the air, the velocity of the wind and the thickness of the swath. The time required for the sward to dry naturally may vary from two to ten days. Again, different plant tissues dry at varying rates. A further material point is that the rate of drying is not constant; evaporation from the freshly cut grass is fast, and the rate falls progressively as the process goes on. Moreover, humidity ordinarily rises during the night, so that hay which has been fit to cart in the evening, even in the absence of dew, may be too damp the following morning.

Most types of herbage, at the hay stage of maturity, have a moisture content of 70 to 80 per cent. Even if it were practicable to determine moisture contents in the field, it would still remain largely a matter of judgment to decide the stage of dryness at which the crop is fit to stack or to bale. Young leafy material not only packs more closely than mature stemmy stuff, but contains a higher proportion of easily fermentable constituents; old material consists more largely of lignified cellulose, which is very resistant to organisms. Again, hay that has been weathered in the field, will have lost a large proportion of its soluble carbohydrate and is much less prone to heat in stack or bale than stuff that has been quickly sun dried. As a rough indication, hay may safely be baled to a moderate density or be put into pike at a moisture content of 26 to 28 per cent. and may be put in stack at a figure of 20 to 22 per cent. If drying is to be continued in bales the hay can be baled at even higher moisture contents.

Even under the most favourable conditions, there will be some loss of nutrients in the course of hay making. Causes of loss are:—

1. Breakage of leaf. If hay is roughly handled in the later stages of harvesting or in the process of collection, the leaves shatter and fall to the ground. Clover and lucerne leaves are much more brittle, when dry, than those of the grasses, and the young grass leaf is more easily broken than that which is moderately mature. Since leafage is much more nutritious than stem, the loss of nutrients by leaf breakage is proportionately greater than the loss in total weight.

2. Living plant tissue breathes so that, if the herbage takes a long time to dry, there is a considerable loss of sugar and starch.

3. Living plant tissue is resistant to attack by the ordinary saprophytic organisms—bacteria and moulds—whereas dead material, in the presence of air and moisture, is more or less rapidly decomposed, the rate depending mainly on the air temperature. Rain does less harm if it falls while the swath is still green, but leads to heavy loss, especially in warm weather, if it occurs after the plants are dead.

4. Heavy rain, occurring after the tissues are dead, leaches out soluble carbohydrate.

5. Heating in the stack or bale is due to oxidation, mostly of the soluble carbohydrates. Heating is at first caused mainly by bacterial action, but later on further damage may be done by moulds, especially in loose material or in pikes or small ricks.

It will be understood that the loss of nutrients varies over a wide range; but estimates based on the yield, dry matter content and composition of standing crops and the corresponding figures for the stacked hay, indicate that the total loss (starch equivalent and protein equivalent taken together) may be 30 per cent. and in some circumstances even 40 per cent.

Hay is an excellent source of vitamin D, but carotene, the precursor of vitamin A, is largely destroyed by oxidation during sun drying. The amount remaining in the cured hay may be judged by its colour, since chlorophyll is destroyed by light and dries at about the same rate as carotene. Hence, green hay is a useful source of vitamin A, while bleached or browned hay contains almost none.

In the days of abundant labour and before the era of cheap imported feeding stuffs, hay making was carried out with great care and with a large expenditure of manpower. The swath was gently turned by hand-rake or pitch-fork, tedding was done without violence, and the material might be gathered into cocks at evening, to be spread out again the following day after the dew had lifted. As drying proceeded the crop was left by day in hand cocks, which were later combined into larger cocks or pikes and, after a short interval, the crop was finally stacked. When required for feeding, the stack was cut out in trusses for ease and economy in feeding.

A saving of labour has been achieved mainly by mechanisation. The past century has seen the introduction of the swath turner, the tedder and the side delivery rake and of a single machine which can be set to perform any of these three operations in turn. Equipment for collection includes several types of sweeps, the hay loader and the buck-rake; while the elevator, the horse or engine operated fork or the stacker largely eliminates hand pitching at the stack. Mechanical cocking and tripoding, though possible, have not been widely adopted, but the hay bogie, the buckrake or the rick lifter enables cocks or pikes to be moved *en bloc* to the rick. Again, baling in the field has become very common in recent years and can be carried out either by a stationary or a pick-up machine. More recently various machines to crimp or bruise the stems of the green plants have been introduced as an aid to quicker drying.

The problem in hay making remains the same in spite of the changes introduced to save man power. The aim is to retain in the hay the largest possible proportion of the digestible nutrients that were present in the cut grass; and to do so the process should be done as quickly as possible to restrict respirational and leaching losses.

The stage of maturity of the grass at cutting time is most important.

The crop is mown, preferably at the time when the bulk of the plants are in flower or coming into flower—*i.e.* when the grasses are shedding or beginning to shed their pollen. At this stage the total amount of digestible nutrients reaches a maximum because, although the weight of dry matter might continue to increase subsequently, digestibility would be reduced through the lignification of cellulose. Cutting the herbage when dry and when there is a reasonable prospect of a dry spell of weather is of great assistance at the start of the drying process. This may mean restricting the acreage cut at any one time; and in so doing it is probable that the batch can be managed better during the subsequent operations.

Grass cut and lying in a compact swath dries slowly and unevenly. The modern technique aims at moving the grass as soon as possible by turner and tedder, so that the cut grass gets the best chance of drying. By doing this before the cut material becomes brittle, there is less risk of losing leaf, which contains much of the more digestible nutrients.

There are many conditions under which the drying process can be accelerated by the use of a roller or crimper, and it is likely that the use of these implements will become more common in future. A roller or crimper can be attached to the mower and operated by a power take-off.

When the grass is sufficiently dry, the simplest procedure is to run the crop into windrows—two or three swaths together—by means of a side-delivery rake, and later, when drying has proceeded to the necessary stage, to stack. Where the stack is to be built in the field a hay sweep conveys loads to the foot of the elevator, on to which the hay is pitched by hand-fork. A gang of five men—one sweeping, two pitching, and two building—may together put up to 20 tons per day. The field is finally raked over and the rakings swept to the stack.

If the hayrick is to be on another site, or if the crop is to be stored in a barn at the homestead, wagons or trailers must generally be used. The buckrake may indeed be preferred for short hauls—up to a quarter or a third of a mile—if the going is level, but on rough land spillage is large.

Stacking from the windrow gives tolerably good results with grassy material cut at a relatively mature growth stage. Indeed, it is doubtful whether such second rate raw material justifies any more expensive process. But with young leafy growth, especially if it contains a high proportion of clover, the system leaves much to be desired. Such material must be very fully cured if heating in the stack is to be avoided and, since it cures slowly, it must be left on the ground, at serious risk, for an undesirably long time. These facts suggest that the making of high quality hay by these methods necessitates an intermediate stage beween the windrow and the stack.

In certain arable areas where the farm staff is large in relation to the acreage of hay, more pains may be taken to secure a first quality product. The hay may be tripoded or cocked from the windrows, and later built into pikes (10-15 cwt. of mature hay) in the field. The practice of cocking and piking is also common on many small farms in upland areas.  Under these conditions the land beneath the swath may be very wet, and it is often desirable to get the partly dried grass into small cocks.  By so doing the land dries more quickly and the risk of loss through rain in the partly dried hay is reduced.  If the cocks will benefit later by being moved or remade, this can be done on drier land.  The hay is often conditioned further in small pikes which can be moved intact for winter storage by hay bogie or buckrake.

A steadily increasing proportion of hay in this country is now harvested by pick-up baler.  Evenness of curing and drying are of the greatest importance, if this process is to be really successful.  A new skill is being acquired in determining when to bale, the size and density of the bales, the safe moisture content for baling under varying conditions and also how far natural drying can be carried out.  It is probable that, in the near future to avoid undue weather risks, a considerable part of the hay crop will be baled at moisture contents 10-20 per cent. above the safe limit for storage, and that this surplus moisture will be removed artificially, quickly and cheaply before the bales begin to heat up.  The final drying would probably be carried out in stacks of bales, so that these need not be disturbed until they are required for feeding.

The prospect then, is that by the use of new techniques hay of high quality, not exposed to undue weathering, will be available in much larger quantities, and at a cost little in advance of that of hay making by ordinary methods.  But there will still remain the need for skill on the past of the farmer to start with nutritious grass and to make the best use of the elements to secure low cost natural drying.

## GREEN CROP DRYING

The removal of a large percentage of moisture from green crops by artificial drying is a costly process.  It can only be justified economically, if the green material is of the highest quality.  Green crop drying has not made much headway on farms in Great Britain, because of the difficulty in providing a continuous supply of grass or other green crops of the necessary quality.  A few co-operative ventures prospered for some time, but the cheaper methods of conservation—ensilage and hay making with some assistance from heat—have  tended to gain ground at the expense of grass drying.  If drying is contemplated on any large scale, then it is necessary to consider carefully whether the cost of the necessary equipment and the labour demands can be met and justified in terms of the output of dried grass or other green crop.  There is also the question whether a sufficient and continuous supply of the type of green material suitable for drying will be available.

With grass, drying will be likely to prove uneconomic if any considerable proportion of the product is of second or third rate quality, and, assuming that the drying is done properly, quality will depend largely on the stage of growth. This is highest in the young stage and deteriorates very rapidly as the plants approach and pass the heading stage. The following figures (nutrient content per 100 lb. dry matter) illustrate the point:—

| Growth stage | Starch Equivalent lb. | Protein Equivalent lb. |
|---|---|---|
| 1. Young leafy . . . . | 60 | 16·0 |
| 2. Leafy . . . . . | 59 | 12·0 |
| 3. Ear emergence . . . . | 57 | 9·0 |
| 4. Flowering . . . . | 52 | 6·5 |
| 5. Seed-setting . . . . | 50 | 4·8 |

It should be borne in mind that material at stage 3 can be efficiently conserved by ensilage and that at stages 4 or 5 by hay making, which processes are much cheaper.

To secure a steady and long continued supply of young material it is necessary to have a series of swards of differing botanical composition. The commoner types of grassland plants are classified, in respect of earliness, as follows:—

*Very Early:* Italian, S.22 and New Zealand short-rotation ryegrasses.
*Early:* S. 24, Irish, and New Zealand perennial ryegrasses.
*Medium:* S. 23 and Kentish indigenous ryegrasses.
S. 26 and S. 143 cocksfoot.
S. 53 meadow fescue.
S. 48, S. 51, and Scottish timothy.
Broad red clover.

*Late:* Lucerne.
Late-flowering red clover.
White clover.

Requirements may be met by three, with perhaps a reserve of old grass to fill the gap in supplies which may occur, in a cold dry spring, between the first and second rounds of cutting. Thus one field might be under Italian ryegrass; a second under S. 24 ryegrass or S. 37 cocksfoot, with S. 100 clover in either case; and a third of S. 53 fescue, S. 48 timothy and S. 100 white clover. It is generally inadvisable to mix cocksfoot with another grass, since the thick leaf bases of the plant are slow drying.

Such a scheme assumes that lucerne cannot be grown successfully. It should be brought into the scheme wherever possible, since it has the advantage, shared with the clovers, that its protein content falls with increasing age much more slowly and less markedly than that of any grass; moreover, its growth is well maintained during dry spells. In some cases lucerne is the major crop, being supplemented only with a relatively small area under Italian or short rotation ryegrass, to make provision for an early start in spring, and to extend the period of operation after mid-September.

Apart from the use of plants of differing degrees of earliness, the supply of material may be smoothed out by the skilful timing and quantitative regulation of nitrogen applications and also by thought in the allocation of the various seeds mixtures between the several fields—early types on the early land and late types on the colder ground. If, for example Italian ryegrass is sown on light, warm soil and receives a nitrogen top dressing in early February, and if S. 37 cocksfoot is sown on heavier land and is top dressed in late March, a sufficiently wide spread of supplies should be assured.

Whenever, despite all care in planning, the dryer fails to keep pace with the growth of the herbage, the best course is to mow an area for silage. To leave it for hay will generally throw the whole programme out of gear.

A full and quick response of the herbage to nitrogen depends upon an adequate supply of other nutrients, and it must be remembered that the drain upon these, under a grass drying régime, is very high. Allowing for the inevitable losses (in particular phosphate fixation) and assuming a yield of $2\frac{1}{2}$ tons of dried material in the season, the fertilizer programme might be made up of annual (autumn) dressings of about 5 cwt. superphosphate (90-100 units $P_2O_5$) and 3 cwt. muriate of potash (180 units $K_2O$) per acre, with about 3 cwt. (60 units N.) of sulphate of ammonia in early spring and 2 cwt. (40 units N.) Nitro-chalk or Nitra-Shell after each cut, excepting only the last of the season. Some prefer to use a compound fertilizer in early spring in place of the autumn application of minerals and the spring application of nitrogen. Further points are that the quantities of nitrogen applied in summer should be related to the proportion of clover in the sward, and that the rate of depletion of the lime reserves of the soil will depend upon the quantity of ammonium sulphate that is used.

Fields for grass-drying must be closely grazed in autumn, and maiden seeds should be repeatedly chain harrowed to break down the stubble of the nurse crop. The presence of any considerable amount of dead herbage or of straw in the first cut will have a very deleterious effect on the quality of the product.

Arable crops and catch crops may often be used to advantage to supplement the produce from long duration leys. Thus a catch crop of rye or of Italian ryegrass sown in July (e.g. after early potatoes) should yield both a late autumn and an early spring cut, and sown later, may yield a cut or even two, before the land is wanted for roots or kale. Where lucerne cannot be grown, a late sowing of oats and vetches will give a good crop at a time when other material is scarce.

It would obviously be useful, in securing fuller employment of the drying plant, if kale could be used during the period from October till December. The one difficulty is that kale must be shredded as a preliminary to drying; the other is the high moisture content of the material. It might appear that the difference between, say, 80 per cent. of moisture in grass and 86 per cent. in kale is not very extreme; but a calculation will show that, for every ton of dry matter produced, the amount of water to be evaporated will be 4 tons in the first case and over 6 tons in the latter. The position is worsened by the fact that kale, in the late autumn, often carries a considerable load of superficial water.

To return to grass, it has already been said that the nutritive quality of the product is related to the age of the plant tissues rather than to the height of the crop. At the one extreme Italian ryegrass, in a growthy spring, may reach a height of a foot or more before there has been any serious decline in nutritive value; at the other extreme a low growing species like S. 23 ryegrass, growing slowly in a period of summer drought, may have to be cut at a height of 4 or 5 in. if a first quality product is to be obtained. These circumstances raise a problem in the choice of harvesting machinery. Fairly long material can be mown and left some little time in the swath—perhaps cut one afternoon and picked up the next. In this case the equipment needed would be a mower and a side-rake (which are normal parts of the farm equipment) and a green crop loader. By contrast, if very short material is once allowed to fall to the ground there will be heavy loss in its subsequent collection. Hence the cut-lift type of machine (see p. 159) must be used, and there can be no wilting.

Wilting in the field, at best, results in some loss of carotene, but this is of little consequence if the product is not to constitute a considerable part of the ration; it will be important if the product is required mainly as a source of vitamin A. Wilting has the obvious advantage of saving fuel and other drying costs, which depend largely on the moisture content of the raw material. With fresh material at 80 per cent. moisture 4 tons of water must be evaporated per ton of product, while with wilted material at 65 per cent. moisture, the figure falls to 1·9 tons.

Another point of importance in relation to costs is that, apart from surface moisture in the form of dew or rain, the dry matter content of growing herbage fluctuates from hour to hour, being ordinarily at a minimum in the afternoon. The same thing happens with grass lying in swath. Hence there is a case for collecting a twenty-four hours' supply between, say, midday and 4 o'clock. But even if it is spread out fairly thinly, the green material will rarely keep cool for more than twenty-four hours. Hence no more should be brought in than can be dried by the afternoon of the following day.

The number of cuts to be made in a season will, of course, vary with seasonal conditions, but must be decided with some reference to the quality of product desired. With five or six cuts—*i.e.* at intervals of four or five weeks—the product will be of high quality, but the yield will be relatively small. This is because frequent defoliation will reduce photosynthesis. Moreover, the cost of harvesting per ton will be high. Three cuts in the season will usually give the highest yield of starch equivalent per acre, but the product will hardly deserve the name of a concentrate.

Sometimes a sward is grazed for part of the year or, more frequently, used to provide a silage crop, and is also cut for drying—perhaps twice—during the season. If grazed, the mower should be run over the field to remove ungrazed tufts or stemmy material, and the land should then be chain-harrowed to level the surface and spread droppings. Grazing should generally be avoided where the cut-lift is to be used subsequently, since this machine, with its cutter bar shaving the ground, requires a very smooth surface and will be apt to collect any remaining dung.

With land of fair average quality under average rainfall, with a fertilizer application of the amounts suggested above, and with four cuts in the season, the total yield of dried grass will ordinarily be between 2 and 3 tons per acre. In areas of high rainfall, with more intensive fertilization, yields of 4 tons per acre are not unusual, and 5 ton yields have occasionally been recorded.

With respect to the necessary degree of drying, it is well to let the process proceed until the moisture content of the grass has fallen to 2 or 3 per cent. It is true that the material would keep in store at a moisture content of 10 or even 12 per cent.; indeed, it will ordinarily pick up this amount under farm storage conditions. But even with careful work it is difficult, even in material with 6 or 7 per cent. moisture, to ensure the complete absence of damp pockets, which may heat up. Many fires have resulted from this cause. Even if drying has proceeded to the 3 per cent. point, it is a wise precaution to delay bulk storage for a few days.

The form of the finished material, for convenience in storage and handling, is another matter of some importance. Longish material will hold together fairly well in a bale, and bales are subject to less wastage than loose material. Short material cannot be made into durable bales, and it is now normal practice to put the material through a hammer mill and pack the meal in paper bags. Paper is preferable to textiles, since it is less permeable to air and therefore gives better protection against he loss of carotene. Many of the larger drying plants process the milled grass into " nuts " and in some cases incorporate cereal meals in order to get a product with the desired protein carbohydrate balance for a particular purpose—*e.g.* a production ration for dairy cows.

## ENSILAGE

It has long been known that watery material such as wet brewery grains, distillery paste and wet sugar beet pulp could be preserved satisfactorily by close packing in pits or clamps. The possibility of ensiling grass and other greenstuff was explored in this country during the eighties of last century, but only a few farmers—mostly those whose circumstances rendered hay making very difficult—were induced to take up the process. The early workers appear to have favoured the production of " sweet " silage, using material at the hay stage of maturity and deliberately encouraging a hot fermentation. It is true that high temperature fermentation yields a product of pleasant aroma and high palatability; but the fermentation is associated with heavy losses through the destruction of digestible carbohydrate and the marked depression of the digestibility of the proteins.

The first widespread development of ensilage took place in the United States, the object being to provide a substitute for mangels and other roots. The crop commonly ensiled was maize which, under American conditions, is much more reliable than roots and also makes much smaller demands on hand labour; moreover, maize, at the appropriate growth stage, is, by reason of its high content of starch and sugar, a very suitable material for ensilage. The normal equipment used was a chaffer blower and a tall cylindrical silo, the walls being made as smooth as possible in order to facilitate compression. The general experience favoured a height of 40 or 50 ft., so that the contents would be compressed largely by their own weight—i.e. with a minimum of treading.

In the early twenties a considerable number of American type silos were erected in Britain, mostly on clay-land stock farms where the cost of root growing had become prohibitive. The favoured material for ensiling was a cereal-legume mixture—ordinarily oats with beans, peas or vetches, or sometimes all three. The crop was cut at a relatively advanced stage of growth—the cereal " in the milk " and the legumes well podded —and a useful product was obtained. The main obstacle to the general adoption of the system was the high cost of the necessary equipment— the silo itself, the chaffer blower and the power unit required to drive the latter.

In the thirties the A.I.V. system was introduced from Finland. This was commonly applied to grassland herbage, mown at a fairly early stage of growth and packed, without chaffing, into relatively small and cheap cylindrical silos of wood, concrete or steel. The A.I.V. system depends upon the addition of enough mineral acid (hydrochloric and sulphuric) to establish from the outset a degree of acidity ($p$H 3 to 4) at which bacterial action is almost completely inhibited. The surface was commonly sprayed with a special material to prevent the development of moulds. In general, conservation was found to be efficient, but the process of filling the silo was laborious, the handling of strong acid was unpopular with workers, and it was necessary, when the silage was fed, to neutralise the contained acid by adding ground chalk.

During the emergency of 1939-45, large numbers of small tower silos were erected and were commonly filled with grass. These served a useful purpose, but the system was generally regarded as too laborious for use under normal conditions.

The pit or clamp systems are now those most widely used; very few now make the silage stack. The pit and clamp have the double advantage that, in filling, the loads can be dumped directly where they are to lie, and that the necessary degree of compression can be secured by carting over the mass during the process of filling and, after filling, by driving a tractor to and fro over the top. Many pits and clamps are now under cover to prevent leaching and loss by rain.

In Britain the commonest material for ensilage is grassland herbage, either from leys or old swards and preferably cut at the stage just before or when the grasses are coming into ear. Younger material may be used if a high protein feed is required, but short grass is difficult to collect with ordinary farm equipment—i.e. a cut-lift or forage harvester type of machine is required. In seasons when hay making is brought to a standstill by wet weather the crop may be salvaged by ensilage, but stuff that has reached or passed the hay stage of maturity, especially if it has suffered weathering in swath or windrow, yields a product of only very low food value. The better plan is to prepare an area for silage and another for hay, if both are to be fed during winter.

*Lucerne, sainfoin,* and *red clover* can be made into excellent silage, though the material must either be wilted or treated with molasses if a good fermentation is to be secured, the point being that the legumes have a high protein content in relation to that of sugar and are therefore prone to undergo cold (butyric) fermentation. Among arable crops the most useful are mixtures of *oats and peas, oats and vetches,* or *oats, beans and vetches.* These have the advantage that they can yield a good product over a fairly wide range of growth stages. Moreover, they can be more easily built than grass into a stable silage stack. *Maize,* as already said, is a very suitable plant for ensilage and in many countries provides the main supply. Varieties are available that, in the southern half of England, attain the proper silage stage (grain well formed but leaves still green) by September. The later maturing types which have sometimes been used are still so immature at the summer's end that they are subject to heavy loss of sugar through the drainage of juice. *Marrowstem kale* has too high a moisture content for the best results, losses by drainage being high. Moreover, it is impracticable to secure much wilting at the season when the crop is harvested, and chaffing is necessary. Otherwise the crop is very easy to ensile, because it does not readily heat even in a loose mass. All that is necessary is to blow the chaffed kale into a heap, preferably in a corner between two high walls, and provide some rough protection from rain. *Sugar beet tops,* if they can be collected in reasonably clean condition, yield a useful silage and being " cold " by nature need little consolidation. *Green pea-haulm* from crops grown for vining is excellent material.

The general principles of ensilage have been outlined at the beginning of this chapter, but the process must be adapted to the nature of the raw material. The object is to ensure a predominance of the lactic-acetic type of fermentation, which is favoured by a moderate degree of aeration at a temperature of about 100° F. Lower temperatures, resulting from a shortage of fermentable carbohydrate or from the over compression of sappy material or both, favour butyric fermentation. Butyric acid is a foul smelling substance which not only reduces the palatability of the silage but imparts a taint to milk and dairy products. Moreover, the objectionable and very persistent smell is complained of by workers and their families.

At the other extreme silage that has seriously overheated (over 120° F.) and is characterised by a dark brown colour and sweet (caramel) smell will not only have lost an excessive amount of digestible carbohydrate but will show a very low figure for the digestibility of its protein. Hence relatively mature material, with a high proportion of grass or cereal should be ensiled quickly and heavily compressed.

A good general plan is to put 2 or 3 ft. of material into the silo, with only light packing, and to allow the temperature to rise to about 100° F. before superimposing further material. This will ordinarily happen in about two days. Thereafter the amount of compression should be regulated according to the temperature of the mass.

Since 1957 there have been many interesting developments in the making of silage. Nowadays most of the silage made in Great Britain comes from grass. Leys or older grass are especially managed and fertilized for a silage crop; the crop is often cut with a forage harvester and blown direct into trailers; the bruising of the green material allows it to pack more closely and evenly in the silo; and a larger proportion of silos are covered—in part due to the introduction of the Silo Subsidy Scheme. Baled silage has been tried but has not proved consistently successful.

It is recognised more widely that good silage can seldom be made with a crop cut wet, and that control of the fermentation process demands care and close attention. There is no general rule that can be given to cover the many conditions under which silage is made, and the farmer's judgment counts for much.

**Pit and Clamp Silage.**—In making a pit silo, or in the siting and building of a clamp or stack, four requirements must be met. The first is drainage. Waterlogging of the lower layers, whether by the accumulation of plant sap or the inflow of surface water or a rise of the water table in winter, will result in butyric fermentation. Hence the site should be high in relation to the surrounding ground and, unless the soil is freely permeable, drains should be laid along each side of the base and be provided with a suitable outlet. Unless there is a firm and permeable bottom a 6 in. layer of hard core or gravel should be laid.

Second, the layout should permit consolidation with a minimum of labour. The least laborious method is to run a tractor over the mass both in the process of filling and after this has been completed. Again, it should be noted that the mass will shrink, horizontally as well as vertically, as fermentation proceeds. Hence if the walls of a pit, or the side walls of a clamp, were to be vertical, air would gain access at the sides, and spoilage would result. The walls should therefore slope outwards, with an inclination of about 1 in 4; for instance, if the walls are 4ft. high or the pit is 4 ft. deep, the width should be 2ft. greater at the top than at the bottom. The material, as it sinks, will then wedge itself tightly between the walls. In order to secure good settlement the walls should be smooth.

Thirdly, since exposure to air causes waste by rotting, the surface exposed should be as small as possible. Obviously, other things being equal, wastage will be higher in small than in large silos, but other considerations are involved—e.g. two lots of material, becoming available at different times, should be ensiled separately rather than in one silo. The occurrence of outside wastage is obviously an argument for a pit or a walled clamp rather than a stack.

Fourthly, in all but the driest areas the silo should either be roofed over or should be domed up and thatched so as to shed rain water.

From the point of view of labour saving, an excavated pit, rectangular in plan and about 5 yd. wide, open at both ends and with a gentle incline at each, has obvious advantages. Where this is to be used over a period of years it is well worth while to have the sides faced with concrete. Where a pit would be subject to waterlogging it is well to keep the silo above ground, when it may consist simply of two parallel side walls composed of concrete slabs with a smooth inner surface and sufficiently strong, well supported and deeply grounded to withstand the heavy pressure that develops during and after filling.

The siting of the silo depends on a balance of considerations. If, on the one hand, it can be adjacent to the fields on which the material is grown, the cost of collection and filling can be kept at a low figure by the use of the buckrake; but if this would imply a considerable distance between the silo and the winter quarters of the stock, then a good deal of winter labour will be involved. In any case, except when the land is light, firm and well drained, the silo should be adjacent to a hard road.

Another question is whether or not the crop should be slightly wilted in the field. American work suggests that a satisfactory fermentation is ensured without the use of molasses if typical grassland herbage, at the proper stage of maturity, is wilted to a moisture content of about 65 per cent. In drying weather this stage might be attained by mowing in the early morning and carting in the afternoon; in ordinary weather it would be attained by cutting one day and carrying the next. But such a procedure is practicable only with grass which is long enough to enable it to be cleanly picked up after wilting, by which time it may have passed the stage of maturity to give a high grade product.

The need to use molasses depends on the nature of the material. Kale, beet tops, oat and legume mixtures at a fairly advanced stage of growth, and also relatively mature grass that has been wilted in the field will, if well managed, develop a good type of fermentation without assistance. Young grassy and especially young clovery herbage are apt to go wrong unless molasses is used. Two gallons of molasses per ton of greenstuff is a usual allowance. The molasses should be diluted with twice its volume of water and sprayed on to each successive layer by means of a watering can with a large aperture rose.

To prevent wastage it is necessary to provide an airtight seal. The silage should be well rolled before the seal is applied. Various types of material are suitable. Soil, ground chalk or ground limestone are commonly used to a depth of 6 in. They should be applied as soon as the silo has been filled and has received its final rolling and the seal itself should also be rolled. The seal is effective in turning off most of the rain if the silo is not covered by a roof, but sealing is necessary even in roofed silos to prevent surface wastage.

**Stack Silage.**—Ensilage may be carried out by building the green herbage into a stack, with a top layer of heavy material to give the required compression. One alternative is to add an upper storey of baled hay or baled straw, and another is to rely on a layer of soil with the addition of large stones if these happen to be at hand.

The exposed surface being much larger than that in pitted or clamped material, the amount of wastage tends to be relatively high. From the point of view of minimising losses, it will be obvious that large stacks are better than small. The system works best with longish material.

Circular stacks which require to be built with a greater expenditure of manual labour and trimmed are now seldom made, though at one time they were the more common form when stack silage was made.

The grass is usually built into a rectangular heap with a ramp leading up from each of the narrower ends. Tractors deposit their buckrake loads as they run over the heap thereby consolidating what has been deposited from earlier loads. The stack is usually built up from 12-15 ft. before settlement at its highest point. The ends are trimmed and thrown up before the stack is sealed.

**Use of Preservatives.**—Various materials, in addition to mineral acids, have been tried as silage preservatives. Sulphur dioxide injected into the mass was found to be useful, but efficient application (from pressure cylinders) proved to be difficult. Materials—complexes of acid sodium phosphate and acid sodium sulphate—have also been tried. They have the effect of a medium strong acid and effect a rapid reduction of the $p$H to a figure of 4·2 to 4·5.

**The Feeding of Silage.**—Well made and fully settled silage commonly weighs between 10 and 12 cwt. to the cubic yard, and dry matter contents range from about 20 to about 28 per cent. A tolerably close estimate of feeding value can be based on the dry matter and crude protein contents, both the protein equivalent and starch equivalent of the dry matter being closely correlated with total protein. The exception is in the case of overheated material, which invariably has a lower feeding value than would be calculated on such a basis. Silage with 15 per cent. or more crude protein in the dry matter is usually designated high grade; that with less than 12 per cent. is classed as low grade.

There has been a great extension of the practice of self-feeding of silage; and for this purpose it is normal to have a depth of settled silage of about 6 ft. If cattle are to be allowed access to the feeding surface for 24 hours each day then 6-8 in. per animal is given. If they are given only limited access then a surface face of 18 in. is desirable, so that all animals (assuming the cattle are dehorned) may feed simultaneously.

**Fodder Conservation Policy.**—There are few farms on which any single method of conservation should be applied to the whole of the available material  Special purpose leys, the more widespread use of fertilizers and improved techniques in making silage and hay open up possibilities in grassland management that could not be foreseen in earlier days.

A well conceived programme of grazing and conservation can assist in the avoidance of labour peaks and in improving sward control. For example, grass mown at the silage stage will produce a better aftermath than that mown later for hay, and will provide grazing at what otherwise may be a period of shortage. The planned programme also assists in ensuring that grass is cut at the right stage of growth whether it be for silage or hay, and therefore that the conserved product is likely to be of higher feeding value.

A good conservation programme then, assists in grazing management as well as in providing nutritious food for winter use. Savings of concentrates through the use of good quality silage and hay can be very substantial. Moreover, concentrates used to supplement good quality conserved grass generally give a better result than when used with poor quality fodder.

The past few years have seen revolutionary changes in our ideas of grassland management. Search now continues to obtain even better methods of saving labour in the making and feeding of hay and silage, and in making these processes less subject to the risk of unsettled weather, which occurs in many parts of Great Britain at the times when silage and hay are ordinarily made.

# PART 3

# FARM LIVE STOCK

# CHAPTER 17

# GENETICS: ANIMAL BREEDING

## ANIMAL REPRODUCTION

IN animal reproduction the embryo develops from a fertilised egg, which is the product of the fusion of an egg cell produced by the female with a sperm cell produced by the male. In some species the fertilised egg divides, giving rise to two or more embryos. One-egg or so-called "identical" twins occur occasionally in cattle, though not in other domesticated animals. A large majority of twins in cattle are " ordinary " or two-egg twins.

The primary sexual organs of the female are the ovaries, and the shedding of the egg from the ovary may be taken as the start of the reproductive process. The ovary, apart from producing eggs, gives rise to internal secretions which control the œstrous cycle. At or about the time of shedding of the egg the period of œstrus (" season " or " heat ") occurs and it is then that mating takes place. The ruptured follicle, from which the egg has been shed, forms the " yellow body " (*corpus luteum*) and so long as this persists œstrus does not recur. Normally, in the non-pregnant animal, the yellow body disappears after a fairly definite period of time, when another follicle ruptures and the animal comes " in season " again.

In the normal healthy cow successive heats recur at fairly regular intervals of about twenty days throughout the year, though in winter the period of heat may be very short. In the mare the interval is about twenty-one days, but œstrus does not recur regularly during winter. In the sow the first heat occurs shortly after weaning, and in the non-pregnant animal recurs throughout the year at intervals of twenty-one or twenty-two days. In the ewe, by contrast with other species, œstrus is more or less confined to the autumn, the main controlling factor being length of day; thus ewes can be brought into œstrus during summer by subjecting them to nightly periods of darkness of twelve or more hours. As would be expected, sheep kept in tropical regions show no breeding seasonality, and the length of the breeding season falls with increasing latitude. The peak of the breeding season is usually somewhat before the shortest day. Again, the length of the breeding season varies from one breed to another. At the one extreme are the wild species, which ordinarily have only one or two heats per year; at the other is the Dorset Horn, which may have twelve or more. Most wild birds produce only two or three clutches during the year, but some, such as the wood pigeon, may have four or five. Domestic poultry may continue in full lay for many months; here, as in the case of sheep, day length has an important influence on ovulation.

Œstrus during pregnancy is abnormal, and it is ordinarily assumed that a female that has been mated, and has ceased to " come in season," is pregnant. But it is not unknown for a pregnant female to show all the symptoms of œstrus and to take the male. On the other hand, the *corpus luteum* sometimes persists in the non-pregnant animal much beyond the usual time—the case of so-called " false-pregnancy."

Single ovulations are normal in the cow and mare. Work is in progress to find out if, by a hormone injection prior to insemination or mating, twinning can be stimulated in the cow, and under what conditions the advantages of twinning can be gained without an adverse influence on her subsequent milk yield or health. In the ewe, double and treble ovulations are common, at least in certain breeds, if the level of nutrition and general well-being is high. Except under mountain conditions, a high proportion of twins is desirable. In the sow, the number of eggs shed at each heat is generally of the order of twenty, but a considerable number of the embryos ordinarily degenerate at an early stage of development. Litters of twenty and over are by no means very rare.

The average gestation period of the mare is about eleven months (340 days), in the cow nine months (280 days), in the ewe five months (150 days), and in the sow sixteen weeks (112 days). There is, however, a considerable range of variation.

Parturition normally coincides with the commencement of lactation, and the distention of the udder with colostrum is one of the signs that parturition is imminent. But animals on a high level of nutrition, and especially those that have been bred for high milk production, may begin to " run out " some time before giving birth. At the other extreme, females of the specialised beef types, especially if they are in very low or overfat condition and have troublesome calvings, may have little or no milk.

After a female has given birth there is a longer or shorter interval before the recurrence of œstrus. In the mare this interval is short— commonly four to seven days. In the cow it is longer and less uniform, but commonly between one and two months. The sow rarely comes on heat while she is nursing a litter, but usually does so on the second or third day after the litter has been weaned.

The age at first œstrus depends to some extent on the breeding of the animal and the level of nutrition. Heifer calves may come on heat as early as six months of age and gilts at about four months. With spring-born ewe lambs some 70 or 80 per cent., on average, come on heat during the shortest-day period of their first year, the percentage being highest in those born early and well nourished throughout their lives. With late-born lambs reared under hill conditions the proportion is low, but it is still necessary to take precautions to prevent mating, which is very undesirable under mountain conditions.

**Artificial Insemination.**—Since a single ejaculation of semen normally contains many millions of sperms, it is theoretically possible for a single male to beget vast numbers of progeny. In practice it is possible, by artificial insemination, to multiply the normal number from five to twenty-five times, and thus to exploit the value of a selected male. There is no great difficulty in collecting semen from the bull, ram, stallion or boar. If the semen is diluted with a nutrient solution and is kept at an appropriate low temperature it retains its vitality, in the case of the bovine, for several days. Moreover, under deep-freeze conditions (—79° C.) vitality is maintained for a period of years. The advantages of deep-freezing are four, viz.: (1) the semen of a particular bull can be made available, in practice, at any time that it may be required (instead of only three or four days per week under cool storage); (2) a stock of semen can be retained after the death of the male animal which has produced it; (3) when there is a limited breeding season (*e.g.* in New Zealand dairy herds) collection of semen can proceed throughout the year, so that only a relatively small number of males need be kept; and (4) the insemination service is less liable to interruption by the occurrence of epidemic disease in the area served.

## THE MECHANISM OF HEREDITY

The egg is a relatively large cell, containing a mass of protoplasm and yolk, together with a small nucleus—a clearly differentiated region with a characteristic structure. The sperm is a very minute motile cell with no yolk and very little cytoplasm (*i.e.* extra-nuclear protoplasm), but containing a nucleus that is similar in size and appearance to that of the egg. The only comparable portions of the egg and sperm are their nuclei, and the bearers of the hereditary characters are in these nuclei. Generally, the one parent has just as much influence on the characteristics of the progeny as has the other.

There are also nuclei in the cells concerned with growth and the carrying out of the normal bodily functions. The division and multiplication of these cells is rather different from that of the germ cells, and so the mechanism of cell division is outlined for each.

The nucleus of a cell that is in normal growth, or is carrying out its ordinary functions, contains a complex network of threads of a readily stainable substance called chromatin. When cell division is about to occur, the chromatin threads condense, thicken and assume the form of a number of generally rod-like bodies called *chromosomes*. These chromosomes are constant in number for all the cells of the individual and (with the significant exception mentioned below) for all the individuals of a race. It can frequently be shown that each chromosome has a definite kind of individuality, for whenever particular members of a set can be recognised by size or shape, a group from one cell can be matched, member for member, with that from another.  A further important fact is that the chromosomes occur in the body cells in pairs, and all the evidence points to the conclusion that of each pair one member is derived from the male, the other from the female parent.    In the ordinary type

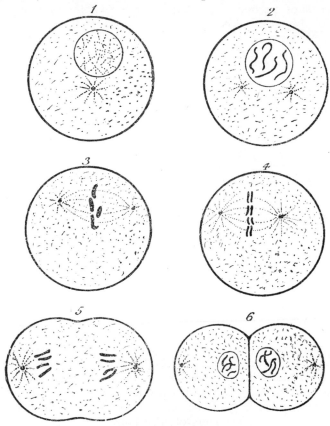

FIG. 17.—Ordinary Cell Division

of cell division (Fig. 17) each chromosome splits longitudinally into two like halves; the latter are drawn apart to opposite poles of the dividing cell, the nuclear wall breaks down and two nuclei are formed, each containing a complete set of the divided chromosomes.

In the division that gives rise to the reproductive bodies—the ova or the sperms—the process is essentially different from that just described. The condensation of the chromatin into chromosomes takes place much more slowly, and when the chromosomes finally appear they are found to be united in pairs. The long preparatory stage is believed to have to do with an exchange of like parts between the paternal and maternal members of each chromosome pair. In any case the two members of each chromosome pair now separate, a further division follows immediately, and four nuclei are produced. The essential point is that the nucleus of each cell contains only half the number of chromosomes that is characteristic of the body cells of the species. Of the four cells, each, in the case of the male, becomes a functional sperm (see Fig. 18). In the case of the female, one becomes the functional egg while the others are cast off as the so-called polar bodies, which can be looked upon as abortive

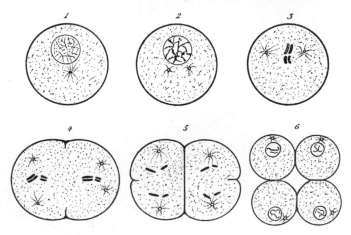

Fig. 18.—The Reducing Division—Formation of reproductive cells
in the male

eggs. When fertilisation occurs the sperm nucleus fuses with that of the egg and the original (or double) number of chromosomes is restored.

A further interesting point is that there is frequently a characteristic difference between the set of chromosomes possessed by the male and by the female respectively. The one sex has a complete double set of chromosomes, the two members of each pair being like. The other sex has either one odd chromosome or else an unlike pair. Thus in the American Fruit Fly, *Drosophila melanogaster* (see Fig. 19), the female has four like pairs of chromosomes, and when reduction occurs, produces, so far as the chromosome content is concerned, only one kind of egg. In the male, three pairs of chromosomes and one member of the remaining pair can be matched in the female set, but the second member of the last pair is recognisable from the others by its shape, which is sharply bent. The male thus produces two sorts of sperm cells in equal numbers, half containing the straight chromosome (or X-chromosome as it has been called) and half the bent or Y-chromosome. It follows that eggs fertilised by the first sort will produce females, since they will possess the constitution symbolised by the formula XX; those fertilized by the second will develop into males, since they will have the constitution XY. The chromosomes thus provide a simple mechanism for the determination of sex. Apart from this, the facts just quoted are important in connection

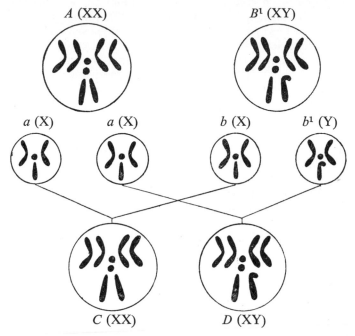

FIG. 19.—The Chromosomes in *Drosophila melanogaster*

*A*, female; *B*, male; *a, a*, ova; *b, b¹*, sperms; *C*, female zygote formed by union of sperm *b* with egg *a*; *D*, male zygote formed by union of egg *a* with sperm *b¹*.

with what is called sex-linked inheritance, a peculiar phenomenon that arises from the circumstance that factors for other characters than sex are carried by the sex chromosomes (see p. 414).

The particular arrangement of the sex chromosomes just decsribed is not universal. It is reversed, for example, in fowls, where the male is *homogametic* (producing but one sort of sperm so far as chromosome content is concerned), while the hen is *heterogametic*, giving rise to two sorts of ova, male-producing and female-producing respectively.

## MENDEL'S FIRST LAW

Such being the mechanism and such the general theory of heredity, let us now turn to some of the observed facts of inheritance. In 1865

Gregor Mendel, as a result of some crossing experiments with garden peas, was led to make an important generalisation regarding the manner in which parental characters are distributed among the progeny. Varieties of peas show a considerable number of definite character differences— *e.g.* some varieties are tall, others dwarf, some have round seeds, others wrinkled, some green seeds, others yellow, and so on. Moreover, the plants are self-fertilising, and varieties, as a rule, breed true to their own particular characters. Mendel's method was to cross two types showing some definite character difference; if the two varieties showed more than one such difference he considered each difference without reference to the others. He reared the hybrid plants and allowed them to become self-fertilised; in the next or second hybrid generation he classified the individual plants with reference to the original parental characters, and counted the members of each group. In one experiment, for example, Mendel crossed an ordinary tall variety with one of the well-known dwarf sorts, both varieties being known to breed true to their respective types. The first-cross plants were tall like the tall parent—indeed, they somewhat exceeded the latter in height. These hybrid talls did not, however, breed true. On the contrary, when allowed to become self-fertilised, they produced tall and dwarf progeny in the proportion (roughly) of three of the former to one of the latter. Mendel's actual figures were 787 tall and 277 dwarf, or 73 and 27 per cent. respectively. When these second-cross plants were tested individually (by making separate sowings of the seeds of each), it was found that all the dwarfs bred true. Of the tall second-cross plants a proportion, about one-third, were found to produce nothing but tall progeny, while the remainder gave talls and dwarfs in the same ratio as did the first cross. These results may be summarised in the following plan:—

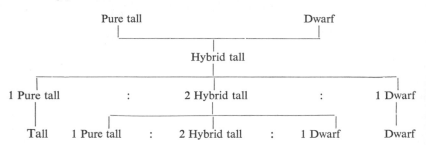

The fact that the first dwarf resembled the tall parent and showed no sign of the dwarf character was expressed by Mendel by saying that "tallness" was *dominant*, and "dwarfness" *recessive*. Dominance, however, is by no means universal; sometimes a hybrid shows a condition somewhat intermediate between those of its parents. For instance, if a red-flowered variety of *Mirabilis jalapa* (Marvel of Peru) is crossed with a

white, the hybrid bears pink flowers. (Fig 20.)  If the hybrid is selfed and
a second hybrid generation is reared, the ratio obtained is 25 per cent. red,
50 per cent. pink, and 25 per cent, white.    The reds and whites so obtained
breed true, while the pinks of the second generation give the three types
in the same ratio as did their parents.    Thus whether or not there is
dominance in a particular case, the general result is the same.    When
hybrids are self-fertilised or interbred they produce, with regard to any

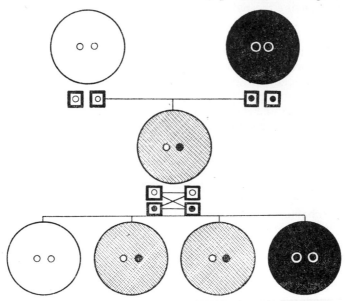

FIG. 20.—Cross between Red and White Varieties of *Mirabilis jalapa*

The large circles represent the parent, first hybrid and second hybrid generations,
and the small circles the genes.    The squares represent the reproductive cells.

particular character, three types of progeny;  the original parental types
are each reproduced in one-fourth of the second hybrid generation, while
the remaining half are hybrids like the first cross.

Mendel not only discovered this general rule of inheritance but he
proposed an explanation of the facts.  His hypothesis still stands.  Subsequent research has brought out much evidence in its support, and has served
to develop rather than to modify the original theory.  Mendel knew
nothing of chromosomes, but the facts regarding their behaviour fit
in remarkably well with the phenomena that he observed, so that to-day
we may best state Mendel's hypothesis in terms of the chromosomes.
We may assume, then, that a " factor " or " gene " controlling, say, the
flower colour of the *Mirabilis*, is borne in one of the chromosomes of the
species.  A red-flowered plant will have a red-producing gene in both

members of the chromosome pair concerned, and since each egg or pollen cell that it produces will receive one member of the pair, only one type of reproductive cell will be produced. The white-flowered plant will contain " white " genes in the corresponding region of its corresponding chromosome pair, and all its reproductive cells will carry the white factor. When the two varieties are crossed it is obvious that the hybrid will have a pair of chromosomes that are unlike with regard to the gene for flower colour, one having the red factor and the other the white. What visible result will be produced by such a combination is not capable of prediction, but in the present case we saw that the hybrid had pink flowers. Now the essential point of the theory is that the two genes do not intermingle but remain throughout the life of the plant as separate and distinct entities. When the reproductive cells are formed, and the two members of the chromosome pair separate, half the ova and pollen grains will receive a chromosome containing the " red " gene, while the other half will get one containing the " white." The pink plant produces, then, reproductive cells that carry not a factor for the pink character but that for either the original red or the original white, and the two classes occur in equal numbers. When the hybrid pink plants are selfed, fertilisation of either type of egg by either type of pollen grain occurs as a matter of " pure chance," so that the following four combinations are equally probable, viz.: " white " pollen grain with " white " egg; " white " pollen grain with " red " egg; " red " pollen grain with " white " egg; " red " pollen grain with " red " egg. The first combination will produce a white-flowered plant, the last a red, and the second and third pinks that are not distinguishable, since it is immaterial whether the red is introduced from the male or the female side. Thus is produced, it is suggested, the ratio of 1 red: 2 pink: 1 white.

The actual numbers obtained in Mendelian experiments are subject to chance variations, and do not, except by chance, give exactly the " expected " ratio. The numbers can be predicted only in so far that we can state the most probable result, just as we can in the case of a series of tossings of a coin. Thus if we make a hundred throws, the most probable single result is fifty heads and fifty tails, but the probability of obtaining fifty-one or forty-nine heads is only very slightly less, and so on through the whole series of possibilities. When large numbers are dealt with, the ratio should approach very closely to theoretical expectation, and this has been the case in Mendelian experiments. For instance, one of Mendel's original experiments, dealing with cotyledon colour in peas, has been fourteen times repeated by different experimenters, and a total of 203,500 second hybrid individuals have been bred. Yellow colour is completely dominant to green, so that the expectation was 3 yellow, 1 green; or altogether 152, 625 yellow and 50,875 green. The totals actually obtained were 152, 824 yellow and 50,676 green—a ratio of 75·1 per cent. to 24·9 per cent.

If the hypothesis that has been outlined above is adequate, it ought to enable us to predict the results of a mating between any two of the three possible types. For example, if we cross the pink (heterozygous [1]) *Mirabilis* back to the parent red form we should expect the following two combinations in equal numbers: " white " pollen and " red " egg cell, giving pink; " red " pollen and " red " egg cell, giving red. Similarly a cross of pink and white should give us pink and white progeny in equal numbers. Results of this sort have been regularly obtained.

Mendel's first law may, therefore, be stated thus: When a dissimilar pair of factors are brought together in crossing they separate again when the hybrid produces its reproductive cells. The separation is clean and complete. The hybrid condition cannot be represented in the sperm or in the unfertilised egg—it can only be produced in the fertilised egg, and then by the union of an egg and a sperm that are dissimilar with regard to the factor in question.

## MENDEL'S SECOND LAW

Mendel's second generalisation was to the effect that when two or more character pairs are considered simultaneously each pair behaves without reference to the others. Since Mendel's time, a very important group of exceptions to this law has been discovered, and the evidence leads to the conclusion that these exceptions arise in cases where two pairs of genes are contained in one and the same pair of chromosomes. With this reservation, Mendel's second law is true. Take, for example, the results obtained in crossing a tall purple-flowered variety of pea with a dwarf white-flowered sort. The tall condition is dominant to the dwarf and coloured is dominant to white. The first cross is, therefore, tall purple. If these plants are selfed and the succeeding generation reared we get the ratios of 3 tall : 1 dwarf and 3 purple : 1 white. But the two dominants do not necessarily go together. On the contrary, the tall group will consist of purples and whites in the ratio of 3 : 1; the whites will consist of 75 per cent. talls, 25 per cent. dwarfs, and so on. Hence the combined ratio is obtained by algebraic multiplication of $(3 T + 1 D) \times (3 P + 1 W)$, giving 9 tall purple: 3 tall white: 3 dwarf purple: 1 dwarf white. It is obvious that very complex ratios will be produced when three or more character pairs are considered simultaneously. It was this complexity, apparent rather than real, that baffled all Mendel's predecessors, and it was Mendel's plan of dealing with one thing at a time that brought out simplicity and order from seeming chaos.

One or two somewhat odd cases must be described in which, though inheritance is strictly Mendelian, the results are complicated by reason

---

[1] Heterozygous, since it received from its parents dissimilar factors for the character now being discussed, a " red " factor from the one and a " white " from the other.

of the effects produced by particular forces.  One of the earliest discovered cases had to do with the inheritance of yellow coat-colour in mice.  The first peculiarity of the case is that yellow mice never breed true; in matings of yellows with yellows the young are about two-thirds yellow and one-third of other colours.  Yellows are never produced from matings of two non-yellows.  If yellow is mated with non-yellow the young consist of equal numbers of yellows and non-yellows.  These facts indicate that yellow is dominant, but that all yellow mice are heterozygous for the yellow condition.  If two such are mated, the expectation would be 1 pure yellow: 2 hybrid yellow: 1 non-yellow, and the only explanation of the facts is that the pure or homozygous yellow is incapable of life.  This has found confirmation in the fact that in yellow × yellow matings a proportion of the embryos die in the early stages of development.  Why the homozygous yellow should be incapable of life beyond this early stage is not known, but it is interesting to note that even the hybrid yellows are not quite normal, being distinctly less hardy than non-yellows, and liable to become excessively fat.  A further interesting fact is that many analogous *lethal factors*, leading to structural abnormalities or functional derangement of such an order as to render the individual incapable of living, have been discovered in several species, including cattle and sheep.

A very striking result of hybridisation was obtained in the course of some of the earlier experiments with sweet-peas.  Two white varieties gave a purple first cross.  This occurrence can properly be classed as a reversion, since the wild parent of our cultivated forms is purple-flowered. These crosses, when left to become self-fertilised, gave progeny in the ratio of 9 purple : 7 white.  In other crosses between two whites, other colours than purple were obtained in the first cross, and sometimes the second hybrid generation contained a mixture of coloured types, the proportion of coloured to white remaining, however that of 9 : 7.  Moreover the whites, when self-fertilised, always bred true; some of the coloured types produced only coloured progeny, while others gave onefourth and still others seven-sixteenths of whites.  The explanation of this case is that colour is produced only in the presence, simultaneously, of two dominant factors.  One of the white varieties contains the first of these factors but lacks the second; the other has the second but lacks the first.  The first hybrid thus contains both dominants and is coloured.  In the second hybrid generation we get as usual a 9 : 3 : 3 : 1 ratio, the last three classes lacking respectively one or other or both dominants, and hence being white.  Many implications of this theory have been tested and the expected results obtained.  The occurrence of different colours in the second hybrid generation is explained by the fact that white sweetpeas may carry various factors capable of modifying colour although, in the absence of the colour factors themselves, these can have no visible effects.

A long series of similar cases might be described; none of them, however, constitutes an exception to Mendel's two laws. The complications arise out of the visible effects of the factors, and the factors themselves behave in the normal way.

## LINKAGE

It was not until some ten years had been spent in active Mendelian investigation that any new principle was discovered. The first cases that failed to conform to Mendel's second generalisation were found in sweetpeas. In one of these cases a variety with purple flowers and an ordinary erect standard petal was crossed with another having red flowers and a hooded standard. It was previously known that purple behaved as a simple dominant to red, and that the erect standard was a simple dominant to the hooded. The first hybrids were purple erect according to expectation. Had the case been normal the second hybrid generation should have consisted of the four possible combinations in the proportions 9 purple erect : 3 purple hooded : 3 red erect : 1 red hooded. The actual numbers obtained were 2036 purple erect : 12 purple hooded : 10 red erect : 654 red hooded. The numbers show that the two dominant factors on the one hand and the two recessives on the other have somehow " stuck together " in a great majority of cases. The numbers, in fact, strongly suggest the simple ratio of 3 : 1—three double dominants to one double recessive. But the other two classes, each containing one dominant only, do occur, though relatively very rarely.

When the cross was made between two parent plants with the same characters in the opposite combinations the result was quite different. Purple hooded crossed with red erect again gave a purple erect first cross. In this case, however, the second hybrid generation consisted of 2969 purple erect : 1369 purple hooded : 1441 red erect. The fourth possible class, i.e. the double-recessive red hooded, did not occur at all. Here, again, the results suggest a simple monohybrid ratio—viz. one-fourth like each of the original parents and one-half like the first cross. It is obvious from the second experiment that the case is not one of attraction between any two characters as such. The point is, however, that the characters are combined in the original parents, these combinations tend to persist and to reappear in the second hybrid generation. The old combinations are broken and new combinations made only in a small minority of cases.

This phenomenon of *linkage*, as it is called, arises whenever two pairs of genes are carried in one and the same pair of chromosomes. For a full explanation the reader is referred to any standard work on genetics.

In the examples quoted above there are *pairs* of Mendelian factors— *e.g.* tall and dwarf in peas, red and white in *Mirabilis*. But many cases are known of *multiple allelomorphs*. Bay, black and chestnut colour in horses constitute such a series—*i.e.* a bay horse may carry the factor for black or chestnut (but not both) while a black may carry chestnut. The dominant grey factor is separately inherited; only in its absence can a horse be of any other colour.

## QUANTITATIVE INHERITANCE

The vast majority of economic characters of farm animals—size, milk yield, egg production and quality of wool—in so far as they are influenced by heredity, depend on a large number of genes whose individual effects cannot be isolated. Such are known as polygenic characters. Moreover, as is well known, such characters are influenced not only by heredity but also by environmental conditions. Thus, a Friesian cow (apart from the possibility that both her parents carried the recessive red factor) will be black and white whatever the conditions under which she is reared. But the expression of her genetic milk-producing capacity will vary with age, disease, level of nutrition, the degree of skill exercised in management and milking and many other circumstances. Under extremely unfavourable conditions her actual milk yield will bear very little relation to her genetic make-up.

Hence a useful distinction can be drawn between the *genotype* and the *phenotype*. The genotype is the result of the random union of gametes produced by Mendelian segregation within the restrictions caused by linkage. The phenotype is determined partly by genetic and partly by environmental forces, and by the interaction between the two.

The relative influences of heredity and environment vary as between one character and another. For example, in the dairy cow the butter-fat content of the milk is much more a matter of heredity, and much less a matter of environment, than milk yield. The proportion of phenotypic variation of a particular quality that is due to heredity is termed its *heritability* and is commonly expressed either as a decimal fraction or as a percentage of the total variation. Thus the heritability of the butter-fat content of milk, within a given herd, is commonly about 0·4 (40 per cent.) while that of milk yield is much less—20 or 25 per cent. Thus it is easier to breed for butter-fat than for milk yield.

## SEX-LINKED INHERITANCE

A complication is introduced in the transmission of certain characters owing to the fact that their factors are carried by the sex chromosomes. In poultry, for example, the male has a like pair of sex chromosomes while the hen has only one functional or gene-bearing sex chromosome. The result of this condition of affairs is illustrated by the behaviour of the barred pattern of the Barred Rock, which is dominant to black and sex-linked. If a pure-breeding barred cock be mated to black hens, the progeny are all barred. In the second generation the males are all barred and the females half and half as to colour. When the cross is made in the opposite direction—black cock with barred hens—the male chicks are barred and the females black (criss-cross inheritance). In the second hybrid generation we get the four classes—black males, barred males, black females, and barred females in equal numbers. The mechanism is illustrated in Figs. 21 and 22.

The explanation of all sex-linked cases is essentially the same. One of the sexes—the female in the case of the domesticated fowl—has only one functional or gene-bearing sex chromosome. This it obtains in every case from its parent of the opposite sex. The other sex has a pair of gene-bearing chromosomes, one derived from either parent, and therefore the normal complement—a double set—of the sex-linked genes. Its visible characters, in the event of the genes being different, are determined by dominance.

Sex-linkage has an important application in poultry breeding. With certain crosses the sexes of the chicks can be distinguished immediately on hatching.

We may now summarise our general conception of heredity. The heredity characters of an animal are determined by a double set of factors or genes—one set derived from either parent. The sole exceptions to this rule are the sex-linked characters which, in one or other of the sexes, are represented by single genes only. Ordinarily each visible character is the resultant effect produced by a pair of genes, whether the two members of the pair be like or unlike; sometimes the effect of one gene is so strong as completely to mask that of its fellow (dominance). When the individual produces its reproductive cells and the chromosomes are reduced to half their original number each egg or sperm cell receives either the one or the other member of each pair of genes—that is, it receives a single set. The mechanism controlling the distribution of the genes between the reproductive cells is such that certain pairs assort quite independently of others. This happens when they are situated in different chromosomes. There is, however, a tendency, definite and measurable in particular cases, for certain genes to stick together in pre-existing combinations (linkage). This, it is believed, is due to their occurrence in one and the same chromosome. Linkage, however, is normally only partial, so that the chromosome cannot be regarded as a permanent or immutable assemblage or genes.

The heritage of a breed or race consists of the sum total of unit characters represented in the chromosomes of its individual members. The great bulk of observed variation between individuals of the same race (in so far as it is not due to conditions of nurture) is due to the process of biparental inheritance. This involves a combination, in each individual, of two sets of genes, one derived from each parent, and a reshuffling of these before they are handed on, in the germ cells, to the next generation. A race will breed true to all its characters only when each and every pair of genes consists of two identical members, *i.e.* when the maternal set of genes is exactly matched by the paternal.

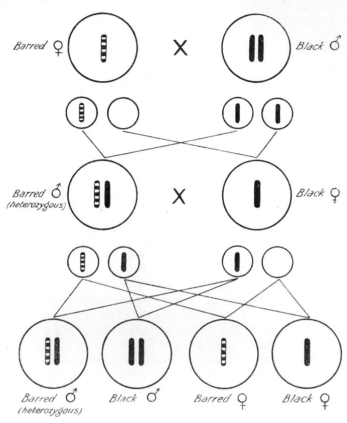

FIG. 21.—Inheritance of Barred Pattern in Fowls

## PURE LINES

It is worth while to look into this last hypothesis and see whether it will stand the test of experiment. The effect of biparental reproduction is to maintain a large number of characters in the heterozygous condition, and thus to produce a large amount of variation. In fact, the whole significance of sexual reproduction seems to be that it makes possible a great series of character combinations and thus gives the race as a whole the power to adapt itself to changing conditions. Among higher animals, therefore, we cannot expect to find true breeding strains unless we employ artificial means to produce them. Many plants, however, have abandoned biparental reproduction, resorting either to vegetative methods or else to self-fertilisation. In either case we get rid of the complexities produced by the reshuffling of genes in each successive generation, and

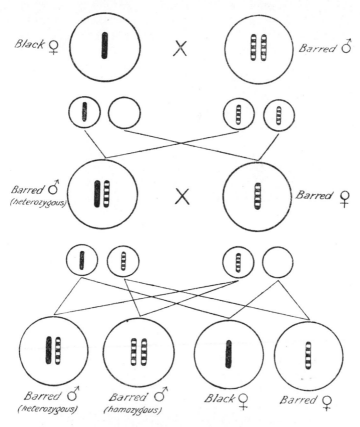

Fig. 22.—Inheritance of Barred Pattern in Fowls

therefore we should expect to find fixed, true breeding strains. Such variations as occur within the strain must be due to causes other than heredity—*i.e.* to environmental causes—and should not be transmitted. This theorem has been put to the test in many experiments, and the results, in every case, have been in agreement with it. For example, if we take a single barley plant, descended, as normally it would be, from self-fertilised ancestors, it will produce a group of progeny having strictly the same hereditary characters as itself. Such a group of progeny, constituting what is called a *pure line*, is fixed, because all its members have

O

the same set of characters in the homozygous condition. Selection within a pure line accomplishes nothing, because selection can produce results only where hereditary differences exist. Cross-fertilisation between plants of the same pure line is likewise without effect, for it amounts to nothing more than a combination of like with like. We are therefore justified in concluding that, as a rule, the individual genes remain constant from one generation to the next, and that the bulk of observed variation among the members of a breed or race is due to reassortment of unit characters and not to any change in the unit characters themselves. This is important from the practical point of view, for it implies that there is a definite limit to the possibilities of selection. When we have obtained a certain combination of characters, all in the homozygous condition, we get no more variations of hereditary value and hence further selection is a ploughing of the sands.

Such is true in the main; the units that compose the hereditary material are of definite constitution, and normally they remain constant. But occasionally, for reasons that are not understood, the genes do change. And when change occurs it is of the nature of a definite step; the new character is fully as constant as the old and behaves as a Mendelian alternative to it. Such sudden and definite changes in the hereditary material are known as *mutations*; they have been seen to occur in most species of plants and animals that have been kept under continuous and close observation; they are not necessarily connected with sexual reproduction—vegetative sports being relatively common. Sometimes they are obvious and startling, more often they are to be detected only upon close scrutiny, and it is certain that many have passed unobserved or have not been distinguished from the ordinary sort of variation due to recombination of factors. Mutations can be produced in plants by treatment with certain chemical substances and by certain ray treatments, but their direction cannot yet be controlled to any appreciable extent. All that the breeder can do is to watch for their occurrence and to perpetuate such as happen to prove of use.

Mutations, as has been said, occur only rarely. In small laboratory animals, which can be bred in large numbers, it has been possible to estimate their frequency. In the fruit fly (*Drosophila*) the total mutation rate is about 0·7 per cent., *i.e.* seven out of every thousand sperms or eggs carry a mutation in one or other of their genes. The total number of genes in *Drosophila* is probably of the order of five or six thousand, so that, on average, the chance of a mutation in a particular gene is slightly more than one in a million. Moreover, of the many mutations that have been observed in farm animals, very few have been of economic value. Yet in the mass, the mutations that have resulted—*e.g.* in the evolution of the superfine merino fleece from the hairy coat of the original wild sheep—have been of immense importance.

# LIVE STOCK IMPROVEMENT

The business of the constructive breeder who sets out to improve his herd rather than merely to multiply it, is to build up a certain combination of valuable hereditary characters—that is, to produce a good type of animal that will " breed true " to its good qualities. Obviously the first essential is a definite object, a clearly conceived ideal type. Moreover, his ideal should be no mere arbitrary standard of " points " but should be laid down with regard mainly to economic considerations—that is to say, our ideal animal should be one which will convert its food into meat or wool, milk or work, as the case may be, with a maximum of efficiency.

In certain cases it is easy to devise a simple and direct test of economic worth. It is so, for example, in the case of milk or of wool production, because it is possible in both instances to determine both the yield and quality of the product and to take such determinations as a basis for selection. The usefulness of a work animal is more difficult to assess, because no final judgment can be reached until the end of its working life. With meat producing animals, again, no complete or definite information can be obtained on such important points as the quality of the meat, or the proportion of carcass to offal, until the animal is slaughtered. In general, however, any direct test is preferable to a mere inference based on the animal's outward appearance, and there is an increasing tendency to apply such direct tests wherever possible. With pigs, for example prolificness can be recorded and the milking capacity of a sow can, for practical purposes, be measured roughly by determining the live weight increments of her piglets during the period when they are solely dependent on their dam's milk. The efficiency of the animal in converting food into meat can be expressed as a ratio between its weight increment and its food consumption, and even on such a matter as the quality of the meat of a breeding animal, inferences can be drawn with some degree of certainty if a few of its litter brethren or its progeny be fattened and slaughtered.

It is important to note that improvement implies the closer adaptation of the animal to the environment in which it is expected to live, and that a breed or strain that has been improved in relation to one type of environment may have been made less well adapted to another. For example, the type of sheep that has been evolved for lowland conditions, which grows and fattens rapidly on abundant and nutritious food, lacks the ability to find its food on a mountian pasture, and its requirements for minerals to make bone and for protein to make flesh, are so high that it cannot collect the necessary supplies of these nutrients from the poor herbage and hence its growth is stunted. Again, when we speak of a highly productive dairy cow we really have in mind a type of animal that is capable of converting a large supply of nutrients into milk. Such an animal may be quite unsuited to a poor upland farm, because her milk production will tend to outrun her intake of nutrients and she will lose condition and powers of resisting disease. As a third example, the bacon type of pig is intended to produce a lean type of carcase with the least possible consumption of food. But if food is restricted in the early stage the development of lean tissue will be inhibited, and heavy feeding at a later stage will result in a large development of fat, so that the final product will not be what is desired. The expression of the animal's hereditary merits thus depends on the provision of appropriate living conditions.

When Bakewell,[1] the great pioneer breeder, started the improvement of British live stock about the middle of the eighteenth century, the farm animals of the country were of very mixed type and of a low average standard of merit. Certain local types were distinguished by peculiarities of size and prevailing colour, but there were no breeds in the modern sense. In all these local types there seems to have been a great amount of variability with respect to useful qualities. Probably there were many individuals with one or other good quality, and occasional specimens showed chance combinations of several valuable qualities; but ancestry was mixed and transmission apparently very irregular. The initial step in the improvement of each breed in turn, by one improver after another has been to collect a herd or flock of the best individuals of the local type and so to get possession of the main qualities that it was deemed advisable to perpetuate in the improved breed. If it happened that several of the characters could be obtained already combined in one individual, then the work of building up the desired combination would be rendered less intricate and tedious. But the main point is that the breeder could not expect, except as a rare piece of good fortune, to get any actual change in the individual unit characters with which he started—a favourable mutation. And hence the real essential in the foundation of a herd was to get together as many good characters as possible, even if this involved the introduction of some bad. For bad characters could be " bred out " whereas there is no known method of producing good characters *de novo*. Apparently Bakewell, when he laid the foundations of his Leicester flock succeeded in gathering together all the characters that were essential to the making of a good long-wooled sheep, mixed up as they were with a greater number of undesirable qualities. On the other hand, his work with the Longhorn cattle of the Midlands was destined to comparative failure, apparently because elsewhere, in the valley of the Tees particularly there was a supply of better raw material—a local type of cattle among which there lay scattered a set of more valuable unit characters.

Having started on a basis sufficiently wide to ensure the inclusion all the characters desired, the breeder proceeds, by successive matings and selection of the progeny, to weed out undesirable characters, and

[1] Robert Bakewell of Dishley in Leicestershire, *b*. 1726, *d*. 1795, originator of improved Leicester sheep and the improved Longhorn cattle, and breeder of cart horse and pigs.

combine the good qualities first in an individual or two and finally in a true breeding strain. This process, it is true, has never yet been carried to the point of complete or final success, yet so much progress has been made that it is important to survey the methods by which it has been achieved.

## MASS AND PEDIGREE SELECTION

The simplest form of selection is what is termed mass or phenotypic selection—the choice of breeding stock on the simple basis of individual merit. The application of this process has given very different results according to the kind of characters to which it has been applied. Obviously the degree of success attained will depend on the accuracy with which the genetic make-up is reflected in the visible or measurable characters. If a certain visible character represents a certain definite and pure (homozygous) condition in the germ cells then we are on perfectly safe ground. Thus if we wished to obtain a race of single-combed fowls from a mixed population, a system of mass selection would give immediate and completely successful results, because we know that a single-combed fowl can have in its germ cells nothing but the " single " factor in the homozygous condition. For various reasons, however, the visible characters of the animal may be unsatisfactory or even quite misleading, as a guide to the qualities that it is capable of transmitting. Characters like egg production in fowls or milk production in cattle are determined in part only by heredity, being influenced to a very marked extent by the conditions of " nurture " in the widest sense. Even when, in the case of a milch cow, we calculate the allowances for the grosser effects of age, time of calving and feeding, we are left with a multitude of varying environmental conditions whose total influence it is impossible to assess. We must therefore proceed on the assumption that milk yield is only in part determined by heredity.

Even when a certain desirable quality is known to be solely a matter of heredity, mass selection often fails to give the desired results. This happens if the character in question is dominant to a corresponding undesirable condition. For example, in cattle the red colour is recessive to most others, and is completely dominant to none [1]; hence reds breed true, and mass selection is immediately successful in establishing a true-breeding red strain. With Angus cattle, on the other hand, the recognised black colour is completely dominant to red, *i.e.* there is no visible difference between the homozygous black, which breeds true, and the black × red heterozygote which throws reds. Red calves occasionally turn up in most herds even though their ancestors may have been black for generations.

There is still another set of circumstances in which simple selection fails to accomplish anything. This happens when a particular quality

---

[1] This statement does not apply to white markings. Some types of white pattern are recessive to solid colours.

is due to a hybrid condition of the germ-plasm. Thus the pink colour in *Mirabilis*, the blue of the Andalusian fowl, and also the roan and the blue-grey colours in cattle, are each due to a heterozygous condition. It seems that one might breed from any of these types for countless generations and still be no nearer to a true breeding strain.

**Pedigree**, when rationally used, forms a valuable aid to the breeder in his work of selection. Pedigree must never be regarded as an end in itself; individual merit must always be considered first—but the two taken in conjunction are undoubtedly a far better guide than either considered alone. The essential questions that a breeder should ask himself in attempting to evaluate a particular pedigree are: (1) what was the average merit of the animal's immediate ancestors? (2) what evidence is there that their good qualities were regularly transmitted from generation to generation? If we have a good individual, the progeny of good and true breeding parents, it is probable that it will transmit its good qualities. The commonest error in the interpretation of pedigrees is that of attaching undue importance to far-back ancestors, and in particular to descent in the direct female line from particular " foundation females." It is quite certain that the average influence of any single animal in even the third or fourth ancestral generation is very slight, and it is doubtful whether in practice there is much to be gained by looking back beyond three generations.

## GENOTYPIC SELECTION

The third and by much the most effective method is what biologists call *genotypic selection*—that is to say, selection on the basis of breeding ability, as determined by actual tests. The special value of this system arises from the fact that it enables the breeder to form a far truer estimate of the hereditary characters than he can do either on the basis of individual merit alone or on the dual basis of individuality and pedigree. We may illustrate the method by reverting to the previous illustration of the red Aberdeen-Angus. If it were a matter of prime importance to get rid of the red colour once and for all, the essential thing would be to breed from parents that were homozygous for black colour. If both parents were homozygous blacks, then the calves would all be homozygous blacks. But even if we made sure of one parent only, we should, for the time being, prevent the appearance of reds, and by continuous breeding from homoyzgous black on one side we should very quickly reduce the number of the black × red hybrids in the herd. In practice this is all that could be done, because it is impracticable to carry out breeding tests with females of the slower breeding species; half the cow's breeding life might be over before one could get presumptive evidence of her germinal constitution. Genotypic selection would therefore be confined to the bull, and the procedure would be to mate him with, say, ten or a dozen red or white or red-roan cows. If he were a homozygous black, all his calves would be black or blue-grey. If he left any red or red-roan calves one could definitely conclude that he was a black × red heterozygote, and therefore he would be discarded.

A similar procedure may be adopted with regard to any other character or group of characters. If the trial matings be made with carefully chosen females, and if the progeny be sufficiently numerous, a picture can be obtained of the germinal constitution of the sire. Thus a guide to the capabilities of a dairy bull could be obtained by comparing the average production of a number of his daughters with the average production of their dams. With meat producing animals, too, a satisfactory basis on which to judge a sire would be the economy of production and the quality of the meat produced by a number of his progeny.

Much thought is now being given to the best types of tests to assess breeding ability. For many years official pig testing stations have been testing the progeny of different sires in Canada, Denmark and other countries; and more recently similar tests have been started in this country. A selected number of progeny are reared, fed and finally converted into bacon under carefully controlled conditions, and the results are used in the selection of the best sires.

For milk production use is now being made of contemporary comparisons. The test consists of comparing the performances of the progeny of one bull with the progeny of other bulls used on the same herd of dairy cows. It is a method which has become possible and more practicable since artificial insemination became widely adopted. Performance and progeny tests for beef bulls first carried out in the United States are also being conducted in many countries. In Great Britain attention is being given primarily to the performance testing of beef bulls to be used for crossing with dairy breeds to produce beef stores. The test consists of recording the performance of a group of beef bull calves over a period of up to twelve months, and later selecting progeny of these bulls for a feeding test. It is hoped to determine if there is a correlation between the live weight gains of the bull calves and their progeny, and also in the economy of the gains. Information is also being obtained on carcass quality. It is hoped that such trials if successful will enable one to select the most suitable beef sires while still relatively young.

Generally there is a quickening of interest as to the methods by which the value of sires can be measured as early as possible in their lives. Clearly, this is now of great importance in those classes of farm livestock where artificial insemination has become established as a common practice.

## FIXING TYPE

When an animal with something approaching the desired set of hereditary characters, has been obtained, the problem arises of maintaining or fixing this combination in a herd or flock or strain. No breeder

has yet succeeded in producing a near perfect animal, or even one possessing a full complement of all the best characters of its breed; yet success
in the breeding of really fine individuals is comparatively common.   It
is far more difficult to build up a herd in which the good qualities are
transmitted in any complete or regular fashion.   Take milk production,
for example.   Individual yields of 2000 and 3000 gal., and even more, have
been obtained.   The best herds, on the other hand, produce averages of
between 800 and 1200, and this under a system of continuous culling—
that is to say, the average is not that of all the females bred but the average
after a considerable proportion of the poorest producers has been discarded
In many countries the average production is 400 gal. or less.   Admitting
that milk production is influenced by many circumstances other than
heredity, one cannot avoid the conclusion that it is extremely difficult
to get a fixed and true breeding strain of heavy producers.   But it is a
more important objective than the securing of a few high individual
records.

## INBREEDING

It has been known since the time of Bakewell that inbreeding—the
mating together of closely related animals—is a valuable aid in the fixing
of type, *i.e.* in the production of strains in which the same characteristics
are regularly reproduced.   The discovery by Bakewell of the value of
inbreeding seems to have been due to the accident of circumstances.   He
had new and original notions as to what constituted merit in a sheep or
a steer, and after he had formed his flock and herd, and had gone some
way with their improvement, he naturally found it increasingly difficult
to obtain, from outside, sires that he considered good enough to introduce.
He therefore turned to home bred sires, and gradually, as his blood lines
became intermingled, he resorted to more and more intensive inbreeding.
On the whole his results were exceedingly good.

This effect of inbreeding, the fixing of type, is readily explicable on
the Mendelian hypothesis.   If we take a group of plants that are heterozygous for a particular character—say a hundred pink-flowered *Mirabilis*
—and cause them to become self-fertilised, 50 per cent. of the progeny
will be heterozygous, *i.e.* pink, while the other half will show one or other
of the homozygous conditions, white or red.   If this generation is selfed
again the whites and reds breed true, while the pinks produce 50 per cent.
of the hybrid (pink) and 50 per cent. of the homozygous (white and red)
forms.   Thus if the various forms are allowed to multiply in the same
ratio, the proportion of heterozygous or non-pure-breeding types decreases
from generation to generation in the series $\frac{1}{2}$, $\frac{1}{4}$, $\frac{1}{8}$, $\frac{1}{16}$, and so on.   After
ten generations of self-fertilisation the pure types would constitute 99·9
per cent. of the population.   Similarly, if we start with a multiple hybrid—
*i.e.* with a plant having a large number of characters in the heterozygous
condition—and if we neglect the complication of linkage the *average*

number of heterozygous characters will be halved each time that self-fertilisation occurs. If, for example, we cross two varieties of wheat that differ in sixteen Mendelian characters, and allow the progeny to self-fertilise for a dozen generations, it may be calculated that over 99 per cent. of the progeny will have automatically reached the homozygous or true-breeding condition.[1] This is in accordance with the discovery, made independently, that in species that are regularly self-fertilised the vast majority of individuals do actually breed true.

Self-fertilisation is, of course, the most intense form of inbreeding that it is possible to conceive, but other forms differ from it not in kind but only in degree. Whenever inbreeding is practised, characters tend to separate out in the homozygous condition, and the closer the degree of relationship the more rapid will be the process of segregation into pure-breeding strains. Continuous out-crossing, on the other hand, tends to keep a maximum of characters in the heterozygous condition, with a correspondingly wide range of possible combinations and a high degree of variability.

It must be pointed out that absolute purity of type, in the Mendelian sense, has never been reached with farm animals. In order to isolate " pure lines " from an ordinary mixed stock we should have to breed very closely for a considerable number of generations. In the case of full-brother-and-sister matings it might take some twenty generations. Nothing approaching this amount of inbreeding has ever been attempted in practice,[2] and so far we can only speak of strains of farm animals as relatively pure. Even in the most carefully selected and most closely bred families there must remain a considerable number of heterozygous characters. That this should be so, in spite of the obvious advantages of pure-breeding types, is accounted for by another, phenomenon connected with inbreeding.

Very generally, when attempts have been made to inbreed through several generations, the breeder has found that his stock deteriorated in some respect—showed a lack of size, or vigour or both; susceptibility to disease; lessened fertility or perhaps complete sterility. The largest controlled experiment with cattle was carried out in the United States with Friesians. One section of the herd was " outbred," each successive herd sire being a carefully selected proven bull which was as nearly as possible unrelated to the females. The other half was closely inbred, each successive sire being a son or brother of his predecessor. The conception rate was three services per pregnancy in the inbred

---

[1] In fact the occurrence of linkage slows down the rate of progress towards homo-zygosity.

[2] A very high degree of uniformity is obviously required in laboratory animals, such as rats and guinea-pigs, which are used for the testing of the strength of drugs and the vitamin potency of foods. Some strains of these animals have been so much inbred that they seem to have reached the condition of pure lines.

section as compared with 1·9 in the outbred.   The birth weight of the calves fell from 82 lb. in the first generation to 63·9 lb. in the sixth inbred generation.   Mortality of calves was much higher among the inbreds than the outbreds.   Milk yield was maintained for the first three generations of inbreeding but afterwards declined.   The cows of the sixth inbred generation gave 31 per cent. less milk and 38 per cent. less butter fat than the original foundation cows.

When we mate two animals or plants, belonging to different inbred strains, the cross-bred progeny often show markedly greater vigour than either parent.   This phenomenon is called " hybrid vigour " or *heterosis*. The theories that have been advanced to account for the facts—the decline in vigour under inbreeding and the gain when two inbreds are crossed —fall into two groups.

On the one hand it is argued that selection for economic qualities in an outbred population will quickly eliminate unfavourable, dominant factors, whereas an unfavourable recessive, unless it is carried by a large proportion of the stock, will escape notice and will persist.   When inbreeding is practised, however, the homozygous recessives will segregate out and, if their number is considerable or their effects severe, the strain will " degenerate."   When we cross two unrelated (or only distantly related) inbred types the chances are that, with respect to the majority of factors, one or the other parent will contribute the favourable dominant so that the cross-bred progeny will have few unfavourable recessive factors in the homozygous state.   This theory appears to accord with most of the known facts.   For instance, in the improvement of self-fertilised crop plants, the common procedure is to make a cross, to allow selfing for a number of generations, and to build up a new strain consisting of the progeny of a single homozygous plant.   Such completely homozygous families may be of high economic value.   Again, with certain laboratory animals—rats, mice, and guinea-pigs—inbreeding has been carried to the stage of almost complete homozygosity, but so far this has not been achieved in the case of any type of farm live stock, the reasons for the difference being probably that it is possible to keep small animals in relatively large numbers, that the generations are shorter and that the higher level of prolificacy gives greater scope for selection.   But it is also to be noted that many of the inbred families of laboratory rats are smaller and less prolific than the outbred populations from which they have been derived.

Another hypothesis, that does not exclude the last, assumes that " over-dominance " (or super-dominance) affects the influence of certain genes—*i.e.* that a favourable dominant can be actually more effective in the heterozygous than in the homozygous state.

Whatever the theoretical explanation, it is clear that inbreeding does not lead to the creation of undesirable hereditary factors, but merely brings to light such as have been hidden.   It does not lead, as was formerly supposed, to indefinite and progressive " running out "; deterioration comes to an end when the homozygous condition has been reached. Obviously, however, if the advantages of inbreeding, in the way of creating true-breeding types, are to be secured without the disadvantage of loss of vigour, inbreeding must be accompanied by rigorous selection, so that, in practice, the degree of inbreeding that should be attempted must depend on the scope for selection. This, in turn, depends on the reproductive rate of the particular animal with which the breeder is concerned; for instance, there is far more scope for selection in poultry than in dairy cattle.

What is called " line breeding " is merely a less intensive form of inbreeding. The term is ordinarily applied in cases where the degree of kinship, between animals mated, is less close than that of full cousins. But statisticians, given an animal's full pedigree, can now place a numerical value on the degree of inbreeding. This expresses the percentage reduction in the original number of heterozygous factors, that would be expected from the occurrence of particular ancestors at two or more places in the pedigree. It is rare to find in ordinary pedigree herds animals that are more than " 10 per cent. inbred."

Very extensive work has been done in the United States over a period of many years in the inbreeding of pigs. With inbreeding many defects have developed, and none of the inbred lines, as such, is useful for commercial production. Performance has been better in two-line and three-line crosses. In this country the production of inbred pigs of two breeds— Large White and Wessex—is in progress at an Animal Breeding Research Organisation near Edinburgh.

The tentative conclusion from all this work so far would seem to be that there may be advantages in the production of inbred lines, and the subsequent use of the inbred boars for crossing. But it will be a costly job, that will require to be carried out over a long period, and there is little immediate prospect of such boars being available for commercial production.

## GRADING AND CROSSING

Where a breeder starts, as is often inevitable, with a collection of females of average or inferior quality he should normally endeavour to " grade up " his flock or herd by the continued use of pedigree sires. Before he begins operations, he should convince himself that one or other of the pure breeds will provide the type of animal he desires, and having once decided on a particular breed he should not lightly discard it for another. Certain of the Breed Societies encourage such grading by admitting to their register " grade " animals with a certain proportion of non-pedigree ancestry. So long as the breeder is in the grading-up stage— *i.e.* so long as he is able to obtain from outside sources sires that are reasonably certain to improve the standard of merit in his herd—there is no particular advantage to be gained by close inbreeding; on the other hand, if he happens to secure a particularly good and impressive sire he should not hesitate to concentrate his " blood," and the experiment of mating him to his own progeny may be worth trying. A breeder who is grading-up may study pedigrees with just as much advantage as the pedigree breeder himself, for if he is content to buy any registered sire on his appearance alone he may get an animal of mixed or inferior ancestry that may bring him serious loss.

**Cross-breeding,** so long as it is carried out systematically, has, for the production of " commercial " animals, certain definite advantages over pure-breeding. Cross-bred animals commonly show the phenomenon of *heterosis* or hybrid vigour—that is to say, are more prolific and more resistant to disease and grow more rapidly than pure breds. Theoretically, of course, it is possible to collect a complete set of desirable dominant factors in a single homozygous strain, but many generations must elapse before this can be accomplished with farm animals. Meantime, such valuable dominants as have been fixed in two breeds can be combined by crossing. Heterosis is usually most marked in the first cross; hence cross-breeding should not be carried beyond this stage or, at the most, beyond that of mating a first-cross female with a pure-bred male. In the latter case the disadvantage of irregularity in the second-cross generation may be outbalanced by the advantages of hardiness and prolificness in the cross-bred dams.

In practice cross-breeding offers the greatest advantages in highly prolific species like pigs and poultry, because in these cases a relatively small proportion of pure matings will suffice to produce the necessary supply of selected pure-bred females. In the less prolific species a large proportion of the females born must be kept for breeding, and widespread crossing involves the retention either of cross-bred females or of inferior pure-breds. In the case of dairy cattle crossing, unless controlled, is very liable to degenerate into " mongrelising." Normally, grading is the better system to pursue in dairy herds.

It is a common misconception that inferior pure-bred sires are good enough for crossing. It is true that there is a limit to the sum of money that can profitably be invested in a crossing sire, and it is also true that animals which are faulty to the eye of the pedigree breeder may be excellent from the point of view of the commercial breeder. But it is only by careful selection of his sires, and by careful study of his results, that the cross-breeding farmer can hope to repeat his successes and avoid recurrence of his failures.

# CHAPTER 18

# THE PRINCIPLES OF NUTRITION

A convenient approach to the study of the nutrition of farm animals is to consider the various chemical compounds which are contained in feeding stuffs and the uses to which they are put in the animal body. The many hundreds of chemical compounds in feeding stuffs are classified by chemists into four major groups. These are: (1) mineral or ash constituents; (2) the nitrogen containing constituents; (3) the fatty and waxy materials; and (4) the carbohyrdates. This classification is a very general one, and each major class contains a multitude of compounds; indeed, the chemical constitution of some is not exactly known. One very important component of feeding stuffs has, however, been left out of the above classification, namely, water. The first step a chemist takes in the analysis of a feeding stuff is to determine its moisture content by heating it at the boiling point of water. He then determines the amount of the other major classes of material in the dry matter. Even the so called dry feeds contain water. Freshly purchased concentrate cubes contain the least, namely, about 10 per cent., hays and straws about 10 to 15 per cent.; grass and green forages between 65 and 85 per cent. The highest water contents are found in turnips and swedes, which often contain over 90 per cent. A high water content, of course, increases the cost of handling and transporting a crop, but at the same time succulent foods such as green crops, roots and silage appear to have a special value which cannot be simply accounted for. A good supply of water for all farm stock is essential, because water is constantly being used to excrete, in solution in the urine and fæces, unwanted waste products arising from the breakdown of food materials in the body. A further loss of water occurs through the skin and in the breath of the animal; in fact, a highly fed dairy cow will lose as much as 4 gal. of water per day by evaporation. In the breakdown of food some water is formed in the body, but this amount goes only a small way to meet these losses. Water requirements of stock are met not only by drinking water but also by the water contained in their feed. In the spring, for instance, heifers grazing on lush pasture receive sufficient water from the herbage they consume, and do not go to the drinking trough. The same is true of sheep which on fresh pasture drink no water, but on old pasture, in dry weather, may drink up to half a gallon per head per day. Table 5 summarises the normal water intakes by farm animals. With the exception of young calves, which never know when they have had enough, and fattening pigs, where a convenient rule is 3 lb. of water to 1 lb. of meal, farm animals are best left to judge their own requirements, and unlimited water should be made available.

**Minerals.**—The ash constituents of feeding stuffs are determined by incinerating the dry material at a dull red heat in a furnace. The unburnt residue consists of silica and the sulphates, chlorides, phosphates and carbonates of calcium, magnesium, potassium, sodium, iron, and a large number of other elements. Some of these others, like copper and cobalt, are of considerable nutritional significance. Others, like boron, aluminium and nickel, while known to be present in minute amounts in animal tissues, do not appear to be essential. The amount of ash in feeding stuffs

TABLE 5

WATER REQUIREMENTS ON DRY RATIONS

| Class of Stock | Weight (lb.) | Water required per Day (lb.) |
|---|---|---|
| Weaning calves . . . . | 150 | 10 to 15 |
| Dry cows . . . . . | 1000 | 70 ,, 80 |
| Milking cows * . . . . | 1000 | Up to 180 |
| Sheep . . . . . | 150 | ,, 10 |
| Weaning pigs . . . . | 30 | 4 |
| Baconers . . . . . | 200 | 8 |
| In-pig sows. . . . . | 400 | 10 to 12 |
| Suckling sows . . . . | 300 | 40 ,, 50 |

* The milking cow requires 1½ to 2 gal. of water for every gallon of milk she produces besides that which she would need if she were dry.

varies considerably. Some feeds, such as flaked maize, contain very little indeed—less than 1 per cent.—while feeds such as fish meal contain more than 20 per cent. Most common feeds contain from 2 to 8 per cent. of ash, calculated on a dry matter basis.

All animals require minerals, and some of these must be given in organic form. Thus the animal must receive at least part of its sulphur requirements in the form of the sulphur containing amino acid methionine. Some mineral elements are toxic when given in large amounts. Thus common salt may easily poison poultry and pigs, if inadvertently they are given doses too large in relation to their water supply. Again, cattle which have access to pastures which have received heavy dressings of phosphate fertilizers and have not been washed by rain may suffer from scours for a day or two. Some minerals are toxic even when only very small amounts are supplied. Molybdenum, which is present in the herbage of certain pastures in Somerset—the so-called " teart pastures," causes severe scouring in cattle. Luckily, the trouble may be prevented by giving cattle a special cake containing copper. There is evidence from experiments with rats that molybdenum is required in minute amounts. These are so small that rations are unlikely to be deficient. Selenium is responsible for a disease of cattle in certain parts of Ireland and the United States. In this case, unfortunately, there is no antidote to the disease and, since selenium is present in the soil of the areas and in all crops grown thereon, it is impossible to carry on any system of live stock husbandry without running the risk of serious loss. Like molybdenum, there is evidence that selenium is also required in very minute amounts. Poisoning by fluorine, which may contaminate pastures through flue gases and industrial smoke from certain modern industries, produces widespread abnormalities of the bones and teeth of cattle and has caused many deaths in several areas of Britain. Of all toxic elements, lead is probably the most important in practice. Every year in Britain many hundreds of calves die as the result of chewing the lead-painted doors of their boxes.

Though certain minerals can cause ill health or even death, much more harm to the productivity of live stock results from a shortage, in their daily rations, of essential minerals. Of these, calcium and phosphorus are of supreme importance. About 75 per cent. of the total ash of the body of farm animals consists of these two elements. Together they make up 99 per cent. of the ash of the bony skeleton, and phosphorus is also contained, in appreciable amounts, in the soft tissues. The rapidly growing young animal, which is laying down both soft and skeletal tissues, obviously has a great need for these elements. Milking animals also have a large requirement, since a gallon of milk contains about $\frac{1}{2}$ oz. calcium and $\frac{1}{6}$ oz. phosphorus. These amounts must therefore be applied in the feed. During early lactation the milking cow draws part of the requirements from her own bones and, later in lactation, rebuilds her depleted bones in preparation for her next lactation. A shortage of calcium and phosphorus leads to rickets and other bone abnormalities. The soils of some large areas, notably in South Africa, are by nature grossly deficient in phosphorus, and the natural herbage is so deficient that cattle grazing it develop the disease aphosphorosis, which is characterised by a stunting of growth and a depraved appetite. Mild forms of this deficiency disease have been seen in Britain.

In meeting the requirements of animals it must be remembered that most concentrates are low in calcium, and that some starchy feeds are very poor in phosphorus as well. The usual home grown mixtures for milk production are generally deficient in calcium, phosphorus and common salt, so that a proprietary mineral mixture or (more cheaply) a mixture of two parts common salt, one part ground chalk and one part sterilised bone-flour should be added to the concentrate ration at the rate of 3 lb. minerals per cwt. Attention to the calcium and phosphorus supplies of pigs is also essential when these are kept and managed under intensive conditions. If the ration is reasonably good the addition of $1\frac{1}{2}$ per cent. ground chalk and 1 per cent. common salt will suffice.

**Trace Minerals.**—Animals that are living under natural conditions, *e.g.* on normal good pasture, are almost certain to receive sufficient mineral nutrients; but if the soil is seriously deficient in a particular mineral, deficiency disease will appear in the grazing animals. Disease will also occur in animals maintained on the conserved forage, in the absence of a supplementary source of minerals. One example is " pining " or " moor sickness " in sheep, which occurs on many hill grazings in Scotland, Wales and in certain parts of England. Sheep confined to these hills or moors lose appetite and become anæmic and weak. The disease is due to the absence from the soil, and hence from the herbage, of the minute amount of cobalt which is necessary to the well being of ruminants. The amount needed by the sheep is extremely small—about 1 part in 10 million of its food. In other parts of the world the disease also occurs in cattle, but in parts of Britain it is virtually confined to sheep. Copper deficiency also occurs on some soils and results in a' pining condition or in scouring and unthriftiness, in cattle. In the pregnant ewe shortage of available copper results in her giving birth to lambs with " swayback." Such lambs may be unable to stand, or can stand and walk only unsteadily with a characteristic swaying of the hind quarters. In certain parts of Britain (notably in Derbyshire) these conditions occur even where the copper content of the soils appears to be normal, and it is thought that the concentration of other minerals, notably sulphates and molybdenum, in the herbage may make the copper unavailable. A further trace element deficiency which occurs in farm practice is that of iron. Copper and iron are needed for the manufacture of hæmoglobin, the red pigment in blood cells. Sows' milk, and indeed all milks, are deficient in these elements, so that sucking pigs that are reared indoors often become anæmic and may die. Dosage with a solution of iron and copper both prevents and cures the disease. Piglets running out of doors can obtain iron by rooting in the soil and are therefore rarely affected. Deficiencies of manganese and iodine have also been known, but only rarely, to occur in farm live stock in this country.

In general, shortage of trace elements is not common, occurring only over a very small range of soil types or under highly artificial systems of intensive rearing. Provided that sufficient calcium, phosphorus and common salt are present in mixed rations and that a fair variety of feeding stuffs is used throughout the year, there is seldom any danger of deficiencies of the other mineral elements.

**The Nitrogen Containing Constituents.**—Returning to our broad classification of the constituents of feeding stuffs, we come to those which contain nitrogen. These include a vast number of different substances, some being of fairly simple constitution, while others are of very great complexity. The most important members of this latter class are the proteins, such as the casein of milk, the albumen of egg-white and gluten, one of the main proteins of wheat grain. Sometimes this whole class of nitrogen containing nutrients is referred to as *crude protein*, and a distinction is made between the actual or *pure protein* and the remainder, sometimes termed " *amides* " but more correctly, *non-protein nitrogen containing substances*. *True proteins* contain some 15 to 17 per cent. of nitrogen and are of exceedingly complex composition. When broken down, an individual protein may yield up to twenty or more relatively simple compounds called *amino acids*. Of these twenty a proportion can be manufactured in the body from quite simple forms of organically combined nitrogen, but ten of them, the so-called *essential amino acids*, have to be provided in the non-ruminant animal's diet in order that it may be able to build up its own body proteins, those of eggs and of milk and the keratin proteins of hair. The non-proteins of feeding stuffs include firstly amino acids and amides, and (in smaller amounts) alkaloids, lecithins, betaines and many other simple crystalline materials. While some of these simple compounds can be used or broken down by the animal, it is only the animo acids, whether derived from the proteins or from the non-protein fraction, that are essential.

The proportion of the crude protein which is in the form of pure proteins varies greatly from one feeding stuff to another. In ripe seeds it is commonly well over 90 per cent., while in mangels it is only about 10 per cent., the remainder, in this case, including some nitrate. In rapidly growing green crops, in which rapid synthesis of protein is proceeding, as much as 50 per cent. of the nitrogen is represented by non-proteins such as the amides asparagine and glutamine. The total content of crude protein also varies widely; for instance, cereal straws contain only 1 or 2 per cent., beans and peas about 25 per cent. and some oil cakes contain more than 40 per cent.

In the digestion of protein-containing feed by simple stomached animals such as pigs, the enzymes of the digestive tract break down the proteins to amino acids. These are absorbed into the blood stream and are later reassembled in the tissues to produce the specialised proteins of muscles, liver, hair, milk and so on. The proteins vary in composition, and when hydrolysed yield various proportions of the common amino acids. Some proteins fail to yield particular amino acids; for example, gelatine, from bones, yields no tryptophan, while gliadin, from wheat grain, yields no lysine and very little tryptophan. The proteins of the pulses tend to be low in lysine. If a pig is given an otherwise adequate ration, with gelatine as the only protein, it fails to gain in weight because of the lack of the essential amino acid tryptophan. Again, if given a ration with wheat proteins as the sole source of protein, its growth rate will be low because of a shortage of lysine. The pig, in synthesising its body protein from the amino acids derived from its food, is limited by the supply of each individual one. Those which it cannot use or which are present in excess are broken down in its liver, the nitrogen being converted first to ammonia and then to urea, which is excreted in the urine. The carbon containing residue can, however, be used as a source of energy and, in part, stored as body fat.

Food proteins thus differ widely in their ability to produce body gains in the pig and other simple stomached animals. The efficiency with which a protein is utilised is usually expressed as its *biological value*. Proteins with a biological value of 100, such as those of whole egg, can be utilised by the animal without wastage. A protein such as gelatine, when fed by itself, can hardly be used at all, and has a biological value of about 25. The proteins of cereals are about 70 per cent. as good as whole egg protein, while those of skimmed milk are nearly as good, having a biological value of over 90. In general, animal and fish proteins, such as those of blood meal, meat meal and white-fish meal, are much superior to plant proteins as sources of essential amino acids. It is broadly true that a mixture of proteins is better than any single protein, since a deficiency of a particular amino acid in one protein is often balanced by an excess in another. For example, better growth is obtained when an all cereal ration, which is deficient in lysine, is supplemented with gelatine, which yields a large amount of lysine. This is true despite the fact that gelatine provides none of the essential tryptophan. The biological value of the protein is unlikely to be a limiting factor in the growth of pigs and poultry if mixed rations are employed, particularly if, as is usual, some fish meal or other animal protein is included in their rations.

With pigs and poultry it is quite certain that the amino acid composition of the food protein is important in relation to growth. By contrast, the importance of biological value to ruminants is much less.

In the ruminant all food first enters the capacious rumen or paunch. Here vast numbers of micro-organisms break down the proteins into their constituent amino acids. This fermentation often proceeds further with the formation of ammonia. The bacteria synthesise the proteins of their own bodies from sources of carbon and ammonia or amino acid. The partly fermented food mass, containing the bacteria, then moves down the digestive tract where the proteolytic enzymes hydrolyse not only the food proteins which have escaped ruminal fermentation, but also a proportion of the bacterial proteins as well. Thus the cow and the sheep assimilate not only the mixture of amino acids directly supplied in their food, but also amino acids derived from the bacteria. In addition some ammonia is absorbed from the gut. The ruminant is able to utilise quite simple nitrogen compounds, such as urea and ammonium salts, as a partial substitute for protein. The explanation is that the bacteria can use these to manufacture amino acids.

Some sulphur, in the form of sulphate, has to be provided to enable the bacteria to synthesise the sulphur-containing amino acids. Studies of the biological value of bacterial protein shows that it is very constant at about 80. This means that the biological value of protein in ruminants will tend towards 80. In the milking cow, for example, the biological value departs very little from a value of 75, irrespective of the type of ration given. Some differences in the value of proteins nevertheless exist. These are associated with the solubility of the protein rather than its amino acid composition. Soluble proteins are readily and rapidly attacked by micro-organisms in the rumen with consequent rapid evolution of ammonia. The rate of ammonia production can then exceed the synthetic capacity of the bacteria and the ammonia is absorbed from the gut, converted to urea in the liver and excreted.

The facts set out go far to explain the observation that dairy cows show very little response, in milk yield, to major changes in the make up of their food protein, and suggest that, for ruminants, the non-protein nitrogen fraction of feeds has a value but little short of that of true protein. For this reason protein requirements of ruminants are best expressed in terms of digestible crude protein rather than as pure protein. A convention which has been adopted for many years is to express protein requirements in terms of " protein equivalent." This is defined as the sum of the digested pure protein plus half the digested non-protein.

**The Fats.**—The next large group of food constituents are the fats. These, as determined by the standard method of analysis, include not only the true fats or glycerides, but resins, organic acids, essential oils, sterols and plant pigments such as chlorophyll and the carotenoids. All these constituents are extracted from the dry, finely-ground feeding stuffs by prolonged treatment with hot ether, and hence they are more correctly known as " ether extractives." In some foods, such as linseed, the glycerides account for the larger part of the ether extractives, while in others—notably the straws and hays—the non-glycerides are the more abundant. In general the glycerides have a much greater feeding value than the non-glycerides, but the latter fraction includes certain very important compounds, notably vitamins A, D and E, which, as we shall see later, are of paramount importance in nutrition.

**The Carbohydrates.**—The carbohydrates of feeding stuffs are generally classified as follows:—

1. *Monosaccharides* or simple sugars, such as grape sugar and fruit sugar, which are hexoses with the general formula $C_6H_{12}O_6$ and the pentoses with the general formula $C_5H_{10}O_5$.

2. *Disaccharides*, which include cane or beet sugar, milk sugar and malt sugar, and have a general formula $C_{12}H_{22}O_{11}$.

3. *Polysaccharides*, which make a very large group of compounds, all of which have a high molecular weight and may be regarded as complex condensations of the simple sugars. They include starches, which are the reserve materials found in many plants, and dextrins, the simpler compounds which arise during the build up or breakdown of starch. In digestion by animals with simple stomachs (pig and fowl)

nearly 100 per cent. of the starches, dextrins and disaccharides are hydrolysed to simple sugars by the action of enzymes secreted into the digestive tract. These simple sugars are then absorbed into the blood stream. The other important group of polysaccharides are those which are generally known as " cell wall constituents " or, more loosely, as fibre. They include a very large number of compounds—pectins, cellulose, lignin, hemicelluloses, pentosans and polyuronides. Of these, the most important are cellulose and lignin. Cellulose is a major component of cell walls and is a polymerised glucose, and yields glucose on hydrolysis. However, none of the enzymes produced by the wall of the digestive tract can carry out this hydrolysis, and simple stomached animals cannot digest cellulose. The immense number of bacteria which are present in the rumen of cattle are, however, able to break down cellulose and, in doing so, supply their host with a source of food it could not otherwise obtain. A little fermentation of the same type does take place in the cæcum of simple stomached animals, accounting for the small amount of cellulose which is apparently digested by these species.

The product of the fermentation in the ruminant is not, however, glucose. When cellulose is fermented by the cow, the gas methane is formed and the simple steam volatile fatty acids, acetic, propionic and butyric acids are produced as well. Some of the cellulose is converted into bacterial starch and some of the energy locked up in the cellulose is liberated as heat. The ruminant does not therefore obtain the whole of the energy of the cellulose which the bacteria break down. The gas methane is of no value, the heat produced is usually a burden rather than an advantage while some of the bacterial starch can escape digestion in the lower part of the digestive tract. The ruminant can, however, utilise the lower fatty acids. The steam volatile acids, which probably account for about 70 per cent. of the energy-yielding compounds the ruminant absorbs, can be used to furnish the energy for maintenance, they can be used to furnish energy for the synthesis of body fat and milk constituents. Acetic acid is incorporated directly into milk fat and propionic acid can be used for the synthesis of milk lactose.

The other important cell wall constituent, lignin, is not attacked by bacteria, nor is there any digestive juice which can break it down. This is of very great importance in the feeding of live stock, since as plants get older lignin is laid down on top of the cellulose layers giving rigidity to the stem, leaf veins and seed coat. This process of lignification makes the plant less nutritious because the cellulose and the cell constituents are protected by the coating of lignin from the action of the bacteria. Lignification accounts for the delcine in the digestibility of hay when cutting is delayed.

The usual way of measuring the amount of woody fibre, i.e. lignified cellulose, is to boil the ground material first in dilute acid and then in dilute alkali. The insoluble residue is called crude fibre. This represents only a rough approximation to the lignin and cellulose content because, lignin is partially soluble in the alkali and cellulose partially soluble in the acid. Thus crude fibre from a late cut hay or a straw is very different, in terms of nutritive value, from the crude fibre of young spring grass. The latter is extremely well digested by cattle and sheep but the crude fibre of straws is not.

New and more specific methods have been devised to provide more meaningful separations of the carbohydrates of foods. These methods allow much more complete characterisations of plant materials to be made and will certainly help to estimate their feeding value. The best available measure of the value of the total carbohydrates of a feed is obtained by feeding experiments in which the digestibility of the crude fibre and nitrogen-free extract is determined.

**The Vitamins.**—In 1906 the late Sir Frederick Gowland Hopkins stated that " no animal can live on a mixture of pure protein, fat and carbohydrate even when the necessary inorganic material is supplied." From his own experiments and others Hopkins concluded that some other substance or substances were required. These were first called " accessory food factors " and later, vitamins. To-day there is an immense amount of knowledge not only about the chemical structure of vitamins, but also their physiological effects both on laboratory rats and guinea pigs and on farm animals and man. The vitamins are classified as either fat-soluble or water-soluble. The fat-soluble group includes vitamins A, D, E and K, and the water-soluble group vitamin C and the members of the vitamin B complex.

**Fat-soluble Vitamins.**—*Vitamin A* is a colourless substance of known chemical constitution which is found in the liver oils of fish and animals. It is formed in the animal body largely from the orange yellow β-carotene, one of the several yellow pigments called carotenoids associated in the plant with the green colouring material chlorophyll. β-carotene is indeed not the only precursor of vitamin A. Yellow maize grain contains crypto-xanthine which is also a precursor of vitamin A. But β-carotene is the most common. All animals have the power of converting carotene into vitamin A, but some do so more efficiently than others. Thus the Guernsey cow produces a yellow milk fat because she passes into her milk a considerable portion of the carotene she ingests. The Ayrshire, on the other hand, given exactly the same ration, converts more carotene into vitamin A before secreting it. The goat secretes virtually no carotene in her milk. Despite the difference in colour the values of these milks in preventing disease due to vitamin A deficiency can be the same. No animal can manufacture vitamin A in its body except from the precursors, and the vitamin A potency of eggs and milk is directly proportionate to the amount of carotene which the hen or the cow obtains from its food.

As would be expected, carotene is largely found in green, leafy materials,

Seeds and common farm concentrates contain very little, even yellow maize being a rather poor source. Carrot roots are very rich in carotene but mangels, swedes, turnips, sugar beet pulp and potatoes supply practically none. Some fish meals contain a little pre-formed vitamin A, but the small amount is sometimes lost during processing. The green leaf is the main and the richest source, and the carotene content falls markedly as the plant matures.

Carotene is not very stable and is rapidly destroyed in the presence of oxygen. Carotene in cut grass is thus largely destroyed in the common process of hay making, and it is only if the hay retains a good green colour that it can be regarded as a highly potent source. The table shows the original carotene content of a crop of grass and indicates the losses which occur when it is conserved in different ways.

TABLE 6

| Material | Carotene content of Material on a Dry Basis, mg. per 100 g. |
|---|---|
| Fresh grass . . . . . | 30 |
| Hay made with little weathering . | 8 |
| Hay, badly weathered . . . | 4 |
| Ensiled . . . . . | 20 |
| Artificially dried . . . . | 26 |
| Hay, badly weathered, after storage for two months in bales . . | 1 |

Artificial drying is clearly the best method of conservation from the point of view of conserving carotene. Bales of dried grass, however, gradually lose their content of carotene through oxidation, this being particularly noticeable on the outside layers. Under most circumstances, dried grass of high quality is the best source of the vitamin. Cod-liver oil, which supplies pre-formed vitamin A has been much used in the past, but when mixed with feeding stuffs its vitamin A value falls off very rapidly, complete destruction occurring within about three weeks. Moreover, under some conditions cod-liver oil is now known to have bad effects on animals. Attempts to stabilise the vitamin A in fish liver oils have been made and these preparations deteriorate less rapidly. It is therefore generally advisable to rely on young green material for meeting vitamin A requirements.

To ensure an adequate supply, it is necessary for the farmer to maintain a supply of fresh, leafy green stuff such as kale, clover, lucerne or grass throughout the year, and to have a reserve of high quality silage or dried grass. Foods that are rich in the vitamin need be given only in small amounts. Three ounces of really young leafy grass will meet the daily requirements of a growing pig and 2 to 3 lb. those of a milking cow.

During the summer and autumn, when green stuff is plentiful, animals are able to store both vitamin A and carotene in their livers and are able to fall back on these stores during periods when their diet is deficient in the vitamin—*e.g.* is composed largely of mangels, straw, corn and cake. Thus, if a calf, which has been running with its dam on pasture, is brought indoors in autumn and is given a ration completely free of the vitamin, it will have sufficient reserve to last for at least five months, Similarly, a pig, given a single large dose of a vitamin A concentrate at weaning, will store enough in its liver to last it until it reaches bacon weight. In milking animals, however, there is a steady drain on the reserves, so they become more rapidly exhausted. This does not mean that the cow will show symptoms of deficiency; in fact, it is necessary to feed a cow on carotene deficient rations for well over a year before failure of reproduction and a general breakdown of her health occurs. She may, however, give birth to a weak or dead or blind calf before she has begun herself to show symptoms of deficiency.

In general, young animals are born with very small reserves of vitamin A in their livers. Moreover, they appear to need more of the vitamin, in relation to their body weight, than do older ones; but they obtain a large amount of the vitamin from the colostrum of their dams, which is a much richer source than full lactation milk. The vitamin A potency of colostrum—due both to pre-formed vitamin A and to carotene—is influenced by the carotene content of the ration which the animal receives during pregnancy. Thus, after a long winter in which rations low in carotene content have been fed, the colostrum will have a low vitamin A value. It will thus be clear that the proper feeding of cows during pregnancy is of great importance from the point of view of the health and viability of the calf.

Vitamin A deficiency in young cattle is not uncommon in this country, and mostly occurs when rations of sugar beet pulp and poor straw are given together with carotene-poor concentrates. The main signs are failure to thrive, night blindness, and, later, total and incurable blindness due to damage to the optic nerves. In pigs, vitamin A deficiency leads to paralysis of the hind quarters and a staggering gait. In chicks, growth is retarded, the birds become weak and emaciated and the membranes of the mouth thickened and pustular. The eyes, too, are often seriously affected. In all animals secondary bacterial infections occur where the deficiency is prolonged, and these may lead to the death of the animal. In this connection there is a great deal of evidence to suggest that many calves, in the late winter, have subnormal reserves of vitamin A. It is possible that the high incidence of scours, pneumonia, and other transmissible calf diseases at this season may be accentuated by shortage of vitamin A.

*Vitamin D* was first identified as a substance, present in cod-liver oil, which was essential for the prevention of rickets. Vitamin D is, in fact, often called the anti-rachitic factor. It is now known that a number of plant and animal sterols, when exposed to the ultra-violet rays of sunlight, become potent as vitamin D. In all, there are at least ten different forms of vitamin D, the most important being vitamin $D_2$ (the form found in plant products such as sun-cured hay and irradiated yeast) and vitamin $D_3$, which is found in animal products, notably in fish oils, and indeed is formed in the animal body itself during exposure to ultra-violet light. The distinction between vitamins $D_2$ and $D_3$ is important because, while both have the same antirachitic value for the laboratory rat and other mammalian species, vitamin $D_3$ is far more effective than vitamin $D_2$ for poultry. Fish oils and irradiated animal sterols are thus much better sources of vitamin D for poultry than are irradiated plant materials.

Vitamin D itself is very sparsely distributed in animal feeding stuffs, but the sterols are fairly widely distributed. Fresh green foods contain very little vitamin D. For example, in rapidly growing pasture grass it is only small dead areas of leaf, which have been irradiated by the sun, which contain any. For the same reason artificially dried grass, not having been exposed to the sun, has a very low vitamin D content. On the other hand, sunshine and " sky-shine " irradiate the skins of animals running out of doors, and hence produce in them a supply of the vitamin. The problem of vitamin D deficiency thus concerns animals which are kept indoors and do not receive sun-cured foods. Obviously animals with very heavy coats, and, in particular, sheep have their skins protected from solar radiation. In winter, sheep receive very little if any vitamin D through sunshine. In this connection it should be noted that ordinary window glass does not allow the short wave-lengths of ultra-violet light to pass through it; and hence, though a building may be well lit, the glass-filtered light will not prevent rickets if the ration is free of vitamin D. Glass substitutes are, however, available which, provided they are kept clean, admit the ultra-violet light.

Unlike vitamin A, vitamin D is not very easily oxidised; in fact, vitamin D was discovered by bubbling oxygen through cod-liver oil, thus destroying vitamin A and leaving the vitamin D unimpaired. The vitamin D activity of hays does not therefore decline during storage, nor does the activity of vitamin D concentrates deteriorate when they are mixed with other feeds.

Rickets, the disease due to vitamin D deficiency, is characterised by a failure of the animal to lay down calcium and phosphorus in its bones. The cartilaginous material is not calcified, the bones become rubbery, so that bent and malformed limbs result. A typical example is bent leg in rams. Rickets, can, however, occur as the result of a deficiency of calcium or of phosphorus in the diet, and it is necessary to the understanding of bone growth to consider calcium, phosphorus and vitamin D together. When the ratio of calcium to phosphorus is abnormal, then vitamin D will often permit normal growth, whereas if the ratio is optimal it may be very difficult to demonstrate any requirement for vitamin D. Vitamin D is not a substitute for calcium and phosphorus, but it enables growth to take place under dietary conditions which would otherwise soon result in unsatisfactory bone formation. Hens given rations low in vitamin D produce fewer eggs of lowered hatchability, and the few eggs that are laid have very thin shells. In chicks, rickets is very common and can be recognised by the ungainly attidues that affected birds adopt to balance their bodies, and by their lame, stiff legged gait. The breast-bone is often bent and the beak becomes soft, rubbery and easily deformed.

*Vitamin E*, when first discovered, was found to be a dietary ingredient essential for the reproduction of the rat. Without it male rats developed permanent sterility, and in pregnant females the embryos degenerated and were reabsorbed. Experiments and practical tests have shown that with cattle, sheep and goats vitamin E, is apparently not concerned with reproduction. Pigs may require it for normal reproduction, and it is known that adult birds, if deprived of it, produce eggs which have a low hatchability.

Though not concerned with reproduction, the vitamin is nevertheless of importance in farm animal nutrition. Under certain conditions associated with rations low in vitamin E content, cattle and sheep develop a muscular disease called muscular dystrophy or " stiff-lamb disease," while poultry develop severe nervous and circulatory disturbances. Many of these muscular diseases and neural disturbances can also be prevented by a compound known as " Factor 3." This has been shown to be an organic compound containing selenium, and selenium as selenite is also effective. The amounts of selenium required are fantastically small, for they are measured in terms of parts per thousand million in diet. Deficiencies of selenium occur in Britain and can be reversed either by giving vitamin E or by giving selenium. One important aspect of the muscle disease in calves is that it follows dosing with cod-liver oil. Though cod-liver oil supplies vitamins A and D it contains unsaturated fatty acids which increase the animal's vitamin E requirements as much as fifty-fold. Small amounts of most proprietary concentrates of vitamins A and D do not have this effect. This is a further example of the complexity of interrelations between dietary constituents. Vitamin E is found in large amounts in green foods and, as with vitamin A, the chief danger of deficiency is in young animals born in the later winter to dams which have received poor rations throughout a considerable time.

*Vitamin K* is concerned with the maintenance of the clotting time of the blood. An animal deficient in this factor may bleed to death from a minor wound. The vitamin was discovered in experiments with chicks. In parts of North America poisoning of cattle by the substance dicoumarol which is present in the moulded lespedeza hay can be cured by giving vitamin K. Deficiency of the vitamin has not been recorded as a cause of losses in Britain.

**The Water-soluble Vitamins.**—*Vitamin C* is required only by guinea pigs, humans and the higher apes, where a lack causes scurvy. Farm animals and birds manufacture the vitamin in their bodies.

*Vitamin B Complex.*—The remaining water-soluble vitamins are all grouped under this one name, and in the last twenty years the number of members of this group has grown to twelve. There are probably others yet undiscovered. No member of the vitamin B complex is required by adult ruminants, the reason being that the micro-organisms of the rumen, besides transforming food proteins and breaking down the fibrous constituents of feeds, manufacture the vitamins of the B complex in sufficient amounts to meet the need of their host. Before the rumen of the young animal is fully established—*i.e.* while it is eating liquid food— it needs a source of these B complex vitamins in its ration, but once the rumen flora is established the need comes to an end. Recent experiments have shown that horses require some members of the vitamin B complex, but it does not appear likely that practical rations would ever be deficient in them. Hence pigs and poultry, and the farm dog, are the only farm animals ever likely to suffer from major deficiencies.

Some of the individual members of the vitamin B complex are listed in Table 7, which summarises what is known about their essentiality in the rations of pigs and poultry.

These requirements have been established by experiments in which highly artificial rations were fed—composed of highly purified feeds, such as raw starch and glucose. These experiments, while they have established that the pig and chick require these members of the vitamin B complex, give no indication of their importance under practical conditions of husbandry. In general, deficiencies of vitamins of the B complex in pigs and poultry are rare, though " curled-toe paralysis " and " perosis " in poultry do appear occasionally. The former is due to a deficiency of riboflavin in the ration, and for best results starting mashes for chicks should contain 5 to 10 per cent. dried whey or dried skim-milk powder, which are rich in riboflavin.

Vitamin $B_{12}$ is found in feeding stuffs of animal origin, such as meat and fish meals. It is also present in small amounts in the residues of the fermentations which lead to the synthesis of antibiotics. The residual antibiotics in these sources of vitamin $B_{12}$ can cause an increase in growth in pigs and chickens. The mode of action of the antibiotics is not precisely known but appears to be through the control of infections in the stock, some so mild that they cause no signs of ill health. It is certain that the poorer the hygienic conditions the greater the initial response to anti- biotics, and there is evidence that the response to them declines with their continued use over several years.

**Food Requirements.**—From what has been said it will be clear that animal nutrition is a very complex science. An animal requires in its food some eight or ten essential amino acids, about fifteen vitamins, and about the same number of essential mineral elements, as well as carbo- hydrates and fats as sources of energy. Ruminants, by virtue of the activity of their rumen flora, can dispense with some of these nutrients.

TABLE 7

THE VITAMIN B COMPLEX

| Vitamin | Other Names | Chief Signs of Deficiency as observed in Experiments | | Agricultural Importance |
|---------|-------------|------------------|---------|-------------------------|
| | | Pigs | Poultry | |
| neurin | $B_1$ | Loss of weight | Nervous disease (polyneuritis) causing abnormal posture | Of little importance, since cereals and millers' offals are rich in the vitamin |
| iboflavin | $B_2$ | Limb stiffness | Curled toe paralysis of chicks | Of importance for baby chicks which should receive some riboflavin supplement such as dried whey or dried skimmed milk if given simplified rations |
| icotinic acid | PP factor (Pellagra preventive) | Severe diarrhœa and loss of appetite | Inflammation of the mouth and darkening of the tongue | Deficiency has occurred in farm practice where rations are restricted to maize and maize products; but lack of the vitamin unlikely in normal practice |
| yridoxine | $B_6$ | Anæmia and fits | Convulsions | Deficiency in ordinary rations unlikely |
| antothenic acid | | Nervous disturbances and "goosestepping" | Failure of growth | Very unlikely to be absent from common farm rations |
| iotin | | Cracked hooves | Poor growth and skin disorders | Very unlikely to be deficient in farm rations |
| holine | | | Hock disorder called "perosis" | Unlikely to be deficient in farm rations |
| olic acid | | Anæmia | Anæmia and poor feather development | Very unlikely to be deficient in farm rations |
| obalamin | $B_{12}$ | Anæmia and poor growth when restricted to rations containing vegetable proteins only | Anæmia and poor growth when restricted to rations containing vegetable proteins only | Of importance as a constituent of the animal protein factor |

Of all these many requirements the one which is of primary importance is energy. It has been estimated that by far the main part of the economic loss that is due to faulty nutrition of farmstock results from failure to meet the animals' energy requirements. These are usually divided into maintenance and production requirements. The requirement for maintenance is the amount of energy the animal must expend on the various processes and reactions of the body which are essential to life. An animal is very unlike an internal combustion engine. When the latter is not being used it does not require fuel. When a milking cow is dry or when a steer is not growing or fattening, it still requires a source of energy to keep it " ticking over." The production requirement is the amount of energy which the animal needs, in addition to its maintenance demand, to support the production of milk, eggs, meat or fat, or to meet the energy lost to the body in muscular work.

Energy requirements are measured in terms of calories. One Calorie can be defined as the quantity of heat energy which is required to raise the temperature of 1 kg. of water 1° C. It is written with a capital C, or called the kilocalorie (kcal), to distinguish it from the " calorie," 1000 of which make up the kilocalorie. A thousand kilocalories make one megacalorie or therm.

The total or *gross energy* value of a feeding stuff, of a particular nutrient or, indeed, of a fuel, is expressed as the amount of heat which it produces when it is burnt completely, the carbon and hydrogen it contains being completely oxidised to carbon dioxide and water. The estimation is made in an apparatus known as a bomb calorimeter. A known amount of the material is placed in a steel bomb in an atmosphere of pure oxygen, and the bomb is placed in a known volume of water. The bomb is then fired electrically, the material burns, and the rise in temperature of the water is noted. The amount of heat given out can then be calculated. When pure fat is burned its calorific value is found to be 4·2 mcal. per lb. Pure starch gives a value of 1·86 mcal., linseed cake 2·1 mcal., and hays, straws and cereal meals about 1·8 mcal. per lb. Anthracite coal gives a value of about 3·6 mcal. per lb. It is obvious that these figures do not give very much indication of the value of the food to the animal, otherwise we would conclude that anthracite coal was a better feed than linseed cake, and that barley meal was about equal in feeding value to wheat straw. Gross energy values only state what energy the food contains; they give no information at all on the amount which the animal can obtain from it.

In the first place, only such portions of the food which can be digested by the animal furnish it with any useful energy. Those portions which appear in the fæces have not been digested. Furthermore, some substances are excreted by the body before they have been completely oxidised Thus the nitrogen contained in the digestible protein of the food is not excreted as gaseous nitrogen, but is locked up in compounds such as urea, hippuric acid and ammonia. These substances are incompletely oxidised and their excretion means a loss of energy to the animal. Again, the fermentations which take place in the rumen of the ox or sheep entail the production of combustible gases, mainly methane or marsh gas, and, under some conditions, hydrogen. This again represents a loss of energy to the animal. To obtain a measure of the useful energy which an animal obtains from its food it is necessary to deduct from the gross energy which it ingests the energy lost in the fæces, the urine and as combustible gas. The balance is called *metabolisable energy*, a term which is better than " useful " energy since, as will be explained later, not all of it can be used by the animal for meeting its requirements for maintenance or production.

The calculation of the metabolisable energy of a ration is made by collection of all the excreta, including the methane produced when an

TABLE 8

Food given

|  | $S_{23}$ ryegrass early cut | $S_{23}$ ryegrass late cut | Poor fescue hay | Flaked maize | Hay and oats 3:1 |
|---|---|---|---|---|---|
| Gross energy intake kcal. . | 100 | 100 | 100 | 100 | 100 |
| Loss in fæces kcal. . . | 17·5 | 37·4 | 45·6 | 9·0 | 35·5 |
| Loss in urine kcal. . . | 7·8 | 3·4 | 3·1 | 3·3 | 8·1 |
| Loss as methane kcal. . | 8·4 | 7·3 | 7·5 | 4·0 | 3·5 |
| Metabolisable energy kcal. . | 66·3 | 51·9 | 43·8 | 83·7 | 52·9 |

exact amount of food is given to an animal. Deduction of the energy losses in fæces, urine and as methane, from the food consumed gives the metabolisable energy. The extent of the losses of energy can be seen from Table 8, which applies to experiments with cattle and sheep.

It is clear that the proportion of the gross energy of food which is metabolised varies appreciably from food to food. Not all the metabolisable energy, however, can be used by the animal for productive processes or for meeting its maintenance requirement. A portion is always lost as heat. This is not surprising, because in the manufacture of milk by the cow, or the synthesis of fat and muscle, a great deal of internal work has to be done. The animal must spend part of the metabolisable energy in the work of prehension, mastication, digestion and assimilation of food, and a further part in the transference of absorbed nutrients to the tissues. Even there, the efficiency of the biochemical transformations involved in the making of new compounds is never a hundred per cent., so that there is a further wastage of dietary energy. The energy expended in the work of digestion and the losses entailed in metabolic transformations of metabolisable energy is eventually given up as heat. This heat may be of value, under certain conditions, for keeping the animal warm, but in general it is a waste product, and, indeed, in very hot weather, is a liability.

For each animal receiving a particular ration there is what is called a critical temperature. This is the air temperature at which the animal's normal body processes generate just sufficient heat to maintain its body temperature at the normal level. If the air temperature drops below this critical temperature, the animal then has to expend energy by shivering, in order to keep its body temperature at the normal level. When chicks huddle together or pigs crawl under their litter, it may be assumed that the air temperature has dropped below their critical temperature. With the adult pig on full feed the critical temperature is about 40° F., with bacon pigs about 55° C. If the temperature falls below these levels food energy is diverted from the usual path of laying down fat and protein in the body and is squandered by the animal merely to keep itself warm. Young pigs and baby chicks have much higher critical temperatures than adult pigs and hens, and thus it is important, when the weather is cold, to provide them with additional heat. The baby pig has a critical temperature of about 85° F. Ruminants, on the other hand, when given normal rations, have very low critical temperatures. Cow shed temperatures below freezing point have no effect on the utilisation of feed by cows. This is largely to be explained by the fact that the extensive fermentations which take place in the paunch produce a considerable amount of heat; thus, while a pig derives about 1500 kcal. from 1 lb. of barley meal, a cow or sheep loses, as heat, about 500 extra kcal. It is thus a mistake to suppose that feed can always be saved by keeping animals warm. This will happen only if the temperature of the surroundings drops to below the critical temperature, and is likely to occur only with pigs or poultry when poorly housed. It is true that, in severe winters, deaths of hill sheep do occur, but the deaths are largely due to the combination of starvation and cold; as the animals get less and less to eat, and thus have less and less waste heat available, the critical temperature rises. A fasting animal has a critical temperature which may be as much as 50° F. above that of one on a normal diet. Thus, if the critical temperature of the hill ewe rises and her reserves of energy in the form of body fat are exhausted, eventually she can no longer equate her heat production with heat losses, so the body temperature falls and she dies. The fleece provides much insulation and sheep with heavy fleeces can withstand severe cold. After shearing, however, and particularly if the sheep are very closely shorn, the critical temperature rises to about 70° F. Losses in weight of ewes after shearing can often be referred to cold weather at that time.

At the other end of the scale high air temperatures impose a considerable strain on the animal's means for getting rid of heat. At high environmental temperatures, cattle and sheep, which have poorly developed sweating mechanisms have to rely in part on the evaporation of water from their respiratory passages to keep themselves cool, and they pant vigorously. As air temperature still rises further the animal is unable to get rid of enough heat and the body temperature increases. This increase appears to result in an acceleration of many of the body processes, and the animal's expenditure of energy thus increases. The temperature at which this increase occurs is called the *point of hypothermal rise*, and between this temperature and the critical temperature is what is called the *range of thermal neutrality*. Within this range the animal's expenditure of energy is not affected by variation of air temperature. Just as a lowered food intake increases the critical temperature so, at the other end of the scale, a lowered intake raises the point of hypothermal rise. In other words, an animal on a high level of nutrition has a relatively poor heat tolerance. This is of considerable importance in tropical countries, since it means that, under hot, humid conditions, high levels of feeding cannot be achieved. Dairy cows imported from temperate regions deteriorate under these hot conditions and give little milk because they cannot maintain the food intake necessary for high milk yield and yet keep their body temperature normal. The tropical breeds of cattle are better equipped to get rid of surplus heat than are those of temperate regions.

If from the metabolisable energy we deduct the amount of energy lost in the form of heat as a result of (1) fermentation in the alimentary tract, (2) the work of digestion and (3) the inefficiency of metabolic transferences within the body, we obtain a difference which is known as *net energy*. The net energy per pound of food ingested is known as the *net energy value* of the food concerned. It represents the energy of the feed which the animal actually uses for maintenance of its vital processes or deposits as fat or protein in its body or secretes in its milk. The maintenance cost, in terms of net energy, is, however, a first charge on the total supply. Only the surplus is available for tissue growth, fat deposition or the production of milk or eggs.

The net energy values of some feeding stuffs and some pure nutrients are given below:—

TABLE 9

ENERGY VALUES IN MCAL. PER LB. AS DETERMINED
WITH FATTENING CATTLE

| Food | Gross Energy | Metabolisable Energy | Energy Lost as Heat | Net Energy Value |
|---|---|---|---|---|
| Earthnut oil | 3·99 | 3·99 | 1·74 | 2·25 |
| Wheat gluten | 2·63 | 2·14 | 1·18 | 0·96 |
| Starch | 1·86 | 1·67 | 0·69 | 0·98* |
| Maize meal | 1·80 | 1·35 | 0·52 | 0·83 |
| Timothy hay | 1·81 | 0·74 | 0·31 | 0·43 |
| Wheat straw | 1·85 | 0·58 | 0·47 | 0·11 |

* In more extensive experiments, Kellner found the average net energy value of starch to be 1·071 mcal. per lb.

It is clear from the table that the proportion of the metabolisable energy which is really of value to the animal as net energy, varies considerably from one feeding stuff to another. Although the gross energy value of wheat straw is slightly higher than that of maize, the fattening steer obtains only about one eighth as much net energy from straw as from maize.

The net energy values of feeding stuffs are not, however, the same for all animals. This was first shown by Oskar Kellner, a famous German nutritionist, who devised the system still used in Britain for the rationing of live stock, and which has since been extended by other workers. Kellner found that when he added 1 lb. of starch to the maintenance ration of a steer, the steer stored 0·25 lb. of body fat each day. Since the energy value of fat is about 4·28 mcal. per lb., the net energy value of starch for the steer was 1·07 mcal. per lb. When the same experiment was made with the pig, however, it was found that the net energy value was 1·50 mcal. per lb. The pig is therefore a much more efficient animal than the steer in utilising the energy of materials such as starch. This difference in efficiency reflects the differences between the digestive process of the two species. The pig has a simple digestive system well adapted to the utilisation of concentrated foods, while the digestive process of cattle involves a massive bacterial fermentation of feeds prior to their digestion lower down the alimentary canal. This bacterial fermentation, though well adapted to make the greatest use of coarse fibrous foods, necessarily wastes a good deal of the energy of easily digestible materials such as starch. The difference in efficiency in the utilisation of starch by the pig and steer does not mean the pig is, in general, superior as a food converter. The opposite conclusion would have been reached if a feed containing 12 to 15 per cent. of crude fibre had been used in the experiment.

Since the net energy value of a feed is the difference between the metabolisable energy it supplies and the expenditure of energy involved in its assimilation, it will be clear that, if the expenditure of energy exceeds the supply, the net energy will be a negative quantity. Such values have been found with sawdust and peat moss. Wheat straw has very little value for ruminants, and for horses is worse than useless, since the horse expends far more energy in eating and digesting it than the straw yields in metabolisable form.

The basis of live stock rationing in Britain is the net energy system outlined above, but energy values are expressed in other units, viz., in terms of a reference substance, starch, rather than as kilogram Calories. The *starch equivalent* of a feeding stuff thus represents the number of pounds of pure starch which would have to be fed to an animal to give the same practical result, in terms of fat deposition, as 100 lb. of the feeding stuff. The starch equivalent system was devised by Kellner, and is essentially the basis of most Continental systems of rationing, such as the feed unit systems of Scandinavian countries.

The determination of the starch equivalents of feeding stuffs is a difficult task. Kellner determined them by experiments with fattening steers in an apparatus which enabled him to measure the storage, by a steer, of both carbon and nitrogen. This was done by confining the steer in a respiration chamber, measuring the carbon lost in dung and urine, and calculating the carbon content of the carbon dioxide lost in respiration and also in the methane produced by fermentation. From the results Kellner calculated the amount of fat stored by the steer when a particular feed was given as an addition to a maintenance ration. He thus found that the addition to the maintenance ration of 10 lb. of linseed cake resulted in the formation of as much fat as was produced from 7·4 lb. of starch. Hence, expressed per 100 lb., the starch equivalent of linseed cake is 74. In the early years of the present century Kellner worked out many starch equivalents, but later realised that a more simple method of determination was needed. He therefore devised a method for calculating the starch equivalent of a feeding stuff from its content of digestible nutrients, *i.e.* from the amount of digestible protein, digestible ether extract and digestible carbohydrates it contained. The energy value of the above nutrients were found to be as follows:—

1. Each pound of digested crude protein supplies as much energy as 0·94 lb. of starch.
2. Each pound of digested carbohydrates supplies the same amount of energy as 1 lb. of starch.
3. Each pound of digested ether extract supplies as much energy as 1·91, 2·12, or 2·41 lb. of starch, the different values being alloted to allow for the varying composition of the ether extract of different feeds. The highest factor applies to oil seeds containing much true fat, and the lowest to hays and straws in which the ether extract is mainly pigment and resins. The intermediate figure applies to cereals.

When Kellner applied these factors to the digested nutrients of feeding stuffs and compared the calculated starch equivalent with his experimental observations made in the respiration chamber, he found that the results failed to agree. The calculated figure was always greater than that actually determined by calorimetry. The difference was greatest in the case of fibrous foods—hay, straw and other coarse fodders—when the calculated figures were often as much as 40 per cent. too high. The reason for this is now known to be concerned with the nature of the fermentation process elicited by the different rations. Roughages give rise to large proportions of acetic acid in the fermentation products in the rumen while concentrated foods tend to produce mixtures of acids comparable to those found when starch is given. Acetic acid is less efficiently used to synthesise fat than are the other fatty acids. To overcome this difficulty Kellner therefore devised two sets of correction factors. One he called

P

" V factors," to be applied to meals and grains. These are simple percentage values indicating the discrepancy between calculated and observed results. Thus a V factor of 97 for linseed cake means that the true starch equivalent of linseed cake is only 97 per cent. of the calculated value. The other corrections for roughages he based on a sliding scale to take into account the fibre content, making a deduction from the calculated figure for each 1 per cent. of fibre in the material. For fresh green fodder the factor used was 0·29, and for the mature hays and straws 0·58. The following example shows how the starch equivalent of a sample of ryegrass hay may be arrived at:—

| | | |
|---|---|---|
| Digestible protein, 4·9 per cent. × 0·94 . . . . | = | 4·61 |
| „ fibre and nitrogen free extract, 41·5 per cent. × 1·00 . . . . . . . . | = | 41·50 |
| „ ether extract, 1·4 per cent. × 1·91 . . . | = | 2·67 |
| | | 48·78 |

*Correction—*
| | | |
|---|---|---|
| Fibre content = 22·9 per cent. × 0·58 . . . . | = | 13·28 |
| *Starch equivalent per* 100 *lb.* . | | 35·50 |

Tables in the Appendix (pp. 783 to 790) give the starch equivalent, protein equivalent and average content of digestible nutrients of most of the common feeding stuffs of the farm.

Most of the starch equivalents used in Britain for live stock feeding have been calculated in this manner; indeed until recent years no direct determinations of starch values had been made in Britain. It must be remembered that the foods used by Kellner in Germany fifty years ago may have been rather widely different from those in Britain to-day. We have new crop varieties, and some new crops such as sugar and fodder beets, new farm processes such as grass drying and modern ensilage. Again, the factory by-products now available for feeding have been more highly processed than those of fifty years ago. It is thus not surprising that many writers have criticised the starch equivalent system, often because they have expected the calculated figures to be more precise than, in fact, they pretend to be. Calculated values are not precise, but the results of practical feeding trials conform fairly closely to expectations based on the book values.

The starch equivalents calculated in the manner given above estimate the values of feeding stuffs to ruminants. As already pointed out, pigs and poultry will make better use than ruminants of some feeds. Armsby for instance, found the net energy value of maize for fattening cattle to be 85 mcal. per 100 lb. and for the pig 120 mcal. It would, of course, be useful to have a separate set of starch equivalents for pigs and poultry, but in general it has been found that the *relative* values of feeding stuffs are approximately the same for different classes of stock. Thus experiments with pigs show the starch equivalent of potatoes to be 20 per cent. of that of maize, while experiments with cattle show potatoes to have 23 per cent. of the value of maize. Obviously hay and straw, which ruminants can and pigs and poultry cannot use, could not be expected to conform to this generalisation, but, for all but fibrous foods, starch equivalents determined with cattle can be used in the computing of rations for other classes of farm stock without incurring too great an error. Data obtained through digestibility trials with pigs are given in the Appendix (p. 790).

It is quite clear that starch equivalents are *estimates* of the amount of energy that animals obtain from particular feeding stuffs. The energy requirements of particular animals are estimates also and can be expected to apply only to the average individual. Two animals may be exactly the same size, yet one may require more food than the other to maintain itself and make a given amount of growth. This is understandable, for one may be a placid individual taking very little exercise and the other a highly strung creature dissipating much more energy in body movement or nervous tension. Again one animal may be making gains containing a great deal of muscle and the other may be laying down a greater proportion of fat. Gains in weight can vary very widely in composition and hence very different amounts of food may be needed to produce the same daily gain. It must be emphasised that a system of rationing according to theoretical requirements is no more than an aid to good stockmanship. Precise rationing of animals according to feeding tables will, on average, give good results; but the knowledgeable stockman realises the inevitable margin of error and makes minor adjustments in the ration of individual animals. Rationing, if done intelligently, prevents waste of food. For example, it was common farm practice, fifty years ago, to feed fattening bullocks enormous quantities of high-protein cakes. Much of this protein was surplus to the animals' needs, and the nitrogen it contained was simply excreted in the urine. Knowledge of energy and protein requirements and values has enabled this waste to be avoided.

In rationing farm stock the primary object is so to adjust the energy and protein supply to enable the animal to realise something near its potential level of production and to avoid waste. As said previously, mineral and vitamin requirements must also be provided for.

**Energy Requirements for Maintenance.**—The maintenance energy requirement of an animal is made up of two parts: the basal or minimal metabolism, and the activity allowance. Basal metabolism measures the heat lost by an animal when it receives no food at all and is lying in a state of complete rest. Very few determinations of it have been made with farm animals. Muscular activity increases the animal's energy loss—even standing without movement increases heat production by

15 per cent. while short bursts of activity such as galloping or struggling increase it as much as threefold or fourfold. In stall fed cattle provision for basal metabolism normally accounts for about 70 per cent. of the total maintenance cost. It has been found by controlled experiments, and confirmed by feeding trials, that the average maintenance requirement (including both the basal allowance and that for activity) of a 1000 lb. ox under conditions of close confinement is 6 lb. starch equivalent per day. This value is only an average, and individual oxen weighing 1000 lb. may have maintenance requirements as much as 25 per cent. more or

TABLE 10

MAINTENANCE REQUIREMENTS OF GROWING AND
FATTENING CATTLE

| Live Weight (lb.) | Maintenance Energy Requirement (lb. Starch Equivalent per Day) | Maintenance Protein Requirement (lb. Protein Equivalent per Day) |
|---|---|---|
| 300 | 2·8 | 0·25 |
| 400 | 3·3 | 0·32 |
| 500 | 3·8 | 0·36 |
| 600 | 4·2 | 0·42 |
| 700 | 4·7 | 0·47 |
| 800 | 5·1 | 0·51 |
| 900 | 5·5 | 0·55 |
| 1000 | 6·0 | 0·60 |
| 1100 | 6·5 | 0·65 |
| 1200 | 6·9 | 0·69 |
| 1300 | 7·3 | 0·73 |
| 1400 | 7·7 | 0·77 |
| 1500 | 8·1 | 0·81 |
| 1600 | 8·5 | 0·85 |

less. Obviously, on average, animals heavier than 1000 lb. will require more and lighter animals less. It has been shown by a careful study of the records made with many species that basal metabolism varies not directly with the body weight but with body weight raised to the power 0·73. The live weight to the power of 0·73 is called " metabolic body size." It is a mathematical expression of the general finding that basal metabolism is roughly proportional to the animal's surface area, i.e. the area from which it radiates heat. This generalisation applies, however, to mature animals only and to basal metabolism only. It does not permit any reliable estimates to be made, by simple arithmetic, of the maintenance requirements of very young animals. Young growing animals tend to have much higher maintenance requirements than would be estimated from their " metabolic body size." Thus the maintenance energy requirement of a mature sheep weighing 100 lb. is approximately 1200 kcal. per day, or 1·1 lb. starch equivalent per day, whereas a young calf of the same weight has a maintenance requirement of 1950 kcal. A young calf only one tenth the weight of an adult cow has a maintenance energy requirement of about one third that of the adult. With adult animals, however, it is fairly safe to use the metabolic body size in computing requirements. Even here, however, it appears that Jersey cows require more maintenance energy in propotrion to their metabolic size than do larger breeds. Indeed, it seems necessary to use slightly more liberal allowances for milking cattle than for others.

TABLE 11

MAINTENANCE REQUIREMENTS OF ADULT MILKING COWS
OF AVERAGE SIZE

| Breed | Maintenance Energy Requirement (lb. Starch Equivalent per Day) | Maintenance Protein Requirement (lb. Protein Equivalent per Day) |
|---|---|---|
| Jersey | 5·5 | 0·51 |
| Guernsey | 6·3 | 0·55 |
| Ayrshire | 6·5 | 0·60 |
| Shorthorn | 7·4 | 0·70 |
| Freisian | 7·6 | 0·70 |

With sheep there are very few estimates of maintenance requirements, but recent experiments suggest that the older results are approximately correct. As with cattle, there are undoubtedly breed differences in maintenance requirement. Hill ewes doubtless expend more energy than a folded flock in searching for their food. The following table gives estimates of requirements for the maintenance of sheep:—

TABLE 12

| Live Weight (lb.) | Maintenance Energy Requirement (lb. Starch Equivalent per Day) | Maintenance Protein Requirement (lb. Protein Equivalent per Day) |
|---|---|---|
| 60 | 0·73 | 0·08 |
| 80 | 0·90 | 0·10 |
| 100 | 1·07 | 0·12 |
| 120 | 1·23 | 0·14 |
| 140 | 1·38 | 0·16 |
| 160 | 1·52 | 0·17 |
| 200 | 1·79 | 0·20 |

Under present day conditions in Britain these figures are of no more than academic interest since the accurate rationing of sheep, even on a group basis, is impracticable. In moving sheep from one pasture field to another, or in settling off an area of forage crop for, say, a week's consumption, or again in deciding whether, or how much, supplementary food should be offered, the farmer or the shepherd must be guided by experience, and by the appetite, bodily condition and general behaviour of the sheep.  It is only where sheep are housed in winter, or fed in " dry lot," that any system of rationing can be applied.

With pigs there have been many experiments, notably at Cambridge, in Denmark and in Germany, in which maintenance requirements have been determined in calorimeters and respiration chambers.  Their practical value is not very great since most pigs grow too rapidly to allow adjustment of their rations on the basis of calculated maintenance requirements. The all meal system aims to provide the pig with a ration containing about 70 lb. starch equivalent per 100 lb. of dry matter, and the daily allowance of meal is periodically adjusted to appetite.  In the later stages of fattening for bacon some restriction of feed is often necessary to the production of good carcass quality, without excessive fat.  With the Lehmann feeding system, the rationing is based on a restricted ration of meal containing sufficient protein and minerals to balance a bulky supplement of potatoes, fodder beet or kitchen waste, which is fed to appetite.

With farm horses the basal metabolism is roughly the same as for cattle of equivalent weight, and the requirement for normal activity, when the horse is not working, is also about the same.  The horse tends to make slightly better use of its feed, for maintenance, than does the ox, largely because fermentative losses are not so great.

**Protein Requirements for Maintenance.**—The requirement of animals for protein is largely accounted for by their need for amino acids to manufacture the proteins of new tissues or of milk.  But animals that are neither growing nor producing milk need protein to replace the nitrogen containing constituents of the tissues, which are constantly being broken down.  An animal on a protein free ration loses nitrogen from its body.  On such a ration nitrogen is found in the faeces, partly in the residues of digestive juices, and partly in the millions of cells that are abraded day by day from the walls of the digestive tract.  Similarly, losses occur in the form of scurf and hair.  The nitrogen in the urine represents the inevitable loss of cell constituents incidental to the normal processes of the body cells.  Maintenance requirements of protein are measured by feeding animals protein free or protein low rations and measuring the total losses of nitrogen from the body.  The figure so obtained represents the minimal requirement of the animal which, for an adult steer weighing 1000 lb., amounts to about 0·2 lb. protein per day.  But the amount of food protein required to prevent this loss is considerably higher, viz. 0·5 to 0·6 lb. of protein equivalent per day. As in the case of basal energy requirements, protein requirements for maintenance are proportionate to metabolic body size and not directly to the body weight.  By contrast with the maintenance energy requirement, however, muscular activity has no effect on maintenance protein requirements provided that sufficient energy is provided in the form of carbohydrate and fat.  Tables 10, 11 and 12 on pages 452 and 453 give the maintenance requirements in terms of protein equivalent of cattle and sheep. Obviously the production of wool by the sheep—containing about some 2 or 3 oz. of pure protein per week—necessitates an additional requirement. Allowance is made in the tables for this extra demand.

**Production Requirements.**—(1) *Energy.*—By definition, 1000 kcal. of net energy (0·94 lb. of starch equivalent) fed to a fattening ox will result in the deposition of 1000 kcal. in the form of fat. This is equivalent to about 4 oz. of pure fatty tissue. The production of 1 lb. of fat in a mature steer thus requires nearly 4 lb. starch equivalent. Fat is not only stored in fat " deposits," *e.g.* the subcutaneous layer and the " caul," but also in the muscles, and without any concomitant storage of water. Hence the deposition of 1 lb. of fat means also 1 lb. of live weight increase. But in animals that are both growing and fattening it is only in the last stages of fattening that 1 lb. of live weight gain represents the gain of 1 lb. of fat. In growing animals part of the energy of the food that is surplus to maintenance is used in the building up of body tissues. Moreover, when protein is laid down in muscles and other tissues it is accompanied by about four times its weight of water. Thus we find that, in young calves, the live weight gain contains only some 10 to 15 per cent. of fat, the remainder being distributed between ash (about 10 per cent.) and protein (15 per cent.), with as much as 65 per cent. of water. The energy value of 1 lb. of live weight gain thus varies widely—between about 800 kcal. in animals growing and laying down muscle and bone, and 4000 kcal. in fully grown fattening animals. Indeed, the energy value of 1 lb. of grain may be actually higher than the value of 4000 kcal. since, in the last stages of fattening, added fat may replace body protein or body water. Hence the amount of starch equivalent required to produce 1 lb. of live weight gain will vary from less than 1 lb. to fully 4 lb. A rough estimate of the requirement per pound of live weight gain can, however, be based on the age of the animal and the rate of live weight gain. Thus a young calf, growing but not fattening, has the lowest requirement. An older animal, being maintained in store condition, will need rather more. A fattening beast requires more in the later than in the early stages of fattening. In Table 13 account is taken of all these variables.

With pigs the same general principles apply but, as mentioned earlier, it is usual to express requirements in terms of total " meal " per day. Requirements are discussed in Chapter 24.

Again, in the case of milk it will be obvious that account must be taken of the variable composition of the product: for example, more food energy will be needed to produce a milk containing 5 per cent. of fat than one containing only 3 per cent. A gallon of milk with 4 per cent. of fat has a calorific value of 3400 kcal., which would suggest a requirement of about 3 lb. starch equivalent. In fact, the need is less because the conversion of energy into milk is more efficient than conversion into live weight gain. The usual recommendation is 2·5 lb. starch equivalent for.

each gallon of average milk containing 3·75 per cent. fat. But practical experience and also experimental evidence indicate that somewhat higher amounts lead to better sustained yields. The best value to use under

TABLE 13

### REQUIREMENTS OF RUMINANTS FOR GROWTH AND FATTENING

*Normal growth without fattening* (growing dairy stock and lambs destined for breeding)—

| CATTLE | | SHEEP | |
|---|---|---|---|
| Age (months) | Lb. S.E. per lb. Live Weight Gain | Age | Lb. S.E. per lb. Live Weight Gain |
| 0 to 3 | 1¼ | 0 to 3 | 1¼ |
| 3 „ 6 | 1½ | 3 „ 6 | 1¾ |
| 6 „ 12 | 2 | 6 „ 12 | 2¼ |
| 12 „ 24 | 2¼ | | |

*Fattening of young cattle and sheep* (baby beeves, fattening lambs and young fattening tegs)—

| | | |
|---|---|---|
| Early stages of fattening . | . | 2 lb. S.E. per lb. live weight gain. |
| Later „ „ . | . | 3 „ „ „ |

*Fattening of older cattle and sheep* (cattle of 2½ years or over, including old cows; sheep over 9 months, including old ewes)—

| | | |
|---|---|---|
| Early stages . . . | . | 2¼ lb. S.E. per lb. live weight gain. |
| Middle . . . | . | 3 „ „ „ |
| Late „ . | . | 3½ to 4 „ „ „ |

present circumstances is 2·7 lb. S.E. for milk containing 3·5 to 4·0 per cent. fat. The amounts of starch equivalent given below are higher than those usually recommended (see p. 500).

*Energy and Protein Requirements for Milk Production*

| Fat-content of Milk (per cent.) | | | Lb. Starch Equivalent (per gallon) | Lb. Protein Equivalent (per gallon) |
|---|---|---|---|---|
| 3·00 to 3·50 | . | . | 2·4 | 0·48 |
| 3·50 „ 4·00 | . | . | 2·7 | 0·55 |
| 4·00 „ 4·50 | . | . | 3·0 | 0·62 |
| 4·50 „ 5·00 | . | . | 3·2 | 0·69 |
| 5·00 „ 5·50 | . | . | 3·5 | 0·76 |
| 5·50 „ 6·00 | . | . | 3·7 | 0·83 |

Even so, intakes of starch equivalent higher than the standards suggested above will result in higher milk production. Much recent experimental work has shown that high planes of nutrition, entailing feeding at levels above those given by feeding standards, will result in substantial increases in milk yield and, incidentally, in body weight. Many of the high average yields of individual dairy herds may be traced to the very high levels of feeding which are employed, but high levels of feeding may not always be profitable.  In general, however, it should be remembered that levels of feeding above the accepted standards are bound to give some increase in milk yield since the law of diminishing returns applies to milk production; but experience has shown that it may take nine months, or perhaps longer, before the effects of a large increase in the feeding level are reflected in an overall economic gain of milk.  A good working rule to apply under present circumstances of food costs and milk prices is to endeavour to feed up to 3·0 lb. S.E. per gallon of milk in early lactation when yield exceeds 45 to 50 lb. per day, and to reduce this allowance to 2·2 lb. S.E. per gallon for cows giving less than 2·0 gallons per day.

For work production there are no reliable figures, and the following are rough guides to feeding working horses:—

*Requirements for Working Horses*

| | Starch Equivalent Required per Working Hour (per 1000 lb. body weight) |
|---|---|
| Light slow work . . . . | $\frac{3}{4}$ |
| Medium slow work . . . | 1 |
| Heavy slow work . . . | $1\frac{1}{4}$ |
| „ fast work . . . . | $1\frac{1}{2}$ |

(2) *Protein.*—The amount of protein required for productive purposes is determined by much the same factors that apply in the case of energy. If the live weight gain is largely protein, as it is in the case of a young and rapidly growing calf, then relatively more protein will be needed than in that of an adult fattening beast, which is storing up little except fat.  As the young animal grows, it, of course, has a rising maintenance requirement but a proportionately smaller need for the build up of tissue.  These two opposites almost cancel out, so that, for instance in the case of growing dairy cattle, a constant daily allowance of 0·9 lb. protein equivalent per head will cover the daily requirement from an age of about five or six months (3 cwt. live weight) to maturity.  A constant allowance of 0·9 lb. protein equivalent over this weight range, having regard to rising energy needs, thus implies a widening of the nutritive ratio of the ration as the animal gets older.  The nutritive ratio may be expressed as that between protein equivalent and the starch equivalent in the ration as a whole. The same figure applies to fattening cattle, good results having been obtained on a daily allowance of 0·9 lb.  In practice, however, more than this amount of protein is ordinarily given, because rations with very wide nutritive ratios are rather unpalatable.  The figure of 0·9 lb. should thus be regarded as a minimum.  A higher allowance will do no harm, and although it may increase the cost of the ration it will often be necessary if the desired level of food consumption is to be attained.  An allowance of less than 0·9 lb. may retard growth.

With sheep and lambs the same general principles apply, and a constant allowance of 0·2 lb. protein equivalent per head per day will suffice for maintenance, growth and fattening in lambs and tegs of ordinary size.

Turning to the dairy cow, it has been shown that milk of high fat content also has a high protein content. Hence the protein allowance per gallon, must vary with the fat content of the milk. In the past it has been customary to feed 0·6 lb. protein equivalent per gallon of average composition; but extensive feeding trials have shown that this figure can be reduced to 0·5 lb. without causing any significant fall in yield. These results may indeed reflect the " margin of safety " in the maintenance part of the ration. A standard of 0·55 lb. P.E. per gallon appears to be a reasonable compromise.

**Appetite.**—There is a fairly definite limit to the amount of food that an animal can eat in a day or at a meal. On the other hand, there is a minimum required to satisfy the appetite. Too bulky a ration will simply be refused, while a too concentrated one, besides not being sufficient to satisfy the animal's hunger, may result in digestive disturbances. The bulk of a ration is usually measured by its dry matter content, but this measure is not entirely satisfactory. Animals will, in general, eat more of high quality foods than of low quality fibrous ones. It is probable that " space-filling " is better measured by the content of indigestible residues, or " ballast," than by dry matter content. The former measure is used on the Continent, but it is not the ideal one. In this country we commonly express appetite, and the need for bulk, in terms of dry matter, recognising, however, the limitations of this measure. For cattle and horses the lower limit is about 15 lb. dry matter per 1000 lb. live weight daily, while normal rations may, in general, contain up to 25 lb. Dairy cows tend to have larger appetites than other classes of cattle; in fact, some very heavy milkers can consume as much as 40 lb. dry matter daily if the total amount is divided into four or five meals and the stockman caters for individuals' preferences. Lean store stock can also deal with slightly more than the usual 3 lb. of dry matter per cwt. of live weight, which is the commonly accepted figure in their case. For sheep 2½ to 3 lb. dry matter per 100 lb. live weight per day is a normal intake. With pigs a good rule is to arrange for the starch equivalent of the ration to be three-quarters of the dry matter content. Pigs will eat about 4½ lb. dry matter per day per 100 lb. body weight when weaned at two months old, decreasing to about 3 lb. as they reach bacon weight.

In general, appetite is expressed per 100 lb. of live weight. But the figures quoted above do not apply to the young calf or to other animals at the suckling stage. These must have a diet of high energy value in relation to its bulk, *i.e.* composed largely of concentrated and easily digested materials, if full growth is to be secured.

There are many other factors which must be taken into account in the practical rationing of animals. The acceptability of foods is one which is often ignored but is of considerable importance. When strange foods are introduced they are often refused by some individuals. Certain breeds, such as the Jersey, tend to be more than ordinarily fastidious. The effect of the feed on the health of the animal is another matter. Unsterilised bone flour might possibly introduce anthrax spores and cause disease, while there is much farming experience to suggest that some feeds are conducive to fertility or, conversely, result in poor reproductive performance. The latter opinion, however, has not been sufficiently examined experimentally. Some foods, such as rice meal and maize, result in the production of too soft a fat in bacon pigs, while others produce a milk fat that is too hard or too soft for butter making. Other feeds, such as turnips and molassed sugar beet pulp, can cause taints in milk. Again, some feeds, such as cotton cake, have a costive action and thus may find a use at particular times when the major part of the ration is too laxative. Conversely, linseed cake is laxative.

Hence, in drawing up rations, it is not enough to adjust the starch equivalent and protein equivalent to the calculated requirements. Individual animals do not conform closely to general rules.

The following examples illustrate the application of the principles set out above.

1. *Daily Winter Ration of a Rapidly Growing Dairy Heifer Twelve Months Old weighing 500 lb.*—The appetite of this animal will be about 14·5 lb. dry matter. For maintenance it will require 3·8 lb. starch equivalent. Normal growth will be about $1\frac{1}{2}$ lb. daily, implying a further 3 lb. starch equivalent and giving a total of 6·8 lb. Protein requirements will be 0·9 lb. If mangels, hay and dredge corn (equal parts oats and beans) are available, the calculation would be:—

| | Starch Equivalent lb. |
|---|---|
| *Energy supply—* | |
| 20 lb. mangels (starch equivalent=6·2) . . . . | =1·24 |
| 12 ,, good hay (starch equivalent=37) . . . . | =4·44 |
| 1 ,, oats (starch equivalent=60) . . . . . | =0·60 |
| 1 ,, beans (starch equivalent=66) . . . . | =0·66 |
| Total . | 6·94 |

| | Protein Equivalent lb. |
|---|---|
| *Protein supply—* | |
| 20 lb. mangels (protein equivalent=0·4) . . . . | =0·08 |
| 12 ,, hay (protein equivalent=4·7) . . . . | =0·56 |
| 1 ,, oats (protein equivalent=7·6) . . . . | =0·08 |
| 1 ,, beans (protein equivalent=19·7) . . . . | =0·20 |
| Total . | 0·92 |

The total dry weight of the ration can be calculated to be 14½ lb. daily. The above ration could then be fed for a period and later be adjusted according to the results secured.

2. *Ration for a Friesian Cow giving* 4 *gal. of Milk containing* 3·75 *per cent. Fat.*—The requirements of the cow would be:—

|  | Starch Equivalent (lb. per day) | Protein Equivalent (lb. per day) |
|---|---|---|
| Maintenance for 1250 lb. live weight | 7·6 | 0·70 |
| Production (2·7 lb. starch equivalent and 0·55 lb. protein equivalent per gallon) . . . . . | 10·8 | 2·20 |
| Total . | 18·4 | 2·90 |

The appetite of this cow will probably be about 3 lb. of dry matter per cwt., *i.e.* 33 lb. daily. Under present-day conditions it is commonly advisable to feed bulky home grown foods for part of the production ration as well as the maintenance ration. A suitable ration would be:—

|  | Starch Equivalent lb. |
|---|---|
| *Energy supply* | |
| 20 lb. marrowstem kale (starch equivalent 9) . . . | =1·80 |
| 20 „ arable silage (starch equivalent 12) . . . . | =2·40 |
| 15 „ good meadow hay (starch equivalent 37) . . . | =5·55 |
| 6 „ crushed oats (starch equivalent 60) . . . . | =3·60 |
| 4 „ cracked beans (starch equivalent 66) . . . | =2·64 |
| 2 „ dried sugar beet pulp (starch equivalent 61) . . | =1·22 |
| ½ „ decorticated groundnut meal (starch equivalent 73) . | =0·36 |
| 1 „ flaked maize (starch equivalent 84) . . . . | =0·84 |
|  | 18·41 |

|  | Protein Equivalent lb. |
|---|---|
| *Protein supply*— | |
| 20 lb. marrowstem kale (protein equivalent 1·3) . . . | =0·26 |
| 20 „ arable silage (protein equivalent 2·0) . . . . | =0·40 |
| 15 „ good meadow hay (protein equivalent 4·6 . . . | =0·69 |
| 6 „ crushed oats (protein equivalent 7·6) . . . | =0·45 |
| 4 „ cracked beans (protein equivalent 19·7) . . . | =0·79 |
| 2 „ dried sugar beet pulp (protein equivalent 5) . . | =0·10 |
| ½ „ decorticated groundnut meal (protein equivalent 41) . | =0·20 |
| 1 „ flaked maize (protein equivalent 9) . . . | =0·09 |
|  | 2·98 |
|  | 2·98 |

In practice the purchased sugar beet pulp, decorticated groundnut meal (or cake), and flaked maize would be mixed with the home grown oats and beans, 2 per cent. of a mineral mixture added and the whole fed at the rate of 4 lb. per gal. for milk produced above the first gallon daily. The ration of marrowstem kale, silage and hay would be sufficient for cows producing one gallon only. The physical condition of the concentrate mixture might be rather fluffy, a difficulty that could be overcome by adding some heavier material such as maize gluten feed or palm kernel cake; both of these are approximately balanced for milk production.

CHAPTER 19

## CATTLE—TYPES AND BREEDS

THE term cattle, originally used to include all classes of live stock, is now generally restricted to oxen, which are included by zoologists in the genus *Bos*. This genus comprises the wild and domesticated buffaloes of Asia, and some two or three wild African species of buffalo; the American and the European Bison; the Yak of Tibet; three species of Asiatic cattle—the Gaur, Gayal and Banteng—all of which are found wild, while the last two are also kept under domestication; the domesticated humped cattle (Zebus) of Asia and Africa; and lastly our European domesticated types. The buffaloes do not cross with the others in the list, but these others cross freely, and the hybrids (or at least the female hybrids) are fertile.

Domesticated cattle are known to have existed in Babylon as early as 5000 B.C. The earliest known domesticated type found in Europe is that known as *Bos taurus brachyceros* or *Bos longifrons*, a very small, slightly built ox with short horns, which was very widespread in the earliest Neolithic (polished stone) period. There is no evidence that it was evolved in Europe, and the accepted view is that it was introduced from Asia as an already long-domesticated animal. This type, sometimes known as the " Celtic Shorthorn," persisted in Britain till Roman times, but on the Continent it was displaced much earlier by a large, strong-boned and long-horned animal known as *Bos taurus primigenius*. This seems to have been produced either by crossing the older form with the native wild species or perhaps by direct domestication of the latter, the old type being meanwhile discarded. The European wild Ox or Urus (*Bos primigenius*) was common in Europe during the Roman period, and the last known specimen was killed in Poland in 1627. It was a very large and powerfully built animal with long horns, and probably brown in colour.

European cattle comprise a great variety of types. Quasi-zoological classifications of these types have been proposed, but none is very satisfactory. As regards the British breeds, they are of very varied and frequently of mixed ancestry. Thus the native cattle before the Roman invasion were small, black or brown in colour, with short horns (*Bos brachyceros*). The Jersey, Kerry and Shetland probably show the largest proportion of this blood. Then, according to Professor Wilson, the Romans brought in large white animals whose descendants have been preserved as the " wild " white cattle of Cadzow, Vaynol and Chartley,

462

now known as Park Cattle. According to another view these park cattle are the direct descendants of the wild Urus. It is certain that the Anglo-Saxons brought over cattle which were probably red in colour and from which the Sussex and the Devon are presumably descended. Possibly the Norse invasions gave us our polled breeds, though occasional polled animals occurred before that time. Much more recently, in the seventeenth century particularly, there was an introduction of large, short-horned and broken-coloured cattle from the Netherlands. These have had a large influence on the Shorthorn and Ayrshire, and probably a lesser influence on several other of our breeds.[1] These types of cattle have intermixed to a considerable extent, just as Celt and Saxon, Norman and Dane have intermixed to form our human population.

For practical purposes we classify cattle according to the object or objects for which they are kept, *i.e.* for labour, beef, milk, or any two, or all three. In Britain, oxen are not used for work purposes, and therefore our classification is into beef, dual-purpose and dairy types. As a matter of fact there is a gradation of types from the Jersey, which is of practically no value as a beef animal, to certain strains of Shorthorns, Herefords and other breeds which have been selected almost entirely on beef points and which produce only enough milk to rear their calves (perhaps 200 to 300 gal.) or sometimes less. Specialisation has been carried further in Britain and America than in most other countries. On the Continent of Europe a considerable majority of breeds may be said to be dual-purpose or triple-purpose, and purely beef breeds are few and relatively unimportant.

We must endeavour to analyse as far as possible the qualities that constitute merit in a beef or in a milking animal. The breeder's ideal is not simply a high quality of meat or a large yield of milk, but beef or milk in such quantity and of such quality, produced at low unit cost, and which will leave a reasonable profit to the farmer. Our aim in breeding must therefore depend on the demands of the consumer, and it is of course true that these may change from time to time. An example of such change is to be seen in some demand for small, tender joints, with a high proportion of lean meat, as compared with the popular taste of a century ago for larger joints of more mature and very much fatter meat. Nevertheless the main characteristics of a good beef or dairy animal have a permanent significance.

It follows from what has been said in Chapter 18 of this section that the efficiency of an animal, whether in the production of meat, of wool, of work or of milk, depends on the ratio that obtains between the total food consumed and the quantity required for maintenance. The animal is always somewhat inefficient in the sense that it must consume a certain amount of material before it begins to produce anything at all. An animal that eats no more than a maintenance ration has obviously an efficiency of zero, and efficiency rises as production increases. Efficiency

[1] See Wilson's *Evolution of British Cattle*, Vinton, 1909.

may be expressed by stating the energy value of the product as a percentage of the energy value of the food digested. On this basis a cow of medium size yielding 750 gal. per annum has an efficiency of 25 per cent. With a yield of 1100 gal. the efficiency rises to 35 per cent. Thus the more our animal eats in proportion to its maintenance ration (so long as the food is efficiently converted into the required product and the animal remains in health) the more economical does the productive process become. Hence, whether for beef or milk production, we want a low maintenance requirement and a capacity to deal with large amounts of food. The maintenance requirement in cattle at rest has been found to be fairly uniform in proportion to the animal's size (see p. 451), but in practice the non-productive consumption does vary within rather wide limits according to the temperament of the animal and according to its opportunities for rest. The energy expenditure is substantially higher (about 15 per cent.) when the animal is standing than when it is lying down; and substantially higher again when it is walking or running. A restless animal may waste a very considerable amount of energy in useless movement. A further point is that high milk production seems to be associated with a relatively high metabolic rate, whereas a lower level of metabolism is associated with rapid fattening.

We must next briefly consider the question of *early maturity*, which is very important in the breeding of all meat-producing types. The newborn animal is short-bodied, shallow-bodied and long-legged. If such an animal be slaughtered and the different tissues of its body separated, it will be found that the proportion of bone and offal (heart, lungs and digestive organs) is very large, that of muscle tissue (lean meat) small, and that of fat very small indeed. As the animal grows the muscle tissue increases much more rapidly than the bone, and the general build becomes longer, deeper, wider and more blocky. At a later stage still, if a full diet is provided, the proportion of fat rises; and when the accumulation of fat has reached the optimum (which depends on the consumer's taste) the animal is ready for slaughter. In the case of the sheep, Hammond found the proportion of bone, muscle and fat in the leg of the new-born lamb to be 100 : 159 : 9, whereas in the mature fat sheep the ratio was 100 : 560 : 285. Now the rate at which these changes occur varies from individual to individual and from breed to breed, and so we distinguish early maturing from late maturing types. It should be understood that early maturity has nothing to do with weight for age. It is rather the capacity to " telescope " the three phases of development which follow one after the other in the late-maturing animal—*i.e.* (1) the growth of bone and offal, (2) the growth of muscle, and (3) the deposition of fat. Thus a South Devon or a Friesian steer at eighteen months old would normally outweigh an Aberdeen-Angus; but the latter would normally have a higher proportion of fat and muscle, and a lower proportion of bone, than the others. Another important point is that while the tendency to mature early or late is an inborn characteristic, the actual achievement of early maturity depends largely on feeding. An animal of the best beef breeding, if it be kept upon a very low ration, will remain narrow, leggy and shallow-bodied; hence there is no object in developing early maturity in strains of animals that have to live through periods of severe scarcity. Indeed an early-maturing type of animal will be permanently stunted by restriction of its food intake to a level that would suffice for the normal development of a slow-maturing type.

The object of breeding for early maturity is to achieve economy in production under favourable food conditions, because the shorter the period taken to produce a finished beast, the smaller is the proportion of the total food that is spent on maintenance. Moreover the early-maturing animal can produce meat that is fat enough while it is still tender.

The other chief aim is quality in the product—the fat animal. This is to some extent a question of the percentage of meat in the animal as a whole. Meat is of far greater value, generally, than the other parts of the body, and hence the type of animal required is light of bone and hide and offal and thickly fleshed. Some of these characteristics are, however, incompatible with other desirable qualities—e.g. a light middle generally indicates a poor feeder. The proportion of the different cuts is also of importance. An animal with its weight concentrated in the back, sirloin, rump and hind quarters, which are the high-priced cuts, will be much more valuable than another with a heavy neck and shoulder and a thin back. But here the differences that exist between different animals are not very large. A further point that determines the quality of the beef is the manner in which the fat is stored. Many unimproved breeds and dairy-bred animals tend to store the fat internally (for example, round the kidneys) and in a thick layer under the skin, the muscle tissues themselves remaining relatively free from fat. The result is that the carcass is wasteful and that the lean meat, when cooked, is tough and dry. In good beef, on the other hand, much fat occurs within the muscles which, when cut across, show a characteristic " marbled " appearance, and the meat when cooked is tender, juicy and of good flavour. This tendency to store fat abundantly within the lean meat is a most important quality in the beef animal. It is what the feeder means when he speaks of his animal " putting on flesh " during the fattening process. A minor point in connection with the quality of the meat is the colour of the fat. Most consumers object to a deep yellow colour, and some dislike a dead white. The colouring matter is largely carotene. Fat colour is in part a question of feeding and in part one of breed. The Channel Island breeds, for example, are characterised by the deep yellow colour of their body fat as well as of their milk. Mangels and sugar beet produce pale fats, while green foods, including green silage, give a deeper colour.

The points of a beef steer are shown in Fig. 23. The general type,

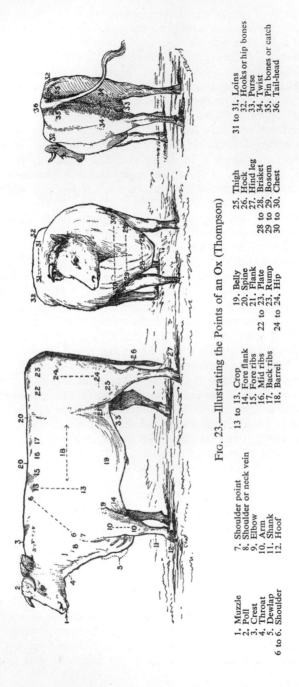

FIG. 23.—Illustrating the Points of an Ox (Thompson)

1. Muzzle
2. Poll
3. Crest
4. Throat
5. Dewlap
6 to 6. Shoulder

7. Shoulder point
8. Shoulder or neck vein
9. Elbow
10. Arm
11. Shank
12. Hoof

13 to 13. Crop
14. Fore flank
15. Fore ribs
16. Mid ribs
17. Back ribs
18. Barrel

19. Belly
20. Spine
21. Flank
22 to 23. Plate
23. Rump
24 to 24. Hip

25. Thigh
26. Hock
27. Hind leg
28 to 28. Brisket
29 to 29. Bosom
30 to 30. Chest

31 to 31. Loins
32. Hooks or hip bones
33. Purse
34. Twist
35. Pin bones or catch
36. Tail-head

which varies from breed to breed only in minor details, is a moderately long but deep and very wide block of meat on short legs. The head should be wide between the eyes and short from eye to nose; the muzzle large, the jaw strong and the eye full and mild; the neck short, and full at its junction with the shoulder; the back wide, and almost uniform in width from crops to pin bones; the shoulder smoothly laid and well covered, not protruding from the general outline of the side nor having a depression behind it; the brisket full, the heart-girth large, and the ribs well sprung or rounded, the middle moderately large, but not " paunchy," and the flank well let down—*i.e.* the underline nearly straight. The animal should be " well ribbed up "—*i.e.* the space from the last rib to the hook should be short; the hind quarters long, wide, level and fairly square in cut, with the hook bones not too prominent; the plates well filled with flesh, the tail-head level and the tail hanging perpendicularly; the thighs thickly fleshed and the flesh well carried down to the hocks; the twist or inner thigh full. The animal should stand on short legs with fine but flat bone, and with the fore legs placed well apart. The flesh should be firm and resilient to the touch, not soft and flabby; the skin not too thin, but soft and mellow to the touch. " Handling " is very important as an indication of feeding capacity.

Turning to milk production, it is of course true that large cows, on the average, yield more milk than small ones. Moreover, it seems to be true that, on the average, large cows yield more milk in proportion to their total food consumption than small ones. The next point may be illustrated by an interesting analysis that was made by Eckles [1] of the differences between a good and a bad Jersey cow. He found that there was very little qualitative difference in digestive capacity—*i.e.* the two animals extracted practically the same quantities of nutrients from like quantities of particular foods. The maintenance requirement was not quite the same, but in the case in question the poorer cow had the advantage—*i.e.* it maintained its weight when not milking on rather less food than the better animal. In the investigation the cattle were fed for a year in such a manner that their body weights remained practically constant. The important conclusion was that the milk yield was proportional, not to the total ration but to the amount of food eaten over and above the amount required for maintenance; and hence the heavier yielder was also the more economical producer.

The causes of unsatisfactory yields may be of three kinds. Firstly, certain cattle milk well for a short time, but " milk down " in condition very rapidly and soon drop off in yield. Here it seems that the mammary capacity may be ample, but the digestive organs are not able to work at sufficiently high pressure to supply the necessary raw materials.

Secondly, there is the type represented in many cows of good beef form. They have ample feeding capacity but the surplus food is diverted

[1] See Eckles's *Dairy Cattle and Milk Production*.

to body fat instead of to milk. If a heavy ration be fed to such an animal it continues to fatten up to a certain point, when the appetite declines, the maintenance energy requirement rises, and a balance between the income and expenditure of energy is restored. In this type it may simply be that the mammary system is not of sufficient capacity to deal with the available nutrients, and that, failing an outlet as milk, the surplus nutrients are converted into body fat. This, on the whole, appears likely. On the other hand it is possible that there is a kind of competition for the available nutrients between the fat-storing cells of the body and the mammary cells, and that in animals that have a marked tendency to fatten, the process of storage tends to take precedence over that of milk production. In this last case we should have to regard the fattening tendency as definitely opposed to high milking capacity. Unfortunately there is no evidence on which to reach a definite conclusion. Some deep-milking cattle do fatten readily when dry.

Thirdly, the activity of the mammary tissues depends on the stimulus of parturition, and a new cycle begins with each calving. The yield during the lactation may be determined, to a considerable extent, by the amount of response to this stimulus, which is caused by internal secretions. Hence these secretions may have an important bearing on milking capacity. It has in fact been shown that milk production can be stimulated—even in maiden heifers—by the injection of hormones, particularly synthetic substances such as hexœstrol and stilbœstrol.

A number of experiments and observation studies have recently been conducted in this country and abroad to determine the effects of different planes of nutrition in the rearing of dairy heifers on their subsequent performance. This is no easy study, nor one on which it is possible to give detailed conclusions. It seems that the plane of nutrition in rearing must be related to the breed, to the intended age of first service and to the intensity of production that is sought. Generally it has been found that moderate planes of nutrition are better in the early stages and that heifers should not be allowed to become overfat before service. This would seem to be of especial importance in the case of dual purpose breeds in which there is a natural tendency to lay on fat at earlier ages than is the case in the pure dairy breeds.

Whole milk for sale should conform (with a reasonable margin of safety) to the British presumptive standard of 3 per cent. butter-fat and $8\frac{1}{2}$ per cent. of other solids. A limited market, at a higher price, can be found for milk of superior quality, for example, under the existing milk-marketing scheme special prices are paid for the milk of Channel Island and South Devon cattle. The consumer also prefers milk with a deep creamy colour which is due to its content of carotene. The colour of milk is partly a matter of the breed and individuality of the cow but is also influenced by the carotene content of the food. The yield of butter or of cream depends mainly, and the cheese yield depends very largely, on butter-fat content so that for these purposes the composition of the milk is important, and attention must be given to the matter in breeding. There is a slight negative correlation between butter-fat content and yield—*i.e.* cattle that give rich milk are generally somewhat smaller producers than those that give poor; and there is a slight positive correlation between butter-fat content and solids-not-fat.

It is difficult to translate into terms of bodily points the physiological qualities that go to make a good cow, and the judging of milch cattle from their appearance is at best rather an unsatisfactory business. The real test is actual performance, with due allowance for age and the other conditions that are known to affect yield. The mean yield over a series of lactations and under ordinary conditions is the best kind of record. Failing this, we must take the record over a shorter period and endeavour to form an impression, from the cow's appearance, of her constitution and general ability to live and thrive in the average environment of her breed.

Of the outward signs of milking capacity the most reliable are the size and " quality " of the udder. The udder should be large, extending well forward along the belly and well backwards and upwards. It should also be wide and deep. A pendulous udder, if short and narrow, is often far less capacious than it appears. The udder should be composed largely of actual secreting tissue, which is elastic, so that the udder is large before milking and has a shrunken appearance and a soft, pliable feel when empty. The teats should be placed well apart and be of a convenient size for grasping—*i.e.* say, from 3 to 4 in. long. After the udder, the size of milk veins, which extend forward from the udder along the belly, is a useful guide among the external characters; but it must be remembered that the milk veins become progressively larger with each lactation. A capacious middle, as showing ability to feed, is also a point of some importance, and a quiet, docile temperament, as indicated by the head, eye and general behaviour, is desirable.

While no substantial correlations have been established between milk yield and individual body measurements, it has been shown that there is a fair correlation between performance and the total " score " for conformation awarded by a competent judge.

The conventional " ideal dairy cow " has many other points that are considered to be indications of deep-milking qualities, but the value of many of these is doubtful. Many cows of " dairy type " are good milkers, but others that are poor as judged by the accepted standards, milk well nevertheless. Briefly, the " ideal dairy cow " is wedge-shaped—*i.e.* she is narrow in the fore end, with sharp withers, and wide in the hind quarters; also, she is relatively shallow in front and deep behind. The eye should be large and placid, the head broad between the eyes—rather longer than in the beef type—and lean; the neck should be long, thin and muscular, the shoulder light and sloping, the withers sharp and narrow; the chest must be of fair depth and not too narrow, otherwise the animal may be lacking in constitution; the middle should be large, the ribs deep, well sprung and placed wide apart, with a wide space between the last rib and the hook; the hind quarters should be lengthy and wide, but the hooks not specially prominent; the thighs should be thin and the tail long and fine. Generally, the animal should be thin in flesh, having a somewhat angular but refined appearance; the skin should be thin, soft and elastic. The colour of the milk is correlated to some extent with that of the skin secretions, as seen, for example, inside the ears and on the end of the tail. Animals that have deep yellow skin generally give deep-coloured, rich-looking milk. Sound legs are necessary if the animal is to have a long milking life. The hind legs should be broad above the hock, and the lower part of the leg should be perpendicular when the cow is standing naturally. The hocks should be wide apart and the gait should be free and easy.

Dairy type is somewhat differently interpreted in the several dairy breeds. The most extreme type is suited only to the best conditions. It is recognised that cattle which are expected to withstand harsh weather or survive periods of scarcity must be rather less refined in form and carry more flesh than the " ideal " dairy cow. Indeed, there is no more important principle in live stock improvement than that of adapting the type of animal to the conditions under which it has to live. The very productive strains of dairy cattle, like the early maturing strains of beef cattle, demand a very high level of nutrition. If this is not provided the cow's high productive capacity becomes a danger to herself.

Unreliable as some of the " signs of milk " are when applied to the cow in milk, they are of still more doubtful value as a measure of the hereditary milking qualities in the bull. The most reliable measure of a bull's worth is the performance of his female relatives, whether dam, sisters, or—most important of all—daughters.

The dual purpose type represents an endeavour to combine milk production in the breeding cow with good fattening qualities in the males and non-milking females of the breed. The recent development of dual-purpose types—e.g. in the Shorthorn—has been regarded by some as a retrograde step: they regard specialisation as essential to the progressive improvement of live stock and look upon the dual purpose animal as at best an unsatisfactory compromise between two essentially opposite types. But there is no proof of actual incompatibility between deep-milking qualities and the tendency to fatten when not in milk, and it is possible to combine to a considerable extent beef qualities and milking tendencies in the same animal. In any case it would seem that dual-purpose cattle are an economic necessity, for under intensive conditions and with the increasing size of the dairy industry there can be no cheap or abundant supply of store cattle except those bred from dairy cows. The efforts that are being made to fix and perpetuate the combination of qualities are meeting with a large measure of success. We now have breeds, the cows of which give an average yield of the order of 8000 lb. while the steers yield good carcasses at under two years old.

## BRITISH BREEDS OF CATTLE

There are, all told, over twenty British breeds of cattle, each of which has its own herd book. No classification can be altogether satisfactory, because each breed shows a certain amount of variation in type from herd to herd, according to the purpose for which the herd is kept, the method of management and the fancy of the particular breeder. Thus there have been dairy herds of Herefords and beef herds of Friesians. We may, however, fairly accurately classify the Hereford, Aberdeen-Angus, Sussex Galloway and West Highland as beef breeds. The Devon may also be included, but a fair proportion of the cows yield more milk than is required for the normal development of the calf. There are five dairy breeds, the Friesian, Ayrshire, Jersey, Guernsey and Kerry. The major dual-purpose breeds are the Red Poll and South Deveon, and minor ones are the Belted Galloway and Dexter. The Shorthorn consists of two main types—the one, represented mainly by animals of Scotch blood, is of extreme beef form, while the Dairy Shorthorn is really a dual-purpose animal. The position is similar in the Lincoln Red Shorthorn and the Welsh Black—*i.e.* each contains beef and dual-purpose strains.

Breeds now of little importance and containing relatively few animals are the Gloucester (dairy), Blue Albion (dairy), Longhorn (dual-purpose) and the " Wild " or Park cattle.

**The Shorthorn** (Plate 37, *A*) originated in a number of closely related types that existed during the early eighteenth century in Yorkshire, Northumberland and Durham. The centre of most of the early work of improvement was the area within a radius of about twenty miles of the town of Darlington. The ancestry of these foundation types, while not fully known, appears to have been mixed. The blood of the old black Celtic, of the red Anglo-Saxon and of the broken-coloured Dutch cattle seems to have been blended in them. There are definite records of importations from Holland as late as 1750, and it is certain that there were many others of earlier date. The cattle of Teeswater, a century and a half ago, were held in high esteem both for beef and milk, perhaps more especially the latter. They were of large size, short horned and of mixed colours, with red-and-white predominating. The Holderness breed was described in 1743 as having " wide bags, short horns and large bodies which render 'em (whether black or red) the most profitable beasts for the dairy-man grazier and butcher."

Some careful selective breeding had been done before 1750, but the earliest of the great improvers were the brothers Charles and Robert Colling of Ketton and Brampton, near Darlington, who began breeding about 1780. They selected the best available animals of the Teeswater type, devoting special attention to fattening qualities, and they inbred very closely. At Charles Colling's famous sale in 1810 the very much inbred bull " Comet " realised 1000 guineas.

The Booths of Killerby and Warlaby in Yorkshire were also, for three generations, famous improvers. They used Colling bulls in the early stages, and produced a type of animal notable for its substance, wide back and thick flesh, but of little account as a milker. Booth cattle were very prominent in the showyard, and were highly prized, over the long period from 1840 to 1880.

Thomas Bates of Kirklevington commenced breeding in 1800, and originated a type of Shorthorn that rivalled the Booth in popularity. His ideal was a dual-purpose animal, and he attached great importance to handling qualities, to style and character and to particular blood lines. He inbred very intensively. Twenty years after Bates's death, which occurred in 1849, his cattle enjoyed a great boom and brought extraordinary prices. After 1890 they fell from favour, but now again Bates blood is in high esteem among breeders of the dairy type.

The Scotch Shorthorn is mainly the product of the efforts of Amos Cruickshank (1808-95) of Sittyton, Aberdeenshire. He was no partisan of the Booth or of the Bates type, and founded his herd by selecting good animals of very varied breeding, Booth blood on the whole predominating. His special aims were a robust constitution, good middle, thick flesh, early maturity and feeding qualities generally. The Scotch type rose very rapidly in favour—first in the United States and, after 1890, in Britain. It remains the popular type of Shorthorn in beef-exporting countries like the Argentine, and British herds are maintained partly with the object of supplying the demand for bulls to export to these countries.

The last outstanding step in Shorthorn history was made in 1905, when a group of breeders started the Dairy Shorthorn Association, with the object of reviving the original dual-purpose type which at that time seemed to be in danger of extinction owing to the high prices prevailing for animals of the Scotch strain. The Dairy section of the breed has made rapid progress since that date.

All British Shorthorns are registered, without regard to type, in Coates Herd Book, established in 1822. This is an " open " register— i.e. animals are eligible for entry if they have a certain number of registered crosses, and need not be descended from registered parents on both sides. The regulations require, for females, four crosses of registered blood, and for males five, so that it is possible by the use of registered bulls for four or five generations to grade up non-pedigree herds until all their members are eligible for entry. Any registered animal may compete in the classes for " Shorthorns " at the leading shows, but males can be shown in the " Dairy " classes only if their dams have passed certain specified milking tests. Cows in milk are also required to produce certain minimum yields.

The special breed points applicable to both types are as follows—Colour: red, or red-and-white, or white, or roan. Deep cherry red and deep uniform roans are preferred; patchy roans, red-and-white, and yellowish or gingery red and roan are regarded as objectionable. The muzzle should be flesh-coloured, a black or cloudy nose being very undesirable. The horn is short, laterally flattened, of fine waxy texture, and free from black. It should not curve upwards, but only forward in the male and forward and inward in the female, remaining about level with the crown.

The *Beef Type Shorthorn* (which, in fact, practically means the Scotch strain) is a large animal, exceeded in size only by the South Devon. Compared with that of most other beef breeds the conformation is more nearly rectangular, the back being wide and very flat and the buttock very square in cut. The type shows remarkable early maturity. The cows are in general poor milkers, sometimes yielding insufficient milk for the normal nourishment of their calves. The coat is abundant and the cattle are reasonably hardy.

The great reputation of the Beef Shorthorn rests on its wide adaptability and on its capacity to stamp its characteristics upon inferior types of animal. It has been a general experience that where the breeder has had of necessity to begin with thin-fleshed, late-maturing " scrub " cows as a foundation, " one cross of the Shorthorn has been equal to two of any other breed." It has been widely used for this purpose in building up the export beef trade of countries like Argentina.

The *Dairy Shorthorn* is numerically important, but in recent years has been losing ground to the specialised dairy breeds. Mature cows in breeding condition weigh about 1200 lb. The general build, as illustrated in Plate 37, *B*, is deep-bodied and roomy with long, level hind quarters, moderately fine shoulders and broad back. The thighs are more fleshy than in the purely dairy breeds. The udder is capacious, and the present tendency in the showyard is to attach great importance to a square level bag with neatly placed and moderately small teats.

The better herds of Dairy Shorthorns, with good feeding, reach average yields of the order of 7000 to 9000 lb. per annum; individual records of over 10,000 lb. are common, but those over 20,000 lb. are rare. The butter-fat content of the milk probably averages about 3.6 per cent.

An Advanced Register for Dairy Shorthorn cows was set up in 1947. The milk yields required for admission are:—

1. After calving at four years of age or more, at least 10,000 lb. milk and 375 lb. of butter-fat.

2. After calving at three to four years of age, 8500 lb. milk and 330 lb. butter-fat.

3. After calving at less than three years of age, 7500 lb. milk and 300 lb. butter-fat.

Higher yields are required where thrice-daily milking is carried out, and the quantities specified must be produced in not more than 315 days. Cattle accepted for the register must be of good general breed type, and special regard is paid to udder conformation.

Dairy Shorthorn steers, when adequately fed, make good-quality beef at about two years old, and selected animals can be finished at eighteen months. When kept as " stores " until two or two-and-a-half years old, and then fattened, they tend to be too large for the average family-butcher's customers.

**The Lincolnshire Red Shorthorn**, or Lincoln Red, is a strain of Shorthorn found chiefly in its name-country. It is of a whole cherry-red colour, large in frame and of robust constitution. The Lincoln Red, like the Shorthorn, consists of beef and dual-purpose strains, which are only rarely interbred. Separate classes are provided at the leading shows for cows of the dual-purpose type. The Lincoln Reds are the prevailing breed in some parts of Lincolnshire, Nottinghamshire, and the adjoining parts of other counties.

**The Northern Dairy Shorthorn** is a recently formed type for which a herd book has lately been established. Its home is in the Dales of Yorkshire and Durham and the upland parts of Lancashire. It is smaller, more lightly built and more active than the typical Dairy Shorthorn and is said to be better adapted to the hilly land and the rather severe climate. Ayrshire blood has been used in the formation of some of the herds.

**The Aberdeen-Angus** (Plate 38, *A*), originated in the old local breeds of Angus and Aberdeenshire. As far back as records go, which is to the middle of the sixteenth century, a proportion of these cattle have been black and hornless, characteristics that have now been practically fixed in the breed. Red calves, and others with white markings, are dropped occasionally, but horns have been completely bred out. The earliest improver was Hugh Watson of Keillor, near Coupar-Angus, who laid his foundation in 1808. Of the other breeders in both counties who carried on the work the greatest was William M'Combie (1805-80) of Tillyfour in Aberdeenshire, who not only improved the breed but succeeded in making its merits generally known. The chief breeding district is still the country lying between Inverness and Perth and eastwards to the sea, the breed being restricted in the more mountainous parts of this region to the straths and glens. Speyside has very numerous herds. There are now many Angus herds throughout the arable districts of Scotland and also in most counties of England and Ireland. The herd book, established in 1862, is a closed register—*i.e.* no animals may be entered except such as are the progeny of parents already registered.

The Aberdeen-Angus is black in colour, with a brownish tinge in the winter coat and in that of the calf, and with often a little white on the underline behind the navel. It is hornless, with a somewhat sharply pointed poll. The Shorthorn, Hereford and Sussex all exceed it in size, but the difference in weight is less than it appears, as the Angus is compact and heavy for its size. The Smithfield weights show that the breed is actually about 4 per cent. lighter than the Shorthorn. The bone is small, and the general symmetry and smoothness of outline are marked characteristics. The back and also the buttock are somewhat more rounded than in the Shorthorn, and the hooks scarcely project from the general line of the side.

As a commercial animal the Angus is an early-maturing beef beast of superlative quality. The dressing percentage is high, the carcass is very free from patchiness, and the beef is fine in grain and well marbled. In open competition at the larger fat-stock shows during the past thirty years the breed and its crosses have won more championships than all others together. The yield of milk, though irregular, is high for a beef breed, and cows with really good dairy qualities occur. The temperament is rather more active than that of most beef breeds.

The Angus is particularly well adapted for intensive feeding and for early beef production. It has not proved so widely adaptable as the Shorthorn, nor so useful under poor range conditions as the Hereford. For grading up thin-fleshed and slow-maturing types it is less useful than the Shorthorn, but for imparting quality to herds that are already improved to some extent, it is excellent. Angus bulls are largely used for crossing with cows of dual-purpose type in the production of commercial beef cattle. If still higher quality is required, the cross-bred females may be mated to pure-bred Angus bulls, producing three-quarter bred progeny. The breed has been an outstanding success under arable or semi-arable conditions—for example, in the maize growing districts of the United States. It has been exported in large numbers. Mated with a white Shorthorn bull the Angus cow produces the well-known and highly valued blue-grey crossbred.

**The Hereford** (Plate 38, *B*).—As early as the beginning of the seventeenth century the cattle of Herefordshire were held in high esteem both as work oxen and for beef. They were large, stoutly built, hardy and generally well suited to be reared and fattened on the fine pastures of the county. Improvement in the direction of early maturity and quality of meat began early. The names of Benjamin Tomkins the younger (1745-1815) and of John Hewer (1787-1873) are the best known—the one amongst the older, the other in a more recent generation of breeders. The herd book was established in 1846 and has been closed since 1883.

As regards Britain, the Hereford was until recently rather a local breed, but it is now spreading well outside its native district. Most of the prominent pedigree herds are found in the English and Welsh counties adjoining the border, from Cheshire in the north to Monmouth and Gloucestershire. The breed is largely represented in Ireland, and has a large place in the United States, Canada, South America and Australia. The breed characteristics are a large size (little inferior to that of the beef

Shorthorn), a deep rich red colour (without any black or dark brown hairs), with white head and underline and generally a narrow band extending along the upper part of the neck and over the crops. Some cattle have a red spot at the eye, which is an advantage in countries of glaring sun. The horn is of medium length, slightly drooping and of a waxy appearance to the tip; the back is wide and thickly covered, the chest deep and capacious and the legs short. The skin is thick but mellow, the coat mossy and very dense and abundant. The Hereford has not the superlative quality of meat of the Angus, nor is it distinguished, even among the beef breeds, for milking qualities. Its chief value rests in the fact that it has, of all breeds, the fullest combination of early maturing and fattening qualities with a robust constitution. It is an excellent " doer " under pastoral conditions, will fatten readily on good grass alone, and abroad has been found to live and thrive on the poorer and drier type of range where no other improved breed can exist. In their home country the cattle are very generally kept out of doors throughout the year.

The **Sussex** (Plate 39, *A*) is native to the Weald district and the marsh lands of Kent, Surrey and Sussex. The breed was originally kept mainly for draft purposes, and continued to supply work oxen for the Wealden clays long after the horse had become the sole draft animal elsewhere. With changing conditions the Sussex has become a beef breed, but it still bears some traces of its centuries-long use in the plough. In weight it is practically equal to the Hereford, but it is less compact, somewhat more muscular in build and rather later maturing. The colour is a deep red, the horn fairly large, spreading, light at the base and dark-tipped; the skin is fine and the coat rather short.

The general conformation is that of a good beef animal, the quality of the beef is excellent, and in hardiness and ability to thrive on poor fare the breed is outstanding. It has met with considerable success in South Africa. The herd book was established in 1874.

The **Devon** (Plate 39, *B*) is native to the hilly region in the north of Devonshire, but spread at a very early date into the adjoining parts of Somerset. Many descriptions dating from the latter part of the eighteenth and early nineteenth centuries show that the breed existed in those days in a form not unlike the modern type. The Devons were described by Marshall (1796) as the best workers he had ever seen, and by John Lawrence, in 1805, as having " for a century past commanded the best price at Smithfield." All writers agree that they were hardy, excellent draft animals and good feeders. Francis Quartly (1764-1856) of Great Champson, Molland, was the greatest individual improver. During the period between 1793 and 1823, when war prices tempted many of the breeders to sell their best cattle and to slaughter their calves for veal, he gradually got together a herd of the best individuals he could find. By continued selection and inbreeding he produced a strain that has since been regarded as the fountain-head of all the best blood.

At the present time the Devon is most numerously represented in North Devon and Somerset, though herds are scattered fairly widely over southern England. On the lower and more fertile pastures of Somerset the cattle are larger and of greater substance, but lack to some extent the refinement of the upland cattle. In appearance the Devon rather closely resembles the Sussex, but is considerably smaller, of a rather brighter shade of red, very frequently with dapple markings. The horns are of moderate length, with an upward tilt in the female. They are of a brownish shade with darker tips. General symmetry of build and smoothness of flesh are marked characteristics. The breed is hardy, well adapted for grazing, and produces beef of choice quality. In recent years more attention has been devoted to dairy qualities, and several pedigree herds are now kept for dairy purposes. In the showyard, however, Devons are still judged as beef cattle. The breed has met with some success abroad, particularly in semi-tropical countries.

**The Galloway** (Plate 40, *A*) is an old breed of obscure origin. Two hundred years ago it occupied, to the almost complete exclusion of other breeds, a very large area in the south-west of Scotland. The extension of dairying in this district has caused it to be largely displaced by the Ayrshire, but on the other hand it has extended into the north and the south-west of England. Like the Aberdeen-Angus, the Galloway is black, polled and of beef type; otherwise it has few points of similarity with the northern breed. In the Galloway the head is very short, with a broad poll and with the ears set on rather low; the neck is rather long; the body is deep, but longer and narrower than in the most highly developed beef breeds. The skin is thick and the coat very abundant, consisting of a very dense mossy undercoat with an outer covering of long fine hair.

The Galloway is one of the hardiest of breeds, whether under the cold and very wet conditions that obtain in winter among its native hills or in districts of intense winter frosts. The cows of most herds live out of doors throughout the year, being brought to lower ground in winter and returning to the higher altitudes soon after calving. The quality of the meat is excellent, and the carcass is never patchy nor wasteful from excess of fat. In recent years the breed has achieved great success in the carcass competitions at Smithfield Show. The Galloway is, naturally, somewhat slow to fatten, yet wonderful examples of early maturity are often seen at fat-stock shows. Judged by the Smithfield weights, the Galloway is nearly 15 per cent. lighter than the Shorthorn at the same age. The Polled Herd Book was originally founded as a common register for Aberdeen-Angus and Galloway herds, but a separate Galloway Herd Book was started in 1877. A dun-coloured strain of the breed is registered in the same herd book.

Crossed with the white Shorthorn the Galloway produces a " blue-grey " that is hardier, if somewhat slower in maturing, than the corresponding Angus cross, and equally esteemed for the quality of its beef.

The Galloway is not noted for dairy qualities, though deep-milking cows do occur.

**The Belted Galloway** is a distinct strain of the breed, separately registered. It has a characteristic white belt round the middle of the body. Some herds are bred upon beef and others upon dual purpose lines. Dun animals carrying the white belt also occur.

**The West Highland** (Plate 40, *B*), or Kyloe, is the native breed of the Western Highlands and Islands of Scotland. The recognised colours embrace various shades of red, yellow, dun and cream, as well as brindled and black, which last formerly prevailed but is now rare. The breed is of moderate size, with large spreading horns and a shaggy coat of straight or slightly wavy hair and a dense undercoat of a fine woolly texture; the form is square and deep, but somewhat lacking in width. The West Highland is exceedingly hardy and well adapted to live out of doors in the wild and exposed surroundings of its home country, where it can subsist on the poorest of grazing. It is a slow grower and difficult to fatten until it is fairly mature; indeed the steers are rarely marketed fat until they are three and a half years of age. The beef of well-fattened beasts is of choice quality. The milk yield is low, being little more than sufficient for the rearing of the calf.

## DUAL PURPOSE BREEDS

**The Red Poll** (Plate 41, *A*) of East Anglia was produced by the blending of two pre-existing local types, viz. the Norfolk Horned, a small and compactly built red beef breed and the Polled Suffolk Dun, which was much praised by early writers, including Arthur Young, for its exceptional dairy qualities. The blending was carried out on a systematic plan and with the avowed object of producing a " new sort " of dual-purpose cattle. The work began in the first decade of last century, when two breeders, John Reeves and Richard England, both of Norfolk, began on the lines indicated. About the same time a breeder named George, farming in the same county, founded a herd of red individuals selected from among the Suffolk Polled cattle. The breed was first recognised by the R.A.S.E. in 1862, and an admirably conducted herd book was started twelve years later. The Red Poll is still far commoner in Norfolk and Suffolk than elsewhere, but there are herds in almost every part of England and a few in Scotland.

The colour is a uniform red, with frequently some white on the udder of the female and a white switch. In size the Red Poll equals the Angus, though it carries rather less flesh and is therefore lighter. Horns or " scurs " are not permitted, and a dark nose is regarded as very objectionable; both of these departures from type are rare. Generally the Red Poll is a well-built and symmetrical dual-purpose animal, although the udder is often not so shapely as could be wished. In the past there has been some irregularity of type, due to the varying importance attached by individual breeders to beef conformation and milking qualities res-respectively, but great progress in the direction of uniformity has now been made. The steers fatten readily at an early age and produce a good quality of beef. In yield and quality of milk many herds compare favourably with those of dairy breeds. Good mature cows will give 8000 lb., and many high individual records, up to twice this amount and more, have been made. The breed is known in the United States and in South America, while there is a growing demand from many of the Dominions, especially the Republic of South Africa.

The **South Devon** (Plate 41, *B*) is numerously represented only in Devon and Cornwall. It differs very markedly from the Devon in being of much greater size. The original colour was a pale brownish red, but the preference is now for the deeper shades. The South Devon is the largest of British breeds, cows in ordinary breeding condition frequently scaling 14 cwt., and bulls in show condition having been known to exceed 30 cwt. The general type, according to the ordinary standard of cattle judges, is rather coarse. Improvement is of comparatively recent date, and a herd book was instituted only in 1891. Milk yields of over 1000 gal. are quite common—several lactation yields of over 2000 have been recorded—and cows of the breed have done well in open milking trials. The average butter-fat content is about 4·3 per cent. and the colour of the milk is a rich creamy yellow. The breed has been largely exported to South Africa, where it is popular on account of its suitability to the climatic conditions and its usefulness for producing trek oxen.

The **Welsh Black** (Plate 42, *A*).—The black, horned cattle of Wales are of great antiquity, although there is evidence that cattle of other colours have existed in the Principality, along with them, from medieval times. Formerly two breeds were recognised. The North Wales or Anglesey was a hardy, slow-maturing beef breed, well known during the past two centuries as producing the highly valued grazing cattle imported into the Midlands for fattening, under the name of " Welsh Runts." In the south was the Pembroke or Castlemartin breed, rather longer and looser of frame and thinner of flesh, prized chiefly for the dairy. The herd books were amalgamated in 1904, when the breed name of Welsh Black was adopted. Of medium size (about similar in this respect to the Red Poll), the Welsh carries rather long, spreading horns. Show specimens often leave little to be desired in respect of symmetry, but the ordinary run tend to be rather high at the rump, rather weak in the thighs and hard " handlers." The steers are generally marketed fat at three years old, when they produce a carcass that is full of lean meat and of very high quality. As said earlier, there are varying degrees of emphasis on beef and milk. Some herds are kept like Galloways, the cows suckling their own calves only. Some are crossed, commonly with a Hereford bull in order to obtain a heavier and earlier-maturing type of store. Other herds, kept on marginal rather than hill land, are kept mainly for milk production.

## DAIRY BREEDS

**The British Friesian** (Plate 42, *B*) is a branch of an ancient breed that has its home in the Dutch province of Friesland, lying north-east of the Yssel Lake (the Zuider Zee). It is only one of several Dutch breeds, but is probably the most highly improved, and certainly possesses the most pronounced dairy qualities. Dutch cattle of the Friesian type have exerted a large influence on other breeds, including our own Shorthorn and Ayrshire, as well as a great number of the lowland breeds of Western Europe. The home province consists largely of low-lying and fertile pastures, and the special centre of the breed, the district round Leeuwarden, is one of exceptional fertility, though its climate is distinctly raw and cold.

During the second half of last century large numbers of black-and-white Dutch cattle, both Friesians and animals of the closely related North Holland type, reached Britain. The cows were chiefly bought for town dairies, and only a small proportion were in consequence kept for breeding; but some herds were established in the early seventies and again about 1890. Few of these were kept strictly pure or managed with any particular care, and the breed, as a whole made little progress until the Breed Society was established in 1909. Thereafter it advanced in favour with extraordinary rapidity, and has continued to increase in numbers ever since. The foundation stock was accepted for the herd book by inspection, and it was impossible to prevent the admission of a proportion of animals of doubtful ancestry. This initial difficulty has since been largely overcome by very strict insistence on the true Friesian markings and type, and by the importation from Holland in 1914, 1936 and 1950, from South Africa in 1922, and from Canada in 1946 of numbers of specially selected animals.

The Friesian is by much the largest of the dairy breeds. The standard colour is black-and-white in clear and distinct patches, though an occasional dun-and-white animal may be seen. A separate herd book has been set up for the red-and-white variety. The feet and switch must be white, and a white star or blaze on the forehead is popular and of frequent occurrence; the head is rather long, the horns short and small with a forward and inward curve; the neck is rather shorter than in the other dairy breeds; the hind quarters are exceptionally wide, and the animals when young or when out of milk carry more flesh on the back and thighs than do most dairy cattle. The mammary system shows great development and the milk veins are very prominent, but the udder is less square and regular than in the Ayrshire.

The special merit of the Freisian lies in its great milking capacity. In the United States and elsewhere the breed holds most of the records for quantity. In this country many individual yields of from 2000 to over 3000 gal. have been recorded, and large herds have averaged over 1000 for cows and heifers together. One cow of the breed has yielded over

PLATE 37

*A.* SHORTHORN BULL

*Farmer and Stockbreeder*

*B.* DAIRY SHORTHORN COW

*Farmer and Stockbreeder*

PLATE 38

*G. H. Parsons, Alsager, Cheshire*

*A.* ABERDEEN-ANGUS BULL

*B.* HEREFORD BULL

PLATE 39

*A.* SUSSEX BULL

*B.* DEVON HEIFER

PLATE 40

*A.* GALLOWAY HEIFER

*Highland and Agricultural Society*

*B.* WEST HIGHLAND HEIFER

PLATE 41

*Farmer and Stockbreeder*

*A.* RED POLL COW

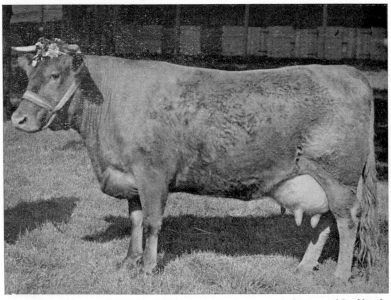

*Farmer and Stockbreeder*

*B.* SOUTH DEVON COW

PLATE 42

C. Reid, Wishaw

A. WELSH BLACK BULL

Farmer and Stockbreeder

B. BRITISH FRIESIAN COW

PLATE 43

*A.* AYRSHIRE COW

*B.* JERSEY COW

*Farmer and Stockbreeder*

PLATE 44

*Farmer and Stockbreeder*

*A.* GUERNSEY COW

*Farmer and Stockbreeder*

*B.* KERRY COW

3000 gal. in each of three successive lactations. The fat-content of the milk is commonly lower than with other breeds. In Holland the average was at one time as low as 3·1 or 3·2 per cent. In Britain, while occasional animals fail to reach the 3 per cent. standard, the average would be more nearly 3·4. There is, of course, much individual variation, and a little careful selection will usually succeed in bringing a herd average up to the normal 3·7 or 3·8. Breeders are now devoting close attention to the quality of the milk.

As a meat producer the Friesian is the best of the purely dairy breeds. The calves are large and feed rapidly into excellent veal. The steers, if given a good start, provide very useful carcasses.

The Friesian is quite ordinarily robust and hardy, but is pre-eminently suited to the better sort of pastures or to arable dairy farms where food is abundant.

**The Ayrshire** (Plate 43, *A*) came into existence some time before the end of the eighteenth century. We have no clear idea of the methods by which it was evolved. The native cattle before the new improved breed displaced them were miserable beasts, " few of the cows yielding more than from 1½ to 2 gal. in the day, at the height of the season, or weighing when fat more than 20 st." Teeswater—*i.e.* early Shorthorn—cattle were imported, and possibly other cattle of more immediate Dutch extraction. There are traditions, too, of " Alderney "—*i.e.* Channel Islands—cattle having been introduced. The centre of improvement was the parish of Dunlop, and John Dunlop of Dunlop was one, and probably the greatest, of the early breeders. The breed, as it spread over the northern portion and finally over the whole of the country, was successively known as the Dunlop, the Cunningham and the Ayrshire. It began to be generally recognised as a distinct and improved breed about 1800, and has ever since been famous as a milker. Thus among the less extravagant estimates of the average yield is that of Sir John Sinclair, who, in 1813, reckoned it at 900 gal., and that of Low, in 1845, who states that " healthy (mature) cows on good pasture " should give between 800 and 900. In the beginning of the present century some strains of Ayrshires deteriorated owing to the neglect of dairy qualities for purely " show " points, but the milk-recording scheme initiated by John Spier, in 1903, has had a very beneficial effect on the utility qualities of the breed.

The Ayrshire is a comparatively small breed, cows in ordinary breeding condition scaling between 8½ and 9 cwt., or, say, four-fifths of the average Friesian weight. Cattle on poor upland farms are, of course, lighter than those found in the more fertile districts. The colour is red or brown with a varying amount of white—a large proportion of white being fashionable. Black-and-white, which is not uncommon among commercial cattle, is an accepted colour, but is not in favour with pedigree breeders. The horns are rather large, set fairly wide apart, and have a very characteristic upward curve. The conformation is very symmetrical and neat,

Q

the back being straight and the lines of the body smooth. The udder is also characteristic, being of great length and width, firmly attached (not pendulous), level in the sole, with small teats squarely and neatly placed. At one time the fashion for " tight vessels " and small teats was carried too far, but this trend has now been righted.

On the poorer sorts of land, at high elevations and in cold climates, the Ayrshire is a very valuable dairy animal. The general average of all the yields recorded in recent years is over 650 gal. with about 3·8 per cent. of butter-fat. Many herds (whole herds, including frequently 20 or 25 per cent. of heifers) have averaged over 800 gal. with a butter-fat content of 4 per cent. or better. Individual yields of 1000 gal. and over are common, so that, in view of its small size, the Ayrshire must be regarded as a highly economical producer of milk. The fat globules are small, so that the milk " creams " slowly, which is an advantage for cheese-making. Ayrshires, whose calves are not required for herd replacements, are now mated regularly to beef bulls to produce beef stores. It is thought that the Beef Shorthorn gives the better progeny. Other breeds commonly used are the Hereford and to a lesser extent the Aberdeen-Angus or Galloway. The quality of calves for stores is found to vary considerably, but numbers of useful crosses are now reared and fattened. Earlier the pure bred Ayrshire steer was seldom reared and fattened for beef.

Ayrshires are largely kept in Canada and the United States, Sweden, South Africa and New Zealand.

**The Jersey** (Plate 43, *B*), which is believed to be of French origin, has existed on its native island for centuries, and no foreign blood has been permitted to be introduced since 1763. A mild and equable climate and a fertile soil render the island very suitable for intensive dairying.

The Jersey is a small breed, the average weight of mature cows being probably under $7\frac{1}{2}$ cwt. The colours are fawn, silver grey, brown and brownish black, either whole or more or less broken with white, and with a characteristic " mealy " ring round the muzzle. The horns are small, with an inward curve, and the head is lean and refined, with the orbits very prominent. The cows are generally very " wedge-shaped " and thin-fleshed, and have an angular but refined and deer-like appearance; the skin is thin and the hair short; the udder is generally both capacious and symmetrical, and the milk veins very prominent. The quantity of milk produced is fair, perhaps good, in relation to the size of the animal. The butter-fat content is very high, averaging somewhat over 5 per cent. The fat globules are large and the milk is deep in colour, so that it creams rapidly and has a rich appearance. As a beef animal the Jersey is of no account.

Under favourable conditions of climate and food the Jersey is greatly prized as a butter cow, and she is also a commercial success where there is a sufficient demand, at a special price, for a high quality of milk. The Island herd book was established in 1866 and a separate English register in 1879. Abroad the breed is most numerously represented in the United States, Australia and New Zealand.

**The Guernsey** (Plate 44, *A*), under which name are included the cattle of Guernsey, Alderney, Sark and Herm, is a larger, less refined, and (in keeping with the less favourable climatic conditions of its home) a more robust breed than the Jersey. The colours are various shades of fawn—red, yellow and brown—the first predominating; white markings are more frequent than in the Jersey. A light or buff-coloured muzzle is preferred, but dark noses are fairly frequent. The skin is of a very deep yellow colour, and the deeper shades are preferred.

Compared with that of the Jersey, the general conformation is rougher. The shoulder is more loosely attached, the wither is thicker and the thighs rather fleshier. A certain amount of slackness of back and a prominence at the tail head are common faults. The Guernsey is a fairly deep milker, good herds averaging perhaps 700 gal. The butter-fat content of the milk is slightly lower than that of the Jersey—probably about 4·8 per cent. on the average—but the milk and butter are richer in colour than those produced by any other breed. The Guernsey grows rather longer and reaches maturity more slowly than the Jersey, which latter is often bred from at a very early age. The bulls, as is common in the case of the other small dairy breeds, are treacherous and troublesome to handle, though here, again, the Jersey is the more extreme type. For veal production Guernsey calves have some little value. The steers mature very slowly and are of poor quality, with an objectionably deep yellow-coloured fat and few steers are reared. The Guernsey is fairly hardy, and thrives in quite exposed situations without exceptional precautions as to shelter or food. There are both Island and English herd books. The breed has been largely exported, the United States being the principal market.

**The Kerry** (Plate 44, *B*) and the **Dexter** are the only remaining native breeds of Ireland. The Kerry is an ancient breed, small in size, neatly built, active and hardy, standing on rather long legs and of distinctly dairy type. The colour is black, with frequently a little white on the udder of the cow. The horns are of medium length, rather thin and curve upwards. On poor hill pastures the Kerry is a commercially useful breed, and gives a creditable yield of milk of rather better than average quality.

The Dexter is of whole black or whole red colour, and of a distinctly dwarfish conformation, with short legs and a heavy head. The general build is compact and blocky, and the breed is a dual-purpose one. The Smithfield figures show that the breed attains rather less than 60 per cent. of the average Shorthorn weight. Monstrous calves, of the so-called " bulldog " type, are much commoner than in other breeds. Indeed, the Dexter appears to be a heterozygous form, producing, when bred pure, 25 per cent. of long-legged " Kerry type " calves, 50 per cent. of true Dexters, and 25 per cent. of " bulldog " calves.

## BREEDS AND NUMBERS OF LICENSED BULLS

No bull may be used for service in Great Britain unless it has been licensed by the appropriate Agricultural Department. There is general agreement that bull licensing schemes have exerted a marked influence in the improvement of British live stock. But their value is now being questioned by those who consider that performance tests could well take the place of licensing, and that the scrub bull would not reappear if licensing were discontinued.

TABLE 14

| Breed | England and Wales | | Scotland | |
|---|---|---|---|---|
| | Year ended 31.3.39 | Year ended 31.3.60 | 1939 | 1960 |
| Aberdeen-Angus . . . . | 783 | 1,105 | 1,395 | 1,274 |
| Ayrshire . . . . . | 554 | 1,298 | 3,830 | 3,380 |
| British Friesian . . . . | 3,086 | 7,084 | 219 | 917 |
| Devon . . . . . | 1,128 | 282 | ... | ... |
| Dexter . . . . . | 16 | 12 | ... | ... |
| Dun and Belted Galloway . . | 6 | 12 | ... | 18 |
| Galloway . . . . . | 241 | 405 | 232 | 494 |
| Guernsey . . . . . | 1,544 | 468 | 10 | 4 |
| Hereford . . . . . | 2,351 | 2,870 | 6 | 353 |
| Highland . . . . . | 4 | 3 | 42 | 24 |
| Jersey . . . . . | 498 | 480 | 18 | 32 |
| Kerry . . . . . | 14 | 3 | ... | ... |
| Lincoln Red Shorthorn . . | 1,300 | 381 | ... | 3 |
| Red Poll . . . . . | 536 | 172 | 4 | 6 |
| Shorthorn . . . . . | 23,897 | 2,156 | 1,272 | 700 |
| South Devon . . . . | 449 | 168 | ... | ... |
| Sussex . . . . . | 238 | 159 | ... | 2 |
| Welsh Black . . . . | 440 | 190 | ... | ... |
| Shetland . . . . . | ... | ... | 20 | 5 |
| Cross-bred . . . . | ... | ... | 2 | ... |
| Polled Shorthorn . . . . | ... | ... | ... | 22 |
| British White . . . . | ... | ... | ... | 1 |
| Total . . | 37,085 | 17,248 | 7,050 | 7,235 |

Table 14 gives the numbers of bulls licensed in England and Wales and in Scotland in two years—1939 and 1960. The figures for the latter year show a steep decline due mainly to the more widespread use of artificial insemination. But the comparative figures for different breeds are interesting in that they show changes in the popularity of the differing breeds in the past twenty years.

The use of beef bulls on dairy heifers and cows, not required to breed dairy herd replacements, has increased markedly in recent years. A very high proportion of these beef cross-breds are bred through the use of artificial insemination.

## COMMERCIAL TYPES AND CROSSES

The following are some of the better types of cattle that are available in quantity, with the main breeding areas in each case.:—

1. *Store Cattle suitable for Fattening at Young Ages.*—Grade or pure-bred Herefords from the Welsh border area and from Ireland; grade Aberdeen-Angus and crosses between Angus and Beef Shorthorns from the semi-upland areas of Scotland and from Ireland; Devons from Somerset and Devon.

2. *Stores for Fattening at Intermediate Ages.*—Crosses between Hereford or Aberdeen-Angus bulls and cows of Friesian and Dairy Shorthorn types from many areas; South Devons and Sussex from their respective home districts; the fleshier types of Dairy Shorthorns from Ireland and northern England; Friesian steers from lowland areas generally; crosses between White Shorthorn bulls and Galloway cows (Blue Greys) from south-west Scotland and northern England.

3. *Stores for Fattening, mainly on Grass, at Older Ages.*—West Highland and Shorthorn-Highland crosses from the Scottish Highlands; Galloways from south-west Scotland, Cumberland and Northumberland; Welsh Black from the mountain regions of Wales.

4. *Dairy Heifers.*—Ayrshires from Lanarkshire, Ayrshire, Dumfries and Wigtown; Dairy Shorthorns from Cumberland, Westmorland, Yorkshire Dales, from Somerset and Wiltshire, and from Ireland; Jerseys, Guernseys and Friesians from lowland areas generally.

5. *Beef-type Calves.*—Single-suckled beef calves are produced mainly in the hill and " marginal " districts of Scotland, northern England, and Wales, and are commonly sold at special auctions in October. The common types are Herefords and their crosses; Galloways and " Blue Greys " (from Galloway cows by a White Shorthorn bull); West Highland and Shorthorn crosses; and Angus and Angus-Shorthorn crosses. Another useful type includes " colour-marked " calves, mainly crosses between Dairy Shorthorn and Friesian cows by Hereford or Aberdeen-Angus bulls.

# CHAPTER 20

# BREEDING AND REARING OF CATTLE—
# MILK AND BEEF PRODUCTION

THE age at which heifers should first be mated depends on their breed, on their individual characteristics and on the system of feeding and general management to which they have been subjected during the earlier part of their lives. Females of the early maturing beef breeds, such as the beef Shorthorn, are sometimes, if they be well grown, mated at fifteen months of age, so that they calve down at two years old. Jerseys are frequently put to the bull quite as early. With breeds like the Dairy Shorthorn—which are about average in rate of growth and development, and are suited to average conditions of food and housing—the ordinary age at first service is about twenty-one months, bringing the first calf at thirty months. It is to be noted, however, that where there is a fixed breeding season—as, for example, in pedigree beef herds, cheese dairies —the choice will fall to be made as between mating at about fifteen months or twenty-seven months so that the heifer may calve in proper season either at two years or at three years old. Again, in whole-milk selling farms it is usually necessary to have a large proportion of the heifers calving in autumn, in order to secure a uniform output of milk throughout the year; and on this account the age for mating may be varied from that which would otherwise be chosen. Animals of the later maturing breeds such as the Galloway and Welsh, should not ordinarily calve before they are three years old, and on the poorest Highland grazings West Highlanders are sometimes not calved down till four. Heifers have been known to take the bull, and to conceive, at as early an age as four or five months, so that they must be kept apart from bull calves from that age until they are considered sufficiently developed to be served.

In view of the many variable factors no precise statement can be made about the optimum age for first mating, but two general points must be borne in mind. First is that gestation makes comparatively small demands upon the heifer's system, whereas lactation, in the case of deep milking animals, makes very heavy demands. Hence an animal that is producing a considerable amount of milk at the age when rapid growth should still be going on, requires a highly concentrated ration if the combined needs for maintenance, growth and milk production are all to be met in full.

On the other hand there is a widespread belief, which has support from experimental evidence, that delay in mating may prevent the full development of the inherent milking capacity.

Bulls of the earliest maturing breeds may begin to be used at ten or twelve months old; those of average development at about fifteen months. Sixty cows may be put as a maximum allotment for a bull of two years old or over, but much depends on the length of the breeding season, which may extend over two or three months only or may cover most of the year. Breeding bulls must be kept in active and thrifty condition by arranging for sufficient exercise, and by so adjusting the ration that the animal is kept in healthy condition without becoming fat.

The ordinary duration of life in cattle is twelve to fifteen years and there are many records of individuals surviving to eighteen or twenty. The average useful life of the dairy cow is very much shorter owing to such troubles as sterility and mastitis. The average milking life is about four lactations.

The average period of gestation is 280 days. Œstrus generally begins to occur at from five to eight weeks after calving, so that it is possible for a cow to bear successive calves at intervals shorter than a year. Where all-the-year round breeding is carried on the period between successive calvings, however, may average about thirteen months. When the calves are wanted at a particular season—e.g. spring in the case of some commercial beef-breeding herds—the number of living calves may reach 90 per cent. under good conditions and in the absence of any exceptional factor such as contagious disease.

The interval between successive " heats " varies a little, the average being about twenty days. Females in good condition come in "season" at all times of the year, but most regularly in spring and summer, and least regularly in late autumn and early winter. The length of the heat period is on the average about eighteen hours, but it varies between six and thirty hours. Œstrus is shortest in mid-winter when it may easily pass unobserved. In the case of cows running out on pasture without artificial feeding, œstrus may occur only during the summer months. Unsuccessful matings are common and are due to a variety of causes. In the absence of widespread disease among the cows, and with a fully fertile bull, about two thirds of the cows may be expected to conceive to the first service. Twin calves are fairly rare—rather above 1 per cent. in dairy herds and about $\frac{1}{2}$ per cent. in beef herds. Fertility in the bull depends upon the number and the activity of the sperms, and these vary over a wide range. Bulls may be infertile either temporarily or permanently.

**Calf Rearing.**—The first period of the calf's life—extending to perhaps six months, when under natural conditions it would be receiving its dam's milk—is one requiring special consideration. The methods of feeding and general management vary greatly according to economic conditions—such, for example, as the local value of milk and milk products, the cost of labour, the rent of the land and the probable commercial value of the calf itself.

Certain general principles must be observed under all conditions if ailments and deaths are to be avoided.  These are:—

1. The calf's powers of resistance to the commoner infections—those that cause white scour, joint evil and pneumonia—are greatly reduced if it be deprived of the colostrum of the dam.  The main explanation is that the colostrum contains " immune bodies " that confer protection against the particular strains of *Bacillus coli* that happen to be prevalent in the premises at the time when the calf is born.  In cases where a cow has died in calving or has failed to come into milk immediately, the calf's chances of survival are reduced unless some substitute is provided or exceptional measures are taken to prevent infection.  Colostrum from another cow in the same herd (either recently calved or approaching calving) is the best substitute for that of the calf's own dam.  The maintenance of a stock of colostrum in deep freeze may also be a useful insurance.

2. Colostrum can be a rich source of vitamin A (and carotene); hence the cow, for some weeks before calving, should have a reasonable supply of green food or other sources of vitamin A.  Green food will also provide a stock of vitamin E, a deficiency of which may cause muscular dystrophy.  Another point is that, whereas colostrum forms a soft curd, milk from a " stale " cow gives a hard curd.  Such milk, if given during the early days of the calf's life, should be diluted with warm water.

3. In order to prevent infection through the open navel, this should be dressed daily with iodine until it dries up.

4. Calves when housed should be kept singly or in small lots in clean, well-littered pens so as to restrict the spread of disease.

5. A calf on an ordinary allowance of milk will drink up to a gallon of water per day, and clean water should be offered freely.

6. Easily digestible concentrates and hay of the best available quality should be offered from the age of about a fortnight.

7. At the first sign of digestive disturbance milk should be withheld for twenty-four hours, and milk diluted with water should be fed for the following day or two.  If there are signs that hard curd is being formed in the stomach, an ounce of sodium citrate solution (15 per cent.) should be added to each gallon of milk fed.

8. The general level of feeding during the first few months of the calf's life should be sufficient to support full growth.  The consumption of a large amount of coarse fodder, induced by a shortage of milk or concentrates, produces a characteristic lean backed and pot bellied appearance.

The feeding of calves for *veal* is a practice best dealt with apart from rearing.  Earlier, it was the usual practice to feed veal calves entirely on whole milk on a generous scale, but at present this is quite uneconomic.

The present method is to feed such calves colostrum for two or three days, possibly whole milk for a short period thereafter and then to use skim milk or a special milk substitute.

Better quality calves are usually reared for milk or beef production. The majority of those fed for veal are surplus calves of less good quality, but excluding the poorest, *e.g.* surplus calves of the smaller dairy breeds. The latter are often slaughtered within a few days of birth and used for the manufacture of dog biscuits.

The object in veal production is to obtain a well fleshed calf weighing 170 to 200 lb. live weight in as short a period as possible, and one which will give a carcass of whitish flesh. To achieve this, veal calves must be fed liberally and are normally kept in a darkened pen and allowed the minimum of exercise.

Feeding should begin, as with all calves for rearing, with colostrum for two or three days, and then the calf may be put on skim-milk or a milk substitute, either directly or after a short period of whole milk feeding. The initial allowance should be about 3 pints of milk per head or its equivalent in a substitute, and the allowance should gradually be increased as the calf grows until at the end of the period it may be consuming some 3 to 4 gal. of skim milk or its equivalent per day.

Calves vary much in their capacity to feed and to increase in weight; as they grow they require more food to produce 1 lb. live weight gain. A useful guide is to aim at an average daily increase in live weight of 2 lb. per day over the whole feeding period.

The methods of rearing that are adopted for animals destined for beef, for the dairy or for breeding, may be classified somewhat as follows: (1) the *natural* system, in which each cow suckles her own calf; (2) the *semi-natural*, where a cow suckles two or more calves during a lactation period; and (3) the *artificial*, where the calf is pail fed, in part or almost wholly, on some substitute for whole milk.

1. The natural method of rearing ordinarily produces the best live weight gains, and the chief ground for departing from it is its high cost. With deep milking cattle the method is not applicable, even when the value of the calf might justify it, because the quantity of milk produced is greater than the calf could take. The natural system is universally adopted in the better herds of pedigree beef cattle, where the value of the calf may ordinarily be expected at least to cover the whole cost of maintaining the cow for the year. In such herds, in fact, the bull calves, if they are intended for early sale, are sometimes transferred, at the age of five or six months, from their own dams to freshly calved and deep-milking nurse cows or may be allowed to suck both. In the production of commercial beef cattle the system is mainly confined to districts where cheap, rough grazing is available, and where the cows can be kept out of doors and look after themselves for the greater part of the year. Galloway and West Highland cows are suitable for this purpose in bleak

districts, and Hereford or Sussex where the climate is less rigorous. The first two breeds will generally be crossed, if conditions permit, with the Beef Shorthorn, in order to obtain larger and earlier maturing calves. Aberdeen-Angus cows, kept on better land and housed in winter, are sometimes used in a like manner, and the value of the calves (for intensive feeding into early beef) is very high. The increased cost of maintenance of the cow is, however, a disadvantage. Commercial beef calves are normally born in late winter or spring.

2. It may be reckoned that, with careful treatment and suitable additional feeding, good commercial calves suitable for early fattening can be reared on 100 to 150 gal. of whole milk—sufficient, that is, to allow a gallon and a half daily for the first hundred days of the animal's life. It is obvious that a reasonably deep-milking cow may be made to rear four calves in a season, and a good milker as many as five or six. Even if we allow a longer suckling period, in order to avoid some of the difficulties, and even if we aim at the production of really well conditioned calves suitable for early beef, an average cow of dual-purpose type should be capable of rearing two or three annually. A deep milking cow (yielding say 5 gal. per day after freshening) may nurse 4 calves for the first three months, 4 more during a second period and 2 more in a third, making 10 in all. The essentials for the success of the system are skilled supervision, a supply of suitable calves and the collection of a herd of cows that not only milk well but accommodate themselves to the scheme of management. Some cows, even when they are quiet to milk, will refuse to suckle other calves than their own, while others show almost complete indifference.

When not more than two calves are to be suckled, close supervision is necessary only during the early stages. After the first few weeks the cow and calves may be put to grass with the reasonable expectation that all will go well. Milk will at first largely satisfy the calves' appetites, and their intake of grass will tend to keep pace with the development of the paunch. If, however, the cow is to have three calves during the first part of the lactation, if these are to be weaned and replaced by others in the middle of her milking period, and the process perhaps repeated a second time, the supervision must be close and constant. Here it is necessary to\keep the calves in pens or paddocks and to bring in the cows twice a day to suckle under the eye of the herdsman.

The purchase of young calves on the open market involves the danger of introducing disease—particularly white scour—and therefore such should be kept apart from the rest of the herd for a week or two. In view of what has been said above on the importance of colostrum, it is generally unwise to buy calves that are less than ten days old, unless the buyer has a freshly calved cow available.

In some cases white scour, which is generally due to invasion of the system by some form of *Bacillus coli*, may cause heavy loss. The point has already been made (see p. 488) that a cow passes on to her calf, in the colostrum, resistance to the types of *Bacillus coli* that happen to prevail in the place where she is kept. But a calf that is moved to another farm will probably be exposed to different types of the organism, so that white scour may occur despite ordinary care in feeding and sanitation. Cure can be effected often by modern drugs in cases of widespread attacks. These are best used under veterinary supervision.

When the cows are made to suckle successive batches of calves, weaning is necessarily both sudden and abnormally early, and hence every endeavour must be made to induce the calves to eat a good ration of concentrated food as the time for weaning approaches. They should commence with a small amount of nutritious and palatable concentrate before they are three weeks old. A mixture of three parts oats or flaked maize, two parts finely broken linseed cake, and one part of fish meal is suitable, and the quantity should be raised, if possible, to 1½ lb. before weaning and to perhaps 2½ lb. immediately after. The calves should have some good hay from the age of two weeks, and in winter, from the age of three or four weeks, some finely sliced roots or silage. Later on the supply of concentrates may be augmented, up to a total of 3 or 4 lb. per head per day. Calves that go to grass before they are six months old should continue to receive a little concentrate for a week or two even if the grazing is very good.

This system is less widely practised at the time of writing. Some of the difficulties mentioned are not easy to resolve, and the cost of supervision can be high.

3. The pail is now regarded as being of less importance in the artificial rearing of calves and its use is often confined to the first few weeks of the calf's life. Milk substitutes are widely used in place of whole or separated milk even for very young calves, and weaning on to dry foods often takes place round about five weeks of age. In pedigree dairy herds, bull calves and sometimes heifers may be fed by the pail on whole milk only, the objects being to obtain the milk records of their dams and at the same time to regulate the ration; but such a practice is not general. Separated milk, which has half the energy value and contains all the protein and ash of the natural milk, may even be available to the farmer at a small fraction of the price of the latter, or if it is not, milk substitutes are readily available and easy to prepare for feeding. Whey, which has nearly one-third of the feeding value of milk, can also be used with a fair measure of success, in the rearing of calves.

Whatever substitutes are to be fed ultimately, the calf should have its mother's milk if possible for a few days after it has lost the obvious qualities of colostrum. This is a desirable start whether the calf is to be retained for rearing or to be sold. Many calves are sold today to farms where there are no milk cows and a good early start is of even greater importance in such circumstances. After that time substitution may begin, and should be spread over a further period of two or three weeks, Where separated milk is used, the additional food—the butter-fat substitute—need supply only the energy and the vitamins (A and D) that butter-fat provides. It must be in a readily assimilable form, but apart from this, it is a matter of indifference whether it consists of oil, starch or sugar. Fats and oils, though formerly much used, are generally unsatisfactory when used in quantity. In crude liquid form they cause digestive disturbances, and in finely emulsified form they are too expensive. Cod-liver oil, formerly given as a source of vitamins A and D, is best avoided, since it has an anti-vitamin E effect, and the essential vitamins A and D can be supplied in pure form. Oats or flaked maize can be used as food to supply energy. The former need not be crushed or ground; indeed, young calves seem to prefer whole oats, and masticate these quite thoroughly. The rate of feeding should be about $\frac{3}{4}$ lb. to each gallon of separated milk. If possible, the milk should be fed quite fresh, being separated immediately after milking and given to the calves while still warm, but with care it is possible to use skim milk preserved with formalin. With separated milk and a fat-substitute a live weight increase of $1\frac{1}{2}$ lb. daily may be expected.

If separated milk is available in large quantities, good results may be obtained by substituting 2 gal. of this for 1 gal. of whole milk, adding a source of A and D to make good the vitamin requirements. The calves seem to suffer no harm by reason of the high protein intake which this method implies.

Whey differs from separated milk in that it lacks not only the fat but also the casein and part of the ash and is now used for calf rearing on a very limited scale. It has necessarily developed some degree of acidity. In order to stop the lactic fermentation, the portion of the whey, that is not to be fed immediately it is drawn from the vats, should be scalded and cooled. It should be warmed before use. Freshly drawn whey is usually warm enough for immediate feeding. It is necessary to use something that is moderately rich in albuminoids as a supplement. A protein equivalent of 20, and a starch equivalent of the order of 70, may be taken as a general guide, and unless fish meal is included, a mineral addition will generally be beneficial. Examples of suitable mixtures are: (1) two parts linseed cake, two parts flaked maize, one part oats, one part fish meal; (2) two parts linseed cake, one part cracked beans, one part middlings, with 1 per cent. each of ground limestone and sterilised steamed bone flour and $\frac{1}{2}$ per cent. of common salt. An average calf may receive $1\frac{1}{2}$ to 2 gal. of whey with $1\frac{1}{2}$ lb. of the supplement. The rate of growth will generally be about half that obtained with a full ration of whole milk.

So far we have discussed the older and better known methods of calf rearing in which liquids—whole milk, separated milk, whey and milk substitutes—have figured prominently. Separated milk and whey are now seldom available on farms and whole milk is too costly to be used in any quantity for commercial calf rearing. Recent research backed by practical experience on rearing farms has shown that calves can be reared successfully with a strictly limited amount of pail feeding and very many calves are now reared on a method in which the feeding of a liquid ceases at about five weeks of age. This newer method relies on calves being encouraged to eat the right kinds of food in sufficient quantity at an early age, so that they do not suffer when suddenly weaned from the pail.

TABLE 15

EXAMPLES OF EARLY WEANING CONCENTRATES FOR CALVES TO BE WEANED FROM 3 TO 5 WEEKS

| Ingredients (lb.) | (a)[1] | (b)[1] |
|---|---|---|
| Flaked Maize | 224 | 196 |
| Bruised Oats | 168 | 84 |
| Molassine Meal | 84 | 56 |
| Soya Bean Meal | 28 | 56 |
| Fish Meal | 56 | — |
| Screened Linseed | — | 56 |
| Dried Skim Milk | — | 56 |
| Cane Sugar | — | 28 |
| Kibbled Locust Beans | — | 28 |
| *Supplements* | | |
| Salt (lb.) | 3 | 3 |
| Vitamin A (i.u.)[2] | 1,000,000 | 1,000,000 |
| Vitamin D (i.u.)[2] | 200,000 | 200,000 |
| Aureomycin or Terramycin (grams.) | 4·5 | — |

[1] Mixture (a) incorporates the more recent developments in the composition of early weaning diets as recommended by the Rowett Research Institute. Mixture (b) was developed by the School of Agriculture, King's College, Newcastle-on-Tyne.

[2] Vitamins A and D should be supplied in dry stabilized form since feeding cod liver oil to calves may cause muscular dystrophy.

[3] Antibiotics at the time of writing may only be used for calves in scientific investigations or on farms under veterinary supervision. Aureomycin and Terramycin are available as Aurofac 2A (1·25 lb. Aurofac 2A supplies 4·5 grams aureomycin) and Terramycin Feed Supplement T.M.9 (0·9 lb. T.M.5 supplies 4·5 grams terramycin).

Calves are started off on colostrum and then fed whole milk at the rate of 8 lb. for each 100 lb. live-weight. They are offered clean water and good hay, the chill being taken off the water especially in cold weather. The drinking of water is an encouragement to eat concentrates—$\frac{1}{2}$ lb. or more at about ten days old. This first ration must be compounded with care. A number of specially prepared compounds are available. Two rations which have proved suitable are given in Table 15. They are extracted from Bulletin No. 10 *Calf Rearing*, Ministry of Agriculture, Fisheries and Food, which gives fuller information on this method and on calf rearing generally.

The present restriction on the use of antibiotics for calf rearing is worthy of mention. Research suggests that the main effect of incorporating an antibiotic in the concentrate mixture for young calves is to reduce fermentation in the rumen; and this results in increased appetite, better food conversion efficiency and more rapid growth. Against this there is evidence that the regular use of antibiotics may lead to the emergence of strains of organisms, which are resistant to the particular antibiotic in use.

Any refused concentrates should be removed and replaced so that fresh food is always before the calves.

Milk feeding is stopped abruptly between the age of 3 and 5 weeks, the actual time being determined according to the strength of the calves and their capacity to eat concentrates. It is better to continue milk until five weeks or later for any calf that has had a set back, is weak or is a shy feeder.

The allowance of concentrates should be raised sharply when milk feeding ceases up to $1\frac{1}{2}$ lb. per day, and then is steadily increased up to about 4 lb. per day when the calves are eight to ten weeks old. After a further month or so the special concentrates can gradually be replaced by an ordinary rearing mixture; and at that stage the consumption of hay will probably be about 4 to 5 lb. per day.

If whole milk feeding is limited only to a week or two and a milk substitute is used to replace it, then it is better to continue to feed the substitute for at least five weeks.

From three to six months all calves while indoors should receive a ration which ensures steady growth, though the level of feeding, for example, of calves for early beef will be more liberal than those being reared for dairy heifers. The ration will normally consist of a general rearing mixture and good hay, or good quality silage probably supplemented by some cereal.

One important point in artificial rearing is worth stressing. No attempt should be made to adhere to rigid rules and quantities, since there is considerable variation in the adaptability of individual calves. Close observation must be maintained and adjustments in diet made according to the progress of the animals. The chief signs of inadequate nutrition are a pot belly, a thin back and costiveness or laxness of the bowels.

The age at which artificially reared calves should be turned out to grass varies with the conditions. The subject has received much attention recently and as the result of experiment and experience, calves are now turned out at younger ages and earlier in spring than formerly.

Autumn born calves often go out in early April or even earlier under favourable conditions; and calves born as late as February are not infrequently turned out now in May.

The pasture should be of good quality and clean (*i.e.* free from husk and stomach worms), and some shade should be available for them.

The calves should gradually be accustomed to bright light, if they have been reared under subdued light, and to their new food. A little supplementary feeding is necessary until they are consuming a reasonable quantity of grass.

In New Zealand very satisfactory results are obtained, in the case of dairy calves, by grazing, without concentrates, from the age of eight to ten weeks. This is done under a modified system of strip grazing, with the calves moving ahead of the other stock.

The general scheme of feeding during rearing varies according to the purpose in mind for the particular animal. If intended to be fattened at an early age it should have a liberal ration with preferably a fair quantity of whole milk in the early stages. Weaning should be late, and should be carried out by easy stages in order that the " calf flesh" may be not lost. At the other extreme, a heifer intended for the dairy is purposely kept rather lean. The belief is that otherwise she may develop an undesirable tendency to fatten, and may probably fail to reach her full milking capacity; but it is always inadvisable to restrict the ration so much as to check the animal's growth.

As regards housing and general management, young calves should be housed, either singly or in small lots, in well-ventilated but not draughty pens, which should be floored with concrete and swept out and freshly littered daily. They will frequently eat their litter if this be not prevented, and the consumption of straw or peat moss may have fatal results. Calves that develop this tendency may be muzzled for the first three or four weeks, a precaution that also prevents their sucking each other about the navel. In summer they should run on fresh and clean grass, and shade during hot weather is a great advantage; but in many districts it is necessary, as a precaution against "husk " or " hoose," to keep the younger animals indoors during their first summer. This applies to such as have not been weaned at the beginning of the grazing season. When heifer calves are to be vaccinated against contagious abortion, the best age is about seven months. Young cattle at grass should not have access to the contaminated water of open ponds, since such water may be infected with the organisms of Johne's disease. Males should be castrated at about four weeks old.

When the period immediately following weaning has been successfully passed, the feeding and management become simple. In summer, young cattle do well on ordinary pasture without artificial feeding, the only exception being in the case of animals that are intended to be marketed fat at an early age—say, before they are two years old. The latter should have an allowance of 2 to 4 lb. of concentrate, unless the pasture is more than ordinarily good. Yearling cattle will require from half an acre to an acre or more of pasture each, according to its quality. In winter, growing cattle may be tied up in stalls, or run in covered courts or partially open yards. In districts where the winter is mild—*e.g.* the south west of England and south west of Ireland—those of eighteen months or more do best out of doors, if reasonably dry and well-sheltered pastures are available. Store animals will thrive when closely confined, but young animals that are being intensively fed must have exercise if they are to be prevented from " going off their legs." An open court, or failing this, a covered court with a daily run on pasture, is preferable even in the case of stores, as the animals grow better coats and are much less liable to suffer a setback when they come to be turned out in spring. The following are examples of winter rations:—

1. For a twelve-months-old store bullock weighing 5 cwt., in an arable district:—

|                                              | lb. |
|----------------------------------------------|-----|
| Swedes . . . . . . . .                       | 40  |
| Oat straw . . . . . . . .                    | 8   |
| Oats and beans or compound dairy cake . .    | 3   |

This supplies about 14 lb. of dry matter (equal to $2\frac{1}{2}$ per cent. of the live-weight), 6·4 lb. starch equivalent, and 0·9 lb., protein equivalent. The maintenance energy requirement is 3·7 lb. starch equivalent, and the surplus, viz. 2·7 lb. starch equivalent, is sufficient for something over 1 lb. live weight increase per day.

2. For a two year old store bullock of 8 cwt., intended for early summer fattening, in a grassland district with a daily run out on pasture:—

|                                       | lb. |
|---------------------------------------|-----|
| Meadow hay . . . . . . .              | 20  |
| Oats, barley or other cereal . . . .  | 4   |
| or                                    |     |
| Grass silage . . . . . . . .          | 70  |
| Oats, barley or other cereal . . . . .| 2   |

These each supply about 9 lb. starch equivalent, and 1·2 lb. protein equivalent. The maintenance requirement is 5·5 lb. starch equivalent, so that the balance available for production would be 3·5 lb., sufficient for fully $1\frac{1}{2}$ lb. live weight increase. In actual practice the full ration of hay or silage would be given only for a short period, say from January till March or April, the quantity being regulated during the remainder of the winter according to the state of the grazing.

## MILK PRODUCTION

A first essential for profitable milk production is a herd of deep milking cows. It is true that the actual yields, as well as the profits, depend very largely on the skill of the dairyman in feeding and general management; but no management, however good, can prove successful if the cattle have a low limit of production. Hence everything possible must be done to secure good foundation stock, and, by careful selection and mating, to maintain or improve the average yield. To this end a system of milk recording is essential. Individual cows, under what may be termed ordinary farm conditions, vary in yield from 200 or 300 to 1000 gal. or more, and accordingly may leave a large profit or a very considerable loss. The average yield of the world's dairy cows is probably under 400 gal., whereas good herds, with a standard of management that is quite attainable under strictly commercial conditions, may reach 800 or 1000 according to breed and frequently more. The composition of the milk varies, too, with the breed and with the individual; in particular the percentage of butter-fat, which is a most valuable constituent, may be anything from 3 to 6, without counting very abnormal individuals. There is no clear evidence as to the hereditary factors that determine production, nor of the mode of their transmission; but we know, in a general way, that milking qualities are inherited, and hence milk records, apart from their value as a measure of the economy of production of individual cows, are of the utmost importance in breeding.

An actual record must always be considered in relation to the conditions under which it is made. Obviously, the size of the cow must be taken into account. The economy of milk production, as has previously been pointed out, depends essentially on the ratio between the production ration and the maintenance ration; the latter varies, not in direct proportion to the live weight but with the three fourths power of the live weight. Thus, for example, a 12 cwt. cow will require about 35 per cent. more for maintenance than an 8 cwt. animal, and hence it may be calculated that 800 gal. from the latter would be as profitable a yield as 1080 gal. from the former. Clearly, too, a record must be considered in relation to the general system of feeding. An insufficient ration will limit the production and prevent the animal from giving any true account of herself.

Age has a well known influence on yield. From the fourth lactation onwards the cow may be considered as mature, and little increase in yield occurs after that time. Naturally, the yield declines ultimately, but the age at which the decline sets in may vary from eight years to perhaps twelve. A heifer calving for the first time at thirty months old may be expected, in her first lactation, to produce about 75 per cent. of her mature yield, and with her second and third calves about 85 and 90 to 95 per cent. respectively. The butter fat content of the milk varies little with age.

The normal lactation may be taken as lasting about ten and a half months. The cow should have at least six weeks'—and preferably eight weeks'—rest before calving, and should be in calf again three months after freshening. An abnormally long period of rest previous to calving has the effect of increasing the yield during the subsequent lactation, up to a maximum of about 15 per cent. above the normal yield. Conversely, if a cow is not rested at all, her subsequent yield may suffer to the extent of 15 or 20 per cent.

Delay in mating has the effect of permitting a longer continued flow, and a cow that does not conceive at all will ordinarily give about 30 per cent. more milk than one which conceives at the normal period of three months after the previous calving. Under the National Milk Records Scheme (England and Wales), the standard lactation period is 305 days—*i.e.* the lactation yield is taken as the amount produced in 305 days from calving. A long period of rest, particularly if the cow be fattened, may have the further result of increasing the butter fat content of the milk during the first few weeks of the subsequent lactation.

Finally, the season of calving has an important influence on the yield. The change from winter to summer feeding usually stimulates the flow, whereas the generally poor quality of autumn pasturage has the opposite effect. This effect is greatest if the change occurs at the time when the yield is beginning to decline, say three or four months after calving. It has been found that a cow calving in December may yield 10 to 15 per cent. more than another of equal real capacity calving in June; but, obviously, no generalisation can be true for all conditions, and the more skilful the winter feeding the less will be the effect of season of calving. Thrice daily milking produces a higher yield than the usual twice milking, and this should also be remembered in interpreting records.

Even when all these factors have been allowed for, an actual record does not necessarily reflect accurately the inherent milking capacity of the cow. The level of nutrition in the herd and the degree of skill brought to bear in its management have very considerable effects on yield.

Many attempts have been made to estimate milking capacity on the basis of short tests—of, say, seven days' duration. It has been shown that with cattle that are fed and managed in the ordinary way there is actually a very high correlation (about 0·85) between the maximum daily yield, at, say, six or eight weeks after calving, and the total yield in a normal lactation. The relationship is, on the average, such that if the maximum daily yield of a winter calving cow is multiplied by 200, there is obtained a very fair approximation to the normal lactation yield. For summer calving cows the factor would be about 185. Thus an average cow, producing, say, 3 gal. a day at her best, might be expected, if she calved in winter, to reach 600 gal. in a normal lactation. Since, however, the correlation is not absolute, the rule is not strictly applicable to the poorer milkers or those that are much above the average. The difference from the average should be multiplied by 0·85, the coefficient of correlation, and the product again multiplied by the lactation factor. Thus if we assume that 600 gal. is an average yield, a 5 gal. cow, calving in winter, should produce in a lactation $(3 \times 200) + (2 \times 0·85 \times 200) = 940$ gal. Similarly, a winter calving cow, yielding 2 gal. at the top of her flow, might be expected to produce $(3 \times 200) - (1 \times 0·85 \times 200)$, or 430 gal., in a normal lactation.

Short period tests, in spite of their inherent value, are of very little use in practice. The difficulty is that it is possible, by special feeding, to stimulate the flow for a short period, as well as temporarily to raise the butter-fat content. Even yearly records are open to objection in cases where the cattle are carefully rested and prepared, though heifer yields are a very useful guide as to subsequent performance in later lactations. Some of the breed Societies now stress the importance of this by setting a high value on the 10,000 gal. cow—*i.e.* a cow which yields an average of 1000 gal. per year over a productive life of ten years.

Milk records, if they are to receive general recognition, must obviously be vouched by an independent authority. In some systems the milk is weighed and tested at regular intervals by the official recorder, but this method is costly if the visits are frequent enough to give an accurate estimate of the yield. The better system is to make the owner responsible for weighing and recording the yield at each milking, and to have the milking inspected, the weights checked and the milk tested for butter fat and solids not fat contents by inspectors making surprise visits.

## FEEDING FOR MILK

The feeding of dairy cattle, if maximum production is to be made possible and waste prevented, is necessarily a somewhat complicated business. Sufficient energy, protein, minerals and vitamins must be supplied to provide for maintenance and something approaching the quantity of milk that the cow is capable of yielding. The maintenance requirement is 0·6 lb. of protein equivalent and 6 lb. starch equivalent per 1000 lb. live-weight. A gallon (10 lb.) of average milk contains 0·35 lb. of protein, so that the protein requirement, per gallon of milk produced, cannot be under this figure. In fact, good results have been obtained with an allowance of 0·45 lb. per gal., but a somewhat higher rate is probably advantageous in maintaining production during the later stages of lactation. The accepted standard is now 0·55 lb. protein equivalent per gallon of average milk (3·75 per cent. butter fat).

The total or *gross* energy value of a gallon of average milk (3·7 per cent. butter fat) is about 3200 kcal.[1] If, therefore, we were to take Kellner's value for the pound of starch equivalent—1071 kcal. of net energy—it would be necessary to feed 3 lb. ($\frac{3200}{1071}$) of starch equivalent for each gallon of milk produced, for the cow must have enough net energy in her food to produce the gross energy in her milk. The value of 1071 kcal. of net energy per pound of starch applies, however, to fattening oxen, and it has been shown that the milking cow is distinctly more efficient as an energy transformer than the fattening steer. The probable explanation of this fact is that the cow has a direct outlet in her milk for protein and carbohydrate, and is not under the necessity, as is the fattening animal, of transforming its whole surplus energy into the form of fat. The difference in efficiency is considerable, amounting to fully 25 per cent. Expressed differently, the pound of starch equivalent yields 1360 kcal. in the form

[1] See page 444.

of milk as against 1071 kcal. in the form of body fat. The quantity of starch equivalent required per gallon of milk of average composition is thus $\frac{3200}{1360}$ or 2·35 lb. approximately. The energy requirement per gallon will, of course, depend on the composition of the milk, notably on its fat content. Moreover, cows that are fed a little in excess of their calculated requirements maintain relatively larger yields, in the later stages of lactation, than those which receive bare theoretical allowances. The optimum level of feeding thus depends on economic conditions, particularly on the relative prices of feeding stuffs and milk. Table 16 embodies the recommendations which are generally accepted, though some individual authorities, regard the figures as somewhat too high for average conditions.[1]

## TABLE 16

### PRODUCTION STANDARDS (PER 10 LB.) IN RESPECT OF MILK IN VARYING QUALITIES

| Fat-content of Milk (per cent.) | Cal. per Gallon | Starch Equivalent | Protein Equivalent |
|---|---|---|---|
| | | lb. | lb. |
| 3·5 | 3170 | 2·40 | 0·52 |
| 3·75 | 3250 | 2·50 | 0·55 |
| 4·0 | 3430 | 2·60 | 0·58 |
| 4·25 | 3510 | 2·70 | 0·61 |
| 4·50 | 3600 | 2·80 | 0·63 |
| 4·75 | 3680 | 2·90 | 0·66 |
| 5·25 | 3820 | 3·10 | 0·72 |

In the case of the cow giving milk of average composition, and where ordinary cakes and meals are to be used as the production ration, the quantity required will be about 3½ lb. per gal. This implies a starch equivalent of 71 per cent. and a protein equivalent of 16 per cent. Such a ration will contain fully 3 lb. of dry matter. As is pointed out in the chapter on nutrition, the cow's food capacity generally lies between 2½ and 3 lb. of dry matter per 100 lb. live weight per day; 3 lb. of dry matter per hundredweight (112 lb.) is a good general figure. Hence if we are dealing with cows of 11 cwt. live weight, with yields running up to 5 gal., maintenance requirements must be met by a ration containing not more than 18 lb. of dry matter (33 lb. total minus 15 required for production). The following are examples of rations supplying the necessary minima of energy and protein (7·1 lb. starch equivalent and 0·71 lb. protein equivalent) for maintenance in not more than the bulk indicated:—

(a) 20 lb. good hay with a starch equivalent of 35.

(b) 40 lb. swedes or mangels with 14 lb. medium hay.

(c) 60 lb. swedes, 6 lb. oat straw and 6 lb. medium hay. (In areas where roots and straw are exceptionally nutritious, e.g. north east Scotland this ration might leave some surplus for production.)

[1] See page 455.

The clear cut line between maintenance and production rations is not possible when silage constitutes a major part of the ration, particularly if the cows are allowed to self feed—a practice spreading quickly. The aim of those who make silage for cows is to make a product that will supply much more than maintenance. Good quality silage is too rich in protein equivalent relative to starch equivalent to provide a balanced food for maintenance. A normal and economical practice is to feed silage so that a ration of silage well within the capacity of the cow plus a few pounds of cereal will supply sufficient nutrients for maintenance and $1\frac{1}{2}$ to 2 gal. of milk. For example, a ration of 80 lb. good grass silage and 3 lb. of crushed oats would supply an 11 cwt. cow with 1·9 lb. of protein equivalent and 12·0 lb. of starch equivalent in about 23 lb. of dry matter. This is sufficient for maintenance and 2 gal. of milk. For higher yields the practice would be to feed a balanced production ration for every extra gallon of milk or the allowance of silage and cereal might be increased to provide one or two more gallons.

Where cows are self feeding silage then it is important to make an estimate of the quantity consumed and the nutrient that it is supplying, so as to give a guide to the supplementary feeding necessary.

As regards production rations, these ordinarily consist of a mixture of three or four distinct materials. The following are suitable standard mixtures to be fed at the rate of $3\frac{1}{2}$ lb. per gal.:—

(a) Two parts maize meal, one part crushed oats, one part bean meal, two parts palm-kernel cake, one part decorticated earth-nut cake.

(b) Two parts maize gluten feed, one part rice meal, one part barley meal, one part linseed cake, one part decorticated cotton cake.

(c) One part coconut cake, one part decorticated earth-nut cake, one part linseed cake, two parts palm-kernel cake, two parts barley meal, one part maize gluten feed.

In the choice of concentrates, apart from questions of price, due regard should be paid to the type of maintenance ration. If this is costive in tendency the production ration should be laxative and *vice versa*. Coconut cake, linseed cake and decorticated earth-nut cake are laxatives, while cotton cakes, dried grains and most of the starchy foods have the opposite tendency.

As with fertilizers so with feeding stuffs, there has been a marked increase in the use of compound cakes, which broadly can be divided into two types—*balanced* and *balancer*, the latter for use, in conjunction with home grown cereals, in specified proportions.

The feeding of very heavy milkers is still something of an art, involving a careful study of individual tastes and appetites. If silage is fed, then it may be necessary to control the total consumption per day in order that the cows will eat other suitable foods. If the older form of maintenance ration is still fed, it will often be necessary in the case of the heaviest milkers to curtail the bulk of that ration by substituting concentrates for part of the more fibrous foods. In other cases a special production ration may be used which will supply the nutrients for 1 gal. of milk in 3 lb. rather than in $3\frac{1}{2}$ lb.

The object of rationing according to yield is to ensure, without waste of food, something approaching the maximum yield of milk of which the cow is capable, while enabling her to maintain herself in good thriving condition. Cases of individual cows becoming too fat or too lean do frequently occur in rationed herds, generally because due regard is not paid to variation in the composition of the milk. In such cases the ration should be altered at discretion.

An important point in dairy cow management is that the cow should be brought into fit bodily condition and accustomed to a fairly substantial ration of concentrates before she calves. This process may commence (with 3 or 4 lb. of cake per day) six weeks before the calving date, and the ration may be raised to 8 or 10 lb. for the last fortnight. A mildly laxative ration is desirable when parturition appears imminent and only a light ration should be fed for the first few days after calving; but thereafter the concentrate should be rapidly increased day by day until it exceeds, by 2 or 3 lb., the allowance corresponding to the actual yield. Excess should continue to be fed so long as the yield shows a tendency to rise, which may be for as long as six or eight weeks. Thereafter the ration should correspond to the actual yield.

The mineral content of the ration requires special consideration in certain cases. The moderate milker receiving a full maintenance ration will normally get enough mineral matter, at least if the bulky foods have been produced on land that contains sufficient lime and phosphate. The heavy milker, on the other hand, will receive a large proportion of her food in the form of cakes and meals. Purchased compounds usually contain added minerals, but home mixed rations may be deficient in minerals, particularly calcium. The addition to the production ration of 3 per cent. of a mineral mixture will be desirable in such cases. One part powdered chalk, two parts common salt, and one part sterilised steamed bone flour form a mixture which has given satisfactory results. As an alternative, blocks of mixed minerals, which are obtainable commercially, may be fixed in the mangers, and the cattle allowed to lick them at will.

The composition of the milk is in the main independent of the feeding, but rations that are low in calcium tend to depress the content of solids other than fat. Chronic undernutrition, produced by the continued use of rations of inadequate energy value, seems to have the same effect. Some materials—such as maize gluten feed, coconut cake, palm-kernel cake and earth-nut cake—have a slight and sometimes only temporary effect in the direction of increasing and the butter-fat content. On the other hand, there is some evidence that rice meal has a depressing effect on the fat content. A high oil content in the ration is undesirable, and it should not exceed 5 or 6 per cent. The character of the butter-fat is markedly influenced by feeding—linseed cake, for example, produces a soft oily butter, while bean meal, coconut cake and palm-kernel cake produce a firm fat. The colour of milk, due largely to its content of carotene, is also greatly influenced by feeding, although, as previously pointed out, it varies with the breed and individuality of the cow. Some breeds, notably Guernseys and Jerseys, pass on carotene in their milk, which accordingly has a deep creamy colour. Cows of other breeds, such as Ayrshire and Friesian, convert a much larger proportion of the food carotene into the colourless vitamin A. The green leafy portions of plants have a high carotene content and hence pasture grass, kale and other green foods impart to milk a desirable creamy tint. The carotene of grass is fully preserved by artificial drying or by low temperature ensilage, but is largely destroyed in the ordinary process of hay making. The point is of importance, since milk of high carotene content has a high vitamin A potency. The amount of food carotene or vitamin A required to maintain the full potency of the milk is not large. It can be provided by about 5 lb. of fresh young grass, by 1 lb. of high quality dried grass.

Before self feeding of silage became common it was general practice to adhere to a pretty strict time table for the feeding of dairy cows, particularly in winter. Where silage is self fed any supplementary feeding is carried out either in the semi-covered yards where the cows normally lie or at milking time. Earlier it had been the practice when silage was given in definite feeds to ensure that it was available immediately after rather than before milking to lessen the risk of taints in the milk. The same practice is observed where large quantities of roots and sugar beet tops are fed. Many cows are now milked in milking parlours in which long fodder is not fed. If milking is done in a cow shed and especially if it is hand milking, long fodder should not be fed before milking as it contaminates the air with dust.

On the question of the preparation of the food it may be taken as a good general rule that roots should be fed either whole or roughly sliced, coarse fodder in the long state and the concentrate in dry form. Straw and hay, when fed long, allow the animal to reject the coarsest and least nutritious portions. For production purposes a mixture of cake (in nut form) with meal is better than meal alone.

A supply of pure drinking water is necessary for cattle in milk, unless the ration contains an excessive quantity of roots. The normal consumption of a cow yielding 2 gal. of milk per day, fed on a dry ration, and in ordinarily cool weather, may be put at 10 gal. daily. Heavy milkers, in hot weather, have been observed to consume up to 25 gal. The most satisfactory method of supplying water, when the cattle are indoors, is by means of automatic drinking bowls. Failing these, water should be offered thrice daily, the last drink being given as late in the evening as is practicable.

In summer, if cattle are on fairly good fresh pasture, it will generally suffice to give $3\frac{1}{2}$ lb. of concentrate for each gallon of milk produced above 3 or 4 gal. The best grazings, for a few weeks during May and June, can support production up to 5 gal. per day. When pastures get bare, much additional food may require to be given, such as cut green forage, mangels in early summer or cabbages later, hay and additional concentrate. Even if grass is abundant its feeding value generally declines from August onwards, and during October it will do little more than provide for maintenance. Deep milking cows on rough autumn pastures should have their grazing restricted, since otherwise they may consume too much of the bulky and innutritious herbage. An average cow requires from 1 to $1\frac{3}{4}$ acres of pasture, according to its quality, when this is managed on the ordinary system, or about $\frac{3}{4}$ acre under a highly intensive system of management.

Pastures during times of active growth or those containing an excessive proportion of legumes—e.g. white clover or lucerne—are liable to cause bloat. Young cattle, fattening cattle and sheep are liable to the trouble. It tends to be most severe in the case of cows in full milk. In some cases the feeding of hay or other roughage before the cattle go to pasture is an effective preventive; and the spraying of pastures with a vegetable oil when the trouble is most expected has proved useful.

Soiling is now seldom practised, but zero grazing is somewhat similar in its aims. The objective in zero grazing is to grow and manage grass so that a portion may be cut each day while still in its most nutritious stage of growth and transported for the feeding of cows. The method involves careful grassland management including liberal fertilizer treatment, suitable equipment to cut and transport the relatively short grass and a labour saving lay out for feeding the cut grass. The advantages claimed are that the cows waste no grass, that poaching of the fields is avoided and that the grass is of good and fairly even quality so allowing a reduction in concentrate feeding. The method is best suited where the pastures are level and lie handy to the feeding centre. At the time of writing it is difficult to predict whether zero grazing will become more common. Many are interested and are keenly studying the costs of this method.

It is worth noting that many summer foods, such as clover, vetches and ordinary pasture grass, are much richer in protein than most home grown winter foods, such as roots and hay. Hence any concentrate fed in summer can be made up to a nutritive ratio of the order of about 1:6 or 7. This may permit the use of a mixture with a high proportion of cereals and one cheaper than the normal production ration.

The cattle should be quietly handled and should have some little outdoor exercise each day. The hoofs may require occasional dressing to prevent their growing too long.

## BEEF PRODUCTION

The type of animal best suited to the production of beef has been sufficiently described in the last chapter. There can be no question that the breeder, if beef if his sole object, should aim at the best possible beef type. But the feeder, if he is nothing but a feeder, may find that the finest commercial type of store commands a more or less fancy price, and that he can obtain a larger profit from a somewhat rougher animal that can be bought cheaper. The value of a young calf, as material for beef production, depends largely on its breeding though rearing can exert a big influence on conformation and the quality of the carcass. Animals with indications of dairy breeding—Channel Island or Ayrshire colours and markings—will rarely produce first grade carcasses.

Calves at six to twelve months of age should show evidence of reasonably good nutrition since inadequate feeding in calfhood usually does permanent harm. Signs of former starvation are small size, a long narrow face, a thin back and a pot belly.

On the other hand, " hard wintering " of older cattle does little permanent harm. In particular, cattle that have been out wintered and fed rather poorly commonly make much better live weight gains, on grass, than such as have been housed and well fed. The latter often lose weight on the spring grass.

Angus, Herefords and Shorthorns of beef type, if they are well fed as calves, and if they are carried on without a store period, can be marketed either as early beef at fifteen to eighteen months or later at eighteen to twenty four months. This system is well adapted to the better sort of mixed farms where breeding and feeding are combined. On the other hand, feeders who buy in stores and who work on a system of rapid turnover prefer cattle of some age because they fatten more quickly. Two years is about the average age for cattle to be put up to feed, and some of the later-maturing breeds are kept till they are three years old or over. Old and heavy cattle, however, sell in a free market at a considerably discount as compared with young, well-finished animals. Under the system of payment according to grade, which operated from 1939 till 1954, the price per cwt. was based mainly on the estimated dressing percentage, and the premium formerly commanded by lightweight young cattle was considerably reduced. With the restoration of free markets in 1954, a considerable premium for cattle of moderate size and good quality has again become established, and many cattle of dual-purpose type are now being fattened at ages corresponding to those of the beef types.

The general scheme of feeding must be adapted to the prevailing economic conditions. If the fattening process is likely, in itself, to be a profitable operation—*i.e.* if there is any considerable margin between the value per cwt. of lean and fat animals, and if feeding stuffs are cheap— the general rule will apply that the more rapid the process of fattening the higher will be the profit. Obviously, if one animal is fattened in four months and another, on a lighter ration, to the same degree in six, the latter is debited with the cost of an additional two months' maintenance, without any compensating advantage. In the past half-century, however, the conditions stipulated have rarely existed, and the winter fattening of cattle had come to be regarded as essentially a means for the disposal and conversion into manure of the bulky and non-marketable by-products of the arable or mixed farm. Hence it was usually good policy to feed a maximum of such by-products, and to confine the use of purchased concentrates to the barest minimum. With the introduction of self-feed silage, however, there is now a prospect of winter fattening at much lower costs and with a reasonable prospect of profit, provided the silage is of reasonable quality and high dry matter content.

The winter ration will depend mainly on the particular home grown feeding stuffs that are available. On arable farms in Scotland the chief constituents will generally be roots and straw, with a moderate allowance of seeds hay in the latter part of the fattening period, but silage feeding is practised by some even in these traditional roots and straw districts. In the eastern counties of England hay is the usual fodder, and sugar beet by-products largely replace roots. In semi-arable districts meadow hay and/or silage will generally be available in quantity and may form the basis of the ration, supplemented by " seconds " grain.

During the progress of fattening, as the animal's appetite for bulky food declines, the allowance of more concentrated food must be increased. Wood's standard for a fattening steer allows 12 lb. of starch equivalent and $1\frac{1}{2}$ lb. of protein equivalent per 1000 lb. live weight. On such a ration a 1000 lb. animal should add nearly 2 lb. daily to its live weight, more in the earlier stages when the live weight increase consists partly of water and protein, less in the latter when the gain is chiefly fat. Good cattle will readily make such an average increase, as between ordinary store and ordinary fat condition. On more highly concentrated rations $2\frac{1}{4}$ to $2\frac{1}{2}$ lb. per day may be obtained. In practice, as has just been indicated, it may often be wise to rest content with a daily increase of $1\frac{1}{2}$ to 2 lb. using a less nutritious ration. In countries where cheap concentrates are available (*e.g.* maize in the corn belts of North and South America) rations with as high a starch equivalent as 18 or 20 lb. are sometimes fed, and the gain may reach 3 or even $3\frac{1}{2}$ lb. per day for short fattening periods. Such rations are often imperfectly digested, and pigs are kept with the cattle to consume the residue.

Cattle that are being fattened for early beef—that is while they are still in active growth—require a more concentrated type of ration than can be fed to mature fattening animals. Straw, even if of good quality is rather too fibrous, and hay should not supply more than a third of the dry matter of the ration. The concentrate mixture must be palatable and the choice of the particular ingredients should depend on ruling market prices. When all the concentrated foods have to be brought, it may be better and less wasteful to use a compound cake.

Much thought has been given in the past few years to the winter feeding of more mature beef cattle. The high costs under the older methods arose chiefly from the high charges for labour in tending the cattle, the growing, transporting and feeding of fodder roots and the subsequent carting and spreading of the manure. Reductions in costs have been made by feeding polled cattle (these take less accommodation and feed together better than horned animals), by spending less time in preparing the feed for the cattle, by the introduction of a food like silage which can be self fed and

*Ration*

| Beginning | lb. | Middle | lb. | End | lb. |
|---|---|---|---|---|---|
| Turnips or | | | | | |
| Sugar beet tops | 80 | Swedes | 70 | Swedes | 60 |
| Oat straw | 14 | Oat straw | 12 | Oat straw | 6 |
| Palm-kernel cake | 4 | Palm-kernel cake | 2 | Seeds hay | 6 |
| Crushed oats | 2 | Barley Meal | 2 | Linseed cake | 3 |
| | | Crushed oats | 1 | Barley meal | 5 |

through mechanical appliances to lift, transport and spread the farmyard manure. The older fattening ration of roots, straw, hay and concentrates fed at stated times each day is being replaced on many farms by self fed silage. Good results with cattle around 10 cwt. live weight are being obtained with about 100 lb. of medium quality grass silage of high dry matter content supplemented by 2 to 6 lb. of cereals.

The table above is given as an example of a winter ration for an arable farm, where roots, straw and hay are available in addition to cereal grains. The cattle are assumed to be about 8 cwt. at the beginning of the fattening period and to be finished at about 10 to $10\frac{1}{2}$ cwt. in four months.

The finishing ration supplies about 1·8 lb. protein equivalent and 13·5 lb. of starch equivalent, the beginning ration about 1·4 lb. protein equivalent and 11 lb. of starch equivalent.

When such rations are used, there are a number of points worth a mention. Palatability is important as well as such considerations as bulk, energy value and protein equivalent.

Some feeding stuffs, such as palm-kernel cake, are not readily eaten at first but are consumed freely enough when the animals have had a week or two to become accustomed to them. An occasional animal will refuse any and every sort of cake. Sprinkling with molasses water, or admixture with any of the commercial condiments, will often be helpful. Again, stores from grassland districts take some time to learn to break roots, and an occasional animal gives up the problem altogether. If it is inconvenient to slice the roots for the whole group, such individuals should be transferred, if possible, to individual boxes and given special feeding. Regarding the preparation of the food generally, roots must be sliced for cattle that are in process of changing the first pair of incisor teeth (say eighteen to twenty-four months old). Otherwise it is doubtful whether any special preparation of the food is profitable. Many experienced feeders give the roots whole, the fodder long, and the cake in the ordinary form of nuts or cubes. On the other hand, some feeders chaff a proportion of the fodder, slice the roots, and mix the two together, with or without the addition of meal. This doubtless decreases the work of mastication and enables the animal more quickly to finish its meal and return to rest, but it involves a large amount of additional labour, and there is no satisfactory evidence that the advantage is sufficient to leave a profit. Heavy root rations are always liable to cause scouring, particularly in early autumn; materials like soya bean, earth-nut and linseed cakes, which have also a laxative tendency, should not be fed with them; undecorticated cotton cake, on the other hand, is an excellent corrective.

The particular details in the arrangement of the ration are of less consequence than strict adherence to whatever scheme is adopted. In practice straw is generally given *ad libitum*, and the racks are filled morning and evening, or oftener if necessary. The roots should be given in two feeds or, if the ration is over 80 lb., in three; the concentrate should also be given in two meals if the amount exceeds 4 or 5 lb. Many feeders believe in allowing a period of two or three hours of entire quietness in the middle of the day. Cattle receiving very large rations of roots will not require drinking water, but, ordinarily, water should be laid on to the yards. The total consumption of water (including any in the food) is generally about 1 gal. per cwt. live weight per day, or approximately four times the weight of the dry matter eaten.

Fattening cattle may be kept in single or double boxes, or may be run in lots of up to twelve or twenty in covered or partially open yards; or they may be tied up in stalls, as are dairy cows (a common practice in the north). Single boxes doubtless give the best results, but the method is expensive both in labour and in housing space. Stalls are economical of space and economical of litter, 5 lb. daily while more than twice this amount is needed in yards. The labour is increased as compared with other methods owing to the necessity of individual feeding and daily removal of manure. The conservation of the manure will be less satisfactory than where it is kept firmly trampled in yards. Partially open courts are wasteful of litter and manure, but are otherwise satisfactory except in very exposed situations.

The method most economical of labour is to run the cattle in covered or semi-covered yards and allow them to self feed silage. If the cattle are to be fattened, rather than maintained in store condition, reasonable comfort and protection from the weather is necessary, otherwise they will fatten slowly and there will be a wide range in the individual live weight gains.

Cattle running together in lots are always liable to disturbance from restless or pugnacious individuals, and if possible, devices should be provided to prevent the " master " bullocks getting more than their fair share of the food.   Polled cattle settle down together better and it is an advantage if they have been grazed together for a month or two before being housed.  A limited amount of stall or box accommodation is useful in order that bullying or frightened or sickly animals may be segregated.

Summer fattening of cattle may be carried out on the best sort of permanent grass without additional feeding, the land carrying a full-sized bullock to the acre and providing, in addition, some autumn and winter grazing for sheep.  Well-managed rotation grass on good arable land will often do as well as this.  Very careful adjustment of the number of cattle to the growth of the grass is necessary if the cattle are to make full progress without cake.  On the one hand, if the grass gets overgrown the fibre content rises and the digestibility falls;  on the other hand, if the pasture gets too bare the cattle fail to get a full ration in the time (about eight hours in the twenty four) that they spend in grazing.  In the first case, the mowing machine should be used to keep the grasses under control.  In the second, the farmer must resort to cake feeding.  The type of stock should also be adapted to the quality of the pasture.  In the chief grass fattening districts of the Midlands the best fields are stocked with steers, the slightly poorer ones with heifers, and those of still poorer quality with barren and other cows culled from dairy herds.  Of average feeding pasture about $1\frac{1}{4}$ acres should be allowed per head, and some concentrate will often be needed during the latter part of the season.  The concentrate used should be one of high energy value and low protein equivalent. Maize germ meal, maize meal, barley meal and rice meal, made up for convenience in cube form, give satisfactory results.  Live weight gain is made at a much lower cost on summer pastures than on winter rations.

The degree of fatness to which cattle should be brought before marketing depends on market conditions.  It must be realised that during the last stage of feeding—that which makes the difference between " good " and " prime " condition—the live weight increase is obtained at a very high cost.  With the demand turning more to leaner meat, a most serious error is to make cattle fatter than the butcher desires, for in this case a low price is obtained for an article with a high cost of production.  Ordinarily fat cattle will dress about 57 per cent. of their live weight, or, say, 8 lb. to the stone.  Prime cattle may reach 62 or 63 per cent., and exceptional animals in very high condition from 65 to 70.  Very lean animals may yield under 50 per cent. of carcass.  The largest items in the "sinkage " are the contents of the alimentary canal (15 per cent.) and the hide (7 per cent.). Dressing percentage will obviously vary considerably with the quantity of food contained in the stomach and intestines; cattle fasted and thirsty may weigh 70 or 80 lb. less than when full.

## CARE AND MANAGEMENT OF BULLS

Bull calves intended for breeding should be kept in growing and thriving condition from the start. Those of the beef breeds are normally nursed by their own dams, though occasionally they are changed over to foster-mothers which yield relatively large amounts of milk. Dairy bull calves are often suckled by cows which, because they are " hard milkers " or for other reasons, are troublesome in the dairy herd. After the calfhood stage, bull calves should continue to be well nourished but not necessarily made fat. They should be housed in airy boxes, kept practically at outdoor temperature, and should have access to an open yard. Exercise is essential, and this may be provided by a run on pasture for an hour or two daily, or alternatively a walk in halter. Subsequent management is always easier if the young animals have been regularly haltered and led about. The feet must be kept in good shape by occasional trimming, and the coat should be kept clean by grooming and occasional washing. A nose ring is inserted before the animal is strong enough to cause trouble— say at the age of ten or twelve months. Either a rope or a pole should be attached (by means of a spring hook) to the nose ring when the bull is led out, but control should normally be exercised by the halter, and the nose ring kept in reserve in case of trouble. If further restraint is necessary, as it occasionally is in the case of older dairy bulls, blinkers may be put over the eyes, so adjusted that the animal can see only the ground in front of it.

Bulls must be inspected for licensing before they are ten months old, and it is obviously important that they should be presented in good condition. Breeders not infrequently complain that bulls are rejected for no other reason than lack of condition, but it is obviously very difficult for an inspector to satisfy himself that the condition of a lean and somewhat ragged specimen is due entirely to its restricted diet. In the case of beef breeds—and to a less extent in that of dual-purpose types— capacity to fatten, and to fatten in the right way, is of fundamental importance, and it is impossible to say with certainty whether a lean animal possesses the capacity in the desired degree.

It is of obvious importance that bulls should be retained until the merits of their progeny can be assessed—*i.e.* in the case of a beef breed for about two years after the animal has been put into service, and in that of a dairy sire fully four years after use has begun. In fact very few dairy bulls are kept so long, chiefly because a large proportion become progressively more difficult to manage as they get older. Another factor is that if an old bull is kept on after his daughters reach breeding age, a second sire is required to mate with these, and the keep of two males is a very heavy charge in the case of the average herd of perhaps fifteen cows. The solution of the bull problem for the smaller sort of dairy farm, is without doubt artificial insemination; but many large scale breeders, and especially owners of pedigree herds, will probably continue to keep their own bulls even if they make some use of the artificial insemination service.

The bull box should be light and airy, and should preferably have access to a large open yard. Failing this yard, opportunity for exercise may be provided by means of an overhead wire with a runner to which the bull's nose ring can be attached by means of a chain, or by one or other of a variety of devices. Where there is a yard outside the box the door communicating between the two may be of the portcullis type and be operated from the feeding passage of the box, or from outside, by means of a wire rope; this arrangement enables the bull to be restricted to the yard while his box is being cleaned and littered, or *vice versa*. It is easy to arrange that the bull may be secured, by his nose ring, from the feeding passage, the animal being brought within reach by the offer of food. Again, a service pen may be so placed and devised that the bull may serve a cow and be put back into his yard without being handled or being given any opportunity to attack his attendant. These various precautions may seem to be unnecessary in the case of good tempered animals, but a proportion of bulls are subject to occasional and unpredictable fits of viciousness.

Apart from the important matter of exercise, the bull must be kept fit by adequate nourishment and yet not allowed to become fat. A suitable ration for a mature animal of average size is 20 to 25 lb. of hay, with a few roots in winter and some green stuff in summer, and perhaps 2 lb. of the concentrate mixture that is fed to the milking cows.

If the bull yard is laid with well roughened concrete the animals' feet may not require much attention, otherwise the hoofs must be trimmed back when they get too long.

# CHAPTER 21

# MILK SECRETION, MILKING AND EQUIPMENT FOR MILKING

DAIRY farming is the exploitation of lactation, the physiological process that occurs within the mammary glands of mammals following each parturition to provide milk for the nutrition of their young.

## THE DAIRY COW'S UDDER

The first signs of the developing udder are to be seen as two lines on the abdominal wall of the calf foetus when it is only about half an inch long. These develop as inverted buds and from these the simple cisterns and ducts develop inwards. At birth the main structure of the udder appears to be mature but in fact only the teats, the teat and udder cisterns and the supporting structures are formed, together with a very rudimentary duct system. After birth, growth of the gland is slow until the onset of regular œstrus cycles when there is rapid growth of the duct systems, though the main development of the udder and the formation of the secretory tissue does not occur until the cow is pregnant. The udder is fully formed well before the end of pregnancy and in the latter stages some of the products of secretion accumulate.

The three stages of growth of the udder of a cow are all controlled hormonally, the first under the influence of the hormones in the blood of the mother, the second by the rise in hormonal activity when œstrus cycles begin and the final stage under the hormones released during pregnancy.

At calving, the udder consists of four quarters or glands, each with its own secretory unit and milk drainage system held within the skin and suspended by strong ligaments to the pelvis and muscular wall of the belly. The two sides of the udder are completely divided by one of the suspending ligaments but the division between front and hind quarters is not readily apparent though functionally they are completely separate.

Each mammary gland consists of *secretory* tissue, that is actively concerned with the manufacture of milk and *connective* tissue that protects and supports it. Within the teat is a small cavity or *teat cistern* which connects directly to a larger cavity, the *udder* or *gland cistern*. Ducts proliferate from this in much the same way as branches leave the trunk of a tree (Plate 45). Ultimately, the minute capillary ductlets end in micro-scopic egg shaped sacs lined with epithelial cells called *alveoli* (Fig. 24).

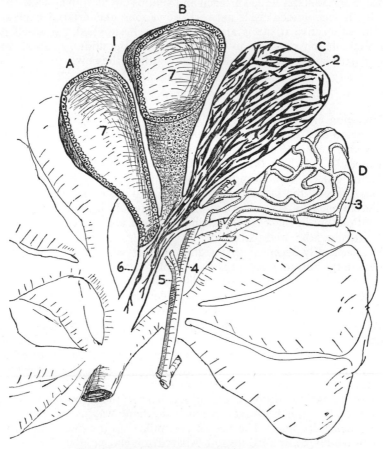

FIG. 24.—DIAGRAM OF A CLUSTER OF ALVEOLI

*A* and *B*. Alveoli with part of walls removed. The wall is made up of a single layer of alveolar cells.

*C*. Alveolus showing myo-epithelial cells (2) lying on the outer surface of alveolar cells.

*D*. Alveolus showing network of capillaries (3). These lie on top of the myo-epithelial cells. 4, Small vein. 5, Small artery. 6, Small duct. 7, Lumen or cavity of alveolus.

(The diagram is not drawn to scale. The branching and arrangement of the alveoli have been simplified to show up more clearly.)

These alveoli manufacture or secrete the milk from precursors drawn from the blood and when fully distended may measure 0·01 in. in diameter.

R

Since milk is derived from blood, up to 10 tons of which may circulate through the udder each day, it is not surprising that the udder has a very extensive and well developed arterial and venous circulation system. Each alveolus is surrounded by a network of venous and arterial capillaries and the connective tissue is also similarly well supplied. A small part of this circulation system is to be seen covering the udder, the milk veins being particularly prominent on the belly wall of the cow.

## LACTATION

Lactation can conveniently be divided into two processes, *secretion* or the manufacture of the milk within the alveoli and its movement from the alveolar cells into the *alveolar lumen*, and *ejection* (commonly called " *let down* ") by which the milk in the alveoli is expressed towards the ducts and cisterns to be removed at milking time. The former is a continuous process, the latter occurs only at milking or suckling. Just as the development of the udder is controlled mainly by hormones so also is lactation, but in this case the main hormones are pituitary and adrenal rather than ovarian and placental.

It is generally accepted that secretion starts after calving because of changes in the hormone balance after the placenta or afterbirth is removed, though this cannot be the reason for the start of secretion with successful pre-milking. Lactation is maintained under the stimulus of the pituitary and other hormones and by the frequent removal of milk.

As the alveolar lumens fill some of the milk passes into the ducts and thence to the gland and teat cisterns. The milk pressure within the ducts rises slowly for the first few hours after milking but then increases more rapidly as the storage areas become inflated with milk, and at the end of a milking interval milk pressures may reach 2 to 3 in. of mercury. At this stage about two thirds of the milk is held in the alveolar cavities and small ducts by capillary forces in much the same way as liquids are held in a medicine dropper. The rest of the milk is in the ducts and cisterns and can readily be drained away. Apart from the capillary forces in the secretory tissue the only barrier to prevent the flow of milk from the udder is the *teat sphincter* at the tip of the teat

When suckling or milking occurs the milk held in the secretory tissue is expressed towards the larger ducts and cisterns and can be removed. The physiological process, giving rise to milk ejection, is brought about by the release of a posterior pituitary hormone but is also initiated and controlled to some degree by nervous stimuli. The hormone, oxytocin, which is involuntarily released into the blood when the cow receives the nervous stimuli associated with the start of milking causes a basketwork of cells surrounding each alveolus to contract. It is transitory in effect because the hormone is fairly rapidly destroyed in the blood and its action is delayed or prevented by the hormone *adrenalin*, secreted into the blood when an animal is frightened or in pain. The nervous reflexes that initiate oxytocin release are either *inborn*, as occurs in suckling, or *conditioned*. An example of a conditioned reflex is feeding concentrates immediately before milking. This becomes a stimulus because it signals that milking is about to begin.

At milk ejection, there is a rapid increase in milk pressure up to twice that before stimulation and after this stage is reached milking should be completed as soon as possible. Even if all the ejected milk is completely removed 10 to 25 per cent. of the milk present in the udder before milking starts is retained in the secretory areas. This is known as *residual milk* and has a fat content of 10 to 20 per cent. While milk ejection is mainly concerned with milk removal there is evidence that it also maintains lactation, the so-called milking stimulus.

After about the fifth month of pregnancy the rate of secretion which has been declining steadily, decreases much more rapidly and most cows cease to make milk after they are eight months pregnant. This decline is caused by ovarian and placental hormones. Changes also occur in the secretory tissue much of which involutes leaving only a framework of ducts, blood and nerve systems and connective tissue on which the secretory cells for the following lactation are built.

## PHYSIOLOGICAL AND ENVIRONMENTAL FACTORS AFFECTING MILK YIELDS

The rate of milk secretion within each milking interval is not constant but slowly declines, the rate of decline being greater with heifers, high yielding cows and those in early lactation. Even with those animals the rate of decline is relatively small for milking intervals of up to 20 hours, and in the case of fat secretion the decline is often not detectable even in a milking interval of 24 hours. Once secretion has declined it does not immediately recover after milking. The recovery may take 24 hours after the milk is removed at shorter milking intervals.

The slowing of secretion in long intervals has always been ascribed to the direct effect of high intramammary pressure. This has not been proved and other factors such as the non-removal of the accumulating milk may be important.

There are a number of management practices which are thought to influence milk yield by a direct effect on the rate of secretion during each milking interval, the most important being the frequency of milking, the equalisation of milking intervals and incomplete milking.

**Frequency of milking.**—There is no doubt that increasing the milking frequency from twice to three times daily will increase lactation yields particularly with heifers and high yielding cows. Analyses of milk records data in the United States of America indicate an increase of 20 per cent. in lactation yield. Because these results are from selected high yielding cows they cannot be regarded as generally applicable and a 10-15 per cent. increase is a more realistic figure. The effect of increasing the frequency of milking on milk composition is to slightly depress the fat content.

**Milking intervals.**—It is generally accepted that when milking twice daily yields are higher when milking intervals are equal at 12 hours. Recent work indicates that for cows yielding up to 900 gal. per lactation the decline in yield following a change to milking intervals of 8 and 16 hours is very small and often undetectable. The fat contents of the milk obtained following equal milking intervals are approximately the same, but with unequal intervals the fat content of the milk is lower after the longer interval though there is no change in the average composition of the day's production. These changes in fat content are not due to varying rates of fat secretion but to the greater quantity of fat in the residual milk after long milking intervals.

**Incomplete milking.**—Possibly the oldest rule of dairy cattle management is that if cows are improperly stripped the decline in lactation yields is greater. Physiologically there are two forms of incomplete milking— that which is concerned with the milk which is not expressed from the secretory tissue at milking time, *i.e.* residual milk, and that voluntarily left by the milker in the udder and teat cisterns, *i.e.* strippings. Because the quantities of residual milk may be up to 5 lb. or more at a milking they are clearly of much greater importance than the small quantities of milk that are left at the end of machine milking and which so much time is taken to remove.

The results of the rather meagre research on incomplete milking show that milk yields are depressed, but it is not surprising to find the effect is not catastrophic and with quantities left of less than ½ lb. per milking the effect is very difficult to detect. Furthermore, although the fat content of the milk obtained is reduced when milk is left in the udder at one milking the fat is not reabsorbed and comes away at the following milkings. In fact, the firmly held belief that careful stripping is necessary to maintain the fat content of milk is incorrect.

In addition to these management factors that affect the rate of secretion during the course of a single milking interval, there are many physiological and environmental factors that affect lactation yields, and several of these cannot be controlled by the farmer. The following are some of the more important factors, excluding the affects of nutrition and disease.

**Size of cow.**—On average, the larger the cow the higher the lactation yields and in general this applies to individual cows within a breed and to different breeds. However, milk yields are not proportionately related to cow size and a group of cows that are twice as heavy as another group of equal numbers will not give twice as much milk per lactation but something less than this. This is because in large cows the proportion of the total weight of the cow that is directly concerned with lactation (*i.e.* the mammary, digestive, blood circulation and respiratory systems) are proportionately less than in the smaller breeds. The choice of breed does not simply depend on size; factors such as hardiness of the breed and chemical composition of the milk are important, as is the fact that the labour required per cow is almost independent of size.

**Age.**—Lactation milk yields increase by about 20 per cent. from first to third calving and after about the fifth calving they usually decline. This change is partly due to change in size of cow and increases are greater in cows that are small at first calving. Examination of lactation curves shows that the maximum daily yields of cows increase for more than three lactations, but this is offset by the lower persistency of lactation of older cows.

Farmers usually arrange for cows to calve when 2 to 3 years old. Calving at two years of age gives first lactation yields 5-10 per cent. below that which might be expected with three year olds, but the cumulative yields in the first four lactations are not affected providing the cow is given adequate food for growth in the first lactation.

**Pregnancy.**—Reference has already been made to the decline in milk yield and change in milk composition as lactation advances. The effect is negligible until the fifth month of pregnancy but is very pronounced by the eighth month. Nutritionally the effect of pregnancy is slight and the reasons for the decline in yield are almost certainly hormonal.

**Dry period and calving interval.**—The length of the dry period and the intervals between successive calvings both influence lactation yields. Dry period length is inversely related to lactation yields. It has been shown that if the dry periods of high yielding cows fall below about six weeks the yield in subsequent lactations is reduced.

A lactation yield is directly proportional to the length of its associated calving interval and also to a small degree related to the preceding calving interval. This is because as calving intervals increase so the effect of pregnancy on milk secretion decreases. Of much more economic importance is the fact that generally the annual output of milk per cow declines with increasing calving intervals because the early lactation periods when the high milk yields are obtained occur less frequently. The length of the calving interval that a farmer aims to get is clearly a compromise. The desire to reduce the calving interval to raise the average annual output of milk per cow has to be balanced against the knowledge that short calving intervals depress yields in the succeeding lactation and it is virtually impossible to reduce the calving interval to less than $10\frac{1}{2}$ months for physiological reasons.

Two important environmental factors that affect the rate of milk secretion are air temperature and month of calving.

**Air temperature.**—The body temperature of the dairy cow is approximately 102° F., a temperature maintained by the heat produced in the metabolism of the body. The regulation of temperature is partly physical (*e.g.* cows lose heat by drinking cold water and expiring air containing water vapour, and conserve heat by the extra insulation of thicker coats in winter). Within the range of air temperature of about 40-70° F. the cow can maintain its body without difficulty by these physical means but outside this range it is forced to change its body function. Lower temperatures do not seriously affect metabolism, body heat being maintained by oxidising more food, but at temperatures above 70° F. and particularly above 85° F. the secretion of milk declines as this is one of the most effective ways of reducing heat production in the body. Regulation of body temperature in high air temperatures becomes more difficult as the humidity of the air increases.

**Season of year and month of calving.**—There is no good evidence that either of these factors influence milk secretion in Britain except through their effect on the nutrition of the cow. Spring and early summer are times of generous feeding with very nutritious food and as such, milk yields are stimulated. Because of this the lactation curves of animals calving in the autumn differ from those in the spring. The milk yields of autumn calvers can be readily maintained during the winter period because they are in that stage of lactation when the natural ability to produce milk is at its greatest. When this begins to decline the secretion is stimulated by the flush of rapidly growing grass and this often results in a marked persistency of lactation. Spring calving cows rise to much higher maximum daily yields because their early lactation coincides with the best season for grass but they tend to be less persistent as the latter part of their lactations occurs during the winter period. Generally autumn calving cows give higher lactation yields, cows calving in November and December giving 5-10 per cent. more than those in May and June.

# MILKING

Just as lactation will fail when milk is no longer secreted into the udder so also it will fail if the milk secreted is not removed.

Physiologically, milking has two aspects, first, ejection or the movement of milk within the udder and second, the removal of milk from the teat cistern through the streak canal at the tip of the teat. The former is a factor of the cow's physiology that is largely, but not entirely, outside the milker's control. The latter is essentially the milker's concern.

We have seen that milk ejection is a two part reflex—the cow receives a nervous stimulus that milking is about to begin and then involuntarily the hormone is released that brings about the expulsion of the milk from the secretory tissue. One of the main tasks for the milker is to give to the cow at the right time those stimuli which will cause the most effective milk ejection and then to remove the available milk from the teat cistern. It is much more important for a milker to be careful in preparing the cow for milking and in this way to reduce the residual milk than it is to be meticulous in removing the very last of the strippings.

Under farm conditions the stimuli initiating milk ejection are largely conditioned, that is they are not inborn but develop because the routines for preparing cows for milking are usually reasonably constant. Because they are conditioned, the strongest stimuli are likely to develop if the work routine that precedes the milking of each cow is very constant, with the operations in the same order each day, the whole routine being carried out within two or three minutes of the start of milking. Pain, changes in routine or fright should be avoided because the resulting release of adrenalin will inhibit the reflex. Furthermore, because ejection is transitory, milking should be completed as soon as is practically possible after the stimulation of the cow.

In any reasonable milking installation these rules can be incorporated in a simple milking routine. Udder washing and taking foremilk can be a very good signal that milking is about to begin and, providing it is done sensibly, the feeding of concentrates just before milking develops into a very strong stimulus. Although in recent years much emphasis has been put on using hot water for udder washing, as far as the cow is concerned details of this sort are not important, though they help to provide reasonable working conditions for the milker.

Once milk ejection has occurred the only essential physical forces required in milking are those necessary to open the streak canal. This is done by increasing the pressure difference between the milk in the teat cistern and the external air. In hand milking the internal milk pressure is increased by squeezing the teat in the palm of the hand, while in machine milking the external air pressure is reduced. In both cases the end of the teat is deformed by the pressure of the milk, the streak canal opens and milk flows from the teat cistern.

## MACHINE MILKING

Many attempts were made in the nineteenth century to perfect a machine for milking but this was not done successfully until about the turn of the century. Even when successful machines were available they were not readily accepted by farmers, and by 1939 only about 10 per cent. of dairy farmers in Britain used them. From this time onwards economic factors forced their acceptance and by 1960 almost all farmers milking over 20 cows and over 85 per cent. of all dairy farmers used them.

Virtually all milking machines used today operate on the same principles. The teats are held in a rubber sleeve or *teat cup liner* which is fixed, usually under tension, within a *metal teatcup*. During milking the cavity within the rubber liner is maintained at a constant vacuum of between 13 and 18 in. of Hg and the air pressure in the cavity between the rubber liner and metal shell alternates about once per second between atmospheric and a similar vacuum to that within the liner. This is brought about by a valve mechanism known as a *pulsator*.

When the air pressures on either side of the liner are equal the liner assumes a tubular shape, the streak canal opens and milk flows into the liner but when the air pressure between the liner and teat cup is atmospheric the liner collapses round the teat squeezing the streak canal and stopping the flow of milk (Plate 46). As milking progresses the teat becomes flaccid and is drawn into the teatcup liner. Often so much teat is drawn into the liner that the flow of milk from the udder cistern to the teat cistern is impeded. When this occurs milk flow virtually ceases until the teat cups are pulled downwards. This manipulation of the teat cup,

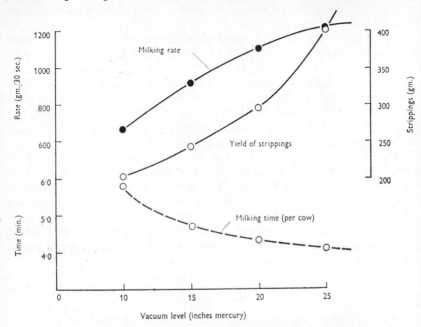

FIG. 25.—The effect of variation in vacuum on milking rate, strippings and milking time.

a routine practice at the end of milking, is known as machine stripping. It is clear from this brief description of mechanical milking that, as far as milk removal is concerned, the main factors are the vacuum, the pulsator and the teat cup liner.

**Vacuum.**—The effect on milking rate of varying the milking machine vacuum can be seen from (Fig. 25). As the vacuum increases so also does the milking rate and consequently milking time is reduced. But raising the vacuum also increases the amounts of milk held as strippings and as a result the decline in milking time when the vacuum exceeds 18 in. of Hg is small. In normal practice the vacuum should not be lower than 15 in. of Hg nor higher than 18 in. of Hg.

PLATE 45

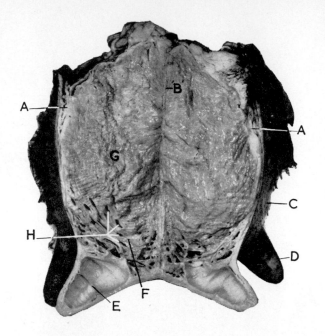

*A.* Cross-section of the Rear of a Cow's Udder

*A.* Lateral suspendory ligament
*B.* Median suspendory ligament
*C.* Skin
*D.* Front teat

*E.* Teat cistern
*F.* Gland cistern
*G.* Glandular substance
*H.* Ducts opening into gland system

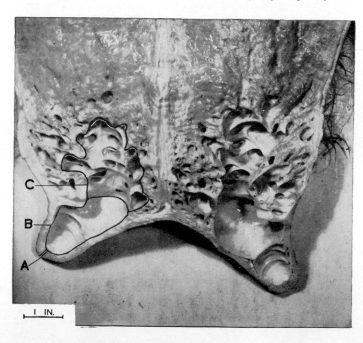

*B.* Cross-section of the Cistern Region of a Cow's Udder
*A.* Teat canal.    *B.* Teat cistern.    *C.* Gland cistern

PLATE 46

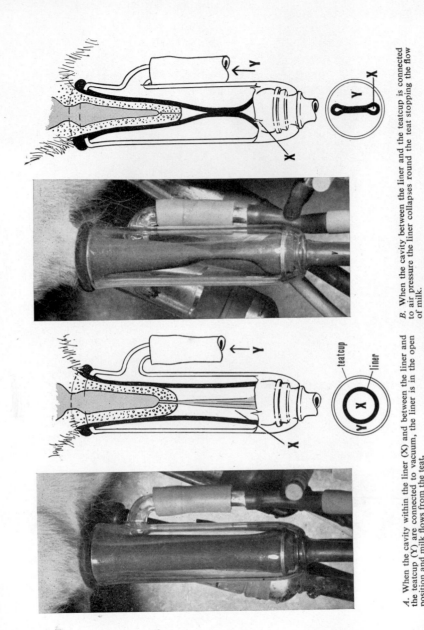

A. When the cavity within the liner (X) and between the liner and the teatcup (Y) are connected to vacuum, the liner is in the open position and milk flows from the teat.

B. When the cavity between the liner and the teatcup is connected to air pressure the liner collapses round the teat stopping the flow of milk.

THE REMOVAL OF MILK FROM THE UDDER
BY MILKING MACHINE

**Pulsation.**—This ryhthmical movement of the liner was introduced into machine milking because it was found that exposing the teat to a constant vacuum restricted the blood circulation causing pain to the cow and, in some conditions, damaged the teat. The collapse of the liner massages the teat and helps to maintain a more normal blood flow but it also stops the flow of milk for up to one half of each pulsation cycle.

ɪ In practice pulsation can be modified in two ways, by changing the frequency of the pulsation cycles, that is changing the pulsation rate and by altering the proportions of each pulsation cycle that the liner is collapsed or open. This altering the balance of the pulsation is known as changing the pulsation ratio. Most milking machines operate at a ratio of 1:1, that is the time that the liner is open is equal to the time that it is collapsed, but today the newer machines operate at ratios of 2:1 or even 3:1.

Both increasing pulsation rate or widening the pulsation ratio give faster milking. The latter is normally the most practical method of increasing the flow rate.

The improvements in milking machine performance that can be obtained by modifying vacuum and pulsation are important. Milking machines operating at a vacuum of 18 in. of Hg with a pulsation ratio of 3:1 milk about 20 per cent. faster than those operating at a vacuum of 15 in. of Hg with a ratio of 1:1. Savings in milking time can only be obtained in this way providing the milker's work routine allows him to take the machine from the cows at the correct time.

**Teatcup liners.**—The design of teatcup liners affects both the rate of milking and, more important, the quantity of milk that has to be removed as strippings. With the liners available in Britain in 1960, milking times of cows vary by about 20 per cent. between designs and the yields of strippings from about $\frac{1}{2}$ lb. to $1\frac{1}{2}$ lb. per cow at each milking. It has been shown that some of the variation in milking rate is due to the tension in the rubber when the liner is fixed in the teat cup, the higher the tension the faster the milking. Strippings are controlled mainly by the liner mouthpiece, the least strippings being obtained with liners with soft flexible mouths. Adding weight to the teatcup assembly will reduce the strippings yields, though with some good designs of liner it is impossible to add weight without the teatcup assembly falling from the udder.

**Milking rate.**—There are very large differences between cows in the rate at which milk leaves the udder during machine milking (Fig. 26). The range in maximum rate of flow is from about 1 to 14 lb. per min., with most cows between 4 and 8 lb. per min. Because of this and the differences between the milk yields of cows their milking times also show considerable variation from about 2 to over 20 minutes, with most cows between 3 and 8 minutes. The large differences between the milking rate of cows are in the main due to anatomical differences, those cows with large slack sphincters at the streak canal of the teat being the fastest milkers. Because of this it is found that the milking rates of individual cows do not vary greatly from day to day or even throughout their lives. This anatomical difference between teats has been found to be highly heritable.

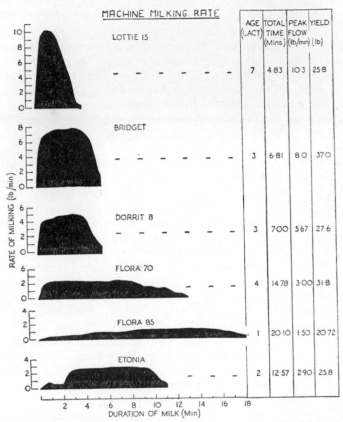

The machine milking rate of six cows in early lactation

FIG. 26.—Showing the variation in the milking rate of six cows in early lactation milked by machine.

Since milking rate is controlled anatomically, it is not surprising that the commonly held view—that cows can be trained to milk quickly or develop slow milking habits when badly managed—has been shown to be fallacious. It is true that milkers can influence the effectiveness of ejection but this does not alter milking rate significantly.

On average, fast milking cows give higher lactation yields than slow milkers, but they are more prone to udder infection.

# HERD MANAGEMENT AND UDDER HEALTH

Mastitis is an inflammation of the udder that follows physical damage or, more common and much more persistent and serious, an infection of one or more quarters by pathogenic bacteria. The bacteria enter the udder either during milking or between milkings, through the streak canal at the tip of the teat. These may set up an infection in the secretory tissue which can be detected by examining the milk. The presence of pathogenic bacteria, a rise in the leucocyte or white cell count and changes in the chemical composition indicate an infection. The infection progressively destroys the secretory tissue but the inflammation is often so slight that it cannot be detected by the milker examining the foremilk and feeling the udder. The course of an infection varies, it may spontaneously disappear, but more often it persists to erupt in a more acute form hours, weeks or even years after the onset. At any one time only about 5 per cent. of infections are in such a mastitic state that they are readily detected by the milker as hard, swollen quarters, clots in the milk and, in severe cases, a raised blood temperature of the cow and loss of appetite. Usually this acute form responds to intramammary therapy with antibiotics though often the infection itself is not eliminated.

Most infections are caused by *staphylococcus aureus, streptococcus agalactiae, streptococcus dysgalactiae, streptococcus uberis* and, less frequently, by *E. coli, Pseudomonas* sp. and *corynebacteria pyogenes.*

The effect of infections can be measured by milking cows with an individual quarter milking machine. In one study with this type of machine 92 infected quarters were found to be yielding an average of 30 per cent. less milk than uninfected quarters of the same cows, with both the solids not fat and fat percentages of the milk produced reduced by 0.3. The main change in milk composition is a reduced lactose content and a rise in the chloride concentration. When infections were eliminated, after treatment with antibiotics, the yields of milk did not recover until the next lactation but the chemical composition of the milk improved within a short time of treatment.

It is common to find over half the cows in a herd are infected, and it has been estimated that these yield about 10 per cent. less milk than uninfected cows. On that basis the true cost of udder disease to agriculture is substantial. In 1960 it was estimated roughly at £10 million per year in Britain; and the survey of wastage from dairy herds revealed mastitis to be the worst single disease and the second most important factor causing wastage from the herds.

Many physiological and environmental factors have been shown to predispose cows to infection. The very large differences in susceptibility between cows have not been completely explained but there is evidence that fast milking, high yielding cows are more easily infected and also those with poor healing skin of the teats. Other factors within the udder' such as the bacteriostatic properties of the milk may also be important. Apart from these differences which are largely genetic, the most important physiological factor is the stage of lactation of the cow. Cows in early lactation and in the first few weeks of the dry period are much more liable to contract an infection. While the incidence is much higher in old cows than in heifers, it has not yet been shown clearly whether this is due to an increase in susceptibility to infection or to the much longer period over which they have been exposed to infection.

High infection rates in individual herds have been attributed to many environmental factors. There is a general belief that milking machines used correctly need not be associated with high infection rates, but, real evidence of the bad effects of poor milking is scanty. The factors that are said to cause infection are milking with machines operating at high vacuum, *i.e.* over 15 in. of Hg, leaving milking machines on cows after milk flow has ceased, *i.e.* over-milking, faulty pulsators, badly designed teatcup liners and incompletely removing the strippings after machine milking. There is experimental evidence that all of these factors except the last can influence infection and mastitis, but the effects are much smaller than is generally believed. What is much more important is the evidence that mastitis occurs, often quite readily, even when all the so-called bad management practices are avoided. Experimental data indicate that the types and numbers of bacteria to which cows are exposed are a much more serious environmental factor. Most infections are caused by bacteria spread from cow to cow on teatcup liners, udder cloths and hands, and pathogens can be recovered from the skin of the teats of almost all cows. Because of this, hygiene routines are used in which the udders and teats are washed with cloths dipped in disinfectant solutions and teatcup clusters are dipped in disinfectant before each cow is milked. These routines do not prevent the spread of bacteria but they greatly reduce the numbers and, properly applied, help to maintain healthy skin on the teats. In this way they reduce the new infection rate though they cannot be regarded as satisfactory methods of control. Nevertheless, at the present time it appears that any effective method of farm prevention will have to be based on the development of more complete yet practical hygiene systems.

The types of infection that cannot be controlled by hygiene during milking are those contracted from soil, dung and airborne bacteria. These are normally infrequent, but gross contamination of the cows in wet and dirty strawyards or in very muddy fields can cause serious outbreaks with these types of infection.

**Control of infection on the farm.**—At the present time there is not a management routine which the farmer can adopt to prevent infections occurring or even to avoid a serious outbreak. But there are a number of ways in which the sensible farmer can minimise the chances of trouble.

Fortunately these are not expensive and most are good management practices from other view points.

1. The only infections that can be eliminated with certainty from a herd are those caused by *streptococcus agalactiae*. This is an important practical step to take because these infections are of the most damaging and infectious type. Eradication can readily be accomplished under veterinary supervision.

2. Reduce the exposure to pathogens by washing the udder with hypochlorite or other effective disinfectant. Adequately clean the milking machine each day and avoid housing cattle under wet or dirty conditions.

3. Avoid all damage to teats particularly at the tip and treat all wounds and sores with antiseptic cream.

4. Reduce dry period infection by lowering milk yields before drying off and dipping the teats in 5 per cent. iodine after the last milking. Give antibiotic treatment to all quarters known to have been infected in the previous lactation.

5. Adopt a sensible milking system, maintain the machine in good mechanical condition and do not let serious overmilking occur.

6. Examine foremilk at each milking and note any swellings and inflammation during machine stripping. This is the farmer's only reasonable way of detecting infection in order that it can be eliminated by antibiotic therapy under veterinary supervision.

In spite of taking these precautions, a herd may suffer a serious outbreak when further more complex routines may be needed. If this happens advice should be sought from the veterinary investigation service of the Ministry of Agriculture, Fisheries and Food acting in consultation with the farmer's own veterinary surgeon.

## MILKING MACHINES

**General Description.** All present day milking machines used in Britain are basically similar, the teat cup assemblies having the same principle of operation. The requirements are a constant vacuum applied to the end of the teat through the bore of the liner, and vacuum and atmospheric pressure alternately applied to the teat cup chamber (the squeeze and release phases). The basic components needed to give these conditions at the liner are: (1) a vacuum pump, usually a rotary type, either oil sealed or dry (using vanes of special carbon ), driven by an electric motor or an internal combustion engine; (2) a pipe system from which the pump exhausts air; (3) an interceptor vessel (" sanitary " trap) to prevent liquid from entering the pump; (4) a vacuum regulator to admit air as necessary, to maintain the required level of vacuum in the system in spite of variations in air admission elsewhere in the machine; (5) a vacuum gauge; (6) a separate pulsator for each milking unit or a master pulsator with pulse relays at each unit, to connect the pulsation chamber alternately to the vacuum system and the atmosphere. Fig. 27 shows the components normally used to give the air pressure conditions needed at the teat cup. There must also be a system for collecting the milk.

The method of disposing of the milk once it leaves the teat cup assembly, which in turn is largely dictated by the method of keeping and milking cows, accounts mainly for the different types of milking machine. The milk from the four teat cup assemblies of each milking unit is brought together in the clawpiece, from which it leaves by the rubber long milk tube. Along with the milk, there will be air that has leaked past the teats

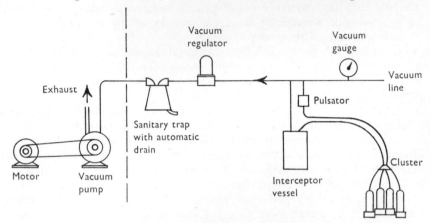

FIG. 27.—Diagram showing the basic components of a milking machine. All types are rather similar. They vary mainly in the length of the vacuum line and the system of collecting the milk after it leaves the cluster.

and carbon dioxide that evolves from the milk under the milking machine vacuum. At some point along the route to the vacuum pump the milk will be intercepted and either held under vacuum as a batch or brought out to the atmosphere. Where cows are milked in a cowshed, the common type of plant is a bucket machine, the portable interceptor vessel giving the name. The units—consisting of a cluster, long milk and pulse tubes, a bucket with an air tight lid carrying the pulsator and the stall tube—are taken to the cows and connected to the permanent vacuum pipeline at stall cocks between each pair of cows. Where milking is done in a parlour or a portable bail, the cows are brought to the milking units. Here the commonest types of installation are direct-to-can and pipeline machines. In the direct-to-can system, the milk from the cluster is intercepted in the can used for despatching milk from the farm. It is usually suspended from a balance which shows both the yield of individual cows and the total amount of milk in the can. With pipeline machines the milk from the cluster may be collected in a weigh jar suspended from a balance (or in a calibrated jar) to be carried away to the milkroom by the pipeline after each cow is milked, or the clusters may be connected to the pipeline. In the milkroom, the milk pipeline may discharge into a series of milk cans under vacuum or into a vacuum bulk tank. Alternatively, the milk may be brought out to atmospheric pressure by some form of mechanical releaser, or by a vacuum operated diaphragm pump or an electric rotary pump, and discharged over a surface cooler or into a refrigerated bulk tank.

There are many variants of these three main types of milking machine.

**Some Practical Features and Routine Maintenance.**—Vacuum pumps should be sited to allow easy access for starting, lubrication and belt tensioning and the use of a standby engine on occasions of electricity failure, and to ensure quietness and cleanliness where milking and milk handling take place, for example in a room or alcove adjacent to the milk-room. " Sanitary " traps are normally fitted above the pump, but a more workable arrangement is a self draining trap fitted close to the pump but in the milkroom, where it is more likely to receive neccessary attention.

The vacuum pipeline system can be a serious source of contamination of the milk if not correctly installed and maintained. When there is an inrush of air at one milking unit, for example when a cluster falls off the cow, there will be a temporary loss of vacuum throughout the plant. This will involve an air flow from the main vacuum line back into the interceptor vessels of the other milking units, such as the buckets and weigh jars. The risk is that a violent surge of air may carry foul liquid from the vacuum line into the milking unit, for inevitably a considerable amount of condensation forms in the vacuum system from vapour given off by the warm milk. The pipeline should be installed with a fall of at least 1 in 80, connections to the unit should enter from above, automatic drain cocks should be fitted at low points, and the pipeline should be washed through with hot detergent solution at least once a month as a routine, and in addition every time milk enters the line accidentally.

The vacuum gauge provides an immediate means of checking at any time during milking whether the vacuum system as a whole is functioning correctly. A fluctuating reading (more than 0·5 in. Hg to each side of the expected reading) indicates a sticking regulator, or untoward incidents such as a stall cock left open by mistake or a displaced rubber connection somewhere in the system. Clearly, the gauge should be fitted where it can be seen most readily during the course of a milking.

Vacuum regulators are almost always of the dead weight type, the weight holding the valve closed until the working level is attained. At this point the vacuum lifts the valve off its seat allowing air to enter at the rate required to make good the excess capacity of the pump. If the valve guide and seat become dirty, sensitivity will be lost and the reading at the gauge will fluctuate. The valve should then be dismantled and cleaned, hot detergent solution being adequate. These valves are designed to operate dry and should not be lubricated. Vacuum regulators will not alter their characteristics with age, at least as far as the maximum vacuum value is concerned. Therefore, each time the regulator is cleaned the accuracy of the gauge can be checked simply by observing that there is no change from the expected reading. The regulator should be fitted where it is least likely to take in dust, particularly, from feeding stuffs, and at about head height so that entry of air can be heard. With all units working and the vacuum gauge showing the expected reading, some air will enter at the regulator if there is no serious loss of function of the pump or undetected leakage of air in the system. When the vacuum is low, no air should enter at the regulator showing that the valve faces are neither dirty nor damaged.

Inadequate pumping capacity is one of the commonest faults in the use of milking machines on farms. This can arise through lack of oil in the pump, gradual loss of function due to wear or the addition of further milking units to an existing installation without due regard to pump capacity. There is a temporary drop in vacuum each time air is admitted to a system as, for example, in evacuating a bucket unit. In the absence of leaks the working level of vacuum should be regained in 3 to 5 seconds if the pump capacity is adequate.

There is a wide variety of pulsation systems which broadly fall into the two groups, individual pulsators at each milking unit or a master pulsator operating a pulsator relay valve at each unit. Transmission of the controlling pulse in the system using relays may be pneumatic for short distances as in parlours, or electric for longer distances as in cow sheds. Control of the pulsation rate may be by the rate of admission of air in vacuum driven pulsators, by pendulum, by synchronous motor or simply by gearing from the vacuum pump shaft to a rotary valve. Now that it is usual to have a short squeeze and a longer release phase of liner movement (wide ratio) all four pulse chambers in the cluster are connected to a single long pulse tube. Failure of the liners to collapse is the most serious malfunction of the milking machine that the operator has to guard against. A useful test is to thrust the thumbs into two liners, the other two teat cups hanging in the cut-off position. If the milker has accustomed himself to the action of the particular liner, any serious change of the movement of the liner from the normal may readily be detected. Each liner should collapse evenly, and close completely below the tip of the thumb.

Milking machine rubberware should be renewed at regular intervals. The life of the various components is not uniform but, so far as renewal is concerned, all rubber parts may conveniently be divided into liners and other rubberware. Components other than liners last for a year or two, and as mechanical failure is rare they are often retained in service when the inner surfaces have become difficult to clean. A sound procedure is to renew all rubberware annually at the beginning of the summer. Liners need to be changed at very widely differing intervals, depending on the milking duty and type of liner as well as other factors. Loss of shape, particularly at the mouthpiece allowing air to enter, is the most obvious indication that the liners should be renewed. All, of course, should be replaced at the one time or the milking efficiency will be limited by the one or two worn liners on each cluster.

## MILK HANDLING EQUIPMENT

Milk is despatched from the farm once a day, either in cans (churns) or by road tanker if the system of bulk collection is practised. The basic requirements of each system are that the milk should be cooled to limit bacterial growth and placed ready for collection with the minimum effort. These are met in a most straightforward way by the refrigerated bulk tank. Once milk is placed in it, cooling to below 50° F. (almost all bacteria already in the milk will not grow below this temperature) is assured, and as the milk is pumped direct from the farm bulk tank to the road tanker no further effort by the farm staff is required. However, very considerable capital outlay is involved in the provision of the bulk tank and possibly of an adequate access road for the tanker; and not all milk production enterprises are large enough to bear the cost. Nor, for various reasons, are all local areas suited to bulk collection. And so, although a substantial increase in this method of milk handling on the farm may be expected, the alternative system of despatch in cans is likely to remain common for some long time.

**Milk cooling with can collection.**—In-can cooling is the obvious choice with direct-to-can milking, and the turbine cooler (Plate 47, *A*) using water from a piped supply is widely employed. The turbine cooler uses about 3 gal. of water to cool each gallon of milk, and enables a can of milk to be cooled to within 5° F. of the temperature of the cooling water in 12 to 15 minutes. The water enters at the centre of the cooler, passes around the loop immersed in the milk, and then leaves by two tangential reaction jets to be distributed over the entire external surface of the can. The loop assembly is mounted in a bearing and rotates as a result of the thrust from the reaction jets, thus stirring the milk to give very much better heat transfer both at the surface of the loop and at the internal surface of the can. The number of turbine coolers required with a direct-to-can installation is not more than the number of milking units and is usually less, as the time necessary to fill cans is considerably greater than the time to cool them.

The turbine cooler has widely displaced the surface cooler formerly used in conjunction with hand milking and with bucket milking machines. Lifting the milk into a pan over the cooler is avoided, there is less apparatus to clean and, more important, it greatly reduces the time spent in carrying milk from the cowshed to the milk room. The cans are carried on a wheeled trolley equipped with weighing and recording gear, and the milker moves this trolley along the cowshed so that the distance between the milking and tipping points is as short as possible. Milk is moved from the cowshed only in lots of two or more full cans.

Surface coolers with a distributor from the bottom tray to fill several cans simultaneously are still used fairly frequently with pipeline milking machines. The alternative system is filling, under vacuum, a series of cans equipped with special lids, gaskets and loop tubes, cooling water being applied externally to the cans from sparge rings during filling (Plate 47, *B*). A higher ratio of water to milk is required with this system 4 to 6:1 than with surface coolers 2 to 4:1 or turbine coolers 3:1.

The present legal requirements for milk cooling on farms are given in the Milk and Dairies (General) Regulations, 1959. Milk must without delay be cooled " either (i) to a temperature not exceeding 50° F. or (ii) if the temperature of the water supply available for cooling is 45° F. or above, to a temperature not more than 5° F. above the temperature of that supply." Water direct from wells and boreholes may always be relied on to be at temperatures not above 55° F., but surface supplies and piped supplies whether private or public may, in the height of summer, attain temperatures even above 70° F. Water cooling can therefore give temperatures from below 60° F. in the most favourable circumstances to about 75° F. under the worst conditions. The effect of cooling in limiting the rate of growth of bacteria falls off very rapidly over this range, although cooling even to 75° F. is useful, particularly in greatly restricting the growth of mastitis staphylococci.

All forms of cooling apparatus using water can also be operated with chilled water from a refrigerated tank. Where there is an acute shortage of water this system may be forced on the farmer, but otherwise a choice has to be made. Is it more satisfactory to take pains to so limit contamination of the milk from all sources (the udder internally and externally, the milking machine, the cooling apparatus and the cans) that even with poor cooling the milk reaches the buyer in an acceptable condition, or to accept the additional cost of refrigeration? Both alternatives have been shown to be effective. Mains water cooling costs about 0·15d. per gallon: the cost of chilled water cooling will vary widely with the daily production of milk, but at present a price of 0·7-1·0d. per gallon is common. Unlike refrigeration associated with farm bulk tanks, chilled water cooling of milk in cans does not at present attract a higher selling price. It should also be noted that, if rapid reheating of milk takes place, much of the benefit, particularly of chilled water cooling, will be lost. Filled cans should therefore not be stored in high ambient temperature conditions. Insulated covers are available to assist in this. Roadside milk stands should be carefully sited and the cans should be shaded.

**Farm bulk tanks.**—At present, the construction and the performance of farm bulk tanks to be used in Britain must conform to a specification jointly issued by the various Milk Marketing Boards. A stainless steel inner milk vessel is required, under conditions of maximum morning load of milk and an ambient temperature of 90° F. the milk shall be cooled to 40° F. within $2\frac{1}{2}$ hours of the beginning of milking, and requirements for accessories such as the closure of the milk outlet, agitator, thermometer, thermostat and dipstick are stated. Measurement of the volume of milk in the tank at the time of collection is by dipstick. A maximum volume per inch depth is specified for the different sizes of tank. The agitator is used for mixing the milk before a sample is taken.

Most of the bulk tanks now available have an ice-building evaporator in the water filled jacket surrounding the inner vessel, with an external layer of insulation and smooth impervious exterior surfaces. (Plate 48, *A*). The stainless steel cover is not insulated. To achieve the specified rates of cooling some provision for rapid melting of the ice on the evaporator coils is necessary. Agitation by air released from holes in a tube at the base of the jacket is usual. It is also necessary to improve the rate of heat transfer by using the agitator to stir the milk during cooling.

There are alternative methods of cooling the inner vessel besides the water filled jacket. Chilled water from a tank under the milk vessel or from a completely separate unit may be pumped to a spray line fixed to the outside of the inner vessel near to the top. Direct expansion cooling may also be used, the evaporator being attached to the bottom of the inner vessel. With this system all the heat from the milk must, of course, be extracted by the condensing unit during the allowed cooling period and bulk tanks larger than about 150 gal. capacity are more expensive than equivalent ones with ice-building evaporators. Moreover, large direct expansion condensing units create problems of electricity supply as the load is high for fairly short times and usually at peak demand periods.

**Milk Strainers.**—A milk strainer usually consists of a vessel into which milk may be easily poured. It has a large diameter outlet fitted with a perforated plate which supports a single service filter disc. There is no evidence that removing debris by straining improves the bacteriological state of milk, but the buyer and consumer, quite rightly, object to extraneous material in milk offered to them. Every effort should be made to prevent its entry, and this is usually the more economical approach.

## CLEANING AND DISINFECTION OF MILKING AND MILK HANDLING EQUIPMENT

The Milk and Dairies (General) Regulations 1959 require that all apparatus coming in contact with milk is so constructed that it can be readily cleaned, and that as soon after use as is practicable it shall be cleaned with or without the use of a detergent and disinfected by means of steam, boiling water or one of the chemicals approved for the purpose.

These operations have two objectives. First, any surface which is to come into contact with food should appear clean. Secondly, since it is not possible to remove all bacteria and their food supplies by practical cleaning methods, a disinfection treatment is given to so reduce the numbers and kinds of bacteria that milk of acceptable bacteriological quality may be produced. Disinfection makes good the deficiencies of the cleaning process—perfect cleaning implying freedom from all contaminating material including bacteria. Thus, although the mode of operation of detergents and disinfectants is quite different, the better the cleaning the more readily may adequate disinfection be achieved. While this distinction is not of prime importance when heat, which can readily penetrate residues, is used, it is of very real importance in the application of chemical disinfectants.

During the last decade or so the use of heat disinfection has greatly declined in popularity. The Milk and Dairies Regulations (1949) for the first time permitted the use of approved chemicals in the place of steam or boiling water for all dairy utensils, although previously chemical disinfection was permitted for milking machines. The effectiveness of heat disinfection has never been in question; the advantage of chemicals is cheapness.

The cost of cleaning and disinfection is not a trifling part of the total cost of milk production. Various surveys have been made which show that the range of costs, in practice, is from 2 to 10 per cent of the total costs. The higher costs appear to be associated more with poor organisation of work routines than with inherent differences in cost of the various systems available, labour costs always being the greatest single item (of the order of 50 per cent.). However, a small output of milk with a given set of equipment will obviously increase the cost per gallon. For example, if one hour is spent per day in cleaning, this represents about 4 per cent. of the total cost of producing 50 gal. of milk, whereas 100 gal. of milk per day could probably be produced at roughly the same costs for cleaning.

Cleaning by brushing the equipment with a warm detergent solution is still the most common and important method, and is applicable to most dairy equipment. A chemical disinfectant may be applied in the washing solution, as a separate solution afterwards or heat disinfection with steam or very hot water may follow washing. Immersion cleaning avoids the drudgery of hand brushing. It is specially suited to direct-to-can equipment but can also be used with bucket milking equipment. Pipeline milking machines, which are increasing in numbers with the growth of bulk collection, cannot economically be dismantled at each milking for hand cleaning. The previous method of cleaning by flushing at each milking and steaming once a day, with complete dismantling for hand cleaning once a week, has now largely given way to circulation cleaning.

For all methods of cleaning, a water supply of the standard required by the Milk and Dairies Regulations is essential. Local supplies may need chlorinating. A piped supply to the points of usage is very desirable. Hot water, needed also for udder washing, is essential for all methods except immersion cleaning, but even then, it is a distinct advantage. Electricity is now finding favour for water heating because of its convenience. Storage units with an immersion heater controlled by a thermostat are common, as are open-topped domestic wash boilers. These have the advantages of cheapness and the ability to produce boiling water if required.

**External cleaning.**—Immediately after milking and before any internal cleaning is attempted, any external soil on the equipment should be removed with a brush and cold water. This operation should not be done over the wash trough. With fixed equipment in a parlour it is convenient to use clean water from a bucket and an udder wash cloth or a brush.

**Hand washing and chemical disinfection.**—Full details of recommended techniques are given in Advisory Leaflet No. 422 of the Ministry of Agriculture, Fisheries and Food. There are three basic processes: (i) *Cold or tepid water rinse.* Most of the residual milk may be removed by rinsing with cold water. With bucket units, it is convenient to draw water from a pail through the cluster into the milking bucket by vacuum. Clusters of direct-to-can units may be thoroughly and quickly rinsed by attaching the long milk tube to the cold water tap, shaking the cluster so that the streams of water from the milk stems contact the liners. If the equipment is not to be washed immediately, steps should be taken to prevent drying out. (ii) *Hot detergent-disinfectant wash.* The equipment required is a wash trough large enough to hold two or three clusters at a time (larger troughs lead to waste of hot water), a set of brushes and a cleaning rod appropriate to the make of equipment, and a general purpose dairy brush. An impervious surface is also necessary for holding the equipment awaiting rinsing after washing and on which to reassemble the equipment. Make up a detergent-disinfectant solution at about 115° F. containing one half pound of dairy detergent and 4 fluid ounces of approved hypochlorite solution per 10 gallons. Alternatively, make up the solution with an approved detergent-disinfectant at the strength stated by the manufacturer. Remove the long milk tubes from the clusters and open the clawpieces. Brush all internal surfaces and place the clusters aside wet with solution so that the disinfectant action continues. Then wash all the other components, disassembling as required so that all surfaces may be brushed. Brush the trough as the washing solution runs to waste. (iii) *Final clear water rinse.* Rinse the components free from detergent-disinfectant at the tap, or in the trough if the water requires to be chlorinated (one fluid ounce per 10 gal.). Reassemble the clusters and lids and store all items on a rack so that they drain completely.

Additional treatments to the above routine at each milking are generally recommended to minimise the effects of gradual deterioration of rubber parts and the build-up of milkstone. Once a week the equipment should be completely dismantled and carefully inspected. Milkstone, if present, may be removed with phosphoric acid or one of the proprietary compounds sold for the purpose. Other possible treatments are weekly heat treatment (water at not less than 185° F. for 2 minutes or steam); a hot detergent solution soak of rubber components (30 minutes at an initial temperature of 185° F.); use of two sets of rubber components week about, with the resting set stored in 5 per cent. caustic soda solution; and wet storage of teat-cup clusters which are placed in a rack and filled with a detergent-disinfectant solution or 0·5 per cent caustic soda solution. The fact that treatments additional to routine brushing at each milking are widely recommended seems to indicate that in practice hand cleaning combined with chemical disinfection is not always applied well enough to be wholly satisfactory.

**Immersion cleaning.**—Full details with illustrations are given in Advisory Leaflet No. 496 of the Ministry of Agriculture, Fisheries and Food. The principle of this technique is to immerse the milk contact equipment for the whole period between milkings in a cleaning solution which is also bactericidal. The solution used is 3 per cent. caustic soda and also contains ethylene diaminetetra-acetic acid (EDTA) to prevent deposition of calcium salts. The equipment is contained in a special basket to avoid air locking and so that it can be lifted in and out of the solution in a bin without splashing.

Before milking the basket is lifted clear of the solution and drained. The components are then transferred to a small wash trough containing cold or preferably lukewarm chlorinated water and are rinsed free from caustic soda. The long tubes are rinsed at the tap. The units are then assembled for milking. After milking, external soil is removed and the units then returned to the trough for rinsing before being partly disassembled and packed into the basket.

At monthly intervals the solution in the bin is renewed. Packs of chemicals are available, the whole contents of a pack being tipped into the bin containing water and dissolved by stirring. At the same time, the equipment is completely dismantled, rubberwear examined and, if necessary, renewed, and all components brought to as-new condition of cleanliness by brushing in warm water. Descaling is generally not necessary.

Immersion cleaning was originally designed for direct-to-can milking equipment. All the components from three milking units may be packed into the basket. The technique may also be used with bucket units, the buckets being separately cleaned with hot detergent-disinfectant solution. Several manufacturers supply suitable direct-to-can and bucket milking equipment, the essentials being a one piece liner assembly which can be freed within the cup for rinsing free from caustic soda, uncomplicated lid assemblies allowing free access of solution and metal parts of stainless steel which is not attacked by caustic soda. A dairy equipped for immersion cleaning is shown in Plate 48, *B*.

**Circulation cleaning of pipeline machines.**—Unlike other methods so far described, circulation cleaning in the early sixties has not advanced to the stage of having a single well established technique. It is generally agreed that steam disinfection is too expensive, that a successful technique must clean all equipment coming into contact with milk, including weigh jars, and that complete dismantling once a week or even once a month is too time consuming to be acceptable. In all present day plants the cleaning fluids are drawn around the circuit by the milking machine vacuum, are separated from air in an interceptor vessel, and are pumped out from under vacuum by an electric pump or a vacuum operated diaphragm pump. Also the cleaning routines recommended by manufacturers are similar, consisting of a pre-rinse and a final rinse both of plain cold water and a warm detergent-disinfectant wash which is circulated for varying periods up to 30 minutes. While the results achieved in practice suggest that current principles will persist, improvements in several directions are desirable. Efforts are being made to modify the milking and cleaning circuits so that fewer manual operators are required to set the plant ready for milking and for cleaning. Also bacteriological results are variable and there is a trend to rather long circulation times at relatively high temperatures (up to 160° F.) which make the process less straightforward than seemed likely at one time.

**Cleaning and disinfection of farm bulk tanks.**—Since the inner vessel of most bulk tanks is permanently in contact with chilled water, the cleaning system must of necessity rely on chemicals applied at rather low temperatures. After the tank has been emptied, the driver of the road tanker will, as part of his duties, rinse the interior with cold water. A hose with a spray nozzle should be provided ready to hand. Before washing the tank, remove the agitator and dipstick and the thermometer and thermostat, if they are fitted inside the tank, and wash these pieces of equipment separately. Add 10 gal. of water at 110° F. containing one half pound of dairy detergent and 4 fluid ounces of approved hypochlorite solution (or a combined detergent-disinfectant made up at the strength recommended by the manufacturer) to the tank. Scrub all surfaces with a long handled brush, paying particular attention to the underside of the bridge, the covers and the outlet closure. Scrub the interior of the outlet pipe as the solution is run to waste. Finally, rinse with chlorinated water (1 oz. per 10 gal.) and drain. It may be necessary to use a descaling compound at intervals.

**Milk cans.**—It is a legal requirement in England and Wales that milk cans be cleaned and disinfected after emptying, that is at the receiving dairy, but there is an equal obligation on the farmer not to place milk in a can which is unfit for the purpose. Unless cans on inspection at the farm are visually clean and quite dry, add about 2 gal. of warm water plus one half fluid ounce of hypochlorite solution to one can, and wet the whole of the interior surface and the lid with the solution, using a general purpose dairy brush. Pour the solution into the next can and repeat the series of operations until all cans have been treated. Then turn the cans upside down to drain.

If the cans are visibly dirty or contain foul liquid, a similar technique may be used with a hot detergent-disinfectant solution, after which the cans should be rinsed with plain or chlorinated water.

## MACHINE MILKING ROUTINES

While a herd of cows is being milked, the milking machine operator spends most of the time repeating a regular sequence of operations associated with the milking of each cow plus occasional jobs such as moving milk in cans and attending to milk cooling. The routine work includes the essential jobs of washing the udder and removing foremilk, putting teat cups on the teats, machine stripping and removing the teat cups at the end of milking. In cowsheds the units have to be moved from cow to cow; in parlours the cows are moved in and out of the stalls. Other jobs such as the feeding of concentrates and the recording of milk yields may be included in the work routine, and machine stripping may be omitted.

The object of a milking routine is to ensure that adequate attention is given to the milking of each cow while allowing the milker to operate two or more milking units. This is possible because the activities of the milker are confined to a few essential operations associated with milking.

A well organised routine ensures that the interval between udder washing, which stimulates milk ejection, and the start of milking does not exceed three minutes; and so milking is completed before milk ejection declines and the milker is available, when milk flow ceases, to machine strip and remove the teat cups. The number and duration of the operations in a milking routine affects the total time the milker devotes to each cow. Reasonable times for routine jobs, based on work study measurements, are shown in Table 17.

Udder washing and foremilking can be completed in 0·5 min., providing the udder and teats are reasonably clean and washing is confined to the teats and the parts of the udder likely to come in contact with teat cups or the hands of the milker. Likewise machine stripping times of 0·5 min. or less per cow are possible with the use of teat cup liners which leave only small amounts of strippings and a suitable milk flow indicator to indicate when the teat cups should be removed. A conscious effort on the part of the milker is also required to remove the teat cups as soon as possible.

A milker spending two to three minutes doing routine jobs on each cow can milk 20 to 30 cows per hour. The elimination of machine stripping or milk carrying in cowsheds can reduce routine times to 1½ min.

PLATE 47

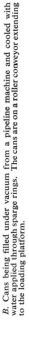

*B.* Cans being filled under vacuum from a pipeline machine and cooled with water applied through sparge rings. The cans are on a roller conveyor extending to the loading platform.

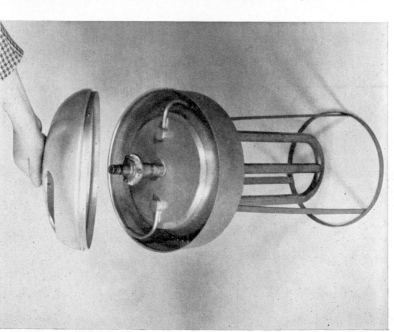

*A.* TURBINE COOLER IN STAND

The top cover has been lifted to show the reaction jets which rotate the stirrer. The holes in the tray, through which water is distributed over the milk can, are just visible.

PLATE 48

*A.* A FARM BULK TANK WITH COVERS REMOVED

The inner vessel is surrounded by a water filled jacket containing the ice-building **evaporator**. The stirrer is in the centre and the dipstick to the right

*B.* EQUIPMENT FOR IMMERSION CLEANING

The basket is lodged in the rim of the bin for draining. Two cans are set ready to receive the units when they have been rinsed and made up for milking

per cow and enable a milker to manage more units and milk up to 40 cows per hour.

**Organisation of milking in cowsheds.**—In organising cowshed milking every effort must be made to reduce the number of visits to the milk room and limit the movement of units in the cowshed.

Time can be saved by feeding all concentrates before the milking clusters are brought into the shed, and by using the udder wash and

TABLE 17

TIME REQUIRED FOR ROUTINE OPERATIONS

| Operation | Time in minutes per cow |
|---|---|
| (a) *In Parlours* | |
| Machine strip and remove cups | ·4 |
| Read and reset balance . . | ·1 |
| Put on teat cups . . . | ·2 |
| Record milk yield . . . | ·1 |
| Change cows . . . . | ·2 |
| Feed concentrates . . . | ·1 |
| Wash and foremilk . . | ·5 |
| Total . . | 1·6 |
| (b) *In Cowsheds:* | |
| Machine strip and remove cups | ·4 |
| Change pail . . . . | ·3 |
| Put on teat cups . . . | ·3 |
| Wash udder and foremilk . | ·5 |
| Move unit . . . . | ·2 |
| Transport and tip milk . . | ·3 |
| Total . . . | 2·0 |

massage as the let-down stimulus. If this procedure involves a change of routine, it should be started at the beginning of a calving season as each cow calves, otherwise difficulties may be experienced with some mature cows. During milking a cowshed can be regarded as an extended two-stall per unit parlour in which units are moved instead of cows. Milking should start at one end of the shed and proceed to the other end so that the units are always close together.

If the cows are grouped according to yield and moved once or twice during a lactation (normally only a few cows would be changed at any one time), milking could start at one end of the shed in the morning and the other end for the afternoon milking, though for the majority of herds it is unlikely that efforts to equalise intervals will prove worth while.

The choice over milk carrying is a simple one. Where bucket units are in good condition and there is good access to the milk room, little expense need be incurred in reducing the number of visits to the milk room.  Milk from the bucket units can be tipped into cans on a wheeled trolley (Plate 49) in the cowshed *and two or more full cans* taken on each visit to the milk room where turbine or sparge ring coolers should be used to cool the milk.  Where one or more cowsheds are some distance from the milk room it may be worth while to move a portable enclosed cooling stand to a suitable point just outside each cowshed in turn so that all movement to the milk room is done after milking.

The grouping of the units, the placing of the udder wash equipment and the movement of the trolley are shown in Fig. 28.  When milk is

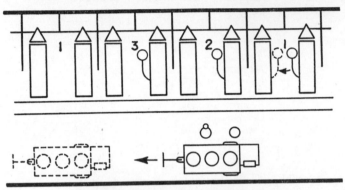

FIG. 28.—Cowshed milking routine showing the grouping of the units and the movement of the trolley.

weighed, all unit buckets should be of equal weight and so available for weighing.

To avoid unnecessary visits to the cow the milker should take the change pail to the stall when stripping the first cow of a pair, so that after the removal of the unit from one cow a journey to the tipping point is not made until the cluster is on the second cow.

When moving from one pair of cows to another the milker should collect the udder wash bucket (with foremilk cup clipped on one side) from the tipping point or trolley and change unit pails at the trolley. Milk weighing should always be done after a unit has been put on the next cow.

The introduction of bulk milk tanks on farms has made it possible to eliminate the carrying of milk from cowshed to milk room.  Milk is transferred from the cowshed to the milk room through a pipeline.

For cowsheds two forms of pipeline milking machines are available. Both, which can be circulation cleaned, will move milk from the cowshed to a bulk tank, or cans standing at lorry platform height in the milk room. One arrangement eliminates the carrying of milk altogether.  It consists of a stainless steel, glass or plastic pipeline over all the stalls in a cowshed, with a side connection between each pair of animals to which the cluster is attached. Milk drawn by vacuum to the milk room may be pumped or released into a bulk tank or over a surface cooler into several cans. Alternatively, milk may be drawn into a series of cans under vacuum and cooled by water from sparge rings on to the necks of the first three or four cans. The cans used for cooling have long inlet tubes so that air is drawn through the milk to cause agitation and accelerate cooling.

The disadvantages of this system are the cost of the pipeline (particularly if there are several cowsheds on the farm), vacuum fluctuations in long pipelines when several units are in use and the need for containers such as buckets when milk yields are recorded. The only milk meter now available is very expensive and is liable to get broken if used in cowsheds and moved frequently. The difficulty and cost of ensuring adequate cleaning of very long pipelines, with covered side outlets every six to seven feet, is a further hazard.

The other pipeline system eliminates the carrying of milk to the milk room but requires the use of buckets in the cowshed. This system should be of particular interest to farmers with several cowsheds and those who wish to weigh the milk from each cow at every milking. The cost of this pipeline system is much less than that previously described because only one length of small bore flexible plastic tube is required. The equipment, which is used extensively in the United States of America, consists of a mobile vessel with a bottom outlet and a ball float which covers the outlet when the vessel is empty. The outlet is connected to a balance jar under vacuum and a releaser or milk pump in the milk room by means of the flexible pipe which is run on or off a reel as the trolley is moved along the cowshed. There are no problems over vacuum with this equipment and only one length of relatively cheap flexible tube is required for several sheds. Moreover, there are no side connections, so circulation cleaning should be more effective. To avoid damage the tube can be hung from ceiling hooks in the cowshed.

Where one double range cowshed is involved a fixed stainless steel line with connections at two or three points may be fixed over the central passage to provide the means of transferring milk from the tipping vessel to the milk room.

**Milking Parlours.** In a milking parlour or movable bail all the equipment is fixed and the cows move through the building during milking. The concentration of all the equipment in a small space, and the collection of milk in cans or a bulk tank enables the milker to make effective use of the milking units with the minimum effort. Even where direct-to-can milking is practised very little time is occupied in moving milk to the adjacent milk room.

All milking parlours can be classified into two basic types; those having a milking unit for each stall and those having a milking unit for each pair of stalls.

During milking the milker carries out a regular sequence of operations for each cow and occasional jobs such as moving cows and attending to cooling equipment. The routine work includes moving the cow in and out of a stall, feeding concentrates, washing the udder, putting on the teat cups, machine stripping and removing the teat cups. In all parlours with one stall per unit, these operations, other than machine stripping, are carried out while the unit is idle and this limits the utilisation of the unit. In parlours with two stalls per unit the unit is idle only while the cluster is transferred from one cow to another in the opposite stall. Thus the total time a unit is associated with a cow (*i.e.*, milking of the cow plus the time the unit is idle while routine work is done for the cow) is about one minute longer in parlours with one stall per unit than in those with two stalls per unit.

The time a cow spends in the milking stall is most important when concentrates are fed during milking. In one stall per unit layouts a cow is in a stall while it is prepared and milked and does not have time to consume more than 3-5 lb. of concentrates. Where a unit is shared between a pair of stalls each cow is in the parlour for almost all the time required for the milking of the two cows and consequently it is possible to feed 6-8 lb. of concentrates per cow per milking.

## ORGANISATION OF MILKING IN PARLOURS

**Stall layouts** (see Fig. 29).—The layout of the stalls in either type of parlour may be abreast or tandem and the cows may stand at the same level or 8 to 36 in. higher than the milker. With two floor levels (one 30-36 in. higher than the other) in tandem layouts, the milker can work standing erect and so reduce fatigue. The difference in levels can be achieved by lowering the floor of the work area or by raising the floor of the stalls and providing steps (not ramps) for the cows outside the parlour. A distinct advantage of two level tandem layouts is that the cows enter and leave the stalls without crossing the work area of the milker.

The layouts of one or two man operated parlours are shown in Fig. 29. In abreast parlours the entrance door should be on the inside and in the centre of the wall facing the stalls and should slide in both directions. This enables the milker to open the door and follow behind a cow entering the parlour.

In three-unit tandem parlours the stalls may be in line, L-shaped or U-shaped. The in-line layout is simplest and fits into a building 25 ft. by 10 ft.

A four-stall four-unit tandem has two stalls on each side of a 4-4½ ft. wide pit. This minimises the distance walked by the milker and the cows entering the stalls. The six-stall six-unit double tandem layout has three stalls on each side of a 5-6 ft. wide pit and each milker operates the units on one side of the parlour.

PLATE 49

Milk cans filled from Bucket Units ready for transport to Milk Room

It is essential that an entrance door be provided for each line of stalls in tandem parlours. A simple arrangement is a self-closing sliding door which can be opened from the pit by means of a drawcord. The door will close satisfactorily if the overhead track is fixed with a fall of some 3-4 in. along its length. A narrow doorway at the entrance end of the pit in tandem layouts enables the milker to get behind any animals hesitating at the entrance doors.

In the conventional two-stall per unit double tandem layout, each unit is shared between the stalls on opposite sides of the operator's pit. Each stall has an entry and exit gate giving access to a passageway along the outside of each line of stalls. Although highly efficient this layout is comparatively expensive for commercial herds.

In Chute and Herringbone parlours there are no side passages and all the cows on one side of the parlour are changed when all the units are in use on the opposite side of the parlour. Batch milking does simplify the work of the milker because fewer doors and gates have to be operated to get cows in and out of the parlour, and if the variation in milking times of cows is not excessive the number of cows milked per hour is not affected.

The Chute parlour with a 4 ft. wide pit can be installed in a building 10 ft. wide. A door at the front of each stall slides inwards across the pit when a batch of cows is changed. The layout with six-stalls and three units is suitable for all herds of 30 to 50 cows milked by one milker. Two such parlours sited side by side or in line with a common central dairy provide an economic installation for herds up to 100 cows milked by two men.

In the Herringbone layout, units are only 3-4 ft. apart compared with the $7\frac{1}{2}$-8 ft. in other tandem parlours, and consequently 3-10 units can be operated in a single parlour. This is a suitable parlour layout where one man must operate 4-5 units to milk 50-70 cows or where two milkers are required to use 6-10 units for herds of 80 to 150 cows.

**Feeding Equipment in Parlours.**—In commercial herds all concentrate feeding may be done in the milking parlour and where this is practised, storage facilities should be provided above or adjacent to the parlour. Mechanical feed meters are now available which can be fitted to any milking parlour and which will dispense concentrates into mangers on the stalls. Although relatively expensive, these meters are preferable to open scoops and can be gravity fed from a loft or by auger conveyors from an adjacent food store. Now that suitable equipment is available for feeding concentrates in Herringbone parlours there is no longer a need for special feeding passages or ties and mangers, at which the cows can be fed in batches immediately outside the parlour.

**Udder Washing.**—A strip-cup and bucket of water for udder washing should be provided for each milking unit and in two-level tandem parlours this equipment should be mounted at a convenient height for the milker.

One stall per unit layouts: one-man operated parlours

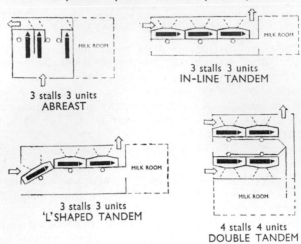

3 stalls 3 units
ABREAST

3 stalls 3 units
IN-LINE TANDEM

3 stalls 3 units
'L'SHAPED TANDEM

4 stalls 4 units
DOUBLE TANDEM

One stall per unit layouts: two-man operated parlours

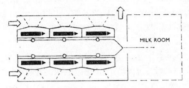

6 stalls 6 units DOUBLE TANDEM

KEY:—

▬▬►    Cows

⇨    Direction of movement of cows through parlour

O    Direct-to-can milking units

——O——·—- Pipeline milking units

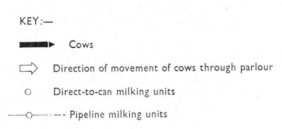

FIG. 29
Stall layouts in milking
parlours.

PARLOU

### ONE-MAN OPERATED PARLOURS

| ONE STALL/UNIT | | TWO STALLS/UNIT |
|---|---|---|
| ABREAST:<br>3 Stalls—3 Units<br>IN-LINE TANDEM:<br>3 Stalls—3 Units<br>'L' SHAPED TANDEM:<br>3 Stalls—3 Units | } For Herds of 20-40 Cows | ABREAST:<br>4 Stalls—2 Units<br>DOUBLE TANDEM:<br>4 Stalls—2 Units<br>CHUTE:<br>4 Stalls—2 Units |
| DOUBLE TANDEM:<br>4 Stalls—4 Units | } For Herds of 30-50 Cows | DOUBLE TANDEM:<br>6 Stalls—3 Units<br>CHUTE:<br>6 Stalls—3 Units |

## Two stalls per unit layouts:  one man operated parlours

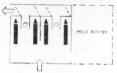

**4 stalls 2 units**
**ABREAST**

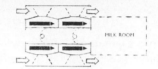

**4 stalls 2 units**
**DOUBLE TANDEM**

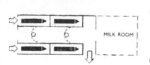

**4 stalls 2 units**
**CHUTE**

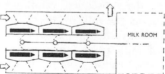

**6 stalls 3 units**
**DOUBLE TANDEM**

## Two stalls per unit layouts:  two-man operated parlours

**6 stalls 3 units**
**CHUTE**

**6 stalls 3 units**
**CHUTE**

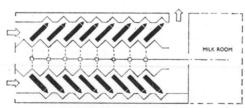

**16 stalls 8 units HERRINGBONE**

| YOUTS | | |
|---|---|---|
| **TWO-MAN OPERATED PARLOURS** | | |
| ONE STALL/UNIT | | TWO STALLS/UNIT |
| DOUBLE TANDEM: 6 Stalls—6 Units } | For Herds of 60-80 Cows | |
| | For Herds of 80-120 Cows { | CHUTE: Two 6 Stalls—3 Units HERRINGBONE: 16 Stalls—8 Units |

**Milking Equipment.**—Both pipeline and direct-to-can milking installations have been designed for milking parlours. Direct-to-can milking with immersion cleaning in caustic soda is the cheapest effective system and is particularly suitable for herds of up to 40 cows milked by one milker. The case for direct-to-can milking is not so strong for large herds milked by two milkers because the movement of cows inside the parlour and the subsequent cooling may lead to difficulties. In double-tandem layouts the milk room should be at one end of the parlour. In designing the layout, thought should be given to the ease of handling of full cans of milk from the parlour into the milk room and on to the collection stand at lorry platform height.

Pipeline milking is essential where milk is collected in bulk and in Herringbone parlours where there is insufficient room for cans. Improvement in the design of pipeline milking machines and the development of simple but effective circulation cleaning processes, which clean all parts of the machine in place (including recorder jars), has eliminated routine dismantling and hand scrubbing.

With pipeline milking the milk room may be sited at one end or on either side of a parlour, milk is delivered into cans at lorry platform height or in a bulk tank, and there is no need for milkers to leave the parlour during milking.

**Collection Yards.**—No parlour can be fully effective unless the cows enter quickly when the entrance door is opened. To facilitate cow movement the collection area should be limited to 15 sq. ft. per cow and preferably rectangular with one end facing the entrance to the parlour. A movable back fence, " electric dog ", operated from inside the parlour, can be drawn along behind the cows during milking so that cows to be milked are always close to the entrance to the parlour. Where possible the collection area should be part of the concrete loafing area used by the cows between milkings, and cows leaving the parlour should be returned to the loafing area without crossing a bedded area. The elimination of separate collection and exit yards reduces the area of concrete which has to be cleaned. If the loafing area is relatively long and narrow it can be cleaned quickly with a tractor and scraper blade.

**Milking Performance in Parlours and Cowsheds.**—The number of cows milked per man-hour is a measure of performance in machine milking; each milker should work independently with a set of milking units. The potential performance of an installation is determined by the milk yields of the cows, the number of stalls with each unit, the number of units and the work routine of the milker.

Measurement of the true milking times of 750 cows in 20 herds, milked with similar equipment operated at a vacuum level of 15 in. of mercury, showed that the average milking time per cow is closely related to the average milk yield at a particular milking. After making a standard allowance of 0·4 minute per cow for machine stripping, the milking times showed an increase from 4 minutes for an average of 10 lb. per cow to 6½ minutes for an average of 25 lb. per cow per milking.

The number of cows milked with each milking unit depends on the time the unit is required for each cow. This is termed the Unit time (Ut) and is the time the unit is on the cows plus the time the unit is idle between cows. In parlours with two stalls per unit all the routine jobs other than changing a cluster from one cow to the next are done while the unit is milking, and consequently the unit idle time should not vary much from the 0·2 minutes per cow required for putting on the teat cups as listed in Table 17. In cowsheds the movement of units increases the unit idle time to 0·7 min. per cow.

In one-stall per unit parlours all the routine jobs other than machine stripping are carried out while the unit is idle between cows and the extent of unit idle time depends on the complexity of the work routine. For the work routines (a) in Table 17, the unit idle time in a one-stall per unit parlour would be 1·2 min. Even with simple work routines, the unit idle time is unlikely to be less than one minute per cow, and consequently the number of cows milked per unit per hour in one-stall per unit parlours is less than in two-stalls per unit parlours.

The number of cows milked with a unit in an hour is the number of times the unit time (in minutes) divides into 60. In practice a milker operates two or more milking units and the maximum number of cows milked per man-hour can be calculated from the formula:

$$P = \frac{60}{Ut} \times N = \frac{60}{Awt}$$

where P = number of cows milked per man-hour, Ut = unit time, N = the number of milking units per man and Awt = available work time (work routine time plus man idle time).

The theoretical performances in two-stall per unit parlours with unit idle time of 0·2 min. have been calculated in Table 18. The performance figures also apply to one-stall per unit parlours having a work routine time of 1·6 min., but not the available work time values in one-stall per unit parlours, because most of the routine work is done when the unit is idle.

Variations in the milking times of cows, differences in times taken by the milker to deal with each cow and delays when all units are not in use at the beginning and end of milking will usually prevent the maximum performance being reached, and Table 18 should therefore only be used as a rough guide to performance.

**Parlour performance specification.**—The choice of the best type and size of milking parlour can only be made after detailed study of the main requirements on the farm where it is to be installed. The more important points to be considered are the herd size, the calving policy, the expected lactation yields, the method of feeding concentrates, the number, duration

S

TABLE 18

## MAXIMUM PERFORMANCE IN MILKING PARLOURS

$$P = \frac{60}{Ut} \times N = \frac{60}{Awt}$$

When P = number of cows milked per man-hour     N = number of units operated per man

Ut = unit time (milking time + unit idle time)   Awt = available work time

| | Type of Installation | | | Number of milking units | | | | | | | |
|---|---|---|---|---|---|---|---|---|---|---|---|
| Unit Time (min.) | † one stall per unit | Cowshed | two stalls per unit | 2 | | 3 | | 4 | | 5 | |
| | Work Routine 1·6 min. | Unit Idle Time 0·7 min. | Unit Idle Time 0·2 min. | P | Awt | P | Awt | P | Awt | P | Awt |
| | Yield lb. | Yield lb. | Yield lb. | | | | | | | | |
| 3·7 | | | 7 | 32 | 1·9 | 49 | 1·2 | | | | |
| 4·2 | | 7 | 10 | 29 | 2·1 | 43 | 1·4 | | | | |
| 4·7 | 7 | 10 | 13 | 26 | 2·4 | 38 | 1·6 | 51 | 1·2 | | |
| 5·2 | 10 | 13 | 16 | 23 | 2·6 | 35 | 1·7 | 46 | 1·3 | | |
| 5·7 | 13 | 16 | 19 | | | 32 | 1·9 | 42 | 1·4 | | |
| 6·2 | 16 | 19 | 22 | | | 29 | 2·1 | 39 | 1·5 | 48 | 1·2 |
| 6·7 | 19 | 22 | 25 | | | 27 | 2·2 | 35 | 1·7 | 45 | 1·3 |
| 7·2 | 22 | 25 | 28 | | | 25 | 2·4 | 33 | 1·8 | 42 | 1·4 |
| 7·7 | 25 | 28 | — | | | 23 | 2·6 | 31 | 1·9 | 39 | 1·5 |

† In one-stall unit parlours the Awt (available time for work on each cow) does not apply. The maximum performance is reached when the milker is fully occupied with routine work, when

$$P = \frac{60}{\text{Work Routine Time}}$$

With work routine times of 1·6 and 1·1 min. the maximum performances would be 38 and 55 cows per man-hour respectively and times of milking each day, the number of milkers and the jobs to be included in their work routine. An example is given in Table 19.

TABLE 19

EXAMPLE ON SELECTION OF A MILKING PARLOUR TO SUIT HERD SIZE AND MANAGEMENT SYSTEMS ON TWO FARMS A AND B

| | Farm A | | Farm B | |
|---|---|---|---|---|
| *Management information* | | | | |
| Total number of cows in the herd | 120 | | 50 | |
| Calving . . . . . | Autumn | | Spring/ Autumn | |
| Maximum percentage of cows in milk . . . . | 90 | | 80 | |
| Maximum number of cows in milk | 108 | | 40 | |
| Number of milkers . . . | 2 | | 1 | |
| Number of cows per milker . | | 54 | | 40 |
| Average lactation yield per cow (lb.) . . . . . | 9000 | | 7500 | |
| Average daily yield lb./cow . . | $\frac{9000}{300}+10$ | 40 | $\frac{7500}{300}$ | 25 |
| Times of milking each day . . | 6.0 a.m. 3.0 p.m. | | 6.0 a.m. 3.0 p.m. | |
| Duration of A.M. milking to be . | | 1½ hr. | | 1½ hr. |
| | | | | |
| *Milking Parlour Performance Specification* | | | | |
| Number of cows to be milked per man-hour . . . . | | 36 | | 27 |
| Average A.M. milk yield/cow . | | 25 | | 15 |
| Concentrates fed per cow per milking . . . . | | Up to 8 lb. | | Up to 5 lb. |
| Type of milking parlour required . | | two-stalls per unit | | one-stall per unit or two-stalls per unit |
| Work routine time . . . | | 1·5 min. | | 1·6 min. |

*Farm A.* Table 18 shows that with four units in a two-stall per unit parlour it is possible to achieve a performance of 35 cows per man-hour providing routine work time per cow is less than minutes. The most suitable parlour for this herd would be a sixteen-stall eight-unit herringbone layout equipped with a pipeline milking machine and operated by 2 milkers. To avoid unnecessary overmilking when the majority of the cows are in declining lactation it would be advisable to reduce the number of milking units to 3 per milker once the average daily yield falls below 30 lb. per cow.

*Farm B. One-Stall per Unit.* With a work routine time of 1·6 minutes per cow a three-stall three-unit tandem or abreast parlour operated by one man milking up to 29 cows per hour would be suitable for this herd. Direct-to-can milking equipment with immersion cleaning in caustic soda solution would be the most economical system for this parlour.

*Two-Stalls per Unit.* A six-stall three-unit chute would also be suitable for this herd and a performance of 35 cows per man-hour would be possible.

**Total number of cows and the calving policy.**—The labour force needed for milking and management is governed by the total number of cows in the herd. The maximum number of cows in milk is affected by the calving policy. On farms where all the cows calve in a short season of a few months each year up to 90 per cent. of the cows may be in milk at the same time. On farms where calving is spread throughout the year the number of cows in milk is never likely to exceed 80 per cent. of the total number of cows in the herd.

**Expected lactation yields.**—Assuming an average lactation length of 300 days the average daily yield per cow can be calculated as follows:—

$$\text{Average daily yield per cow in lb.} = \frac{Average\ lactation\ yield}{300}\ \text{lb.}$$

Where calving is seasonal the milking parlour must be planned for the average daily yield when the majority of cows are at the peak of their lactations. With an average lactation yield of less than 8000 lb. per cow the average daily yield

$$= \frac{average\ lactation\ yield}{300} + 5\ \text{lb.}$$

In herds with lactation yields of 8000-12,000 lb. of milk per cow the average daily yield

$$= \frac{average\ lactation\ yield}{300} + 10\ \text{lb.}$$

**The number, duration and times of milking each day.**—Normally cows are milked twice daily and the proportion of the daily yield obtained at each milking depends on the intervals between milkings. If, for example, morning milking begins at 6·0 a.m. and afternoon milking at 2.0 p.m., the morning milk yield is likely to be two-thirds of the daily milk yield. In order to allow sufficient times for work, other than milking in the course of a reasonable working day of 8-9 hours, morning milking should be completed in $1\frac{1}{2}$ to 2 hours.

**Concentrate feeding policy.**—If all concentrate feeding is done in the milking parlour during milking, the quantity of concentrates to be fed per cow at a milking will have a bearing on the type of parlour required. One-stall per unit parlours are suitable for herds in which not more than 3-5 lb. of dry concentrates are fed at a milking. In two-stalls per unit parlours it is possible to feed 6-8 lb. of dry concentrates per cow at a milking.

**The milker's work routine.**—The routine work for each cow can normally be completed in $1\frac{1}{4}$ to $1\frac{3}{4}$ minutes depending on the number of operations included in the work routine.

# HOUSING FOR DAIRY COWS

The majority of dairy cows is housed during the winter months either tied in stalls in traditional cowsheds or loose in covered yards. In some areas of south and south-west England cows are outwintered and milked in movable or fixed bails.

**Cowsheds.**—Traditional cowsheds provide suitable accommodation for milking cows under conditions which allow for individual rationing of all foodstuffs, but considerable manual work is necessary to distribute

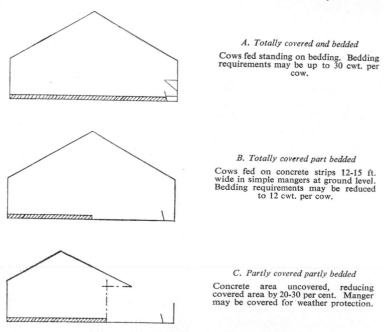

*A. Totally covered and bedded*

Cows fed standing on bedding. Bedding requirements may be up to 30 cwt. per cow.

*B. Totally covered part bedded*

Cows fed on concrete strips 12-15 ft. wide in simple mangers at ground level. Bedding requirements may be reduced to 12 cwt. per cow.

*C. Partly covered partly bedded*

Concrete area uncovered, reducing covered area by 20-30 per cent. Manger may be covered for weather protection.

FIG. 30.—Loose housing for dairy cows.

foodstuffs and bedding and to remove dung at least twice daily. Furthermore, cows must be released each day for exercise outside the cowshed.

Modern designs of cowsheds have facilitated the use of mechanical equipment for the transport and distribution of foodstuffs and bedding and the removal of dung by provision of large doors, wide feeding passages and dung channels, but it has not been possible to eliminate or reduce the frequency of any of the daily tasks associated with cowshed management.

**Loose housing for dairy cows.**—The loose housing of dehorned cows in covered or semi-covered yards (Fig. 30) enables simpler systems of management to be practised in which more effective use can be made of mechanical equipment. Concentrates can be fed in rationed quantities in the milking parlour during milking while roughages such as silage or hay can be fed in simple open mangers in the yards allowing 2 ft. of manger per animal. A further simplification in management is possible where animals are allowed to self feed silage or hay from a clamp 5-7 ft. high. The length of the feeding face is restricted to 6-9 in. per cow and a portable barrier is used to control the animals and prevent wastage. This method of feeding eliminates handling of silage.

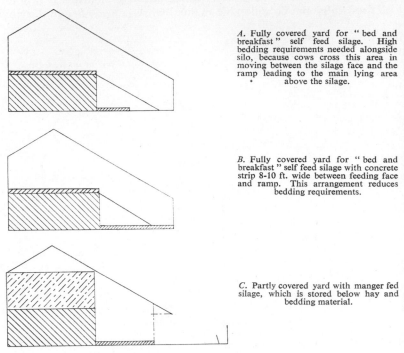

*A*. Fully covered yard for " bed and breakfast " self feed silage. High bedding requirements needed alongside silo, because cows cross this area in moving between the silage face and the ramp leading to the main lying area above the silage.

*B*. Fully covered yard for " bed and breakfast " self feed silage with concrete strip 8-10 ft. wide between feeding face and ramp. This arrangement reduces bedding requirements.

*C*. Partly covered yard with manger fed silage, which is stored below hay and bedding material.

FIG. 31.—Loose housing of cows with facilities for feeding of silage

In fully covered and completely bedded yards with approximately 80 sq. ft. of floor area per cow fresh bedding is put down each day and the accumulation of dung and straw is removed at the end of the winter period. The disadvantage with this system is the quantity of bedding material used which may amount to 30 cwt. or more per cow (3 to 4 times as much as is used in cowsheds) during the winter period.

The quantity of bedding required may be reduced to 10-12 cwt. per cow by providing a bedded area of 40 sq. ft. per cow and an unbedded concrete area of 30-40 sq. ft. per cow with mangers along the side away from the bedded area. Much of the dunging occurs when cows are feeding and the provision of a concrete feeding area reduces the soiling of bedding.

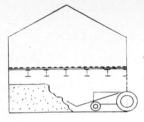

A. High level slatted floor, 8-9 ft. above ground floor. Dung is removed by fore-loader.

B. Low level slatted floor, 1 ft. above ground floor. Shallow channels hold 6-9 in. of water into which dung falls. Channels are drained when sluice gates raised. Dung disposal by vacuum tank or irrigation plant.

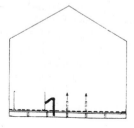

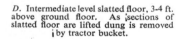

C. Intermediate level slatted floor, 3-4 ft. above ground floor. Slatted floor is lifted in sections and dung removed from ground floor.

D. Intermediate level slatted floor, 3-4 ft. above ground floor. As sections of slatted floor are lifted dung is removed by tractor bucket.

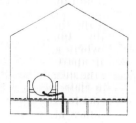

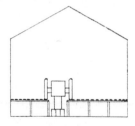

E. Intermediate level slatted floor, 2-3 ft. above ground floor. Dung falls into 6-9 in. of water and is pumped out by vacuum into distribution tank.

F. Slatted feeding area alongside bedded area of cattle yard.

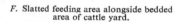

FIG. 32.—Possible slatted floor systems.

Daily cleaning of the concrete area is necessary but this can be done quickly and effectively with a tractor-mounted scraper.

In low rainfall areas the concrete feeding and loafing area need not be covered but suitable provision must be made for the disposal of the slurry scraped from the yard, and the open fronted covered yard must be properly sited to afford adequate protection for the cows and the bedding from wind and rain.

The installation of a slatted floor over a collection pit in the feeding area makes daily cleaning unnecessary.

**Bed and breakfast self-feed silage.**—An overall reduction in the area of yards is possible where sawdust or wood shavings are used for bedding and the animals self-feed in a covered silo (Fig. 31). The top of the silage is littered to a depth of 12-15 in. and used as the main resting area. A ramp situated at the end away from the feeding face provides access to the lying area. A limited additional bedded area is sited alongside the silage clamp but the total area of the building need not exceed 60 sq. ft. per cow. This management system is most successful where cows do not walk over the bedded area alongside the silo to get to and from the feeding area.

**Slatted floors.**—The two major problems associated with the loose housing of dairy cows, *i.e.* the cleaning of large areas of concrete and the use, storage and handling of large quantities of bedding materials may be solved by the introduction of raised slatted floors. Loose housing of cows in slat floored pens in insulated barns has been practised successfully in Norway and Iceland for some 10 years. In order to ensure adequate trampling through of the dung the floor area per cow is restricted to 35-45 sq. ft. per cow and a light sprinkling of sawdust on the 5 in. wide concrete or hardwood slats keep the animals clean and the floor relatively dry.

Much useful information is being obtained at the time of writing on the use of slatted floors for dairy cows in Britain. Injuries to hooves, legs and teats did occur in slat floored housing where groups of 20-100 animals were confined on slats 3 in. wide and 2 in. apart. The reduction of gaps between the slats to $1\frac{1}{2}$-$1\frac{1}{4}$ in. has reduced the incidence of injuries but the unyielding nature of wood and concrete slats and the slippery surfaces do not appear to provide sufficient comfort for the larger breeds of dairy cows. Work is now in progress to produce more comfortable slatted or perforated floors which would be self cleaning. Possible arrangements are illustrated in Fig. 32.

## CHAPTER 22

## SHEEP AND GOATS

SHEEP and goats, with certain intermediate species, are generally regarded as forming one group of the Cavicornia or hollow-horned ruminants.

The true sheep comprise a considerable number of wild species which fall into two rather distinct natural groups. The one includes the Mouflon (*Ovis musimon*) of Corsica and Sardinia, together with the closely related species of Cyprus (*O. cypria*) and of Asia Minor (*O. orientalis*), and the Urial (*O. vignei*) of Persia, Northern India and Tibet. The other group consists of the Argali (*O. ammon*) of Western Siberia and the Altai, Marco Polo's sheep (*O. Poli*), and the Bighorn of Northern Siberia (*O. nivicola*) and of the Rockies (*O. montana*). The true goats include the Markhor (*Capra falconeri*) of Afghanistan and the common wild goat or Bezoar (*C. aegagrus*) of the Caucasus, Persia and Crete. The Steinbok and the Tur are included in the genus *Capra*, while the Bharal or Blue Sheep of Tibet, the Barbary Sheep and the Tahr of Nepal and Kashmir represent types intermediate between sheep and goats, and are referred to as separate genera.

Nothing is known for certain regarding the origin of domesticated sheep. The view most widely held is that the Asiatic Mouflon supplied most of the foundation stock, but the Urial and even the Argali have sometimes been regarded as the ancestors of some domestic types. The older view, to the effect that the wild ancestor must have been quite different from any surviving species, is not now accepted. The common goat is descended from the Bezoar, and the Cashmere goat from the Markhor, while the valuable Angora is generally believed to have been derived from a cross between the two.

Sheep are valued commercially for their mutton and wool, and occasionally also for milk. With some breeds, such as the Merino, wool is the primary product, while British breeds are kept mainly for mutton—wool being a secondary, but an important consideration. The points of the mutton sheep correspond rather closely to those of the beef ox, the valuable qualities being a tendency to fatten early in life (early maturity)—a thick covering of lean meat and an even and not wasteful distribution of the fat. The head varies greatly with the breed, but should be of good depth and width, strong of jaw and broad through the nose; the neck moderately short and thick at its junction with the body; the body deep, wide and square; the shoulder top wide, level and well covered; the chest deep and wide, and the ribs well sprung or rounded; the shoulder neatly laid and thickly covered, and the region behind the shoulder well filled up; the hind quarters long, broad and level, with the width well carried out to the rump; the gigot or leg of mutton thickly fleshed, and the flesh well carried down, both inside and out. The back should be wide and level throughout, thickly covered with firm, muscular flesh; the legs moderately short and set well apart, the bone neither too coarse nor too fine, but clean and hard. The thickness of the tail is a useful measure of condition or fatness. The carriage should be stylish and springy, indicating activity and robust health.

Sheep's wool is commercially by much the most important fibre of its kind, although other wools and hairs—for example, mohair, cashmere, alpaca and camel's hair—are all used as textiles. Wool is used in the manufacture of a great variety of articles. The chief are articles of clothing for the inhabitants of the colder regions of the world, carpets, tapestries and blankets. The characteristics of the wool fibre on which its value mainly depends are as follows:—

1. *Length.*—This varies from under 1 in. to over 2 ft., the coarser wools being generally the longer. Other things being equal, the longer wools are the more valuable.

2. *Uniformity in Length of the Different Fibres in the Staple.*—This is important, because, for certain purposes, the short fibres require to be separated and put to a different use, bringing a lower price.

3. *Strength and Elasticity.*—Strong, elastic fibres suffer a minimum of breakage in the process of manufacture and naturally give a strong yarn. Fine fibres are stronger in proportion to their size than coarse. The staple should be free from any weak part or " break," as wool with such a " break " cannot be combed without great wastage. The condition is generally due to the sheep having suffered a severe check during the period of growth of the wool. In Britain the common causes of a "break" in the staple are a period of undernutrition or partial starvation, which may affect the whole flock (particularly in the case of hill sheep), and illnesses of various sorts. The weaker part of the fibre is that produced at the end of the period of malnutrition—*e.g.* just before the commencement of fresh growth on a hill grazing. In extreme cases the sheep casts part or the whole of its fleece.

4. *Fineness.*—the mean diameter of the fibres may vary from about $\frac{1}{1500}$ in. in the finer Merino wools to $\frac{1}{600}$ in. or more in the coarser long-wool fleeces. The smaller the individual fibres the finer the yarn that can be spun from them, and in yarns of the same weight the finer wool gives a softer and fuller character, which in turn gives the finished cloth a better appearance and " handle." Softness is due chiefly, but not entirely, to fineness of the individual fibres.

5. *Crimp.*—The aptitude of the different fibres to interlock depends on the fineness and extent of the waviness or " crimp." Fine Merino will often show more than twenty waves to the inch, while most Longwools

give only three or four. Crimp also gives springiness or elasticity to the finished cloth. Felting further depends on the number of epidermal scales and on the extent to which their upper edges project. Fibres with a smooth surface, like those of the Lincoln or Wensleydale sheep, are naturally slippery. On the contrary, Merino or Down wool (which has the appearance under the microscope of a series of irregular flower pots set one inside the other) felts readily. The wool of a healthy sheep will rarely felt or " cot " on the sheep's back because the fibres lie parallel, with the serrations all pointing in one direction, and because of the coating of oily secretion. " Cots " or felted fleeces do occur, and have a low value.

6. *Colour.*—A clean white or pale lemon coloured wool can be dyed to any desired shade, whereas coloured wools, or those containing a proportion of black or brown fibres, have a restricted use. Hence dark fibres are objectionable, and every endeavour should be made by the breeder to eliminate them by selection. Certain natural coloured wools— *e.g.* " moorit " (brown) Shetland—have a higher value, for special purposes, than white wools.

7. *Lustre.*—Wools with large, flat, epidermal scales have a bright shiny appearance, whereas if the scales are small and the surface rough the wool is dull in appearance. High lustre and felting qualities are obviously incompatible.

8. *Behaviour to Dyes.*—True wool absorbs dye differently from what is called kemp, which is a coarse and generally brittle fibre with a characteristic dead white appearance. It does not absorb dye in the ordinary dyeing process, and hence causes unsightly marks in the cloth. Here, again, the breeder should make every effort to get rid of the fault by careful selection of his breeding sheep. Kemp is commonest in the wool of mountain breeds, and generally increases with the age of the animal.

9. *Uniformity of the Different Portions of the Fleece.*—Previous to its manufacture, fleeces are " classed " according to their general quality, and each fleece is then " sorted " —*i.e.* it is pulled to pieces and these are placed in separate lots according to quality. Classing is done either by the producer, the merchant or in many cases by woolgrowers' co-operative societies. Sorting is normally carried out by the manufacturer who, however, may re-sell the lots that do not meet his particular requirements. Sometimes, as in the best Merino wools, the fleece is practically uniform throughout. In most sheep the quality varies according to the part of the body from which the wool is taken. That from the shoulder is generally the most valuable, being deep in staple, uniform and fine. The neck wool is often finer, but is much less uniform; that from the breech, on the other hand, is both coarse and irregular. The wool sorter divides the fleece into different " counts," the count representing the number of hanks of yarn (each 560 yd. long, according to the Bradford system),

that could be spun from 1 lb. The count, as usually applied, is a measure of fineness, although in actual spinning the length of yarn that can be got from the pound of wool varies with the length as well as with the diameter of the fibres. A good average Merino fleece might give wool of 64 quality from the back part and 70's from the front. A typical Longwool (*e.g.* Lincoln) fleece sorted into its separate counts is shown in

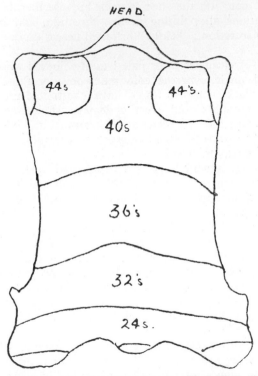

FIG. 33.—Counts of different parts of a Lincoln fleece.

Fig. 33. Skirtings, cots, brand marks and soiled locks are removed before or during the process of sorting.

Wool is manufactured by either of two methods. In the *worsted* process the raw material, after scouring, is combed so that the short fibres are removed. The latter are sold as " noil " to the woollen manufacturer, while the long fibres, arranged parallel to each other in a sort of rope, form " wool tops." The tops are spun into a rather firm, hard thread, the cloth made from which has a distinct thread structure and a bright appearance. The important qualities in worsted wools are length, strength, uniformity, trueness, elasticity, lustre and fineness. High felting qualities are generally not required. In the second or *woollen* manufacturing process the short fibres are not removed, length being unnecessary. The material is carded—that is, it is teased out into a thin web in which the fibres run in all directions. The carded " sliver," or rope, is condensed and spun without further treatment. The cloth is more or less felted by moisture and pressure, so that the fibres are interlocked in all directions and the thread becomes indistinct. The important qualities for this purpose are fineness, softness and felting properties. A break in the staple is an unimportant defect, and lustre is not wanted, since the haphazard arrangement of the fibres would, in any case, conceal any natural lustre of the wool.

The value of natural or " greasy " wool will, of course, vary with the proportion of fatty and sweaty matter that it contains, as well as with its moisture content. The " yield " of scoured wool, after the removal of the " yolk," may be has high as 80 or 85 per cent. in the Longwools, and may fall to 60 or even as low as 30 per cent. in some Merinos. The general run of British wools gives an average yield of about 80 per cent. of the unwashed weight. Vegetable impurities, such, for example, as straw, burrs, grass seeds or fibres—*e.g.* from jute packs or hemp string—are all very objectionable in wool, since they do not absorb dyes in the same manner. They are often difficult to separate, and their presence in large quantities may render it necessary for the wool to be carbonised (treated with acid and heat) in order to destroy them. Hence every endeavour should be made to keep them out. As extraneous matter is readily picked up during shearing, this process should be carried out on a clean floor or on a tarpaulin. Sheep are commonly branded after clipping. Tar should not be used for this purpose, but one of the materials officially approved by the wool trade. Sheep are frequently coloured (" bloom dipped ") for sale purposes, and some of the materials used for this purpose permanently discolour the wool; such should be avoided. Shearing should never be done when the fleece is damp, otherwise the wool will deteriorate in storage. The fleeces must be stored under dry conditions.

From the farmer's point of view the weight of the fleece is obviously an important consideration. This depends on the size of the sheep and on the length and density of the fleece. Density is judged by grasping firmly with the hand. Single fleeces of modern breeds vary from 2 or 3 up to 15 lb., and exceptionally up to about 30 lb.

The wool breeds of sheep, as distinct from those in which mutton is the prime consideration, are all derived from the Merino of Spain. The Spanish sheep is now of little account but its descendants have covered a great proportion of the globe, and many distinct types have been evolved, notably in Australia, the United States, Germany and France. Of these the American " C " type and Delaine Merino, as well as the French Rambouillet, are relatively large, robust, smooth-bodied sheep, with wool of good length (3 in.) and moderately fine quality, and capable of producing lambs of good quality for slaughter. At the other extreme is the American " A " type, small and of very poor mutton form, with a very wrinkled skin and a heavy clip of very fine but short and very greasy wool. Merinos are best adapted to dry and at least moderately warm climates, and are a profitable type of stock for land at a great distance from centres of population.

## BRITISH BREEDS

Omitting a few of minor importance and the Roscommon and Galway breeds of Ireland, there are thirty-two British breeds of sheep, falling into three main groups:—

(*A*) **Longwools** embrace the Leicester, Border Leicester, Wensleydale, Lincoln, Cotswold, Devon Longwool, South Devon and Kent or Romney Marsh. These are, broadly speaking, the largest breeds. They are white-faced (except the Wensleydale), hornless, and have a fleece of long lustre wool which is used for worsted manufacture. They mature fairly early and fatten readily, but the mutton, at least of the older animals, tends to be coarse grained and poor in flavour and readily becomes too fat.

(*B*) **Shortwools** include six breeds that are ordinarily spoken of as Downs, and seven others. The Downs are hornless, with dark faces and legs, and generally a short, close fleece of relatively fine quality which is suitable for hosiery manufacture. Most have a strong flocking instinct and are docile, so that they are easily kept in folds. The mutton is generally of very good quality, with a high proportion of fine grained lean meat and a fine flavour. Originally associated with the Chalk Downs, they have now spread all over Britain, except the mountains, and are kept under a great variety of conditions. The Down breeds are the Southdown, Shropshire, Suffolk, Hampshire Down, Dorset Down and Oxford Down. The Oxford is not a typical member of the group but is intermediate between the Down and Longwool types. The remaining short wooled breeds are the Dorset Horn and the Western or Wiltshire Horn (white-faced horned), the Ryeland and Devon Closewool (white-faced hornless), the Kerry Hill (speckled-faced hornless), the Clun Forest (dark-faced hornless) and the Radnor (brown or tan-faced).

(*C*) **Mountain Breeds.**—These have little in common except their generally small size, good quality of mutton and their ability to live on mountain or moorland grazings. They include the Scottish Blackface, Swaledale, Lonk, Rough Fell and the Dales-bred, all belonging to the black faced, coarse wooled, horned type. The Derbyshire Gritstone is sometimes grouped with these, but is softer wooled and hornless. The others are the Cheviot, North-country Cheviot, Welsh Mountain, South Wales, Herdwick, Exmoor Horn, Dartmoor and Shetland. The quality of the wool varies widely even within particular breeds. The coarsest is used for carpet making, the intermediate for Harris and other strong tweeds, and the finest for hosiery and flannel.

The Leicester (Plate 50, *A*) is the oldest, or at least was the earliest improved of the Lonwgool breeds. It was evolved by Bakewell between 1755 and 1790 from the pre-existing Old Leicester type. The latter was large and coarse, late maturing and of poor mutton type, though it bore a good fleece of long combing wool and was hardy and prolific. Bakewell effected a very great improvement in early maturity and in mutton qualities generally, but it is generally acknowledged that he allowed the fleece to deteriorate and the fecundity to decline. Bakewell's type would doubtless carry far too much fat for modern taste, but fat meat was in demand at his time. During and after Bakewell's time the Dishley Leicesters spread all over the country; they gave rise, as an offshoot, to the Border Leicester, and they were used in the improvement of all the other Longwools and of some other breeds as well. With the change of taste in favour of smaller and leaner mutton, the breed, as a commercial sheep in its pure-bred form, has declined in popularity, but it is still useful for crossing purposes.

The modern Leicester is a medium sized Longwool of low set and blocky conformation. The carcass weight of mature ewes is from 100 to 140 lb., rams reaching 200 lb. The head is wedge shaped, the nose slightly Roman and rather thin at the bridge; the hair on the face white with a bluish tinge and dark spots, and the lips and nostrils dark. The forehead is covered with wool, the ears are bluish or white, long and thin; the neck is short and thick and is carried almost horizontally. The fleece is fairly dense, of good length, and is fine, curly and highly lustrous. The count is about 46/40. Good ewe flocks will clip about 10 lb. per head and tegs 12 to 14 lb. The mutton is of fair average Longwool quality.

The chief centre of the breed is now the Wolds in the East Riding of Yorkshire. Some flocks are still kept pure for ordinary commercial purposes, but there is a growing tendency to cross the Leicester ewe with the Suffolk ram in order to obtain a leaner type of mutton with better flavour; other flocks are maintained in order to produce rams for mating with Mountain, or more generally, with " Masham " (Wensleydale × Blackface mountain) ewes. Abroad, the breed has been successful in Australia, New Zealand and Tasmania, and to a less extent in South America. It is also found in Canada and the United States, but there it has been merged to some extent with the Border Leicester.

The Border Leicester (Plate 50, *B*) is descended from Dishley sheep that were brought to the Scottish Border district from about 1800 onwards. Whether or not any Cheviot blood was introduced in the formation of the Border type has been much disputed. English Leicester rams continued to be imported by Border breeders until about 1850, but since that time the types have been kept distinct. By 1869 the two types had so far diverged that the Highland Agricultural Society (now the Royal Highland) decided to institute separate classes for each.

This breed is of similar weight to its relative, but is higher on the leg, with a high and straight underline. The head is long, rather thin through the nose and light behind the ears. The nose is aquiline, the whole head free from wool, and the lips and nostrils black. The ears are large, white with occasional black spots, and carried rather high. The neck is distinctly long, but thick at its junction with the trunk, and the head is carried gaily and high. The breed is exceptionally wide and level of back, and is very easily fattened. The modern tendency is to aim at a rather short and dense fleece. The wool is wavy and lustrous, with an average count of 48/44; 10 lb. is reached as an average clip in the best flocks, and 14 lb. is a common clip for well bred and intensively fed ram hoggs. The Border Leicester is fairly hardy and extremely prolific. Flocks kept under good conditions will often produce 170 per cent. of lambs, and the ewes are good milkers. The chief use of the breed is the production of rams for crossing with Cheviot and Scottish Blackface ewes. It is admirably adapted for mating with the smaller and leaner breeds owing to its combination of size, early maturity, and a thin head—which last feature is important in connection with parturition. Border Leicesters are largely bred in Northumberland and Cumberland and throughout all the lowland districts of Scotland, and the breed is common in Northern Ireland. A blue faced strain with a finer fleece is bred in the vicinity of Hexham and is preferred locally for crossing with the blackfaced mountain breeds. The Teeswater is somewhat similar. The Border Leicester has been largely exported, and is probably the most widely known of the Longwools. In Australia it is the most numerous of all British breeds, and gives excellent results when crossed with the Merino.

**Half-bred** (Plate 51, *A*) or Border Leicester × Cheviot ewes are a common type of breeding stock on arable farms north of Yorkshire, and are an important commercial type in many grassland districts in the Midlands and elsewhere in England.[1] They are hardy, very prolific (rarely giving less than 150 per cent. of lambs) and excellent mothers. When crossed again with Oxford, Suffolk or other Down rams, they produce an excellent type of butcher's sheep.

**The Wensleydale** (Plate 51, *B*) was produced originally by crossing the Dishley Leicester with an old, large, white faced breed known as the Teeswater " Mug." The characteristic blue face and legs were derived from the half-bred Leicester ram " Bluecap," born in 1839. The modern type was fixed about 1860.

The Wensleydale is a large framed sheep, rather long of leg and long of body. The depth of rib is good, but the back is less broad than that of the Leicester. The head is strong, highly carried on rather a long neck, and the forehead carries a tuft of wool. The fleece is long, similar in quality to that of the Leicester (46/40) but with a higher lustre. It is

---

[1] In many parts of England Half-breds are erroneously called Border Leicesters. In parts of Yorkshire the name Bamshire (from Bamburgh, Northumberland) is used.

PLATE 50

*A.* ENGLISH LEICESTER RAM

*Farmer and Stockbreeder*

*B.* BORDER LEICESTER EWE

PLATE 51

Brown & Co., Lanark

*A.* HALF-BRED SHEARLING RAM

*B.* WENSLEYDALE RAM

PLATE 52

*J. T. Newman, Berkhampstead*

*A.* Lincoln Longwool Ram

*Farmer and Stockbreeder*

*B.* South Devon Shearling Ram

PLATE 53

*A.* KENT OR ROMNEY MARSH SHEARLING RAM

*Farmer and Stockbreeder*

*B.* SOUTHDOWN SHEARLING EWES

PLATE 54

*A.* SHROPSHIRE SHEARLING RAM

*B.* SUFFOLK RAM LAMB

PLATE 55

*Farmer and Stockbreeder*

A. HAMPSHIRE DOWN SHEARLING RAM

B. OXFORD DOWN SHEARLING RAM

PLATE 56

*A.* DORSET HORN SHEARLING RAM     *Farmer and Stockbreeder*

*B.* RYELAND SHEARLING RAM     *J. T. Newman, Berkhampstead*

PLATE 57

*Farmer and Stockbreeder*

*A.* Scottish Blackface Shearling Ram

*Farmer and Stockbreeder*

*B.* Swaledale Ram

PLATE 58

*A.* Cheviot Shearling Ram

*C. Reid, Wishaw*

*B.* Welsh Mountain Ram

*G. H. Parsons, Alsager, Cheshire*

PLATE 59

*Alex. Booth, Hensingham*

*A.* HERDWICK RAM

*Farmer and Stockbreeder*

*B.* EXMOOR SHEARLING EWES

divided into locks of about pencil size and is open in character. Good ewe flocks average up to 9 lb. of wool. The face and legs are of a very characteristic deep blue-grey colour. Some strains produce a considerable proportion of black lambs.

The Wensleydale is probably the hardiest of the Longwools, but is notably narrower in build than the Leicester or Lincoln and is distinctly later maturing. The mutton is of good quality with a remarkably high proportion of lean meat for a Longwool. The breed is mainly found in the North and West Ridings of Yorkshire and in Lancashire. Its chief use is the production of rams for crossing with the various blackfaced mountain breeds, both in the north of England and in the south-west of Scotland. Crosses with Swaledale ewes are known as Mashams (Massams) and those with Scottish Blackface ewes as Yorkshire Crosses. Masham ewes are often mated back to Wensleydales in the lower lying farms, producing " twice-crossed " lambs. Both sorts are very useful commercial sheep for winter feeding. The Wensleydale is also the favourite breed for crossing with Herdwick ewes.

**The Lincoln** (Plate 52, *A*).—Before the era of live stock improvement for meat production there existed in Lincolnshire a large, coarse breed of sheep, with a remarkably good fleece of long, strong, lustrous combing wool. For long the breeders of the Old Lincoln sheep held out against the introduction of Dishley Leicester blood, but eventually crosses were made, and the modern Lincoln undoubtedly owes something to the outside blood, which, although it temporarily diminished the size of the sheep and the length of wool, improved the fattening qualities and symmetry.

The Lincoln is the largest British breed. Mature rams in show condition occasionally reach 400 lb. live weight, and the average weight of the wethers (at twenty two months old) shown at Smithfield in the 1930s was practically 3 cwt. The Smithfield weights show the breed to be about 12 per cent. heavier than the Leicester. Ordinary commercial tegs reach carcass weights of 80 to 90 lb. at twelve months old. Compared with the English Leicester, the Lincoln is more massively built and has a rather longer and stronger head, which is generally carried a little higher. The ears are always more or less dotted with black. The wool is of great length, that of hoggs frequently exceeding 18 in.; it is very dense on the pelt, wavy, lustrous and strong, but distinctly coarser (about 44/36) than that of the Leicester. The locks are as broad as two fingers and are less completely separated than in the Leicester. The clip is heavy; 12 lb. is not an uncommon average in good flocks, while ewe hoggs often give a stone and heavily fed ram hoggs as much as 2 st. of wool. In the show type a good deal of wool is carried on the hind legs below the hocks, and there is a top knot of long locks.

The Lincoln is quite hardy, commercial flocks being kept on the fairly high and exposed wold and " heath " land of its native county.

It is not remarkable for fecundity, 130 per cent. of lambs being considered a satisfactory crop. The quality of the mutton, at least of the older sheep, is generally poor. In Britain the breed has not spread far beyond its native county, most of the leading flocks being found in Lincolnshire and south-east Yorks. Abroad, especially in Australia and Argentina, the breed is in great favour on account of its value for crossing with the Merino. The cross-bred is large and readily fattened, and yields a heavy fleece of useful medium quality wool. The well known Corriedale breed, originally formed in New Zealand but now widely distributed throughout the world, was produced by fixing the characters of this cross, with some infusion of Leicester blood.

**The Cotswold,** formerly kept in large numbers on the limestone farms of Oxfordshire and Gloucestershire, is still of some importance in the United States, but only two or three British flocks survive. It is nearly as large as the Lincoln and of somewhat similar type but with a somewhat coarser type of fleece.

**The South Devon** (Plate 52, *B*) is a large, robust type of sheep found in Cornwall and South Devon, In many respects it resembles the Lincoln but is longer in body and, on the average, less squarely and massively built. The wool is dense, long and curly, but coarser (about 36/32) than in the Lincoln, particularly at the breech. The mutton is of relatively good quality, with a high proportion of lean meat.

**The Devon Longwool** is smaller than the last (roughly equal to the Leicester in size) but somewhat irregular both as to size and type. The fleece is similar to that of the South Devon. The quality of mutton is again above the ordinary Longwool standard. The Devon is the predominant Longwool breed in North and East Devon and Somerset, but is giving way, like other Longwools, to smaller, leaner and hardier breeds. For fat lamb production Devon and South Devon ewes are crossed with Down rams, the Dorset Down, Hampshire and Suffolk being commonly used.

**The Kent or Romney Marsh** (Plate 53, *A*) is an old breed native to the rich but cold, exposed and damp grassland district from which it is named. Like all Longwools the modern breed is indebted to some extent to the Leicester, but it has retained many of its original characteristics and is in many ways the most distinct of the Longwool breeds. Of these it is the smallest, the mean weight being perhaps 5 per cent. less than that of the Leicester. It is low of leg, stout-limbed and long-bodied. Often it is low at the shoulder and deficient in heart girth in proportion to its development of hind quarter. The forehead is very wide and generally carries some short wool; the nostrils are black. The wool is denser than that of any other Longwool and is much finer in quality (50/46) though shorter and less lustrous, and sometimes rather coarse at the breech. The wool is classed as demi-lustre. The fleece is heavy, ordinary commercial flocks yielding an average of 8 or 9 lb., and pedigree flocks usually reaching over 10 lb. The Romney is hardy, does well on grass without hand feeding, and is relatively immune from such diseases as foot rot and liver fluke that so frequently affect sheep on wet land. The sheep graze singly, rarely flocking of their own will. The breed is not notably prolific, giving perhaps 120 per cent. of lambs under ordinary conditions.

The Kent sheep is very numerously represented in the south eastern counties, although a considerable proportion of the ewes are crossed with Southdown, Hampshire or other Down rams. The lambs so produced fatten readily and are of excellent quality. Abroad the breed is very popular, notably in New Zealand, but also in South America, Australia, the Falkland Islands and elsewhere. New Zealand now competes with England in supplying pedigree sheep of this breed to other countries.

**The Southdown** (Plate 53, *B*) was the first Shortwool type to be improved, and was used in the improvement or formation of all the modern Downs, just as was the Dishley Leicester in the production of the modern Longwool breeds. The Southdown has existed for several centuries on the chalk hills of Sussex, and the old type, before the improvers set to work, was described as a small, dark-faced and occasionally horned breed, long in the neck, light in the fore quarter, long and narrow in the back, with a light, thin fleece. The hind quarter was well developed, and the leg thickly fleshed. The first of the great improvers was John Ellman of Glynde, near Lewes, who started farming about 1780 and bred Southdowns with great success for fifty years. He avoided close inbreeding and, unlike Bakewell, devoted close attention to the fleece and to the breeding qualities. Also he increased rather than diminished the size of his breed. Ellman's chief successor in the work of improvement was Jonas Webb, of Babraham, Cambridge, who began about 1821.

The Southdown is distinctly the smallest of the Down breeds and attains, at maturity, less than two thirds of the weight of the Lincoln. Full grown rams of the better sort, in fat condition, weigh about 200 lb., and good ewes in breeding condition about 130 lb. The general build is very neat, compact and symmetrical. The head is very wide, short from the eyes down, of an even mouse colour and is wooled over the forehead, but not round the eyes or over the bridge of the nose. The ears are short and are covered with short wool. The leg of mutton is remarkably thick and heavy. The wool is short (about $2\frac{1}{2}$ in.), dense and very fine (60/56), comanding the top price per pound for British wools. The clip in good ewe flocks may reach $4\frac{1}{2}$ lb. or occasionally more. For quality of meat the breed is unsurpassed, and as a winner of carcass competitions it occupies a place comparable to that of the Aberdeen Angus among cattle. The lambs mature and fatten very early and produce small fleshy joints with very little bone.

The breed is reasonably hardy, but below the average of the Down type in prolificness. Up till 1939 Southdown rams were largely used for crossing, and the cross-bred lambs, though small, ordinarily commanded a premium over all other market types. The loss of this premium under war-time conditions resulted in a great decline in the demand by commercial sheep breeders for Southdown rams, but there has been a renewed demand since then. The breed is still in widespread use in New Zealand for crossing with Romney Marsh and Corriedale ewes for the production of choice quality lamb.

**The Shropshire** (Plate 54, *A*) originated before 1850 in Shropshire and Staffordshire. It was produced from local sheep by crossing with the Southdown, and possibly in earlier times and to a less extent, with the improved Leicester. Of these local types the two most important were those of Morfe Common, near Bridgnorth and of Cannock Chase in Staffordshire. The new breed first attracted attention at the Royal Agricultural Show in 1853, and in 1859 it was definitely recognised by being given separate classes. Although the type has changed considerably since those times, no further outside blood has been introduced.

In size the Shropshire stands about half way between the Southdown, which is the smallest, and the Oxford, which is the largest of the Down breeds. The head is wide above and short. The former breed standard called for wool down to the nose, but a " clean " face, with the wool restricted to the poll, is now laid down. The change is to be commended, since wool on the face tends to collect grass seeds and burrs. The face and legs are of a soft black colour, sometimes a little mixed with grey. The ears are short and pointed. The general form is square and blocky, on short strong legs that are wooled almost down to the feet. The fleece is dense, of good length (fully 3 in.), and of typical Down quality (56/50). In good flocks the average clip will reach 7 lb. The wool is relatively free from dark fibres, though some are generally to be found about the head and legs. The Shropshire is very early maturing, and hence excellent for fat lamb production. The quality of mutton is good, but the carcass lacks something of the smoothness of that of the Southdown, and can easily be made too fat. The fertility is high, 150 to 160 per cent. of lambs being common. The breed is fairly hardy, adapts itself well to a great variety of conditions, and the rams are very useful for crossing with the leaner and later maturing types of ewe. In Britain it is still most numerous in Shropshire and the adjoining counties. From about 1920 there was a marked decline in numbers; on the one hand the breed lost ground to the Suffolk and Oxford for crossing with Longwool and half-bred ewes and, on the other, as a foundation for commercial ewe flocks, to the Clun and Kerry Hill.

**The Suffolk** (Plate 54, *B*) was formed in the first half of the nineteenth century by crossing the blackfaced Norfolk Horned breed with the Southdown. The former had existed in East Anglia from early times, and was a very active, hardy and prolific breed producing a light fleece and a very lean carcass. One small flock still survives. By 1850 the new type had been fairly well fixed, and by 1859 it was recognised locally as a definite breed. In 1886 separate clasess were provided for it, for the first time, at the Royal Agricultural Show.

Though slightly inferior in weight to the Oxford, the Suffolk is one of the larger of the Down breeds. The head is rather long, generally quite free from wool, and, with the legs, of an intense glossy black colour. The neck is rather long, the bone stout, and the legs free from wool. The fleece is of fair length and density and of typical Down quality (58/52). A good average clip would be 7 lb., but some choice flocks reach 9 lb. Dark fibres in the wool are rather common, and the lambs are dark or parti-coloured when born. The mutton is full of lean meat and of very high quality. In carcass competitions in Britain the Suffolk competes strongly with the Southdown and the Mountain breeds. The prolificness is relatively good. When the ewes have access to abundant green food at mating time, 150 per cent. or more is common.

In Britain large numbers of rams are used for crossing with Longwool ewes, the crosses being so good that they form a favourite type for exhibition at fat stock shows. In the north they are now perhaps the most popular breed for crossing with half-breds, and are also used on Cheviot draft ewes. The centre of the breed is still East Anglia, but there are many flocks in other districts of England and in Scotland. Canada, U.S.A., South and East Africa and Chile have been the principal foreign markets.

**The Hampshire Down** (Plate 55, *A*) owes its origin to the crossing of Southdowns with two old local types, the dark-faced, horned, Berkshire Knot and the Wiltshire, a white-faced, horned and very light-wooled sheep that is still in existence. The breed was formed in the first half of the nineteenth century, and was first recognised by the Royal Agricultural Society in 1861.

The early Hampshire was nearly as large as the Suffolk, though shorter legged and more blocky. The recent trend has been towards a smaller type more nearly resembling the Southdown. The ears are long and are carried rather low. The wool on the head reaches below the level of and generally surrounds the eye. The shoulder top and breast are generally very wide and the leg is well developed. The wool reaches about 3 in. in length, is of nearly as good quality as Southdown and is very uniform (58/56), but only moderately dense, and dark fibres are rather frequent. A good average clip would be 6 lb. The face and legs are of a deep, rich, brownish black.

Hampshires are very rapid growers, lambs reaching great weights at weaning. They do not fatten quite so readily as Shropshires, nor do they produce so fine a quality of carcass as the Southdown. The breed is well adapted for folding on arable land, and is the favourite on the mixed Down and arable holdings on the chalk formation, where the ewes generally lamb in January, and many of the lambs are sold fat in spring. The ewes breed earlier in the year than those of other breeds, excepting

the Dorset Horn and Dorset Down.  The Hampshire is not very prolific,
a lambing percentage of 120 being regarded as good.  In many flocks a
large fall of lambs is not specially desired, as twins cannot easily be got
ready for the early lamb market.  The heavy head and wide shoulder of
the old type discouraged the use of the Hampshire for crossing with the
smaller sort of ewes, but recent years have seen a considerable refinement
in these points.  Abroad, the Hampshire has met with a considerable
measure of success in many sheep countries, and especially in North America, where it is now the most numerous of British breeds.

**The Dorset or West Country Down** was formed by mating Southdown
rams with Hampshire ewes, and by crossing the product with the native
western Down type.  It may be described as generally similar to the Hampshire; it is, however, slightly smaller and rather more blocky in build;
also, it shows more refinement in the head and bone, and has a distinctly
lighter colour of face and legs.  The wool resembles Southdown in quality
(58/54).  The ewes breed very early in the year, and often lamb down in
November and December.

**The Oxford Down** (Plate 55, *B*) is another breed that owes its origin
in part to the same early types as produced the Hampshire, having been
formed between 1830 and 1850 by crossing these with the Cotswold.
Some Southdown blood was also introduced.  Crossing of Downs and
Longwools is often done in commercial flocks, but the Oxford is the only
case in which the cross-bred type has been successfully fixed.  The breed
was first granted separate classification at the Royal Agricultural Show in
1862.

The Oxford is the largest and heaviest of the Downs.  In some respects
it most nearly resembles the Shropshire, but apart from the difference in
size the Oxford has a much longer and less dense fleece, and less wool on
the head and legs.  There is a top knot of long wool, and the face colour
is uniform dark greyish brown—lighter than in the Shropshire.  The head,
too, is longer, and the ears longer and thinner.  The clip is heavy, reaching
an average of 9 lb. in the better flocks.  The wool is coarser than that
of the other Downs (52/48), and indeed only slightly finer than Romney
Marsh.  The Longwool blood shows up, too, in the carcass.  As lambs
or young tegs, Oxfords give meat of good quality, but at a greater age, say
towards a year, the carcass tends to become fat and coarse, and the size
of the sheep passes beyond the desirable limit.  Oxford rams are very
suitable for mating with the older ages of half-bred ewes.  The breed is
found throughout Britain, with its centre in Oxfordshire and Gloucestershire.  Abroad it has proved successful in most districts where food is
plentiful.  The ewes are very prolific.

**The Dorset Horn** (Plate 56, *A*) is an ancient breed native to Dorset
and the adjoining parts of Somerset, Wiltshire and Hampshire, including
the Isle of Wight.  The breed is of medium size with white face and legs,
and is horned in both sexes.  The nose is pink or flesh coloured, never

black as in the Longwools. It is about similar in weight to the Shropshire, but is longer in body and generally more loosely built, with a lighter fore quarter and a somewhat narrower back. The wool is as fine as that of any of the Downs, excepting only the Southdown and Dorset Down, but is rather less uniform in quality (56/50). It is clear white in colour when scoured, and is free from dark fibres, whereas that of most Downs is creamy white, and often contains black or brown: 5 lb. is reckoned a good average clip for ewes. Lambs are normally shorn in their first summer and clip $2\frac{1}{2}$ to 3 lb. The quality of the mutton is good, but the carcass usually lacks the thickness of flesh of that of the typical Down. The breed is quite hardy, and well suited to the chalk farms of its native district, consisting of rather poor arable and dry semi-upland pastures. The ewes are very prolific, frequently giving 150 per cent. of lambs, and are excellent milkers. Their most striking peculiarity is that they will often take the ram as early as April or May, thus lambing in October-November. Milk fed fat lambs may thus be produced by Christmas. Dorset and Hampshire Downs have something of the same peculiar habit, but not in the same degree. Occasional sheep of other breeds also breed out of season. Dorset Horn ewes are used for the production of " out-of-season " lamb, which now is in competition with the extensive importation of frozen lamb, chiefly from New Zealand (Canterbury lamb). A proportion of Dorset ewes will breed twice a year, but no satisfactory or standard system of this kind has ever been found possible. Three crops in two years are not unusual. The ewes cross well with Down rams, such as Shropshire, Dorset Down and Hampshire, giving excellent lambs for early fattening. The breed has been extensively exported to Australasia and North America.

The **Wiltshire Horn** (or Western) Sheep is an old breed that at one time was nearly extinct but has been revived. A considerable number of small flocks are to be found in Northamptonshire and Anglesey. The Western is a sheep of good size, somewhat resembling the Dorset Horn, but of rougher conformation. The skin is often spotted with black, and the breed is peculiar in that it produces practically no wool. Such fleece as it possesses generally falls off in spring. The breed is hardy, and thrives well on grass throughout the year. The rams are used, especially in North Wales and the English Midlands, for crossing, the crossbred lambs being quick growers and coming early to market.

The **Ryeland** (Plate 56, *B*) is descended from a very small and very fine wooled breed that was common in the West Midlands during the eighteenth century, and probably much earlier. In most districts this type seems to have been bred out of existence by repeated crossings with Leicesters, but in the poor and sandy tract in south Hereford (Ryelands) many of the original qualities were retained, along with something of the size and fattening qualities of the Dishley sheep. The Ryeland is still a comparatively small breed, lighter than the Shropshire but heavier than the Southdown. The face is of a dull white colour with dark nose, and is wooled down to the eyes. The general symmetry is good and the sheep is well covered with firm flesh. The wool is of good quality (56/50), not so fine as Southdown, but deeper in the staple and of a clear white colour. Good flocks give an average clip of about 6 lb. The carcass is blocky and thickly fleshed, but with rather more fat than that of the Downs The rate of growth of the lambs is only fair. The Ryeland is moderately prolific, and thrives on cold, damp and inferior land with a minimum of hand feeding. It is kept entirely as a grassland breed, *i.e.* it is rarely folded on arable crops. The home of the breed is still the southern part of the Welsh Border area, but a few pure bred flocks are maintained in many parts of England. At one time the Ryeland seemed to stand in danger of being ousted by the Shropshire, which is its neighbour on the north side; now its competitors are the Clun Forest and the Kerry Hill.

The Kerry Hill (Wales) occupies a position intermediate between that of the Down and that of the true mountain breeds. Geographically, and to some extent as regards its descent, it is midway between the Shropshire and the Welsh Mountain. Its home is the Kerry Hills district of Montgomeryshire. In size it approaches the Shropshire. The face and legs are black and white, with the black concentrated at the nose and feet, and there is a tuft of wool on the forehead. The wool is of Shropshire type, but generally somewhat coarse on the breech (56/48). The ewes are very prolific and good nurses. The quality of the mutton is good. The Kerry ram is the most commonly used for crossing with Welsh Mountain ewes, and again the Kerry ewe is often crossed with the Suffolk, Shropshire or Hampshire for the production of fat lambs. Some exportations have been made, but the breed has not yet become generally known abroad. The Breed Society dates only from 1899, although the breed has existed in very much its present form for about eighty years.

The Devon Closewool is native to the area lying between Barnstaple, South Molton and Blackmore Gate in North Devon. It is derived from crosses between the Devon Longwool and the Exmoor Horn. Some of the flocks date from the end of the nineteenth century, but it was not until 1923 that a Breed Society was formed. Intermediate in size between the two parent breeds, and hornless, the Closewool otherwise approaches more nearly to the Exmoor Horn, being compact in build, thickly fleshed, and carrying a dense fleece of useful medium-quality wool (50/46). It may be described as like a small Romney Marsh, but it is shorter-bodied in relation to its height. The Closewool is a hardy breed, admirably suited to semi-upland conditions and living on grass for the greater part of the year.

The Clun Forest is an old local breed which originated in the Clun district of Shropshire, and was formerly restricted to the hilly districts of Shropshire, Radnor and Montgomery. It is related to the Kerry Hill but carries more Shropshire blood. The breed is dark faced, hornless, of medium size and, like the Kerry Hill, is notably hardy and prolific. It may be said to be intermediate between the Down and mountain types. The weight of fleece is about 6 lb. and the quality of the wool is similar to that of the Ryeland.

In recent years the breed has risen in popularity very rapidly, and it is now to be seen in large numbers not only in the Welsh Border country but in the Midlands and south. The ewe flocks thrive on pastures with little hand feeding, and are said to require very little shepherding. The wether tegs are frequently fattened on roots and settle down well in folds. If the ewes are mated to Down rams—*e.g.* Hampshire or Suffolk—the lambs fatten readily on leys and reach good weights.

**The Radnor** is native to its name county, and in its economic characters resembles its geographical neighbours, the Clun and the Kerry Hill. The original breed was tan faced like the Welsh Mountain, rather small and very hardy. Some crossing with the Kerry Hill and Shropshire increased the size with some sacrifice of hardiness.

**Mountain Breeds.**—The blackfaced mountain type seems to have been first known in the Pennine Chain, and all the modern varieties of it appear to have a common origin in that district.

Of these the **Scottish Blackface** is now the best known and is the most numerous of all British breeds. It must have reached the southern uplands of Scotland several centuries ago, but was not introduced into the Highlands till about 1770. Previous to this time the Highland grazings were stocked mainly with cattle, and what few sheep there were belonged to the old Celtic soft wooled type, which is still to be met with on some of the Western Isles. The Scottish Blackface (Plate 57, *A*), when reared in a true mountain environment, is a small sheep, but when heavily fed for fat stock shows it reaches a weight greater than that of the Southdown or Ryeland. The face and legs are either black or "brockit," *i.e.* black with white patches, the latter being preferred, though excess of white is objectionable. The head is rather short and, in show specimens, very deep and strong at the nose. The horns of the ram are large, coming out level with the head and forming a wide spiral. The fashionable type of wool is long, nearly reaching the ground, and of a coarse and hairy character (40/28) but free from kemp. Some stocks have a finer and softer wool that can be used for rough overcoatings and blankets, but most of the wool goes for carpet manufacture. The average clip under mountain conditions is probably about 4 lb., and the best flocks rarely exceed 5 lb. The general conformation has been immensely improved in recent times, and the modern sheep has a good back and leg of mutton, though the wither, as in all mountain types, is often narrow and sharp. The quality of carcass, whether as lamb or mutton, is first class. The tail is naturally shorter than in other breeds, reaching only to the hocks; as in other mountain breeds, it is frequently left uncut.

The Blackface occupies practically all the heather-clad or " black " hills of Scotland and Northumberland up to altitudes of 3000 ft. The highest grazings formerly carried wether stocks, the male sheep being kept on till they were two, three or even four years old, but almost all such stocks have been displaced by breeding ewes. Most of the lambs not required for breeding are now sold as stores in autumn or fat after a run on better keep on lower ground. On the higher grazings the Blackface is kept pure, while on the lower hills the ewes are crossed with Border Leicester or, in some districts, with Wensleydale rams. The cross lambs, known in the first case as " Greyfaces," " Mules," or " Crossbreds," and in the second as " Yorkshire Crosses," make excellent mutton at from seven to fifteen months old, though some are sold as fat lambs. The cross-bred ewe lambs may be kept for breeding for fat lamb production. The Blackface is exceedingly hardy. Generally, the ewe hoggs destined for breeding are sent to the low country to be wintered (on grass only), though provision may be made to winter some at home. The ewes live on the mountain throughout the year and get little or no artificial feeding except in times of stress in preparation for lambing. The ewes are prolific. Under hill conditions twins are not generally wanted, but good draft ewes when taken to the low country give up to 140 per cent. of lambs.

The Lonk is found in the mountainous district of west and south-west Yorks, east Lancs, and north-west Derbyshire. It is a larger, longer bodied, and rather longer legged sheep than the Scottish Blackface, with often more white in the face. The tail is long. The fleece is considerably finer (50/44) and both denser and heavier (6 to 7 lb.) than that of the Scottish. The quality of the mutton is excellent, but the breed is distinctly less hardy than either the Scottish Blackface or the Swaledale. Wensleydale and Leicester rams are those principally used for crossing, where this is practised.

The Swaledale (Plate 57, B), another useful and hardy breed, is also somewhat larger and longer bodied than the Scottish Blackface. The fleece is shorter and finer in front but is coarse on the breech, and kemp is quite as common. The face is black or dark grey with a " mealy " (grey) nose, and the legs are spotted. There is usually a good deal of black wool on the nape and throat. Swaledale lambs are said to fatten rather more readily than Scottish Blackfaces and the ewes to milk rather better, but the hardiness is probably not so good. This breed is found from Swaledale westwards to the Pennines and into Westmorland. Where crossing is done the Wensleydale ram is used, and the female progeny, known as Masham ewes, are a common type of breeding stock on grassland farms.

The Rough Fell, also known as the Kendal Rough Sheep, is a closely related breed found in an area centred on Kendal and embracing parts of the West Riding of Yorkshire and of Westmorland. It is larger, somewhat rougher in conformation, and shorter wooled than the Scottish

Blackface, and shows a brownish tinge in the face. It is regarded as a hardier sheep than either the Swaledale or the Lonk.

**The Dales-Bred** is a rather larger type with a heavier fleece. It is found on the lower and better grazings in the same area. The wool approaches that of the Scottish Blackface in quality (40/32) and the ewe fleece averages about 5 lb. Older ages of ewes are commonly crossed with Wensleydale or Teeswater rams.

**The Derbyshire Gritstone**, native to the High Peak district of Derbyshire, has the softest wool (50/46) and the closest fleece of all the breeds of the Blackface type, and is further distinguished by the absence of horns. The face and legs are mottled with black and white.

**The Cheviot** (Plate 58, *A*) is regarded as derived from the ancient Celtic tan faced breed, and would thus be related to the Welsh Mountain and to the old soft wooled sheep of the western Highlands and Hebrides. It has existed on the hills of southern Scotland from very early times, though formerly the breed was much smaller and probably finer wooled than now. There are some records of crossing with Lincolns and Leicesters about the end of the eighteenth century, but the improvement in size and in mutton qualities has been accomplished mainly by selection. The Cheviot is of medium size, reaching, when intensively fed, about the same weight as the Shropshire. The size of hill bred sheep naturally depends on the abundance and quality of the herbage. Mature rams of the best class, in show condition, weigh over 200 lb. The head and legs are white, with occasionally a shade of tan, and covered with rather hard, short hair. The head is rather short and very strong through the nose; the ears short and carried very high, giving the animal a very characteristic alert appearance. Short horns still occasionally appear—perhaps to the extent of 5 per cent.—in males. The tan colour of face is gradually being eliminated. The wool is of fine quality (56/48) but with a harsher handle than typical Down wool, of medium length (3 to 4 in.), and quite dense on the pelt. It is largely used for the manufacture of tweeds. Kemp is not common, but does occur. Mountain flocks clip from 3½ to 5 lb., and the better sort of ram hoggs reach 10 or 12 lb. The general conformation is good. The body is distinctly long and the back sometimes slack; the hind quarter is generally good, but the fore quarter, as in most mountain breeds, tends to be proportionately light and the shoulder rather sharp. The mutton quality is excellent, and the breed and its crosses (especially those from Southdown and Suffolk rams) are often very successful in carcass competitions. The Cheviot is hardy, but distinctly less so than the Blackface. In Scotland and the north of England it is chiefly to be found on the lower and more grassy hills, the heather land being given over to the Blackface. Cheviots are also kept as " park " sheep, *i.e.* on semi-upland enclosed land, and are then wintered with some turnips and other artificial food. The breed is prolific under good conditions and the ewes are excellent milkers. Hill Cheviots are very active and difficult to confine.

There are two main centres of the breed, the one in southern Scotland and the north of England and the other in Caithness and Sutherland. North country sheep are larger and leggier, somewhat less compact in build, and longer of head and ear. The ears also are carried lower. They have finer but rather more open coats and tend to be less well clad over the belly. They require rather better food conditions than the true hill type of the Border area. A separate flock book for North Country Cheviots was established in 1946.

On the better hill farms the older Cheviot ewes are crossed with Border Leicesters, and on certain farms only Half-bred lambs are produced, the Cheviot ewe stock being replenished from outside sources. Half-bred ewe lambs are in very keen demand for breeding, and command a much higher price than wethers of the same cross. Half-breds produced from north country Cheviot ewes are larger and more prolific than the corresponding progeny of Border ewes, though they require somewhat better food conditions. Draft Cheviot ewes are mated either with Border Leicesters or Suffolks. Cheviot ewes and ewe lambs are often taken far south into England for breeding purposes, and there are colonies in Brecon and on Exmoor. The breed has met with some success in Canada, the United States and New Zealand.

**The Welsh Mountain** (Plate 58, *B*) is an original Celtic breed that has been kept almost free from extraneous blood. It is the smallest of the breeds here described, reaching about half the weight of the Leicester or Oxford and not much more than two thirds that of the Southdown. The Welsh sheep is rather long bodied, light in the fore quarter, and the face and legs are either all white or have patches of a light tan shade— the latter being commoner and preferred. The rams only are horned. The breed embraces several types, including a larger improved type on the more fertile farms with some low ground and smaller types on true mountain land. The wool of improved sheep is short, fine and dense, comparable to Shropshire or fine Cheviot in quality (54/46), but that of the true mountain type is often coarse at the breech and contains much kemp. An average clip for ewes is $2\frac{1}{2}$ lb., rams reaching 5 or 6 lb. The mutton is comparable in quality to that of the Southdown, Cheviot or Blackface, and indeed is regarded by many judges as the finest procurable.

The Welsh is a hardy breed, living on the higher mountains during summer and being brought down to lower levels for wintering and lambing. The sheep are very active and rather wild, and hence are very difficult to confine. The ewes are excellent breeders and nurses. Draft ewes may be mated with Southdown rams to produce choice small fat lambs. For larger fat lambs the Wiltshire Horn is preferred. Where the produce is to be carried on to the teg stage, Kerry Hill or Clun rams give good results. The breed is found throughout the whole of the mountainous district of Wales, the population being densest in the north. A black strain of the breed exists, but is generally kept in lowland parks.

Recently numbers of Welsh Mountain ewes have been mated with the Border Leicester for the production of a Welsh Half-bred. This Half-bred is finding favour as a cross-bred ewe for the production of fat lamb, particularly on lower lying grass farms. It is rather smaller in size than the Border Leicester × Cheviot Half-bred.

**The South Wales Mountain** is a rather leggy type with a very kempy fleece, suitable only for carpet manufacture. It is found in Glamorgan and Monmouth and in parts of Carmarthen and Brecon. It is the largest of the Welsh types.

**The Herdwick** (Plate 59, *A*) is a breed of rather striking peculiarities found in the bleak, exposed fells of the Lake District. Its origin is quite unknown, although there is a tradition that the foundation stock came from a Scottish or Norwegian vessel that was wrecked on the Cumberland coast two or three centuries ago.

The size is rather less than that of the Blackface mountain type though varying a good deal with the quality of grazing. The rams are generally but not always horned, while the ewes are hornless. The face and legs of the lamb are of a deep blue black colour, becoming grey and sometimes eventually white with age. The wool, particularly that on the belly, is often mixed with grey; it is long and coarse (40/32) and contains much more kemp than that of the Scottish Blackface. Ewes clip from 3 to 5lb. according to conditions, and rams up to 9 or 10 lb. The shoulder top is generally sharp and the breed is late maturing, but the mutton is of fine texture and flavour. The ewes are sometimes not allowed to bear lambs till they are three years old—a year later than the normal age. The Herdwick is generally regarded as the hardiest of all British breeds; the sheep subsist largely on heather and juniper, and survive long periods of storm. Draft ewes taken to the low country are generally crossed with Wensleydale, Leicester or Border Leicester rams, and the progeny make excellent butcher's sheep. The Wensleydale is the ordinary cross under hill conditions. The breed is declining in numbers owing to the progress of afforestation in its home area.

**The Exmoor Horn or Porlock** (Plate 59, *B*) is an ancient breed native to Exmoor and the Brendon Hills in North Devon and West Somerset. It is of small size, horned in both sexes, with white face and legs and a black muzzle. The fleece is of the Cheviot type, but rather longer and stronger and coarser at the breech (56/40). Ewe flocks give clips up to 5 lb. The general conformation is compact and neat, with a peculiarly rounded symmetry. There is rather frequently a deficiency behind the shoulder. The breed is hardy, but the ewes generally get some roots and hay in winter. The mutton is of good quality.

**The Dartmoor,** like the Oxford Down, Kerry Hill and Clun, cannot rightly be classified in any of the three main groups of breeds. Though originally a Moorland breed, the Dartmoor has been so increased in size and improved in form that it must now be considered a Longwool.

Like the true Longwools it owes something to Dishley Leicester blood.

It is larger than any of the mountain breeds proper, and hornless— short stubs being seen exceptionally in rams. The face and ears are white with black spots, the latter generally somewhat concentrated towards the nose. The fleece is long, curly and lustrous, of coarse Longwool quality (36/32), and the clip is heavy. The sheep is long bodied, strong limbed and well covered with firm flesh. The ewes are wintered on grass and hay, and lamb in the beginning of March. The breed is rather late maturing but produces yearling wethers of fine quality. Older ewes are crossed either with Down or with South Devon rams. A white-faced strain is separately registered.

**The Shetland** is an interesting breed, so far little improved, but with certain potentially valuable characteristics. It is very small, slow maturing and thin-fleshed, though the texture and flavour of the mutton in well fed sheep are good. The colour is black, grey or brown (moorit), often with white patches, or entirely white. The white and moorit wools command the highest prices. The fleece is light and of very mixed quality but contains a proportion of very fine soft wool which commands a higher price than that of the Southdown. In Shetland the sheep are not shorn, the loose wool being picked off at intervals and the finest sorted out for the local industry of shawl-making. The breed, like others in Northern Europe, is naturally short tailed. The rams are horned, the ewes generally hornless. At one time the breed occupied the whole of the Shetland Islands, but it has given way to some extent before the Blackface. Crosses with the Cheviot are useful both for wool and mutton.

## COMMERCIAL TYPES AND CROSSES

It will be clear from references in the preceding pages that certain areas of the country breed far more sheep than can be fattened locally, and that some districts will have surpluses of pure-bred or cross-bred ewe lambs suitable for breeding. The surplus is sold, and is moved into areas where the flocks are not self-supporting. The following are the more important classes of stores and breeding animals that pass through markets:—

**Store Lambs.**—A variable and rather small proportion of mountain wether lambs are sold to butchers direct from the grazings where they have been bred; the bulk are marketed as stores in August and September. The main sources are the Highlands and southern uplands of Scotland, the northern counties of England, the Pennine region and Wales. The mountain breeds have a limited capacity for growth, and in any case are not very suited for folding on roots, hence the great majority are fattened on pastures, aftermaths and rape, and reach the fat market mainly from October to December. They yield small carcasses of between 25 and 35 lb., which in normal times command a high price per pound. Ewe lambs are in demand for breeding, and in most areas only culls can be bought at prices which make it possible to fatten them at a profit. The typical produce of the lower hill areas in the same regions and in Caithness and Sutherland is a cross between a mountain ewe, *e.g.* Blackface and Cheviot, and a Longwool ram. The Border Leicester × Cheviot ewe lambs (Half-breds) are in great demand for breeding, and few are fattened as tegs; but the wether lambs are a fairly important class of store. The breeders' demand for Longwool × Blackface ewe lambs (Greyface, Mule, Masham) is not so great, so that many of these, as well as the wethers, are available for fattening. Greyface and similar crosses are commonly run on lowland pastures for the earlier part of the winter and finally fattened off on roots, hay and concentrates, reaching the fat market mostly from March till May; they produce good carcasses of the size 40 to 55 lb..

Apart from mountain and hill areas, the chief sources of store lambs are: (1) part arable farms in southern Scotland, Northumberland and Cumberland (crosses between Suffolk or Oxford rams with Half-bred or Mule ewes); (2) the Welsh border area (Kerry Hill and Clun and crosses of these breeds with Down rams); (3) Kent (Romney Marsh wether lambs and crosses between the Southdown ram and the Romney Marsh ewe); (4) the chalk area, from Dorset to Norfolk (mainly Downs, such as Hampshire, Suffolk and Hampshire-Oxford crosses). Recently, a higher proportion of the lambs from these areas have been fattened on the farms where they were bred. Those available for sale as stores are available earlier than those bred on the hills, the largest sales taking place in June and July. The more forward lots are fattened off on aftermath and rape. The remainder are folded on roots and provide the bulk of the supply of spring mutton. There is now a strictly limited market for these heavier carcasses.

**Ewe Lambs.**—The mountain sheep farmer normally retains the best of his ewe lambs for his own flock, selling his " seconds" to farmers in lower hill areas, who use them to produce cross-bred lambs. As already noted, there is a sale for some of the cross-bred progeny for breeding, the demand for Half-breds being especially strong. Many downland farmers also make up lots of " second " ewe lambs which are bought by other breeders.

**Young Ewes.**—Some breeders hold over their surplus ewe lambs and sell them at about eighteen months of age (theaves or gimmers), when they are ready for breeding. There are also some specialists who have suitable areas of lowland pasture and who buy ewe lambs and sell them as theaves a year later. Many breeders in the Welsh border counties keep all but the poorest of their ewe lambs and sell these females at two and a half or three and a half years old.

**Draft Ewes.**—Under comparatively rigorous conditions for any particular breed the death-rate among ewes tends to rise after about five years. On the other hand, rich land tends to make ewes too fat for breeding. Hence it is often advantageous to draft ewes from poorer to better farms at " three-crop " (four and a half years old) or " four-crop " (five and a half years old). The latter are often fattened with their next crop of lambs, but the former may produce two further crops of lambs in the second flock. There is a large demand for draft ewes, the sales mostly taking place shortly before the breeding season, *e.g.* in May for Dorset Horns and Dorset Downs, and in September to October for mountain breeds.

## SHEEP BREEDING, REARING AND FEEDING

It seems necessary to begin this section with an explanation of the names that are applied to sheep of the different sexes at various ages. Age in sheep is reckoned from the time of shearing, which in this country is normally done for the first time at the age of fourteen to sixteen months, and at yearly intervals thereafter. The term *lamb* is not very precisely limited, being sometimes confined to the period before weaning and sometimes extended to cover the first six, eight or occasionally ten months of the animal's life. However, at some time in autumn, spring born lambs become in the north *hoggs* or *hoggets* and in the south *tegs*. The sex is also denoted, males being known as tup or ram lambs, tup hoggs, ram tegs; castrated males as wether or wedder lambs, wedder hoggs; and females as ewe lambs. In some districts the term *chilver* is used instead of ewe lamb. After shearing we denote the males as shearling rams or tups and shearling wedders respectively. The terms *diamond tup* and *dinmont* are also applied at this age. The female at shearing becomes a *gimmer* (north) or *theave* (south). Thereafter we have two shear rams, wedders or ewes. Ewes may also be distinguished according to the number of crops of lambs they have borne, as two-crop, three-crop and so on. In some districts it is customary to denote age by the teeth, as two-tooth, four-tooth, but these terms are less satisfactory on account of the variation in dentition according to breed and environment.

The average period of gestation in sheep is about 147 days, varying a day or two with the breed. The ordinary practice is to complete preparations for lambing about a week before the elapse of five calendar months from the time of turning out the ram. Females are normally mated for the first time as gimmers, to lamb at two years old, though the practice of mating well grown ewe hoggs in autumn is now fairly common in lowland commercial flocks. Such hoggs in good condition will frequently take the ram at an age of seven or eight months, and will then lamb at a little over a year, giving a lamb crop of 60 to 70 per cent. In-lamb tegs should receive specially liberal feeding during the last month of pregnancy. Ram lambs, especially those of the quicker growing breeds like Hampshires and Oxfords are often used for breeding at seven months old or little more. They should, however, be alloted a smaller number of ewes than old sheep, generally not more than thirty or forty. Shearlings and older rams, so long as they remain active, may have from forty to fifty ewes under mountain conditions, and from sixty to eighty when the flock is in enclosed fields. Where it is desired to make the fullest use of a specially good ram, the ewes, as they come in heat, are taken one by one to the ram for a single service. A " chaser " ram is employed to seek out the ewes that are in season. A piece of sacking is tied round the chaser's middle to prevent him from serving.

The time of mating is limited in part by the time of occurrence of heat in the ewe. Thus Dorset Horns will frequently take the ram in May, Dorset Downs and Hampshires as early as June or July, while mountain ewes rarely come in heat till late September or even well on in October. In most breeds the onset of œstrus is governed mainly by the hours of daylight—i.e. the ewe begins to come in season with the shortening day. The control of the cycle is by the pituitary body, and it is possible, by injecting pituitary extracts, to make ewes breed at any season. Apart from this the time of mating is fixed by the breeder in accordance with the average climatic and food conditions prevailing in spring. Thus in the south of England, on arable farms, lambing may begin in December or occasionally earlier, while on Highland grazings it does not commence till late in April. The customary dates for turning out rams in various flocks are usually closely adhered to from year to year, and vary from the end of July (early Hampshires) to mid-September (Lincolns), mid-October (Half-breds), 10th November (average Mountain Cheviots), and 22nd November (Blackface Mountain). Rams are left in the flock for about six weeks, which is ordinarily long enough to ensure that practically all the ewes will conceive. The period of œstrus in the ewe lasts about twenty seven hours and recurs, if she does not conceive, after about sixteen days. A six weeks' breeding season thus covers at least two and, in a majority of cases, three œstrous periods. In lowland flocks, where the ewes will have close attention at lambing, it is necessary to record the dates of service. To this end the ram is smeared between his forelegs with colouring matter so that he leaves a mark on each ewe that he serves. At the end of, say, each week, the ewes that have taken the ram are given a distinguishing mark, which remains till spring as an indication of the date of lambing. At the end of sixteen days the colour on the ram is changed to a darker one, so that the ewes not holding to the first service can be immediately known by the fact that they are marked with two colours. Any such should be examined, and if necessary, clipped about the tail and inside of the thighs. The longer wooled breeds are generally so clipped before tupping begins. Occasional ewes that have failed to hold to the first service should be placed with another ram in case the second service should also have proved ineffective. If many ewes are being twice marked another ram should be procured; in large flocks it is best

T

to run two or three rams together with a combined allotment of ewes, as the accident of one ram proving infertile will then cause comparatively little loss. If, however, the rams fight, this plan must be abandoned; also, the method is not applicable in pure bred flocks, where matings are made with close regard to individual merits and faults. Under ordinarily good conditions and on low ground the proportion of barren or " eild " ewes should not exceed 1 or at most 2 per cent., in hill flocks it may reach 3 or 4 per cent. in ordinary seasons.

The number of twins, or at least of double conceptions, depends partly on the inherent fecundity of the ewes and partly on their treatment before and during the mating season. The smallest number of lambs will be obtained when the ewes are lean and weak, very fat or are going back in condition. The highest birth rate is obtained if the ewes at mating time are in moderately lean but rapidly improving condition. This is assured —if the sheep have been in low condition after the previous weaning— by bringing them on slowly till within a week or two of tupping, and then by flushing on rape, young seeds or other fresh nutritious food. Flushing causes an increased proportion of the ewes to breed early, *i.e.* at the season when there is the greatest chance of multiple ovulations. Failing a supply of fresh green food the ewes may be given up to a pound per head of concentrate daily, avoiding specially fattening materials. Oats are very suitable. The proportion of multiple ovulations (*i.e.* of heats at which two or more eggs are produced) is highest in the earlier part of the breeding season, this explaining the well-known fact that more twins are usually born at the beginning than at the end of the lambing season. Delay in mating after the time when the ewes would begin to take the ram will thus reduce the proportion of twin births. Sometimes twins are not wanted—as, for example, in mountain flocks; ram breeders, too, if they sell their output as lambs, do not want a high proportion, as a good single ram lamb is often worth more than a pair of moderate twins. Draft ewes, which are usually sold off the hill in autumn, to be kept for a further one or two years under lowland conditions, will generally be wanted in lamb earlier than the normal time, and must be brought forward in condition more rapidly than the rest. To this end their lambs are often weaned earlier than those of the other ewes. Rams often require special attention during the breeding season. Longwool or other lowland rams put out among mountain ewes must be in good breeding condition and receive a feed of concentrates once a day at least, otherwise they will very rapidly become reduced in condition.

In countries where the winter is very severe, such as the northern United States and Canada, breeding ewes are housed in cool barns during winter, going out for exercise only. In this country they are always wintered out of doors. Ewes of the hardier mountain breed are left on their usual pastures, being gathered to the lower and sheltered areas only at the prospect of snowstorms. Many flocks live without hand feeding unless or until they are in rather severe straits, which is only in the wildest weather or when the ground is covered with hard-frozen snow. If given hay unnecessarily they tend to stop foraging for themselves. Usually the supply of hay on hill farms is limited and too much should not be used during the early part of the winter. The hill shepherd endeavours to save the lower areas of the pasture during late summer and autumn, so that he has a reserve of natural herbage for winter food. Weak ewes, however, must be taken in from the hill and kept in enclosures near the homestead, where they can receive whatever special attention or feeding is necessary.

There is a growing tendency to give hill ewes some supplementary feeding to prepare them for lambing. The evidence now available suggests that this is an important factor in raising the weaned lamb percentage of hill flocks from say 60 to 70 per cent. to a figure nearer to one lamb per ewe. Great ingenuity must be exercised by the shepherd to arrange the feeding so that the ewes do not stop foraging for themselves. For example, the supplement may only be given every few days, and the place of feeding may be varied. Where supplementary feeding say of a lower grade concentrate is carried out successfully the ewes come to lambing fitter, the lambs are stronger and losses after lambing are much reduced.

On lowland pasture farms the sheep may run on grass without any additional food during the early part of the winter. Later on they are given up to 2 or 3 lb. of hay, according to the condition of the pasture, and sometimes, from a month before lambing, a moderate ration of cake and corn.

On arable or semi-arable sheep farms the winter management varies greatly according to breed, the amount of roots and such like foods available, and the time of lambing. Half-bred ewes in the north, due to lamb in March and April, are usually run on grass without extra feeding until towards Christmas. As the pasture gets bare they are given a limited ration of turnips, say ½ ton per hundred ewes per day. Later they will generally be folded on turnips for half the day or overnight, returning to the pastures at other times and receiving perhaps a little hay in addition. When roots are abundant ewes are sometimes folded permanently on the crop; but the method is not always satisfactory, the ewes getting into a soft and unhealthy condition. In any case they should be put back on pasture, with a restricted root ration and some hay, a few weeks before lambing is due to begin; they also benefit by daily exercise, such as may be given by driving the flock daily to and from an outlying field. A light daily ration of concentrates will be given from six weeks before lambing in order to bring the ewes into good condition for milking. In March, just previous to lambing, the ration might be: turnips, 20 lb.; oats, peas and dried grains, 1 lb.; hay, ½ lb.—varying, the hay particularly, according to the amount of rough herbage on the pasture fields. Draft ewes in the lower districts, that are due to lamb perhaps a month later, and are to be fattened along with their lambs, are given more liberal treatment.

In the south on those very few farms where folding is still practised a common succession of winter foods is: (1) turnips, (2) swedes and marrow-stem kale grown in alternate strips, (3) swedes and thousand-headed kale, and (4) swedes. Folding takes place over a long period. A few mangels are often valuable, after lambing, in tiding over the flock until " seeds " or other summer food is available. Clover, lucerne or sainfoin hay or pea haulm, may replace the seeds hay of the north. The aim is, however, the same—to keep down costs during the early stages of pregnancy and, by adding concentrates later, to ensure strong lambs and a plentiful flow of milk. In one series of experiments it was found that half-bred ewes which gained 20 lb. of live-weight during their period of pregnancy produced quite as large and as vigorous lambs as others which were more heavily fed and gained 50 lb. in weight. On the other hand, a third group which were more poorly fed, so that they barely maintained their weight, produced a large proportion of very weak lambs, many of which could not suck.

On sheep farms where the arable land is heavy, as, for example, in many districts of Northumberland, folding in winter is impossible. In such cases the root crop is stored in autumn and the daily allowance is thrown out to the ewes on grass.

To sum up, we now know that heavy losses of ewes and poor lambing results are more likely if the ewes approach the critical lambing season in poor condition. Under all conditions the aim should be to ensure that ewes come forward to lamb in good hard condition but not overfat, *i.e.* through good but not too liberal feeding and plenty of exercise. Such ewes are more likely to avoid such troubles as twin lamb disease; the lambs are stronger at birth, and the ewes have more milk to rear them. Profitability turns larger on the number and quality of the lambs, hence the importance of good management for the ewes.

Before lambing, the ewe flock should be collected and looked over to see that the teats are clear of wool, otherwise the lambs will be liable to seize and swallow locks of wool in their attempts to suck. Gimmers (theaves) often have to have a considerable amount of wool removed. The operation is known as " udder-locking."

Lambing, in hill flocks, goes on in the open, and generally on the mountains, though in some cases the ewes are brought down to lower enclosed pastures. It generally begins in the second or third week of April and continues throughout the greater part of May. Each shepherd, who will have a " hirsel " of perhaps twenty five or thirty score of lambing ewes under his charge, is given a temporary assistant (or at least a half share of the time of such an assistant) for the busy and critical period of four or five weeks. This arrangement makes it possible for the sheep to be seen at least two or three times a day, and will generally ensure that assistance is available in cases of difficult or protracted labour. The chief causes of heavy mortality are snow or heavy rainstorms; in the first case the lambs may be buried, or simply exhausted by the cold and the heavy going; in the latter they are very liable to be drowned in attempting to follow their dams over swollen torrents. In bad weather the sheep are gathered into the naturally sheltered areas on the lower ground. Even in good lambing seasons weak ewes and those with weak lambs require to be brought down and fed, but the main part of the flock should be made to travel the ground in a regular way. The natural habit of hill sheep is to spend the night on the hill-tops, to move down to the valleys in the morning and up again in the afternoon, grazing as they go. When the lambs are young, however—and especially if the ewes are in low condition —many will tend to lag behind and to remain on the lower ground, which would then soon become foul with droppings; very heavy worm infestation may result. Hence the shepherd must see that all that are able do actually go up the heights in the evening, and this often entails heavy work. The earliest herbage on mountain grazings is the " Draw Moss " (sheathing cotton-sedge or cotton grass), *Eriophorum vaginatum* which grows on marshy land. On grazings where this is not abundant, care must be taken to preserve it by avoiding over-drainage, and the sheep should have full access to the marshy areas in early spring.

A considerable part of our mountain grazing in Scotland and Northern Ireland is infested with sheep ticks (*Ixodes ricinus*) which carry two specific diseases (Louping ill and tick borne fever) and also cause loss by producing abscesses and blood poisoning (pyæmia) in young lambs. The ticks are most common on coarse, dense bottomed herbage where the humidity is high; hence any treatment that will promote a finer sward and reduce humidity will help to control the pest. Drainage, the employment of cattle to eat off the coarse stuff, and burning are all helpful, while repeated dipping of the sheep tends to kill off the parasites. Lambs are most susceptible to tick borne disease, and it is best to try to protect them by smearing with an anti-tick salve. Hoggs may be protected from louping ill by a vaccine usually used in March before they come home.

Considerable areas of hill-grazing from Bodmin Moor in Cornwall to the north of Scotland are deficient in cobalt. Cobalt deficiency leads to reduced numbers of lambs, which make very poor growth. The areas in question have been recognised in the past as " pining " land, but the condition has been diagnosed only in recent years. Good results have been obtained by applying cobalt sulphate, at the rate of 2 lb. per acre, to the pastures and also by providing salt licks containing cobalt. The more certain preventive is to dose the ewes in autumn with 200 to 400 mg. of cobalt, and to drench the lambs in spring and again in summer.

Ewes on mixed farms will have been classified in autumn into five groups according to the period (week) in which they are expected to lamb. Each batch in succession, as it comes due to lamb, is removed to the lambing field, which should be a good dry pasture with the best available natural shelter. Artificial wind breaks, consisting of thatched hurdles or sheep nets stuffed with straw, and set up in the form of a cross, should be placed here and there. In or near the lambing field should be a lambing shed with a hut in which the shepherd and lambing man spend alternate nights. The shed is usually a permanent structure; some farmers prefer temporary shelters on the ground that they are less liable to harbour disease, but permanent erections, if they receive a thorough annual disinfection, are not open to serious objection. The shed consists of a series of pens, about 4½ or 5 ft. square, with a low roof and arranged to form a hollow square (Fig. 34). In ordinary cases the central yard is

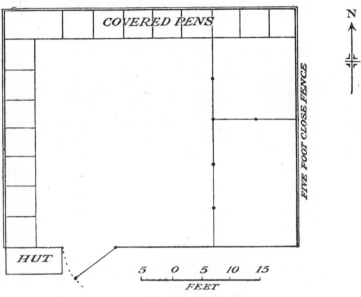

FIG. 34.—Lambing Yard.

open, but for valuable pure bred flocks the whole may be roofed in. In any case, the shed should be on dry ground with a sheltered situation and a southern exposure.

During the day the ewes go out in the lambing field; at night they are confined in the central yard of the lambing shed, which should be well littered with dry straw. Ewes lambing at night are placed one in each small pen. Assistance in lambing should not be given too soon, and the assistant should thoroughly disinfect his hands before and after each case. Each ewe and her lamb or lambs may be given a distinguishing dot of colour, in order to avoid any possibility of subsequent confusion; but as a ewe generally keeps in touch with one of her lambs it is often considered sufficient to mark the twins. Generally there will be a proportion of triple births, as well as a few orphan lambs. On the other hand, there will be many singles and a few ewes whose lambs die. There should be a reassortment, by transferring lambs, so that the flock is made to consist entirely of singles and doubles. In cases where a lamb has died its skin should be tied over the back of the stranger, when the latter will generally be adopted at once. Other devices, such as that of rubbing the ewe's nose in whisky to deprive her temporarily of her sense of smell, are successful in other cases. Refractory ewes may have to be tied up by the neck for a few days in order to prevent maltreatment of foster lambs. In any case, reassorted families must be kept penned together until it is seen that they have settled down. Gimmers (theaves) should not be given second lambs if ewes are available.

The ewes and young lambs are kept in the more sheltered fields near the centre of operations for a week or two, and are then put out in lots to the ordinary pastures. On enclosed farms the flock will be split up into lots of similar age, gimmers with double lambs being given the best grass, ewes with singles the worst. Feeding with roots, hay and concentrate must be continued until grass or other supplement e.g. silage or a forage crop becomes available. This may be as early as mid-April in the south, often after mid-May in the north. When grass becomes plentiful, supplementary feeding is withdrawn, or may be transferred from the ewes to the lambs. Soon after lambing is completed the lambs are docked, males not required for breeding are castrated, and ear-marking with the flock mark may be done—although it may be postponed until after weaning. In pedigree flocks the sheep are given individual ear tags or are tattooed in the ear with individual numbers. In hill flocks the " gathering " is taken as an opportunity of enumerating. In mountain sheep the tail is often left long (for protection), but all lambs that are likely at a later stage to receive roots or concentrates are better docked.

Lambing percentages vary greatly with conditions. Mountain flocks in normal years may give from 60 to 120 lambs per 100 ewes—less on the poorer and higher ground, more on the lower and better sort of grazings. In years of storm and flood the lamb crop may be as low as forty or fifty, and occasionally the ewe lambs will barely be numerous enough to replace losses in the older sheep. Probably the average of lowland flocks all over the country is about 130 per cent., and the most prolific flocks reach an average, over series of years, of about 160.

In the north and west, sheep are generally kept on pasture throughout the summer. In the south and south-east, especially on the Chalk and Oölite formations (semi-upland and rather poor arable), the traditional practice (now fast being superceded) is to run the ewes on Down pasture, if this forms part of the holding, during only part of the day; for the rest the flock is folded on forage crops—rye, trifolium and winter vetches in spring; clover, sainfoin, lucerne, spring vetches, mustard and rape in summer; rape, mustard, kale and turnips in autumn. The folding system is very expensive in labour as compared with ordinary grazing, and on this account has declined very greatly during the past forty years; it is a method by which a considerably larger head of stock can be kept than otherwise is possible, on the drier sort of land where pasture is not very productive.

The stocking of pastures so as to get the best results can only be decided by trial. The best seeds pastures will carry three ewes with double lambs per acre; ordinary pasture perhaps two ewes (with, say, three lambs) per acre; good grassy hill land about one per acre, and the poorer sorts of mountain land as little as one ewe to 5 or even 15 acres. On the best permanent grass it may be wise to put on no more than two ewes and their lambs to the acre and to complete the stocking with cattle; heavier stocking with sheep tends to increase the incidence of internal parasites, such as stomach worms. Most mountain grazings have a recognised carrying capacity which, however, can be improved by treatment, *e.g.* by application of lime and phosphate. In most cases it is, of course, economically unsound to manure the whole area of the grazing, but highly beneficial results may be obtained from dressing quite small areas of the better land, especially if these can be enclosed and the grazing therefore managed more effectively. The direct feeding of mineral mixtures (ground limestone, steamed bone flour and common salt) is beneficial on hill grazings that are very deficient in minerals. Common salt should be provided in all cases; this can most conveniently be done by placing large lumps of rock salt under simple shelters.

Most sheep pastures are improved by the addition of a small number of cattle—say a store bullock or a cow and calf to every five or ten ewes. They keep the grasses from becoming coarse and from running to seed.

Of the various special incidents of the summer season, shearing is the first. In the south this is done as early as the beginning of May; in north country low ground flocks about the beginning of June, and in the highest mountain grazings as late as the first or second week of July. The date is determined mainly by the time of natural " rise " of the wool, which becomes apparent a few weeks after the return, with the spring, of a vigorous thriving condition. The time occupied in clipping depends on the type of wool that the sheep carries. With Shortwools, less than a score will represent a day's work for a good hand shearer, while with Blackfaces, where an inch of wool or more is left on, fully five score per day can be shorn. In wool producing countries like Australia, where sheep shearing is a specialised occupation, and power driven machines are generally used, the number clipped in relation to the quality of the work is far greater. Machine shearing is now normal practice in many British flocks. Sheep may either be washed in clean stream water a week before clipping, or may be shorn in the grease. There is a loss of weight, generally from 10 to 20 per cent., if washing is done thoroughly, but the washed wool brings a proportionately higher price. Washed wools can be more accurately valued by buyers.

The time for summer dipping is generally about three weeks after clipping, when there is just wool enough to carry the dip. Summer dipping has the double object of killing external parasites (keds, ticks and scabmites), and of warding off attacks of blowfly. The dip formerly used, based usually upon sodium arsenite and sulphur, has been replaced by one containing usually both D.D.T. and benzene hexachloride (Gammexane) with sometimes arsenical compounds as well. The great advantage of the new insecticides is that they give protection against blowfly, and against reinfestation by skin parasites, for a much longer period than the older materials—generally for a period of about six weeks. In the use of all dips it is important to observe the directions of the makers; some shepherds tend to use stronger solutions than those recommended. Ewes and lambs are generally dipped at the same time. If it should be found necessary to dip a breeding flock when the lambs are very young it is essential to work with very small lots of sheep, otherwise the ewe and her lamb may fail to recognise each other after the operation. Reference has already been made to smearing lambs with an anti-tick salve.

During July and August shepherds must be continually on the outlook for sheep that have been " struck " by the fly, and the affected parts must be dressed as early as possible. The most successful preventive treatment so far discovered is dipping or spraying with a preparation of D.D.T. Spraying, as compared with dipping, makes for great economics both in time and materials. Apart from preventive dipping or spraying, the clipping off of locks of dirty wool from about the hind quarters is important, as the fly is attracted by smell. Dip that is heavily contaminated with faeces is worse than useless as a fly deterrent, so that the bath must be frequently emptied and refilled with clean material.

Lambs on pasture are very liable to infestation with a variety of stomach-worms and it has been a routine practice, in many flocks, to drench them with a weak solution (1 per cent.) of copper sulphate. This is effective against the commonest species (*Haemonchus contortus*), but in other cases it has been necessary in the past to use either a drench of copper and nicotine sulphates or arsenical preparations. The drug phenothiazine is very effective against most of the common stomach and intestinal worms except *Nematodirus* and the very common twisted stomach-worm (*Hæmonchus*). The eggs of the former can over-winter from one season to the next. Where lambs show symptoms of heavy worm infestation—poor general condition, scouring and anæmia—it is well to have the droppings examined in order to determine the species of worms concerned. The most appropriate treatment will depend on the prevalent species. Where *Nematodirus* is serious, it is a common practice to so manage the grazing that lambs graze new grass or a pasture on which sheep have not grazed for twelve months. This aim is also secured on some farms by front or sideways creep grazing—a method which allows of heavy stocking and high production per acre, but which demands close and constant supervision to ensure that the grass is grazed at the right stage of growth.

Weaning is generally done when the lambs are from three to four months old, *i.e.* between May and August, according to the date of lambing. At weaning the ewes are put out to the poorest and barest pastures, in order that the flow of milk may be dried off, while the lambs are given the best and cleanest grass available, fields having generally been rested for the purpose; or they are folded on fresh forage crops. Clover aftermaths are ideal for the purpose, only in this case the herbage must be dry when the lambs are turned on, otherwise many of them may get hoven (bloat). Most store lambs are disposed of by the breeders at large sales, which commence in June, July or August, according to the district; at the same time, or generally a little later, the breeder buys in ewe lambs to replenish his breeding flock, unless a proportion of the home bred lambs is being retained for the purpose.

Draft and cull ewes are disposed of at other special sales in July, August or September. On most arable farms, and on better mountain grazings, ewes are kept in the breeding flock until they are of a certain definite age. This is generally four and a half years (four-shear or three-crop), but sometimes a year more. On the poorer mountain grazings, where sheep have a special value when acclimatised[1] and accustomed to the ground, there is no definite age for drafting, but each ewe is retained in the flock so long as she remains active and healthy. Even in flocks where ewes are drafted out at a fixed age, the younger ewes must be looked over and unhealthy animals, bad milkers and ewes with defective teeth or udders culled out. Draft ewes are brought in to good pasture, or folded on forage crops, as soon as the flow of milk has ceased, and are brought forward rapidly so that they may be in good condition for early tupping. Generally, the draft lot is examined and culled, so that the major part may be sold as fully guaranteed, *i.e.* certified correct in udders and mouths. A second lot will be made of those that are broken-mouthed but otherwise correct, while unhealthy animals or those with defective udders, are sold separately for fattening.

Hill ewes after weaning and until, say, October, are herded on to the higher parts of the grazing in order to conserve the lower areas for winter use. Lambs that are not sold at weaning time are allowed to rejoin the flock after about ten days, by which time the ewes' flow of milk will have ceased.

---

[1] There is good reason for the belief that the main factor in acclimatisation is that the stock has been mildly attacked by (and has built up immunity from) louping ill and tick-borne fever. Immunity to the former disease can now be conferred artificially. As mentioned on page 581, both diseases are carried by the tick *Ixodes ricinus*, which also causes septic infections (pyæmia) in young lambs.

In autumn sheep must be kept off marshy ground and water meadows, as otherwise they are liable to pick up large numbers of liver fluke larvæ. When it seems likely that infestation has occurred, the sheep should be treated two or three times, at monthly intervals, commencing in September with male fern or ethyl hexachloride. On wet grazings this may be a matter of routine.

Winter dipping is done during spells of good weather in autumn, generally in October, but either before the commencement or after the close of the tupping season.[1]

Besides skin parasites, maggots and liver flukes, all mentioned above, there are many diseases and parasites of sheep that must be guarded against. Foot-rot is common in most breeds when they are kept on wet land, and is a serious cause of unthriftiness. There are two kinds of foot-rot—one affecting only a few individuals, the other virulent and infectious. One important piece of knowledge about the latter is that it can only survive on pasture for about two weeks in the absence of sheep. This gives a valuable line on control. The feet of infected sheep should be trimmed very carefully, on concrete or other hard surface so that the parings may be swept up and destroyed, and treated with 10 per cent. formalin or 10 per cent. tincture of chloromycelin. All apparently healthy sheep should go through a 5 per cent. copper sulphate or formalin foot bath before they go out to clean pasture. The affected sheep should not be mixed with the others until the lesions are healed.

Garget or udder clap, inflammation of the womb after lambing, scour in lambs, lung-worms and tape-worms, lamb dysentery (which can now be prevented either by vaccinating the ewes or by injecting the lambs with serum), sturdy, louping-ill or trembling and braxy (which can be prevented by vaccination), scrapie, tick-borne fever, pulpy kidney, and several other troubles are often responsible for serious loss. In each case the flockmaster must endeavour to avoid such loss by general good management as well as by special preventive measures.

Great progress has been made in recent years in the prevention of a number of sheep diseases and the cure of others. Lamb dysentery, pulpy kidney, louping-ill and braxy can now all be prevented by vaccination. The losses from many others can be restricted by good general management, as in the case of intestinal worms; and each year some newer method of treatment seems to come to the flockmaster's aid. It is therefore well worthy seeking veterinary advice so soon as the onset of trouble seems likely.

Sheep often get all the water they require from plant sap, rain and

---

[1] In certain parts of the country there are Government regulations requiring dipping to be done at least twice a year, and between certain specified dates. Sheep moved from an area which is scheduled for scab into a " clean " area are required to be dipped twice, the second dipping being between eight and fourteen days after the first. There are good grounds for hope that sheep-scab has been completely eradicated.

dew, and under such circumstances do not drink; but in spells of dry weather they do so freely, and water should be offered in all cases of doubt.

Ewe lambs for breeding may be selected from home bred stock if this be kept pure; indeed, on the poorer mountain grazings, home bred sheep are much more likely to survive than others introduced. On the other hand, breeders who produce cross-bred lambs for the butcher should obtain ewe lambs from others who specialise in the breeding of such. In either case the animals should be selected carefully and individually, and the number bought or retained may well be 10 or 20 per cent. greater than actual requirements, in order to allow for subsequent culling. Hoggs intended for the breeding flock should be so wintered as to keep them in healthy growing condition, but should not be made fat. Those from mountain grazings have generally to be wintered on low ground, and those from extensive mountain districts like the Scottish Highlands have sometimes to travel a hundred miles or more for wintering. Such are, almost invariably, wintered on grass alone, even if this means that they become rather reduced in condition. Root feeding is undesirable because after such artificial treatment the sheep do not take kindly to their native hillsides. Recently the practice of home wintering on slatted floors has been tried out with some success. The hoggs run our during the day and are housed at night, usually receiving an allowance of hay.

Ewe hoggs on arable or semi-arable farms may run on grass until well on in the autumn, when they are folded on roots for a gradually increasing period of the day. Later on, in January, or earlier or later according to the time of commencement of root feeding, the temporary incisor teeth begin to break off, so that roots must thereafter be fingered and fed in boxes. An allowance of 16 lb. of roots (hardy yellow turnips or swedes) and $\frac{3}{4}$ lb. of hay will suffice for those of ordinary size (about 100 lb. live-weight); or if they can be induced to eat sufficient good silage, they will winter well on it, possibly with a little cereal supplement. If such materials are not available in sufficient quantities, the bulkier concentrates such as dried grains, sugar beet pulp and oats may be used, mixed with a little chaffed oat straw or pea haulm. As soon as grass is available the hoggs will go out on the poorer and higher fields, the better pastures being, of course, reserved for the ewes. They will be shorn a week or ten days before the milking ewes, because the wool " rises " earlier. They join the ewe flock generally some weeks before the mating season, or when the old ewes are drafted out. In some flocks the gimmers (theaves) are not put to the ram until two or three weeks after the ewes, the object being to secure better weather and food conditions at their lambing time.

**Fattening.**—Lambs of the earlier-maturing breeds can be brought to slaughter weight and condition as early as ten weeks of age. Under conditions of free markets the most popular carcass weights are probably about 25 lb. for the small hill breeds and 35 to 40 lb. for others. In general (apart from cast ewes) the great majority of animals reach the meat market at ages ranging from three to fifteen months, though very occasional lots of two-year-old and even three-year-old wedders of mountain breeds are still seen.

The earliest fat lambs are usually the produce of draft ewes—the latter are purchased by farmers of the better arable land between July and September. Either fully guaranteed ewes or broken-mouthed ones ones (if they are young) may be bought—the latter being generally cheaper but requiring to have their roots cut during winter. Some are sold already tupped; others will generally be put to the ram without delay. They must have a considerable amount of hand feeding during the winter, and concentrates must continue to be offered until the arrival of the spring flush of grass. As soon as the lambs will eat they are fed with concentrate, either along with their dams or separately. Separate feeding may be arranged by placing the lamb troughs in an enclosure with lamb creeps in the surrounding fence. The creeps may consist of special hurdles with apertures that can be adjusted to the size of the lambs and with wooden rollers on the top and sides to avoid any risk of the lambs being caught.

Traditional lamb foods are complex mixtures containing such materials as linseed cake, bran, broken peas, kibbled or flaked maize, oats, with broken locust-beans to make the mixture palatable. Compounds in the form of lamb nuts are, however, more convenient and less wasteful. If folding is practised the lambs are run before the ewes, *i.e.* they are allowed access to the standing crop by means of hurdles through which the ewes cannot pass, the latter following on to clean up. As soon as the lambs are fat (the ewes will generally be fat enough) they are marketed together with their dams. Early lambs of this sort, weighing perhaps 70 to 80 lb. live-weight or 35 to 40 lb. carcass, command a high price; but the ewe will often bring less than she cost the previous autumn. Shropshire Southdown, Suffolk and Oxford rams are perhaps those most widely used for the production of such lambs, but Leicesters and Border Leicesters give good results with Down ewes.

The produce of draft ewes is succeeded on the market by selected single lambs from regular breeding flocks on the better arable farms, and by June and July lambs of many breeds, not excluding pure bred Black-faced Mountain, will be found on the fat markets. In all cases there will have been no store period—the processes of rearing and fattening having been combined. Later on there come lambs that have been reared as stores, weaned, very frequently sold by breeder to feeder, and finished off by the latter. The most forward of these, weighing perhaps 80 lb. or more at four months old, will be fattened, in a period of a few weeks, on clover aftermaths, rape or other forage crops, receiving about 1 lb. per day of nutritious concentrate; they make rapid gains, as high as 4 or 5 lb. weekly. Hampshires, Oxfords and crosses of these with Longwool and

Half-bred ewes are the favourite types for this system. Less forward lambs, including those of many mountain breeds, may be very well finished on rape or rape and ryegrass mixtures.

Lambs for hogging are carried on as stores, first on grass or forage crops and later on roots, until they are considered sufficiently grown to be fattened. Their general treatment meanwhile will be the same as that of ewe tegs for breeding. Heavy sheep give joints that are too large for modern taste, and bring a lower price per pound. Moreover, live weight increase becomes more expensive as the limit of growth is approached. There is also a desirable pitch of fatness beyond which it is easy to go with the fatter breeds like Oxfords and Leicesters. Lambs and young tegs are rarely too fat—the difficulty is usually to get them fat enough—but large fat carcasses, especially during spring and summer, are generally in very limited demand. As a rule, therefore, tegs are kept as stores as cheaply as possible, until they weigh from 50 to 80 lb., according to breed, and are then put up for fattening—the latter process occupying two or three months.

Lambs of mountain breeds, and crosses such as Mashams and Mules (Greyfaces), may be wintered on grassland with little or no hand feeding and fattened on grass during the ensuing spring and early summer. This, naturally, is most successful when no breeding flock is maintained, the pastures being stocked in late summer with cattle only; the object being to leave a good bite for the winter and to avoid trouble from internal parasites. The rate of stocking in winter must, of course, be fairly low. The same practice is feasible with lowland breeds and crosses, but the sheep, at perhaps fifteen months old, are much beyond the size desired by consumers.

The following points require attention in winter feeding with roots. In the early part of the winter feeding season—October and November—roots are liable to cause scouring and other disorders. The change from grass or summer forage crops to root feeding should therefore be made gradually, and the root ration should at first be limited. If wet weather occurs and sheep on the root land become uncomfortable, they should be returned to pasture and have the roots conveyed to them. Thirdly, a proportion of the roots should be stored so that there may be no need to feed them in a frozen condition.

The choice of hay is important with feeding sheep. Pure legume hay —red clover or lucerne, for example—is usually freely eaten and is valuable on account of its high protein and mineral content. Even with this, however, unless it has been cut at an early stage of growth, fattening sheep will tend to reject the stemmy portions, and a certain amount of wastage must be permitted if the sheep are to make rapid progress. When mixed hay is fed the animals tend to pick out the clovers and leave the grasses. Grassy hay—meadow or ryegrass—especially if it has been over-ripe when cut, is not liked by sheep, and it is frequently difficult to get fattening tegs to consume more than ¼ to ½ lb. unless the other ingredients in their diet are severely restricted. This, in turn, naturally interferes with the rate of progress.

Feeding sheep are occasionally housed in cool airy sheds. Housing may result in a substantially improved live weight increase if it happens that outdoor conditions are bad. But in dry weather, even if it be very cold, outdoor sheep do quite as well.

In spring and summer, hoggs or wedders of the later maturing breeds are fattened on grass or forage crops, with or without the addition of concentrates. Fat sheep may be clipped as much as a month before the normal time for breeding stock.

Hoggs in wool—but with the wool dry and clean, and in fair marketable condition—may yield from 48 to 52 per cent. of their live-weight as dressed carcass, the average of market sheep being nearer the former figure than the latter. Newly shorn sheep give about 5 per cent. more. Heavy and very fat wethers may dress up to 65 per cent. or occasionally more.

## GOATS

Goats are valued either for their fleeces or their milk. In the first class are the Cashmere and the Angora, of which the latter is by far the more important commercially.

The Angora is native to the province of that name in Asia Minor. It is of a whole white colour, small in size (60 to 100 lb. live-weight), and horned in both sexes. The fleece (mohair) varies a good deal in quality, but in the best specimens is extremely fine, silky and lustrous. Typically it is from 8 to 10 in. long and hangs in separate and well-defined ringlets. Four pounds is an average weight of fleece, but superior specimens shear 6 lb. and occasionally up to 14 lb. Fine mohairs have a distinct use in the manufacture of plushes, velvets and bright lustre materials, and command a price comparable to that of fine wool The quantity used annually in the Bradford district runs into thousands of tons. The flesh of the young and fat Angora is said to be good. The breed is not very prolific, twins being rare and the annual increase being generally under 80 per cent. Angoras require a dry climate but are otherwise hardy, and thrive under semi-arid conditions where sheep do not prove a complete success. The chief mohair-producing countries in order of importance are South Africa, Asia Minor and the United States (western and south-western states).

Milch goats are of several breeds; the best known are the Toggenburg and Saanen (Swiss), the Nubian and the Maltese. In Britain we have the imported Swiss and Nubian types, as well as somewhat ill-defined sorts like the Anglo-Swiss, Anglo-Nubian and Anglo-Nubian-Swiss derived from crosses of the foregoing with the native type. Goats' milk is comparable in composition with cows'—somewhat more variable though probably, on the average, rather richer in fat and poorer in other solids. It is often more easily digested by delicate persons. It can be reckoned to be free from tubercle bacilli. Does of good type reach yields of 3 to 5 qt. per day and occasionally up to 2 gal. The lactation period is ordinarily five or six months, but may extend to nine or ten. Lactation yields of over 400 gal. have been recorded in ten months, and the average in good recorded herds is over 200 gal. Goats, as is well known, will live on almost any sort of herbage, and in mountainous districts, or wherever food is scanty, they form a valuable source of milk. It seems unlikely that they will ever become commercially important in lowland districts where improved dairy cattle can be kept.

# CHAPTER 23

# HORSES

THE horse family (*Equidæ*) forms part of the group of Perissodactyla or odd-toed ungulates. Zoologists include all members of the family, whether horses, asses or zebras, under the genus Equus.

The Zebras, which are found only in Africa, include the now extinct Quagga (Cape Colony), the True or Mountain Zebra (south-western Africa), Burchell's Zebra (Transvaal), Grevy's Zebra (Somaliland) and two or three more species or sub-species related to one or other of the foregoing. None of the zebras has attained any importance as a domesticated animal, although specimens of several species have been successfully broken both to harness and the saddle. Grevy's Zebra has generally been regarded as the most promising from the utility point of view.

The Wild Asses embrace two African types, the Somaliland and the Nubian; and two Asiatic, the Onager of Syria, Persia, Arabia and India, and the Kiang of Turkestan, Mongolia and Tibet. Domesticated donkeys are generally regarded as of purely African origin, but some authors have supposed that Onager blood has been blended with African in some of the larger breeds.

The only truly wild horse now existing is the *Equus Przevalskii* of the Gobi Desert and north-western Mongolia. Whether or not this wild species has been concerned in the origin of our domesticated horses is somewhat uncertain; that it is not the sole ancestor is fairly generally agreed, most authorities supposing that at least three distinct species are represented among our modern breeds. Although these original species have been crossed and intermingled to a considerable extent, we may still distinguish fairly pure representatives in the Celtic pony (*Equus celticus*) of the Western Isles; the Arab and Barb (Oriental light-legged type), and the Shire and Belgian (Western heavy-legged type).

Hybrids between horses and zebras, asses and zebras, or horses and asses may be produced with comparative ease, but the hybrids with rare and doubtful exceptions, are sterile. Of the hybrids the only one of much economic importance is that between the male donkey or jackass and the mare, the mule. The opposite cross, between a stallion and a she ass, is of much less value on account of its smaller size.

As a preliminary to a description of the various types of horses some explanation of points and gaits is necessary. **The points** are shown and named in Fig. 35. Of the things that go to the making of a good horse, some are related to the special purpose for which the particular animal is to be used, *e.g.* draft, harness or saddle. Other things are regarded as desirable in all breeds and types, and these may now be briefly mentioned. The head should be of good width between the eyes, and the eyes themselves prominent and of good size. These points denote intelligence and

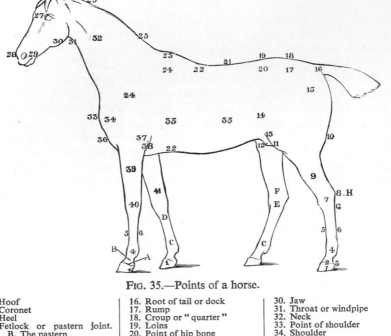

FIG. 35.—Points of a horse.

| | | |
|---|---|---|
| 1. Hoof | 16. Root of tail or dock | 30. Jaw |
| 2. Coronet | 17. Rump | 31. Throat or windpipe |
| 3. Heel | 18. Croup or " quarter " | 32. Neck |
| 4. Fetlock or pastern joint. | 19. Loins | 33. Point of shoulder |
|    B. The pastern | 20. Point of hip bone | 34. Shoulder |
| 5. Cannon Bone | 21. Back | 35-35. Front ribs and short |
| 6. Back sinew or tendon | 22-22. Girth or chest measure- |    ribs behind, forming the |
| 7. Hock |    ment |    barrel |
| 8. Point of Hock | 23. Withers | 36. Chest or breast |
| 9. Second thigh or gaskin | 24-24. Shoulder blade (*sca-* | 37-34. True arm (*humerus*) |
| 10. Haunch or lower buttock |    *pula*) | 38. Elbow |
| 10-20. Thigh | 25-25. Crest | 39. Arm (or fore arm) |
| 11. Stifle | 26. Poll | 40. Knee |
| 12. Sheath | 27. Forehead | 41. Chestnut, castor or callosity |
| 13-14. Flank | 28. Muzzle | |
| 15. Hip joint | 29. Nostril | |

Seats of Common Diseases

| | | | |
|---|---|---|---|
| A. Side-bone | C. Wind-gall | E. Spavin | G. Curb |
| B. Ring-bone | D. Splint | F. Thorough-pin | H. Capped hock |

docility. The nostrils should be large and open to permit of free breathing The neck should be of good length. The shoulder should be moderately sloped back, as an upright scapula almost invariably makes for a stilted gait. The back and loin should be short, nearly straight, and thickly clad with muscle in order to give strength. But too short a back is often associated with a lack of freedom of movement, especially at the trot. The hind quarters should be long and wide, and not too steeply sloping to the tail. Large fore arms and thighs are important as indicating strength. Chest and middle should be deep in order to give, on the one hand, space for heart and lungs, and on the other, capacity for food. For similar reasons the ribs should be well sprung or rounded. The knee should be large, the hock broad and the cannon bones flat, *i.e.* the tendons should be large and set well back from the bone itself, in order to give the necessary strength and freedom of movement. A fair length and moderate slope of pastern are necessary in order to break the concussion when the foot meets the ground, but too much length or slope involves weakness. The feet should be wide in proportion to their length, the soles concave, and the substance of the hoof tough and durable. The legs should be well knit under the body, and should be moved freely and straight.

**The gaits** natural to most horses are the *walk*, *trot* and *gallop*. Some horses develop, also naturally, either the *amble* (or running walk) or the *pace*. The chief additional gaits to which horses may be trained are the *canter*, which is a restrained and modified gallop and the *rack* or " single-foot." Of these various modes of locomotion the simplest are the trot and pace. The trot is a diagonal two-beat gait—that is, the off fore and near hind move together and meet the ground at the same time, making one beat; the near fore and off hind similarly move together and produce the second beat, the intervals between the beats being the same. Young horses frequently " strike " or " click " when at the trot, the toe of the hind shoe meeting the sole of the fore shoe just as the former is meeting and the latter leaving the ground. In the trot the rider generally posts; that is, he rises in his stirrups in unison with one or other pair of legs—generally with the near hind and off fore—and thus escapes the jolt of the second beat.

In the pace (which is rarely found except in American pacer-bred animals) the left pair and the right pair of legs move together, as in a camel's " trot." This sidelong gait is both uncomfortable and unsafe for a rider, but in a harness animal it is not objectionable, and is on the average slightly faster than the trot.

The walk, amble and rack may be grouped as symmetrical four-beat gaits—that is, each foot is moved in different time from the others and makes a distinct beat, while the movement of the left leg, in each case, is similar in amount and opposite in time to that of its right fellow. The chief difference between the three is in speed. The amble is performed at a rate intermediate between those of the walk and trot. It is a good saddle gait, comfortable for the rider and easy for the horse, and is favoured in many countries where long distances have to be travelled. The rack is performed at a speed faster than that of a sharp trot. It is a showy gait, and a comfortable one for the rider, who has nothing to do but to sit still in the saddle, but it makes very heavy work for the horse; animals are trained to it with difficulty, and it is regularly developed only in the American saddle breed.

The canter and gallop are unsymmetrical gaits, *i.e.* the movements of the one leg are not matched by those of its fellow. A horse may canter or gallop either right leg leading or left leg leading, and may be trained to strike off in either way or to change the leg at the rider's will. In the gallop the four beats follow each other in very rapid succession and there succeeds a relatively long interval in which each leg in turn leaves the ground, and the horse is suspended in mid-air with all four gathered under him. The canter is a very comfortable gait for the rider, and in saddle-bred animals it forms an easy one for the horse.

The particular gaits that are required vary with the purpose for which the animal is to be used. Heavy draft animals perform all their work at a walk, but should be able to trot freely and easily on occasion. The principal gait of the harness animal is the trot (or alternatively and exceptionally, the pace), but a free and rapid walk is also to be desired. Ordinary saddle horses should be trained to walk, trot, canter or gallop at the rider's will, while the American (" gaited ") saddle horse is required to show five distinct gaits, viz., the walk, trot, canter and rack, together with the walking trot, or one or other of two somewhat similar slow movements.

From the utility point of view, horses (including ponies) are classified as saddle, harness, draft and pack. The first type is required to carry a rider, the second to draw a light vehicle at considerable speed, the third to pull and the last to carry loads at a moderate or slow speed.

**The Saddle Horse.**—In this country, the hunter and the polo pony may be taken as representative types of saddle horses. The former is typical of the larger, the latter of the small sort of animal for actual utility purposes.

Hunters are classified according to the weight they are judged to be capable of carrying in the field. One system is to make 12 st. the minimum for the light-weight class, and 13 st. 7 lb. the minimum for the heavy. More elaborate classifications are adopted at the larger shows. The qualities specially desired in a Hunter may be summarised as follows:—

1. *Speed.*—He must be fast at the gallop and should show a collected and easy movement at the walk, trot and canter. Very high action is generally incompatible with great speed and is not wanted.

2. *Staying Power.*—He should be able to gallop at a good speed over three or four miles of ordinary mixed country, taking fences as he goes. Staying power can never be finally judged without actual test, but a large nostril, a good width between the angles of the jaw, and a deep capacious chest are useful indications of it.

3. *Strength.*—The muscles chiefly used in galloping under a rider are those of the back, loin and hind quarter. The back and loin should be short, wide and thickly covered with muscle, while the quarter should be

long, wide and strong, the muscles carried well down towards the hocks, and the gaskin or second thigh wide from front to back.

4. *Durability.*—The limbs and joints must be strong enough to withstand the stresses to which they are subjected. The heaviest of these occur during jumping—on rising they are greatest in the hock, and on landing in the tendons and ligaments of the fore legs and the bones of the pasterns. Hence broad clean hocks—neither too straight nor too bent—and large bone and tendons in the fore leg are points of great importance.

5. *Temperament.*—The animal must have plenty of courage and yet be susceptible to such training as will place it completely under the control of its rider. This may be judged to some extent by the appearance of the head, the expression of the eye and the carriage of the head and ears. A long neck, fine at its junction with the head, generally makes for easy control by the bit, whereas a short, thick neck generally means difficulty in control. Jumping ability, which is largely a matter of temperament, cannot be judged except by trial.

6. *The Comfort of the Rider.*—The withers should be high and fairly thin to provide a comfortable seat. The gaits should be smooth and easy and the stride long, the feet being carried rather low, especially at the canter and gallop. Good length and slope of pastern also make for comfort by breaking the impact of the leg on the ground.

In size, hunters range from about 15·1 to nearly 17 hands,[1] most being between 15·3 and 16·2. The weight-carrying capacity is not a function of height but rather of general build, the shorter legged and stronger boned animals being generally up to greater weights, if somewhat slower, than the taller and finer-boned types.

The polo pony may best be described as a weight-carrying hunter in miniature, with, if possible, a greater measure of intelligence, in order to permit of greater refinements in training. Great nimbleness and particularly cleverness in turning are necessary in playing ponies.

The American or gaited saddle horse is an interesting type that has been developed in the direction of great style and symmetry, combined with high endurance at moderate speed, and a great measure of comfort for the rider. It is inferior to the hunter in strength, speed, and fencing ability.

**Harness Horses** are now bred in very small numbers and the interested reader must refer to other works for information about them.

**Draft Horses.**—Of chief importance to agriculture is the draft type, more especially the heavy draft; the qualities desirable in the latter may be summarised as follows:—

1. *Strength.*—This is to some extent proportional to weight, but depends also in large measure on the development of particular muscles and on the efficiency of the transmission of the available power through the limbs. The back and loin should be short, wide and thickly covered

[1] The height of horses is measured to the withers, and the unit used is the hand = 4 in.

with muscle, while the quarters should be long, wide and well muscled down to the thighs. Arms and gaskins should be broad, with the muscles prominent. For the transmission of power, the legs should be closely knit to the body and placed well underneath it; they should be moved freely and straight. Serious defects under this head would be a long and bare back, narrow quarters and thin upper thighs, wide waddling action in front, or a tendency for the hocks to twist outwards when they are submitted to the strain of draft.

2. *Endurance.*—Lung space—a deep, capacious chest—is of importance, but perhaps of rather less consequence in the draft animal than in horses that work at a high speed. Most horses that fail to stand up to severe and long continued work in draft do so from an insufficient capacity for food. The good feeder, who can be known by his well-rounded ribs and deep capacious belly, will generally be found to have great endurance, whereas the tall, light ribbed animal with flat sides readily goes weak and out of condition.

3. *Wearing Qualities.*—Apart from unsoundnesses like roaring and stringhalt, the useful life of the draft animal is terminated, in a large majority of cases, by some breakdown in the feet and legs. The common troubles are sprain of the tendons, ring-bone, side bone and navicular or other disease of the foot. Hence special attention must be paid to " underpinning." The cannon bones should be of good size, but must show quality, *i.e.* they should be clean and hard, with the tendons well set back and large, giving the leg a markedly flat shape. The pasterns should be of good length (they can, however, be too long) and should slope at about 45°. The foot should be wide at the hoof head, neither flat nor steep, and the substance of the hoof should be tough and strong.

4. *Speed.*—The draft animal should have a long stride and a free, straight, active and easy walk. An animal with a short-stepping, stilted action either cannot walk out at a reasonable speed, or does so with a great wastage of effort. The animal should be able to trot freely and rapidly when required, but there is no particular advantage in high knee or hock action.

5. *Temperament.*—The draft horse should have pluck and energy, without being highly strung or intractable. His head will show less refinement, but more strength than that of the saddle type; it should be carried fairly high and the expression should be alert.

A height of 17 hands is sufficient for a heavy draft animal, if he be thick of body and proportionately built. Many good horses are under this height, and females are generally considered big enough for breeding if they reach 16·2. A good weight for a mature gelding in working condition is 14 to 15 cwt., or, say, 1600 lb. The largest stallions in show condition occasionally exceed a ton (2240 lb.), though 18 cwt. or 2000 lb. is more usual.

The light draft type may be described as something intermediate between a heavy draft and either a weight-carrying hunter or a harness horse. It shows less weight and strength than the heavy draft, but more activity and speed. Since it has to perform a good deal of its work at the trot, it should show freedom and ease in this gait, and should be hard-limbed and sound of feet to withstand the heavy wear and tear of fast work on hard surfaces. In general, the light draft type is not a very profitable one to breed, since the market requirements for vanners and light lorry animals are now very small. It makes a useful farm horse for the lighter classes of soils, and on certain farms for miscellaneous light tasks.

The pack type of horse is one of very minor and decreasing importance, since its use is confined to districts where the roads are not fit to carry vehicular traffic. The most generally useful sort of animal for the purpose is a large pony or small sturdily built horse, sure-footed, active and docile.

## BRITISH BREEDS

**The Thoroughbred** or English racehorse (Plate 60, *A*) is of almost pure Eastern blood. It may be said to have originated in an importation of some forty mares—mostly Barbs—made by order of Charles II. During Charles's lifetime these mares were kept as a Royal Stud, and at his death they were sold and dispersed throughout the country. Of many stallions imported before and after that time, by much the most important were the Byerly Turk, imported in 1689, Darley Arabian (1706) and Godolphin Barb (1724). The blending of these different blood lines, together with long continued and rigorous selection on the basis of race-course performance, has produced an animal that is far superior in speed to any modern Oriental breed, and is by much the fastest horse in the world.

Modern Thoroughbreds show a good deal of variation in type, chiefly because there has been little or no selection except that based on racecourse performance. The height varies from the one extreme of under 14·2 to the other of over 17 hands, the average being probably between 15·2 and 15·3. The head is lean and refined, the eye large and prominent and the nostril wide. The courage of the breed is proverbial, but the temperament is sometimes highly strung and occasionally vicious. The neck is long, rather thin and muscular, with a large windpipe, and is carried rather low. The chest is capacious, but deep rather than wide, and the shoulder is preferably but by no means invariably well sloped. The back and loin are very generally short, straight and muscular; the croup is commonly of good length but varies in conformation, being sometimes level with the tail set on rather high, sometimes rather steeply drooping. The bones are clean and hard, with the tendons sharply defined and well set back. Small " weedy " bone and long slight pasterns are objectionable. The movement should be smooth and easy, the stride long and the legs carried rather low. The commonest colours are bay and brown, with chestnut, grey and black following in order of frequency. From the utility point of view Thoroughbreds vary greatly in value. Natural toughness, stamina, courage and speed are constant assets, but it is only when these qualities are combined with strength and wearing qualities that they make for commercial value. The long legged, slightly built and light boned animal is often a good flat racer, but otherwise is of very little use. Such "weedy" animals, if they fail to win on the racecourse, are almost worthless. On the other hand, the stoutly built and big boned animal, even if he is not fit to win races, forms an ideal saddle-horse sire and possesses distinct commercial value. Many breeds of light-legged horses are indebted to the Thoroughbred for endurance, speed and courage.

**The Arab** (Plate 60, *B*) has a history that stretches back to about the beginning of the Christian era, and the purity of the breed has been jealously maintained for the greater part of this long period. Knowledge of pedigrees extends over many generations. Careful selection, with very special attention to such qualities as courage and endurance, has been carried on by the Arabs for a long period, and the modern breed is distinguished by these qualities in a very marked degree. From the Thoroughbred, to which he is closely related, and which he resembles in a general way, the Arab is distinguished by several fairly constant characters. On the average he is smaller, 14·2 hands being perhaps the average height. The head is wider between the eyes and tapers more towards the nose; the neck is more arched, the head is carried higher and the shoulder is more oblique; the croup is generally longer and typically more level, with the tail higher set on; the withers are commonly rather thicker.

In speed the Arab is far inferior to the Thoroughbred but capable of carrying a heavy weight in proportion to his size and is unexcelled in endurance; many animals have been ridden 50 or 60 miles a day for several days on end. In long-distance tests the breed is generally supreme. An Arab Horse Society has been established in England, and published the first volume of its Stud Book in 1919.

**The Hunter and the Polo Pony** (Plate 61).—Hunters generally carry a large proportion of Thoroughbred blood, the other elements in their breeding being very varied. "Clean bred" hunters are by no means unknown, but it is exceptional to find Thoroughbreds with the necessary bone and substance to carry heavy weights. The type required in flat country such as the Midlands is different from that suited to hilly areas; the latter must be short legged and sure footed rather than specially fast. The polo pony breed will contain the blood of several native breeds of ponies such as the Welsh, Exmoor and Dartmoor, blended with that of the Thoroughbred and Arab. A Hunters' Improvement and National Light Horse Society has recently been formed.

**Ponies.**—Of the native British ponies, the smallest and certainly one

PLATE 60

*Clarence Hailey, Newmarket*

*A.* THOROUGHBRED STALLION

*B.* ARAB STALLION

PLATE 61

*A.* Hunter Gelding

*G. H. Parsons, Alsager, Cheshire*

*B.* Polo Pony, mare and foal

PLATE 62

*A.* HIGHLAND PONY MARE

*B.* WELSH PONY

PLATE 63

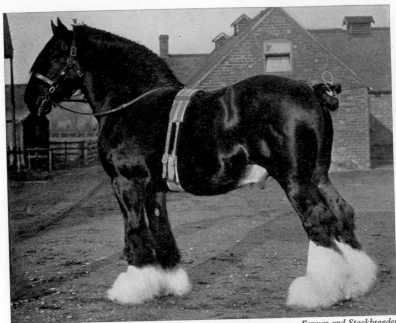

*Farmer and Stockbreeder*

*A.* SHIRE STALLION

*Scottish Farmer*

*B.* CLYDESDALE STALLION

PLATE 64

*A.* Suffolk Stallion

*B.* Percheron Stallion

of the oldest breeds is the **Shetland**. Standing generally under 40 in. in height (the maximum height for mature animals is 42 in.), the Shetland is very stoutly built—rather like a heavy draft animal in miniature—and very strong for its size. In their native isles the ponies are used as pack animals, *e.g.* for the carrying of peat. Being generally docile and easily trained, they are very popular as riding ponies for young children.

**The Western Isles Pony** or light-type Highland pony, is native to the Hebrides, some of the best and most typical being found on Barra. It is generally between 12 and 13 hands high and is of good saddle conformation, though often steep of shoulder and rather sickle hocked. The quality of bone is excellent and the breed is very active and exceedingly hardy. It is used, like the Shetland, principally as a pack animal.

The heavy or Mainland type of **Highland Pony**, frequently spoken of as the Garron (Plate 62, *A*), is found in the Central Highlands of Scotland, notably in Perthshire. Averaging nearly 14½ hands in height (the maximum allowed by the breed standard) the breed is very stoutly built, distinctly drafty in type, with rather heavy shoulders and thick withers. The neck is highly crested, the mane abundant. The bone is sometimes too round and the legs carry, in winter, a good deal of long feather. Distinguished for his great hardiness and longevity, the Highland pony is used by the smaller glen farmer as an all purpose horse—for riding, driving, hauling and carrying; during the stalking and shooting seasons they may find employment in carrying deer or game. Grey is the more common colour.

Of rather similar type to the last is the **Fell Pony** of Cumberland, Westmorland and West Yorks. It is generally some 2 or 3 in. smaller than the Highland, but is built on the same general plan—thick and short of leg, with large bone. It is believed to be descended from the old Galloway pony, which was famed for its toughness and strength. The **Dales Pony** of East Yorks and Durham is similar to the Highland pony but generally bay or brown in colour. It is larger than the Fell pony and might almost be regarded as a small draft horse, since many specimens exceed 14·2 or even 15 hands in height. The general conformation is rather massive, but the breed is both sure footed and fast. In past times many were employed for pack work, and some are still taken for colliery work: their chief use is for farm work on the smaller holdings of the Dales.

**The Exmoor and Dartmoor** are ponies of saddle type. The latter stand about 12·2 hands, the former perhaps 2 or 3 in. less. They have well bred heads, good shoulders and hard bones, but, rather frequently, drooping quarters and sickle hocks. Crossed with small Thoroughbred or Arab sires, they produce excellent riding ponies.

**The New Forest** type shows rather less breeding than the foregoing, and generally a heavier and more upright shoulder; the legs are better built. Forest bred specimens run from 12·2 to 12·3 hands.

The **Welsh Pony** (Plate 62, *B*) has existed from very early times on the moors and mountains of Wales and is a breed of very considerable importance, forming perhaps the most valuable foundation stock for the production of saddle ponies. Two types are recognised and are registered separately in the Stud Book. The smaller and lighter type (under 12 hands) is of saddle conformation, while the larger (up to 12½ hands) has higher action and is more of the harness type. In general these ponies are very hardy and enduring, and show great freedom and speed in movement.

The **Welsh Cob** is derived partly from the foregoing, with an infusion, in early times, of some Thoroughbred, Arab and Hackney blood. Typical specimens measure from 13·2 to 14·2 hands, have durable limbs and show high-stepping action and considerable staying power. They are used as riding animals by farmers in the remoter parts of Wales.

The **Heavy Draft Breeds** now recognised in Britain are the native Shire, Clydesdale and Suffolk, and the recently introduced Percheron and Belgian. The Clydesdale is the breed of Scotland and the four northern counties of England and is the chief of the draft breeds in Ireland. The Suffolk is native to East Anglia and has only recently spread beyond the borders of this province. The Shire is found throughout the rest of England and Wales, excepting only mountain and moorland districts.

The **Shire** (Plate 63, *A*) is regarded as the direct descendant of the Old English war horse or Great Horse. This latter was derived partly from the horses that existed in Britain before the Roman invasion, partly from heavy horses that were introduced at various times, chiefly from Flanders. In olden times the Great Horse was valued for his ability to to carry the immense weight of armour of the mounted knight, and various kings of England from John to Henry VIII—were at considrable pains to maintain or increase the size and quality of the breed. Until the eighteenth century the bulk of field work was done by oxen, and the use of the horse as a draft animal has taken place since then. Now in Britain the tractor has very largely replaced the draft horse.

Careful and systematic breeding of Shires has been carried on since the middle of the eighteenth century, and some modern pedigrees go back a hundred years or more. In the days before the formation of a breed society (1878) there was a good deal of variation in type from one district to another, but the breed has been levelled up by continuous interbreeding of the local variations. Of the early Shires it may be said that many were weighty and powerful animals; but upright pasterns and steep, narrow hoofs, a want of quality in bone and unsoundness like side-bone, were common faults. The aim of the Shire breeders has been to eliminate these defects, while preserving or even increasing the size and weight. The strict veterinary inspection of all animals competing at the shows of the Shire Horse Society has had a very beneficial effect.

The modern Shire is probably the weightiest of all horses, though the

Belgian is sometimes regarded as first in this respect. Mature stallions of the best class, measuring generally 17 hands or over, often reach a weight of 20 cwt. when in show condition. The head is heavier and coarser than in other British breeds and the eye is smaller. Typically the back is short, wide and very strong; the ribs both deep and widely sprung, giving a middle of great capacity; the quarters very wide and powerful, but often somewhat short and drooping. The fore arms and thighs are of great size, and the bone should measure at least 11 in. below the knee and 12 in. below the hock—the larger the better, so long as it is clean and flat. The pasterns are of moderate length and preferably well sloped. The feet are generally of good size—wide at the heels and open at the hoof head. The " feather " is long and straight, and rather strong in quality. Curly or wooly feather is regarded as objectionable. Common colours are bay, brown and black, with grey, chestnut and roan less prevalent. The mare, apart from her smaller size and the feminine character in her head, is relatively longer in body and shorter legged than the stallion. The temperament of the Shire is commonly very docile. In general the animal gives the impression of great strength and massiveness. He is an excellent feeder and has great endurance on slow work.

The Shire, while fairly popular in many foreign countries, has not on the whole competed very successfully with other draft breeds.

A cross between the Shire and Clydesdale combines a good many of the best qualities of the two breeds.

**The Clydesdale** (Plate 63, *B*) had its origin during the first half of the eighteenth century in the interbreeding of the native horses of the Upper Ward of Lanarkshire with colts introduced from England; some at least of the latter were of Flemish breeding. The most famous of the pioneer breeders was John Paterson of Lochlyoch who, about 1715, introduced from England a black Flemish stallion which has been regarded as the foundation sire of the breed. The earliest horse to which pedigrees can now be traced is " Glancer," foaled about 1810, and probably descended, in the female line, from the Lochlyoch stud. Occasional crossing with Shires was done up till about 1890, and a good many three quarter blood Clydesdales, with the Shire cross, are entered in the earlier volumes of the Stud Book. Many breeders believe that the separation of the breed from the Shire was a mistake, as the original differences were not very marked. At times the breeds have drifted very far apart, but the less massive and cleaner legged type of Shire that is now preferred is not very different from the heavier boned sorts of Clydesdale.

The Clydesdale is similar in height to the Shire, the stallion being 17 hands or over and the mare about 16·2. The general build is less massive, the legs being proportionately longer, and the body neither so deep nor so wide. The head shows more quality and refinement, the eye being larger and the muzzle finer. The neck is rather longer and more crested, the head more gaily carried, and the shoulder has on the average more slope. The back is more frequently faulty than in the Shire, being sometimes too long, hollow and rather bare of muscles. Flatness of rib and shallowness of heart or belly are commoner faults. The quarters are usually longer and more level, but narrower when viewed from behind. The arms and gaskins are not so large and are shorter in proportion to the length of the cannon. The bone of the Clydesdale is much smaller but is harder, flatter and cleaner, and the feather, which is more silky in quality, is confined to the back of the leg. The pasterns are longer and have more slope; the feet are relatively larger and wider but with a more frequent tendency to flatness. The Clydesdale, as a breed, is very free from leg troubles like grease, side-bone, ring-bone and navicular disease, and the average working life is exceptionally long. The breed is also remarkable for its straight, free and close movement, and shows great ability and cleverness in handling loads. In general it may be said that the Shire excels in weight and strength and in endurance; while in speed, agility and wearing qualities the Clydesdale is pre-eminent. The temperament of the Clydesdale is more mettlesome and nervous than that of the Shire; he is more troublesome to break and requires more horsemanship on the part of his driver. Another point of difference is that the Shire matures at a much earlier age than the Clydesdale, so that the difference in weight is far more marked at the yearling or two-year-old stages than in aged animals. Clydesdales are of all the ordinary colours, bay and brown predominating, while chestnut and grey are rare. White faces and legs are almost constant features, and splashes of white on the belly or white hairs irregularly mixed throughout the coat, are becoming increasingly common.

The Clydesdale is a common draft breed in Canada, New Zealand, Australia, the United States and many other countries. Broadly speaking it is less popular than the Percheron. The chief defects of the breed, as urged, e.g. in the United States, are its tendency to flatness and shallowness of rib and narrowness of build, with a consequent inability to keep in condition when exposed to heat or cold or subjected to severe work or scarcity of food.

**The Suffolk** (Plate 64, *A*) is the least numerously represented of the three native draft breeds. It has been recognised as a distinct local type for several centuries, but some infusion of trotting blood was made over a hundred years ago. The average height is 1 or 2 in. less than that of the Clydesdale or Shire, but the weight is not notably less than that of the Clydesdale. The general build is thick, wide and low set. The ears are rather short, the neck crested, the chest deep and wide, the barrel large, the ribs well-rounded and the quarters wide and heavily muscled, though often rather steeply sloping. The bone is rather light, but not more so than in many modern Clydesdales. The legs carry practically no feather. The pasterns are rather short and upright, especially the hind ones. The feet formerly showed a tendency to flatness but the breed has been greatly improved in this respect. The Suffolk is active, but the movement is not so straight and true as in the Clydesdale. The colour is some shade of chestnut, with sometimes a white spot or blaze on the face. White feet are regarded as objectionable. The outstanding merit of the Suffolk is his constitution. When well fed he puts on a great reserve of fat, and he is easily kept. On ordinary work he can go long hours without food, and stands exposure and scarcity very well. In draft he is remarkably steady and he lives and works to a long age. The mares are exceptionally regular breeders. The Suffolk was long in obtaining recognition outside his native district, but several studs now exist in other parts of England.

**The Percheron** (Plate 64, *B*) derives its name from the old French district of La Perche, lying within a radius of some forty miles from the town of Nogent-le-Rotrou, situated about a hundred miles south-west of Paris. The breed contains a good deal of the same blood as the other draft breeds, but was influenced to a considerable extent by the introduction of Eastern (Arab) blood. In coaching times the Percheron was used chiefly for road work, and its evolution into a heavy draft breed has occurred since the widespread development of railways. Its main characteristics may be summarised as follows:—

The height averages 16·2 for stallions and 16 hands for mares. The weight is rather great in proportion to the height, but even by this measure the Percheron is perhaps the smallest of the heavy draft breeds. The head is rather lean and shows a good deal of breeding. The neck is highly crested and the shoulder long and oblique, the chest deep and wide. Width and strength of back and roundness of rib are very striking characteristics, but the depth of back ribs is not so uniformly good. The quarters are wide, but often short and generally rather steeply drooping, the tail being set on low. The bone is fairly hard and fine though somewhat round, and the legs are free from long hair. The pasterns are somewhat short and upright, and the feet of reasonable size, shapely and very sound and durable. The hind leg has often too much set—*i.e.* is too crooked —to please the eye of British judges, and the hock is often lacking in breadth and is too round and fleshy. The movement is sharp, with rather high knee action at the trot, but the front action is not so straight as is desired. The temperament is very good—docile, yet active and willing. The common colours are grey and black, with bay and brown rare. The Percheron is the favourite draft breed in the United States, where it owes its popularity to its clean legs, its quiet temperament, good constitution and its high power of endurance on rather fast work. Importations of pure bred Percherons into Britain were of no importance until 1918, when the British Percheron Horse Society was formed.

**Belgian** horses were imported into Britain in considerable numbers for the few years up till 1939. The breed is a very old one, related to the Flemish animals which played a part in the formation of the Shire and Clydesdale breeds. The Stud Book dates from 1886. The general build of the Belgian is heavy and compact, with a very large girth in proportion to the height. The neck is short, the back straight and strong, the rump rather short and drooping. The short legs are practically devoid of feather. The bone is rather round and the feet tend to be small. The temperament is very docile and the horses are willing workers. The commonest colour is chestnut, though bay, brown and roan also occur.

## THE FARM HORSE

The very marked decline in the number of farm horses indicates how quickly they are being replaced by tractors and generally by the mechanisation of much farm work. There are still a number of farms on which one or two horses are kept for short haulage jobs, but there seems little likelihood of horse numbers rising again. The demand for older draft horses for industry—at the docks and railway depots—has also declined very markedly. The number of farmers who breed draft horses regularly is relatively small.

## HORSE BREEDING

Breeding animals should be chosen primarily for individual merit, and should preferably be of pure breed and of good pedigree. Continued and indiscriminate crossing should be avoided as it gives a greatly increased chance of " misfits." In the breeding mare, quality, trueness to type and roominess of body are more importance than size (height). Freedom from any hereditary tendency to unsoundness is most important. The list of diseases that are held as disqualifying stallions from registration under the Horse Breeding Act includes cataract, roaring or whistling, bone spavin, ring-bone, side-bone, navicular disease, shivering, stringhalt and defective genital organs.

Fillies may be mated for the first time either at two or at three years old. The question whether it is advisable to breed at the earlier age should be decided according to the animal's size and condition, and whether it is desired that she should make the fullest growth of which she is capable. Colts at two years old may serve a limited number of mares— generally not more than a dozen. Three-year-olds should be restricted to about sixty and aged horses to about eighty. Much, however, depends on the individual characteristics of the stallion, on his constitution, and the effectiveness of his services.

The period of gestation averages rather more than eleven calendar months and varies quite commonly as much as a fortnight either way. It is longest in mares that foal in winter or early spring and shortest in those that foal in summer. The first heat begins four to seven days after foaling and ends on the tenth to the thirteenth day after foaling. The average duration of the period of heat is seven days, but there is much variation. It is longest in early spring, especially in a cold spring, and gets shorter in summer and autumn. The average time between successive heats is twenty one days, but the best way to calculate the time of onset is to count sixteen days from the end of the previous heat. The foaling season may be at any time between January and September. With Thoroughbreds, where age is counted from the beginning of the year, and where two and three year olds are very often trained and raced, it will obviously be advantageous to have the foals early, and most are dropped between January and March. For ordinary farm horses in this country the most convenient season is April to June, since this entails a minimum of housing and attention for the young animal. In countries where summer work is heavy and winter work very light, it is sometimes arranged to have a proportion of the foals dropped in autumn.

In general the fecundity of the mare is far below that of other domesticated animals. An occasional animal conceives regularly, year after year, at her first service; but it is far commoner for mares to come back to the stallion several times, and the proportion that remain barren after repeated services throughout the breeding season may reach 40 or 50 per cent. A service two to four days before the end of the œstrous period is much more likely to be effective than one in the first day or two or on the last day of the heat. Indeed if a mare is still on heat three days after service it is advisable to serve her again. The proportion of conceptions depends partly on the male. Some stallions will settle 80 per cent. of their mares, while others, under identical circumstances, will beget very few foals, and a small proportion of apparently normal animals are almost or quite sterile. To ensure good results the stallion must be carefully fed on a good mixed ration, should not be too fat at the commencement of the breeding season and should have regular exercise during the idle part of the year. As regards the mares, those at grass are more likely to conceive than those kept in stables and on dry feeding. Mares that are on hard work and lean, and on the other hand such as are over-fat, are much less likely to conceive than such as are in natural thriving condition. Twins are rare and are not wanted, since they are generally undersized even when mature.

Ordinary farm mares are generally required to work regularly during the greater part of the year. It is only when the prospective value of the foal is very high in proportion to the cost of maintenance of the mare that breeding, in itself, is likely to produce a profit. Provided that the mare is in the charge of a skilled and reasonably careful horseman, she may do all classes of farm work during the first six or seven months of pregnancy. In the latter part she should not be put between shafts and should be excused from any exceptionally heavy jobs, but may continue to work in chains right up to the time of foaling. It is a serious mistake to rest the mare for the last few weeks if this entails shutting her up in a box and leaving her without exercise; but if it is possible to turn her out to grass she may go idle without taking harm. The approach of parturition is indicated by a gradual slipping or relaxation of the muscles about the tail head and a swelling of the udder; generally some two days before foaling a waxy secretion will appear on the ends of the teats. As the time approaches, the mare should be placed at nights in a roomy box, and after the appearance of the wax should be kept under close observation. The period of labour is generally short—often less than an hour—and false presentations are comparatively rare. Retention of the cleansing is more dangerous than with other animals.

Some patience is frequently necessary in getting the foal to suck, but interference should be delayed as long as possible. After foaling, the mare should have laxative and nutritious foods—bran mashes, oatmeal drinks and clover hay. After two or three days, if the weather be genial, mare and foal may begin to go to grass for a short period, which period is extended day by day until after two or three weeks they may be left to lie out at nights. In the case of foals born early in the year, exercise should be regularly given until the weather conditions permit of the animals being turned out. When the foaling falls in summer excellent results are often obtained by turning the mare into a clean and sheltered paddock and allowing her to remain out altogether, Where foaling boxes are used they must be thoroughly disinfected for each new case and must be kept clean.

After foaling, the mare should be left idle for at least a month, and with advantage until the time of weaning. When work is pressing she may be given light jobs, but should not be overheated nor kept apart from the foal for more than two or three hours at a stretch. If, occasionally, the mother should be put to severe work or overheated, some of the milk should be drawn by hand before the foal is allowed to suck. The age for weaning may be about four months—or up to six months if the mare is not required for work. The separation should be complete and final; the foal must be closely and securely confined out of hearing of the mare, and the latter should be put into regular work in order to dry off her milk. After three or four days' confinement, during which time it is usually fed on bran, oats and hay, the foal may go back to pasture—preferably with a companion.

If weaning has occurred fairly early in the year, and if good pasture is available, no additional food will at first be necessary in order to keep the weaned foal in thriving condition. Backward animals, or such as have been weaned at an early age, will benefit greatly from a daily mash of bran and crushed oats soaked with separated milk. As the season advances and pastures get bare and less nutritious, the foal should get one feed per day, and later, during the winter, two. A suitable ration for midwinter might be: crushed oats, 4 lb. and bran, 2 lb., divided into two meals, and good clean hay. During periods of frost and snow a little long hay may be thrown out in the field, and many breeders give two or three swedes a day. The foal should be out whatever the weather conditions for some part of each day, but should—except in mild districts or in sheltered situations—be housed at night in a freely ventilated box. With the return of grass in spring, hand feeding may be discontinued, and in April or May the animal may begin to lie out.

Castration is generally performed at a year old or as soon thereafter as the weather is sufficiently mild. Very warm weather should be avoided. The operation involves more danger than with the other species of farm animals. No one but a skilled veterinary surgeon should be trusted to carry out the operation. Apart from this the only special attention necessary is to the feet. These should be kept well rasped down so that the frog rests on the ground, otherwise the feet will become long and narrow and an undue strain will be put on the pasterns. On ordinarily soft land the feet will require to be dressed at intervals of four or six weeks.

Young horses grow and thrive best when they are given a wide range of moderate pasture and when they are running with other stock, preferably cattle. When kept by themselves on a small area they graze very irregularly and are more liable to suffer from intestinal worms. Only Thoroughbreds are normally given grain (oats) while on summer pastures, and then only to hasten growth for early racing.

During the second winter, if fair rough pasture be available, hand feeding may be confined to a shorter period—say January to March—and the ration may be lighter and less concentrated. Six pounds of grain with a similar amount of hay may ordinarily suffice, but the quantity must depend on the animal's condition and the climate. In no case should the animal be made fat, and it will usually be all the better if it reaches the spring in distinctly lean condition. During the third summer ordinary pasture will again suffice.

The usual age for **breaking** the farm horse is two and a half years. Some Shires are put to work at two, and Clydesdales, in breeding districts or where the winter work is light, are often left till nearly three. In any case the whole process should not be left until the animal is of age to start work. As a young foal it should be made to understand the use of the halter and that there is no means of escape from it. This first lesson may involve a severe struggle. Thereafter it should be gradually accustomed to being handled and to having its legs lifted. When these processes have not been gone through at an early age the preliminary " gentling " of the grown animal is much more difficult.

The first stage of the breaking proper is to put on harness and lead the animal about, in order that it may lose the sense of irritation and alarm at the contact of the tackle. Thereafter it should be driven on long reins for an hour or so at a time, until it answers to the bit; two or three lessons will generally suffice. Care must be taken to avoid damage to the mouth, as repeated bleeding, even if slight, causes the bars (on which the bit rests) to become insensitive. These lessons may be combined with or

U

followed by training in draft, which is best started by means of men pulling against the animal on long rope traces, the pressure on the shoulders being applied gradually while the animal is in motion. Finally, it may be harnessed along with a steady but active horse in the plough, with at first an additional leading rein and a man alongside. Work in shafts should be postponed for a few months. Judgment must be exercised in the matter of the time to be allowed for each stage. Some animals can be put almost straight into work while others may require a week or two of preliminary training. Fractious animals should be trotted round on the end of a rope—preferably on heavy going such as fresh ploughed land—before each lesson. This preliminary exercise should proceed until the animal is tired enough to be amenable to discipline, but not to the point of exhaustion.

Most horses continue to grow in size and strength until they are about seven years old, and a good animal, barring accidents, may be expected to remain fit for regular work until the age of from fourteen to eighteen years, after which it may fill the post of odd horse for two or three years more. The average working life probably does not greatly exceed ten years, say from three to thirteen years old.


## FEEDING OF WORK HORSES

In Britain, oats and hay form the usual basis of the ration for work horses; and provided the oats be sound and not too new, and the hay be clean and hard, there are no other feeding stuffs that are so wholesome or so generally useful. Of the various hays, timothy, ryegrass and good meadow hay are all very satisfactory. Clover is less good, since it is too laxative for animals on severe work. Dusty hay is objectionable in that it spoils the wind, and mouldy or ill got material should be avoided if possible. For the winter months, when work is often irregular and the day is short, oat straw, if of good quality, may be substituted for hay, and in such circumstances forms a useful fodder. It is too low in nutritive value for animals on hard continuous work. In northern clay land districts bean straw is sometimes used as a substitute for hay. It is less nutritious than hay, and the concentrated ration must be correspondingly heavier.

Of concentrates other than oats, maize is sometimes used, 3 lb. giving the same energy value as 4 lb. of oats. If it is to form a large part of the ration it must be introduced gradually, and it gives the best results when mixed with oats and dry bran in order to lighten it. Barley makes a good horse corn but wheat is unsatisfactory, being liable to produce colics unless fed with care. Rye is worse. Beans are good up to a moderate proportion—say one eighth of the grain ration. Crushed linseed or linseed cake is an excellent conditioning food for animals that are run down, but it is too laxative to be fed in quantity to animals on severe work; 1 or 2 lb. of the former or 2 to 4 lb. of the latter are common amounts to feed daily. Molasses or one or other of the various molassed foods is sometimes added as an appetiser to the grain ration, and is useful for shy feeders. A bran mash in place of the usual evening feed of grain may be given on Saturday nights as a matter of routine, in order to prevent, by its mild laxative action, the possible ill effects of the following day's idleness. It is specially important when work during the preceding week has been continuous and hard.

On farms where summer work is not very heavy the work horses usually run at grass, and are given a feed of 5 or 6 lb. of concentrate for each half-day that they work. They must be stabled and hardened up before the regular autumn work commences.

The amount of the daily ration must be determined according to the size of the animal and the amount and severity of the work being done. A full-sized, active, heavy, draft animal, on hard and continuous work, will require quite 20 lb. of oats—or its equivalent in other grain—per day, along with nearly the same weight of good hay. The following are examples of rations for a farm horse of average size—say 1400 to 1500 lb. live-weight:—

| Light or Intermittent Work | Medium Work | Continuous Heavy Work |
|---|---|---|
| 12 lb. oats. | 16 lb. oats. | 10 lb. maize |
| 8 „ hay. | 16 „ hay. | 5 „ oats. |
| 10 „ oat straw. | 10 „ swedes. | 5 „ bran. |
| 20 „ swedes. | | 14 „ hay. |

The actual expenditure of energy depends to a greater extent on the speed at which the work is performed than on the hours worked or the pull. Hence in the north, where it is the custom to drive horses rather hard, rations tend to be heavier than in the south. In the Midlands and South of England, 12 lb. oats and about 14 to 16 lb. of hay, may be taken as an average ration. In periods of complete idleness the grain ration must be severely restricted, as many ailments arise from overfeeding at such times.

Grain should be bruised and a proportion of the fodder may be chaffed, and grain and chaff fed together. This prevents the animal from bolting the grain. Feeding, when on full work, should be done three times a day, and a full hour should be allowed both for the morning and for the midday meal. Water should be given freely four times a day—always before feeding, or, at least, not immediately after a meal. Exception should be made only in the case of an animal in very overheated and overtired condition; in such cases the horses's thirst should be quenched gradually with half a bucketful of lukewarm water at short intervals until he is satisfied.

Horses at work should be groomed once a day. Legs should not be washed often, but should be allowed to dry and then be brushed out. In periods of idleness during winter an hour's exercise should be given at least every second day. Exercise is the more necessary if the animals are suddenly thrown idle after a spell of hard work.

Shoeing should be done at intervals of six or seven weeks, or oftener in cases where the feet are thin or liable to break. New shoes are not necessary on all occasions. At the onset of winter, but before the coat is fully grown, farm horses may be clipped trace high—*i.e.* the coat is removed only from the chest, belly and thighs, while the head, neck, back, quarters and legs are left untouched. This plan allows the horse to keep reasonably cool at work and yet leaves the natural protection against rain on the one hand and mud on the other. The end of November is generally a suitable time to clip, and the operation is usually repeated in January. The stable should have ample head room and should be well ventilated and well lit. Stalls should be 6 ft. to 6ft. 6 in. wide, and the length from manger to back wall should be about 18 ft. Overhead racks are undesirable because of the risk of hay seeds and dust getting into the eyes and nostrils.

Careful routine management must be accompanied by a close watch over individual animals, and early attention must be paid to common ailments such as sore shoulders, " weeds " (lymphangitis), colics, colds and lamenesses. Horses that are in lean and unthrifty condition should have their teeth examined and filed if necessary. Intestinal worms are another frequent cause of a failure to thrive. A supply of rock salt in the manger will generally help in the maintenance of health.

## ASSES AND MULES

Donkeys are now seldom used in this country for farm work. They were generally to be found on the smallest class of holding, for which they were suitable, having small food requirements. Abroad, they are used as riding and pack animals. The larger breeds, which produce jacks suitable for mule-breeding, are the most valuable. The breeds that are held in the highest esteem for this purpose are the Catalonian (Spain) and the Poitou (France). The former has unusually good symmetry and action and reaches a height of 14 to 15 hands; the latter is a breed of great weight and substance and large bone, and is generally from 15 to 16 hands high. The females are about 2 in. smaller in each case. Other well known breeds are the Maltese, the Majorca and the Andalusian. Mules are preferred to horses both for farm and city work in warm climates. They are very sure footed, and hence valuable as pack animals in mountain regions; they also possess great endurance and are not fasitidious feeders. They are bred in great numbers in most Mediterranean countries and also in the warmer regions of both North and South America. Big mules can be bred only out of big mares. The offspring of a horse and a female donkey (hinny) has its fœtal growth restricted and remains undersized in later life.

# CHAPTER 24

# PIGS

THE pig belongs to the non-ruminant section of the Artiodactyls (even-toed hoofed animals). The wild pig is a forest animal, feeding upon acorns, beechmast and other seeds, roots, worms, grubs and occasional small mammals. It consumes relatively little in the way of grass or other herbage. The digestive system is closely similar to that of man, except that there is more active bacterial digestion of cellulose in the large intestine. The wild sow normally farrows only once a year and the average litter is about four.

All our domesticated swine are believed to have descended from two closely related species—*Sus scrofa*, indigenous to Europe and North Africa, and *Sus vittatus* of Eastern and South-Eastern Asia. The latter is distinguished chiefly by its wider and shorter head.

The earliest known domesticated pig, *Sus scrofa palustris*, existed in Neolithic times, its remains being found along with those of the small short horned type of cattle (*Bos brachyceros* or *longifrons*) and the small sheep of the same period. The domesticated pig of early historic times in Europe appears to have been closely related to the local wild type— long legged with a long snout, heavy shoulders, short body, light hind-quarters and a coat of coarse bristles. During Saxon times large herds were maintained, the animals being herded, for a considerable part of the year, in the widely prevalent oak forests. More recently pig keeping was largely associated with dairying on the one hand and with corn growing on the other. On butter making farms the traditional foods were skim milk, wheat offals and barley meal, and on cheese farms whey, wheat offals and beans. On corn farms the chief foods, as would be expected were, tail corn and millers' offals, supplemented by beans or peas. In either case the breeding sows and young animals, wherever conditions permitted, had a run on pasture in spring and on stubbles during autumn. Still later, pigs came to be associated with commercial potato growing.

During the latter part of the eighteenth and in the early nineteenth centuries there was a considerable infusion of fresh blood by crossing with the so-called *Sus indicus*, introduced both directly from its home area in China and Siam, and indirectly through Mediterranean types, notably the Neapolitan. The Chinese differed from the native type in being smaller, shorter faced and very markedly earlier maturing—*i.e.* with a much more pronounced tendency to fatten while young. The admixture resulted in an animal that was smaller and less active than the indigenous type and easier to fatten, but of less fecundity. Among modern breeds the Chinese influence is most obvious in the Berkshire and Middle White, least so in the Tamworth and Large White.

Most of our present day breeds have been evolved, or at least have been moulded into their present forms, within the past seventy or eighty years. Previous to the formation of the National Pig Breeders' Association in 1884, there were no breed societies and no herd books. Up till that time breeding was conducted in a rather haphazard fashion, and although there were local types known as the Berkshire, Tamworth and Yorkshire, their characteristics were very variable, and often widely different from those of the modern breeds that have inherited the names.

Pigs are valued almost solely as meat producers, but the meat may be utilised in different ways, and different types have been evolved to meet the varying requirements. Moreover, consumer demand and methods of utilisation vary in different countries. In Britain, before the war there were four main market types—(1) in the north, a relatively large and fairly fat pig, for bacon; (2) in the south, a lean and long pig of about 200 lb. live weight (or 150 lb. carcass weight), for the Wiltshire bacon trade; (3) cutters with a much wider weight range than that demanded by the Wiltshire curer (the method of utilisation was to cure the hams and sometimes the forehams and belly cuts, and to sell the rest of the carcass as fresh meat); (4) the London porker, of about 70 lb. carcass weight, which was retailed as pork joints. In all cases trimmings and much of the edible offal were normally converted into sausage and brawn, while surplus fat was rendered into lard.

At present the pattern is rather different. The demand for pig meats has risen substantially and now accounts for some thirty per cent. of the total meat consumption. About one third of our home production goes for pork, and the demand is less for the light weight porker and more for the cutter type of pig. Another third goes for bacon and the remainder for manufacture. The recent trend has been a steady and substantial rise in pig meat for manufacture: and one that seems likely to continue with the increasing demand for packed and tinned products and the development of supermarkets.

A newer development for Britain relates to the heavy pig of some 260 lb. live weight. Those, who favour that type, claim that the right type of bacon pig, fed ad lib. to that weight, can be used effectively and economically to produce a variety of products, e.g. packed and vacuum packed bacon and hams, pork, sausages and pies. The fat, surplus to that for bacon and ham, is trimmed off and used in the manufacture of the other products such as sausages and pies. Experimental work on the economy of the heavy pig is continuing. It is as yet too soon to say whether for example such a pig may be a serious competitor with the pig suitable for Wiltshire bacon.

The weights mentioned above represent much less than mature weights —*i.e.* they are for animals still in active growth. Good specimens of the larger breeds, at maturity but in breeding condition, range from 300 to 400 lb. live weight in the case of sows, with boars about 100 lb. heavier. Exceptionally large animals, in very fat condition, reach weights of the order of 1000 lb.

Of all our farm animals the pig has the greatest capacity to accumulate body fat, more especially in early life. Hence early maturity, which is one of the chief objectives of the breeder of beef cattle and sheep, in the case of the bacon pig, can very easily be carried to excess. It is therefore well that the selection of breeding stock, with the object of the right degree of early maturity, should be made when the animals have reached market weight—*e.g.* in the case of bacon breeds, at about six or seven months old. An animal which attains the desired body proportions at, say, five months old on normal feeding, will be too short and blocky, and will tend to yield an over-fat carcass when it reaches bacon weight.

The importance of the correct degree of early maturity is illustrated in Plate 65. The typical Large White, slaughtered at 100 lb. live weight, yields a carcass with too much bone and too little fat, but when grown to 200 lb. gives a carcass of well balanced proportions. The typical Middle White gives a good blocky carcass at 100 lb. but, at the higher weight, is too short, too heavy in the fore-end and altogether too fat for any purpose.

Though the type of pig is important, it is only one factor in influencing the character of the final product. It is possible by restricted feeding in the later stages to delay maturity or by ad lib. feeding to hasten fattening. Restricted feeding on a concentrated diet does tend to increase the cost of food per pound of carcass weight. Indeed, one of the claims by those who favour the heavy pig is that in total, live weight gains can be made more economically by following ad lib. feeding, provided that a cheaper ration is fed after the pig is 140 to 150 lb. live weight.

The conformation desired in a pork pig, to be finished at an early age, is comparable to that of a beef type of cattle or a mutton type of sheep. The highest priced cuts are obtained from the back and loin (roasts and chops) and the ham (leg of pork). Hence a wide, thickly fleshed back and a heavy ham are wanted. At the age of five months or so, pigs are still in rapid growth and, if fed on a well-balanced diet, are unlikely to be over-fat. In the selection of breeding stock at porker weight a blocky conformation and thick fleshing should be the main criteria. Great length of body is incompatible with the degree of early maturity required.

The bacon type is longer bodied, rather higher on the leg and more lightly fleshed than a pork animal of similar age. Since the side (back rashers and streaky bacon) and the ham provide the most highly priced cuts, great length, combined with a full, plump ham, are the main desiderata. The shoulder and jowl should be light. The side should be of uniform depth throughout and thick at the flank. In score card systems of grading, length of body in relation to weight is emphasised, the other major points being a plump ham, a moderate thickness of back fat ($1\frac{1}{2}$ in. or not exceeding 2 in.), a thick belly wall (streak) and a light head and shoulder. The firmness and whiteness of the fat are also taken into account, soft carcasses being penalised; but the quality of fat is determined by feeding (see p. 633) rather than by breeding.

The distinguishing characteristics of the bacon and pork types are to some extent fixed in the various breeds. The Large White, the Landrace and Tamworth are essentially bacon breeds. The average type of Berkshire, being shorter, wider and smaller of frame, is admirable for pork and useful for small bacon. Other breeds of intermediate type, with a certain amount of selection and appropriate management, can be successfully used for either purpose. The more important British breeds are arranged by Hammond in the following groups. There is a considerable variation as between strains within each breed.

*Pork—*
   Berkshire.
   Middle White

*Dual Purpose—*
   Essex.
   Gloucestershire Old Spot.
   Large Black.
   Long White Lop-eared.
   Welsh.
   Wessex.

*Bacon—*
   Landrace.
   Large White.
   Tamworth.
   Welsh.

Cross breds are frequently preferred for commercial purposes. Thus the Berkshire × Middle White cross is admirable for small pork, while a dual purpose sow—*e.g.* the Wessex—may be mated with the Middle White for pork or the Large White for bacon. The arguments for and against cross breeding are set out later (see p. 625).

Apart from the special points desired for particular purposes, certain qualities are desirable under all circumstances. Robustness of constitution is one. Breeders of all classes of livestock tend to believe that constitution is correlated with certain points in conformation—for instance, a wide head or a capacious chest. In fact, there is no convincing evidence of any such correlation in the pig. Hardiness and thriftiness

PLATE 65

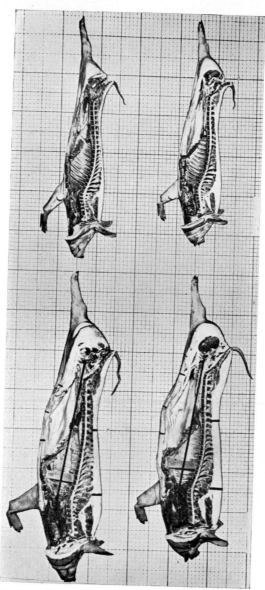

Carcasses of Middle White (right) and Large White (left) at
100 lb. live weight for Pork (top) and 200 lb. live weight for
Bacon (below)

can be improved only by the continued weeding out of weakly animals or such as fail to attain a satisfactory rate of growth. Another requirement is sufficient strength of limbs to carry the body and to permit a reasonable degree of activity, which is very important in the breeding sow. The legs should be reasonably stout and fairly straight and the pasterns short and nearly upright. The temperament should be docile and quiet; nervous or savage or excitable animals are almost invariably unsatisfactory and, in particular, the temperament of the sow has much to do with the casualty rate among her young. Prolificacy is of great importance and, although there is a wide range of variation in the size of successive litters from the same sow, there is a considerable degree of heritability. Hence breeding animals of both sexes should be chosen from among the progeny of prolific dams.

The growth rate of the sucking pig during the first three weeks of its life (a point of great economic importance) depends partly on its inborn capacity for growth but much more on the level of milk production of its dam. Hence sows whose litters bear evidence of poor nutrition should be discarded. Each pigling, within the first day or two after it has been farrowed, has its own teat; hence the maximum number that can be properly nursed is the same as the number of the dam's teats. In general, females should not be retained for breeding unless they have at least twelve well formed and regularly spaced teats. Since teat number is inherited from both parents, the rudimentary teats of the boar should be examined with the same standard in mind. Gilts with ten teats or even fewer are not uncommon.

Most breed societies publish special registers of sows that have attained certain standards of performance in breeding and nursing—for example, an average for four successive litters, born within a period of twenty two months, of eight piglings reared to weaning age.

Finally, colour is of some importance. On the one hand white breeds are somewhat liable to suffer from sun scald when exposed to intense sunlight, though trouble of this kind is rare in Britain. On the other hand, black animals are liable to seedy cut, i.e. the appearance of patches of dark coloration in the streaky rashers. The pigment can occur in the rudimentary mammary tissue of male pigs as well as in females.

Two procedures have been devised for the assessment of economic qualities in pigs and these should be used in conjunction as guides to the selection of breeding stock. The one is known as *pig recording*, records made being of the number of young born in each litter, the number reared to the normal weaning age (eight weeks) and the individual weights of the piglings at that age. It is a useful refinement to record weights at three weeks of age as well as at eight, because the growth rate during the first three weeks is a measure of the milking propensity of the sow; subsequent growth is largely influenced firstly by the quality of the food and on the skill exercised by the pigman in inducing the piglings to take to the trough at an early age.

Official recording commonly ceases at weaning age, but the pig keeper will be well advised to keep other records for his own guidance—of the age at slaughter of individual animals and of their carcass weights and carcass grades. The total food used and the total live weight increment of the herd, year by year, is a further useful measure of the overall efficiency of management. It is, of course, necessary to have a suitable weighbridge in order to arrive at the efficiency of food conversion even for the herd as a whole; but a weighing machine is a worth while investment in any case since otherwise it is likely that individual animals, when sold, will fall outside the weight range to which the maximum price applies.

The other aid to improvement is *litter testing*, designed to assess the breeding value of individual boars. A reasonably accurate measure of a boar's merit can be obtained by selecting four of the heaviest weanlings (two gilts and two hogs) from each of three litters sired by him. The selected animals are moved to an official testing station, are kept under strictly controlled conditions and are individually fed on a standard, balanced food mixture. Records are kept of food consumption, live weights at slaughter, carcass weights and scores for carcass quality. The average food cost (in terms of pounds of meal per pound carcass weight) and the average carcass quality of the twelve progeny, taken together, constitute a good measure of the sire's breeding value. In theory the same progeny test can be applied to sows, but the dam will be of rather advanced age before the test results for samples of three litters can become available; the results from any much smaller sample of progeny would be subject to a large margin of error. Litter testing has long been in use in Scandinavian countries and has proved an important aid to improvement both in conversion efficiency and in carcass quality.

Until fairly recent times the ordinary basis of selection of breeding stock has been visual inspection, either by breeder or prospective buyer or show judge. Breed societies have recently, however, required members to provide returns of numbers born and reared in every litter from which any pigs are to be registered. It is thus possible to build up an extended pedigree of any animal, with all the evidence of the prolificacy of its female ancestors and of their ability to rear their young.

In recent years there have been interesting developments in official pig testing and recording. These were fostered and are now being developed by the (British) National Pig Breeders' Association and a new body, the Pig Industry Development Authority. There is now provision for the testing of the progeny of boars through official testing stations, and a National Accredited Scheme has been set up by the Pig Industry Development Authority under which records are kept of important commercial aspects of pig production, *e.g.* number of pigs born and reared and live weight gains.

# BRITISH BREEDS

There are twelve recognised breeds, each with its own pedigree records. A number are under the care of the National Pig Breeders' Association.

**The Large White** (or Large Yorkshire) (Plate 66, *A*) is derived from an early North Country type, large in size and either all white or white with black spots. Probably it contained very little Chinese or Neapolitan blood. The evolution of the modern breed began, before 1850, in the industrial districts of the West Riding of Yorkshire, the pioneers being largely factory workers. In 1851 a weaver of Keighley, Joseph Tuley, exhibited at the Windsor Royal Show a pig of the improved type which attracted much notice.

The Large White is a pig of great size, being exceeded only by the Lincoln Curly Coat. Mature boars reach 7 cwt. in good breeding condition and up to 10 cwt. when fully fattened. The head is of medium length and dished, but the nose is not turned up. The ears are of medium length and incline forward but are rigid. The skin is fine and carries a moderately abundant coat of silky hair. The breed standard calls for pure white skin and coat, but occasional animals show small patches of dark skin and, more rarely, of black hair. The general conformation is that described for the bacon type—light in head, jowl and shoulder, with great length of body, moderate depth of side and plump but smooth hams. Broadly speaking, growth continues long and maturity is relatively late, but in this respect there is some variation between strains. All strains can produce a first class bacon carcass at the age of six to eight months, and some are quite suitable for the production of medium weight porkers.

The Large White is, according to available records, the most prolific of all our breeds, the average number born per litter being over ten. But the sows are sometimes less docile than could be wished, so that losses of piglings, in the first few days of life, are higher than in certain other breeds. Milk production is good, and the young grow rapidly.

The Large White is widely distributed over Great Britain and Ireland, with some concentration in the north and east. It has been largely exported to other bacon producing countries, including Canada and New Zealand, and has been used in the formation of many overseas breeds.

**The Landrace** (Plate 66, *B*) is derived from the Danish Landrace. Some seventy years ago the Danes started to produce a bacon pig that would be suitable for their export trade to Britain. By systematic selection and testing they established a breed which has become widely known for its quality and uniformity of type. Pigs from this Danish stock were bred later in a number of European countries, and it was from Sweden that the first importation of Landrace came to Britain in 1949.

The Landrace was crossed extensively with the Large White in the early years after its introduction, and there was some infiltration of Large White blood in the building up of the breed in this country.

The British Landarce Pig Society was formed in 1953 to register all pedigree Landrace pigs for breeding and to preserve those qualities in the breed which were the outcome of the long and patient plan for improvement in Scandinavian countries. The popularity of this new breed in Britain can be gauged by reference to the table of licensed boars on page 622.

The conformation is that of the bacon type—small head and neck, light shoulders, a great length of side and good hams. The breed can also be used to produce pork of good quality. It has established itself as a good show pig, having won a number of the highest awards in carcass competitions.

The sows are quiet mothers, prolific and the economy of live weight gain is good.

**The Middle White** (Plate 67, *A*) was formed by the blending of the blood of the Large White with that of the now extinct Small Yorkshire, which latter was a small, short-faced, fine-boned and excessively fat animal such characteristics reflecting the very high amount of Chinese blood that it carried. The Middle White was recognised by the Royal Agricultural Society in 1882, but the type was not fully fixed until twenty years later. Sanders Spencer, of Holywell, St Ives, Hunts, played the leading part in developing the breed.

In weight the Middle White is about 20 per cent. less than the Large White and is probably the smallest of our breeds, though but little below the Berkshire and the Tamworth. The head is short, dished and the snout turned up; the ears of moderate size and carried erect; the jowl is sometimes heavy and the general build is rather short, wide and compact; the breed is low legged and the coat is thicker than in most other breeds. The Middle White, maturing very rapidly, formerly shared with the Berkshire the trade for small porkers, and the decline in its numbers is to be explained by the disappearance of this market. The modern tendency has been to breed for greater length of body, a lighter shoulder and a leaner type of carcass. The sows are less prolific than those of the Large White, and the growth rate of the young is less. Boars of the breed are useful for cross breeding with sows of the larger and leaner breeds, and have proved very valuable overseas in the grading up of unimproved stock.

**The Berkshire** (Plate 67, *B*) originated, as its name implies, in the Thames Valley. Culley, writing in 1789, describes Berkshires as " generally reddish brown with black spots . . . large ears hanging down over their eyes, short-legged, small-boned and exceedingly inclined to make rapidly fat "; but other descriptions vary widely from this, and it seems that there must have been a great diversity of types. The modern breed is of a rather rusty black colour, with white points—tail, face and feet.

It is, according to Smithfield weights, slightly heavier than the Middle White. It is smaller framed than the Tamworth but about as heavy. The head is rather short but the snout is not turned up. The ears are rigid but incline forward. Body conformation is similar to that of the Middle White, but the hind quarter is typically more level. The Berkshire is less prolific than the larger and longer breeds and the young sometimes make slow growth in early life.

The outstanding merit of the Berkshire is the quality of its meat at the small porker stage of development. At one time pure bred Berkshires were supreme in the Smithfield pork carcass competitions, but the breed has suffered, like the Middle White, by the loss of its special market. Abroad, the Berkshire is widely popular, its dark colour being an advantage in sunny climates. The types developed in the United States, Canada and Australia are generally longer bodied and leaner than the original.

**The Large Black** (Plate 68, *A*) is an old breed which came into prominence only after the founding of its Breed Society in 1899. The foundation stock came partly from Cornwall and Devon and partly from Suffolk and Essex, but the original differences in type have long ago been eliminated. The breed is widely distributed in Britain and has been largely exported, especially to warmer countries.

Animals of the breed reach weights only slightly less than Large Whites of comparable age. The head is of moderate length, the ears long and lopping, the tips reaching to the nose. The hair is jet black, fine and generally rather abundant, but the skin is not deeply pigmented. The general build is intermediate between that of the Large White and Tamworth on the one hand and the Berkshire and Middle White on the other; in other words, the conformation is that of a dual purpose animal. The shoulder is notably light in relation to the ham, but the flesh is often less smooth than that of the Large White. The sows are remarkably docile and seem to be able to build up bodily reserves, during pregnancy, with very little food other than good grazing. The average size of litter is about nine as compared with ten for the Large White, but the casualty rate is substantially less. The Large Black sow, crossed with the Large White boar, gives a product with much of the bacon quality of the sire and a mainly white coloration. The cross bred has the advantage of the good mothering ability of the dam.

**The Tamworth** (Plate 68, *B*) has its home in the Midlands, particularly the district about Birmingham. It is of comparatively small weight, long bodied and relatively narrow in build, with a very long straight snout and red (chestnut) colour. The breed was at one time reduced to small numbers, and prolificacy (probably through inbreeding) declined seriously, but importations from Canada have helped to restore fertility and vigour. The Tamworth is slow maturing, but its long smooth side, neat shoulder and firm flesh makes it very suitable for the production of high quality bacon.

The **Wessex Saddleback** (Plate 69, *A*) and the **Essex** (Plate 69, *B*) are of similar type and colour—black and a white saddle over the shoulders and forelegs. The Essex breed standard calls for white hind feet and a white tip to the tail, whereas in the Wessex the hind feet and tail should be black. Both breeds are liable to produce a proportion of all black individuals, the probable explanation being that the wide belted and all black types breed true, while the animals with narrow belts are often heterozygous—*i.e.* they throw wide belted, all black and narrow belted progeny.

The ears are of medium size, with a forward pitch, but rigid. They have more forward inclination in the Wessex. Both breeds are hardy and the sows milk well. The Wessex is slightly the larger.

The Saddlebacks are, after the Large White, the most numerously represented breeds, and the cross between the Large White boar and the Saddleback sow is very popular with commercial breeders.

The **Gloucester Old Spots** (Plate 70, *A*) is an old local type which was little known until the establishment of a herd book in 1914. In conformation it approaches the Large White. The pig is hardy, prolific and a good grazer.

The **Lincoln Curly Coat** (Plate 70, *B*) is larger than the Large White, more heavily fleshed and rather coarser in bone. The coat is abundant and curly. **The Long White Lop-eared** (Plate 71, *A*) is, apart from colour, closely similar to the Large Black. Its home district is Devon and Cornwall. **The Welsh** (Plate 71, *B*) is similar, but rather longer and leaner in build. It is gaining in popularity by reason of its hardiness and good carcass qualities.

There is an almost complete unanimity that the number of British breeds is unnecessarily large. The needs of the industry could probably be met by half the present number—two bacon breeds, perhaps two dual purpose types selected for prolificacy and mothering ability, and an early maturing pork breed.

All boars are required to be licensed by the Agricultural Departments.

TABLE 20

| | Number of boars licensed in England and Wales | |
| Breed | 1954 | 1960 |
| --- | --- | --- |
| Large White Yorkshire . | 19,051 | 12,703 |
| Wessex Saddleback . . | 1,371 | 715 |
| Essex . . . . | 1,031 | 351 |
| Large Black . . . | 620 | 253 |
| Welsh . . . | 985 | 342 |
| Landrace . . . | 251 | 5,356 |

The preceding table gives the numbers of new licences issued in 1954 and 1960 in England and Wales for boars of six of the well known breeds, and indicates the progress made by the Landrace.

# BREEDING

Well grown and liberally fed gilts begin to come on heat at the fifth or sixth month of age, and from that time until they are large enough for mating they should be kept apart from boars. The minimum age for breeding, for good results, is about eight or nine months in the case of the female. But the actual criterion should be size, and a body weight of about 175 lb. in store condition may be taken as a reasonable standard. Earlier mating often results in an unsatisfactory first litter and may cause permanent stunting of the sow's growth. Some breeders prefer to delay mating to an age of ten or even twelve months. Young boars (brawns) may begin to serve at seven or eight months of age.

The female comes on heat, except when pregnant or nursing, at intervals of twenty to twenty one days throughout the year, so that it is possible to arrange for litters to fall at any season. Œstrus is rare while a sow is in milk, but occurs very soon after her litter has been weaned, very commonly on the third or fourth day. The period of heat lasts forty to sixty five hours, and the onset is heralded, some two days in advance, by a swelling and reddening of the vulva. Ovulation occurs towards the end of the heat period, so that sperm from a service soon after the onset may have lost its vitality before the eggs are shed. The ordinary rule is to mate during the second day of œstrus and, in case the sow is still on heat the following day, to mate a second time. It should also be borne in mind that the first service from a young male, or from one that has been rested for some time, may be ineffective because of the inactivity of the sperm. In this case a second mating should follow a few hours after the first. Except under these exceptional circumstances there is nothing to be gained by mating twice during the same œstrus period. Sows are more likely to conceive at the first heat after weaning than at subsequent heats.

Since the gestation period is sixteen weeks (varying only a day or two one way or the other), and since litters are normally weaned at eight weeks of age, the breeding cycle is completed in just under six months. Some sows, in fact, farrow at half yearly intervals throughout their breeding lives, but the average interval between litters is between six and seven months.

It is sometimes argued that eight weeks is too early an age for weaning, but it must be recognised that the period of lactation of the sow is very short. In most cases the peak milk yield is reached about three weeks from farrowing, and the milk flow has commonly dropped to a low level by the eighth week. A surer method of preventing a set back at weaning than that of extending the suckling period, is to induce the young to begin eating at the earliest possible age, and to use specially nutritious food during the suckling period and for a few weeks after weaning.

It is possible to wean young pigs at 2 to 3 weeks of age, but careful supervision is necessary to ensure success. The young pigs in this case, should be given a special compound mixture including vitamins and an antibiotic and the feeding of solid food should begin at about 5 days. Weaning is effected by removing the sow from her pigs at 5 days and doing all possible to get the pigs to eat the compound mixture. The advantages claimed for the system are that the sow comes in season earlier and so there is a possibility of obtaining five litters in two years rather than the normal four.

Some prefer to wean early but defer the actual weaning until the young pigs weigh about 20 lb. It is doubtful if there is much advantage in this modification of the early weaning method. At the time of writing few are practising early weaning and it is doubtful if in commercial practice it is resulting in the substantial benefits that were once claimed for it.

In large commercial herds, provided with adequate housing, the usual aim is to have the farrowings evenly distributed throughout the year and so to achieve a regular flow of marketable pigs. Any other system makes for periodic congestion of housing and to fluctuating demands for labour. But if the available buildings are poorly insulated, damp or otherwise unsatisfactory, farrowing in the dead of winter is best avoided.

The useful life of a sow may ordinarily extend to four or five years or six to eight litters. But since there is always a wide choice of gilts for replacement, sows that have proved unsatisfactory should be discarded after one or two farrowings. Specially valuable pure bred sows may be retained till an age or eight or even ten years, though they generally become progressively less prolific after their fifth year. Individual litters vary in number from one or two to more than twenty, and the average reaches about ten in the more prolific breeds. With first class management numbers reared can reach an average of nine per litter or eighteen per year, but a figure of eight per litter, with an average interval of seven months between successive farrowings (giving an output of fourteen progeny per sow per year), can be taken as satisfactory under the conditions of commercial farming. Gilts' litters tend to be one or two less in numbers than those of sows in their prime, but something depends on the age at first mating.

Very large litters are not desirable. More than twelve should not be left on a sow since, even if she has fourteen functional teats, the hindmost pair usually give very little milk. Many breeders limit numbers to ten for sows and eight for gilts, but with good stock and good management twelve and ten respectively may be permissible.

Surplus piglings, if healthy and vigorous, may be easily transferred to another newly farrowed sow, with a small litter of her own, if such happens to be available. A sow will commonly raise no objection to

PLATE 66

*A.* Large White Boar

*Farmer and Stockbreeder*

*B.* Landrace Gilt

*W. Richardson*

PLATE 67

*Farmer and Stockbreeder*

*A.* MIDDLE WHITE SOW

*Farmer and Stockbreeder*

*B.* BERKSHIRE GILT

PLATE 68

*A.* LARGE BLACK SOW

*Farmer and Stockbreeder*

*B.* TAMWORTH BOAR

*Farmer and Stockbreeder*

PLATE 69

*Farmer and Stockbreeder*

*A.* WESSEX ' SADDLEBACK ' SOW

*B.* ESSEX SOW

PLATE 70

*A.* GLOUCESTER OLD SPOTS SOW

*Farmer and Stockbreeder*

*B.* LINCOLN CURLY COATED SOW

*Farmer and Stockbreeder*

PLATE 71

*Farmer and Stockbreeder*

*A.* LONG WHITE LOP-EARED SOW

*Farmer and Stockbreeder*

*B.* WELSH GILT

foster piglings, even if these are of a different colour from her own. If no foster mother is available the surplus pigs (being, of course, the poorest of the litter) should be killed; any such action should not be taken until about the third day after farrowing, since most casualties occur during the first two or three days.

As regards systems of breeding, the simplest system of breeding is, to select a particular pure breed and to aim at progressive improvement by selection, with such aids as pig recording and litter testing, or at least, by examining all the data about prolificacy, efficiency of food conversion and carcass quality that can be got together. This is the system that has been applied with marked success in Denmark.

Many commercial producers in this country prefer a system of crossing. Where the process is confined to first crossing, the plan is that the sows should be of a breed combining prolificacy, milking ability and mothering qualities with reasonably good conformation—e.g. the Wessex—and to cross with a boar likely to be prepotent for growth rate and carcass quality—the Large White or the Landrace.

Apart from the advantage of combining the desirable qualities of the two parents there is the argument that first-cross animals are more vigorous and faster growing than pure breds—i.e. that crossing, as such, results in hybrid vigour. The experimental evidence in support of this contention is not very conclusive, a fact that may be explained on the assumption that hybrid vigour depends on the heterozygous condition of certain particular pairs of genes, and that it will be largely a matter of chance whether a cross bred animal will be more heterozygous, with respect to the factors concerned, than a pure bred.

Sometimes crossing is carried a stage further with the object of taking advantage of hybrid vigour in the sow. Thus one might cross the Large White with the Wessex, and mate the cross bred females back to the Large White. Going still further, some American commercial producers follow a system of rotational crossing, using three breeds. Breed A is mated to breed B, the cross bred sows to a boar of breed C, the produce of the last to a boar of breed A, and so on.

The obvious objection to all systems of cross breeding is that either two pure breeds must be maintained or, alternatively, that the breeder must rely on others for a continuing supply of pure bred gilts as well as of boars. In the latter case he cannot himself follow any system of progressive improvement.

Where the decision is in favour of a single pure breed, there remains the question of the degree of inbreeding that should be adopted—a question raised in Chapter 17.

Still another system, also discussed in Chapter 17, aims at the production of highly inbred families, in each of which the least desirable genes have been bred out, and then crossing up two or more of these families for the production of commercial stock—i.e. the same technique as is used for the production of hybrid maize. The process has been carried near to completion in the United States. The production of inbred families is proceeding under the Animal Breeding Research Organisation near Edinburgh. Though later results are promising no practical application arising from this work can yet be recommended.

## SOME PRINCIPLES OF HOUSING

There is a great variety of housing systems for pigs. The choice depends on a balance of considerations, having regard to the local climate, the soil type, the size of the enterprise and the available supply of capital and labour. The major objectives should be: (1) the provision of environmental conditions that will conduce to full health and vitality—warmth, comfort and opportunity for the necessary minimum of exercise; (2) the control of parasitic infestation and contagious disease; (3) the prevention of nutritional disorders—especially piglet anæmia; (4) reasonable capital cost; and (5) economy of labour.

No system so far devised can be said to be the best under all circumstances and in all respects, and decisions must be reached on a balance of considerations.

1. The pig, being a forest animal in nature and thus having opportunity to seek shade in hot weather and shelter in cold, has developed a narrow range of tolerance in regard to environmental temperature. It should be noted also that high air humidity intensifies the adverse effects both of heat and cold. Animals in show condition are subject to heat stroke and young pigs are very susceptible to cold. The most common fault in farrowing sheds is that they are too cold in winter. A condition, mistaken at times for piglet anæmia, has been closely associated with chilling, due either to too low an air temperature (sometimes combined with high humidity) or to poorly insulated flooring. The optimum environmental temperature for a baby piglet, at rest, is probably about 80° F., a level that can be maintained inside a well strawed nest in a building with an air temperature of about 65° F. and with a well insulated floor. Where the air temperature is liable to fall below 65° some form of artificial heating for the nest should be provided. One possibility is floor heating by means of resistance wires; another is an electric heat lamp suspended about 2½ ft. above the nest; or, failing a supply of electric power, an oil lamp. Space heating, by stoves or hot water pipes, is unsatisfactory, because (apart from its high cost) high temperature throughout the building results in a high rate of ammonia production from urine.

All this may be thought to be at variance with the experience that piglets generally do well, even in winter, in the common type of simple wooden hut, of triangular section, with free access to the open; but it has been shown that the temperature maintained at the back of a well-bedded hut is generally much higher than that prevailing in a permanent farrowing shed with the usual amount of air space and the common amount of ventilation.

Casualties in cold buildings are due either directly to chilling or indirectly through the tendency of the young piglets, in the absence of any source of warmth, to crowd round the sow and thus to risk being overlaid.

Where existing buildings have poorly insulated floors, a sleeping platform of wood or other non-conducting material may be provided. If the air space is excessive a ceiling may be added at a convenient height.

A useful check on the adequacy of the temperature in the farrowing quarters is the seasonal variation in piglet casualty rates and in average weaning weights. Thus, if, in summer, the piglet death rate is 5 per cent. and the average weaning weight 35 lb., and if the corresponding winter figures are 15 per cent. and 26 lb.—a not uncommon relationship—the likely explanation is that the farrowing quarters are too cold.

Cold tolerance, of course, increases with body size but also depends on bodily condition, since the layer of back fat acts as a blanket. Warmth continues to be of importance in piglets at the post-weaning stage and also in the case of sows in very reduced condition following lactation. Given a dry bed, well grown stores and mature animals, in good condition and run in sizeable groups, require no special consideration; but for economy of live weight gains temperature control is very important.

As regards exercise, breeding sows during pregnancy, breeding boars and gilts intended for breeding require a fair amount of freedom and should either be kept in yards or have an outdoor run. Stores and fatteners will generally get all that they need in sties.

Trough room is important both in order to ensure that all pigs in a group have equal opportunity to feed but also because over-crowding at meal times may lead to fighting. One foot per head is the common allowance for pigs up to bacon size, but the optimum is probably rather more.

A very important measure is the provision of a creep in the farrowing pen, so designed as to keep out the sow and admit her young. Food, preferably in the form of pellets or small nuts, should be offered in the creep from the age of three weeks.

Considerations of general comfort are important in relation to the choice between the indoor and outdoor systems. On free draining light land, a good sward can with ease be maintained in pig paddocks, and young pigs benefit from outdoor exercise. But with poorly drained soil in a wet climate the pens soon becomes a quagmire and so much mud is carried into the huts that it is impossible, in practice, to keep the interior dry.

2. As regards parasites, the most prevalent types—the lung worm, the round worm of the intestine and the stomach worm—are very liable to be picked up from contaminated ground, and unless the animals are

frequently treated, fixed paddocks rapidly become pig-sick. Moreover, a sward stocked entirely with pigs deteriorates rapidly so that there is little grazing, and the manure is then largely wasted. Hence permanent runs have to be periodically rested from pigs—*i.e.* must be stocked with some other type of animal.

The system greatly to be preferred is one in which the whole installation is moved at intervals of a few months to a fresh site with a clean and well established sward.

There are three possible modifications of the hut and run system. The one employs a fold unit—*i.e.* a hut with an attached unroofed pen, mounted on wheels or skids, which can be moved to clean ground at intervals of a few days or even daily. Under another system the sow is tethered by means of suitable harness and chain to a peg which is driven into the ground a few yards from the entrance to the hut, the young pigs being allowed free range over the pasture. A third is to confine the sow, by means of an electric fence, to a small area surrounding her hut, the height of the wire being, of course, sufficient to allow the piglets to range outside.

The wide dispersal of pigs under the outdoor system is a favourable factor in relation to the spread of certain contagious diseases. This is not true of swine erysipelas, which is caused by an organism that can live in the soil. In any case this trouble, as well as swine fever, can be controlled by immunisation. Virus pneumonia (pig influenza), however, since the infection can be air borne, is much more prevalent under the indoor system—at least where farrowing is carried out in a building that accommodates a number of litters.

3. The commonest nutritional disorder is piglet anæmia associated with a low iron content in the blood. The danger arises from the fact that iron is virtually absent from sow's milk, so that the piglet, though born with a certain reserve, soon becomes dependent on some other source. Green herbage and soil are the natural sources, so that piglets with access to the land are never affected. Moreover, if the pregnant sow spends part of her time out of doors, the piglings, at birth, will have considerable reserves. Under the indoor system the trouble can often be prevented firstly by feeding greenstuff to the sow during pregnancy, and secondly by placing a fresh turf or a spadeful of soil, in the farrowing pen daily. In other cases it is necessary to resort to dosage of the piglings, in their second week, with iron salts.

4. The prime cost of housing is, of course, greater in the case of a permanent building than that of movable huts, together with pig fencing for the surrounding paddocks. On the other hand, the rate of depreciation on the latter is much the higher.

5. Labour costs are reduced by concentrating pigs in large groups, with well planned arrangements for feeding and the removal of dung. The feeding of scattered groups involves a large expenditure of time.

Moreover, it is very difficult to achieve the proper degree of supervision, particularly of farrowing sows, if these are in dispersed individual huts over a large area.

A few miscellaneous points may be added.

Some breeders are accustomed to use farrowing crates in order to restrict the movements of the sow and prevent the young being trodden or overlaid, but it seems that the desired result can generally be achieved by providing a warm nest to which the sow has no access. Opinions differ as to the value of farrowing rails, which have the object of saving piglings from being caught when the sow lies down against the wall of her sty.

While strong pig netting is necessary to confine a boar, breeding gilts and pregnant sows, running in groups, can be controlled by an electric fence.

The usual size of farrowing huts is 8 by 10 ft., while indoor farrowing sites should ordinarily be 10 by 10 ft. Where a number of farrowing or feeding pens are grouped together in the same building, each, as a precaution against the spread of disease, should have independent drainage.

The housing system need not be either a purely indoor or a purely outdoor one. One popular arrangement is to have a block of farrowing pens in a permanent building with small runs to which the animals are given access for a short period every fine day; to have a yard or two, opening on to a large paddock, for breeding gilts and in-pig sows; to use an all indoor fattening shed with a series of pens of varying size, so that groups of weanlings, as they grow, can be moved from the smaller to the larger, while backward pigs, when their sty mates have gone for slaughter, can be placed in the small pens. Re-grouping should be avoided so far as possible, since this leads to fighting. Sows in very reduced condition at weaning should be kept by themselves until they have fully recovered strength and activity. Such needs should be foreseen in planning.

## FEEDING

The digestive organs of the pig are of a very different type from those of the purely herbivorous animals. The capacity of the alimentary canal is, in proportion to the size of the animal, about half what is found in the ox, sheep or horse. There is no provision, such as is made in the paunch of the ruminant or the cæcum of the horse, for holding a large quantity of bulky, fibrous food while it undergoes bacterial digestion. Despite the smallness of its digestive tract the pig, on full diet, eats more, in relation to its size (and in terms of dry matter), than other farm mammals. This implies that the process of digestion is much more rapid. Bacterial digestion does occur in the large intestine, but is capable of dealing with only a small amount of cellulose. Hence the proportion of fibre in the diet must be kept low.

While cellulose digestion is much less efficient than in the ruminant, the more readily digestible materials—starch, sugar and protein—just because they are not subjected to bacterial action, are more efficiently utilised by the pig.

The pig's capacity for growth and fattening is remarkably high since its high energy intake is coupled with a maintenance requirement that is little greater than those of the other farm animals. A steer of 9 cwt., on full feed, consuming 25 lb. of dry matter, with some 13 lb. of starch equivalent, may make a daily live weight increase of about 2 lb., whereas a pig of 200 lb. weight, on a ration providing 6 lb. dry matter and about $4\frac{1}{2}$ lb. starch equivalent, may be expected to gain about $1\frac{1}{2}$ lb. per day. Moreover, the proportion of carcass weight to live weight is substantially higher in the pig. Such comparisons should not be pressed too far, since the steer can utilise straw, hay, pasture grass and other cheap, bulky material in relatively large quantities.

In general, if the pig's capacity as a converter of feed into meat is to be fully exploited, its rations must provide a large quota of energy in small bulk. It is only in case of the pregnant sow or the full grown boar that the concentrate can be economically cut down by any large amount and replaced by grass or green food. Considerable use can, however, be made of roots, especially potatoes and fodder beet, since these contain only small amounts of fibre.

The fact that pigs require a highly concentrated diet has led, at times, to serious mistakes in feeding. The traditional foods—barley meal and wheat middlings—are poor in regard to both the quantity and quality of their proteins and have a very unsuitable ash balance—a deficiency in calcium, an excess of phosphate and a shortage of common salt. The traditional supplement was skim milk (or, alternatively, whey with beans or peas), and when this was used in adequate amounts good results were obtained.

Young pigs—up to the age of four or five months—make maximum growth only if they have a proportion of animal protein in their diet; the usual sources are white fish meal, meat meal, meat and bone meal and separated milk either in liquid form or dried. Skim milk appears to have some special merit in promoting health and growth. After the age indicated, quite satisfactory growth and development can be obtained on rations containing vegetable proteins only. The oil content of the ration should be kept fairly low, especially in the later stages of fattening, in order to avoid the carcass fault of soft fat. Unsaturated oils are particularly objectionable, so that herring meal should be used in small amounts only. White fish meal and meat and bone meal contain substantial amounts of calcium and phosphate, and when used so that they supply the greater part of the protein in the ration, the addition of minerals may be unnecessary  In most other circumstances, it is sufficient to add about 1½ lb. per cent. of ground chalk and ½ lb. per cent. of common salt to the meal mixture.  Most proprietary pig meals contain added minerals, often in great variety.

Iron deficiency, as mentioned earlier, is the cause of nutritional piglet anæmia, which may develop in cases where the piglets have no access to soil before they begin to take solid food—*i.e.* during the second and third weeks of age.  The symptoms are commonly most severe at about the tenth day.  It can be prevented by administering daily, during the second week of life, a small dose of ferrous sulphate.

As regards vitamins the only likely deficiencies will be of A and $D_3$, the former only where insufficient greenstuff is fed, and the latter only in animals that get little or no direct sunlight or sky shine.  In case of doubt on either score, about 1 per cent. of cod liver oil may be added to the mash once or twice a week.

The total energy value of the food, in relation to its dry matter content, is of great importance.  For growing and fattening animals and for lactating sows the starch equivalent should be about 75 per cent. of the dry matter, or about 65 per cent. on an air dry basis.  Sucking pigs and those newly weaned should have a rather more concentrated diet—say, a mixed meal with a starch equivalent of perhaps 68.  For pregnant sows and growing gilts a figure of 55 will suffice, this being ordinarily arrived at by feeding a limited amount of meal along with grazing, or with green stuff such as kale, cabbage, clover or roots.

The protein balance should be varied according to the need of the animal.  The young pig (up to the age of about four months) and the nursing sow have high requirements—a ratio of protein equivalent to starch equivalent of about 1:5, or, in other words, about 13 per cent. protein equivalent in the mixture.  Thereafter the protein equivalent may be reduced to about 11½ per cent. and finally, in the later stages of the bacon pig's life, to about 10 per cent.

The following are examples of mixtures suitable for the three groups in a breeding and feeding herd:—

|  | 1<br>Nursing Sows<br>and Weaners<br>per cent. | 2<br>Growing Pigs<br>3 to 5 months<br>per cent. | 3<br>Over 5 months<br>of age<br>per cent. |
|---|---|---|---|
| White-fish meal | 7 | 4 | ... |
| Bean meal | 7 | 9 | 13 |
| Barley meal | 25 | 30 | 35 |
| Flaked maize | 25 | 25 | 20 |
| Weatings (Middlings) | 35 | 30 | 30 |
| Minerals | 1 | 2 | 2 |
| Starch equivalent | 68 | 67 | 67 |
| Protein equivalent | 13 | 11·5 | 10 |

A variety of ready mixed foods are available on the market, either as meals, feed nuts or pellets; and where the requirements for a particular group of pigs are small there is a strong argument, on grounds of convenience, for their use.   Where home grown and purchased foods are used together, the mixture should be balanced.   Sometimes a balanced compound is supplemented by tail corn or potatoes, and the protein balance is then seriously altered.

The creep feeding of sucking pigs is discussed later (see p. 635).

A variation of all meal feeding is to use a mixture like No. 2 above up till the point where consumption reaches 3 or $3\frac{1}{2}$ lb. per day and thereafter to keep the meal ration constant, adding boiled potatoes, sliced fodder beet, or sterilised household swill to appetite.   Since all these materials have a low protein content, the overall nutritive ratio of the combined ration falls progressively as the proportion of meal to other materials decreases.   This scheme is known as the Lehmann system, after the German worker who devised it.   The system is now little practised.

Under many circumstances, it appears that the incorporation of a small amount of antibiotic material—usually aureomycin or procaine penicillin—increases growth rate and the efficiency of food conversion. Typical results are 10 per cent. faster growth and 5 per cent. improvement in conversion.   The main explanation appears to be that the bacterial flora of the digestive tract are controlled and minor digestive upsets are thus prevented, but the precise mode of action is not fully understood at the time of writing.

With regard to the preparation of the food, all hard grains must be either ground or soaked, otherwise they may escape digestion.   Experiments in the feeding of dry meals (as against a thick slop) have shown no constant or important differences, but there is more risk of waste by dry feeding of meals.   Except for the farrowing sow, the slop should be of thick consistency, especially in cold weather.   If dry meal or a thick slop is used, water, if not provided in drinking bowls, should be offered twice daily;  but with a mixture of one part meal to two parts of water (by weight) it is generally found that pigs will drink only during periods of hot weather.   Cooking should not be done except in the case of potatoes (whose starch grains in the raw state tend to escape digestion) or in that of materials of doubtful soundness.   Household swill must, by law, be boiled as a precaution against foot and mouth disease.

Where pigs are intended to be fed to appetite, the dry meal may be offered in self feeders, of which several types are procurable, water being provided from troughs or drinking bowls.   In general, growing pigs are frequently given all that they will eat, and there is little or nothing to be gained by restriction.   On the other hand, breeding gilts and pregnant sows will get much too fat unless the concentrate is restricted;  moreover, it is generally economical to compel them to consume a large proportion of grass, greenstuff or roots.   Again, all but the more extreme types of bacon pigs tend to get too fat to command the best price if, in the last month or two, they are fed *ad lib.*

During the last few weeks of the bacon pig's life the effect of feeding on the quality of the carcass should receive consideration. On the one hand, excessively watery foods—roots, whey or distillery paste—should be fed only in moderate amounts. On the other hand, materials that contain any considerable amount of unsaturated oil should be avoided as likely to produce soft carcass fat. Examples are maize germ meal and, to a less extent, maize itself, rice meal and linseed cake. Fish meals derived from herring, mackerel and other non-white fish impart a taint to the flesh. The best finishing materials are barley, potatoes and beans.

Food consumption is ordinarily reckoned in terms of dry meal, 4lb. of cooked potatoes, or about 5 to 6 lb. of fodder beet, or 8 lb. of swedes being reckoned as 1 lb. of meal equivalent. On this basis a pig of 50 lb. live weight will consume about $2\frac{1}{2}$ lb. of meal (5 per cent. of its weight); one of 100 lb. about $4\frac{1}{2}$ lb.; 150 lb., $5\frac{1}{4}$ lb.; 200 lb., $6\frac{3}{4}$ lb.; 250 lb., $7\frac{1}{2}$ lb. (3 per cent. of the body weight). A pound of meal per month of age is a useful approximation. A common practice in production for Wiltshire bacon, at around 200 lb. live weight, is to feed to appetite until consumption reaches 6 lb. per day, and thereafter to restrict the ration to this amount.

## GENERAL MANAGEMENT

Pregnant sows should have ample opportunity for exercise, preferably in the open air and, in summer, on pasture. Many unsatisfactory litters and many casualties among the young result from sows getting fat and lazy. In summer a rough but rain proof shelter, with access to pasture, can provide for a group of up to twenty. The same shed, with perhaps some additional provision against wind or driving rain, can be used in winter if the land is reasonably dry: otherwise a partially open yard is preferable.

Sows that finish lactation in a seriously reduced condition should have a short period of good feeding before they join the group, otherwise they may be bullied and prevented from getting their full share of food. The requirements of a pregnant sow, for maintenance and the rebuilding of body reserves, are met by about 6 lb. of meal equivalent. Good ordinary pasture or an abundant supply of good greenstuff or roots will meet about half of these requirements, so that the actual allowance of concentrates may be about 3 lb. per day. Indeed, on good clovery pasture satisfactory condition may be restored with 2 lb. of concentrate. For sows on pasture, feed nuts are more convenient and less wasteful than dry meal or slop; these will be fully consumed if scattered thinly over the ground, and all the animals will have the opportunity of getting fair shares. In winter the supplementary foods may be largely potatoes or fodder beet, in which case meal or nuts with a rather high protein content should be used. The allowance of concentrate should be increased to 4 lb. at mid-gestation and to 6 lb. about three weeks before farrowing. If sows are kept indoors during pregnancy, with only limited amounts of green stuff, it may be well to incorporate a trace of iron salts in their food, with the object of ensuring that their young will be born with good reserves of iron and will thus be unlikely to develop anæmia. Five to 10 gm. (say ¼ oz.) per head per day is sufficient.

Sows will ordinarily have been served before they join the group but some may return to service; the group should therefore be looked over daily for signs of œstrus.

Each female, some ten or fourteen days before she is due to pig, should be moved to her farrowing quarters in order that she may be appropriately fed and have time to become accustomed to her surroundings. The udder should be washed with soap and water to get rid of any worm eggs that may be present on the skin. Her ration should be about 7 lb. of meal equivalent, mostly in concentrate form, rather laxative, and moderately rich in protein. Weatings (middlings or sharps), with the addition of perhaps 5 per cent. of fish meal and 5 per cent. of linseed meal, is a popular diet. An alternative is an ordinary sow and weaner mixture, with the addition of perhaps 20 per cent. of bran. Only a small amount of green food should be given. The pen should be kept clean and well littered with straw, and the animal should be occasionally handled and petted.

Milk ordinarily appears in the teats about a day before the onset of birth pains, and, soon after, the sow will be seen to gather litter with her mouth and make a nest. Any long straw should now be removed and replaced with clean cavings or short straw; baby pigs are liable to become entangled in long litter and may fail to reach the teats or be overlaid.

Nobody except the regular attendant should be present at farrowing, and there should be no interference except in the very rare cases where help is clearly needed. In many cases, once parturition has begun and is seen to be proceeding normally, the sow can be left for intervals of an hour or so.

The chief danger is from an excited or nervous sow savaging or even eating her young or treading or lying on them, the risk being greatest with the first litter. If trouble is feared, the piglets, as they are born, may be removed to a warm box or barrel and kept covered up until farrowing has been completed and the dam has settled down. To help in avoiding such risks farrowing crates are sometimes used. Sows that have once killed a litter should not be bred from again. The piglings' mouths should be examined and, if the incisors are very prominent or if the sow is evidently suffering pain during suckling, the teeth should be nipped off with pliers. It is an advantage to leave a light over the farrowing pen for a few nights.

During the first two days after farrowing the sow will take little food and should be offered only a thin slop of middlings or—if she is in very weak condition—some warm milk. Her demands will remain small for a further few days and will generally be met by a daily ration of 6 or 7 lb. meal, fed as a slop, and divided into two feeds. Many breeders withdraw green food entirely during the first week lest the sow's milk cause some digestive disturbance in her young. By the end of the first week the flow of milk will have greatly increased, and it ordinarily continues to rise during the succeeding fortnight. The ration must therefore be raised to 10, 12, or even, in the case of large sows with large litters, 14 lb. of meal per day (in three feeds) with a small allowance of greenstuff. A rough rule is some 2 lb. for the sow and 1 lb. for each piglet, but few sows will consume more than 14 lb. The concentrate should be well balanced (see p. 631).

During the second and third week the attendant should watch for symptoms of anæmia since, even if a sod is placed in the sty daily, it may be neglected. If the skin and, especially, the ears develop a yellowish instead of the natural pinkish tinge, and if there is any tendency to scour, iron salts should be administered daily until the piglets are seen to be eating or nosing at the sod (see p. 628). The easiest means of prevention is to let the piglets out to grass for an hour or two daily.

Farrowing may take place outdoors in folding units and the young pigs then run out with the sow. They do not suffer from iron deficiency under such conditions. If folding units are used for winter farrowing, especially where the land is heavy, it may be preferable to move them on to a concrete base which can be kept reasonably clear of standing water and mud.

Young pigs in their first few weeks are very sensitive to cold; and whatever system of farrowing is adopted, it is necessary to give them a warm, dry bed free from draughts. Artificial heating of part of the farrowing pen, where the young pigs receive their creep food and can lie, is now commonly provided in new or improved farrowing pens.

To ensure continuing rapid growth after the sow's milk yield begins to drop, as it commonly does three weeks after farrowing, the piglets should be induced to eat as soon as may be. They must be encouraged with palatable and nutritious food which, since it must be constantly accessible to them, must be out of reach of the sow. Wet mash, though palatable when fresh, quickly turns sour, and dry meal is apt to be wasted. Thus small nuts or pellets are the best form, and should be rich in protein and minerals and vitamins and low in crude fibre. Some pigmen, if interest does not develop, sprinkle the food with milk. Appetite should develop fast and, by weaning time, consumption should have reached fully 1 lb. per day.

Males not required for breeding should be castrated about the fourth or fifth week of age; if the operation is delayed until near weaning time the animal suffers a double check. Rigs (cryptorchids) should be fed off before they are five months old since, after this time, their flesh develops the strong flavour of boar's meat.   The normal age for weaning is eight weeks.   It is preferable, at weaning time, to remove the sow, rather than piglings, from the farrowing sty.

Regarding the rate of growth, piglings weighing 2 to 3 lb. at birth should reach an average of at least 35 lb. at weaning—unless the litter is very numerous, when the two or three smallest may bring the figure down.   Some New Zealand authorities mention 40 lb. as attainable in practice, but the assumption is that separated milk is available in unlimited amount.   A 35 lb. average is attainable without milk given well selected stock and good management.

After weaning the growth rate, starting at about $\frac{3}{4}$ lb. per day, progressively rises to about $1\frac{1}{2}$ lb. per day at six to seven months (200 lb. live weight).   For a further month or two the rate of gain remains about constant and thereafter declines.   Breeding gilts, which should be kept in growing condition but not fattened, will ordinarily make rather less than three fourths of the weight increases of bacon pigs.   A table of weights for age is given in the Appendix.

The rate of live weight gain and the economy of gain (food consumption per pound live weight increase) are two important considerations. Up to a point the two go together; assuming that the maintenance requirement is constant in relation to body weight, and that surplus nutrients are devoted to growth without fattening, a fast growth rate will be associated with a low total food consumption per pound of live weight gain.   On the other hand, the formation of body fat requires much more food energy than the growth of bone, muscle and vital organs.   It will be obvious that over-fattening is doubly undesirable for, on the one hand, the food cost per pound of carcass will be enhanced, while the carcass will be valued at a lower price.

As indicated earlier different views are held about the size of carcass that can be produced at the lowest cost per pound.   The cost of the weaner per pound of carcass weight will obviously be high, since the cost of maintaining a sow for six months as well as depreciation, must be divided over the litter.   In the early stages after weaning the economy of gain is very high, and it progressively falls with age.   On the other hand, older pigs can consume increasing amounts of relatively cheap food—waste potatoes, fodder beet and swill.   The overall result is that there will often be little difference in costs, per pound of carcass weight, within a range of 200 to 250 lb. live-weight.   Porkers of half this size are substantially more expensive to produce, per unit of carcass weight; one calculation makes the difference about 25 per cent.

With regard to the level of feeding there is general agreement that animals being reared for slaughter should be fed concentrates to appetite— as much as they will clean up in about twenty minutes—until the age of five to six months (by which time the consumption will be about 6 lb. per head per day).   Thereafter, the allowance should be restricted to about

6 or 6½ lb. daily, if the aim is a light bacon pig not too fat. In the early stages full consumption should be encouraged either by providing three meals daily or, alternatively, by feeding twice daily and allowing access to a self feeder. Feeding to appetite after the age of six months will, in many cases, result in an overfat carcass, but if there is a market for such pigs, there are advantages for example in labour saving through *ad lib.* self feeding. The poorest carcasses and the poorest returns for food consumed result from under-feeding in the early stages (which restricts growth and the development of muscle) followed by over-feeding in the latter part of the animal's life, which leads to a large accumulation of expensive and unwanted fat.

In the rearing of breeding gilts the objective is to secure nearly full growth with very little fattening. This can best be achieved by reducing the allowance of concentrates to about three fourths of the amount that would be appropriate to a fattening pig of the same age, and by allowing the animals to satisfy their hunger by grazing, or by consuming such bulky foods as kale, clover and roots to appetite.

The control of diseases and parasites is of prime importance. The most disastrous of the commoner infections is Swine Fever, and unless there is a high degree of isolation from possible sources of infection, vaccination should be carried out as a routine. The incidence of Swine Erysipelas varies much as between districts, and veterinary advice should be sought on the desirability of immunisation. Outbreaks of coughing may be due to virus pneumonia, and veterinary advice should be sought.

Periodic worming is desirable even if there is no obvious sign of infestation, since it is much cheaper to prevent a build-up than to deal with one after it has occurred. The best of known medicaments is sodium fluoride, its only disadvantage being that the dosage must be accurately adjusted to the size of the animals, varying from $\frac{1}{4}$ oz. at weaning time to $\frac{5}{8}$ oz. at maturity.

A watch should be kept for the appearance of lice, which generally first show about the ears. A soapy emulsion of derris, applied to the skin with a brush, will kill the living specimens but not the nits, so that treatment should be carried out twice with an interval of a fortnight.

The droppings should be watched. If the animals are constipated a mild laxative should be administered by way of the food, *e.g.* the addition of some bran may be considered. Scouring may be a symptom of serious disease; on the other hand, it is often due to particular foods—*e.g.* unripe fodder beet.

Outbreaks of fighting may occur, sometimes when lots of well grown animals are reassorted. It may happen that one particular animal is set upon by all its pen mates and be seriously injured or even killed. In general, the introduction of strangers should be avoided; it is rarely practicable to keep each litter separate from start to finish, and weanlings rarely give much trouble. At more advanced age resentment of strangers is much stronger. Sometimes the trouble starts when the pigs outgrow their trough room, and needs in this respect should be borne in mind when the pens are being filled. In large herds a plan, that both economises space and conduces to peace in the herd, is to run the weaners in batches of thirty or forty in yards and, when they are perhaps four months old, to divide the batch into evenly sized small groups for transfer to the fattening pens.

# CHAPTER 25

# POULTRY

THE domestic fowl appears to be descended from *Gallus bankiva*, a species of wild fowl indigenous to that region of Asia comprising Burma, parts of India and Sumatra. By the beginning of the Christian era the birds probably reached Europe, their domestication and spread having been due partly to their value as food producers but also largely because of the sport provided by cock-fighting. Fowls have proved themselves to be particularly adaptable; they have been moulded into a large number of breeds and varieties, each possessing special characteristics.

In order to get a broad view of the management of poultry, it may be helpful to compare the life of the wild bird under natural conditions with that of the modern fowl kept for commercial purposes. The wild Jungle Fowl breeds only once a year, lays a clutch of eggs, broods and incubates the eggs, and looks after the young for as long as is necessary. The young reach sexual maturity at a year old. Moulting takes place once a year or oftener.

Breeds used in poultry farming have been selected so that the short natural laying period has been extended to a period of perhaps ten months, and the natural clutch of a dozen or more eggs has been increased in many cases to over two hundred. To get this high production, birds have been so bred that they seldom go broody and do not pause in laying during winter. In order to reduce the costs of maintaining unproductive birds, modern fowls have been developed to reach sexual maturity and commence laying under six months old. In commercial practice the time of hatching is adjusted so that the young birds lay a large proportion of their eggs during winter, which because it is the unnatural season, is the time of relative scarcity and high prices. But fowls that are producing eggs in the winter season require to be protected by suitable housing and provided with ample and correct food. During winter the production of eggs may be stimulated by providing artificial light.

Birds have also been selected for table production. A recent tendency has been to concentrate on breeds and crosses to produce light weight carcasses ready for the table in ten weeks or so, and at low costs of production.

Poultry farming in its various branches is now a major industry. Its value in Great Britain is one sixth of the total agricultural production and one quarter of that of meat and live stock products. It is a subject not easy to cover in much detail in a chapter. Here, an attempt has been made

to give a broad picture of the industry—some notes on its history and
future, a description of the main sections of poultry farming and a few
references (see p. 655) to assist in the follow up of any particular point.

**Recent Developments.**—The poultry industry was built up gradually
after the 1914-18 war; it had attention focussed on it with the intake of
ex-service men. By 1928-29 the 200 egg breeding hen had become quite
common, although the national average was nowhere near this. As
today so then, the main turnover in money terms lay in egg production.
This section expanded quickly in the early 1930's with the introduction
of laying cages and battery and cage brooding. Coinciding with this
development, there was a rapid rise in problems relating to disease,
mainly of the paralysis type, and in mortality. By the mid 1930's it was
not unusual to have to cull 40-50 per cent. of a flock of point of lay
pullets with paralysis or leg weakness, as it was then known. At that time
it should be remembered advisory services were very limited and the
knowledge of nutrition was much more scanty than it is today. Knowledge of disease was also sketchy, and we lacked the drugs, e.g., sulphona-
mides, which are in such wide use today. Losses under intensive production especially were very heavy.

Table poultry was a specialised business dealing with a luxury trade—
very much a case of a chicken at Christmas and on special occasions; and
the birds were normally killed at greater weights than today. There was
little mechanisation applied in production.

On the marketing side the position was dominated by the widely
fluctuating seasonal price which was a reflection of the fact that most
birds were housed extensively and artificial lighting was not generally
practised. It was common to find mainly March hatched birds which
came into lay in August or September, many of them going into a moult
over the winter; and so in winter there was a shortage of home produced
eggs and a price rise, and consequently a need for more imports. At that
time we produced about 60 per cent. of our consumption of eggs, and
these were marketed in a variety of ways. Imported eggs, notably those
from Denmark and Holland, were as fresh as the home product and were
often marketed more attractively.

The poultry industry then entered the 1939-45 war with major problems
regarding disease (which probably arose from insufficient knowledge
both of disease and nutrition) and with fundamental problems in marketing.
In one way, the emergency lessened both of these evils. On the one hand,
owing to feeding stuff restrictions, flocks were drastically culled, whilst
the more intensive forms of production were reduced. The death rate
became lower and the disease position improved, particularly in regard
to paralysis or leg weakness. On the marketing side problems were
solved simply because demand exceeded supply and eggs being scarce,
presented no problems in marketing. In the same way, the table poultry
industry, whilst declining on a specialised basis, became a lucrative side

line in the absence of other meat products. Laying hens for example, would sell out at well over their rearing cost at the end of the laying year.

There were many depleted flocks at the end of the last war. It was noticeable that the flocks which had increased, were mainly on the larger farms where grain and other feeding stuffs were available. From then onwards the national flock continued to grow, though feeding stuffs rationing continued for some years.

There were three interesting features of the expansion during these years. Some farmers increased their poultry flocks without consideration of capital cost. Others planned expansion without using much capital. We saw agricultural buildings, bullock yards and other outbuildings being converted into temporary straw yard houses, the working assumption being that while production might not reach the optimum, it showed a profit on the relatively low capital cost per bird involved. The third and more recent trend has been towards intensive production in cages, deep litter or on wire floors, with the emphasis on low labour costs and a large number of birds per man—a swing towards automation (Plate 72).

Much attention has also been given to methods of increasing output through genetic improvements and better feeding. This is reflected in increasing output per bird. In 1946 the average production was estimated at 90 eggs; by 1960 this figure had risen to nearly 180 eggs per bird. The supply position had also changed. The pre-war 60 per cent. production of the country's needs had increased to almost 100 per cent.

It was during this interesting period of development that the British Egg Marketing Board was formed.

There were also changes in table poultry production. It soon became apparent that it was not economic to produce the very large table bird. For example, the 10 lb. Christmas chicken could well be costing 4/- in feeding stuffs to put on 1 lb. live weight in the latter stages of feeding. The change, springing partly from the 1946 mission to the United States, was to the so-called broiler, the production of a small 3½ lb. live weight table bird at a low cost. The success of this production method is tending to encourage the wider and more regular use of poultry meat in the general household. The production of these small table chickens may reach 100 million a year at the time of writing. Even that total represents a consumption of only 9 lb. per head. The corresponding figure in the United States is 34 lb.

One trend is common to both egg and poultry producers. The importance of " know-how " and testing work in breeding, and the need for capital for research and development is tending towards large undertakings and the reduction in numbers of the middle-sized operator. The pattern in future may well be a few really large scale organisations, and a great number of small family-labour units carrying a few hundred birds each. Already the need for integration has become apparent alike in the

X

breeding and production sides of the industry, and has led to the formation of public companies of a size undreamt of in earlier days.

The industry may conveniently be considered in the following four sections, each of which is interdependent upon the others to some extent.

**Breeding and Hatching.**—Both the table bird and egg production sides of the industry cover the main operations in breeding and hatching. In recent years the trend has been towards greater specialistaion and away from the dual purpose type of fowl which can produce both layers and table poultry. The machines for incubation, the nutrition problems and disease control are broadly the same for both table and egg production. It is worth noting that the big demands of the broiler industry for hatching eggs have produced an entirely new breeding group which, unlike normal laying birds, is housed almost always intensively. Broiler chicken are almost always bred indoors while birds for egg production are still bred out of doors in some cases. A second difference is that it seems easier to breed birds for table than for laying. This is because table birds are being bred for features, all of which are easily measurable, i.e., body confirmation, weight, feather colour and so on, and improvement in table poultry seems to have made relatively greater strides since its inception. Quite recently however, it has become important to take into account the laying ability of the broiler breeders so that they may produce an ecomonic number of hatching eggs. Here the table producers are running into exactly the same problems that are facing the egg industry; it is relatively easy to get improvement for characteristics that have a high heritability and can be seen or measured, but egg production has a heritability perhaps as low as 5 per cent. This then is a difficult problem not yet solved in terms of the best method or practice. Under present practices, breeding output is about one pullet per breeder per week; in other words, a flock of 500 breeding hens will produce in the region of 500 saleable pullets per week. This is a broad and useful ready reckoner but a minimum only if birds are housed intensively.

**Egg Production.**—In cash turnover this represents the greater part of the industry. It also accounts for the greater part of the sales value to the ancilliary trades, e.g. feeding stuffs, house manufacture and so on, a fact sometimes overlooked in the publicity accorded to the recent emergence of the table poultry trade. The egg production section today is tending to specialise in birds which lay more eggs as a flock, i.e. on a highly productive flock, which lays eggs of good size, although not necessarily in the " specials " grades, and at a lower feed conversion rate than their forebears. At the present time with feed costing around 4d. per lb., it is most important to reduce the number of lb. of feeding stuffs consumed in the laying year, and this is attracting the attention of all major breeders. It seems that the most rapid advances may be made by the use of smaller birds because a smaller bird can lay as many eggs, but it has less body to maintain and, therefore, burns less fuel and uses less food. But this may not be the whole story, for there is evidence that there are productive strains of larger birds which lay eggs at a lower feed conversion. It should also be remembered that while the small bird eats less food, it tends in many cases to produce smaller eggs, and the present market shows a demand for the large egg.

The rise in the average annual production of birds in Great Britain from around 90 eggs in 1946 to about 180 in 1960 seems substantial—doubled output in fourteen years. Yet today this higher output is not recognised as economic. It is probable, on present estimates, that a bird has to produce at least 160 eggs before it has paid all outgoings.

The major present trend then is towards the intensive production of eggs, especially as the bigger units get under way. Popularity in housing swings between the battery and deep litter, and there are good reasons in support of both. Broadly, battery cages are more useful for the individual who is concerned with the optimum efficiency in output—it is possible to handle and cull so much more easily in cages. On the other hand, the large scale deep litter unit appeals very much to the larger commercial man who is concentrating on a reduction in labour charges.

**Table Bird Production.**—This section shows the greatest recent change. Today we see a vast, integrated and most efficient section of the industry, producing in a manner which, at the best, equals any other form of chicken meat production in the world. The output of broiler chicken is now thought to be 100 million a year and plans have been made for a substantial increase in the next five years. It is felt that profitability will drop and this is acknowledged by most major producers. But it is considered that this form of meat production will persist, especially if the rise in the output can be geared to match an increase in consumption.

**Allied Trades.**—The poultry farmer is now very dependent on allied traders in his efforts toward more efficient and cheaper production.

Incubation is in part now out of his hands. In housing and equipment, new designs for buildings and labour-saving appliances appear each year and are of great assistance to him, under conditions of production where their capital cost can be justified.

Great advances have been made in the provision of drugs for disease control. Conditions often now arise where it is better and cheaper to purchase mixed feeding stuffs with or without additions rather than to home mix.

The poultry industry is also becoming more dependent on adequate storage facilities, *e.g.* deep freeze and cold stores for poultry meat.

# THE PRODUCTION OF GROWING STOCK

**The Egg.**—A hen laying 200 eggs per year produces about five or six times her own body weight in eggs. A simple post mortem of a layer would show the ovary with the yolks in various stages of growth. When fully formed and ripe the enclosing sac breaks and the yolk falls into the oviduct. Here layers of thick and thin white are deposited and covered with a shell, the whole process taking between 17 and 21 hours.

The same processes are carried through in the fertile egg, except that after mating the sperm swims up to fertilise the egg towards the top of the oviduct, before the white and shell are added. Fertile eggs may be found in as little as 24 hours after mating and one mating may last up to twenty-one days, but it would be usual to wait only one week after removing the male before regarding the eggs as unfertile. Where males of different breeds or families are being interchanged, ten days should be allowed between the turnover of cocks. As stated earlier it can be reckoned that one mated female will normally produce one pullet chick for sale per week. This may be exceeded under intensive conditions but the figure is useful as a safe estimate on which to base forward sales.

**Intensive v. Extensive mating.**—Intensive mating or breeding has become more common in recent years and there are two basic reasons for this. It is possible to obtain a higher egg production and, therefore, a higher chick output per group of females. The birds are less affected by outside weather conditions; and it is thought with some justification that where birds are going to live in an intensive environment it is well to breed them within such an environment. But there are a few points worth noting. Intensively housed birds are very susceptible to infection through the introduction of outside stock, *e.g.* a breeding cockerel may have a slight cold and where he is added to birds housed extensively with plenty of air, running in and out in all weathers, it is not likely that this will affect the layers. But, if a male bird with a slight cold, perhaps one not noticeable, is introduced to an intensively kept flock, the result could prove serious, giving a drop in production and general unthriftiness. It follows that the best method is normally to introduce the male birds at the time when the females are housed, *i.e.* they should be reared under similar conditions and housed together. There is still something to be said in favour of extensive breeding stock, especially where lighting is not to be used, because many birds in this country are still housed extensively or semi-extensively. It may be possible to so condition a flock that their progeny will not perform well unless they are given lights and it is still argued that the extensive bird is more healthy than the intensive one— an extremely debatable point with little scientific background.

By tradition we mate 10 or 12 heavy breed females and 15 light breed females to one male. In recent years these numbers have been increased. The tendency is to undermate rather than to overmate, and the former may do more harm. A useful ratio for both heavies and lights is 1 to 15. Perhaps the more important point is the conditions under which the birds are mated. There are advantages in arranging troughs, hurdles, nests and so on behind which mating may be done in some privacy and where th male, who is perhaps not the toughest in the group, can work without being disturbed by his seniors.

The choice of system in brief should be governed by the type of bird to be bred, the market for the product of the mating and the time of year when the mating takes place.

**Incubation.**—Incubation has of late become a specialised side of poultry farming. The tendency is towards incubation in large units, and for the sale of day old chicks from these centres to the many customers, who wish them for rearing. Farm incubation has indeed little place for the smaller egg producer. The practice would involve the provision of suitable incubation and rearing equipment at a considerable capital cost. It is certainly not worth spending capital on such equipment unless a high annual output in the form of sales is likely to be realised; it would be better instead for a producer to devote capital to the furtherance of egg or table production.

Machines are made in two types, with natural or forced draught, and range in capacity from some 50 to 15,000 eggs. Thus all requirements can be met in terms of size and throughput and operations are relatively simple.

**Rearing.**—The main object is to provide the right conditions for the production of growth, with the minimum of labour and capital. To do so, demands quite a lot of ingenuity and planning.

Let us first look at feed. Future layers or table birds will weigh about two pounds when eight weeks old. Thus the chick, which is just under two ounces when a day old, multiplies its weight sixteen times in eight weeks. (At this rate an average human child would weigh eight stones at two months old.) Chickens then are extremely fast growing and demand a high intake of the right type of feed. It is necessary to provide high quality, balanced and palatable food and give ample opportunity for eating, *i.e.* plenty of trough space (see p. 650). Any restriction on feed space creates competition and the big chicks get bigger and the small ones lose ground in the hustle that arises. Lack of feed space can be the greatest cause of ragged or irregular growth in a flock. Adequate light is also important.

Chicks require some grit, insoluble grit, for grinding—the general tendency is usually to provide too much. If a young chick with a high food requirement is given the opportunity to eat a lot of grit, it will often do so, thus loading its gut with unnecessary material and restricting the intake and throughput of nourishment. The best rule is to make up the total requirements for a week and to feed a quantity which the chicks will clear up in about half an hour.

It is now possible to add a number of vitamins and of drugs to assist in growth promotion and disease control. It is a useful general rule not to add anything unless it is actually wanted. It is preferable to keep drugs in hand as a control measure rather than to use them as a continuous precaution, and it is cheaper.  Additives generally are no substitute for intelligent, sound husbandry, and the aim should be prevention and where possible, the acquirement of a natural immunity, with drugs always in reserve as a control measure.  But there are conditions and environments where this general advice would not be applicable.  For example, in the intensive rearing of broilers, to be killed at an early age, the aim would be disease prevention.  Here, good husbandry might control the onset of a disease such as coccidiosis so well that although the chicks had the disease, mortality was very light.  But even a minor outbreak of disease under such an intensive system would check growth and be most serious to the owner.  This, therefore, would be a case where additives would be used from the start to try and prevent outbreaks.

Intensive rearing is now estimated to be cheaper than extensive rearing, chiefly because of high labour costs.  But this depends much on the lay out of the enterprise and how the work involved fits in with the general work organisation of the farm in question.  It is possible for one girl to rear up to 3,000 birds in movable folds; this is comparable with the labour requirements of many intensive houses.  The product of the extensive rearing system is still more readily sold as a layer.

There is an incredible range of variation between intensive and extensive rearing.  For example, rearing can begin in wired tier brooders for three weeks and then be carried on outside in hayboxes, or may be done inside on floor brooders for six to eight weeks and then the birds may be put in arks or range shelters.  It is especially important on a farm to integrate the chosen system with the general work of the farm and with the ultimate housing of the birds as laying stock.  Care should be taken not to adopt too complicated a system.  It is easy in theory to plan the movement of birds from one unit to another, but in practice this may work out both laborious and too expensive.

## THE LAYER

There is a great variation in the management of layers and in the different types of housing available.  Let us look at some of the considerations in making a choice.

**Extensive Systems.**—There are two main systems.  The slatted floor house is generally some 8ft. by 6 ft. on skids or wheels and is capable of being towed to different parts of the farm.  Birds are each allowed about $\frac{3}{4}$ sq. ft. floor.  The units generally run in house loadings of 70 and the flock to 1,000 birds or more.  This system is better on good pasture, and bulk movement at least once a month is necessary in order to avoid fouling and soiling the grassland.  Provision for cleaning the dropping boards and removing manure is essential.  It is a system employing a cheap form of housing and one that has some value in grassland improvement.  The houses are difficult to light and winter egg production is not always satisfactory. This type of unit is becoming superceded under modern conditions, except where it is used for a breeding flock on a small farm unit with family labour.

A second system is the movable fold. The fold is some 20 ft. by 5 ft. and houses 20 to 30 laying hens. The essential feature of the system is that the folds are moved daily, apart from weekends, and the birds thus cover the whole of the available grassland leaving it well manured and the grass well aerated and scratched. It is possible under this system for an operator to attend to up to 3,000 birds if he is serviced, *i.e.* receives weekly deliveries of food, and water is readily available. The fold is relatively a low cost unit and fits in well on the poorer type of soil where arable crops are grown with a short grassland break. But again it fails in respect of egg production in inclement weather. The method is not now favoured and is tending to die out in favour of more intensive housing.

**The semi-intensive house.**—This is a fixed house about 30 ft. by 12 ft. and carrying 1-2,000 layers. The house does not move but the layers have a free range over the surrounding land. The system has been used a great deal in the past on small 5 to 20 acre holdings. It involves the use of much wire netting and does not permit grassland control; the cost of keeping the grassland cut is quite an item. A considerable amount of walking or travelling time for the attendant is also involved, and this is not economical. Perhaps the best commercial use of such a unit may be on small hilly 50 to 100 acre farms where the house is sited in the corner or sometimes in the centre of a field and left empty or unused when the particular field is under cultivation. This system is losing favour on the specialist holding, and finds favour only as a low efficiency unit where family labour is available.

**Laying Cages** (Plate 73).—Birds are housed three tiers high in single or double bird cages, back to back. This relatively old system still finds favour with many today in terms of economy of production. Walking time is reduced to a minimum and it is possible for one man to look after up to 5,000 birds, depending upon the degree of mechanisation built into the cages. Obviously with such units special attention must be paid to hygiene and ventilation. The capital cost is greater than with other systems. It is necessary to provide both cages for the birds and a house for the cages, and the cost per bird is slightly higher than is normal for a deep litter unit. But the system finds favour with many and is specially suited to the man who is striving for the best return from limited labour and is concentrating upon maximum efficiency per cage. It is relatively easy in this system to spot birds which are not pulling their weight and to remove them and cash them for table; and so though labour costs may be higher than in modern deep litter units, the efficiency is greater because it is possible to keep a much more individual eye upon the birds and thus remove any passengers. It is the ultimate cost per dozen eggs that is important.

**Deep Litter.**—This can be the cheapest system in respect of labour costs. It is possible under ideal lay outs for one man to look after up to 10,000 birds, *e.g.* where the unit is so designed that feed is delivered in bulk and distributed by machine; and the eggs can be collected, packed and cleaned in a central egg store within the building itself, thus avoiding labour handling charges. As the labour costs per bird are reduced through increasing the number of birds per man there is a real risk of loss of efficiency. For example, let us compare culling in battery cages and deep litter. In cages it is relatively easy to remove non-profitable birds. It is known precisely what food is costing and if a bird is not laying sufficient eggs to more than cover these costs, it can be removed. On the other hand, it is far from easy to cull deep litter birds. There are the problems of handling up to 5,000 birds in a house and of determining not only whether a bird is laying but whether it is laying profitably—a decision which is difficult even to those of long experience. There is little doubt that in many cases efficiency declines through the retention of numbers of birds with low production. Despite this drawback, deep litter units have become popular and undoubtedly will remain so because such large numbers of birds can be handled by one man.

**Feeding for Production.**—The method to be adopted depends largely on the system of housing and management, and the intensity of production. On free range the method of wet mash and grain is still sometimes used, though the labour involved with wet mash is curtailing its use. Intensively, all mash or all pellets or a combination of both is the normal practice. Feeding may be *ad lib.* or on a controlled quantity basis.

There is a trend towards the wider use of pellets, which permit of a constant qualitative control of food. Grain balancers are also in general use. Here, the aim is to provide a supplement with extra protein to balance the lower protein content of the grain. Whatever the method, if high production is the aim, the bulk and quality of the total feed must be such that the bird can eat sufficient to cover the needs of maintenance and production. If lower production only is required then birds can be allowed to balance their own diet. But then the level of production may fall short of what the owner thinks desirable.

There is a wide choice of foods and of compounds suitable for poultry feeding. Typical rations are given as a guide to the making up and mixing of suitable foods for different classes of poultry; and some notes are added about possible substitutes, rates of food and water consumption and trough requirements.

Grit is required in two forms:—

(*a*) insoluble for grinding—small gravel and flint grit.
(*b*) soluble for the production of egg shells and a supply of lime— oyster shell or limestone.

When very small quantities of certain ingredients are used, they

PLATE 72

*I. W. Rhys*

*A.* Fore Loader removing Litter

*I. W. Rhys*

*B.* Elevator removing Litter from Breeding Pens

PLATE 73
SINGLE BIRD CAGE LAYING UNIT

PLATE 74

B. TURKEY—DIMPLED BRONZE

A. TURKEY—BROAD WHITE

W. A. Motley

PLATE 75

AN EXPERIMENTAL GROUP OF
BROILER CHICKENS UNDER INFRA
RED HEATING

should be thoroughly mixed together with a small part of the ration before being added to the bulk. If Cod-liver oil is used it should be pre-mixed with a small quantity of cereal.

**The chick ration** is designed for normal rearing for the first 6-8 weeks and is suitable under intensive or extensive conditions. A small corn feed may be given daily from the age of 3-4 weeks, but should not form a major part of the daily ration until the chicks are 7-8 weeks old.

### POULTRY RATIONS

*Parts by weight*

| Ingredients | Chick Ration | Growers Ration | Layers A | Layers B | Breeders A | Breeders B | Broilers A | Broilers B | Turkey Starter | Turkey Grower | Turkey Breeder |
|---|---|---|---|---|---|---|---|---|---|---|---|
| Wheat | 25 | 30 | 25 | 25 | 25 | 25 | 38 | 45 | 25 | 20 | 25 |
| Oats | 25 | 30 | 25 | 25 | 25 | 25 | 10 | 15 | 25 | 35 | 25 |
| Barley | 25 | 30 | 25 | 25 | 25 | 25 | 15 | 15 | 25 | 20 | 25 |
| Grass-meal | 5 | 5 | 5 | 5 | 5 | 5 | 5 | 5 | 5 | 5 | 5 |
| Fish Meal 60 per cent. | 9 | 7 | 5 | 5 | 5 | 5 | 10 | 5 | 10 | 5 | 5 |
| Meat and Bone Meal 46 per cent. | — | — | 5 | 5 | 5 | 5 | — | — | — | — | 5 |
| Decorticated Earth-nut Cake Meal | 5 | — | 5 | 10 | 5 | 10 | 15 | 10 | 10 | 10 | 5 |
| Dried Skim Milk | 2 | — | — | — | — | — | 2 | — | 2 | — | — |
| Unextracted Yeast | 2 | — | — | — | — | — | 3 | 3 | 3 | 2 | — |
| Limestone Flour | 1 | 1 | 1 | 1 | 1 | 1 | — | 1 | 1 | 1 | 1 |
| Steamed bone flour | 1 | — | 1 | 2 | 1 | 2 | 1 | 1 | 2 | 3 | 1 |
| Manganesed Salt | ½ | — | ½ | 1 | ½ | 1 | ½ | ½ | ½ | ½ | ½ |
| *Additional Ingredients* | | | | | | | | | | | |
| Vitamin D I.u's per lb. | 150 | 150 | 400 | 600 | 400 | 600 | 400 | 400 | 600 | 600 | 600 |
| Riboflavin mg. per lb. | — | — | — | — | 1 | 1 | ·5 | ·5 | ·5 | ·5 | 1 |
| Pantothentic Acid mg. per lb. | — | — | — | — | — | — | — | — | — | — | 5 |

**The growers ration** is designed for use on range or confined grass runs. It is designed to be fed fifty-fifty with corn. Where free range on good short grass ley is available delete grass meal, vitamin D, and reduce the fish meal to 5 per cent.

Two **layers rations** are shown. They are basically the same, but A is designed to be fed as " all mash " and B to be fed with a 2 oz. evening feed of corn. Both rations are balanced for intensive production.

Here again two **breeders rations** are also shown, A as an " all mash " and B where 2 oz. of corn per bird is fed. This ration is designed to cover the production of hatching eggs, and for this purpose should be fed at least one month before eggs are taken for hatching.

**The turkey starter ration** is designed to carry turkey chicks intensively for the first 8 weeks.

**The turkey grower ration** is designed for intensive use. Where birds are on good grass range, a simpler ration can be fed from 10 weeks onwards, and the addition of 7 per cent. white fish meal to ground cereals will provide for satisfactory growth.

**The turkey breeder ration** is designed for the production of hatching eggs under intensive conditions.

The following notes indicate the possibilities of the substitution of different feedstuffs.

On an energy basis wheat offal is worth only 80 per cent. of wheat or barley, *i.e.* 10 parts wheat offal are needed to replace 8 parts wheat or barley. If wheat offal is used up to say 15 per cent. of the ration, it should be of first-rate quality and preferably from a " low extraction " flour.

Decorticated earth nut cake meal can be replaced by either extracted soya bean meal or sunflower seed oil meal without materially affecting the protein or amino acid content of the ration. Pea or bean meal or maize gluten feed up to 10 per cent. of the ration can be used but their protein value is only half of the three vegetable proteins mentioned above and an adjustment will therefore be needed. It is generally the practice to use at least one third of the total protein from animal origin.

**Milk products.**—Separated milk to drink *ad lib*. will replace the yeast and/or dried skim milk, and 5 per cent. fish meal in the chick ration. Separated milk can also be used to provide the protein requirements of laying birds under some conditions.

Grass meal is fed as a carotene or vitamin A supplement. A high carotene quality meal of about 14 per cent. protein is satisfactory. It should have a good colour and a declared carotene content.

**Grinding.**—A $\frac{1}{8}$th sieve with a hammer mill is normally satisfactory. The meals should be coarsely ground, as fine floury meal will blow away and tends to stick to the beak and clog the nostrils. Where a high wheat content is used, *e.g.* the broiler ration, this becomes especially important, and in general, the softer non-milling wheats are much more suitable.

As a rough guide, 100 chicks to 8 weeks will consume about 5 cwt. of food, 100 pullets reared to 6 months will require approximately 25-30 cwt. and 100 layers will require 5 tons per year.

Ample trough space is needed especially with mash feeding. The following figures give a rough guide per 100.

**Adults:**

    20 ft. trough space (double sided) for all mash.

    15 ft.  ,,    ,,  ( ,,    ,,  ) for mash and grain.

**Chicks:**

    1-2 weeks    10 ft.

    3-8 weeks    20 ft.

    **after** 8 weeks  25-30 ft.

Water consumption per 100 birds will be roughly as follows:—

**Chicks:**

| | | |
|---|---|---|
| 1-2 weeks | 4 quarts daily | |
| 3-6 weeks | 7 ,, | ,, |
| 7-18 weeks | 12 ,, | ,, |

Adults at point of lay 3-4 gallons daily increasing to 6 or 7 gallons daily at 60 per cent. production.

Two or more waterers are better than one, especially with large numbers.

Do not use galvanised containers for liquid skim milk.

**Hygiene.**—In a general consideration of hygiene a line must be drawn between an ultra clean and controlled environment that produces birds liable to succumb to adverse stresses or exposures or, on the other hand, an environment that by reasonable exposure enables birds to create their own immunity and to resist disease. This is a major problem for the man who is producing poultry for sale. It would seem that in future much more attention is likely to be given to breeding and rearing for differing conditions of management. With broiler production for example, birds are only kept for a relatively short period, and the objective is to make the maximum use of additives and preventive drugs to obtain the best and most economical production. For birds required to face more rigorous conditions and to live longer it is probably best that they should be reared under hardier conditions, so that there should be no sudden break in their growth.

## PRODUCTION FOR TABLE

Here we are concerned with geese, ducks, turkeys and chicken.

**Geese.**—These birds contribute only a very small fraction to the poultry output. They are profitable when reared in relatively small numbers, with little or no labour, and where good grass together with homegrown " seconds " are available. Geese are best disposed of around the traditional September market as " green geese ", for with good pasture they may be sold in good condition with little additional feeding. An alternative market for geese is Christmas, but such birds take a large amount of feed, if they are to be well finished. On most holdings there will normally be some grazing, but from October to February even on good grass, geese, although fit and healthy, will be in a lean condition. If birds are required in fat condition during winter then they must be well fed and this extra feeding may not be economic. On the other hand, the September market finds the birds in naturally good condition before the lean period of the winter begins.

**Ducks.**—Like geese, ducks are normally kept in this country in small lots, but a few large table units do exist. In Lancashire and Norfolk the larger units often work on a contract basis for large scale packers who sell a branded product. The more common table bird is based upon the Aylesbury and its crosses, with which extremely good growth rates are possible. The birds are finished for killing around eight weeks old and will produce a good feed conversion on relatively poor quality feed stuffs. It is important to market at around this eight weeks stage as the birds grow a further set of feather shortly afterwards; this results in deterioration of the carcass, poorer feed conversion and increase in costs.

**Turkeys.** (Plate 74)—Great changes have taken place in the turkey side of the poultry industry in the last twenty years. The turkey hen laying under the hedge has been replaced by an artificially lit flock supplying incubators; while the old fiction that the turkey is a delicate and difficult bird to rear has successfully been exploded. Factors that have enabled these great changes to take place are improved nutrition, the use of lighting to get hatching eggs at the time required and the selection for growth and meat carrying characteristics. In this period also new knowledge on cold storage has become available and marketing techniques have been much improved. Turkeys now can be killed and stored in prime condition, long before Christmas; and turkey is available for the consumer all the year round.

Three main changes have improved production and revolutionised turkey management. Firstly the nutritional requirements of the turkey have been investigated more thoroughly and understood, and the use of synthetic vitamin additives with modern diets has assisted in increasing egg production and in improving the hatchibility of the eggs and the health of the young birds.

The turkey hen had two faults in the past. On the one hand she did not produce a large enough number of eggs and upon the other, she tended to produce those eggs at a time to suit herself, only in summer. This meant that round the year production was difficult, and the summer egg produced far too large a bird at Christmas for the modern market. Through selection and the use of light it has been possible to effect considerable improvements. The turkey hen has been selected for increased egg production in the same way as for poultry, *i.e.* using trapnesting together with individual family and flock recording; and through lighting it is now possible to produce the 100 eggs, which the turkey hen normally lays, at the time of year to suit the breeder and his customers. Lighting does not necessarily increase egg production but assists in obtaining the eggs at a time when the breeder requires them. The turkey hen should be lit about four weeks before the eggs are required and the stag, or breeding male, should receive lighting about 8 weeks before the eggs are required. This helps sexual development in both the male and the female, and brings them to the same stage of development for mating.

In the same period we have seen major forward steps in disease control.

These have taken two forms; on the one hand blood testing has enabled the carrier to be eliminated from the breeding flock; and antibiotics and drugs have been helpful both in the control of disease and in increasing growth rate.

**Table Chicken** (Plate 75).—These birds, killing at between 3 and 4 lb. at 10-12 weeks of age, are offered at a competitive price with meat. The co-operation of large retailers has helped to make this production possible. It is quite common now to find broilers, graded as to size and quality offered, clean and attractive, in the big multiple stores.

When these chickens were first introduced they were reared in lots of 1,000, but the size of the lots rapidly increased, and today it is common to find 5,000 as the smallest unit. It is the usual practice to allow two to three weeks between batches for the cleaning out of the house.

The requirements of this special trade have produced many problems especially with regard to feed conversion and the control of disease. Over the past ten years these have largely been solved. The feed conversion ratio has been reduced whilst disease is now well controlled by extremely good hygiene and the use of drugs and additives. The production of these chickens in this way has called for skills not common in the older type of poultry farmer. Management has now to plan a constant through-put, control it with the minimum of labour, use all mechanical devices and always keep an eye on the end product and marketing trends. It must always be willing to try new ideas and at the same time use them so as not to upset the output which has already been sold weeks ahead. The labour actually working on the job need not necessarily have had a poultry training, in fact, many think they were better without it. The job is one of strict routine, quiet movement and accurate observation. In fact, it is one which a really skilled poultryman of the old school would probably find most distasteful.

It is within this section of the industry that we have seen one of the most interesting developments in this country in recent agricultural history. Here, a group of producers is combining together for two main reasons. The first is to make sure of a constant weekly output. For example, twelve people each with a 5,000 bird house could produce 5,000 birds per week, *i.e.* they deliver their output to a packing station in rotation. As an extension of this we find a group of people owning or acquiring its own packing station and putting its own brand name on the market. The second common interest concerns finance. Here, the group is interested in obtaining the maximum price for its product and also such financial advantages as arise from group buying of all its many requisites. Thus it would not be uncommon to find a group buying chicks, feeding stuffs, appliances, houses and even obtaining credit from the same source. The advantages arising from such financial discounts are pooled and shared out to members in a variety of ways. The system certainly seems to work and to be here to stay. Again, with a group it is possible to employ a type of skilled technician which the average operator working on his own could not afford to employ. Amalgamations of such groups could well result in a few really big organisations handling the whole of the broiler trade in the country.

## PRESENT TRENDS

Food represents about 60 per cent. of the cost of producing eggs and table poultry; and so there is a continuing search for means by which food conversion rates can be improved and the intensity of production increased. In the past there has been a good deal of wastage in feeding and many new types of equipment have been devised to assist in reducing this waste.

Poultry farming has become a specialised branch of farming, and is now being regarded as a business rather than a side-line of general farming. Many systematic analyses are being made of the inputs and outputs of differing systems of poultry farming. The preparation of budgets and the analyses of accounts are accepted as a necessity for the specialist unit to ensure that it is being run on efficient lines; and preliminary budgeting is clearly of importance before a new unit is set up. Recording is also necessary to check up on performance. Recently the Agricultural Economic Departments of many of our Universities have been giving rather more attention to poultry costing, and there is now available much useful financial information to guide both the established poultry farmer and the would-be entrant to the industry.

Capital requirements vary widely with the system adopted, i.e. whether intensive or extensive. Labour saving devices are in keen demand, and there is often now a conflict as to how far labour can be saved and production intensified without running into serious trouble through a breakdown in the health of the birds or so undermining their stamina that production tends to fall.

One or two examples are given here to illustrate present thoughts on future development. Is the present type of laying cage satisfactory? Could it be smaller and so cheaper? Would there be a serious loss in efficiency if cages were constructed to hold three, four or five birds? Possible modifications in cage construction would of course lead to other alterations, if the plant were to be as fully automatic as possible. The decision in each individual case will depend largely on the amount and quality of labour available and the degree of intensity of production which it is estimated will pay best.

The tendency in deep litter houses is to reduce the area per bird to between one and two feet, including a pit. The pit would be constructed to take the greater part of the droppings and the food and water troughs would be carried over the pit.

The complete wire floor is also being used more commonly with a view to reducing labour. Here, it is important to ensure that ventilation is adequate and there is reasonable control of humidity.

It may be that in the future intensive houses will be windowless with a controlled environment and that birds will be reared in these units from day olds and remain there for the rest of their economic lives. The unit may then consist of several wings with a central food and egg handling store. This type of layout would provide ease in cleaning and enable a fresh lot of birds to be brought in without disturbance to the remainder of the flock. There would be an economic advantage in that the period of maximum egg prices tends to move a little each year and if for example, one third of the flock was hatched in October, one in January and one in April, then the producer could have two thirds of his flock in good lay at any stated period; and the division into sub-units would enable him to retain part of his flock for another four to six weeks if the circumstances demanded it.

**References.**—More detailed information on certain aspects of poultry farming is available in the following bulletins of the Ministry of Agriculture, Fisheries and Food.

| Number of Bulletin | Subject |
| --- | --- |
| 148 | Incubation and Hatching Practice |
| 152 | Methods of Intensive Poultry Management |
| 146 | Poultry Breeding |
| 174 | Poultry Nutrition |
| 8 | Poultry on the General Farm |
| 54 | Rearing of Chickens |
| 168 | Table Chickens |
| 67 | Turkeys |
| 70 | Ducks and Geese |

# PART 4

# FARM ORGANISATION AND MANAGEMENT

# CHAPTER 26

# LAND AND ITS EQUIPMENT

THOSE who choose farming as a vocation do so for various reasons. To make a living or a financial profit is very often the chief motive, but it is rarely the only one. Many find satisfactions in farming that cannot be measured in terms of money or material things. In this book, however, we are concerned not with farming as a complete way of life but only with its technical and business aspects.

It has often been pointed out that technical skill in the production of crops and live stock products does not of itself ensure financial success in farming. Such success depends also upon competence in the organisation and management of the farm as an integrated business. Such competence derives partly from personal qualities—for example, the gift of inspiring the confidence and winning the co-operation of the farm staff and the inborn powers of judgment that are required in weighing alternative plans and reaching sound decisions. But it is also true that management, to be successful, must be based upon economic, and business principles, and it is these principles that form the subject matter of this section.

Something must first be said about the various particular objectives that farmers, according to their varying circumstances, may have in mind, and about the origins and development of our present day farming systems in this country.

Agriculture, which dates from early neolithic times, was originally adopted as a more reliable way of securing the necessities of life than the older economy which was based on hunting, fishing and the collecting of seeds and roots. The early cultivating peoples grew such plants as cereals, pulses, roots and other vegetables for food, and cultivated flax, cotton or some other fibre plant for clothing. They built their huts out of the most easily available materials, thatching them in many cases with cereal straw. They made household utensils out of flint or other minerals, wood and moulded clay. The early stockmen lived on meat, milk and various milk products. They used for clothing and for tents either skins or else felted or woven cloths made of wool or hair. The early mixed farmers, by a combination of crop and animal husbandry, achieved a more varied diet, eased their burden of work by harnessing cattle to their implements, and in some cases at least, discovered in animal manure a means of maintaining the fertility of the soil. The first farmer immigrants into Britain, who arrived about 4500 years ago, possessed cattle and sheep, and cultivated barley, wheat, beans and flax.

These various forms of ancient subsistence farming were common in many parts of the world until comparatively recent times, and they survive in places at the present day.

The next stage was the emergence in each little community of a relatively small class of specialist craftsmen—the smith, the potter and the weaver and, later on, the joiner or builder, the miller, the shoemaker and others. In such communities each craftsman provides some particular service and is paid in kind—largely in food. Generally there is a very limited amount of long distance trade, restricted to such metals or other necessary raw materials as are not locally available.

This form of economy, in which the village or other small community is substantially self supporting, prevailed in most countries throughout mediæval times, and it persists to-day, with only minor modifications, over large parts of India, China and other countries. Normally, under such conditions, about four out of every five families devote the major part of their energies to food production, though the farmers' womenfolk spin, collect and prepare fuel and brew. Conversely it is usual for the specialist craftsman and his family to cultivate a small piece of land and produce part of their food. In other words, the separation between farming and manufacture is only partial.

The early development of commercial farming—the production of food for sale—was associated with the development of cities. Thus the concentration of a large urban population in Rome created a market for large quantities of agricultural produce, and led to the setting up of commercial farms producing wheat and olive oil for cash sale. Again, so far as this country is concerned, the earliest cash farmers were concerned with the feeding of London, which long remained the only large town. Originally London's citizens, like those of other towns until much later times, combined farming with other concerns, cultivating pieces of land outside the city walls and keeping cows that daily walked out to near-by pastures. But as London grew, the adjacent lands came to be needed for the production of perishables, like vegetables and milk, so that non-perishable foods had to be drawn from farther afield. By the seventeenth century, butter was being brought by pack horse from the Vale of Aylesbury and Suffolk. Cheese, produced in the Wiltshire Vale, was taken overland to the Upper Thames and thence to London by barge—some even came from Cheshire by sea. Wheat and malt were brought by coastal shipping from East Anglian and south coast ports, and also by barge from the Upper Thames Valley. Fat stock was driven on foot, in summer and autumn, from as far as Norfolk and Leicestershire. By this time, therefor, some farmers in many parts of the country were looking more and more to a distant market for a cash income, were specialising in the particular crops or live stock products that would procure them the largest cash incomes, and were thinking less and less of their land as the direct source of consumption goods for their families. But these were still a small proportion of the whole.

Another early development of business farming, with more pronounced specialisation, was the cause of a great popular outcry in Tudor times. This was the replacement of the old system of subsistence farming by a cash economy based on the production of wool for export. The object was to acquire foreign exchange for the purchase of imports—chiefly luxury goods like silks, other fine textiles, wines and spices. The main grounds of the popular complaint was not the diversion of land from food production, for it seems that agricultural improvement, at the time in question, was more than keeping pace with the slow growth of population. The serious concern was over the wholesale depopulation of the areas concerned. These areas were largely the chalk and limestone uplands of the south eastern half of England, though the sheep business was found elsewhere—for instance, the monks of the great Border abbeys had extensive sheep farms in the Cheviot Hills. This type of farming, like farming for the London market, was restricted to relatively small parts of the country, but it was of great importance as the basis of overseas trade. Up till the fifteenth century the chief export was unmanufactured wool, but as time went on, most of the home produce was worked up by cottage spinners and village weavers into finished cloth.

The widespread changes that constitute the industrial and agricultural revolutions had gained considerable momentum by 1760 and continued for the greater part of the following century. One impelling reason for the reorganisation of farming was the unprecedented increase in population, arising out of the fact that the death rate, especially among children, had been markedly reduced through the progress of medical science. The population of Great Britain roughly trebled in the hundred years, and since there was still no source of substantial food imports, more intensive cultivation of the country's soil was imperative. The period was one of large scale reclamations of moor, marsh and forest. Also, with the objects of higher production and improved efficiency, the old open field manors of eastern England and the Midlands, with their scattered strips of tillage land and their very unproductive commons, were replanned, enclosed and converted into farming units of a size that would admit of economic production. A similar process occurred on the old townships of lowland Scotland. New crops—potatoes, roots and clover—were introduced; phosphate, derived from bones and coprolites, was applied with astonishing effect; towards the middle of the nineteenth century the invention of the drain tile was exploited on an immense scale on the heavier and wetter lands; nitrogen fertilizers such as guano, Chilean nitrate and sulphate of ammonia were introduced about the same time. All these efforts were indeed not enough for full success. There was serious dearth in the eighteen-forties, but the achievement was immense.

The other great change of the times was the concentration of manu-factures with the object of utilising water and, later on, steam power, and otherwise exploiting mass production methods. Spinning and weaving, which had formerly been carried on in cottages in the agricultural districts, moved to the Yorkshire dales and other regions where water power was available, and where, in many cases, the adjoining land was poor. Iron smelting—formerly carried on in small units in forest country—moved, as coke replaced charcoal, to the coalfields. The introduction of the steam engine greatly increased the demand for coal, with a consequent increase in the number and size of mining villages. Thus a large proportion of the people ceased to have any concern with food production, while the remainder gave up their industrial activities and concentrated on agriculture. Hard roads, canals and later railways were built to carry the vastly increased amount of long distance traffic between farm and city.

It was inevitable, under these circumstances, that little farms and small-holdings should have been thrown together to make big farms; the old small holders, having formerly lived partly by cottage industries, had not enough land to provide a living by farming alone. It was natural, too, that the old system of farming, producing a bit of everything should give way to more specialised forms. Thus Cheshire, Ayrshire and the Somerset Vale took more and more to cheesemaking; the heavy land farmers of Essex and Suffolk specialised in wheat; the light arable farms of the Eastern counties concentrated on grain and winter meat. Similarly, Kent expanded her orchards, and Aberdeenshire, especially after the invention of steamships, set out to supply the London demand for choice quality beef. The Scottish mountains specialised—probably over-specialised—in sheep.

But the changes were not everywhere so marked or so complete. Devon and Cornwall were already, before the revolution, laid out in small farms of enclosed fields, and they were too far from the new manufacturing regions to attract the attention of the new type of business farmer. In many Midland areas the enclosure and redistribution of the village lands was done in a half hearted fashion, so that many farms to-day consist of separate bits and pieces. In Wales there was no wholesale change such as occurred in the West Highlands of Scotland; the holdings remained small and the mountain sheep walks, continued, in many cases, to be held in common: part time holdings persisted in Yorkshire, Lancashire and elsewhere in the vicinity of the scattered wool and cotton mills.

Another fact is that specialisation to the point of monoculture—the concentration upon a single crop—has never developed on any consider-able scale in this country. This has proved a wise limitation, for the general experience of such systems—*e.g.* " bonanza " wheat farming in western North America, cotton farming in the southern United States, sugar cane growing in some of the West Indies—has shown that one-crop farming is rarely successful in the long run.   In some cases the breakdown has resulted from soil erosion or exhaustion, in others from epidemic plant disease; sometimes from a fall in demand for the single commodity produced, and sometimes through a combination of these and other factors.    Apart from the advantage of producing more than one cash product, it has often proved wise to retain an element of subsistence farming alongside the commercial enterprises.   Thus even the farmer who relies mainly on sugar beet, grain and beef for his money income may well provide directly his own family's needs in the way of milk, eggs, poultry, bacon, potatoes and other vegetables.   The best balance between the two types of production depends on circumstances; in general, subsistence production is important only on small farms that produce one or two commodities for sale and employ little or no paid labour.

Up till the thirties of last century this country remained substantially self-supporting in regard to food.   It is true that standards of nutrition, especially in the industrial towns, had become far from adequate—partly by reason of the irrational preference for white bread, but mainly because of inadequate supplies of health foods such as milk and dairy products, meat, eggs and fresh vegetables.   The food situation deteriorated during the forties—partly because the population continued to rise after the reserves of cultivable virgin land had been largely exhausted and partly on account of bad seasons and the outbreak of potato blight.   The repeal of the Corn Laws (1846) marked the recognition of the fact that the country would for the future require substantial imports of staple foods.

It was not until thirty years later that British farmers felt the weight of overseas competition in the home food market.   Wool was the only important product which other countries could deliver in British markets at a substantially lower price than that which home farmers had considered profitable, and the situation was at least partly met by a change of emphasis from wool to meat by British sheep breeders.   British farming in the fifties and sixties attained as high a level of efficiency and intensiveness as was to be found anywhere in the world, and tenant farmers, despite high rents, earned large profits.

But the invention of the reaper and later of the string binder (1878) together with the building of a railway network over the North American Continent changed the situation.   Wheat prices especially, dropped to unprecedented low levels—ultimately falling, in the early nineties, to a level of about five shillings a hundredwieght.   This change caused a major financial crisis, marked in various parts of the country by bankruptcies of tenants and the failure of landowners to find others.   Naturally the crisis was most acute in the clay land areas that had been devoted largely to wheat production.   The depression spread to other areas with the commencement, in the last decade of the century, of large scale imports of frozen meat.   Most other European countries met this situation by heavy import duties on grain and other foodstuffs, taking the view that the preservation of their agriculture was more important than a lowered cost of living for the urban population.   This course was not without its disadvantages, tending on the one hand to perpetuate obsolete methods of farming and on the other to handicap manufacturers in competition for the export markets that the new countries provided.

In any case, British farmers worked under great difficulties in the thirty years that began with the disastrously wet and cold season of 1879. Much of the poorer land, especially in the uplands and the clay counties, was left to tumble down to poor pasture.   Rents fell, and buildings, drainage and other equipment deteriorated, while the number of farm workers greatly declined.   In some areas, a solution was found in switching production to such commodities as milk, potatoes, vegetables, fruit, poultry and eggs, which, with the rising real incomes of urban consumers, were in increasing demand.   Milk displaced wheat as the most important product of British agriculture.

Scarcity of goods and currency inflation towards the end of the first World War led to high prices and large farming profits; but prosperity was short lived, and subsequent losses very quickly outweighed the gains. The period between the wars was again one of depression, but the underlying causes were essentially different from those which had operated in the eighties and nineties; British farmers now suffered in common with those of other countries and with many groups of manufacturers.   Agricultural depression was, in fact, more acute in many overseas countries, including Canada, Australia and the United States, than in Britain.   Indeed some British farmers were in a position to take advantage of the situation by expanding their dairy, pig and poultry enterprises through the increased use of imported feeding stuffs, which were in plentiful supply at very low prices.

The outbreak of the second World War, with the prospect of something approaching siege conditions, forced a major change in the whole structure of British farming.   The emphasis was naturally placed on the essential foods—cereals, potatoes and other vegetables, sugar beet and milk—and the tillage area was greatly expanded.   By a combination of price incentives, appeals to patriotism, recruitment of women workers, rationing of scarce raw materials and equipment, the provision of various services by County Committees and other means, production was raised to a level that surpassed the highest expectations.

A number of dietary surveys, carried out in this and other countries during the inter-war period, showed that, despite the low prices and apparent surpluses of many foodstuffs, a large proportion of the world's population were inadequately fed.

In 1943 the United Nations Conference on Food and Agriculture, which met at Hot Springs, discussed the long term problem of achieving adequate levels of nutrition and made a number of important recommendations.

The chief grounds for anxiety about future food supplies appeared to be: (1) the continuing rapid increase of world population, (2) the approaching exhaustion of the once large reserves of fertile virgin land, (3) the high rate of wastage of soil resources by erosion, and (4) the magnitude of the gap between the food supplies and the nutritional requirements of the world even before the outbreak of the second World War.

The conference recommended a large number of long term measures designed to mitigate the situation. Among these were: (1) the expansion of agricultural research, educational and advisory services, (2) the provision of better facilities for the supply of capital to promote the expansion and improvement of agriculture, (3) the provision of fuller security of tenure for farm tenants, (4) measures for the control of prices at such levels as might be expected to encourage the expansion of production, and (5) measures to prevent erosion and other forms of wastage of soil resources.

For some ten years after the second World War national agricultural policy was directed to the overall expansion of output, with emphasis on those commodities which could be produced in Britain at relatively low costs and which were in short supply. Production in the United Kingdom rose to over 60 per cent. above the average for the period 1937-39. More recently home production of certain commodities such as milk and eggs has caught up with consumption, and the emphasis now is directed to lowering costs of production and to finding better methods of marketing to meet modern demands. It seems that in the immediate future much more study will be given to bulk handling of farm materials, the consolidation of agricultural holdings, and to the presentation of produce to the consumer in attractive forms.

The agents that are used in agricultural production are land, capital (including buildings and other improvements, implements and machinery, animals, seeds and manures) and labour. The land may be utilised in various ways—as, for instance, arable, pasture, meadow, orchard or woodland. Capital and labour may be applied in varying measure, intensively or extensively, as we say. Crop produce may be marketed as such—e.g. wheat or potatoes—or may first be converted into animal products—e.g. roots, hay and straw used to produce meat. Sometimes material may be purchased to permit of the profitable disposal of home produce—as fish meal to make possible the efficient utilisation of unmarketable potatoes. Sometimes it may happen that a single enterprise, like wheat production, apple growing, sheep breeding or milk production may constitute in itself the most economic system of farming for a given set of conditions. More frequently the most economical employment of land, labour and capital can be achieved by dovetailing together a strictly limited number of distinct enterprises.

How to use land; how to equip it; what crops to grow and how to dispose of them; what labour to hire and how to employ it—all to the end of maximum net profit over a period of years, without deterioration of the land and having regard to all the local conditions—such is broadly the problem of organisation.

## LAND

Land, the first essential agent of production, varies in quality and in value (and here we are considering value based solely on its suitability for farming). That value depends not only upon the original nature of the soil and the climate, but also upon any improvements in its condition that have been made by human agencies as well as its situation in regard to supplies of raw materials and its accessibility to markets for its produce. The measure of its value is the true or economic rent, *i.e.* the income it is capable of yielding over and above the usual return on capital and the usual rewards for labour and skill in management. The theory of economic rent is that the poorest or the least accessible land that will be used for agriculture is such as will only just repay the application of capital and labour, but will leave no margin. Such land may be said to be on the margin of cultivation, or simply marginal. Any land that is more fertile or more accessible to markets, will produce a return over and above the current return to capital and labour, which surplus constitutes economic rent. The rent that a piece of land will produce cannot, however, be determined without reference to the amount of capital and labour applied to it. The kind of land that is just worth farming, and the degree of intensity of cultivation that it is worth while to apply to land within the margin of cultivation, will change with changing economic conditions. Thus in the middle of last century much poor and heavy land in Essex was growing corn, while thousands of square miles of prairie, capable of growing better wheat with less labour, were lying idle. A rise in wages coupled with a lowering of transport costs reversed the position, and the prairie lands were broken up while Essex farms fell derelict. But later, owing to other changes, such as a growing world demand for wheat and the development of the London milk market, these Essex farms again came within the margin of cultivation.

The conception of fertility is a composite one, implying an estimate of the quantity and quality of produce that the land is capable of yielding in relation to the amount of human effort expended on it. Fertility depends on a great variety of circumstances, such as the presence of plant foods and the absence of plant poisons in the soil; the behaviour of the soil towards moisture; its ease or difficulty of cultivation; the amount, regularity and seasonal distribution of the rainfall; the temperature conditions and sunshine. It will be obvious that there can be no permanent measure of fertility, because progress in agricultural technique affects the potentiality of various types of land in very different ways. For example, the discovery of the use of lime or of potash; the invention of tile drainage or of tractors; the introduction of the potato or of wild white clover—all these and many other introductions to agriculture have brought about changes in our estimates of the relative values of different lands. Not only so, but estimates of fertility change from time to time and from place to place with changing economic conditions, as witness the Downs and the Fens in prehistoric as compared with modern times; at present the Fens are incomparably the more fertile, yet we know that the high, thin, chalky soils were the first to be brought under cultivation, while the fen lands were almost the last. Before the age of railways, relatively poor sandy land within wagon range of London had a high value because, with the ample available supplies of city stable and cowshed manure, it was suitable for the production of vegetables and soft fruit which could not be transported from far afield; at the time in question land in Bedfordshire, now used for vegetable production, was still farmed on the sheep and barley system and commanded only a small rent. The development of rail and later of lorry transport, together with the growth of London markets, resulted in the development of market gardening in Bedfordshire and, later on, in the silt lands of Lincoln and Norfolk.

Again, between 1880 and 1939, a large area of clay land, once devoted to rather intensive cereal production, was laid away to grass and fell greatly in value. More recently the development of power tillage, with a consequent reduction in costs, together with a recovery in cereal prices, has favoured a change to corn and ley farming.

Under nature every piece of land has a certain type of flora, the resultant of the soil and climatic conditions. Thus we may distinguish between steppe or prairie, moorland, natural forest of various types and many others. Moreover, each type of flora supports a particular type of fauna.

Agriculture, in the widest sense, may be said to include all schemes that are employed by man in order to increase the usefulness to himself of the plant and animal life that the land supports. Such interference may be slight, consisting, for example of nothing more than the aiding of useful species of plants and animals by attacking their natural enemies (game preserving and forest conservation), whereas in its final stage agriculture aims at the complete suppression of the greater part of the natural flora and fauna (weeds and pests), and substitutes one or more selected species, which are modified and cared for in order to develop their maximum usefulness. The larger the human population to be supported and the greater its wants, the greater will be the extent of our interference with nature, i.e. the more intensive will agriculture become.

Lands are classified, from the agricultural point of view, according to the product for which they are specialized, thus:—

1. *Game and Fishing Preserves.*—Wild animals under some degree of protection.
2. *Forest.*—Trees grown for timber and bark, where utilisation involves felling.
3. *Orchards and Plantations.*—Trees or other perennial plants for fruit, leaves and latex, where utilisation does not involve felling.
4. *Garden and Nursery Lands.*—Plants requiring or repaying highly intensive treatment and individual care.
5. *Farm Lands:*—
   (*a*) Grass—herbaceous plants—for grazing or mowing.
   (*b*) Tillage—plants propagated annually.

The boundaries between these different classes are, of course, not hard and fast. Thus between farm and garden, garden and orchard, there is an insensible gradation among cultural schemes. Moreover, two purposes may be combined, as in the case of hill grazings that are also grouse moors, or orchards or woodlands that are also grazings. Again, among farm lands many are worked on a system of alternate grass and arable husbandry. The first problem of organisation is to allot the land to the particular purpose for which it is best suited, *i.e.* to whichever mode of utilisation is likely to produce the largest net return. Let us look at the various types in the foregoing order:—

**Game**, from the fact that it is kept in the wild state, is capable of yielding a very small return measured in actual produce. It can only be regarded as a profitable product either where land is of very little value for other purposes (*e.g.* mountain or heath), or where, in wealthy communities, there are people who are prepared to pay relatively large sums for sport. The letting of fishing rights may go with a letting for game.

The preservation of game on land that is being used for another purpose—whether forestry, agriculture or horticulture—generally reduces its value for such other purpose; moreover, game animals, since their feeding is not under control, are capable of doing an amount of damage that is quite out of proportion to the amount of food they consume—*e.g.* when they attack crop plants in the seedling stage. Some species that are valued as game are, however, either harmless or actually beneficial. The partridge and the quail feed mainly on weed seeds, and their preservation interferes with farming only in that a certain amount of nesting cover must be provided. Where there is a good demand for sporting rights a certain amount of game may pay, *i.e.* may add to the net value of the land even if some damage is done. The amount that is permissible depends on the system of utilisation that is being applied. In general, the more intensive the cultivation the less place there is for game: thus on our mountain grazings the preservation of game can be profitable;

on the better sort of grasslands, in established woodlands and on the less intensively worked types of mixed farms, it may be quite in place; whereas, under intensive arable conditions, and still more in gardens and nurseries, game (except for example, partridges) must be reduced to a minimum.

**Forest Lands**, of which timber is the chief product, are dealt with in various ways, and produce forests of many different types. One outstanding feature is the long period that is required for trees to mature, or even to reach such a size as to enable them to be utilised at all. Forty, eighty or even considerably over a hundred years are common lengths of rotation. This implies, almost unavoidably, a relatively high capitalisation; for even if we suppose a small figure for preparation of the land and planting, and a low annual rental of the land, the initial and current charges, lying out at compound interest over such periods, eventually grow to very large sums. Again, the produce of cultivated—*i.e.* of planted and tended—forests has had to compete in the past with that of natural forests in various parts of the world, so that the gross income has been limited. As the world's forest reserves have been depleted, the price of timber in relation to the general level of prices has risen. On the other hand, it is impossible to predict the extent to which, in the course of fifty or a hundred years, other materials—such as steel, concrete or plastics—will be substituted for timber. Under existing conditions it is only where land has a low agricultural value that forestry can be an economic success. If, for example a piece of land is worth, as grazing, 5s. an acre for annual rent, it will be doubtful, even if it is fairly well suited for afforestation, whether forest could give as high a return. The Forestry Commission, which is in control of State afforestation in Britain, has acquired most of its land at prices below £4 per acre, whereas ordinary farm land, worth perhaps, £20 to £30 per acre in 1939, had risen, at the time of writing, from £60 to well over £100.

On the other hand, many forest trees have, as compared with practically all agricultural and horticultural crop plants, very low requirements for soil nutrients. Also, since land under forest requires no tillage, trees can be grown on steep or rocky ground which cannot profitably be farmed. Hence timber can be produced with success on land whose only alternative use would be as rough grazing. Again, forestry can be successfully practised on slopes so steep that they would be subject to soil erosion under any form of agriculture, not excluding grazing. In countries where erosion is a serious problem, large areas of eroded land are being reafforested. Forests once established employ relatively little labour and require little equipment—circumstances that give forestry a place, along with sheep and cattle ranching, under extensive conditions, *i.e.* where land is cheap in relation to the other agents of production. Timber is costly to transport by land but cheap to carry by water, so that proximity to rivers is an important consideration. Trees are more liable than are agricultural and other crops to destruction by wind and fire, and the degree of risk and the possibilities of protection must be taken into account in deciding for or against afforestation.

There are a few exceptions to these broad facts—*e.g.* the timber of the cricket bat willow, when it is of high quality, is very valuable, and the production of high class material requires a highly fertile soil. Moreover, the trees reach maturity in a comparatively small number of years.

For particular plots of land of limited area forestry should be regarded as an alternative to agriculture. There are, it is true, woodlands that have a certain grazing value, but such combined utilisation is rarely economic. The feeding of pigs in forests of oak, beech and Spanish chestnut is an exception, making possible the utilisation of a valuable by-product without disadvantage to the forest itself.

If, however, we have in mind not individual plots of ground but large districts, we may find that farm and forest are not alternatives but are economic complements one of the other, *i.e.* a suitable allocation of land to each will produce a higher average return than could be obtained from either by itself. This may happen even when the land within the area does not vary sensibly in quality. Examples are to be found in regions where transport is expensive or difficult and where the population has to depend mainly on local produce. Here the farm lands produce the materials for food and clothing, the forest those for house and fuel. Again, in many of the colder parts of the world, agriculture provides full employment during only part of the year—the frost free period—whereas in forests the greater part of the work, including felling and disposal, can be done in winter. Thus the two industries together can employ labour more economically than could either alone. The British Forestry Commission, in connection with its afforestation schemes, creates numbers of smallholdings and guarantees a certain amount of employment in forestry to its tenants; and in the development of large areas it is prepared to modify its planting programme to assist certain needs of the hill sheep farmer.

Woodlands may also, in certain cases, be properly regarded as minor adjuncts to farms, being maintained for the purpose of producing the quantity of timber necessary for fences and the like. In exposed districts, woods in the form of shelter belts may be of considerable value to the farm, and in hot climates trees are useful for the provision of shade for live stock. In such cases timber production becomes a secondary consideration. The provision of cover for game is a further use of woodlands, but this need not greatly interfere with their main purpose.

**Orchards and Plantations** other than of timber trees (*i.e.* sugar maple, rubber, coffee and nuts), resemble forests in so far that they are formed of perennial plants that usually require to stand for a period of years before they begin to yield. They have thus the same general feature of a high capital requirement. The productive stage is, however, usually reached a good deal earlier than in the case of forests; moreover, the yield of the individual trees is sustained over a number of years, and tends to remain fairly constant from one year to another. Orchards and plantations also differ from forests, and resemble garden lands, in that the labour requirement—for spraying, pruning, harvesting, curing and packing of the produce—is high. In many cases cultivation of the soil is necessary or desirable, so that there must be no serious obstacles to tillage; but since this tillage is normally not very intensive, great ease of cultivation is not essential. Many of the products of orchard lands, unlike timber, carry away considerable amounts of manurial substances, so that the soil should generally be fertile chemically. Wind shelter and immunity from spring frost are also important. Frost pockets occur where cold air (being heavier than warm air) flows downhill and forms pools in hollows. Moreover, hedges and shelter belts can act as dams, preventing air drainage. The siting of orchards must, therefore, be based on a careful survey of air drainage conditions. Much information is now available as to the value of different areas in this country for orchards. Considerable depth of soil is necessary to provide a sufficient reservoir for rain water, and adequate drainage is important. Capitalisation, current charges and gross returns per acre all tend to be higher in fruit-growing than in ordinary farming, and the yield and quality of the produce are at least as dependent on soil and climate as are those from annual crops or grass. Land suitable for fruit growing often commands a rent or a price which could not be paid by the ordinary farmer.

**Market Gardens** may be regarded as the more intensively worked types of arable farms; the kind of crop, a plant propagated annually and grown in pure culture, is essentially the same; the chief difference is that the gardener confines himself to those species or varieties which, because of their capacity to yield crops of high value per acre, repay more intensive cultivation and individual treatment, whereas the farmer is restricted to such as are fairly robust growers and can be dealt with by cheap wholesale methods. Many crops—such as potatoes, carrots, peas, celery and cabbages—are common to both systems, and many holdings are cultivated on a system intermediate between the two. Moreover, large scale farming methods have in many cases been successfully applied to crops (*e.g.*, green peas and carrots) formerly grown on a garden system. Much garden produce is perishable, or at least has a maximum value when quite fresh, whereas farm crops and their products can generally be stored for considerable periods and can be handled and marketed in quantity and cheaply. Then, also, all garden stuff is intended directly for human food, whereas much farm produce is converted by live stock into secondary products.

One outstanding feature of the market garden is its high labour requirement. Few farms, apart from the transitional type of holding mentioned above, employ more than two persons per hundred acres, whereas in market gardens the labour may rise to one person per acre, or with glass, much higher. The capital investment, apart from glass, is not proportionately high, chiefly because the rate of turnover is very rapid.

In respect of physical conditions, the gardener's crops are by definition of a less robust type than those of the farmer. Moreover, one of the main objects of the market gardener is to produce, as nearly as may be, a regular supply of fresh material at all seasons of the year. These facts both point to the selection of land so situated that the growing season reaches the maximum length for the locality and where the climate is relatively mild and equable. Hence in Britain a low elevation, proximity to the sea, a southern exposure and shelter from winds, are all of importance. For the same reason the soil should be of a warm, early type, *i.e.* light and well drained. The last point has a double importance, for, since a succession of supplies must usually be aimed at, the soil must be of such texture that it can be worked and a tilth secured, at many different seasons and under many different weather conditions; it is true, however, that modern methods of preservation—particularly deep freezing—are tending to reduce the importance of a succession of supplies. The heavier the soil the more is the cultivator restricted as to his time of seeding. Moreover, stiff clays, even at the best, can scarcely be got into the state of tilth necessary for the smaller seeded and more delicate of the gardener's crops. Chemical fertility is to the gardener relatively unimportant. His costs are so high, mainly owing to the large amount of labour employed, that even very intensive manuring involves only a relatively slight addition to the total. At the same time it must be borne in mind that the lightest sands cannot be worked successfully unless organic manures, as well as fertilizers, are available. Without the former the moisture supply will be liable to fail, growth will be interrupted and the quality of the produce will suffer. The use of catch crops for green manuring is one method of meeting the growing shortage of farmyard manure, which was formerly the most common form of organic manure.

The ultimate form of intensive gardening is cultivation under glass, *i.e.* with both a climate and a soil that are very largely artificial. In this case most of the physical conditions are under control, and the natural quality of the land loses its importance. The cost of heating, however, is relatively high in cold climates and exposed situations and winter sunlight is of great importance.

Probably more important than any of the natural conditions is the economic situation of the land, *i.e.* its proximity to markets, the amount of competition from other industries for the available labour and the state of development of means of transport and of methods of marketing. Hence market gardening originally tended to become concentrated near centres of population. In recent times more rapid transport and low-temperature storage have worked towards a wider diffusion of the industry. Thus London's supplies of vegetables were mostly produced, up till about 1850, in the zone within a night's journey, by wagon, of the city. With the coming of railways, vegetable production spread on to suitable land, in Bedfordshire and elsewhere, as far as 50 or 60 miles out. Still later, mechanised road transport, permitting direct movement from field to market, led to a further widening of the zone, *e.g.* to include the silt areas of south Lincolnshire. Air transport obviously provides further possibilities, at least for such commodities as have a high money value in relation to their weight.

**Nurseries** devoted to the propagation of perennial plants (*e.g.* fruit and forest trees) are akin to gardens in their high labour requirement, but are found under a greater variety of soil and climatic conditions. They tend to be established on the more easily tilled soils and under the more favourable climatic conditions.

**Agricultural Lands** include pastures, meadows and arable fields. If the cultivator allocates a given area for an indefinite period to one purpose or the other, we speak of permanent pasture, meadow or arable, but it will be obvious that no scheme of allocation, if it is to depend on economic considerations, can be truly permanent. Changes in supply and demand or developments of transport may force the breaking up of grassland in one area and the laying down of arable to grass in another. Improvements in methods of tillage, or in the techniques of pasture production and many other causes, may have a like effect in one direction or the other. The alternative to such permanent allocation of the land is to adopt some scheme whereby the land is put under tillage and grass during alternate and more or less definite periods of years. The three possible systems are therefore: (1) permanent grass (including both pasture and meadow) (2) permanent arable, (3) alternate husbandry; and it is necessary briefly to set down the main considerations that should guide the farmer in deciding for one or the other.

1. In the first place, the gross return from arable land, measured in terms of quantity of human food, is generally higher than from grassland. Broadly speaking the money value of the output is also higher; but the most intensive forms of grassland milk production, with heavy fertilizer usage, frequent re-seeding, strip grazing and grass drying or ensilage, gives as high gross returns as all but the most intensive forms of arable cropping. In general, arable farming is the more intensive system of the two, and, other things being equal, will tend to prevail wherever the land is fertile and of easy access to markets. The less fertile or the less accessible the land the more will it tend to be left in grass. Land that falls below a certain level of fertility, whether owing to a short growing season, insufficient warmth or rain or sunlight or to chemical or physical deficiencies of soil, will fail to leave any net return under arable farming. Similarly, at long distances from markets, ports, railways or good roads, land may become not worth ploughing. Much of this land that is beyond

the margin (in the economic sense) of arable cultivation is still capable of paying a rent under the less intensive system of grass husbandry.

2. The next question is that of the difficulty or ease of cultivation. The expenditure on grassland is not only low, but varies within comparatively narrow limits. In the case of arable fields the expenditure is not only higher but varies, with soil and climatic conditions, within far wider limits. Thus level, free working soils situated in districts of moderately low rainfall are those which tend to be kept under arable cultivation. Great tenacity of soil, steep slopes, excessive rainfall and liability to flooding, all add materially to cultivation costs and so favour the alternative of grass farming. It will be obvious that economic conditions, such as the relation of wages to prices and the possibilities of using labour-saving devices, will also have an important bearing on cultivation costs. These questions are treated in Chapter 28.

3. Apart from the question of tillage costs, the conditions that constitute maximum fertility for grass and for arable crops respectively are different. The most striking difference is in the matter of moisture requirement. Grassland is covered (throughout the year) with a more or less dense herbage, whereas arable ground is unoccupied for at least a part of the year, and is only sparsely covered with vegetation for a further season. Hence the moisture requirement of grass is much the higher, with the result that grass tends to predominate in regions of high rainfall, on the more retentive soils, and for example, on river flats where there is a supply of water from the subsoil. Again, arable crops, most of which are required to ripen, are benefited by dry weather for this process [1] and for their harvesting; whereas with grass, prolonged vegetative growth, which is favoured by continuously moist conditions, is what is wanted. This connection between moisture and cropping is very easily traced if rainfall and cultivation maps of this country be compared. Again, arable crops pass through phases, such as the seedling, the flowering and the ripening stage, when they are liable to suffer disastrous damage from climatic agents like late or early frosts, summer hail, wind, rain, fog or drought. These may act either directly on the plant or may produce damage by encouraging insect pests or fungoid diseases. Grass suffers relatively insignificant damage from such causes. Hence under very uncertain climates land has very little value for arable purposes and yet may be very valuable for grass.

4. The agricultural situation of a piece of land (*e.g.* its position in relation to other land and its accessibility to the farm buildings) may also prove a determining factor. Within the individual farm a limited area of pasture quite close to the farm buildings is a convenience of obvious

---

[1] In certain areas—*e.g.* parts of Wales, the West of Scotland and West of Ireland—the difficulty of corn harvest is partly caused by the high rainfall, but even more by the high average relative humidity of the atmosphere. The drying of crops is protracted because the air is so often almost saturated with moisture.

Y

value. Apart from this the more distant or less accessible fields will tend to go to grass, while the land of easier access will tend to be kept as arable. The question of water supply to grazing stock is another point that must be borne in mind when a scheme of allocation is under consideration.

Regarding the two modes of utilising grassland, it is obvious that wherever there is a definite winter season, where anything approaching intensive methods of stock feeding are adopted and where there is no sufficient supply of arable land products, part of the produce of grassland must be conserved by one means or another. Seasons of drought, whether of regular or occasional occurrence, fall to be provided for in the same way. Mowing and conservation (hay making, ensilage or artificial drying) involve a considerably higher expenditure than grazing, so that the more productive of the grasslands will usually be set apart for conservation. Relative freedom from obstacles is also of importance. Apart from this, lands that are too wet to carry stock or are unhealthy for grazing animals, will tend to be alloted to permanent meadow.

Very frequently it happens that the most profitable system for a particular farm includes both arable and grass. Apart from the question of the distribution of risks, it is often desirable that a certain quantity of live stock should be permanently maintained, e.g. dairy or regular breeding stock. And in such cases it will generally happen that pasture provides the cheapest summer food, and assists through conserved products in meeting the winter requirements available from arable cropping.

In alternate (as opposed to merely mixed) husbandry there is the further important advantage that grassland accumulates nitrogen and humus, whereas tillage exhausts the soil of these very important constituents, if steps are not taken to replace them. Moreover, weight must be given to the fact that temporary grass, at least in the earlier years of its existence, is commonly much more productive than permanent grass under similar conditions. This is because, except under systems of management that are not always practicable, less productive and nutritious plants tend to increase at the expense of the best pasture species. The broad result is that a given standard of productiveness can be maintained, under a system of alternate husbandry, with a lower expenditure in labour and manures than under a system of permanent division into arable and grass. On the other hand, land under the alternate system requires a measure of double equipment—it must be fenced and supplied with water if it is to be grazed, and for arable purposes it must have roads. Added to this is the additional expenditure for periodic reseeding with grasses and clover and the risk of failure that attends the laying down of land to grass. The latter obstacle to alternate husbandry assumes most importance on the heavier soils, on which a suitable tilth for the smaller seeds is difficult to obtain, and in the drier areas. In reaching a decision for the one or the other system of mixed farming, the one set of considerations must be balanced against the other. If the land of a farm is tolerably uniform in fertility and accessibility, and its soil of fairly uniform texture, and if grass is not too difficult to establish, alternate husbandry should generally be preferred. If, on the other hand, the land of a farm includes rich and poor, high and low, heavy and light, or if it is difficult to lay down to a good sward, then a permanent division may be the more profitable scheme. Recent progress in the technique of pasture making (including sowing without a cover crop) and management is tending towards the increase of alternate husbandry. Under conditions that are unsuitable for arable crops there is the possibility of breaking up and directly reseeding grassland when its productivity has declined.

## CAPITAL

Farm capital includes all the equipment that is necessary to make the and productive. It is usual to draw a distinction between such forms of capital as are practically inseparable from the land—buildings, roads, drains—and such as are readily separable—implements, live stock, annual crops. Obviously this distinction is not absolute, e.g. a wire fence is movable, but the cost of moving it may represent a considerable part of its value; a hill sheep flock is readily movable, but its value in the market may be less than its value on its native grazing. A sum spent in manuring with nitrate of soda is probably recoverable within a year, one spent on basic slag in perhaps three or four years and one spent on liming perhaps not in ten years. However, the broad distinction is important, especially in countries such as Britain, where the landlord and tenant system prevails. Here the fixed capital is the property of the landlord, and interest on it is included in the rent, while the movable capital is furnished by the tenant. Questions regarding the quasi-permanent forms of capital are settled by custom, by covenants in leases or by law. Improvements carried out by a tenant are classified into various groups in the Agriculture Act, 1947, the Agricultural Holdings Act, 1948 and the Agriculture Act, 1958. There are those to which the landlord's consent is required in order that the tenant may have a right to compensation. others to which the consent of the landlord or the approval of the Minister of Agriculture are necessary; and yet others in respect of which no consent is required. There is also a list of the operations carried out by a tenant during his last year of a tenancy in respect of which he is entitled to compensation.

**Landlord's Capital.**—*Buildings*, apart from dwelling houses, comprise implement sheds, storage accommodation for produce—e.g. corn lofts, hay sheds and straw barns, and accommodation for stock. It will be obvious that the number, size and quality of the buildings necessary will depend, among other things on the climate; the longer and the more severe the winter the more commodious and the more substantial must the buildings be. Hence in the north of Scotland the capital represented in buildings generally bears a high proportion to the freehold value of the land, whereas in the south of England the capital so invested is upon average considerably less. Again, the necessary capacity of the buildings depends on the number of stock maintained during winter. This is generally greater on arable and semi-arable than on grass farms, because of the larger stock of machinery and the storage space required for crop produce. Thirdly, the accommodation required depends on the type of stock that is to be kept. Thus winter feeding cattle and dairy cows or pigs kept on the indoor system, require much housing, whereas sheep and outwintering store cattle require little. The provision of buildings will often be outside the tenant farmer's province and it frequently happens that he must modify his system to fit in with the existing buildings; if, however, it is within his control he must endeavour to satisfy himself with regard to any proposed addition or alteration, that there is a likelihood of an economic return on the outlay that would be required.

The stage has been reached in many parts of Britain, when it is necessary to make a decision whether substantially to repair and modify old farm buildings for new uses and to provide labour saving layouts or to build anew. Many existing farm buildings were built one hundred or more years ago and, though very substantial, are not well suited to modern requirements. In a number of such cases it is better to build anew. Where this is done, it is general to build structures that can be adapted for alternative uses with an expected life of from 25-50 years. The introduction of the Farm Improvement Scheme a few years ago came at a most appropriate time. Under this scheme grants of one third of the approved cost may be made for the erection of new farm buildings and certain other items of fixed equipment. The applicant for the grant must satisfy the Minister of Agriculture that his plan is sound economically and that the proposed alterations are those that would be likely to be accepted by a prudent landlord.

Apart from the question of the amount of available accommodation which influences the stock carrying capacity of the farm, its arrangement from the point of view of economy of labour is assuming greater importance. The chief points are connected with the handling of the bulky materials, such as roots, straw, hay and farmyard manure. With ideal buildings and with all materials delivered to his hand, a man can attend over one hundred fattening cattle while under the worst conditions the number may be as low as thirty. The position of the buildings is also a point of importance. This, where the land is of uniform quality, should be as central as possible. In other cases the ideal position is nearer to the most fertile and most intensively worked portions. Access to public roads is also an important consideration as affecting the most convenient point. Access to the various storage buildings, stockyards and cowshed should be so arranged that there will be a minimum of interference between vehicles and live stock. On very large holdings subsidiary homesteads may be desirable.

*Fencing* of subdivisions of the farm becomes necessary wherever grazing and cropping are carried on together; also, on purely grazing land, fences are essential if the grazing animals are to be properly controlled and the herbage is to be fully utilised. In general the more intensive the system of grazing the smaller must be the individual enclosures. On the poorer types of grassland, *e.g.* hill grazings, the erection of fences will often not be justified economically. Fences may be either temporary or permanent. Hurdles, sheep netting, electrically charged wires and various forms of folds are used in certain cases in preference to fixed fences.

The cost of fencing per acre (where the shape of field is constant) varies inversely as the square root of the area; *e.g.* if one field is four times the size of another, the length of fence required will be only twice as great or half as much per acre. Fencing imposes a considerable burden on the land. For example, if we erect a substantial wire fence for 5s. per yd., the outlay will amount to £11 per acre for 10 acre square fields, or to £5 10s. per acre for 40 acre square fields. These sums will represent annual charges, including interest and upkeep, of perhaps 13s. and 6s. 6d. per acre respectively.

The number of fields in the case of farms run on a system of alternate husbandry should not be less than the number of years in the rotation, *i.e.* a four course farm should have at least four fields, and a seven course farm at least seven fields. It is often necessary, in the interests of efficient management of the temporary grasslands, and especially when several different classes of stock have to be provided for, to increase this number —say two or three fold. But very small subdivisions such as exist in many parts of England lead to great inconvenience in working, as well as to a very considerable loss in the total cultivable area.

Fields should be rectangular, unless natural obstacles impose some other shape; irregular shapes involve a very considerable loss of time in cultivation. For large fields (say 30 acres or more), square is generally the most convenient shape. Smaller fields should preferably be oblong, in order to give a longer furrow and so more economical working.

*Roads* are a necessary adjunct to the arable farm; the type necessary is dependent on the nature of the traffic they have to carry, particularly on the amount of heavy winter carting. Thus if sugar beet or potatoes are to be carted off and dung carted on, a tolerably well built road is essential; whereas if roots are to be folded, the carting is reduced to seed, artificial manure and such produce as cereals, and the provision of the necessary access may cost little or nothing. A useful guide to road making is a Ministry of Agriculture, Fisheries and Food Bulletin, *The Road of Local Material*.

*Drainage*, either natural or artificial, is essential under British climatic conditions if the maximum returns from arable land are to be obtained. The cost of tile drainage varies from £80 to £120 per acre, representing an annual charge of up to £7; and drainage can only be expected to be carried out if the probable increase in the annual value of the land reaches such a figure. Mole drainage, of course, provides a cheap substitute on heavy land of suitable configuration. At the time of writing (1961), State grants up to 50 per cent. of the approved costs could be obtained for all approved schemes of land drainage.

*Water supply* is of obvious importance. The carting of water for stock is very expensive, and a reliable supply of uncontaminated drinking water is an asset of great value. Open ponds which collect surface water are dangerous to the health of live stock, particularly in spreading Johne's disease among cattle. Apart from the amount and purity of the supply, the temperature of the available water is a material point on dairy farms. On this may depend the efficient cooling of the milk. Deep well water is to be preferred, since it maintains a low temperature in summer. State assistance can now (1961) be obtained for approved water supply schemes.

Other forms of improvement—*e.g.* clearing of forest land and removal of stones—may represent large capital sums. All the foregoing forms of capital investment must be taken into account in assessing either the freehold or the annual value of a farm. It does not follow, of course, that the value of a farm is the original value of the unimproved land plus the actual sums spent in equipment and improvement, because the actual value of an improvement may bear very little relation to its original cost. Buildings may become obsolete—*e.g.* ill adapted to a new system of farming which is otherwise desirable—while they are still structurally sound, and stone walls or hedges, made at considerable cost, may have become impediments to mechanised tillage. The capital value of land, of course, varies with the rate of interest that can be obtained on long-term investments of other kinds. The actual method used by land valuers is, firstly, to estimate the annual rental value to a good tenant. From the gross rental is deducted any fixed outgoings (land tax, tithe redemption annuity) and also the estimated annual cost of repairs and maintenance. The capital value is then calculated as so many years' purchase of the net rental—*e.g.* twenty, twenty-five or forty years' purchase according as the current rate of interest is 5, 4, or $2\frac{1}{2}$ per cent. If there seems to be opportunity for making improvements that are likely to return more than the normal rate of interest, some addition will generally be made to the value so arrived at.

**Tenant's Capital.**—The movable capital of the farm, or tenant's capital, may be conveniently dealt with under the following heads:—

1. *Standing Capital*, corresponding to the machinery and plant of the manufacturer, and consisting of things which are used continuously or

repeatedly for productive purposes, and are replaced only when they are obsolescent or more or less worn out:—

(a) tractors and work animals.

(b) permanent dead stock—*e.g.* implements, machinery.

(c) fixed or regular live stock, *e.g.* dairy herds or breeding flocks maintained at a constant level.

2. *Working or Floating Capital*, corresponding to the manufacturer's stocks in hand or in process of manufacture, and constituting that portion of the capital that is turned over and is continually changing its form. On an arable farm in midsummer this would be represented by such items as growing crops and unexhausted manures; in winter by roots, hay, straw, unsold grain or potatoes, tillages, dung, fattening cattle and so on. If we imagine the case of a farmer taking over a bare farm, the working capital would be held in cash at the beginning of his occupancy, and the amount required would be calculated as the sum necessary to meet all current expenses until such time as the farm was expected to become self supporting. The chief heads under which expenditure might be required are:—

(a) seeds.

(b) lime, manures and fertilizers.

(c) feeding stuffs.

(d) temporary stocks of animals for the utilisation of surplus roots hay and straw.

(e) wages

(f) rent, rates, taxes and insurances.

(g) miscellaneous—implement repairs, veterinary attendance, expendable stores such as coal, oil and binder twine.

In practice, when the tenancy of a farm changes hands, the new occupier is ordinarily required to take over from the old, at the valuation of a third party, such parts of the investment of the former as cannot conveniently be realised otherwise. On the other hand, if an outgoing tenant has allowed the land to become foul, has failed to maintain a reasonable level of soil fertility and has neglected fences and ditches, he is chargeable with the extra cost of restoring the land to a proper state of cultivation. The custom in many districts is to hand over this sum to the new tenant, who in turn binds himself to leave the farm in good condition. The valuation of the tenant right is a matter for a professional valuer, who must be acquainted not only with the law but also with the procedures and bases of valuation agreed by the professional bodies. Formerly the business was complicated by the existence of a great variety of local customs which had the force of law, but many of these complications were removed by the 1947 Agriculture Act and the Act of 1958.

**Farm Tractors.**—Over a great part of Britain oxen were at one time largely used for farm work. In this country ox teams were gradually replaced by horses, chiefly between 1750 and 1840; but in many other countries oxen, and even cows, are still largely used. About 1850 steam tillage became possible and many people believed that steam power would largely replace horses. But the common unit of steam tackle—a pair of heavy engines drawing ploughs and cultivators by cable—proved too costly and was not sufficiently adaptable to the variety of tillage operations. Moreover, steam power was unsatisfactory for farm transport. Tractors with internal combustion engines assumed some importance during 1917-18, but numbers declined again soon afterwards. Since 1930 there has been a rapid development of mechanical tillage, with a continuously growing population of tractors of various types (tracklayers, heavy and light wheeled models, row-crop types and small market-garden types). The rate of increase in the numbers of tractors was greatly accelerated during the war years and since. In 1939 there were about 55,000 farm tractors in England and Wales. At the time of writing the number is probably around 400,000. As the number of tractors has increased the number of horses has decreased, but the reduction in the horse population has not been so great as might have been expected, even after making allowances for the greatly increased tillage acreage since 1939. This is probably due to the tendency on many farms to retain a horse or two to do odd jobs for which they are more suitable than tractors, and as a reserve of power for peak load periods.

The range of tractors is now considerable. At one extreme there are small single or two wheeled horticultural types and at the other very powerful tracklayers. The smallest of the horticultural types can be fitted with a variety of attachments, but their power is so low that they can be used only for light work such as hoeing. Slightly larger models of the same general design are suitable for ploughing and some are fitted with rotary cultivators; but the high powered (4 to 8 h.p.) two wheeled tractors are often difficult to handle on heavy work. The larger tracklayers are usually contractor's machines, since only very large farmers can justify the capital outlay involved. It is from the tractors falling between these two extremes that the farmer makes his choice. They include the medium powered tracklayers and the medium and high powered wheel tractors. Tracklayers cost more than wheel tractors of similar horsepower and their track equipment may be expensive to maintain, especially when used much on sharp sandy soils. They are, therefore, only chosen when the work is too heavy or the slopes too steep for wheel tractors. If the amount of that type of work is not sufficient to justify the purchase of a tracklayer it may be more economical to employ a contractor or to equip a wheel tractor with half-tracks. In the latter case the half-tracks would be replaced by wheels for the lighter work of the spring and summer.

A number of surveys have been carried out to determine how the farm tractor is used. Most figures agree that rather more than a third of its working time is spent on transport and that the bulk of the remainder is on field operations. Stationary work accounts for only a small portion of that time. This would tend to point to the need for versatility, particularly on the smaller farm where only one tractor is used. There is little doubt that the introduction of the pneumatic tyre has probably played a bigger part than any other single factor in making possible the substitution of tractors for horses or other draft animals on farms not only in Britain but also abroad. Transport work on some farms can often be done with special transport vehicles or motor lorries, but it should be remembered that no economies are effected if, in providing special transport vehicles, tractors suitable for that work are left idle.

Many implements, such as grass mowers, binders, small combine harvesters, potato diggers and harvesters, some of which were formerly driven through their land wheels, are now driven from the tractor power take-off. Power driven machines have many advantages, but on most tractors the speed of the power shaft is constant at rated engine speed. Soil conditions for certain operations may be such that a low forward speed is essential, but when the tractor is operating a power driven machine, forward speed cannot be adjusted by manipulation of the governor control lever. If it is, the mechanism of the machine is slowed down and its efficiency reduced. Because of this, modern tractors are often fitted with a wide range of gear ratios so that forward speed can be adjusted by choosing the gear to suit the conditions while maintaining rated engine speed. A very low bottom gear, giving a speed of half to one mile an hour, is necessary for operations such as mechanical potato planting and transplanting of cruciferous crops, and when choosing a tractor the farmer should take into account such special needs as these.

There is no simple yardstick for determining the number of tractors required to work a given acreage efficiently and economically. So much depends on the intensity of production, organisation and management, and soil type, that farm size may be of minor importance. For instance, on a heavy land arable farm the number of days in the year when it is possible to work the land may be so much smaller than on a light land arable farm that it requires a larger number of tractors for a given acreage. By having adequate tractor strength full advantage can be taken of spells of suitable weather.

Again, recent surveys do show that the arable acreage per farm tractor is decreasing steadily. In part this is due to the common practice of small farmers to buy second hand tractors. On the larger farms, tractors that are pretty fully employed, are often sold when they have run for about two thirds of their useful lives. These are bought by smaller farmers at relatively low prices and may perform effectively for a number of years the cultivation and haulage tasks associated with the smaller acreages.

The cost of tractor work is influenced greatly by the type of tractor and the number of hours worked in the year. Certain fixed costs such as licence, insurance and some part of depreciation do not change regardless of the hours worked. Other costs such as fuel, oil, repairs and maintenance do. If the fixed costs are spread over more hours, then the total cost per hour decreases. The following table from the bulletin, *The Farm as a Business*, Ministry of Agriculture, Fisheries and Food illustrates the point.

TABLE 21

### TRACTOR COSTS PER HOUR ACCORDING TO TYPES AND ANNUAL USE

| Type of Tractor | Hours worked annually | | | | | | | |
|---|---|---|---|---|---|---|---|---|
| | 500 | | 750 | | 1000 | | 1250 | |
| | s. | d. | s. | d. | s. | d. | s. | d. |
| V. O. (small) | 5 | 0 | 4 | 0 | 3 | 9 | 3 | 6 |
| V. O. (medium size) | 5 | 0 | 4 | 3 | 4 | 0 | 3 | 9 |
| Diesel (small) | 6 | 0 | 4 | 6 | 3 | 9 | 3 | 3 |
| Diesel (medium large) | 6 | 3 | 4 | 9 | 4 | 0 | 3 | 6 |
| Tracklayer | 10 | 0 | 8 | 0 | 7 | 0 | 6 | 6 |

The costs are based on price levels in 1955.

There is some difficulty in separating out depreciation from other items of expenditure in any analysis of tractor costs. Depreciation should be related to the work done, for a tractor's useful life is more closely associated with the hours worked than with its age. The normal practice, however, is to calculate depreciation at the rate approved by the Inland Revenue Authorities. At the time of writing this is " five fourths of the basic percentage rate (22½ per cent. for farm tractors) to the written down value in the inventory at the end of the previous year." It is therefore, difficult to give average values in the break down of operating costs. Fuel and lubricants normally account for more than half these costs.

**Field Implements.**—To keep down the cost per acre of tractor operations it is essential to have implements that are capable of loading the tractor to as near to full capacity as is possible. Converted horse implements which were in the past frequently used with tractors were not always suitable because they were seldom strong enough to withstand tractor haulage and because they did not provide an adequate load. Wide tractor implements are usually required to give a sufficient load, although it is sometimes possible to compensate for a narrow implement by travelling at a higher speed. There is, however, a limit to the speed at which certain cultivations can be done and an alternative arrangement is to do two cultivations at once by using narrow implements in tandem—for example, seed harrows behind a corn drill or harrows behind a roller. There are other operations, such as the hoeing of root crops, that make very light work and cannot provide an adequate load for a medium powered tractor; neither can they be performed at high speeds. These operations until recently, were often done by horses, but the horse and the skilled horse hand are disappearing, and much row work in Britain is now done with wheeled tractors.

Increasing the width of an implement does not necessarily give a proportionately greater rate of working. In an N.I.A.E. survey [1] the average rates of ploughing in acres per hour per furrow for one, two, three, four and five furrow ploughs were ·29, 0·22, 0·16, 0·15, and 0·16. The significance of these figures especially in so far as a medium powered wheel tractor is concerned, is the difference in output per furrow between the two and three furrow ploughs. The three furrow plough had a rate of working only 9 per cent. higher than the two furrow, whereas an increase nearer to 50 per cent. might have been expected. In practice a medium powered tractor with a three furrow plough has frequently to work in bottom gear, whereas with a two furrow plough it can be used in second gear almost all the time. Tractors fitted with pneumatic tyres operate more efficiently the higher the forward speed, so that it is preferable to provide them with ploughs that they can handle in second gear. Generally this means a two furrow plough, but there are types of soil on which it may be a three furrow. Another fact brought out by the survey is that rate of ploughing is not proportional to the power available. Wheel tractors of over 35 belt horse power ploughed 0·53 acre an hour comparedwith 0·47 acre an hour by tractors of less than 20 b.h.p. Although there may be a tendency for the more powerful tractors to be used on the heavier land, the more probable explanation of the small difference between the rates of ploughing quoted is, as already mentioned, the inability of a high powered wheel tractor to use the power available as drawbar pull.

The equipment necessary to work a farm is determined by the type of farming and the size of farm, but there is no close relationship between the size of farm and the amount of equipment. It may not always be advisable for a farmer to purchase all the machines and tools that he could conveniently use. Certain operations such as very deep ploughing, subsoiling, mole draining, spraying and lime spreading that are done only occasionally require special equipment and sometimes very powerful tractors. It is more economical to leave such work to contractors.

There is also a possibility of sharing with one's neighbours. Co-operative ownership and use of machinery is practised on a small scale, and the practice has never appealed widely either to large or small farmers. Much more interest is now being shown in the idea. The farmers' organisations in Britain supported by the leading banks have drawn up a scheme by which Machinery Syndicates can be formed on an approved plan. Those farmers, say six or so, who form a syndicate are required to enter into a definite form of agreement as to the running of the syndicate and the operation of any machines and equipment that it owns. The scheme is in its early days. but promises well, particularly in the purchase of expensive but very necessary machines and equipment, for which there is insufficient work on any one farm to justify the outlay. Success depends

[1] " Operation Rates for Basic Cultivations," *Agricultural Engineering Record*, Vol. I, Winter, 1946-47, p. 162.

much on the leader of the syndicate and the mututal confidence that its members can establish with each other—hence the advantages of a small membership, not more than six. One of the big problems to-day is how to reduce the cost of mechanisation on the small farm, and the syndicate scheme may prove at least a partial solution to this difficulty.

The equipment for a one tractor farm generally includes one or two ploughs, a cultivator, a set of light and of heavy harrows (and possibly of disc harrows), a roller, a seed drill, a fertilizer drill and a grass mower, a tool bar with row crop attachments, a binder (or small combine harvester) and at least one trailer. The farming system, the organisation and management and the situation of the farm all have an influence on how many acres should provide a full year's work for any given machine or piece of equipment and when it should be duplicated. The following table, (p. 685) is a rough guide in considering the mechanisation of any particular farm.

The author's comment is that these figures represent reasonable efficient performances, and not average figures such as would be obtained in a survey covering all farms.

On the question of the provision of barn machinery it is again difficult to lay down principles of general application. On the larger arable and mixed farms (with one or two hundred acres or more under arable crops annually) it will generally be found profitable to instal a complete equipment and there may be a special case for doing so on even smaller farms, where live stock production is intensive.

Other standard equipment comprises a weighing machine, ladders, sacks, stack and wagon covers, ropes, and so on. Additional equipment is required for the various classes of stock: for sheep feeding a supply of netting or hurdles, troughs, corn bins, hay racks and root cutter; for pigs, either self feeders or food steaming plant may be necessary; and for the dairy, milking machine, churns, cooler, separator and steriliser according to the method of disposal of the milk. A milking machine is now a normal piece of equipment where the number of cows in milk exceeds ten to twelve.

**Live Stock.**—The live stock carrying capacity of a farm is based mainly on the amount of home grown food available and the quantity of purchased feeding stuffs that is available or that may be used profitably. Other important considerations are the accommodation for live stock and sometimes the quantity of litter available.

On some farms the main income may be derived from the sale of crops such as grain, potatoes and sugar beet, and the function of the live stock is to convert the by-products of the farm into marketable form and to assist in maintaining soil fertility. On others, live stock and their products may provide 80 per cent. or more of the farm income e.g. in milk, and the objective will be generally to maintain as many live stock as the farm can carry conveniently. Clearly, any calculations as to stock carrying capacity

## Table 22

## EFFECTIVE CAPACITIES OF FIELD EQUIPMENT *

| Implement or Machine | Normal Working Speed m.p.h. | Average Rate of Work Acres/ft. width/ hour | Field Capacity of Typical Implement | | Potential Acreage per implement per season in average conditions [1] Acres |
|---|---|---|---|---|---|
| | | | Width of Implement ft. | Average Rate of Work Acres/hr. | |
| Ploughs . . . . | 2½ | 0·18 | 3 | ½ | 125[2] |
| Rotary cultivators . . | 2 | 0·15 | 5 | ¾ | 150 |
| Cultivators . . . | 3 | 0·25 | 7 | 1¾ | 200 |
| Harrows, zig-zag . . | 3 | 0·25 | 12 | 3 | 350[3] |
| Harrows, disc . . | 3 | 0·25 | 8 | 2 | 200 |
| Rolls . . . . | 3 | 0·28 | 18 | 5 | 500 |
| Fertilizer distributors . | 3½ | 0·25 | 8 | 2[4] | 200 |
| Corn drills . . . | 3½ | 0·25 | 8 | 2 | 200[5] |
| Combine drills . . . | 3 | 0·18 | 8½ | 1½ | 175 |
| Tractor hoes . . . | 2 | 0·15 | 8 | 1¼ | 100 |
| Down-the-row thinners . | 2 | 0·15 | 8 | 1¼ | 100 |
| 3-row ridgers . . . | 2½ | 0·21 | 7 | 1½ | 125 |
| Potato scufflers . . | 3 | 0·25 | 7 | 1¾ | 150 |
| Mowers . . . . | 3 | 0·25 | 5 | 1¼ | 150 |
| Swath turners/side rakes . | 3½ | 0·30 | 10 | 3 | 200 |
| Hay sweeps . . . | 6 | 0·10 | 10 | 1 | 100 |
| Pick-up balers . . . | 3–4 | — | — | 1½–2 | 300[6] |
| Binders . . . | 3½ | 0·25 | 6 | 1½ | 120 |
| Combine harvesters 4–6 ft. | 2 | 0·15–0·2 | 5 | ¾–1 | 100 |
| ,, ,, 8 ft. | 2 | 0·13–0·16 | 8 | 1–1¼ | 160 |
| ,, ,, 12 ft. | 2 | 0·11–0·15 | 12 | 1¼–1¾ | 240 |
| Potato planters . . | 1¼ | 0·11 | 4⅔ (2-row) | ½ | 60 |
| Potato spinners . . | 2 | 0·15 | 2⅓ | ⅓[7] | 75 |
| ,, elevator diggers . | 2 | 0·15 | 2⅓ | ⅓[7] | 75 |
| ,, harvesters . | 1½ | 0·10 | 2⅓ | ¼ | 60 |
| Sugar beet harvesters . | 3 | 0·17 | 1½ | ¼ | 80 |
| Spraying machines . . | 4 | 0·25 | 16 | 4 | 300 |

[1] Above this acreage a second or larger implement is likely to be needed, or it may be necessary to adopt alternative methods.

[2] The implement could do much more, but "timeliness" may make it necessary to have two ploughs above this acreage. Similarly, timeliness is a limiting factor for most of the equipment in this table.

[3] Refers to one kind of harrow only. Several sets of different weights may be needed even for much smaller acreage.

[4] Rate of work much lower with heavy dressings.

[5] Different types may be needed.

[6] Total of hay and straw.

[7] Determined by pickers rather than by equipment.

* *Farm Mechanisation Management* by Claude Culpin, 1959, Crosby Lockwood and Son Ltd.

will be affected according to whether live stock constitutes the primary or secondary group of farm enterprises.

While the relationship between live stock, crops and grass is important on most farms, there are a few farms where live stock production is carried out wholly with purchased feeding stuffs and litter, land being required only for buildings, with perhaps a small open space for exercise. This was a common system in town dairies, where such by-products as milling offals and brewers grain and green foods were carted to deep milking cows. The cows were sold fat for slaughter as they dried off. Few such dairies now exist. Intensive production with little land is now practised in broiler houses and sometimes with pigs. In those types of production food is a major item of cost and the price of feeding stuffs relative to the return obtained for the live stock product is an important consideration.

**Summer Stock.**—A convenient method of calculating stock for pasture is to reduce the various classes of grazing stock to a common basis. A suitable unit is the food requirement of a dairy cow of average size ($10\frac{1}{2}$ cwt.) yielding 2 gal. of milk daily. Throughout the greater part of the grazing season such an animal will do quite well on pasture of ordinary quality without any additional feeding and may be reckoned to require a ration of 12 lb. starch equivalent per day. In the table (p. 687) the daily food requirements of various classes of stock are set down; an assumption is made regarding the amount of starch equivalent fed in the form of concentrates, the difference giving the amount of starch equivalent that would necessarily be derived from grass. In the last column is given a number or fraction representing the pasture units to be allotted to each animal of the various types.

The value of pasture, of course, varies within wide limits, both as to the weight of grass produced and its feeding value. First class British pastures, leaving out a limited number of exceptionally rich ones, may produce about 8 tons of green grass per acre during the season, with a starch equivalent of about 12—say nearly 1 ton of starch equivalent, which is just equal to 12 lb. per day for a six months' grazing season. An acre of such pasture is therefore equivalent to 1 unit in the table on page 687. Other types of pasture will carry stock in something like the following proportions:—

|  | Units per Acre |
|---|---|
| Finest permanent fattening pastures and first-year seeds pastures on best arable land    .    :    .    .    . | $=1\frac{1}{4}$ |
| First-class permanent pastures and first-year seeds pastures on average arable land    .    .    .    .    . | $=1$ |
| Average permanent pastures and pastures of second and subsequent years on average arable land    .    .    . | $=\frac{2}{3}$ |
| Poorer lowland and average semi-upland pastures    . | $=\frac{1}{2}$ |
| Hill pastures    .    .    .    .    .    .    .    . | $=\frac{1}{5}$ to $\frac{1}{3}$ |
| Mountain grazings    .    .    .    .    .    .    . | $=\frac{1}{50}$ to $\frac{1}{5}$ |

The aftermath from seeds leys, cut once for hay, may be taken as representing about or slightly more than one-third of the total annual output; that from permanent grassland that has been cut for hay will

TABLE 23

| | Live Weight | Total Daily Ration (Starch Equivalent) | Concentrate Ration (Starch Equivalent) | Grass Ration (Starch Equivalent) | Pasture Units per Head |
|---|---|---|---|---|---|
| *Cattle* | Cwt. | | | | |
| Milch cows yielding 2 gal. per day | 10½ | 12 | ... | 12 | 1 |
| Fattening bullocks | 10½ | 13½ | 1½ | 12 | 1 |
| Dairy and store stock— | | | | | |
| 6 to 12 months | 4 | 6 | ... | 6 | ½ |
| 12 „ 18 „ | 6 | 7½ | ... | 7½ | 3/5 |
| 18 „ 24 „ | 8 | 9 | ... | 9 | ¾ |
| Cattle for early fattening— | | | | | |
| 6 to 12 months | 5 | 7½ | ... | 7½ | 3/5 |
| 12 „ 18 „ | 7 | 8½ | ... | 8½ | ⅔ |
| 18 „ 24 „ | 9 | 10 | ... | 10 | 5/6 |
| *Sheep* | Lb. | | | | |
| Breeding ewes, large with twin fattening lambs | 200 | 5 | 1 | 4 | ⅓ |
| Do. with single fattening lambs | ... | 3¾ | ¾ | 3 | ¼ |
| Do. with twin store lambs | ... | 4½ | ½ | 4 | ⅓ |
| Do. with single store lambs | ... | 3¼ | ¼ | 3 | ¼ |
| Breeding ewes, small, with twin lambs | 120 | 3¾ | ¾ | 3 | ¼ |
| Do. with single lambs | ... | 3 | ½ | 2½ | 1/5 |
| Yearling sheep— | | | | | |
| Fattening | 100 | 1 3/5 | 2/5 | 1 1/5 | 1/10 |
| Store | 100 | 1 1/5 | ... | 1 1/5 | 1/10 |
| Fattening weaned lambs | 80 | 1½ | 3/10 | 1 1/5 | 1/10 |
| *Horses* | | | | | |
| Draft mare (and foal) | 1500 | 15 | ... | 15 | 1¼ |
| Yearlings | 700 | 8 | ... | 8 | ⅔ |
| Two-year-olds | 1000 | 10 | ... | 10 | 5/6 |

usually represent from a fourth to a third of the total output, depending on the time of cutting. In the pre-war period (1936-38) the area of lowland pasture per live stock unit was about 1·5 acres, in addition to 0·7 acres of hay aftermath, making the equivalent of about 1·7 acres of full-season grazing. This rate of stocking was certainly below the optimum. In 1946 the corresponding figures were 1·2 acres of pasture and 0·6 acres of aftermath, making the equivalent of about 1·4 acres of full-season grazing per unit. This represented, despite the substitution of temporary leys for a considerable proportion of permanent pasture, something rather above the optimum. The optimum rate of stocking, under present conditions, would probably give an average figure of ¾ unit per acre, *i.e.* the equivalent of 1·2 acres per cow. This would imply about 1·6 acres of grassland—1·0 acre of full-season pasture and the aftermath from 0·6 acre taken for silage or hay.

Carrying capacity can be raised above the ordinary level by the use of nitrogen fertilizers and the adoption of a system of rotational grazing. It depends, too, on the proportions of the various classes of stock placed upon it. It is least when the stock is exclusively sheep or horses, and is probably greatest when the stock comprises a large proportion of sheep and store cattle. Stocking must further depend on the amount of winter grazing that is wanted; if a considerable amount of autumn growth is to be left as wintering, the pasture must be not fully stocked in the latter part of the summer season.

The following calculation shows the application of the foregoing data.

A mixed farm of fair fertility provides 20 acres first-year seeds pasture, 40 acres second and third year seeds pasture, and 80 acres secondary permanent pasture. The number of units would accordingly be:—

|  | Units |
|---|---|
| 20 acres first-year seeds . . . . . . | = 20 |
| 120 ,, second-year and permanent pasture . . | = 80 |
| Total . . | =100 |

The stock carried might be:—

|  | Units |
|---|---|
| 32 dairy cows . . . . . . . | =32·0 |
| 8 heifers, six to twelve months, at ½ unit . . | = 4·0 |
| 8 ,, twelve to eighteen months, at ⅗ unit . | = 4·8 |
| 8 ,, eighteen to twenty-four months, at ¾ unit . | = 6·0 |
| 150 large breeding ewes— |  |
| 80 with single lambs, at ¼ unit . . . . | =20·0 |
| 70 ,, twin lambs, at ⅓ unit . . . | =23·3 |
| 50 yearling ewes, at 1/10 unit . . . . . | = 5·0 |
| Total . | =95·1 |

It will generally be wise to adjust the permanent stock of the farm to 10 per cent. or so, below the theoretical carrying capacity, otherwise in seasons of drought the farmer will be faced with the alternative of selling stock in a bad market or of purchasing large quantities of expensive concentrates. In favourable seasons the surplus grass may be ensiled, otherwise the pastures should be topped by the mower to prevent the plants running to seed.

Under very intensive systems of pasture management, with rotational grazing and heavy nitrogenous as well as other manuring, the carrying capacity of the middle grades of pasture in regions of ample rainfall can be increased by some 50 to 100 per cent. The same relative increase cannot be secured on first class pastures; on the poorest classes—e.g. mountain grazings—the response would not be commensurate with the cost of the intensive treatment.

The stock carrying capacity can also be raised by providing keep for difficult seasons—in early spring by rye and by Italian or short rotation ryegrass, and in autumn by undersown Italian ryegrass.

**Winter Stock.**—For winter stocking, general rules cannot be laid down because the requirements of different classes of animals are not even roughly comparable. The following facts may, however, be usefully stated.

*Litter.*—After deduction of the quantity necessary for thatch, covering clamps, littering horses if any, the wheat and a good deal of the barley straw produced will normally be used as litter for housed cattle or pigs. The allotment may vary within wide limits. Where straw is scarce, and regarded as a commodity of considerable value—e.g. on semi-arable dairy or north country cattle feeding farms—5 lb. per head per day, for full-sized cattle in stalls, is ample. For cattle in covered courts, a daily allowance of 12 to 16 lb. per head (varying somewhat according to the quantity of roots fed), will ensure the animals a comfortable bed and the production of the best quality of farmyard manure. Where the cattle are running in partially open yards, and where the object is rather to tread down a maximum quantity of straw into manure, 20 or more lb. per head may be allowed and farmyard manure of still fair quality be produced. The allowance for young stock kept indoors may be reckoned at between 1 and 2 lb. per 100 lb. live weight per day. The allowance for pigs may be calculated on the same basis, though in the more modern type of house, with its dunging passage, very little is needed.

On farms where litter straw is scarce and expensive to buy, a number of alternative materials are being tried—sawdust and wood shavings. A few farmers in such conditions are also turning to slatted floors, and the number seems likely to increase as more experience is gained about the most suitable type of slats, the management of live stock on slats and the best and most economical methods of moving the accumulated farmyard manure.

*Fodder Straws.*—The use as fodder of large quantities of cereal straw can be attained practically only with cattle. On cattle feeding and dairying farms the whole of the available oat straw is generally used as fodder if there is sufficient other material to serve as litter. Barley straw is used as fodder in districts where oats are not a satisfactory crop. For cattle on full production rations the maximum daily ration of straw will be about 12 to 14lb. per 1000 lb. live weight. A larger proportion makes the ration too bulky in proportion to its energy value. Cattle being kept at little over maintenance level—*e.g.* dry cows—may consume up to 20 lb. per 1000 lb. live weight per day. Straw is not necessary if other roughage, such as hay, is available and can be used economically. Where there is a possibility of selling straw this method of disposal should be considered, but the market is a variable and limited one. If farmyard manure can be bought in exchange, the whole of the straw may be so disposed of, but where this is not possible the proportion to be sold must be decided according to the nature of the soil of the farm, especially with regard to its humus content. Thus, black fen soils require little farmyard manure, and the bulk of the straw may be sold. At the other extreme, light soils in the drier districts decline in fertility when farmyard manure is withheld over a period of years, and the selling of straw is generally to be avoided altogether. The extent to which straw should be converted into dung depends also on the kind of crops grown. Mangels, potatoes and many market garden crops benefit from applications of organic manure.

*Hay*, since it is a primary product and not a by-product, must be regarded quite differently from straw; that is to say, no more need be produced than can be used profitably. Hay has an energy value that is from 50 to 100 per cent. higher than that of straw, and its content of protein is from three to ten times as high.

Hay may be regarded as indispensable for horses on regular work, the annual allowance per head varying from 25 to 30 cwt., according to the type of horse used and the distribution and amount of the work to be done. For young horses in winter a certain amount is generally necessary, 5 to 10 cwt. per head representing their requirement where they have a good range of winter pasture.

For cattle up to one year old, hay will generally form part of the winter ration, and the minimum allowance may be put at about 1 per cent. of the live weight per day. Sheep fattening or wintering on roots generally receive hay at the rate of $\frac{1}{2}$ to 1 lb. per 100 lb. live weight daily; to grass-wintering sheep and cattle, hay may be supplied regularly or only during spells of severe weather.

At the other extreme, *e.g.* on some grassland dairy farms, hay forms the basis of the winter ration, and may be fed to cattle at the rate of fully 2 per cent. of their live weight daily. On others, the conserved grass may be fed as silage or both silage and hay may be fed.

*Silage*, if well made from immature grass, has a high starch equivalent and a protein equivalent normally varying with its dry matter content. The quantity eaten depends largely on dry matter content, which should, if possible, be over 25 per cent. Silage of that quality can be used as a substitute for hay and in addition normally supplies extra protein for production. The value of silage is now appreciated more widely, particularly by those who have devised satisfactory arrangements for self feeding.

Silage from mature crops of oats and legumes or from grass in an advanced stage of growth is of less value, but proves useful for dry and store stock, and can be a useful substitute for roots and hay.

*Roots*, having a high energy value in relation to their dry matter content and being succulent and very palatable, form a satisfactory complement to straw in the feeding of all classes of cattle. With the introduction of precision drilling and mechanical singling the costs of growing the crop have been reduced considerably, and there are indications that the acreage of roots for live stock feeding may rise.

The maximum root ration for growing and fattening cattle may be reckoned at about 8 per cent. of the live weight daily. At this rate an average bullock would consume 7 to 8 tons, or somewhat under $\frac{1}{2}$ acre of an average crop, in a six months' feeding period. For dairy cows about three fourths of this quantity should be regarded as the upper limit, the energy requirement of the ration being made up in other ways. The economic ration in particular cases depends on the ease or difficulty of growing the crop and the cost. Where hay is fed in place of straw the root ration may be reduced or eliminated entirely.

Sheep may receive relatively more roots than cattle—up to 15 per cent. of the live weight daily for full production, and, even in maintenance and low production rations, roots usually take a more prominent place. It is to be noted that the cost of the crop to sheep is less than to cattle, since normally sheep consume a considerable proportion of their roots in folds, and lifting and carting is thus avoided.

Fattening and breeding hoggets of the larger lowland breeds may be given 1 cwt. per week, allowing for a certain amount of wastage, or 1 ton in a winter feeding period of five months. Breeding ewes of the larger lowland types require about the same quantity, but the use of roots depends much on the date of lambing and on the amount of pasturage and other food available.

*Kale* has a higher dry matter content than roots and is normally fed in smaller quantities. Moreover, fibre constitutes a larger proportion of its dry matter, so that if it is substituted for roots on a dry matter basis the net energy value of the ration will be reduced. The equivalent of a ration of swedes, straw and concentrates can be obtained with a kale, straw and concentrate combination only if the straw is somewhat reduced and the starchy concentrate—*e.g.* oats or maize meal—is increased. On dairy farms it is a common aim to provide about 40 lb. of kale per cow per day from early October till Christmas. This implies about 1$\frac{1}{4}$ ton or perhaps $\frac{1}{12}$ acre per cow.

The amount of by-products, such as small potatoes, tail corn and sugar beet tops affects the carrying capacity of the farm to a minor extent. Considerable quantities of home grown grain are fed to stock, but these, when normal imports are available, are to be regarded as alternatives to purchased concentrates and thus hardly enter into stocking calculations.

**The Working** or **Floating Capital** comprises that part which is regularly turned over—that is to say, realised and reinvested. The rate of turnover varies with the nature of the product. In a fresh milk dairy, capital is invested in food and labour, and a return obtained from sales of milk practically concurrently, with the result that the amount of working capital required is negligible. In producing a spring cereal, the capital represented by seed, manure and tillage will be laid out for a period of from six months to a year; that spent in threshing may be realised again almost at once. If grass seed be sown with the cereal crop, the capital so invested will be realised only after one or more years; and if the grass be manured with basic slag the return may be expected to be spread over a period of years.

In practice the amount of floating capital required may be arrived at in either of two ways. Firstly, taking a farm at any season of the year, the working capital actually invested at the moment may be added to the prospective outlays that will require to be made up till such time as current receipts may be expected to equal or exceed expenditure. Thus if we enter an arable selling farm at Candlemas (2nd February), the outgoing tenant having disposed of the whole of the previous season's crop, we should pay for tillages that had been carried out, for grass seed and wheat seed already sown and for manures and unexhausted residues. We should then proceed to estimate our probable outlays, under the heads of seeds, manures, wages, feeding stuffs, rent, insurance and sundry maintenance charges up till, say, September or October, when sales on a considerable scale would commence, and our investment would cease to grow.

Alternatively, the total investment of floating capital may be estimated directly for the particular season of the year when it will be at its maximum. Thus in the foregoing case we should estimate the probable investment represented in the crop and manurial residues, just after the completion of harvest, and the sum so obtained would represent the maximum working capital required.

It will be obvious that where the requirements of working capital vary considerably from one season to another the farmer may find it in his interest to obtain credit for part of the year rather than to have a large amount of capital lying idle at other seasons. The investment in the main items of floating capital on an arable farm, over a period of a year, is shown in Fig. 36. The farm grew 100 acres grain, 30 acres potatoes, 30 acres roots and 30 acres hay. The live stock consisted entirely of cattle

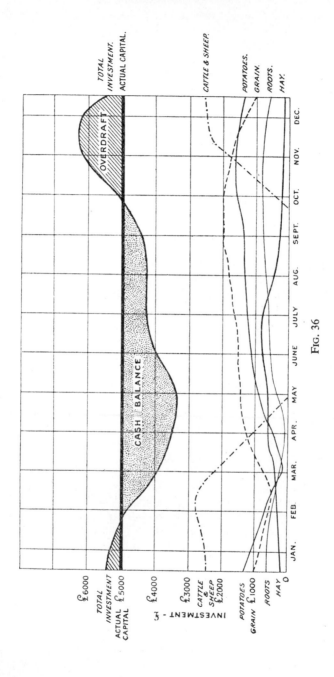

FIG. 36

and sheep which were bought in autumn to consume the roots and straw and were sold fat between February and May. The actual working capital was £5000. In April and May, after the winter stock had been sold, the farmer had a cash balance of £1500. In November, because the winter stock had to be purchased before any considerable amount of the grain and potatoes had been realised, he had an overdraft of about the same amount. The exact amount of working capital that it would be profitable to employ on this farm, *e.g.* whether £3000, £4000, or £6000, would depend on the relationship between farming profits and bank interest. Obviously, if a farmer could make 12 per cent. on his working capital and the rate of overdraft interest were 6 per cent., it would pay him to borrow more freely.

## FARM LABOUR

**Labour requirements** may be claculated on the basis of the acreages of crops grown and the numbers of the various classes of live stock maintained, with an allowance for overheads, *i.e.* work involved in the maintenance of roads, drains, ditches, fences and equipment generally, the wages of a bailiff (or of such part as pertains to general supervision), and any other work time that cannot be charged up to a particular enterprise. A common figure for overheads is about 15 per cent.

The following figures are derived from the investigations of farm economists as reported in the Farm Management Survey. The unit used is the man day (8 hours). There is, as would be expected, a considerable range of variation as between one farm and another—apart from that due to varying degrees of efficiency in labour organisation. Thus in respect of crops, the labour expended on tillage will vary with soil type, size and shape of fields, the average distance from field gate to homestead and the quality of farm roads. Labour expenditure per acre on harvesting or hay making will vary with climate and the size of the crops. In the case of live stock there is considerable variation as between different systems—*e.g.* deep litter as compared with free range poultry keeping, or the yard and parlour as compared with the cowshed system of dairying. Even when the system is essentially the same—*e.g.* yard feeding of cattle—much will depend on the layout of the buildings in relation to convenience in feeding, littering and dung handling. Recently, attention to method study has resulted in changes which in some cases have reduced labour requirements very markedly. The figures given on page 695 are averages.

In estimating the number of regular workers required for a particular farm, the total man days are calculated from the acreages of the various crops and the numbers of the different classes of live stock, and an addition, commonly of 15 per cent., is made for overheads; next, a deduction is made for the estimated amount of casual labour to be employed (for such tasks as potato lifting and beet singling) to give the amount of work remaining to be done by the regular staff. The number of man days (each of 8 hours) available is influenced by the statutory regulations, which from time to time are varied, and the amount of overtime. Most farm workers do overtime at the busiest seasons of the year. With these

*Crops and Grass: Man Days per Acre*

Wheat, oats, barley and rye—
    Binder-harvested . . . . . . 4
    Combine-harvested . . . . . 2
Beans and field peas . . . . . 3–5
Potatoes . . . . . . . . 20
Turnips and swedes (folded) . . . . 10
Mangels, sugar-beet and fodder-beet (hand topped) . . . . . . . 20
Kale and cabbage (carted). . . . . 14
Pasture . . . . . . . . $\frac{1}{2}$
Hay and silage. . . . . . . $2\frac{1}{2}$

*Live Stock: Man Days per Head per Year*

Dairy cows—
    Hand milked . . . . . . 19
    Yard and parlour . . . . . . 12
In-calf heifers . . . . . . . 2
Bulls . . . . . . . . 3
Other cattle— .
    2 years and over . . . . . . 2
    1 to 2 years . . . . . . 3
    Under 1 year . . . . . . $4\frac{1}{2}$
Lowland sheep—over 1 year (including ewes with lambs . . . . . . . $1\frac{1}{2}$

Pigs—
    Breeding sows . . . . . . 5
    Stores and fatteners . . . . . $1\frac{1}{2}$
    Overall (breeding, rearing and fattening) . . $2\frac{1}{2}$

considerations in mind the following man day figures give a guide in calculating the total available labour—Stockman 350, Tractor driver 320, General worker 300. An average figure for a farmer is 300.

A rather widely variable factor, which affects requirements in the way of regular staff, is the extent to which the farmer may depend upon contractors. In areas where contract services are available it may be profitable to use these, especially for operations that require special machinery or exceptionally high powered tractors—deep ploughing and cultivating, combine harvesting of corn; weed spraying or mechanical beet harvesting.

Minimum wage rates for prescribed hours of work are laid down by the Central Wages Boards for England and Wales and for Scotland respectively. There are separate rates for adult men, adult woman and young workers, according to age.

Piece work rates can be applied to certain farm operations. In general, the system has obvious advantages where the quantity of work done is readily measurable and its quality can be assessed. In some areas such operations as hedging, ditching, root singling and sugar beet harvesting, are normally done at piece work rates, whether by regular employees or by casual workers. On some large dairy farms the head herdsman is in fact a contractor, employing what assistance he requires and being paid on the gallonage of milk produced.

Various forms of bonus payments are in use, especially for stockmen—for instance a bonus for numbers of pigs reared in excess of a given number per litter, or of lambs reared in excess of a standard number per hundred ewes.

Profit sharing schemes have been operated in some cases, but are open to the difficulty that farm profits are subject to many influences other than the efficiency and assiduity of the staff—for instance a drought or bad harvest may deprive the workers of a bonus payment that their efforts may have fully deserved. This difficulty has prevented their general adoption.

# CHAPTER 27

# THE CHOICE OF FARM ENTERPRISES

THE first problem that arises in the organisation of the farm is the selection of enterprises—the choice of the particular commodities to be produced on the farm. Selection from among the various possibilities should never be arbitrary but should be based on a thorough understanding of all the conditions, natural and economic, under which the farm will have to be managed.

The chief marketable products of British agriculture are cereal and other grains; potatoes and other vegetables; sugar beet; fat cattle, sheep and pigs; wool; milk, butter and cheese; horses; eggs and table poultry; fruit, flowers and glass house produce. In certain cases (as, for example, that of beef) the process of production is often divided into two or three stages, so that, in fact, there are more departments in the industry than there are marketable products.

**Grain.**—While it is of course true that the various cereal crops have different individual requirements in regard to temperature, moisture and fertilizers, yet it is possible to lay down certain principles regarding corn-growing generally. It is to be understood that the production of grain for sale is the question immediately under discussion. The use of cereals for the production of stock food is dealt with later.

The conditions affecting the economic success of cereal cultivation are briefly as follows:—

1. *Climate.*—The operations of seeding, and more particularly that of harvesting, are most cheaply and most efficiently performed under dry conditions. Under the best conditions—such as prevail, for example, in the great wheat belt of North America—cereals may be regularly combined from the standing crops and put in store without a need for artificial drying. In the wetter areas of our country there is additional expense and more risk of damage at harvest. The moisture requirement of cereal crops is on the whole low, and full yields may be obtained with a rainfall of from 20 to 25 in. per annum if other conditions are suitable. A rather high amount of sunshine is beneficial both in respect of yield and quality. Thus cereals are most profitably cultivated in the drier and sunnier districts—that is to say, in the east of Britain rather than in the west.

2. *Soil.*—Compared with other annual crops, cereals are easily satisfied as regards tilth. This arises partly from the fact that they are relatively

frost hardy and can be sown either in autumn or early in spring, when moisture is plentiful in the soil, and partly from the fact that the seeds are large, can be sown at a fair depth and germinate readily. Cereals are therefore relatively safe crops on the more extreme types of arable soil. This fact is exemplified in the high proportion of the arable area devoted to cereals on such different soils as the heavy clays of Essex and the thin dry soils of the Chalk.

3. *Markets.*—Cereal grain has a fairly high value in relation to its weight, is non-perishable and with modern facilities is easily and cheaply handled and transported. Hence proximity to market means relatively little in the value of the produce. Cereals are included in the list of farm products for which prices are guaranteed under the Agriculture Act, 1947.

4. *The Scale of Production.*—Before the use of the threshing machine became general, in the early part of the nineteenth century, there was no marked relation between the size of the enterprise and the unit cost of production of cereals. Even when mechnical threashing became normal, the needs of the small producer could largely be met by the threshing contractor with his movable equipment. Again, the early reapers were so cheap that their purchase did not impose a heavy burden on the small farm. The horse drawn binder, a more costly piece of capital, was capable of handling some 70 acres of corn, and units of lesser size were placed at some disadvantage. The introduction of reliable medium powered tractors, some twenty five years ago, and of the power take-off binder, enabled practically all the field work to be mechanised, and provided the farmer with an opportunity to make a substantial reduction in costs if his cereal acreage was of the order of 100 acres or more. This opportunity was not open to the small producer. In the thirties the high powered tractor, capable of pulling three or four furrows and the combine harvester (used in conjunction with a grain dryer), made possible a further substantial reduction in costs (and also in harvest risks) in large units. Cost accounts seem to suggest something like 150 or 200 acres as the minimum size for maximum economy in production. But the additional cost per acre, for a unit of half this size, is not very large, especially where the straw is required or can be profitably used as litter or fodder for cattle.

5. *The Labour Requirements* of cereals, compared with those of other arable crops, can be brought down to a rather low figure (see p. 695). Hence high wages do not in themselves mean that cereals cannot be profitably grown. Of more consequence from the point of view of organisation is the seasonal distribution of labour. On the whole this is very uneven; in one actual set of records, 37 per cent. of the total tractor labour for the barley crop on a group of farms was applied during March and April, and a further 37 per cent. in August and September; the remaining 26 per cent. was spread over the remaining eight months of the year.

Since seed time and harvest are the periods of pressure, the area of cereals that can be grown will depend partly on the supply of trained labour at these times and partly on the length of the periods over which planting and harvesting can be spread. The sowing of proportions of both winter and spring varieties will ease the pressure of work at seed time, and in districts where winter oats, winter barley and spring wheat succeed, the harvest can likewise be spread over a longer period, because the two former mature earlier, and the last later, than the main crops. Earlier and later ripening varieties can also be chosen. In the extreme north and at high elevations, where there is often barely time for the crops to be sown, ripened and harvested within the limits of the season, the growing of corn for market ceases to be an important object.

6. *Capital Investment* per acre is comparatively low. Costs of production under typical British conditions amounted to something of the order of £8 or £10 per acre in the period 1930-39. Costs now range from as little as £12 to more than £20 per acre, with an average of about £15.

7. *Weeds* formerly set a rather strict limit to the frequency of cereal crops and hence to the proportion of cereals on the arable acreage as a whole. Few of the rotations in widespread use implied a higher proportion than half of the land in corn. The increasingly effective control of weeds, by means of selective weed killers, has changed the situation in regard to what used to be the most prevalent of corn field weeds—charlock and wild radish, poppy and corn buttercup. But annual grass weeds (wild oats and slender foxtail) as well as perennials like couch and bind weed still set some limit to the frequency of cereal crops. It is possible in the south and south-east, especially where ample power is available, to carry out a considerable amount of cultivation (stubble cleaning) after the grain crop has been removed from the land; hence in dry and early districts the proportion of cereals may be greater than in the wet and late areas. In the main cereal growing districts corn often now occupies 60 per cent of the arable acreage.

8. *The utilisation of straw* has a rather important bearing on the profits of grain growing. It has a considerable value, notably where other conditions tend to favour the cattle industry (dairying, rearing or feeding). The larger the place occupied by cereals in the system, the less does the value of the straw become, until in the extreme case it is sometimes regarded as of little worth and is burnt.

The special requirements and preferences of wheat, barley, oats, and rye in the matter of soil and climate, and also the relative yields of grain and straw, are dealt with in Part 2.

**Beans** and **Peas** grown as seed crops had by 1939 become rather unimportant in Britain, occupying an area equal to about 5 per cent. of the cereal area. There was some increase during the war and post-war periods, when imported high protein feeding stuffs were scarce; but production of pulses for animal food has again declined.  On the other hand there has been an increase in the acreage of peas for human consumption.

*Peas* are more costly to harvest and more susceptible to damage by wet weather than are cereals, and the factors chiefly affecting their distribution are the amount of sunshine and of summer rain.  Their cultivation is mainly confined to the eastern and south-eastern counties of England from the East Riding of Yorkshire to Surrey and Sussex, Worcester being the only notable exception.  The proportion of the crop is largest in Kent, Essex, Suffolk and Lincolnshire.  Pea straw (from the ripe crop) is comparable in energy value to the better cereal straws and has a protein content equal to that of average meadow hay.  It is commonly used for sheep feeding.  The dried haulm from picking peas has a higher feeding value, almost equal to that of hay, and the fresh material (especially that produced on farms where substantial acreages are grown for canning or freezing) makes excellent silage.  The pea crop is expensive to grow and rather speculative, but the returns in good years are high.  An increasing proportion of the crop consists of the so-called garden varieties, which are partly harvested green—either for immediate consumption or freezing or canning—and partly ripened, threshed and either marketed as dry pulse or else processed and canned.

*Beans* have somewhat the same preferences in regard to climatic conditions as peas, *i.e.* they do better in the drier and sunnier districts of the east than in the wetter and duller western districts.  On the other hand, the crop is much less dependent on good harvest weather, being, in fact, considerably less susceptible to damage by rain than the cereals.  The result is that the northern limit of cultivation is higher than that of peas, as evidenced by the considerable areas grown in Scotland as far north as Perthshire.  On the other hand, the distribution is more strictly governed by soil conditions, there being a close correlation between the clay area and the bean area in various districts.  Beans can be summer-tilled more economically than cereals, though they do not form a really satisfactory fallow crop.  In northern districts, where the crop is liable to be somewhat under-ripened, bean straw has a high feeding value.  The feature of unreliability in yield (caused in this case by the incidence of frost damage, aphid attack, chocolate-spot disease and other factors that are not fully understood) is shared with the pea crop; the amount of variation from year to year in the average British yield is about half as large again as in the case of wheat.  The bean acreage declined almost continuously during the half-century preceding 1939.  It increased, as said, during the war, but has since declined again.

**Potatoes.**—Next to cereals, potatoes are by far the most important of our market crops.

1. *Climate.*—Potatoes thrive under a wide range of climatic conditions and their distribution is governed to a very minor extent by the incidence of sunshine, rainfall and temperature.  But the incidence of late and early

frosts is an important consideration, and freedom from the former is generally the governing factor in locating early potato areas. Another rather important point is that a cool and not too dry climate gives healthy and vigorous stocks, whereas in hot and dry regions stocks readily become affected with diseases such as mosaic and leaf-roll, which markedly reduce yields. The demand for Scottish seed from English growers tends to maintain the area of the crop in the North. Northern Ireland also exports a considerable tonnage of seed potatoes to England.

2. *Soil Conditions* have a very large influence on production costs. The best soils are deep, free working loams; the worst are heavy clays. Good crops may be produced on heavy land if deep ploughing and thorough tillage are carried out; but in wet autumns the lifting of the crop is difficult and costly. In low rainfall areas, if the earlier maturing main-crop sorts are grown they can be lifted successfully in all but quite exceptionally wet years. The heaviest yields are obtained from the better fen and silt soils, the finest quality from red loams. The crop withstands a considerable degree of soil acidity and may suffer if the lime content of the soil is high. The high incidence of common scab militates against potato production on some soils, chiefly light loams.

3. *Markets and Transport Facilities.*—The weight of marketable produce per acre is about six times as high from potatoes as from grain. Transport and handling charges are therefore a consideration, which should be borne in mind in harvesting, storing and dressing for market. Potatoes grown in the more highly favourable districts command a readier sale, particularly at times when supplies may be in excess of demand.

4. *Uncertainty of Returns.*—The variation in yield in potatoes from year to year is rather high according to the British Agricultural Statistics, about 50 per cent. greater than in the case of wheat. Moreover, potatoes do not keep for more than a few months, so that a surplus from one harvest is of little or no use in making good a deficiency in the next. The result is that, in an uncontrolled market, prices tend to fluctuate violently from year to year, making the crop a highly speculative one.

The main purpose of the Potato Marketing Board, set up in 1934, was to control the marketing of the crop and to steady market prices. Each farm (except those growing less than one acre) was allotted a certain basic acreage, and the Board was empowered to exact payment for permission to increase this basic acreage. Also the Board prescribed the use of riddles of certain sizes, in order to prevent the sale of small tubers for human food. The size of riddle was also adjusted according to the available supplies and the anticipated demand. Factories for the processing of surplus potatoes (*e.g.* for manufacturing starch or alcohol) were also set up by the Board. These measures were successful in their object of reducing price fluctuations.

Under the Agriculture Act, 1947, prices of potatoes, together with those of other basic farm products, have been guaranteed by the State at levels calculated to leave a margin of profit to the efficient producer. The Potato Marketing Board has recently resumed operation and now works very closely with Government Departments in all matters relating to the growing and sale of this crop.

5. *The Labour Requirement* of the potato crop is very high—from five to ten times that of a cereal. Other expenses, *e.g.* that of seed, being also high, potatoes can be cultivated most profitably on fertile soils, where a high gross return can be obtained. On poorer lands, a return commensurate with the expense can rarely be obtained, and the farmer must look to crops that give moderate returns at a lower cost.

The seasonal distribution of labour varies greatly according to circumstances. If conditions permit the cultivation of both early and late varieties—as, for example, in parts of Lincolnshire—the crop may give a very uniform distribution, planting extending from February till April, summer cultivation from April till July, lifting from June to November, marketing from June to May and preparation of the land for the succeeding crops from August to April. If one or other of the chief types (earlies, second earlies or maincrops) is grown to the exclusion of the others, there will be periods of pressure at planting and harvest, especially the latter. The ordinary staff of the farm will usually be quite insufficient to harvest the crop, so a supply of casual labour is necessary and the amount of that labour available often limits the acreage that can be grown. As regards the fitting in of potatoes to the general labour scheme, planting of earlies is generally done before the sowing of spring corn and that of maincrops between the seeding of the spring cereals and the preparation of the land for roots. Early varieties are usually lifted between the hay and cereal harvests, a period when on many arable farms there is little other urgent work. The harvest of second early sorts covers the period of cereal harvest, when the regular farm staff will generally be fully occupied, so that additional labour may have to be secured for the potatoes. The maincrop harvest follows the cereal harvest, and must be completed before there is a likelihood of severe frost. The rate at which lifting should proceed, and therefore the quantity of casual labour that is necessary, depend upon the acreage to be harvested and on the length of time available between cereal harvest and the onset of winter. Broadly speaking, the work is more urgent, and the supply of casual labour must be greater, in the north than in the south. The lifting and storing of mangels and sometimes the lifting of sugar beet is work that falls to be carried through about the same period of the year, and this should be taken into consideration in estimating labour requirements. A part of the crop is now gathered with mechanical harvesters, and the search continues for even better tools which will harvest the crop with a minimum of damage to the tubers. More of the crop is now stored in ventilated stores, where some control of humidity and temperature are possible. When well stored wastage is reduced. There is also another advantage in that the crop can be sorted and dressed during winter under cover, and so the operation is not dependent on the weather.

6. *Capital Requirements.*—The cost of special implements (planter, row-crop equipment, digger and dresser) is not large in relation to an area of the order of 25 acres or more. Large scale growers often find it desirable to erect special houses for chitting the sets, and for storing the crop in order and to enable dressing to proceed indoors during winter. In this case large sums are involved. The floating capital represented in the crop is of the order of £100 per acre.

7. *Manuring.*—Potatoes respond to heavy manuring, and in particular they give a higher average money return than any other crop from dressings of farmyard manure. But black fen land can be quite well farmed with little dung, and in some coastal areas seaweed is used as a substitute for farmyard manure. On early potato farms a similar purpose is served by feeding off catch crops of ryegrass and rape. In the silt and warp districts it is common to take the crop after a one-year clover ley, the aftermath being ploughed in as green manure, and in the moister districts temporary leys, through their contribution to the humus content, render heavy dunging less necessary.

8. *Diseases and Pests.*—As is explained earlier (Part 2, Chapter 10), the acreage of potatoes that can be grown on a particular farm may be restricted by the occurrence of diseases and pests, in particular eelworm. Eelworm control necessitates a wide crop rotation, so that the potato acreage on infested land should not exceed 20 per cent.

9. *The By-products* of the potato crop consist of small and damaged tubers which can be used only for stock feeding. In small quantities they can profitably be fed to cattle, but when the quantity to be dealt with is considerable it will be more economical to feed them to pigs, for which they may supply rather more than half the energy value of the ration. Where medium sized tubers can be sold for seed purposes the amount of non-marketable material is comparatively small, averaging perhaps under 10 per cent.

**Sugar beet** became an important crop in Britain from 1922, when the Government freed home grown sugar from excise duty; in 1925 it was given a substantial subsidy. Factories were erected in various localities, being most numerous in the eastern counties of England. Now the price of sugar beet is guaranteed under the Agriculture Act, 1947. The crop is grown on contract for the factories, at the previously determined price per ton (washed weight), varying according to the sugar content of the roots. Seed is supplied by the factory, and dried pulp, in amounts corresponding to the quantity of beet supplied, is offered back to the growers.

1. *Climate and Soil.*—The climate in the main arable districts, from Fife to Devon, is quite favourable to beet culture. Farther north the

crop does well in favoured localities. In the north the upper limit of
profitable cultivation is probably about the same as that of wheat, viz.,
500 to 700 ft. above sea level. So long as the soil has good depth, and is
not sour, the crop can be profitably grown on a wide range of types, from
light sandy to heavy loams.

2. *Distance from Factory and Transport Facilities.*—Proximity to the
factory is a very important factor. A farmer within 3 miles of the factory
usually delivers his beet at a total transport cost of a few shillings per
ton. There is an arrangement within the terms of the price structure by
which the factories pay a proportion of the transport costs of the more
remote growers.

3. *Labour Conditions.*—The hand labour requirement of the crop
was high, but is rapidly being reduced by such practices as pre-emergence
spraying, precision drilling and mechanical gapping and harvesting. Well
over 60 per cent. of the crop is now lifted with mechanical harvesters.

4. *The Value of the By-products* (tops and pulp) varies in importance
according to the system of farming. The value of tops is greater where
sheep are kept, and that of pulp probably where dairy cows or winter
fattening cattle are a feature of the farm.

The capital involved is considerably lower than in the case of potatoes,
the cost of production per acre, apart from transport, being about three
fifths of that of potatoes. The largest difference is in the cost of seed.

**Hay.**—The making of hay, definitely for sale, is restricted usually to
areas that are fairly close to a market. In times past the chief market was
for the feeding of city horses and mine ponies, but with the replacement
of these by mechanically driven vehicles the demand for hay declined very
markedly. There is still a considerable trade between the south-east of
England and the western uplands. The demand is very variable from
year to year, depending upon the weather during the hay making season
in the pastoral uplands and on the severity of the winter.

Other crops, grown on farms on a very restricted scale, are hops and
mustard. Flax and linseed are now seldom grown. Vegetables such as
cabbage, cauliflower, brussels sprouts, carrots and onions are grown in
certain areas as farm crops; and there are now fairly well defined districts
in which grass, clover and root seeds are grown.

**Hops** have a very heavy labour requirement and involve a large capital
expenditure on such needs as kilns, poles and wire. They repay very
liberal manuring and very intensive treatment generally. Hop growing
is a highly specialised business. Yield and quality are closely dependent
on soil and climatic conditions, a deep, medium or heavy loam or marl
on an open well drained subsoil, abundant sunshine, shelter from strong
winds, freedom from late and early frosts and a dry picking season being
all important. Hop growing in Britain is almost entirely restricted to
two main areas, viz., Kent, Sussex and Hampshire on the one hand, and
Hereford and Worcester on the other. Even within these areas it is only

in comparatively small districts that the crop occupies a large proportion of the land. The Hops Marketing Board controls the acreage of the crop and the marketing of the produce.

**Brown Mustard** (for seed) is a crop that can be grown most profitably on deep, fertile, rather moist soils. It requires to be harvested within very narrow limits of time and is easily damaged by bad weather, so that a dry harvest period is very important. The area required to supply market requirements is not very large, and the crop is closely restricted to a few specially suitable districts in the east of England, principally in the fen districts of Lincoln, Cambridge and Norfolk.

**Flax** has received much artificial encouragement during periods of war but does not appear to be destined to occupy any permanent place in British agriculture.

**Linseed**—*i.e.* varieties of flax grown for seed—requires little labour (less probably than the average cereal), and the product has a high value in proportion to its bulk. It tends rather to be grown in districts remote from markets where suitable land is cheap, *e.g.* in Argentina. The crop is of value where a cereal crop has been destroyed and it is too late to resow.

The growing of **Vegetables** as field crops depends on suitable soil and climatic conditions which permit of early sowing and regular daily harvesting, on the availability of the necessary labour and on the prospect of a market. Success turns largely on the managerial ability of the farmer. Carrots as field crops are now cultivated in Lindsey, the Isle of Ely, the East Riding of Yorkshire and Norfolk, onions and brussels sprouts in Bedfordshire, broccoli in Cornwall and celery in the Fens.

The principal **Seeds** produced in Britain (apart from cereals and pulses) are clovers, grasses and roots.

**Clovers** are all dependent on insects for fertilisation, so that the seed yield is very closely governed by the amount of summer sunshine. They are also very susceptible to damage from wet weather at harvest. Consequently, the clover seed industry is mainly confined to the south-eastern half of the country from Somerset to Lincolnshire and to certain small areas in Cornwall, the Severn Valley and parts of Wales. Considerable quantities of clover seed are imported from New Zealand, France and Canada, where climatic conditions are more favourable to production than anywhere in Britain. But the closer adaptation of the home strains to their native conditions enables British seed to command a higher price than imported, and thus gives the home grower a compensating advantage. Sainfoin seed is produced on the more highly calcareous soils in low rainfall districts. In the past relatively little success was achieved in the production of lucerne seed in Britain, but the introduction of newer techniques holds out some promise of better results.

**Grass Seeds.**—Up till the thirties British requirements of grass seeds were met for the most part by imported supplies. The chief exceptions

Z

were the ryegrasses—of which considerable quantities were grown in Cambridge, Ayrshire, Stirling and the North of Ireland—and timothy, grown mainly in Stirling. With the growing demand for certified seed of bred strains of grasses the culture of the more common species for seed has increased and spread to many other areas. Good crops are now harvested in counties as widely separated as Hereford, Hampshire, Lincolnshire and Northumberland.

**Root Seeds** can be grown over a somewhat wider range of climate, but give the most satisfactory results where the winter is fairly mild, the summer dry and the soil deep and fertile. Lincolnshire, Essex and Kent produce the main supplies.

## LIVE STOCK

Live stock is a feature of practically all systems of farming that have endured in Britain over long periods of time. In the past, where live stock were not kept, other methods were adopted to maintain soil structure and fertility. For example, stable or other organic manure was bought in for use on numbers of market gardens; on other stockless holdings reliance was placed on green manuring and the ploughing in of crop residues. Of late, the number of farms without live stock has risen, particularly in areas suitable for cereals, where mechanised corn growing has become almost the sole enterprise and source of farm income. It is too early to predict how long this type of monoculture is likely to be successful. There are risks of a deterioration of soil structure and of a build up of certain pests, *e.g.* eelworm, which could eventually bring falls in cereal yields, and indeed leave the land less valuable for alternative types of farming. So far, evidence points to little reduction in the level of organic matter, except in one or two areas of lighter soil, but there are doubts as to whether soils under continuous corn growing are working so kindly as they once did. Over a large part of the lower lying lands in Britain, however, a short or longer ley is a feature of the rotation, and live stock are usually associated with it. British farms are " mixed ", *i.e.* live stock and sales crops, and each contributes substantial amounts to the gross income.

There are very many circumstances in which live stock assumes the position of the primary department —where, that is to say, cropping is arranged to supply the needs of the stock rather than *vice versa*. It should be noted that about three quarters of the total product of British agriculture reaches the market in the form of live stock products—milk and other dairy produce, meat (including poultry meat), eggs, wool and hides.

**Sheep.**—Sheep husbandry is carried on under a wide diversity of conditions and there is a correspondingly wide variety of systems, with particular breeds or crosses adapted to each. A few general statements can, however, be made. Sheep are generally kept in conjunction with cattle. One argument for mixed stocking is that it tends to reduce the incidence of parasitic diseases to which sheep are very susceptible. Though this argument has lost some of its force through the introduction of much improved preventives against the more widely prevalent and troublesome parasites, it is still true that cattle and sheep are, up to a point, complementary rather than competitive in the utilisation of pasture—*i.e.* mixed stocking with sheep and cattle gives a higher output than stocking with either alone. But careful planning is necessary, especially to cover periods of scarcity of keep.

The mountain breeds of sheep are extremely active and hardy, can travel far in search of food and are highly selective in their grazing habits, so that, given sufficient range, they can utilise herbage that no other class of animals, except goats, could live on. Mountain pastures are indeed no exception to the rule that mixed stocking is an advantage, and a small proportion of cattle helps to control the coarser types of herbage plants which tend to increase when sheep constitute the whole of the stock. At one time mountain ponies were kept for the purpose in view, but the market for these has virtually disappeared. The difficulty in achieving the optimum balance between cattle and sheep, from the point of view of maintaining the value of the herbage, is that of wintering. Even mature cattle of the hardiest breeds require some hand feeding, and young cattle on typical hill and mountain farms must be housed.

On the best types of grassland, whether used for meat or milk production, a common practice is to stock with a large proportion of cows or of fattening cattle, as the case may be, and possibly a small proportion of sheep. The case for the introduction of sheep requires to be studied for each individual farm. If they are to be kept, then they should be managed so as not to interfere with the early bite of grass in spring for the dairy cows, and provision is necessary to ensure that neither the cows nor the sheep suffer through lack of suitable keep such as occur during periods of drought. In some areas of good grass—*e.g.* Romney Marsh— sheep form the main grazing stock, and store cattle fill the role of scavengers. A frequent deterrent to the introduction of sheep on farms, hitherto stocked with cattle alone, is the considerable cost of providing and maintaining sheep proof fencing.

Up till about the beginning of the present century the folded flock, commonly of one or other of the Down breeds, was a common feature of arable farms on the lighter soils, such as those of the chalks and oolite and the sandy and light loam areas of the Eastern Counties. The sheep were close folded during the greater part of the year, and a complicated system of forage cropping was required to ensure a succession of food supplies. This association of sheep with corn production on light land goes back for several centuries and became widespread with the introduction of root crops and clover. The chief reasons for its marked decline have been the rise in wage rates—the growing of crops for folding and the daily change of fold involving a very high labour charge—and the increased supplies of fertilizers which have provided a partial substitute for " the golden hoof." Some few pedigree flocks of the Down breeds are still run on the folding system throughout most of the year.

On mixed farms the usual function of the arable land is to keep the breeding flock during the latter part of the winter and early spring— perhaps late January until April—and to fatten the progeny as lambs or tegs either on rape and kale in autumn and early winter, or on roots and concentrates in later winter and spring.

A few general points remain to be noted.

On most arable farms there are supplies of by-products that can best be utilised by sheep—pickings on stubbles, sugar beet tops, catch crops and winter grazing on cattle pastures. On large farms the utilisation of such by-products may justify the keeping of sheep throughout the year or at least for part of it.

A flying flock of breeding ewes is more suitable to certain conditions than a regular breeding flock. For example, draft ewes from upland flocks may be run on cattle fattening pastures from September onwards and sold fat, with their lambs, in June-July, thus utilising the winter foggage and the spring flush of grass. The absence of sheep from the land over a period of months greatly reduces the incidence of parasitic troubles. Again, the fattening of purchased lambs, on clover aftermaths, rape, other catch crops or on roots, is a widespread practice not only on typically mixed farms but on those where the emphasis is on cash crops.

**Cattle** form on the whole the most important class of farm stock. This arises partly from the variety of their useful products—beef, milk, butter, cheese and leather—and partly from the large proportion of coarse and fibrous foods, such as straw, hay and inferior grass, that may figure in their diet. It is true that pigs will convert certain classes of foods into meat much more economically than will cattle, but this applies to a limited number of foods of relatively high digestibility. Sheep also may be more efficient meat producers where herbage is sparse, and under British climatic conditions, require less labour and equipment because they do not need winter housing. But there are many farms that can be carried on without the aid of either sheep or pigs, and very few that can be run permanently without a stock of cattle.

The production of **Milk** for direct sale was confined until recently to districts within fairly easy reach of markets, but developments in the way of cooling plant and rapidity of transport markedly extended the zone in which market milk is produced. The operations of the Milk Marketing Boards have tended still further to reduce the disadvantage of remoteness from consuming centres. At the time of writing there is a surplus of milk in excess of the requirements for the liquid milk market, and consideration is being given to ways and means to keep that surplus within manageable dimensions and to create a larger consumer demand for liquid milk.

In past times, when the output of milk greatly exceeded the liquid milk consumption, there were many summer producers who manufactured butter and cheese. At the time of writing their number is very small. As the liquid milk market has expanded and better facilities have become available for collecting milk from outlying farms, many of these farmers have striven towards a more level output of milk throughout the year. On arable, mixed or grass farms there are now much better prospects of maintaining productive rations for dairy cows throughout the year at reasonable costs. Modern developments in grassland—to given early bite, an expanded grazing season, improved conserved products—have helped the grassland dairy farmer to reduce his feeding costs; and the arable or mixed farmer in addition to the produce of leys, can use arable land by-products and crops such as kale to assist in winter feeding. Suitable concentrates are also available through the large home production of by-products from wheat milling, brewing, oil and seed extraction. The greater bulk of home made butter and cheese is now manufactured in factories.

Cows, especially those of the smaller and more active breeds, are capable of quite a high measure of production on land where cattle do not readily fatten. Hence the dairy industry tends to become established on land of moderate fertility rather than in the very best pastoral districts. The selling of whole milk gives much more rapid returns than rearing or fattening, so that the amount of floating capital required is low and its turnover rapid.

Whole milk production is a business requiring skill and close supervision. It is not a suitable business to occupy a minor place in the farm economy but cost accounts show that efficiency in milk production is not dependent on large scale operation. Low costs are frequently shown by producers with 10 or 12 cows.

**Cheese** is from five to ten times as valuable, weight for weight, as whole milk, and is, in the case of most standard varieties, practically a non-perishable commodity. The market therefore is open to world competition, and the industry tends to be carried on wherever natural conditions permit the production of milk at a cheap rate, and where land is of low value on account of its distance from markets. The natural conditions in question comprise a long, mild and rather moist growing season, so that the cattle may be at pasture for the greater part or the whole of the lactation period, and preferably a mild winter, so that the cost of winter housing and feeding may be kept low. Cheese making is ordinarily carried on for part of the year only—the season of cheap food. All the cattle calve down in spring, so that most of the milk may be produced during the grazing season and so that the winter ration may be as light as possible. With moderately good market facilities it may be most profitable to combine cheese making during summer with milk selling during winter, at which latter season the price obtainable for milk is higher. Cheese making involves more floating capital than milk selling, since produce is not ordinarily marketed till it has matured, being then perhaps three or four months old. The yield of cheese per gallon (10 lb.) of milk varies, according to the variety made, from about 0·8 to 1·1 lb. Farm house cheese making was reduced to very small volume during the war, but since the demand for liquid milk had fully been met at the time of writing, some revival seems possible, particularly for the choicer type of product.

Whey is a by-product whose utilisation is a matter of considerable difficulty. It contains fully one third of the net energy value of the milk and, on the basis of composition, a gallon has about the same value as a pound of cereal meal; but its perishable nature and its very high water content reduce its usefulness where it is produced in large quantities. Limited quantities can be utilised for calf feeding, and large quantities— up to 2 gal. per day and per 100 lb. live weight—may be fed to pigs. Pig feeding is therefore a useful complement to farm cheese production. Some part of the output of factories is concentrated by evaporation and sold as a feeding stuff, or used for the extraction of milk sugar.

The manufacture of **Butter** or the separation and sale of cream are alternatives to cheese making. With milk of average composition the yield of butter may be taken at about 0·4 lb. per gal. as against 1 lb. per gal. for ordinary hard cheese. The low price of imported butter, together with the guaranteed price paid by the Milk Marketing Boards for liquid milk has caused a marked decline in farm house butter making. Dairy factories, supplied with surplus milk, now manufacture the greater part of our home produced butter; and the output during summer is considerable. In other countries, also, butter making has become a factory rather than a farm industry. The separation and sale of cream is also largely a factory industry. The by-product, separated milk, has a much higher food value than whey. On the basis of its energy value and protein content it is worth about twice as much as whey; actually, owing to its mineral content and the high biological value of its protein, its value for many purposes is proportionately much greater than the difference its energy value and protein content would imply. It is one of the disadvantages of the factory system of butter making that the cost of transporting the separated milk back to the farm is heavy in relation to its value.

**Calf Rearing.**—There is a considerable advantage to be gained by the home rearing of a sufficient number of heifer calves for the replacement of the milking cows as these have to be disposed of. Until quite recent times it was commonly reckoned that the number of heifer calves to be retained for herd replacement should be about 25 per cent. of the number of milking cattle. But progress in the control of tuberculosis, mastitis, contagious abortion and other causes of wastage has reduced the average replacement figure to 20 per cent. or less. Better selection of those to be retained as replacements is therefore possible.

Apart from that rather special case, calf rearing tends to develop in districts remote from markets where the land is of moderate quality and where soil and climate are ill suited to the production of market crops. For example, in Cumberland and Westmorland, cattle under one year are normally about as numerous as cows and heifers in milk, whereas in Cheshire the latter are more than three times as numerous as the former. In general, cattle breeding is an alternative to sheep breeding and will have the preference on the moderately fertile mixed farms, especially those of small size.

From the age of six or eight months cattle require comparatively little labour and individual care, and may be quite as successfully reared by the large farmer as by the small. Where arable and pastoral districts occur fairly near together there is a considerable transference of cattle from the one to the other in spring and back again in autumn.

**Summer Fattening** of cattle is generally carried on where highly productive and nutritious pasture, either permanent or temporary, is available. There is the alternative, it is true, of stocking such land with the largest and most productive types of dairy cows, as is done, for example, in Holland; but although the precise causes are not understood, pastures of the finest quality frequently give a relatively better return from beef than from milk. Cows will often give quite satisfactory yields on land where cattle fatten only slowly, and hence, where the area of specially rich pasture is limited, it tends to be set aside for fattening.

The **Winter Fattening** of cattle provides, on the whole, the most convenient method for disposal of straw and for its conversion into the best quality of farmyard manure. Risks are comparatively small, and individual care and attention are less necessary than with dairy cows or calves. The choice as to whether cattle are to be fed as stores or fattened in winter depends on a number of considerations, *e.g.* types of feeding stuffs available, purchase price of stores if bought for winter yarding, relative prospects of profit through selling as forward stores in spring, fattening at grass or fattening during winter. In the north in districts where roots and straw have a distinctly higher fattening value than elsewhere, the ration may consist largely of these foods, supplemented by a variable amount of concentrates according to the expected length of the fattening period. In other areas self feed silage is being used more widely, either for stores or fattening cattle. With the latter it is important that the animals should have reasonable comfort so that they may make the best use of their food.

**Pigs.**—It has been pointed out that pigs have a special value in the utilisation of certain by-products from other departments—notably whey in cheese dairies and unmarketable potatoes. This accounts for the fact that, in the past, counties like Cheshire and Wigtown on the one hand and the Holland division of Lincoln on the other, had large pig populations. The decline of farm house cheese making resulted in the fall in numbers of pigs in the dairy counties.

There is a further connection between the proportion of arable land and the ratio of pigs to other stock—due, of course, to the fact that grass forms a food complete in itself for cattle and sheep, whereas pigs, in so far as they are kept on home produced food, require a large proportion of grain. Thus Suffolk, Essex, Cambridge and Lincolnshire have normally a much higher pig production, in proportion to other stock, than Devon and Wales.

Climatic conditions also play a part. In exposed situations and in cold and damp climates pigs suffer more than cattle and sheep. Outdoor pig breeding requires a well drained soil as well as a fairly sheltered situation. In very cold and exposed areas well constructed and rather expensive buildings are required. Hence, broadly speaking, the density of the pig population decreases, in Britain, from south to north. At one time, proximity to sources of various industrial by-products—e.g. milling offals, distillery and brewery by-products—and to supplies of swill from shops, hotels and households, was of considerable advantage and pigs, therefore, tended to concentrate in certain industrial districts and in suburban areas generally, but to-day that advantage has largely disappeared.

Owing to the relatively quick rate of reproduction, the pig population of this country was subject to rather marked fluctuations, which caused corresponding price changes. When prices were low, breeding operations tended to be unduly curtailed and the populations fell considerably. This in turn produced a rise in prices which lead to some over-production, followed by a fall in price. The average time covered by one of these price cycles was between three and four years, so that the common saying " two years up and two years down " was not far from the truth. In recent years various steps have been taken to reduce wide fluctuation in prices.

Pig production can be conducted quite economically on a small scale. It can be a suitable business for the small holder, provided that the pig unit is regarded as a real source of income and the necessary care and attention are available at important times, e.g. at farrowing and in the care of the new born pigs.

In ordinary times, with feeding stuffs abundantly available, pig keeping can be carried on largely or entirely on purchased feeding stuffs, so that the scale of the pig enterprise may be independent of the size of the farm. Thus expansion of the pig herd is one of the few ways open to the family farmer who has surplus capital and labour and who is precluded, by the nature of his land, from intensifying his crop production. The chief alternative under such conditions is to expand poultry production. One deterrant to specialisation in pigs that has operated in the past has been the risk of epidemic disease, especially swine fever and swine erysipelas, but these particular diseases can now be controlled by vaccination.

On larger farms there is a marked tendency to base the size of the pig enterprise on the capacity of one skilled pigman, possibly with a lad or other assistant. The size for a one-man unit, for bacon production depends on the layout of the buildings and the degree of mechanisation in feeding. It might run to 50 sows and their produce, *i.e.* about 500 head in all.

**Horse Breeding.** up till twenty years ago, was a fairly important enterprise on many farms, but the progressive decline in the demand for all classes (except saddle horses and ponies) has resulted in the virtual cessation of breeding of draft horses as a commercial enterprise.

**Poultry** and pigs, as already noted are alternative outlets for capital and labour on farms that would otherwise be below an economic size. Specialisation in poultry is now much more common and intensive production using little land has been steadily on the increase in recent years. Many small flocks are still kept on general farms, and it is now realised that the management of these requires to be more thorough if they are to contribute a reasonable quota to the farm income. There are opportunities on general farms to use certain by-products for poultry production to supplement bought-in foods.

**Pedigree Stock Breeding** is governed by somewhat the same conditions as those set forth for commercial stock, but two or three other considerations must be borne in mind. A considerably larger amount of capital is needed, partly because the individual animals are more valuable and partly because returns are less certain. Pedigree breeding, especially with certain breeds at certain times, tends to become a hobby with some people, and then there is a risk of over-production of animals of moderate merit. A high degree of skill and expert knowledge are necessary to financial success, which can be far greater than that from ordinary commercial stock but is more difficult to achieve.

## THE PRODUCTION OF FOOD FOR STOCK

There remain to be discussed questions relating to the production of food for stock.

**Winter Food.**—The following table expresses average yields of the more important feeding crops in terms of cwt. per acre of dry matter, starch equivalent and protein equivalent.

The relation of energy value to total dry matter (column 3) has an important bearing on the value of feeding stuffs, varying with the type of animal to be fed and the other feeding stuffs that are to be used in conjunction with the one in question. Roughly speaking, the starch equivalent of the ordinary types of production rations should bear the following proportions to the dry matter contents: for pigs somewhat over 75 per cent.; for sheep 50 to 55 per cent.; and for growing and fattening cattle 40 to 50 per cent. Thus, for pigs, grain (especially barley) can largely be used in compounding satisfactory rations. Roots and especially fodder beet can be employed to a limited extent if they are balanced with more concentrated sources of energy. Hay of ordinary quality is, by

TABLE 24

| | Dry Matter per Acre cwt. | Starch Equivalent per Acre cwt. | Starch Equivalent as percentage of Dry Matter | Protein Equivalent per Acre cwt. |
|---|---|---|---|---|
| Turnips (16 tons) . | 27·2 | 14·1 | 52 | 1·3 |
| Swedes (16 tons) . | 36·8 | 23·4 | 64 | 2·2 |
| Mangels (20 tons) . | 48·0 | 24·8 | 52 | 1·6 |
| Cabbage, drumhead (20 tons) . . | 44·0 | 26·4 | 60 | 3·6 |
| Kale, marrowstem (20 tons) . . . | 56·0 | 36·4 | 65 | 5·6 |
| Meadow hay, good (24 cwt.) . . . | 20·4 | 8·6 | 42 | 1·0 |
| Clover hay, good (30 cwt.) . . . | 25·5 | 11·7 | 46 | 2·1 |
| Grass silage, medium quality (6 tons) . | 27·0 | 13·9 | 51 | 2·6 |
| Oats— | | | | |
| Grain (20 cwt.) . | 17·4 | 11·9 | 68 | 1·5 |
| Straw (25 „ ) . | 21·5 | 5·0 | 23 | 0·2 |
| Barley— | | | | |
| Grain (22 cwt.) . | 18·7 | 15·6 | 83 | 1·4 |
| Straw (20 „ ) . | 17·2 | 4·6 | 26 | 0·1 |
| Beans— | | | | |
| Grain (16 cwt). . | 13·8 | 10·6 | 77 | 3·2 |
| Straw (24 „ ) . | 20·6 | 4·6 | 22 | 0·4 |

itself, insufficiently concentrated to support a high level of production even with cattle and must be supplemented with roots or concentrates or both. Silage from grass, if well made, is better from this point of view. If large quantities of straw are to be utilised for feeding, considerable quantities of roots or grain or both must be used in conjunction; the one exception is the winter maintenance of mature or nearly mature cattle, which can sometimes be done almost entirely on straw. Under the less intensive systems of farming the object of winter feeding may sometimes be maintenance only and not production. Here the question of the ratio of energy to dry matter is of much less importance, a relatively bulky ration being desirable. Where the protein supply is of importance— e.g. notably on dairy farms—the cost of production of this constituent becomes a matter of moment. Good quality silage and hay, kale and beans have a special value to the dairy farmer. On fattening farms the choice will generally fall to the cheapest source of net energy—often, for example, roots and straw or silage with a cereal supplement. The fore going general facts should be borne in mind. The actual choice of feeding crops will depend greatly on considerations of soil, climatic and labour conditions.

**Mangels** have a high maximum yield and are thus suited to the better soils: they thrive best where the amount of sunshine is high; they produce relatively heavy yields on deep and rather heavy soils. The labour requirement is high; the growing season is long and the crop is very susceptible to frost damage, so that the seasons of sowing and harvesting are restricted within rather narrow limits—*i.e.* little latitude is allowed in the seasonal distribution of labour. In many districts the crop competes for labour with both the sugar beet and the potato crops, and both in spring and autumn.

**Turnips** and **Swedes** are relatively more successful than mangels on the poorer soils; they require more rain and less sun. As they are specially dependent on fine tilths at seeding, they are unsafe on the heavier soils and in districts liable to summer droughts. The growing season is shorter and the susceptibility to autumn frosts much less, so that they are, relatively, more successful in the north. They are grown mainly in the north of England and in Scotland.

**Kale** and **Cabbages**, being specially suitable for autumn feeding and having roughly the same soil and climatic requirements as mangels, are grown under the same conditions as the latter crop. They are specially valuable where pastures are liable to fail early, *i.e.* in dry districts, and where highly intensive feeding is carried on—*e.g.* on dairy or pedigree stock farms. Kale has the notable advantage over roots that it can commonly be fed *in situ* to cattle as well as to sheep.

**Hay.**—Apart from silage, hay forms the chief alternative to roots and straw as the basis of winter feeding. Hay is largely grown in pastoral districts—*i.e.* in regions of heavy soil and of fairly high rainfall—whereas roots are relatively more important on the lighter soils and the drier climates.

Hay can be made from a variety of plants—from annuals such as peas and oats to perennials like lucerne and timothy and mixtures of grasses and clovers, either sown as leys or growing in a permanent sward. Of the plants grown in the more purely arable districts, *i.e.* in leys of short duration, clover predominates in the drier and ryegrass in the moister districts. For long duration leys, lucerne, either in pure stand or with cocksfoot is valuable particularly in areas of light soil and low rainfall.

Timothy and meadow fescue, in combination with one of the larger types of white clover, probably give the highest yields of nutrients under good management. Such hay leys produce in general much higher yields than the permanent meadows discussed in Chapter 26 of this section.

The labour required for the hay crop is concentrated in a short period, but is light when the available labour saving machinery is used. The hay crop is, of course, subject to heavy weather risks, and the average loss of nutritive value, taking one season with another, may exceed 30 per cent. Where the acreage of hay is small in relation to the labour supply or there is risk of excessive wastage, then newer techniques may be used to minimise the risk and part of the grass at least can be conserved as silage.

**Grass Drying.**—Artificial drying is by much the most efficient method of conservation in the sense that loss of nutrients is reduced to an almost negligible proportion. The figure is commonly of the order of 2 or 3 per cent., which compares with average figures of about 25 per cent. for silage and over 30 per cent. for hay. But there is difficulty in being able to dry more than a proportion of the crop when at its highest nutritive value; and the high cost of artificial drying can only be justified if the product is of first class quality. Even then the product may be expensive in comparison with that of high and medium protein concentrates. There is only a very limited demand for high quality dried grass as a source of carotene in animal rations.

**Grass Silage.**—The making of silage has not so far appealed to very many farmers, but the quantity of grass ensiled has tended to rise slowly in recent years. Grass cut just before the flowering stage and well ensiled provides a bulky food with a higher ratio of protein equivalent to starch equivalent than all but the very best hay; and good silage can provide for more than a maintenance ration for dairy cows and fattening cattle. It is also a useful food for calves and stores, and for sheep, once they have become accustomed to it. The advantages of grass silage can be summed up briefly thus:—(1) ensiling grass helps in good grassland management—the area cut early for silage provides good aftermath grazing in summer; (2) losses in making silage can be reduced with reasonable care to less than those in hay making; (3) the cost of making silage need not be high, if the job is well organised; (4) self feeding of silage is a practical way of reducing labour costs and can be quite effective with store, fattening and dairy cattle, provided they receive in total a properly balanced ration.

On most farms where the practice is to make hay, it would be an advantage also to make some silage; and on others it might be better to to conserve all grass for winter feeding as silage.

Arable crops are now seldom grown for ensiling.

**Oats.**—Cereals occupy a fairly large place in any system of arable farming because of their low cost of production when grown in conjunction with other crops. A certain proportion of concentrates must be employed in compounding most types of rations, and the cereal grains can be used, with purchased concentrates, as good and cheap sources of energy. The practical question for the arable farmer is not whether cereals shall be produced but whether the grain grown shall be consumed on the farm or sold and replaced by purchased concentrates. The answer to this depends on the relative market values of home grown grain and market concentrates and on the transport costs involved in making the exchange. Oats are a very important cereal for stock feeding purposes. For horses, cattle and sheep the grain forms a healthy, palatable and, broadly speaking, a well balanced food, but for pigs the fibre content is somewhat high. The straw yield is relatively large and its feeding quality, particularly when the crop is grown in the cooler and moister districts, is high.

**Barley** grain has a higher energy value than oats; it is less suitable for horses but more valuable for pigs, and is now being used more widely for cattle and sheep. The straw is less in yield, and perhaps on the average of lower feeding value, though in the drier and sunnier districts, where oats do not flourish, the latter statement does not hold good. Recently the acreage of barley has been increasing and that of oats declining; early varieties of barley yield well even in the north.

**Wheat** is regularly used as a feeding stuff for poultry, but for other classes of stock it is used only when it is procurable at a low price in relation to maize, oats and other feeding grain. In times when the grain is very cheap it may constitute 50 per cent. of pig feeds and perhaps 25 per cent. of the concentrate mixtures for sheep and cattle. The straw is of very low energy value. Rye is still less desirable from both points of view.

**Beans,** as appears from the table on page 714, are specially valuable on account of their high production of protein. In the period of 1930-39, imported high protein cakes, such as earthnut, soya bean and cotton, were available at prices so low as to make bean growing unprofitable. The cultivation of the crop revived during the war, but has declined again as increased quantities of imported high protein feeding stuffs have become available. Yields of the crop are very variable, even under conditions that would seem to favour the crop.

**Total requirements** in the matter of winter foods, depend on the length of the winter season. They are, for example relatively high in the northeast and low in the south-west of Britain.

**Summer Food.**—It has already been mentioned that, on the whole, cattle and sheep can be maintained in summer more cheaply on pasture than on arable crops. In winter arable land products may form the more economical source of food. Hence there is some migration of stock from pastoral to arable districts in autumn and back again in spring. In mainly arable districts, where herds of dairy cows or breeding flocks of sheep are kept, grass in summer provides the cheapest food. The system of pasture management to give the best returns depends very much on conditions. The poorest and highest mountain pastures do not give an adequate return either for fencing or manuring—or, indeed, for anything but the least costly improvements. Grass that is worth a few shillings per acre is generally most economically managed in large enclosures, and rarely pays for any fertilizers other than the cheaper forms of phosphate, *i.e.* mineral phosphate or slag. Fattening pastures are always intensively managed from the labour point of view, and there is often little scope for improvement by manuring. An intensive system, involving strip grazing and frequent nitrogenous manuring, offers the best prospects of success on grassland of moderate fertility, is more easily applicable to milking cattle than to other classes of live stock, but promising results are being obtained through new techniques in intensive management for other classes of live stock, *e.g.* sheep and fattening cattle.

Arable forage crops grown for soiling or for folding may be used as a substitute for pasture, but though somewhat more productive than pasture, the cost of production per acre is high. Modern practice is tending more and more to plan grassland management to cover possible periods of shortage. For example, there is a wide introduction of special purpose leys; possible summer gaps can be filled by the aftermath following an early cut for silage; lucerne either in pure stand or with a companion grass can be used as a reserve; grass silage may be kept in reserve to supplement the grazing in spring and in autumn. In addition crops such as rape and kale are useful in helping to bridge the gap between summer and winter feeding. Kale has the advantage that under suitable conditions it can be strip grazed and is sufficiently winter hardy to stand at least until Christmas.

# CHAPTER 28

# SYSTEMS OF FARMING

## 1.—THE CO-ORDINATION OF ENTERPRISES

SUPPOSING that one has formed an opinion regarding the commodities that might be produced economically under a given set of conditions, the next problem is that of fitting together the separate enterprises into a general scheme that can be run economically as a whole. It is necessary to state some of the guiding principles to be kept in mind when this is being done.

### Seasonal Distribution of Labour

Wages, on most farms, constitute the largest single item of expenditure, and it is convenient to take the labour organisation as the starting point in constructing the farming system. The aim is to ensure productive work for all the labour that is employed at any particular season and sufficient workers to perform in due season all the work that falls to be done.

Under a majority of circumstances the cost of labour in relation to its quality is lowest when constant employment is given. Exceptions are to be found where other industries—such, for example, as forestry or fisheries—offer seasonal employment; under such circumstances it may happen that labour can be obtained at a cheaper daily rate if the worker is offered a seasonal rather than a yearly contract. But in general, casual labour is relatively expensive, and in many cases skilled casual labour is virtually unobtainable at those seasons when it would be required. The working of overtime in busy seasons is, of course, another alternative, but overtime scales of pay are higher than ordinary rates, and the working of much overtime inevitably leads to some loss of efficiency. Hence the seasonal distribution of farm work should receive careful and constant consideration, and seasonal demands must be levelled up to such an extent as to make the labour as productive as possible in relation to its cost.

The same considerations apply to horse labour, but this on most farms has become a relatively minor item in total costs. The cost of running a tractor, per working hour, will of course vary immensely with the number of hours worked, but the cost of maintaining an idle tractor is small.

The operations of the farm, regarded from this point of view of the seasonal distribution of work, may be roughly grouped in four categories—

1. such as have to be performed regularly, as a matter of daily routine —*e.g.* milking and the feeding and tending of live stock.

2. such as can be performed efficiently or successfully only within narrow limits of time, and may be, in addition, dependent on weather conditions—*e.g.* hay making, cereal harvest, mangel and potato raising, seeding of spring crops and singling of roots.

3. such as fall to be carried out at certain approximate periods of the year, but are not strictly limited as to time and weather—*e.g.* winter ploughing, storing of swedes, carting of farmyard manure.

4. such as can be performed equally well at any season or in any weather—*e.g.* road mending, building repairs, and the overhaul of implements, machinery and other equipment.

Operations in the first category present little difficulty except the unavoidable one that they have to be performed seven days a week; the last group usually presents no difficulty at all. It is the other categories, and particularly the second, that must receive careful attention when the general system is being worked out. Broadly speaking, a large proportion of any one crop leads to difficulty in organisation because there is usually an optimum time for each operation—seeding and harvesting—and hence too large an area will involve either the employment of casual labour at generally high rates or the spreading out of the necessary work beyond the desirable time limits. As an example of the working out of the seasonal distribution of labour we may take an east coast arable farm, growing a fair variety of crops, and farmed, say, on the Eart Lothian six-course rotation of (1) spring oats, (2) maincrop potatoes, (3) winter wheat, (4) turnips, swedes and sugar-beet, (5) barley, and (6) one year ley for hay and silage.

The following might be approximately the normal dates of the more critical operations:—

| | |
|---|---|
| Oat sowing . . . . . | 7th to 21st March. |
| Barley sowing . . . | 1st March to 15th April. |
| Potato planting . . . | 1st April to 1st May. |
| Root sowing . . . | 20th April to 20th May. |
| „ thinning. . . . | 1st to 25th June |
| Ensilage . . . . | 7th to 20th June |
| Hay-making . . . . | 25th June to 10th July. |
| Summer cultivation of potatoes and roots . . . . . | Till 20th July. |
| Wheat, barley, and oat harvest . | 10th August to 25th September. |
| Potato lifting . . . | 1st to 20th October. |
| Wheat sowing . . . | 25th October to 30th November. |

While the labour distribution obtained on this system is, on the whole, very satisfactory, the following disadvantages and difficulties should be noted:—

1. There is a large preponderance of spring sown crops, with the result that there is frequently great pressure of work in April. Late sowing of barley is a common consequence, particularly where roots are fed off late. Casual labour must generally be obtained for potato planting, if this is not done by machine.

2. Root thinning will often clash with ensilage and, if germination is delayed, with hay making. Further, successive sowings of roots may come to the hoe simultaneously, and casual labour may be required to ensure timely singling.

3. There is liable to be a gap between the completion of summer cultivations and of hay harvest on the one hand and the commencement of cereal harvest on the other; all the cereal crops tend to ripen together, making the harvest a time of great pressure. The introduction of a proportion of early potatoes or of spring sown silage crops would bring useful work into the slack period mentioned, without, however, easing the problem of the cereal harvest. But harvest pressure can be relieved if most of the area is harvested by combine. The substitution of winter for spring oats serves both ends, but apart from the fact that winter oats are not entirely reliable in the northern areas, the preparation of the land for this crop involves the loss of the hay aftermath.

4. The late ripening of the potato crop, taken in conjunction with the possibility of severe early frost, makes the potato harvest an exceedingly pressing business, and there is frequently great competition for the available pickers. By following the potato crop with wheat, the seeding of the latter crop is liable to be unduly delayed. Occasionally no opportunity of sowing wheat occurs, and there is a certain derangement of the system through the substitution of a spring cereal.

Difficulties such as those in the foregoing example are found in most systems. Not only is it impossible to plan a perfect distribution of labour that would adapt itself to all probable seasonal variations in weather conditions but the question is only one of many that have to be considered, and imperfections in one direction must be accepted if there are compensating advantages in some other.

It should not be overlooked that there may be better ways of doing many farm operations and at less cost for labour. Method study may give a lead to the modifications in organisation and in the methods of doing certain jobs that could well result in more labour being available for essential tasks that must be done within a given time.

Fig. 37 illustrates an actual case of seasonal distribution of man labour on a mixed farm in the Midlands about the period 1925. The total area was 540 acres, of which, in the year in question, 290 acres were under arable crops and 250 under permanent grass.  On the acreages of the several crops grown and the numbers of stock kept, the labour requirement at the period might have been estimated at just over 5000 man-days—equivalent to the full time of 17 men.  The staff regularly employed was 16 men and 2 boys.

The chart shows that the labour distribution was fairly even, the extra time devoted to the live stock in winter being roughly balanced by the greater requirements of the arable in summer.  Miscellaneous labour

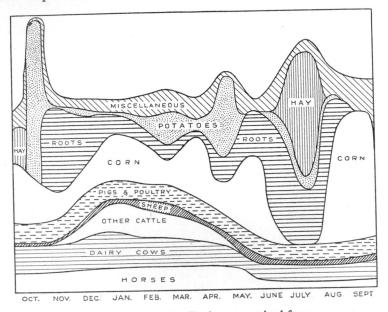

Fig. 37.—Labour distribution on a mixed farm.

was fairly uniform throughout, showing that there was no period when it was found necessary to resort largely to fill-time jobs.  A large number of casual hands had to be employed for a short time in lifting potatoes, but such employment was generally unavoidable.  There were peaks, too, at the time of potato planting (April to May), and again in July when root thinning clashed with hay making.  Broadly speaking, however, the organisation was successful from one point of view—that is to say, productive work was available for the whole staff at all seasons of the year.

Judged by the other test—the timely performance of important work—the organisation is seen to have been faulty.  Potato planting was not finished until mid-May; in May and June a great deal of time had to be devoted to the weeding of corn crops.  Such work has now largely been eliminated by the introduction of chemical weed killers.  Hay making had hardly begun in June and continued until August (overlapping, in fact, with the corn harvest), with the implication that much of the hay must have been far past the optimum time for cutting. Summer tillage of roots continued till the end of August, long after harvest was in full swing, and the harvest itself was not completed at the end of September. Moreover, the number of working hours recorded was consistently higher than normal. It is clear that there was always more to do than could be comfortably managed, and that overtime must have been the rule rather than the exception. Either, then, the regular staff was inadequate, or else its organisation was inefficient. In cases such as this, where work was chronically behind the calendar, it sometimes sufficed to get some tillage done by a contractor, enabling the regular staff to overtake arrears. Apart from the obvious and immediate advantage of such a step the psychological effect on the farm staff was often very beneficial. Workers inevitably lose heart when the work of the farm is badly behindhand.

Labour distribution is affected not only by the proportions of the various crops grown but also by the order of their succession in the rotation. Obviously one must aim at allowing sufficient time for the necessary cultivations between the harvesting of one crop and the sowing of the next, with a certain margin against the possibility of unfavourable weather. For example, where roots are left on the land for winter folding, the choice of a crop to succeed them is limited to such as may be sown fairly late in spring; or again, if aftermaths are wanted for autumn grazing, they cannot, in many districts, be followed by winter wheat.

### Weed Control

A second requirement that any permanent scheme of farming must fulfil, is to provide means for the control of weeds. A clean farm is one of the chief marks of an efficient farmer, but this end, like others, must be attained with due regard to economy. There are five chief methods of control.

1. **The Uses of Smother Crops.**—Here the object is to suppress the weeds through the agency of the competition of the crop. Kale, silage crops and late potatoes are perhaps the most useful from this point of view because, with such, a dense, luxuriant vegetative growth is desirable in itself. On the other hand, barley, for example, does not lend itself to such use, because great vegetative luxuriance is incompatible with high quality of the produce. The smothering effect of cereals depends mainly on the length of straw, which is related to the density of the shade cast. Short straw may be desirable from other points of view, but a compromise may be sought in the case of foul land. Obviously, the greatest degree of reliance can be placed on this method where the land is fertile, where the moisture supply is fairly abundant, and where, owing to favourable economic conditions, a somewhat intensive system is justified. On poor, dry soils the method has a very limited application.

2. **The Alternation of Arable Crops with Grass, and, in certain cases, of Hay with Pasture.**—The particular weed species that flourish in the one type of environment generally die out more or less rapidly in others. Thus charlock and runch multiply in spring corn, while slender foxtail, wild onion and corn buttercup increase in winter corn; yellow rattle and soft brome are weeds of meadows; and ragwort and creeping buttercup of pastures. Alternate husbandry generally is regarded only as an aid in weed control; other and more active measures are necessary in addition. A ley and corn rotation, without row crops, is practicable in some areas. Ordinarily two or three corn crops are followed by three or more years under grass, the ley being used for hay (timothy, timothy-fescue mixture) or for grazing, or both. In many areas it is desirable to break up the ley at midsummer, so that the land may be bastard fallowed in preparation for the first corn crop. With full mechanisation, the system is highly economical of labour.

3. **The Inclusion of Row Crops in the Rotation.**—This has long been regarded as the chief method on all the lighter and medium soils in this country—on all soils, that is to say, where potatoes, roots and kale form reasonably reliable crops. Any crop may, of course, receive a certain amount of intercultivation, but it is only where the individual plants are fairly large, permitting the use of horse implements, or of tractors with row-crop equipment, between them in their early stages, that such intercultivation can be carried out at a moderate cost. At the best, the amount of hand labour required is heavy, and it is only where intensive systems are justified that frequent row crops can be profitable. Generally, a proportion of one cleaning crop to two cereal crops provides ample opportunities for weed suppression; but a less proportion than this will usually be effective if some of the other methods of weed suppression are practised—such as stubble cleaning or chemical weed killing. Much, however, depends on the type of soil; well drained and fertile clays are notably less liable to weed infestation than sandy or chalky soils.

Row crops, of course, will fail to prove effective if the young plants fail to compete with the early growth of weeds. Sugar beet, and particularly carrots, are easily smothered by weed competition.

4. **Cultivation in the Absence of a Crop.**—Such cultivation may be carried out in the same season that an ordinary crop is grown (spring or autumn cleaning); it may extend over a part of the ordinary growing season, the remainder being occupied by a quick maturing crop such as a single cut of hay or a green forage crop (bastard fallowing); or finally, it may extend over a full season (bare fallowing). The first of these methods is obviously limited in its application by climatic conditions. In the colder and wetter districts the ordinary cereal crops must be sown as soon as the ground becomes workable in spring, and are harvested so late that little or no autumn cultivation is possible; whereas in the south,

where harvest is early, a great deal of cleaning may often be accomplished in autumn.

Bastard fallowing involves the sacrifice of part of the summer season. Hence, in districts where the amount of summer heat and sunshine constitutes a limiting factor in production, it becomes a costly operation. There are other districts, however, of low rainfall and of long and hot summers, where the limiting factor, so far as climate is concerned, is not heat but moisture. In such cases the soil may be able to store up most of the rain that falls during the period of the fallow, and the partial sacrifice of one crop may be justified by the increase obtained in the one which follows. Hence it is that in the south-eastern counties the bastard fallow is often an economical method of weed control. Another form of partial fallow, widely used in the chalk and limestone areas, is, in effect, a spring fallow followed by rape—or, more commonly, a crop of kale or turnips—sown in June or July.

Bare fallows, too, may be introduced for other purposes than that of weed control. In dry farming systems they are employed with the object of storing up a season's rainfall, on the principle of using two years' rain for one year's crop. Again, at the polar limits of arable cropping they become necessary because there is not time, within the limits of a single season, to prepare the land and also to grow a crop. Under our conditions bare fallows are useful in that they expose the soil to weathering agents and lead to improved tilth, but their chief object is that of cleaning the land. On all soils except heavy clays, the bare fallow is regarded as a last resort in the struggle against weeds, to be used only where other methods cannot be employed—that is to say, where neither roots nor potatoes can be planted with much chance of success. Ill drained clays require the most frequent fallows both because they quickly become foul and because opportunities for spring and autumn cultivations are very limited. The acreage of bare fallow fluctuates widely from year to year, rising in seasons when the spring is unfavourable for tillage. The fallow acreage in England and Wales was as high as 535,000 in 1937 but is now ordinarily about 250,000.

5. **The Use of Weed Killers** which has increased rapidly with the growing range of materials, has greatly widened the farmers' choice of cropping systems—enabling weed control to be achieved with much less resort to fallows and row crops. At the time of writing, however, certain weed species—*e.g.* wild oat, couch, and other stoloniferous grasses and bracken —could not be controlled effectively at a reasonable cost by any practicable chemical treatment.

## The Maintenance of Soil Fertility

**Humus.**—The importance of maintaining an adequate organic matter content in arable soils is well recognised. Under certain special sets of circumstances—for example, on black fen soils or where plentiful supplies of organic manures such as seaweed or city refuse are available at low cost—the farmer may be free to grow such crops and to dispose of them in such ways as will bring the greatest immediate returns. But under many circumstances he must arrange that a greater or less proportion of the organic matter of his crops is returned to the soil as manure. The precise proportion that should be maintained between sales and home consumption, in order to secure, in the long run, the maximum net return, is very hard to determine. It depends, for one thing, on the physical characteristics of the soil. On deep, well watered, alluvial lands like the Scottish carses or the Lincolnshire silts, considerable amounts of hay and straw, as well as grain, may be sold off year by year with very little harm. On the other hand, thin light soils on chalk and those of sandy or gravelly nature, as well as the stickier clays when occurring in dry districts, fall off in cropping power if a large proportion of the organic matter that they produce is not returned to the land. It depends, too, on the staple crops of the farm. Wheat, owing to its deep-rooted habit and to its relative indifference to tilth, is much less dependent on the humus content of the soil than say, oats, with their high moisture requirement and shallower root system.

The necessary supply of humus may be provided (1) by green manuring, (2) by the folding of animals on annual forage crops, (3) by laying the land away to temporary pasture or (4) by the application of farmyard manure or compost. In most actual cases two or more of these methods are used in conjunction. Under green manuring we may include the ploughing in of crop residues such as sugar beet tops and the leaves of other root crops which is a widespread practice, and also the ploughing in of clover or seeds aftermath, which is done to some extent on farms that carry little live stock in summer. The crops specially grown for green manuring are normally catch crops, because the sacrifice of a full season's crop for this purpose can rarely be justified. Hence the conditions under which green manuring becomes a part of the system are those under which catch crops are likely to succeed—light soil, fairly abundant rainfall and mild winter climate. Even where catch crops succeed it will ordinarily be desirable to feed them off rather than to plough them in directly. The yield of catch crops is, however, uncertain, and their utilisation for feeding may involve large market transactions in live stock, in which case transport charges and sales commissions may be likely to amount to more than the crop is worth. The type of plant used for green manuring requires some consideration. Very highly nitrogenous material, such as immature clover or vetch, decomposes with such extreme rapidity that the nitrogen may be lost, as nitrate, before the following crop is able to make use of it; moreover, under the highly aerobic conditions prevailing in light soils the bulk of the organic matter is quickly dissipated. Thus it would seem that where a cereal is under-sown with the idea of producing a sward to plough in, a mixture of Italian ryegrass with clover or trefoil may be preferable to a legume alone. The carbon nitrogen ratio of the material to be ploughed in may be still further widened by leaving a long stubble when the cereal is harvested. In special cases the use of a full season crop for green manure may be profitable. Many horticultural crops are much more exacting in the matter of tilth and soil moisture conditions than the general run of farm crops. With the diminishing supplies of stable manure, increasing use is being made of composts and green manures, the most widely used species for the latter purpose being Italian ryegrass sown at a high seed rate.

The grazing of temporary leys and the folding of summer forage crops are to be regarded as alternative methods of serving the same ends—the provision of summer food for stock and the direct return to the soil of a large proportion of the organic matter produced. The cultivation of annual forage crops for summer folding involves more or less continuous cropping, and the main conditions which render this possible are a free working and well drained soil and a moderately high and evenly distributed rainfall. Under such conditions arable forage crops are more productive than grass, though the labour charges are necessarily much higher and the cost of seed is greater. On heavier soils as well as where the growing season is shorter and the rainfall less evenly distributed, the grazed ley is usually preferable. Arable folding has declined greatly in recent years with the rising cost of labour in relation to the value of farm produce.

The folding of summer and winter forage crops and the grazing of leys tend to predominate in the less intensive arable systems and where live stock occupies a position of primary importance in the farming scheme. These methods permit of the maintenance of fertility at a cost sufficiently small to be in keeping with the rather low gross income obtained from the land. On the most valuable arable soils such methods interfere with the primary object in view, which is the production of marketable plant products. In such cases the live stock must be maintained chiefly on the by-products of the system, and house feeding of stock, with the production of farmyard manure, becomes the chief means of keeping up the humus content. The handling and transport of large quantities of feeding crops and dung is a costly business, and can pay only when the gross income is kept at a high level.

**Phosphates.**—The problem of maintaining the chemical fertility of the soil is more or less bound up with that of the upkeep of the humus content, because all organic manures contain quantities of phosphates, potash and nitrogen. As regards phosphatic fertilizers, it is easy to lay down a general policy. Practically all systems of farming involve the removal of phosphate from the land, and it is the exception to find a soil that can be farmed successfully over a period of years without recourse to phosphatic manures. These are relatively cheap, and they do no harm when applied in quantities somewhat larger than are necessary. Large single applications may be undesirable because, especially in acid  soils, the phosphate forms highly insoluble compounds with iron and aluminium; but in general, phosphate should never be allowed to become the factor limiting production but should be applied almost up to the limit of its capacity to produce yield increments.  Harm has been shown to have resulted from excessive use of phosphate on intensively cropped market gardens and particularly in greenhouses.

It is difficult to lay down any general guidance about the quantities required to maintain full productivity, since soils vary in their capacity to fix phosphoric acid in unavailable forms.  Occasional determinations of available phosphate are a valuable guide to the level of application required, though even with such information it is well to carry out occasional field trials to discover the response actually obtained.  On most British soils a substantial saving can be obtained by the use of combine drills and other equipment for placement of fertilizers.

**Potash.**—With potash the position is somewhat more complicated. Where only live stock and their products are sold off the farm, the drain of potash is negligible;  even when grain is sold as well, the loss is comparatively small;  but when potatoes, roots and hay are sold in addition, the loss becomes considerable.  A good crop of potatoes, for example, removes as much potash as is contained in 2 cwt. per acre of the sulphate. Different soils, too, show very different potash requirements, heavy soils generally making little or no response to applications, while sandy and peaty soils, chalk lands and gravels often show very marked responses. Again, it is possible to economise in the use of potash manures by care in the conservation of dung and urine and by growing especially deep rooted species that reach down to subsoil reserves.  For practical purposes potash may be considered as not liable to be washed out of the soil, but on some soils there is a material loss by fixation.  In such cases, again, an economy can be achieved by placement.  In general, the principle to be followed is the same as in the case of phosphate.  It is generally most profitable to meet the demands of the plant in full, and it is safer to err in the direction of excess rather than in that of deficiency.

**Nitrogen.**  The economic aspects of nitrogen usage are somewhat complex because supplies of soil nitrogen are obtainable from three separate sources:  (1) the leguminous plant, (2) the residues of purchased feeding stuffs and (3) nitrogen fertilizers.

The introduction of clover, as a regular rotation crop, was the first step, in point of time, towards the provision of adequate supplies of soil nitrogen.  Later came imports of guano and natural nitrate, together with some quantity of by-product ammonia from gas works.  At about the same period (mid-nineteenth century) came greatly increased imports of oil seeds, particularly linseed, which were fed to live stock not only with the object of obtaining well balanced rations but with a view to the production of nitrogen rich manure.  Up till the twenties of last century supplies of imported high protein feeding stuffs continued to be large and prices continued low, while nitrogen fertilizers were relatively scarce and costly. Hence British farmers continued to rely, in the main, on legumes and cake fed dung. Since that time there has been a rapid expansion in the output of synthetic ammonia and nitrate, at low cost, while imports of protein feeding stuffs have fallen and prices have risen. The consequence has been a large increase in the use of nitrogen fertilizers.

Farm practice has, however, changed too slowly, and the average rate of usage in Britain is still, at the time of writing, substantially below that which would have yielded the maximum profit. Moreover, modern crop varieties, particularly of cereals, are capable of responding to, and of repaying with profit, higher applications of nitrogen than the sorts which were formerly available; and there has been a time lag in adjusting the level of nitrogen usage to the changed character of crop plants.

With regard to the nitrogen residues of feeding stuffs, there are, of course, numbers of farms—heavily stocked dairy holdings and those with large pig units—where purchased feeding stuffs are bought in large amounts. But with modern standards of dairy hygiene, conservation of the cow manure is commonly very poor. Purchased feeding stuffs can indeed constitute a source of fertilizer nitrogen, but it is no longer economic (as it once was) to feed protein in excess of the animals' needs in order to produce nitrogen rich manure.

Turning to the place of legumes, pulse crops—peas and beans—are relatively inefficient in nitrogen fixation. Moreover, their residues (roots and root nodules) are quickly nitrified between harvest and the onset of winter, and the nitrate is largely lost in the winter drainage. It is only the herbage legumes—clover, lucerne and sainfoin—that add substantially to the stock of soil nitrogen, and their efficiency is increased when they are grown in association with grasses. A well balanced clover grass sward has been known to raise the stock of soil nitrogen by an amount equivalent to that contained in a dressing of 10 to 12 cwt. (200-240 units of N.) of ammonium sulphate per acre. Thus with the introduction of truly perennial types of herbage legumes (especially white clover) it became possible, under a six course rotation including a three year ley, to maintain quite a high level of production with little resort to nitrogen fertilizers.

Two systems of farming, however, rely mainly on fertilizers. Under intensive arable cropping, with little live stock, nitrogen fertilizers may be profitably applied, in considerable amounts, to all crops except beans and peas; optimum (most profitable) dressings are ordinarily between 2 and 4 cwt. per acre. The other case is that of intensive grassland farming (see pp. 369-373). A system based on carefully selected plant material, utilised by strip grazing with grass drying or ensilage, can give profitable returns, in the form of milk, for successive applications of nitrogen fertilizer in amounts totalling 5 to 8 cwt. per acre per year.

**Lime.**—The maintenance of soil fertility also involves the control of soil acidity, which is generally best accomplished by means of fairly frequent and moderately small dressings of lime. Heavy dressings at longer intervals involve the sinking of additional capital and increased wastage from the soil, without any compensating advantage. Some economy in lime may be effected by the continuous use of lime-saving or lime-containing fertilizers, *e.g.* nitro chalk in preference to ammonium salts, and basic slag or mineral phosphate in preference to superphosphate.

In certain high rainfall areas, where leaching is increased by the sulphuric acid content of the rain (as happens in smoke polluted areas) the rate of loss of lime from near neutral soil ($pH$ 6·5) is so high that the cost of maintaining the lime status at this level may be prohibitive. This is particularly likely where other factors, such as climate, set a somewhat low limit to the productivity of the land. In such cases the only economically possible course may be to restrict cultivation to those species, such as oats, potatoes and grasses, that show a high degree of tolerance to sour conditions, and to abandon any attempt to cultivate such crops as barley, sugar beet and red clover.

### Plant and Animal Hygiene

The control of diseases and pests, both of crops and of live stock, is one of the constant concerns of the farmer and must receive due consideration in relation to the general farming scheme. When the natural mixed herbage of the ground is replaced, say, by a crop of swedes, or when the natural animal population is replaced by a flock of sheep, the farmer is disturbing the balance of nature and is giving to the enemies of these particular species an opportunity, such as they never enjoy under natural conditions, to increase and multiply. Sometimes the consequences are not serious; thus healthy crops of mangels or barley can, with reasonable care, be produced for several years in succession on the same land; and pastures may be stocked entirely, season after season, with fattening cattle, without any particular ill consequences to the animals.

Even when pests are potentially very harmful it may be cheapest and best to deal with them directly. Thus no farmer would think of modifying his general system of farming because of bunt attacking his wheat; in this case there is a cheap and satisfactory method of control. In other cases direct measures are only partially successful. For example, liming is useful against finger and toe in *Brassicas*, but it may be necessary, in order to keep the disease completely suppressed, to grow susceptible crops only at long intervals. Then, there are cases where no direct method of control can be economically applied, and where attack can be escaped only by introducing more or less fundamental changes in the farming scheme. Thus, if land becomes infested with potato eelworm, there is at present no satisfactory method of control except the adoption of a rotation in which there is a minimum interval of four or five years between successive potato crops. In other areas the farmer may be obliged to reduce his corn acreage because of a build-up of cereal root eelworm, or an increasing incidence of such diseases as eye-spot and take-all.

## 2. EXAMPLES OF BRITISH FARMING SYSTEMS

The following descriptive accounts, with relative financial data, are given as illustrations of the general principles of farm organisation. Prices, wages rates and so on change frequently and the figures therefore should only be taken as a very rough guide.

### A.—North Wales—Mountain Sheep Farm

#### Natural Conditions and Land use

The typical Welsh mountain farm comprises, firstly, a small area of arable land round the homestead, which is commonly on the lowest part of the farm and at no very great altitude; secondly, a larger block of enclosed land (known as the *ffridd*) stretching up to perhaps the 1000 ft. contour and sometimes including a proportion of improved or improvable land; and thirdly, a still larger area (or, alternatively, common grazing rights for a prescribed number of sheep) on the highest land.

Rainfall varies greatly according to elevation and aspect and may reach 70 in. and even 100 in. on the western aspects of the higher slopes. Winter in the valleys is relatively mild, but on the high ground snow may lie for long periods.

The soils on the steeper slopes are thin, stony and heavily leached, and here the herbage, despite the high rainfall, is liable to suffer from drought. The herbage consists mainly of *Nardus* (wire grass) and Sheep's Fescue. On gentle slopes lying below steeper ones the soil is well supplied with seepage water, and here the dominant species is commonly *Molinia*; where drainage is impeded there are accumulations of peat, with typical mountain bog flora. The deeper and more fertile land, up to elevations of some 1200 ft., is very liable to invasion by bracken. In the absence of steep slopes, rock outcrops and boulders, such land may be ploughed, limed and fertilized and, after one or two pioneer crops, be reseeded with good grasses. The typical soil of the valley bottoms is a silty loam.

#### Economic Situation

The area is thinly populated and, apart from stone or slate quarrying in certain localities, stock breeding is the only important industry. Main highways are few and minor roads are generally poor. Many farms are without piped water supplies or electric power. Most are small, some too small to provide full time employment for the farm family. The following description applies to one of the larger.

#### Allocation of Land and Stocking

The total extent of the holding is about 1300 acres. The enclosed arable, round the homestead, is 40 acres and is divided into small fields. It is farmed on a long ley rotation, with some 10 acres annually under oats and rape. The leys are grazed in early spring by the weaker ewes, and the later growth is mown for hay or silage. The flock may have to be gathered to the enclosed land during periods of snowstorm and be fed on hay. The rape is ordinarily used for fattening the most forward of the wether lambs.

The ffridd extends to some 240 acres and is in a ring fence. Ten acres has recently been enclosed and reseeded (as part of a scheme under the Hill Farming Act), and a further area is being similarly improved.

The open mountain is legally common grazing, but in the present case, as in many others, the flock of each owner is trained to keep to its allotted area.

The whole flock is run on the open mountain from early June until weaning time in late August. At mating time, again throughout the lambing period, and also at times when snow threatens, the ewe flock is confined to the ffridd. Otherwise, during winter, the sheep have the run of both this and the open mountain. Some hay is usually mown on the better patches of the ffridd. The ewe lambs that have been retained for flock replacement are sent to lowland pastures for wintering, leaving in November and returning in April. The rams are kept in the enclosed fields from September until mating time in November.

Apart from the flock of Welsh Mountain Sheep the only live stock is a herd of twenty Welsh Black cows, mated to a Hereford bull, some twenty or thirty poultry, and a house cow.

### Rental

Rental values are governed not by acreage but by such factors as the stock carrying capacity of the farm, the average death rate among the ewes, the normal lambing percentage, the risk of major losses (mainly by snowstorm) and the average size and quality of the lambs. Figures vary from 2s. or 3s. per ewe on the poorest grazing to 6s. or more on the best—leaving out of account those farms which are capable of wintering their ewe lambs or of fattening a substantial proportion of the wether lambs. The cost of low ground wintering for the normal quota of ewe lambs frequently exceeds the rent of the farm. Middle-grade farms, such as the present example, are stocked at a rate of one ewe to every 2 or 3 acres of total area.

### Labour

Five or six hundred ewes provide full employment for a shepherd who, however, requires a whole time assistant during lambing and occasional help at other times. In the present example the farm staff consists of the farmer himself and two paid workers.

### Tenant's Capital

The following estimate of the investment (at 30th September) is based on the assumption that the wether lambs and surplus ewe lambs have been sold, while the season's calf crop is still on hand. (The actual situation might be different—*e.g.* some wether lambs might have been retained for fattening, to be sold in October-November.)

*Live Stock:*

| | | |
|---|---:|---:|
| 550 breeding ewes and yearlings at 110s. | £3025 | |
| 200 stock ewe lambs at 75s. | 750 | |
| 12 rams at 200s. | 120 | |
| 20 cows and in-calf heifers at £65 | 1300 | |
| 1 bull | 150 | |
| 16 calves at £30 | 480 | |
| 2 light horses at £40 | 80 | |
| poultry | 50 | |
| | | £5955 |

*Equipment:*

| | |
|---|---:|
| Implements, Harness, Miscellaneous Stores | £600 |

*Miscellaneous:*

| | |
|---|---:|
| Oats, hay | £400 |
| | £6955 |

**Annual Expenditure**

| | |
|---|---:|
| Rent . . . . . . . . . | £200 |
| Wintering 200 ewe lambs at 30s. . . . . | 300 |
| Replacement of rams . . . . . . | 80 |
| Replacement of cows and bull . . . . . | 200 |
| Wages . . . . . . . . . | 1100 |
| Fertilisers, lime, seeds and feeding stuffs . . . | 200 |
| Depreciation on implements and horses . . . | 120 |
| Sheep dip and miscellaneous . . . . . | 100 |
| | £2300 |

**Annual Income**

| | |
|---|---:|
| 160 draft ewes at 70s. . . . . . . | £560 |
| 220 wether lambs and 20 ewe lambs at 60s. . . | 720 |
| Wool . . . . . . . . . | 450 |
| 16 calves at £40 . . . . . . . | 640 |
| Miscellaneous (including subsidies) . . . . | 500 |
| | £2870 |

## B. East of Scotland Arable Farm

Throughout Eastern Scotland, up to elevations of the order of 800 ft., ley farming is traditional and all but universal. The general level of cropping intensity—the duration of the ley and the proportion between cash crops and fodder crops—varies according to soil type, rainfall, elevation and other circumstances. The main live stock enterprises are beef and mutton production and dairying. In regard to the two former, the emphasis throughout the higher and less fertile regions is on the production of store stock, while in the more fertile and more largely arable farms it is on fattening; under intermediate conditions rearing and fattening are combined. The cereal crops, in order of importance, are barley, wheat and oats, but on many farms the most important cash crop is potatoes, grown mainly for seed. In the areas of lower rainfall, as far north as Angus, sugar beet is a minor enterprise.

The system exemplified below is one of moderate intensity, and is typical of the lowland parts of the counties of Angus, Perth and Fife.

### Natural and Economic Conditions

The farm lies at an elevation of 150 to 200 ft. with a southerly exposure. Mean annual rainfall is 27 in. The mid-winter climate is similar to that of the Eastern Counties of England (except that the hours of daylight are shorter), but the summer is cooler (some 5° F. lower) and the growing season is some three weeks shorter.

The parent material of the soil is glacial drift, derived mainly from Old Red Sandstone material. The soil is a free working loam of good depth, with some stones and gravel; it is naturally lime deficient.

The area is well served with roads and railways, and there is some coastwise traffic with the south. There is a local market for distilling barley and there is a beet sugar factory. The once large market for milling oats has declined, but the area supplies seed oats for the adjoining upland regions. A considerable amount of farm produce—ware potatoes, fat cattle and sheep—goes to Glasgow and Northern England, and there is an export of seed potatoes to England.

### Allocation of Land

The total acreage is nearly 300, of which 20 are under permanent grass. The traditional rotation is a seven course, viz.: (1) oats after ley, (2) potatoes, (3) wheat or oats, (4) roots, (5) barley, (6) seeds and (7) seeds. A common modification is to extend the ley for a third year and to follow with potatoes, thus omitting an oat crop. This applies to about half the land on the farm described.

The root break is allocated to swedes (20 acres), turnips, kale and rape (10 acres), and sugar beet (10 acres). Of the 100 acres of temporary grass, about 20 are mown once for hay and a further 20 once for silage.

Conditions for the production of virus-free seed potatoes are not quite ideal; hence half the total potato acreage is planted with material obtained from adjoining high-lying districts.

### Tractor, Horse and Man Power

There are two medium and one light tractor, two horses, and six full time workers.

### Live Stock

There is an attested breeding herd of non-pedigree Aberdeen-Angus cows producing about thirty calves annually. These are suckled singly by their dams. The calving season is January-March. The produce is sold at a little more than two years old—mostly in March-April at live weights of about 10½ cwt., the quality being choice. About six heifers are retained annually to replenish the breeding herd.

There is a flock of about eighty half-bred (Border Leicester × Cheviot) ewes. Some twenty-five replacements are purchased annually as gimmers (yearlings). The ewes are mated to Suffolk rams to lamb in March, and ordinarily rear about 140 lambs. Single lambs are sold fat off their dams in July; the remainder are finished, mainly on aftermaths, and sold fat by October-November.

Since the farm can carry rather more stock in winter than in summer, some ten to twelve attested store cattle are ordinarily bought in Autumn to be sold fat in May. Again, if there is a surplus of aftermath and rape, some forty to sixty Blackface mountain wether lambs may be bought and sold fat in October-November.

The ewe flock is wintered on grass, with a run over beet tops in autumn, and silage later, and receive about 2 lb. per head of concentrates from February until there is sufficient growth of pasturage. The breeding cows are wintered on oat straw, roots and a small allowance of silage, the weaned calves on roots, hay, oats, and a pound or two of linseed or other oil-cake. Fattening cattle have a liberal ration of roots, with oat straw at first and hay later, along with about 4 lb. of concentrates, mainly oats.

### Manures and Fertilizers

The general scheme of fertilizer treatment is as set out below. Quantities are varied according to circumstances.

*Applications per Acre*

|  | Dung | Ground Lime-stone | Units of Nitrogen (N) | Units of Phosphate ($P_2O_5$) | Units of Potash ($K_2O$) |
|---|---|---|---|---|---|
|  | tons | cwt. |  |  |  |
| Oats after ley . | ... | ... | ... | ... | ... |
| Potatoes after three-year ley | ... | ... | 40 | 80 | 120 |
| Potatoes after oats . | 15 | ... | 60 | 80 | 120 |
| Wheat . | ... | ... | 40 | ... | ... |
| Swedes | 10 | 40 | 30 | 100 | 60 |
| Sugar beet | 10 | 40 | 40 | 60 | 120 |
| Turnips, etc. . | ... | 40 | 30 | 60 | 60 |
| Cereal after roots (undersown) | ... | ... | 30 | 40 | ... |
| Hay . | ... | ... | 20 | 40 | ... |
| Pasture . | ... | ... | 20 | ... | ... |

Permanent pasture: lime and phosphate at intervals of four years.

Half the pasture (for early bite) receives about 2 cwt. of nitrogen fertilizer.

**Crops**

Normal yields are: oats, 28 cwt.; wheat, 30 cwt.; barley, 28 cwt.; early potatoes, 4 tons seed plus 2 tons ware; maincrop potatoes, 5 tons seed plus 3 tons ware with about 1½ tons for stock feed; swedes, 25 tons; sugar-beet, 10 tons; hay, 2½ tons. All straw, hay and roots and also the bulk of the oats are consumed on the farm.

The cereals are harvested by combine harvester and/or binder. Potato storage is in clamps (pits).

**Capital**

The following is based on an August valuation (*i.e.* before the commencement of the cereal harvest) when investment is near its peak.

*Standing Capital:*

| | | |
|---|--:|--:|
| 2 work horses at £40 | £80 | |
| 3 tractors (at half new prices) | 1050 | |
| Field implements (at half new prices) | 1900 | |
| Oil engine, thresher, and other barn machinery | 1000 | |
| | | £4030 |

*Crops and Crop Produce:*

| | | |
|---|--:|--:|
| 100 acres cereals at £15 | £1500 | |
| 40 „ potatoes at £80 | 3200 | |
| 40 „ roots at £30 | 1200 | |
| 40 „ new seeds at £6 | 240 | |
| 50 tons hay at £10 | 500 | |
| 100 „ silage at £2 | 200 | |
| | | £6640 |

*Live Stock:*

| | | |
|---|--:|--:|
| 33 cows at £70 | £2210 | |
| 30 suckling calves at £25 | 750 | |
| 30 yearlings at £55 | 1650 | |
| 80 ewes at £11 | 880 | |
| 80 weaning lambs at £7 | 560 | |
| | | £6050 |

*Miscellaneous:*

| | | |
|---|--:|--:|
| Straw, feeding stuffs, and miscellaneous stores on hand, unexhausted manurial residues | | £800 |
| | | £17,520 |

**Annual Expenditure**

| | | |
|---|--:|--:|
| Rent at 70s. per acre | | £1050 |
| Insurance | | 250 |
| Carriage | | 400 |
| Labour | | 3000 |
| Casual: Potato planting, harvesting, dressing, and miscellaneous | | 500 |

*Seeds:*

| | | |
|---|--:|--:|
| Seed potatoes—20 acres at £30 | £600 | |
| Roots | 30 | |
| Cereals | 300 | |
| Grass seeds | 200 | |
| | £1130 | |

| | | |
|---|--:|--:|
| Fertilizers and lime (cost *less* subsidies) | | 1000 |
| Purchased feeding stuffs—20 tons at £35 | | 700 |
| Fuel and oil, implement depreciation, fencing, veterinary charges, etc. | | 2300 |
| Flock replacement (purchases of yearlings *less* sale of cast ewes) | | 300 |
| Herd replacement (depreciation on bull) | | 100 |
| | | £10,730 |

**Annual Income**

Crops:

| | | |
|---|---|---:|
| Wheat—40 acres, 1200 cwt. at 25s. . . . . | | £1500 |
| Barley—20 acres, 560 cwt. at 25s. . . . . | | 700 |
| Oats—20 acres, 560 cwt. at 22s. . . . . . | | 616 |
| Seed potatoes (*less* retained)—160 tons at £25 . . | | 4000 |
| Ware potatoes—100 tons at £10 . . . . . | | 1000 |
| Sugar beet—100 tons at £7 . . . . . | | 700 |
| | | £8516 |

Live Stock:

| | | |
|---|---|---:|
| 24 home-bred fat cattle at £100 . . . . . | | £2400 |
| 5 cast cows at £40 . . . . . . . | | 200 |
| Gross profit on 12 store cattle at £10 . . . . | | 120 |
| 140 lambs at £8 . . . . . . . | | 1120 |
| Gross profit on 40 purchased lambs at £1 . . . | | 40 |
| Wool . . . . . . . . . | | 100 |
| | | £3980 |

Miscellaneous:

| | | |
|---|---|---:|
| (including ploughing grant) . . . . . . . | | £500 |
| | | £12,996 |

## C. Cotswold Arable Farm

### Natural Conditions

This is thin limestone brash country 400 ft. to 900 ft. above sea level; on the whole it is flat but there are many dry river valleys. The annual rainfall is 26-28 in. The grazing season starts late and the winters are long and cold. The geological formation is oolite and the soil is derived from the parent material and contains a high clay fraction.

### Economic Situation

The area has enjoyed prosperity over a long period due to the margins obtainable from corn growing. While barley is the main crop, an appreciable acreage of winter wheat is grown behind the leys which form the basis of the farming pattern. The problem has always been to match the output of the grass with the output of the corn which on most farms amounts to 50 per cent. of the total acreage. Present trends are for a more intensive use of grass through dairy cows and fat lamb production.

### Allocation of Land

The farm extends to 480 acres. Of this 120 acres is unploughable permanent pasture, 360 acres is in a rotation of three years ley, winter wheat and two spring barley crops.

### Manures and Fertilizers

The leys receive 3 cwt. per acre of complete fertilizer per annum. The wheat receives 3 cwt. of a low nitrogen compound in the seed bed and 4 cwt. of sulphate of ammonia as a spring top dressing, while the barley is sown with 3 cwt. of complete fertilizer and 2 cwt. of sulphate of ammonia—all in the seed bed. The permanent grass receives nothing.

### Yields

Average yields are 30 cwt. per acre of winter wheat, 26 cwt. of barley. Hay yields fluctuate widely from 25 cwt. to 40 cwt. per acre.

### Live Stock

There are 400 ewes lambing in March with an average prolificacy of 150 per cent., 40 single suckling cross bred beef cows are maintained, calving down in January with the aim of producing a 5 cwt. calf for sale in the autumn.

### Labour

There are four men. The farmer himself works physically about three hours per day on average. The rest of his time is taken up with managerial duties.

### Capital

The following would represent the capital investment as at 1st March:—

*Live Stock:*

| | | |
|---|---:|---:|
| 400 ewes at £8 | £3,200 | |
| 8 rams at £10 | 80 | |
| 40 heifers at £50 | 2000 | |
| 38 beef calves at £20 | 760 | |
| 1 Bull at £100 | 100 | |
| | | £6140 |

*Equipment:*

| | | |
|---|---:|---:|
| 1 Grain Dryer | £980 | |
| 4 Tractors at £350 | 1400 | |
| Field equipment, *e.g.* ploughs, drills | 1125 | |
| 1 Combine | 1250 | |
| 1 Baler | 500 | |
| Miscellaneous grass equipment | 700 | |
| | | £5955 |

*Miscellaneous:*

| | | |
|---|---:|---:|
| Cultivations, hay, straw, seeds, fertilizers on hand | £4416 | |
| | | £16,511 |

### Annual Expenditure

| | | |
|---|---:|---:|
| Rent | £1440 | |
| Labour | 1980 | |
| Machinery and Power | 2400 | |
| Feeding stuffs | 650 | |
| Seeds | 720 | |
| Fertilizers | 1380 | |
| Cattle | | |
|   Replacement of cows, 8 at £65 | 520 | |
|   Replacement of bull at £40 | 40 | |
| Sheep | | |
|   Replacement of ewes, 130 at £8. | 1040 | |
|   Replacement of rams, 3 at £20 | 60 | |
| Miscellaneous | 960 | |
| | | £11,190 |

2 A

**Annual Income**

| | |
|---|---|
| Wheat, 60 acres at 30 cwts. at 25s. . . . . | £2250 |
| Barley, 120 acres at 26 cwt. at 25s. . . . . | 3900 |
| Lambs, 600 at £6 . . . . . . . | 3600 |
| Cattle, 38 calves at £42 (including subsidy) . . . | 1596 |
| Cull Cows, 6 at £50 . . . . . . . | 300 |
| Cull Ewes, 95 at £4 . . . . . . | 380 |
| 150 acres of Straw at £3 . . . . . . | 450 |
| Miscellaneous (including ploughing subsidy) . . . | 720 |
| | ———— £13,196 |

## D. Severn Vale Dairy Farm

**Natural Conditions**

The country is low lying (100-200 ft.) well sheltered but sloping towards the River Severn on the west. The geological formation is mainly lower lias clay, with middle lias above and an outcrop of oolite at the high eastern side. Most of the fields are high in lime but a narrow outcrop of sand is slightly acid. Rainfall is about 30-35 in.

**Economic Situation**

The farm is situated within easy distance of small towns. There is a large dairy collecting centre near and communications by road and rail are excellent.

**Allocation of Land**

The farm extends to 88 acres of which 8 acres are in permanent grass. There are 3½ acres of potatoes some kale and 11 acres of wheat. The remaining area is in Timothy, Meadow Fescue, Cocksfoot leys with 4 acres of Italian Ryegrass for early grazing.

**Rotation**

Potatoes/Kale, Wheat, three years ley.

**Manures and Fertilizers**

Leys have an annual application of 4 cwt. per acre of a complete compound fertilizer. Italian Ryegrass has additional Nitrogen for the early bite, potatoes 6 cwt. compound plus 15 tons farmyard manure, wheat 3 cwt. compound and a spring top dressing.

**Yields**

Wheat average 30 cwt. per acre. Potatoes 11 tons per acre.

**Live Stock**

The dairy herd consists of 23 high yielding Friesian cows and heifers with 20 followers. 25 Clun cross ewes are normally kept over winter and sold with lambs at foot. Five Wessex gilts have been kept outdoors. There are no poultry.

**Labour**

The farm is run by the farmer and one man but contractors are employed for corn harvesting and casual labour is brought in to handle the potato harvest.

## Capital

The following would represent the capital investment as at 5th May:—

### Live Stock

| | |
|---|---:|
| 23 cows and heifers at £70 | £1610 |
| 5 heifers in calf at £55 | 275 |
| 6 yearlings at £35 | 210 |
| 9 calves at £12 | 108 |
| 5 sows at £30 | 150 |
| | £2353 |

### Miscellaneous:

| | |
|---|---:|
| Cultivations, seeds, fertilizer in hand | £410 |

### Equipment:

| | |
|---|---:|
| 1 tractor | £310 |
| 1 mill and mixer | 395 |
| 1 potato spinner | 75 |
| 1 mower | 70 |
| Milking Machine and Plant | 250 |
| Cultivation tools. | 200 |
| | £1300 |

## Annual Expenditure

| | |
|---|---:|
| Paid Labour | £820 |
| Purchased food | 1826 |
| Seeds | 251 |
| Fertilizers | 416 |
| Rent | 260 |
| Contract | 68 |
| Power and machinery | 483 |
| Miscellaneous | 256 |
| | £4380 |

## Annual Income

| | |
|---|---:|
| Milk | £3828 |
| Cattle | 730 |
| Sheep | 192 |
| Pigs | 192 |
| Crops | 631 |
| Sundries | 204 |
| | £5777 |

### E. Cheshire Dairy Farm

The holding here described lies in the southern part of the Cheshire plain. Specialisation in dairying, chiefly cheese production, began very early, the product being sent to London by sea before the days of canals or railways. Specialisation has since increased, but the great bulk of the milk is now sold on the liquid market and there is very little farmhouse cheese making. Coincident with the change in milk disposal there has been a marked trend from summer to year round milk production. Up till 1939, however, the general practice was to use pasturage and home grown bulky foods in conjunction with purchased concentrates. During the last war intensified grassland management set free land for the production of cereals and beans, and outputs of milk were well maintained. Since the war there has been some decline in tillage and more dependence on purchased feeding stuffs, but the output of milk has risen.

### Natural Conditions

The farm lies at an elevation of about 150 ft. The situation is sheltered and the configuration flat. Annual rainfall is about 30 in. The winter is fairly mild, but the land lies rather wet, so that stock must be housed in winter to avoid damage to swards. The geological formation is Keuper Marl with some boulder clay, giving rise to fertile clay loam or clay soils. The lime status varies from good to moderate.

### Economic Situation

Industrial Merseyside to the north and the Pottery district to the south are each about thirty miles distant. The area is well served with roads, and most farm requisites can be delivered from works or mills by road. Electric power is generally available.

### Allocation of Land and Cropping

The total area is 210 acres. Some 60 acres of the lightest land is old arable, farmed on a six course rotation, viz.: (1) oats; (2) fodder roots and kale; (3) wheat or oats (undersown); and (4) to (6) a three-year ley, commonly mown for hay or silage in both the first and second seasons (the after-growth being grazed) and grazed during the whole of the third. Thirty acres of heavy and rather poorly drained land are permanent meadow, the aftermaths being grazed by dry cows and young stock. Sixty acres more is under a ley-and-corn rotation, ordinarily (1) wheat, (2) oats and beans, and (3) to (6) ley which is commonly mown for silage in its first year, being too tender to carry cattle. The remaining 60 acres are permanent pasture.

### Fixed Equipment

There is a cowshed for seventy five, with calving boxes, calf house and yards for older dry stock. The milking machine and hammer mill are electrically driven. There is adequate Dutch barn space for hay and corn.

### Manures and Fertilizers

The permanent pasture has a dressing of about 5 cwt. basic slag at intervals of four years. Permanent meadows are dunged at intervals of four years and receive about 3 cwt. per acre of complete compound in the intervening years. Root crops have about 15 tons per acre of dung, with 4 to 6 cwt. of appropriate compound fertilizer. Wheat following ley receives only a light spring application of nitrogen. Second corn crops and seeds hay have 3 cwt. of a nitrogen-phosphate compound. About 20 acres of pasture is dressed, for early bite with nitrogen. Average usage of lime is about 20 tons per annum.

### Crop Yields

Meadow hay, $1\frac{1}{2}$ tons; seeds hay, $2\frac{1}{2}$ tons; oats, 22 cwt.; wheat, 26 cwt.; mangels, 40 tons; kale and swedes, 20 tons.

### Live Stock

The attested dairy herd comprises eighty grade Friesian cows and about forty-five followers. The remaining live stock consist of three breeding sows (the produce being sold as baconers) and about 100 head of poultry.

Maiden heifers and some of the poorer cows are artificially inseminated to produce Aberdeen-Angus cross calves. These, and the male Friesian calves, are sold at the age of a week or two.

### Labour

The regular labour force is five men and a lad. Some casual labour may be employed at hay time.

### Capital

The following estimate is based on a Lady Day (25th March) valuation:—

*Equipment* (at half new prices):

| | | |
|---|---:|---:|
| 2 tractors, tillage implements | £2000 | |
| Barn machinery, poultry houses | 400 | |
| Dairy equipment | 700 | |
| | | £3100 |

*Cattle:*

| | | |
|---|---:|---:|
| 75 cows at £80 | £6000 | |
| 45 other cattle at £40 | 1800 | |
| Bull | 150 | |
| | | £7950 |

*Other Live Stock:*

| | | |
|---|---:|---:|
| 3 sows at £25 | £75 | |
| 30 other pigs at £10 | 300 | |
| 100 head poultry at 25s. | 125 | |
| | | £500 |

*Miscellaneous:*

| | |
|---|---:|
| Hay, straw, and feeding stuffs; growing crops and maiden seeds; residual manurial values | £1200 |

| | |
|---|---:|
| | £12,750 |

### Annual Expenditure

| | |
|---|---:|
| Rent—£4 per acre | £840 |
| Labour | 3000 |
| Feeding stuffs—55 tons at £35 | 1925 |
| Seeds | 250 |
| Fertilizers and lime (*less* subsidies) | 600 |
| Replacement of bull | 100 |
| Tractor, fuel and oil, electricity, repairs and depreciation of equipment, veterinary charges, consumable stores, carriage and insurance | 1600 |
| | £8315 |

### Annual Income

| | |
|---|---:|
| 60,000 gallons milk at 3s. | £9000 |
| 40 calves at £4 | 160 |
| 36 bacon pigs at £16 | 576 |
| 20 old, barren and casualty cows at £25 | 500 |
| Eggs | 80 |
| Wheat (production *less* usage for poultry) | 200 |
| | £10,516 |

# 3.  ADJUSTMENT OF THE FARMING SYSTEM TO CHANGING CONDITIONS

No rigid farming scheme can be expected to produce maximum profit over any long period of time, and since neither economic changes nor technical developments can be predicted with assurance, flexibility is an important objective in farm planning.

This has particular importance in relation to farm buildings and other fixed equipment.  In the past, farm buildings have often been sited and planned with much too little regard to possible changes in use; there are many old horse stables that cannot be satisfactorily converted into cowsheds, piggeries, grain stores or tractor sheds; many old cattle yards that cannot readily be adapted to permit of mechanised foddering or dung handling; implement sheds so sited that they cannot be enlarged to accommodate the growing range of equipment, particularly such large machines as the combine harvester or the tractor drill.  Again, there are many examples of massive stone walled buildings that have remained structurally sound long after they have become obsolete.

In general, then, buildings should be of such dimensions as will permit of a variety of uses.  Much thought has been given to this subject, and there is now a supply of mass produced pillars and roof trusses, in a limited number of standard sizes, which provide for a large number of uses.  Where highly specialised buildings are in question, it may be true economy to build in relatively cheap materials with a view to a relatively short life.

Again, many farms have been laid out and divided up with stone wall or hedge and ditch fencing, on the assumption that an existing cropping plan, and the existing types of field implements, would long continue to be appropriate.  In many districts fields are too small and too irregular in shape to permit of the full and economic use of tractors and tractor drawn tools.  Movable or temporary fences have many advantages.

The more important kinds of adjustments that may fall to be considered are set out below, with examples.

1.  **Substitution of One Enterprise by Another.**—Perhaps the commonest incentive to substitution is a change, or an expectation of change, in the relative profitability of an existing enterprise and a practicable alternative. But other considerations may arise—*e.g.*, a change in the supply of labour, a change in the farmer's capital resources or some major technological development.

During the past half century many farmers were led to the view that milk offered better prospects than beef production.  Population was increasing, and consumption per head was rising as the nutritive value of milk became more widely recognised, while the liquid milk market was not open to overseas competition.  Again, there was increasing scope for higher yields, by reason of progressively better control over bovine disease and advances in breeding, feeding and management. On the other hand, with developments of meat preservation—particularly freezing and chilling—and with the opening up of the grasslands of the new countries, there was reason to expect increasing pressure of imports of meat.

The change over from beef to milk involved additional capital investment (in buildings and dairy equipment), the training of workers in milk production, and the acquisition by the farmer himself of new knowledge and skills. But, in general, the change did, in fact, result in improved profitability.

At the time of writing it appeared that there might be a balance of advantage in a reverse change. Consumption of liquid milk had ceased to increase and yields of milk, per cow, were rising; world supplies of dairy produce—butter, cheese and evaporated milk—were ample, and costs of production of those commodities, for various reasons including climatic conditions, were lower in certain overseas countries than in Britain. At the same time, the production of beef was tending to give way, in certain overseas countries, to other enterprises, while the growth of population in many of the meat exporting countries was reducing the quantities of beef available for export. But the balance of argument for the change (from milk to beef) varied as between one farm and another. The small farmer would suffer a decline in gross income, and the family farmer might find it difficult to secure full employment for his available labour force, while the large scale farmer might be able to reduce his wage bill and give more time and thought to his other enterprises.

2. **A Change in Form of an Individual Enterprise.**—An existing system of producing some particular commodity may be outmoded by some step of technical progress, by a change in economic conditions or by some combination of these and other circumstances.

Towards the end of last century the close folding system of sheep husbandry, once typical under light land arable conditions in the south-eastern half of England, became uneconomic, partly by reason of the fall in cereal prices, partly because increasing supplies of fertilizers, at lower prices, provided a cheaper means of maintaining soil fertility, partly because sugar beet gave a better return than folded roots, and partly because the labour cost of folding (in relation to prices of mutton and wool) rose to a level that could hardly be borne. The alternatives open to the farmer were to turn over from the folding system to leys and grass sheep husbandry (which involved capital expenditure on fencing) or to abandon the sheep enterprise altogether. The latter alternative was commonly selected in the Eastern Counties, while in the south the former was often preferred.

Again, in recent times the colony house system of poultry keeping has in many cases been replaced by one or other of the intensive systems—the deep litter house, the laying battery or the hen yard. The one incentive has been a reduction in labour cost and the other a more favourable pattern of seasonal production—a higher proportion of winter eggs. The change has been facilitated by the development of electricity supplies in rural areas.

Recent times have seen two rather widespread changes in the organisation of milk production. The milk-and-feed system, under which herd replacement was by the purchase of mature cows at or near to calving and the cattle were sold as they dried off, suffered over a period from the circumstance that the farmer could hardly qualify for the premium offered for tuberculin tested milk. Hence many producers proceeded to build up self contained herds, rearing all necessary replacement stock. Recently, however, there has been a great increase in the supply of tuberculin tested heifers, and many small producers have reverted to their former practice on the ground that milk production from mature cattle yielded higher profits and provided fuller employment than the combination of milking and rearing.

Other milk producers, long accustomed to purchase the bulk of their concentrated feeding stuffs (because these could be bought at prices below the farmer's own cost of production) and, for the rest, to depend on ordinary pasturage and hay, were obliged, by the war time scarcity of feeding stuffs, to intensify their grassland management and to set aside land for the production of cereals and kale. When imported concentrates again were available in ample supply, some farmers, especially in areas unfavourable to arable farming, reverted to their former practice. In many cases, however, the intensification of grassland management and the improvement in conservation methods had proved profitable in themselves, and the choice was between continuing the war time system or expanding milk production with purchased and home grown feed.

3. **Changes in the Number or in the Balance of Enterprises.**—The classical arguments for a high degree of diversification—the combination of many enterprises—are the spreading of economic risks, the reduction of biological risks (soil borne disease, animal disease), efficient utilisation of cash crop by-products (straw, sugar beet tops, tail corn) by means of live stock, the maintenance of soil fertility and the provision of productive work, throughout the year, for the regular workers.

The force of these arguments has, however, tended to decline. Under the existing conditions of guaranteed prices and assured markets for many commodities price risks have been greatly reduced. Measures other than the rotation of crops and mixed stocking are available for the control of diseases and pests; fertilizers are a cheaper source of plant nutrients than the residues of imported concentrates; and the mechanisation of cereal production and hay making has relieved the pressure of work at hay time and harvest.

The positive arguments for increased specialisation—*i.e.* for a reduction in the number of enterprises comprising the traditional system—are firstly that the individual worker will commonly be more efficient as the variety of his tasks is reduced; secondly, that specialised equipment (the combine harvester, pick up hay baler or beet harvester) can be expected to be economic only if used up to something approaching full capacity; and thirdly, that, with the accelerating rate of technical progress, it becomes increasingly difficult for the farmer himself to maintain a high level of efficiency in the management of each and all of a large number of enterprises.

Despite these broad arguments for simplification of the farm system, individual circumstances may and often do call for an addition to the existing enterprises. The commonest objective is perhaps that of securing full employment, under changed conditions, for an existing number of workers. On the larger farms, employing four or more workers, the benefit from measures to increase the productivity of labour may be realised either by a change in the balance of enterprises, by raising the general level of intensity of production or by dispensing with a worker. But the same choice is not open to those farmers (the great majority) who employ one or two workers.

Thus if with a two man dairy unit we install a milking machine and modern milk handling equipment, and provide improved facilities for feeding and cleansing, we may be able to run the herd with one full time and one half time worker, and it may be impracticable to increase the size of the dairy herd by the amount necessary to provide the desirable full employment. In such a case the appropriate solution may be to set up a half man pig or poultry unit as an addition to the existing enterprises. Again, many family farms are too small in acreage to provide either full employment or an adequate standard of living under the traditional farming system. In such case the most promising approach may be to add an enterprise that will use no considerable acreage of land—a pig or poultry unit or a glasshouse.

4. **The Level of Intensity.**—Apart from the question of the make up of the farming business, the enterprises comprising it and the balance between them, the farmer is concerned to get, in each enterprise, the optimum level of intensity—*i.e.* with regard to each element of input (labour, fertilizers, feeding stuffs) the level that will give the maximum profit.

Although the distinction is never quite clear cut it is possible to divide the inputs for the production of a given commodity into *fixed* and *variable* costs. For example, in the production of potatoes the land must be worked to a tilth, seed must be bought and the crop must be harvested. There are only minor savings to be made by scamping the tillage, by planting less than the standard quantity of seed or in harvesting a 5-ton as compared to a 10-ton crop. On the other hand, manures and fertilizers may be applied in widely varying amounts, and it is important to find the optimum level, *i.e.* the application that will achieve the highest level of profit.

The response of crops to manures and fertilisers is subject to the law of diminishing returns—*i.e.* each successive addition to the dressing produces a lower response than the preceding one. The point may be illustrated by the response of a particular variety of potatoes to farmyard manure at varying levels, and the following table sets out the data for a particular case:—

| Plot No. | Farmyard Manure, tons per acre | Yield, tons per acre | Yield Increment (tons per acre) for each Successive Addition |
|---|---|---|---|
| 1 | 0 | 4·6 | ... |
| 2 | 4 | 5·9 | 1·3 |
| 3 | 8 | 6·7 | 0·8 |
| 4 | 12 | 7·4 | 0·7 |
| 5 | 16 | 7·8 | 0·4 |
| 6 | 20 | 8·0 | 0·2 |

Assuming a constant price (or cost) per ton for dung, the most profitable application will depend on the price realised for the crop. In the following table the value of farmyard manure is put at 30s. per ton and a calculation of profitability, for each level of application, is made for three levels of potato prices, £6, £9, and £12 per ton:—

| Plot No. | Cost of Farmyard Manure £ | Yield, tons per Acre | Total Value of Crop per ton at | | | Value of Crop, less cost of Farmyard Manure | | |
|---|---|---|---|---|---|---|---|---|
| | | | £6 | £9 | £12 | £6 | £9 | £12 |
| 1 | Nil | 4·6 | 27·6 | 41·4 | 55·2 | 27·6 | 41·4 | 55·2 |
| 2 | 6 | 5·9 | 35·4 | 53·1 | 70·8 | 29·4 | 47·1 | 64·8 |
| 3 | 12 | 6·7 | 40·2 | 60·3 | 80·4 | 28·2 | 48·3 | 68·4 |
| 4 | 18 | 7·4 | 44·4 | 66·6 | 88·8 | 26·4 | 48·6 | 70·8 |
| 5 | 24 | 7·8 | 46·8 | 70·2 | 93·6 | 22·8 | 46·2 | 69·6 |
| 6 | 30 | 8·0 | 48·0 | 72·0 | 96·0 | 18·0 | 42·0 | 66·0 |

It thus appears that the most profitable dressings of farmyard manure were about 4 tons, 10 tons, and 13 tons respectively. In no case was the full dressing as profitable as something less.

The figures below illustrate the application of the law of diminishing returns to the application of sulphate of ammonia to wheat, in the absence

| Rate of Application cwt. per Acre | Yield, cwt. per Acre | Added Yield, cwt. per Acre | Value of Added Yield | Cost of Added Fertilizer | Net Value of Additional Yield |
|---|---|---|---|---|---|
| | | | s. d. | s. d. | s. d. |
| Nil | 21·0 | ... | ... | ... | ... |
| 1 | 24·0 | 3·0 | 88 6 | 13 5 | 75 1 |
| 2 | 25·8 | 1·8 | 53 1 | 13 5 | 39 8 |
| 3 | 26·8 | 1·0 | 29 6 | 13 5 | 16 1 |
| 4 | 27·5 | 0·7 | 20 8 | 13 5 | 7 3 |
| 5 | 27·9 | 0·4 | 11 10 | 13 5 | —1 7 |

of farmyard manure, on good land. The calculation is made at prices ruling in 1952-53—13s. 5d. per cwt. for sulphate of ammonia and 29s. 6d. per cwt. for wheat.

It thus appears that on average the most profitable dressing under the conditions prevailing was 4 cwt. per acre. The responses, however, varied from one trial to another, being influenced by such factors as soil type, climatic conditions and the variety of wheat grown. Under certain soil-climate-variety combinations the risk of lodging, at the higher levels of nitrogen, would be a material consideration in deciding the level of nitrogen dressing.

The optimum level of the variable inputs (e.g. as fertilizers) depends on the relationship between the variable and the fixed or near fixed costs. But it also depends on the degree of technical skill of the farmer. The point may be illustrated by the relationship of milk yield per cow, to profitability. The potential yield of a cow depends on the skill of the farmer in such matters as breeding and rearing. And actual yields depend on the farmer's efficiency in controlling disease, in compounding rations and on that of the cowman in day-to-day operations, including milking. The substantially fixed costs—provision and maintenance of buildings, the wage cost of milking, milk handling and cleansing, and providing the maintenance ration—constitute a large proportion of total costs.

The law of diminishing returns applies, but only in small degree, to the output of milk—for instance, the production of the fifth gallon per day costs somewhat more, in nutrients, than that of the third. The overall result is that, within wide limits, high yield makes for low cost per gallon. Moreover, the larger profit per gallon, on the higher yield, ordinarily results in a marked increase, with increasing yield, in the margin of profit per cow. The relationship between yield and profit margin may be illustrated by the data below derived from the National Milk Cost Investigation, 1949-50.

|  | Yield Group |  |  |  |  |  |  |
| --- | --- | --- | --- | --- | --- | --- | --- |
|  | A | B | C | D | E | F | G |
| Mean yield (gal. per cow) . | 407·0 | 514·0 | 600·0 | 687·0 | 771·0 | 861·0 | 1035·0 |
| Labour (hours per cow) . | 148·0 | 129·0 | 139·0 | 139·0 | 150·0 | 161·0 | 184·0 |
| Food cost per cow (£) . | 26·4 | 30·3 | 34·0 | 38·1 | 42·9 | 47·9 | 57·9 |
| Net total cost per cow (£) . | 48·3 | 54·9 | 58·9 | 64·3 | 70·4 | 76·7 | 89·2 |
| Returns per cow (£) . | 55·6 | 71·1 | 82·3 | 95·8 | 109·2 | 122·4 | 148·4 |
| Farm cost per gal. (pence) . | 28·5 | 25·6 | 23·6 | 22·5 | 21·9 | 21·4 | 20·7 |
| Margin per gal. (pence) . | 4·3 | 7·6 | 9·4 | 11·0 | 12·1 | 12·7 | 13·7 |
| Margin per cow (£) . | 7·3 | 16·2 | 23·4 | 31·5 | 38·8 | 45·7 | 59·2 |

In certain enterprises it may, however, be possible, by a change of system, to achieve a major reduction in fixed costs. In the case of milk production such a saving can be achieved under the outdoor or bail system.  The capital cost of the milking bail is small by comparison with that of a set of permanent buildings, while there is a reduction in labour costs of cleaning and manure carting.  Again, bulky materials such as hay and silage can often be consumed in the fields where they have been grown, thus eliminating transport costs.  Hence it can happen that a yield per cow of 700 or 800 gal. from a bail herd may leave as large a margin per cow as one of 1000 gal. under the traditional cowshed system. Soil and climatic conditions, however, may preclude the former.

# CHAPTER 29

## MEASURES OF ECONOMIC EFFICIENCY

IN the previous chapter the basic elements of an economic farming system have been described, but the farmer still needs to have methods whereby he can measure the business efficiency of his enterprise. The appearance of crops and grass, the apparent quality of live stock and the timeliness of seasonal operations all serve to provide a good physical appraisal of the standard of farming, but they give no guide to the actual margin of profit or the way in which that profit is achieved.

In many manufacturing industries the commonest measure of efficiency is the cost of production of the finished article, and at one time it was thought by many that cost accounting could serve the same purpose in farming. It is indeed possible, to some extent, to allocate inputs—labour, fertilizers, feeding stuffs and so on—between the various enterprises that constitute the business, and to put values upon such by-products as straw and farmyard manure; but the basis for the valuation of by-products is largely a matter of guesswork. Again, labour is ordinarily charged at flat rates as between one task and another, whereas in practice the return per man hour varies widely as between one task and another. In any case the determination of enterprise costs necessitates a very elaborate system of accounting including, for example, a detailed time sheet for each man and a separate record for each field or group of live stock.

The degree of difficulty varies as between one enterprise and another. It is, for instance, small in the case of a pig or poultry unit run mainly on purchased feeding stuffs. By contrast, the cost of the winter fattening of cattle can be arrived at only by making a series of assumptions about the value of unsaleable commodities such as roots, straw and farmyard manure. Finally, the production cost of a particular commodity may vary widely from year to year by reason of differences in weather conditions and it is difficult to make proper allowance in such cases.

Not only is it necessary to detect weaknesses in husbandry techniques, but also to identify and define weaknesses in the management and organisation of the farm business. Cost accounting may reveal the level of costs of the individual enterprises, but it does not follow that the lowest unit cost results in the highest profit. For example a dairy farmer producing 20,000 gal. of milk at a cost of 2/- per gal. and selling it at an average price of 3/- per gal. will make a profit of 1/- per gal. or £1000. If he has the necessary facilities to produce an extra 5000 gal., it will pay him to do so even if this extra milk may cost 2/6d. per gal. to produce. His overall average costs will rise to about 2/1¼d. but his *total profit* will increase by £125.

The chief measure of overall efficiency is profit, the total income that the holding yields. Profit is the balance between receipts (including home produce consumed by the farm family) and expenditure, with a correction for the difference between opening and closing valuations. In some cases —particularly the smaller farm—it may be well to divide the income into two parts:—(a) the notional wages earned by the farmer and any member of his family in operational work, and (b) the remainder, which represents interest on capital plus the reward for management. The latter part is described as " Management and Investment Income ". There is nothing to be gained by splitting the last into interest on capital, a notional salary for management and a balance of profit. The profit is commonly expressed on a per acre basis, but this is inappropriate in certain cases, *e.g.* mountain sheep farms or glasshouse holdings.

The farmer will endeavour to attain the highest level of profit that is consistent with good husbandry. His objective will be the maintenance of high profits over a period of years rather than maximum profit in any one year. To this end he will seek to arrive at both the best balance of enterprises for his farm, and the optimum yields for those enterprises. Cost accounts will show that certain enterprises consistently make more profit than others, and there is thus the temptation to cut down or eliminate those low profit enterprises and to expand and concentrate on the more profitable ones. Farming, however, is not as simple as this. A farm is not a collection of separate and independent departments but an organic whole, and policy decisions are unlikely to be soundly based when each enterprise is studied in isolation. In the case of a dairy farm showing a profit of £30 per cow it might be concluded that the addition of 5 more cows would increase the total farm profit by £150. This is not necessarily the case because the extra cows might well be handled by the same labour force and without the provision of new or modified buildings. In other words there would be no increase in the overhead or fixed costs, and the profit on the extra cows would be substantially higher than the average of £30 per cow being earned by the existing herd.

## ANALYSIS OF THE FARM BUSINESS

To overcome the difficulties encountered in farm cost accounting it is necessary to apply a series of tests or yardsticks based on simple physical and financial farm records. Such analytical methods consider the farming system *as a whole* and determine its economic soundness, pinpoint the main technical weaknesses and provide measures for assessing the efficiency of utilisation of resources such as labour, feeding stuffs and machinery.

All farm management analyses rely on the availability of certain basic farm records. These are:—

(a) a financial statement of Income and Expenditure under the main headings. This can be derived from the accounts which most farmers have prepared for them by a professional accountant.

(b) a record of crop acreages and the disposal of crops, *i.e.* the proportions sold and fed on the farm.

(c) numbers of each class of livestock, preferably for each month of the year or at least quarterly.

(d) yields and sales of all livestock products.

(e) use of feed, both home grown and purchased, as between different classes of live stock.

With the aid of these records it is then possible to proceed with a detailed analysis of a farm business, stage by stage. The first step is to

### Example—75 acre dairy farm—South West

|  | £. s. | £ s. | £ s. | Average Similar Farms £ s. |
|---|---|---|---|---|
| **Output** (per acre) |  |  |  |  |
| Cattle |  | 4 10 |  | 4 5 |
| Milk |  | 53 0 |  | 38 4 |
| Poultry and Eggs |  | 8 5 |  | 10 8 |
| Crops |  | 6 |  | 2 1 |
| Other receipts |  | 4 2 |  | 2 4 |
| Total (Gross Output) |  | 70 3 |  | 57 2 |
| *Less*: Food purchases | 20 2 |  | 15 12 |  |
| Seed purchases | 1 12 |  | 1 4 |  |
|  |  | 21 14 |  | 16 16 |
| Net Output |  | £48 9 |  | £40 6 |

|  |  | Per Acre £ s. | Per Acre £ s. |
|---|---|---|---|
| **Expenditure** |  |  |  |
| Labour |  | 9 8 | 12 18 |
| Machinery |  | 7 16 | 7 4 |
| Fertilizers |  | 4 12 | 2 18 |
| Rent, rates, etc. |  | 4 2 | 2 12 |
| Miscellaneous |  | 5 4 | 4 10 |
| Total |  | £31 2 | £30 2 |
| *Profit:* |  | £17 7 | £10 4 |

convert the farmer's trading account into a per acre statement which shows at a glance the way in which the output of the farm is made up and the various constituents of the cost structure. This lay out also allows for a quick comparison with similar farms or with average figures published at frequent intervals by University Agricultural Economics Departments.

*Gross Output*—Total sales corrected for the difference between opening and closing values—is not, in itself, a good measure of overall production. For instance, if a farmer buys twenty store cattle in spring, at £60 per head, spends £2 per head on feeding stuffs, and sells the cattle at £80 per head, the measure of his output is not £1600 but £1600 minus (£1200 + £40), *i.e.* £360. Again, if a potato grower spends £20 per acre on seed and the crop realises £80 per acre, the output should be reckoned at £60.

Purchases of livestock, of feeding stuffs and of seeds are the most important variables as between farm and farm, and hence the measure generally applied—commonly called Net Output—is arrived at by deducting from total sales (corrected for valuation differences) the total expenditure on live stock, feeding stuffs and seeds. In a particular area the figures for farms of 100 to 150 acres were:—

| Farm Type | Gross Output per Acre | Net Output per Acre |
|---|---|---|
| Mainly dairying   .    .    . | £38 | £24 |
| Cash cropping   .    .    . | 51 | 41 |
| Cropping with livestock (other than dairying   .    .    . | 33 | 24 |

It will be seen that there is considerable difference in the ratio between the gross and net figures as between one farming type and another.

Since the wage bill is by much the largest item of expenditure on a majority of farms it is clear that some measure of output per man is necessary to the assessment of efficiency. Since, however, wages rates vary according to the age of the worker and the amount of overtime work, and since casual labour may be employed, it is sounder in principle (and, incidentally, easier in practice) to make the calculation in terms of wages, or of work units (notional man days) per 100 acres. Even so, as might be expected, there is no regular relationship between such a figure and profitability. One particular area gave the following figures in a particular year:—

Man Days per 100 acres.

| Farm Type | Group Average | Six most Profitable Farms in Group |
|---|---|---|
| Dairying—under 150 acres   .    .    . | 1052 | 970 |
| „        over 150   „    .    .    . | 847 | 909 |
| Cash cropping—under 150 acres   .    . | 940 | 940 |
| „        „        over 150   „    .    . | 731 | 758 |
| Cropping with live stock—under 150 acres | 665 | 683 |
| „    „    „    „   —over 150   „    . | 693 | 750 |

In particular cases this kind of calculation may show that a farm is grossly over or under manned. But a much more useful figure, which is no more difficult to determine, is net output per £100 paid in wages.

It would obviously be useful if we could express net output in relation to the third major factor in production—the tenant's capital (including loan capital) invested in the farm business. In some cases net output per £1000 capital has been used in the assessment of efficiency. The difficulty is the practical one that the figures for capital, as shown in the accounts of costed farms, may bear little relation to the amount actually invested. For example, dairy herds and other regular breeding stocks are commonly valued on the herd basis, *i.e.* at figures that take no account either of changes in actual prices or of progressive improvement in quality. Again, depreciation of plant and machinery is ordinarily calculated at the maximum rates allowable by the Inland Revenue authorities, and many items in annual valuations—*e.g.* unexhausted manurial values—are often entered in annual accounts at nominal figures. In short, net output per unit of capital, whether or not it could be estimated in a particular case, would be of little value on account of the lack of good data from costed farms.

If a particular farm (as judged by comparison with others of similar type) is showing an unsatisfactory profit, the first broad question is how much of the explanation lies in excessive expenditure and how much in subnormal output. As regards output, the relevant data that can generally be assembled are:—

1. approximate yields per acre of arable crops and hay, and quality of the products.
2. output of live stock products per acre of pasture and fodder crops.
3. live stock production figures—*e.g.* milk sales per cow; egg production per bird; weight of piglets at weaning; and age and weight of cattle, sheep and pigs at slaughter.

Crop yields must, of course, be assessed not in relation to national averages but in relation to local standards; and, even so, allowance must be made for the inherent fertility of the particular farm or field. In certain areas, however, there are rather clearly defined soil types, and in some cases approximate figures for normal yields are available. For example, the following are the approximate five year average yields for each of eight soil types in East Anglia:—

|  | Wheat | Barley | Oats | Sugar Beet | Potatoes |
|---|---|---|---|---|---|
|  | cwt. | cwt. | cwt. | Tons | Tons |
| Norfolk loams . . | 22·2 | 18·7 | 21·7 | 10·4 | 6·5 |
| Suffolk   „    . | 24·3 | 19·5 | 22·1 | 11·6 | 8·4 |
| Essex boulder clays . | 22·7 | 19·9 | 19·4 | 10·6 | 7·6 |
| London clays   . . | 23·9 | 20·0 | 20·5 | 10·6 | 7·7 |
|    „   chalks  . . | 21·9 | 19·0 | 19·1 | 8·9 | 6·1 |
| Cambs.-Hunts. clays . | 20·1 | 17·5 | 16·1 | 9·3 | 6·5 |
| Black fen    . . | 27·7 | 21·8 | 24·1 | 12·4 | 8·9 |
| Silt (alluvium) . . | 33·4 | 26·4 | 26·3 | 13·8 | 10·0 |

If, in a particular case, yields are poor in relation to the inherent possibilities of the local climate and the particular soil type, an effort should be made to identify the reasons. The commonest are probably (1) the use of ill adapted varieties, (2) inadequate usage of fertilizers (especially nitrogen), (3) ineffective weed control, (4) late sowing or planting, (5) imperfect control of diseases and pests, (6) inefficient tillage, (7) avoidable wastage in harvesting or storage. The quality of crop produce is of varying importance as between one crop and another, and there is, in some cases, a degree of incompatibility between high quality and high yield.

*Net Output of Live Stock Products per Forage Acre.*—The efficiency of live stock production may be assessed by relating the net output of live stock products to the acreage of grass and forage crops, including land used for hay and silage, and such other crops (oats and beans) as are used for stock feeding. Where a substantial proportion of the food require- ments of pigs and poultry is produced on the farm, and where either of those enterprises is on a considerable scale, the calculation should embrace the whole of the live stock. Where such circumstances do not obtain, it may be well to confine consideration to the grass eating animals, and examine the pig and poultry enterprises separately. In the latter case the net output is derived from sales of milk, wool and live stock (with allow- ance for change in valuation), with deductions for purchased feeding stuffs and of grass seeds and forage crop seeds. The following illustration applies to a small farm devoted mainly to milk production but carrying a small flock of sheep:—

**Sales**

| | | |
|---|---|---|
| Milk . . . . . . . . | £2850 | |
| Wool . . . . . . . . | 120 | |
| Sheep . . . . . . . . | 650 | |
| Cows, heifers and calves . . . . . | 600 | |
| Increase in live stock valuation . . . . | 120 | |
| | —— | £4340 |

**Purchases**

| | | |
|---|---|---|
| Sheep . . . . . . . . | £280 | |
| Cattle . . . . . . . . | 180 | |
| Feeding stuffs . . . . . . . | 650 | |
| Seed (grass, beans) . . . . . . | 90 | |
| | —— | £1200 |

| | |
|---|---|
| Net live stock output . . . . . . . . . | £3140 |

Fodder acreage:

| | |
|---|---|
| Grassland (pasture, hay and silage) . . . . . | 87 |
| Kale and roots . . . . . . . . | 8 |
| Oats and beans . . . . . . . . | 14 |
| | 109 |

$$\text{Live stock output per forage acre } \frac{£3140}{109} = £28 \text{ 16s.}$$

*Net Output per Work Unit.*—The efficiency of labour use over the farm as a whole is obtained by dividing the total net output by some measure of the labour employed. Some economists use " work units "—*i.e.* either the man hour or the man day, the latter being taken at eight hours. Others use the total wages paid; the answer is thus expressed in terms of net output per man hour, per man day, or per £100 of wages.

The measure of efficiency may be derived from either of two sets of data—the average work units per acre of crops and grass and per head of live stock or the average man day units for the appropriate size and type of farm.

In the former case the theoretical labour need is calculated from the average work units per acre of crops and per head of live stock, with an addition of 15 per cent. for overheads, and the amount of labour used on the particular farm is compared with the calculated need. In the latter case the labour used per acre is compared with the average figure for costed farms of the appropriate group. For example, if a particular light land arable farm of 130 acres uses 9.5 man day units per acre, as compared with the average of 7.3 for the appropriate group, it would appear that the labour use is rather seriously inefficient.

The degree of efficiency of pig and poultry enterprises can best be measured by physical rather than financial data, one reason being that output is little affected by climatic or soil conditions, and another that physical inputs and outputs can be easily recorded. Average figures are as follows:—

**Poultry**
  *Food Requirements:*
    Laying birds—

| | | | | | |
|---|---|---|---|---|---|
| Range or deep litter | . | . | . | . | . 20 cwt. per year |
| Battery (cages) | . | . | . | . | . 25 „ „ „ |
| Rearing | . | . | . | . | . 7 „ per head |

  *Egg Production:*

| | | | | | | Year | Winter |
|---|---|---|---|---|---|---|---|
| Battery (cages) | . | . | . | . | . | 200 | 100 |
| Hen yard | . | . | . | . | . | 180 | 80 |
| Free range | . | . | . | . | . | 150 | 60 |

  *Man hours per Bird per Year:*

| | | | | | |
|---|---|---|---|---|---|
| Battery (cages) | . | . | . | . | . 2·8 |
| Hen yard | . | . | . | . | . 1·9 |
| Free range | . | . | . | . | . 2·6 |

**Breeding Pigs**

| | | | | | |
|---|---|---|---|---|---|
| Litters per sow per year | . | . | . | . | . 1·6 |
| Pigs born alive per litter | . | . | . | . | . 9·2 |
| „ „ „ year | . | . | . | . | . 15·2 |
| Pigs weaned per litter | . | . | . | . | . 7·5 |
| „ „ sow per year | . | . | . | . | . 12·4 |

**Bacon Pigs.**—Weaning till slaughter (at 200 lb. live weight). 4·25 lb. meal per pound live weight gain = 6½ cwt. per pig.

A number of techniques devised to assist in the solution of farm management problems is described in the following pages. The systematic study of the business of farming is still relatively new, and newer techniques as they are brought forward, require to be tested out under a wide range of practical conditions before the suitability of each can be decided. At the time of writing, there is evidence that for the solution of certain management problems each of the techniques described has distinct value; and ways in which they can be made more simple and easy in practice are now being sought.

While sound farming is likely to remain a matter for personal judgment and experience, the scope for judgment in many farming matters is becoming less obvious as the need for precision in many operations increases in importance. The intelligent use of the techniques of farm business management can improve the results arising from sound farm organisation and planning.

In some farming systems the farmer now uses considerable quantities of expensive resources, and his profit will largely be governed by the level of efficiency under which these resources are converted into saleable products. Farm management analysis reveals defects in past performance. The keeping of basic financial and physical records provides the farmer with the data for use in future analyses, and so enables him to derive real benefit in his planning ahead.

## FARM BUDGETING

A farm budget consists of estimates of capital and labour requirements and of expenditure and income for a particular holding to be operated on some new plan. In some cases a radical change of the existing system may be contemplated—for example, a change from an all grass system, with cattle fattening and sheep breeding, to one of ley farming with cereals, potatoes and milk production as the main enterprises. In such cases a complete budget for the new system is required, and its estimated profitability is compared with the known profitability of the existing system. At the same time estimates are made of labour and capital requirements.

More commonly the change contemplated is less revolutionary, in which case the better approach may be by partial budgeting *i.e.* the estimation of the effects of the proposed changes on capital and labour requirements and on profitability.

A budget must, of course, be based on some set of assumptions about the economic conditions that will obtain in the future; for instance, we may assume that there will be no material change in costs or prices, or that this relationship will become more or less favourable. Again, the assumption may be that the existing relationships between the prices of different farm products will continue to obtain or, alternatively, that the existing relationship will change—*e.g.* that beef prices will tend to rise and milk prices tend to fall. It is often desirable to consider two or more alternative farming plans and to estimate their relative profitability under two or more sets of assumptions in regard to future trends of costs and prices.

In preparing a budget for any farm situation there are four items to be taken into account:—

(a) extra income
(b) costs saved
(c) income foregone
(d) extra costs

Items (a) and (b) would be on the credit side and items (c) and (d) on the debit side of the budget.

**Example:** Minor charge—

To increase an existing pig unit by 5 sows.

In this case it is assumed that the extra work can be handled by the existing labour staff and that no new accommodation is required.

From the records of the existing pig unit the following information is available:—

| | | |
|---|---|---|
| Average no. of pigs weaned per sow per year | | 16 |
| Average food consumption ,, ,, ,, ,, | | 28 cwt. |
| ,, ,, ,, per pig (weaning to bacon weight) | | 6¼ cwt. |

The budget would be as follows:—

(1) Extra Income:—

|  | £ | s. |
|---|---|---|
| 80 baconers at £17 10s. = £1400 . . . . | 1400 | 0 |

(2) Extra Costs:—

Feed:—

|  | £ | s. |
|---|---|---|
| 5 sows at 28 cwt. per cow at 32s. per cwt. | 224 | 0 |
| 80 baconers at 6¼ cwt. meal at 30s. per cwt. | 750 | 0 |
| Depreciation at £3 10s. per sow . . | 17 | 10 |
| Miscellaneous costs at 12s. per pig fattened | 48 | 0 |
| Total Extra cost | 1039 | 10 |
| Extra Profit | £360 | 10 |

The budgeting procedure for a major change can be used to compare the financial possibilities of various plans. The following example [1] prepared by the Farm Economics Branch of Cambridge University illustrates the method. The farm is 158 acres, fairly typical of a considerable group, situated on a reasonably fertile boulder clay soil in East Anglia. Table 25 sets out the existing organisation. The cows provided milk for the

[1] " Planning a Farm for Higher Productivity," Report No. 41, 1954.

farmer's household and the farm staff, while the store cattle were used mainly to convert straw into farmyard manure.

TABLE 25

| Crops: | Acres | Live Stock: | Nos. |
|---|---|---|---|
| Wheat . . . . . | 37 | Horses . . . . . | 3 |
| Barley . . . . | 37 | Milk Cows . . . . | 2 |
| Oats . . . . . | 4 | Calves . . . . . | 2 |
| Sugar beet . . . | 12 | Store cattle . . . | 12 |
| Fodder beet . . . | 2 | Boar . . . . . | 1 |
| Mustard seed . . | 12 | Sows . . . . | 6 |
| Red clover . . . | 10 | Laying hens . . . . | 200 |
| Mixed seeds . . . | 8 | | |
| Fallow . . . . | 4 | Sold annually— | |
| Permanent pasture . . | 28 | Capons . . . . | 200 |
| Waste and buildings . . | 4 | Weaner pigs . . . | 78 |
| Total acres | 158 | | |

The average trading account is set out in Table 26.

TABLE 26

| Purchases and Expenses: | | Sales and Receipts: | | |
|---|---|---|---|---|
| Rent . . . . | £307 | Wheat . . . | £1100 | |
| Labour . . . | 998 | Barley . . . | 840 | |
| Seed and fertilizers . | 592 | Sugar beet . . | 864 | |
| Feeding stuffs . . | 785 | Seed crops . . | 458 | |
| Live Stock . . . | 582 | | | £3262 |
| Fuel and machinery . | 593 | Cattle . . . | £678 | |
| Other expenses . . | 580 | Pigs . . . | 429 | |
| | £4437 | Poultry and eggs . | 845 | |
| Farm Income . . | 777 | | | 1952 |
| | £5214 | | | £5214 |

The regular farm staff consisted of three men and one girl. The womenfolk of the farm were employed to single most of the beet crop, and an additional male worker was employed for a period of about ten weeks for the grain and root harvest. A contractor had regularly been employed to combine harvest a substantial part of the corn crop.

Five provisional plans were examined, by partial budgeting, from the point of view of increasing the level of profitability.

Plan 1 has the object of reducing the regular labour force by one man. This implies mechanisation, especially aimed at reducing labour needs at the three peak periods—the late spring, cereal harvest and beet harvest. The plan necessitates the purchase of a mid-mounted tractor hoe, a combine harvester and a mechanical topper and digger for the sugar beet crop. The partial budget under this plan is shown in Table 27.

This plan would leave the output virtually unchanged and would require the investment of something between £1500 and £2000 of additional capital, but is estimated to produce fully £300 of additional profit.

TABLE 27

| Additional Expenditure: | | Reduced Expenditure | |
|---|---|---|---|
| Depreciation and upkeep of new machines . . . . | £172 | Wages of one man . . . | £294 |
| Casual labour or overtime . | 51 | Contract combining (no longer required) . . . . | 196 |
| | | Threshing (no longer required) . | 52 |
| | £223 | | |
| Additional profit . . . | 319 | | |
| | £542 | | £542 |

Plan 2 envisages the retention of the existing labour force and equipment, together with an increase in net output. Crop yields are already fairly high but the permanent pasture is understocked. With moderate usage of fertilizers, 16 acres would suffice to carry the existing head of stock, permitting 12 acres to be added to the tillage area. The crop chosen must be one which will not compete for labour at peak periods, and peas (for threshing) would appear to meet this requirement. The partial budget for this plan is shown in Table 28.

TABLE 28

| Increase in Expenses: | | Increase in Receipts: | |
|---|---|---|---|
| Overtime labour . . . | £11 | Peas sold . . . | £360 |
| Extra tractor and machinery expenses . . . . | 32 | | |
| Fertilizers . . . . | 70 | | |
| Seed . . . . . | 108 | | |
| Upkeep of fence . . . | 6 | | |
| Combine harvesting (by contract) | 48 | | |
| | £275 | | |
| Additional profit . . . | 85 | | |
| | £360 | | £360 |

Plans 3, 4, and 5 assume that the existing labour force is retained while the scheme of mechanisation adopted in Plan 1 is carried through, the labour so released being used to increase output.

Under Plan 3 the store cattle and the pigs would be replaced by a dairy herd, composed of fifteen cows with followers. This change, though it would add substantially to the farm income, would involve some reorganisation of the cropping, the replacement or re-training of labour, and an adaptation or an addition to the farm buildings. Moreover, as appears from Table 29 on page 760, the estimated profitability is lower than that of Plan 4.

Plan 4 is based on the intensification of the pig and poultry enterprises—the carrying on of the pigs to bacon weight (instead of selling these as weaners) and the doubling of the laying flock. The existing buildings will accommodate the extra stock, provided that the store cattle

TABLE 29

| Increase in Expenses: | | Increase in Receipts: | |
|---|---|---|---|
| Wages . . . . . £243 | | Pigs . . . | £1320 |
| Feeding stuffs for pigs and | | Poultry and eggs . . | 629 |
| poultry . . . 963 | | Wheat . . . . | 70 |
| Pig replacements . . 95 | | Barley . . . | 96 |
| Depreciation of poultry batteries 50 | | Reduction in Expenses: | |
| Miscellaneous costs . . 69 | | Seed and fertilizer . . | 15 |
| Reduction in Receipts: | | | |
| Cattle (net) . . . . 72 | | | |
| | £1492 | | |
| Additional profit . . . 638 | | | |
| | £2130 | | £2130 |

in winter are reduced from twelve to six. The total amount of farmyard manure produced will then be substantially maintained. The only cropping change indicated is the replacement of a few acres of ley by barley or other cereal for feeding to the pigs and poultry. The labour saved by mechanisation under Plan 1 would be sufficient to meet the needs of the pig and poultry enterprises. Table 29 shows that (as compared with Plan 1) the additional profit is estimated at £638, implying a total profit of £1734.

TABLE 30

| Increase in Expenses: | | Increase in Receipts: | |
|---|---|---|---|
| Additional use of— | | Peas sold . . . | £360 |
| Tractor and implements . £33 | | | |
| Combine . . . . 18 | | | |
| Seed . . . . 108 | | | |
| Fertiliser . . . 70 | | | |
| Upkeep of fence . . 6 | | | |
| | £235 | | |
| Additional profit . . . 125 | | | |
| | £360 | | £360 |

Plan 5.—It will be obvious that the change envisaged under Plan 2— the reduction in the acreage of pasture to make room for peas—will be equally appropriate as a modification of Plan 4. Indeed, unless the number of summer cattle is maintained, the redundant acreage of pasture will be larger than 12 acres. Plan 5, however, assumes 12 acres of peas.

The calculated effect of introducing the pea crop will, however, be different from that set out in Table 28, for the reason that there will be no need to have the crop harvested by contract. The appropriate calculation is made in Table 30.

TABLE 31

| | Plan 1 | Plan 2 | Plan 3 | Plan 4 | Plan 5 |
|---|---|---|---|---|---|
| | Present Organisation | Mechanisation | Pea Crop | Mechanisation plus Dairy Herd | Mechanisation plus Pigs and Poultry | Mechanisation plus Pigs and Poultry plus Pea Crop |
| *Revenue—* | £ | £ | £ | £ | £ | £ |
| Wheat . . . | 1100 | 1100 | 1100 | 1100 | 1170 | 1170 |
| Barley . . . | 840 | 840 | 840 | 1058 | 936 | 936 |
| Sugar Beet . . | 864 | 864 | 864 | 864 | 864 | 864 |
| Seed crops . . | 458 | 458 | 458 | — | 458 | 458 |
| Peas . . . | — | — | 360 | — | — | 360 |
| Crop sales . . | 3262 | 3262 | 3622 | 3022 | 3428 | 3788 |
| Milk . . . | — | — | — | 1425 | — | — |
| Cattle . . | 678 | 678 | 678 | 214 | 354 | 354 |
| Pigs . . . | 429 | 429 | 429 | — | 1749 | 1749 |
| Poultry and eggs . | 845 | 845 | 845 | 845 | 1474 | 1474 |
| Livestock sales . | 1952 | 1952 | 1952 | 2484 | 3577 | 3577 |
| Total sales . | 5214 | 5214 | 5574 | 5506 | 7005 | 7365 |
| *Expenditure—* | | | | | | |
| Wages . . . | 998 | 755 | 1009 | 1031 | 998 | 998 |
| Seed . . . | 116 | 116 | 224 | 226 | 104 | 212 |
| Fertilizers . . | 476 | 476 | 546 | 526 | 473 | 543 |
| Feeding stuffs . | 785 | 785 | 785 | 616 | 1748 | 1748 |
| Livestock . . | 582 | 582 | 582 | 93 | 425 | 425 |
| Contract . . | 328 | 80 | 376 | 80 | 80 | 80 |
| Fuel and machinery | 593 | 765 | 625 | 786 | 765 | 816 |
| Other costs . . | 252 | 252 | 258 | 466 | 371 | 377 |
| Rent . . . | 307 | 307 | 307 | 307 | 307 | 307 |
| Total expenses . | 4437 | 4118 | 4712 | 4131 | 5271 | 5506 |
| Farm income. . | 777 | 1096 | 862 | 1375 | 1734 | 1859 |
| Net output . | 3731 | 3731 | 3983 | 4571 | 4728 | 4980 |
| Increase in output per man (per cent.) | — | 26 | 6 | 21 | 28 | 35 |

Table 31 gives estimates of revenue and expenditure, farm income and net output under the existing system and also under each of the five plans, together with a measure of the output per man in each case. It will be noted that the prospective income from Plan 5 is considerably more than double that obtained under the existing system.

It remains to consider the effect of any major price changes upon the relative profitability of the existing system and each of the five plans. The calculated effects of a number of downward changes in prices are set out in Table 32.

TABLE 32

| | Present Organ- isation | Plan 1 | Plan 2 | Plan 3 | Plan 4 | Plan 5 |
|---|---|---|---|---|---|---|
| | £ | £ | £ | £ | £ | £ |
| Farm Income at present prices . | 777 | 1096 | 862 | 1375 | 1734 | 1859 |
| 1. Pig prices fall 15 per cent. . | 713 | 1032 | 798 | 1375 | 1472 | 1597 |
| 2. Pig prices fall 10 per cent.; poultry and eggs 20 per cent. . . | 566 | 885 | 651 | 1206 | 1265 | 1390 |
| 3. Milk prices fall 10 per cent. . . | 777 | 1096 | 862 | 1232 | 1734 | 1859 |
| 4. Crop sales fall 30 per cent. . . | —201 | 118 | —224 | 469 | 705 | 722 |

It will be observed that, under each of the assumptions, Plan 5 retains its place as the most profitable.

## PROGRAMME PLANNING

In recent years agricultural economists have developed new techniques for formulating the best combination of enterprises on any particular farm, to produce the highest level of profit. One such method of profit maximisation has been developed in the United States of America and is known as Programme Planning. This method selects those enterprises which give the highest return in relation to the limiting factor, whether it be land, labour or capital.

The first step is to classify the farm costs into *fixed costs*, *e.g.* such as regular labour, rent and depreciation, and *variable costs*, *e.g.* seed, fertilizer, feed, casual labour and machinery running costs. Surplus income over and above the variable costs is termed " *gross profit* ", from which the fixed costs have to be met.

The next step is to list the possible enterprises for a particular farm and the levels of yield and variable costs for each. To do this it is essential to make a sound physical appraisal of the farm and to take account of what is permissible in the way of good husbandry.

The following example [1] illustrates the method:—

1. Land—72 acres medium/light soil

2. Labour—Farmer ⎱
          1 man  ⎰ Totalling approximately 620 hours per month
          1 boy

3. Possible Enterprises       Limit

   (a) Crops

   | | |
   |---|---|
   | Potatoes | 10 acres |
   | Sugar Beet | 10 acres |
   | Wheat | — |
   | Barley | — |
   | Oats | — |

   (b) Stock

   | | |
   |---|---|
   | Cows | 20 head |
   | Beef | 30 head |
   | Sheep | — |
   | Pigs | 200 baconers |
   | Poultry | 500 layers |

4. Enterprises in order of Gross Profit per Acre (see Tables 33 and 34).

| | £ | s. |
|---|---|---|
| Potatoes | 70 | 4 |
| Sugar Beet | 40 | 18 |
| Cows | 37 | 12 |
| Sheep | 27 | 0 |
| Wheat | 25 | 16 |
| Barley | 25 | 7 |
| Oats | 24 | 10 |
| Beef | 19 | 10 |

In this example, only two factors of production will be considered—land and labour. Adequate capital will be assumed, as will the reliability of the assessment of managerial ability reflected in the levels of yield and variable costs. A single method of production will be considered for each enterprise. Gross profits are calculated on an annual basis.

Pigs and poultry have not been ranked in the list of gross profits per acre since they can be managed with virtually no land and are regarded in this example as eligible only to provide profitable employment for any spare labour after putting the land to its most rewarding use.

### Choice of Enterprise

Having now established what resources are available, what enterprises are possible and the margin over variable costs (gross profit) which each is expected to yield, certain questions can be posed and answered concerning a rational choice of enterprises. Assuming for the moment that

[1] " New Tools in Farm Management "—G. B. Clarke and J. White. N.A.A.S. Quarterly No. 49.

## TABLE 33

### CROP GROSS PROFITS

| Enterprise | Yield | Price per Ton | Gross Income (a) | Variable Costs Seed | Fertiliser | Casual Labour | Fuel | Spray and Haulage | Total (b) | Gross Profit per Acre (a less b) |
|---|---|---|---|---|---|---|---|---|---|---|
| | | £ s. | £ s. | £ s. | £ s. | £ s. | £ s. | £ s. | £ s. | £ s. |
| Potatoes . | 10 tons | 12 — | 120 — | 15 — | 16 — | 10 2 | 5 14 | 3 — | 49 16 | 70 4 |
| Sugar beet . | 12 tons | 6 5 | 75 0 | 1 2 | 14 — | 7 — | 3 — | 9 — | 34 2 | 40 18 |
| Wheat . | 25 cwt. | 29 — | 36 5 | 2 15 | 2 16 | 2 2 | 1 16 | 1 — | 10 9 | 25 16 |
| Barley . | 25 cwt. | 28 — | 35 — | 2 14 | 2 10 | 2 2 | 1 7 | 1 — | 9 13 | 25 7 |
| Oats . | 25 cwt. | 27 — | 33 15 | 3 — | 2 10 | 2 2 | 1 13 | 1 — | 9 5 | 24 10 |

## TABLE 34

### LIVE STOCK ANNUAL GROSS PROFITS

| Enterprise | Yield | Price | Gross Income (a) | Variable Costs Concentrates | Grass | Replacement cost | Miscellaneous | Total (b) | Gross Profit (a less b) | Acres/Head | Gr.Profit per Acre |
|---|---|---|---|---|---|---|---|---|---|---|---|
| | | £ s. | £ s. | £ s. | £ s. | £ s. | £ s. | £ s. | £ s. | | £ s. |
| Cows . . | 800 gal. +calf | 3 / +1½— | 132 — | 31 — | 8 7 | 15 — | 10 — | 74 7 | 57 13 | 1·8 | 37 12 |
| Sheep . . | 1½ lambs+ wool | 6+ / 1 10 | 10 10 | 0 10 | 1 3 | 1 10 | 0 12 | 3 15 | 6 15 | ¼ | 27 — |
| Beef . . | 9 cwt.+Calf Subsidy | 8+ / 9 5 | 80 — | 16 10 | 9 10 | 15 — | 5 — | 46 — | 35 5 | 1·8 | 19 10 |
| Sows . | 16 weaners | 5 — | 80 — | 45 — | — | 6 — | 2 — | 53 — | 27 — | — | — |
| Poultry (100 birds). | 1500 doz. eggs | 3s. 6d. | 262 — | 160 — | — | 40 — | 5 — | 205 — | 57 — | — | — |

TABLE 35

LABOUR PROFILE (HOURS)

| Enterprise | Jan. | Feb. | Mar. | April | May | June | July | Aug. | Sept. | Oct. | Nov. | Dec. | Gross Profit |
|---|---|---|---|---|---|---|---|---|---|---|---|---|---|
| | | | | | | | | | | | | | £ |
| 10 acres Potatoes | 100 | 100 | 120 | 190 | 120 | — | 50 | — | — | 680 | 190 | — | 702 |
| 10 acres Beet | 30 | 30 | 30 | 100 | 130 | 310 | 130 | — | — | 100 | 360 | 140 | 409 |
| 36 acres Milk: | | | | | | | | | | | | | |
| 20 Cows | 300 | 300 | 300 | 280 | 220 | 160 | 220 | 220 | 220 | 240 | 280 | 300 | 1353 |
| 20 acres Grazing | — | — | 5 | 20 | 3 | — | — | — | — | — | — | — | — |
| 16 acres Silage | — | — | 32 | 16 | — | 96 | — | — | 32 | — | — | — | — |
| 16 acres Corn | — | — | 16 | 16 | 16 | 16 | 16 | 48 | 160 | — | — | 32 | 400 |
| Totals | 430 | 430 | 503 | 622 | 489 | 582 | 416 | 268 | 412 | 1020 | 830 | 472 | 2864 |

enough labour is available to handle any technically acceptable combination of the possible enterprises, then the answer to the question of
the order in which possible enterprises should be selected is shown in
Tables 32 and 33, *i.e.* potatoes first with a gross profit per acre of £70 4s.
and beef last with a gross profit per acre of £19 10s.

Selection 1—as many acres of potatoes as possible. In this case 10
acres. The programme so far planned would be:—

| Crop | Acres | Gross Profit |
|------|-------|--------------|
|      |       | £            |
| Potatoes | 10 | 702 |

Selection 2—as many acres of sugar beet as possible. In this case
10 acres. The programme so far planned would then be:—

| Crop | Acres | Gross Profit |
|------|-------|--------------|
|      |       | £            |
| Potatoes | 10 | 702 |
| Sugar Beet | 10 | 409 |
|          | 20 | 1111 |

Selection 3—as many cows as possible. In this case $(20 \times 1 \cdot 8) = 36$
acres can be devoted to cows. The programme then becomes:—

| Crop | Acres | Gross Profit |
|------|-------|--------------|
|      |       | £            |
| Potatoes | 10 | 702 |
| Sugar Beet | 10 | 409 |
| Cows (20) | 36 | 1353 |
|          | 56 | 2464 |

Selection 4—as many sheep as possible. In this case only 16 acres
of land are left so the final programme becomes:—

| Crop | Acres | Gross Profit |
|------|-------|--------------|
|      |       | £            |
| Potatoes | 10 | 702 |
| Sugar Beet | 10 | 409 |
| Cows (20) | 36 | 1353 |
| Sheep (64) | 16 | 432 |
|           | 72 | 2896 |

If all the judgments about this farm were correct and had been fully
stated, the programme under Selection 4 would be the most profitable.
Reconsideration of these judgments, whether of yields, variable costs,
gross profits, possible enterprises and their limits or even of the amounts
of the fixed factors, is not only possible at every stage but is directly
encouraged by spotlighting important factors to consider.

At Selection 2 (if not even at Selection 1) ten or twenty acres of roots on a 72 acre farm will immediately suggest possible difficulties in handling the peak periods of labour need, even with a regular labour force of two men and a lad. It would be wise to take a look at a labour profile compiled from standard labour requirement data. Could potato harvesting be started in September and beet harvesting be delayed until November? Late beet harvesting will be dependent in part on enterprise selections after No. 2. If live stock come in rather than corn and the beet tops are needed for feeding them, a late start may be difficult.

In the variable costs for beet and potatoes a total of £171 for casual labour on the twenty acres has been allowed. Is this enough, or would it be better to spend a bit more to ensure that regular labour was available for other farm enterprises? If more is spent, then gross profit from roots will be reduced, but this reduction might be more than offset by the gain from being able to handle a 20 cow dairy herd in preference to either sheep or corn.

Every week of labour taken away from root harvesting will mean a reduction of about ½ acre for potatoes or approaching an acre for beet— a loss of £35-40 of gross profit. Would more be earned by taking this labour from roots to allow some other enterprise to be undertaken, or is investment in mechanised root harvesting a better answer?

Perhaps at Selection 3 the idea of a 72 acre farm with 20 acres of roots and a 20 cow dairy herd with yet a further 16 acres left for either sheep or corn may seem unduly intensive. This is a good reason for trying the effect on the programme selection of reducing the regular labour to two men or even one man—dividing the enterprise gross profits per acre by the labour requirement per acre and ranking them for selection in descending order of gross profit per hour or per man day.

At Selection 4 some perfectly valid objections to sheep may be brought forward. Having regard to earlier selections, sheep may not be very satisfactory due to shepherding difficulties and inadequate grazing control. If this is so, each acre taken from sheep and transferred to corn will reduce profits by something less than £2, but having regard to the variability of much of the data on which this difference of gross profit depends, it cannot be taken too seriously. The following programme would have certain advantages, particularly as regards the provision of straw and the cereal ingredients of the cows' rations.

|  | Crop | Acres | Gross Profit |
|---|---|---|---|
|  |  |  | £ |
| Selection 1 | Potatoes | 10 | 702 |
| „ 2 | Sugar Beet | 10 | 409 |
| „ 3 | Cows (20) | 36 | 1353 |
| „ 4 | Corn | 16 | 400 |
|  |  |  | 2864 |

The programme has been planned on the basis of dairy heifers being bought in at £100 each and fetching £40 after a 3 year herd life. Rearing something like 6 heifers a year could be considered. If the variable costs of taking a heifer calf to 2½ years were £50 with a land requirement of 2 acres, then the gross profit per acre would be £25. Among the considerations influencing a decision on this question would be the fact that land taken from corn for rearing would not affect total gross profit, but land so taken from milk production would reduce gross profit by some £11 per acre.

A specimen labour profile for this programme is set out in Table 34, and its implications would need to be considered in relation to the particular circumstances of the farm.

It should be noted that an estimate of net farm income is made after fixed costs have been deducted from the total gross profit of the completed Programme.

This then is the basic nature of Programme Planning. It seeks to make direct use of the information, gleaned by record and account analysis and farm appraisal, to build up an appropriate schedule of variable costs and gross profits for possible enterprises. It then attempts to use this information in the light of technical knowledge and the rules of good husbandry to guide enterprise selections and decisions on their size. The aim is to secure the greatest long term cash margin over costs that the farm resources can achieve.

## GROSS MARGINS

In all budgeting procedures it is essential to distinguish between fixed and variable costs. If a farm plan is to be changed the variable cost items, such as feed or fertilizer, can be re-allocated and measured; the fixed or overhead costs, on the other hand, may hardly change at all, especially if the alteration is a minor one. If a farmer decides to grow an extra 10 acres of barley the extra returns might be £320 and the variable costs for such items as seed and fertilizers, £80. Provided the existing farm staff and machinery could handle the extra acreage of barley and the farmer has incurred no extra cost, such as overtime, the gross margin would be arrived at as follows:—

£

10 extra acres barley = 320
*Less* seed, fertilizer, fuel =  80
<hr>
Gross Margin <u>240</u>

*i.e.* £24 per acre

The *Gross Margin* can therefore be defined as Output less Variable Costs. The Farm Economics Branch, Cambridge University have developed a method of planning changes in farm organisation by the use of gross margins. To do this it is necessary to prepare gross margin values for the various crop and livestock enterprises, appropriate to the area in which a particular farm is situated, on the basis of local knowledge and experience. It is then possible to prepare budgets for such changes in farm organisation as the introduction of a new enterprise, the substitution of one enterprise for another or in the preparation of a completely new farm plan.

Supposing a farmer wishes to substitute 10 acres of oats for 10 acres of barley and that he has the labour and equipment to deal with this simple change the budget would be set out as follows:—

| Losses | £ | Gains | £ |
|---|---|---|---|
| Gross Margin for Oats | | Gross Margin for Barley | |
| 10 acres at £18 | 180 | 10 acres at £24 | 240 |
| Increase in profit | 60 | | |
| | 240 | | 240 |

In calculating gross margins for live stock enterprises it is usual to regard, as cash crops, any cereal crops fed, and to allocate to them their full market value. By doing this the farmer is able to judge whether it is more profitable to market his cereal crops through live stock or to sell them direct as grain. Fodder crops, such as kale, rape and mangels, and pasture, hay and silage can be regarded as part of the live stock enterprise and only their variable costs for such items as seed and fertilizer are included. The gross margin for milk production could thus be calculated as follows:—

Dairy Herd (40 Cows)

| | £ | |
|---|---|---|
| Milk Sold | 5000 | |
| Sale of calves | 400 | |
| Valuation increase | 110 | |
| | 5510 | |
| Less stock purchased | 60 | |
| Output | | £5450 |
| Less Variable Costs:— | | |
| Purchased feed | 1600 | |
| Home Grown Grain (Market price) | 240 | |
| Sundries e.g. Veterinary services | 260 | |
| Fodder crops e.g. seed, fuel, fertilizer | 420 | |
| | | £2520 |
| Gross Margin | | £2930 |

2 B

If this herd requires 100 acres of grassland and fodder crops then the gross margin per acre is £2930÷100 = £29 6s. and the gross margin per cow is £2930÷40 = £73.

## LINEAR PROGRAMMING

In previous farm management procedures, farming systems have been analysed in order to detect weaknesses and various measures to rectify these weaknesses are evaluated by such techniques as budgeting, illustrated in Tables 25-32. Other things being equal, the farmer will adopt the plan showing the best long term profit potential. However, there is no certainty that this is in fact the plan that will give the highest long term profit from the land, labour and capital available on his particular farm. To arrive at such optimum solutions a technique has been developed in the United States of America known as *linear programming*. This technique relies on the accurate formulation of a problem in order to produce an acceptable solution. The preparation of an accurate statement of a problem that is susceptible to such an analysis requires considerable skill and expertise, and a high speed digital computer is needed to cope with the calculations. The procedure is under examination at the time of writing for possible use in Britain.

# CHAPTER 30

# MARKETING

FARM products may be marketed by a wide variety of means. It is impossible to enter here into all the details, but it seems necessary to state the general principles and to give examples of the commoner marketing channels.

The first principle of marketing is to provide the prospective buyer with all the information that he needs in order to be able to form a true estimate of the value of the particular article.

1. The first means to this end is to present the actual article that is for sale and at the same time to answer in advance any questions that an intending buyer might be likely to ask. This is the procedure most commonly used in the case of breeding animals and store stock. Thus a lot of ewes may be penned in a market or offered through an auction. The seller will state whether or not the ewes are guaranteed correct in udder and whether they are whole or broken mouthed; whether they are all of the same age or whether of mixed ages. In the case of a dairy cow the age, if known, may be stated, and the animal may be guaranteed correct of bag. The date of last calving or the probable date of the next calving should also be stated. If the cow has been milk recorded her yield may be given, and is she has a pedigree this should be set out, with any relevant information about her ancestors. Information so given carries a guarantee of accuracy and a buyer may, if he finds that he has been given incorrect information, repudiate the purchase.

2. The bulk of the commodity may not be exposed, the buyer being shown a *sample*. This is the method of selling corn in this country. The farmer either takes to market, or sends to an agent, a small quantity of his grain and a sale is negotiated. The buyer has naturally the right to repudiate the contract if he can show that the bulk does not conform to sample.

3. The sale may be on *specification—i.e.* a guaranteed description of the article. Thus a seller of artificial fertilizer is required by law to state the percentage content of nitrogen, potash, water soluble phosphoric acid and insoluble phosphoric acid which the fertilizer contains; a seller of certain classes of feeding stuffs (oil cakes and meals, compound feeding stuffs), the percentage content of albuminoids (protein), oil and fibre. Seeds are sold on a guarantee of purity and germination. Potatoes are sold in size grades, and with a general guarantee of quality—*e.g.* the

variety is stated, the bulk is guaranteed to be substantially sound and free from blight and to have been dressed over a specified riddle.

In certain cases, it is important to note, a form of words used to describe an article is held, in law, to give an implied guarantee. Thus if a farmer sells seed oats he is giving an implied guarantee of a minimum germination, or if he sells Majestic seed potatoes, an implied guarantee of a certain percentage purity of that variety. Similarly, barley meal means a meal, made from barley with not more than a definite percentage of impurities, which has not been treated by sifting.

4. Commodities may be sold by *grade*, which grade is determined by an authority who is entirely independent. Thus Canadian wheat is graded as No. 2 Manitoba Hard, and the various grades are bought and sold unseen. Similarly, bacon pigs, supplied to factories, may be graded according to carcass measurements and paid for at rates which vary with the grade. Fat cattle, during the war and up till 1954, were purchased by the Ministry of Food, and the individual animals were graded according to their estimated dressing percentage (dressed carcase weight as a percentage of live weight). Milk is graded in this country according to the standard of hygiene maintained in its production, and there are special premiums for the milk of tuberculin tested cows and for milk derived from the Channel Islands breeds. In other countries the scale of payment is related to the average content of butter fat. Sugar beet is paid for, by the factory which has contracted to receive it, on washed weight and sugar percentage.

We may next classify and shortly describe the actual means of effecting a sale.

1. The simplest method is by *private treaty*. A seller or his agent approaches a likely buyer, or *vice versa*, and the price and other conditions of sale are arranged. A slight modification of this is what is sometimes called *private auction*. In this case, for example, corn merchants assemble at a certain place and time and a farmer presents a sample of seed oats to one after another until he obtains what he considers a satisfactory offer. In deciding which offer to accept he naturally considers not only the price bid but also the credit of the bidder.

2. In certain parts of the country the normal method of marketing store stock and dairy cattle is by public auction. The same method may be applied to pedigree animals, and to a variety of commodities including growing crops of potatoes, grass keeping and fodder roots. Auction is the usual procedure at farm sales, when a tenancy has changed hands. The sale is conducted by a licensed auctioneer, who lays down certain conditions of sale. Ordinarily he does not bind himself to accept the highest or any bid: he lays down conditions regarding payment; he generally permits the seller, if he so desires, to set a reserve price on each lot, or he may allow the seller to make one or more bids for his own property; and he lays down a certain procedure to be followed in the case

of disputes. Finally, he insists that the goods sold shall conform to any warranty or specification which the seller gives, either verbally or in writing. In large markets this method of selling is generally satisfactory. Small auction sales are frequently spoilt by the formation of buyers' rings; *i.e.* a group of buyers delegate one of themselves to bid on behalf of the group, and the stock so purchased is later divided up.

3. A modification of the ordinary auction system, which is widely used in other countries but is rarely found in Britain, is the *Dutch auction*. Here the lot is put up at a price which is considered to be above its value, the price is reduced by stages until a bid is made, when the lot is at once sold. The first bidder (instead of the last) thus becomes the purchaser. In Holland the system is mechanised by having a pointer, which is moved by the auctioneer, travelling round a dial on which the price series is marked Each customer has an electric button by which he can stop the pointer at the price which he is prepared to offer. The pressing of the button also lights up the buyer's registered number and the sale is immediately registered by a clerk.

4. Sales may also be effected through *commission agents*. A commission agent is prepared to undertake the sale or purchase of a particular commodity and makes a charge, generally on a percentage basis, for his services. A seller on commission may sell in bulk, on sample or by grade or description. An example of this system is seen at Covent Garden market in London. The grower consigns his fruit or vegetables to his commission agent, generally after a telephone inquiry about the expected supplies and demand. The commission agent gets in touch with likely wholesale buyers, sells the goods for the best price obtainable, collects the proceeds, deducts his commission and marketing charges and remits the balance to the seller. In many cases the commission agent supplies the necessary containers for the goods, making a special charge for their use. Dead meat was sold in Smithfield and other markets by the same procedure up till 1939.

5. A sale may be effected by an agreement between the buyer and seller to accept the decision of a third party on the price at which the goods shall change hands. Thus in the case of a change of tenancy the outgoing and incoming tenant may agree that live and dead stock, growing crops and tillages shall be valued by a single individual. A modification of this procedure is that each party appoints a valuer to act on his behalf, and the two valuers appoint an arbiter or oversman to give a decision in case of disagreement. Sale at the valuation of a third party may be applied to any kind of article.

6. Still another method of sale is to put an article up for *private tender*. The offer of sale is advertised in the press or by circular, or both, to possible buyers. Time is allowed for the inspection of the goods and written tenders are received up till a specified date. The letters of tender are then opened and the highest offer is ordinarily accepted.

7. Goods may also be produced by the farmer *on contract* at pre-arranged prices. In the case of sugar beet the farmer contracts to grow, for a certain factory, a given acreage of beet, and to deliver the total produce to the factory at times and under conditions which are arranged. It is also a common practice in certain areas to grow potatoes for merchants on contract. The land is taken at a certain sum per acre, the farmer applying farmyard manure, doing all tillage, sometimes supplying planters and, less commonly, pickers as well. The merchant on his part supplies seed, fertilizers and the balance of the labour.

Many farmers are also accustomed to buy forward their requirements in the way of feeding stuffs and fertilizers. Thus a farmer may contract, say, in July, for his winter supplies of cake and meal, to be delivered at the prices fixed when the contract is made, over the period when he expects to require them.

It should be noted that in certain cases sales can be made only through specially authorised persons or bodies. Thus all hops are grown under a quota scheme of the Hops Marketing Board and sales of hops must be arranged through that Board. All sales of milk by producers, except producer-retailers, are made through the Milk Marketing Boards, which collect the proceeds and, after making necessary deductions, remit the balance to the producer.

While in this country most auctioneers, dealers, merchants and commission agents are ordinary individuals or companies trading for profit, any of their functions may be carried out by voluntary Farmers' Co-operatives. The members of these Co-operatives subscribe the necessary share capital, the interest on which is a first charge on profits. Surplus profits are distributed as a trading dividend, *i.e.* the sum received by a member is determined by the amount of his trading with the Society. Co-operative Societies may collect, pack, grade and transport farm produce or farm requirements as well as buy and sell on behalf of their members.

Every sale should be made with a distinct understanding regarding the time and method of payment. In certain cases the terms are cash on delivery; in many cases, however, the seller allows to the buyer a certain amount of credit. Thus certain auction companies supply live stock to farmers on an instalment system. In other cases there is three, six or even twelve months' credit at the price agreed, with the option of a discount for cash. Sometimes rather indefinite credit is allowed, subject, of course, to a prearranged rate of interest on the sums remaining outstanding.

In the sale of agricultural produce there is frequently a good deal to be gained by careful grading of the produce. If a farmer has 300 store lambs to sell he will generally obtain a higher average price if he sells in well assorted lots of, say, 50 rather than in lots run off at random. The advantage to the purchaser is obvious, for he will be able to have all the lambs fat within a relatively short space of time, and will have, in turn, a comparatively level lot to sell. With commodities such as fruit and vegetables careful grading is very important; standard packages should be used and each package should contain the same quality throughout.

In certain cases the difficulty arises that the farmer has only a small quantity of produce and that of mixed quality. The clip of wool from a small flock is a case in point. Most wool buyers require large lots of uniform quality, and hence a small mixed lot attracts very little attention. One satisfactory method of dealing with this problem is to form a Co-operative Woolgrowers' Society, which employs an expert to class the fleeces and to make up large batches for sale. Some wool brokers are prepared to deal with mixed lots in the same way.

With certain commodities, especially such as are liable to damage in transit, packing as distinct from grading is an important point.

The Ministry of Agriculture in the period between the wars established National Marks for most classes of fruit and vegetables, as well as eggs and many other commodities. Inspectors were employed to ensure that goods sold under a particular National Mark Grade actually conformed to the prescribed standard.

One further point in connection with marketing is the cost and method of transport. There is generally the choice between rail and road transport, and sometimes the one and sometimes the other will be the cheaper. As regards railway rates, there is often a relatively low rate per ton for large consignments—*e.g.* a full wagon load of cattle or sheep or a six ton lot of fertilizer or feeding stuffs. Speed of delivery and risk of damage or deterioration must, of course, be considered as well as cost.

Under the Agriculture Act, 1947, price guarantees are provided for wheat, rye, barley, oats, potatoes and sugar beet; for fat cattle, sheep and lambs, pigs sold for slaughter (whether for pork or bacon); for milk and eggs.

With the return to private trading in these commodities in 1954 new methods were devised for implementing the price guarantees. The general aim is to make good any deficiency between the market price and the guaranteed price, but the method employed varies as between one particular commodity and another.

The methods at present in use are:—

(i) sale to a central organisation on contract at the actual guaranteed price, *e.g.* sugar beet.

(ii) sale to a central organisation at the guaranteed price, adjusted to market conditions, *e.g.* milk, eggs, wool.

(iii) sale of the product in a free market, the producer receiving a deficiency payment representing the difference between the guaranteed price and the average market price, *e.g.* wheat, rye, fat cattle, sheep, pigs.

(iv) price support by acreage payment, where all producers receive a sum per acre related to the difference between the guaranteed price and the average market price, *e.g.* barley, oats, mixed corn.

(v) Market Support Fund linked to deficiency payments. In the case of potatoes the market can be strengthened in years of heavy surplus by the contribution to a market support fund by the Government and the Potato Marketing Board.

## THE MARKETING OF FARM CROPS

Guaranteed prices for cereals are implemented by means of deficiency payments which allow farmers to sell their grain in the free market. The rate of the deficiency payment will depend on the difference between the national average market price and the guaranteed standard price.

(a) **Wheat.** The standard price for wheat, fixed at the Annual Price Review, is subject to seasonal variation, rising from the time of harvest until the end of the cereal marketing year. If the average realised, over a particular price period, falls short of the standard price, the difference is made good by the Government. The seasonal prices for the 1961 harvest when the basic standard price was 26/11d. were as follows:—

| | | |
|---|---|---|
| July-September | 24/6d. | per cwt. |
| October-November | 26/- | ,, ,, |
| December-February | 28/6d. | ,, ,, |
| March-April | 29/- | ,, ,, |
| May-June | 29/6d. | ,, ,, |

All sales must be registered in order to qualify for deficiency payments and the grain must be sold to an approved merchant and certified by him as millable.

(b) **Rye.** The system is the same, except for the standard price.

(c) **Barley, Oats and Mixed Corn.** Whereas wheat and rye are ordinarily grown for sale, large quantities of barley and oats are consumed on the farms where they are grown. It would thus be impracticable to base deficiency payments on quantities sold and prices realised. The deficiency payment is therefore based on the acreage grown and on the national average yield. This system results in relatively high returns per cwt. in cases where the yield is low, and in relatively low returns per cwt. in cases where the yield is high.

The production of barley rose from $2\frac{1}{4}$ million tons in the year 1954/55 to $4\frac{1}{4}$ million tons in 1960/61, and the rate of subsidy for the 1960 crop was nearly half the market price, which was out of all proportion to the support for any other commodity. In order to ease this marketing problem and to prevent excessive offerings of barley immediately after harvest the Government have introduced a scheme to provide growers with an incentive to hold barley till later in the season.

(d) **Potatoes.** The guarantee is implemented through a support price system, operated through the agency of the Potato Marketing Board. The market price of potatoes, unlike that of grain, is little affected by imports, and the purpose of the guarantee is to protect producers against low returns in years of high yields. The support price is fixed at a somewhat lower level than that which would be appropriate to a fixed price. Since transport and marketing costs vary from area to area, separate support prices are obtained in the five regions into which the country (Great Britain and Northern Ireland) is divided. In order to strengthen the market in years of heavy surplus and low prices, the establishment of a Market Support Fund was arranged in 1961.

(e) **Sugar Beet.** This is grown under contract with the British Sugar Corporation. The basic price applies to beet of 16.5 per cent. sugar content, and the actual price of each consignment is determined on the basis of its sugar content, with a deduction for tare (dirt tare and top tare). The Corporation bears transport costs in excess of those for a haul of about 40 miles. The contract price is normally for beet delivered to the factory, based on the weight of clean beet of a sugar content of 16·5 per cent. with an addition or deduction of 9d. per ton for each 0·1 per cent above or below that percentage.

Conditions of soil and climate, distance from the factory and sugar content are thus the main factors which determine the returns on the sugar beet crop. An extra ton in yield and an additional half per cent. in sugar content, together with a saving of 10/- per ton on freight can increase profits by about £15 per acre.

## THE MARKETING OF LIVE STOCK

Fat cattle, sheep and pigs can be sold by the farmer through any channel he may decide is best in his own interests. To qualify for any guarantee payments, however, they must be presented at an appointed certification centre and be certified as qualifying for such pyament and marked in such a way that they can be identified. Auction marts, slaughter houses and bacon factories can be appointed certification centres and approved for the purpose.

**Fat Cattle** attract guaranteed prices for steers and heifers; fat cows are not eligible. Animals must weigh not less than $7\frac{1}{2}$ cwt. live weight or 450 lb. dressed carcase weight. Guarantee payments cease at 15 cwt. live weight or 950 lb. dressed carcase weight. In order to qualify the animal must also, in the opinion of the certifying officer have a killing out percentage of not less than 54 per cent.

Certified animals also attract a quality premium of 5/- per live cwt. for Grade I steers of not more than $11\frac{1}{2}$ cwt. live weight (750 lb. d.c.w.) or Grade I heifers of not more than $9\frac{1}{2}$ cwt. live weight (620 lb. d.c.w.). This differential of 5/- per live cwt. between the rates of Grade I and

Grade II cattle was applied in 1961/62 by increasing the average rate of guarantee payment for home bred cattle by 1/11d. for Grade I and reducing it by 3/1d. for Grade II. In addition to this, high quality cattle normally fetch a higher price per cwt. in the market so that the additional price realised for a Grade I beast over a Grade II can be as much as £8 to £10 on a live weight of 11 cwt. This is the reward which the farmer gets for good finish.

The guaranteed price for fat cattle in the year 1961/62 was 167s. 0d. per live weight. Not only is this average guarantee subject to quality variations according to Grade, but it is also broken down into a seasonal scale of weekly standard prices. These reach their highest level in April and fall to their lowest in October. The object of this seasonal scale is to provide an incentive for feeders to market their cattle during those months when supplies tend to be shortest and to avoid the period of autumn glut, when large numbers are coming off grass.

The guarantee payment is announced in advance of the week to which it relates. This is subject to a stabilising adjustment to ensure that the actual average market price, plus the announced guarantee payment, does not differ from the standard price for the week by more than 7/- per live cwt. either way.

The seasonal guaranteed price variation is quite considerable and there is a drop in price between the end of July and the end of September of about £6 on a 10 cwt. beast.

A farmer may sell his cattle for beef by live weight or he may sell on a grade and deadweight basis at an abattoir. The former system is still preferred by the majority though the latter probably gives a return more nearly related to the quality of the animal.

**Sheep and Lambs,** excluding ewes and rams, qualify for the guarantee payment on estimated (or actual) dressed carcase weights of not less than 17 lb., provided the quality is satisfactory to the grader. There is no upper limit to the weight at which live sheep or their carcases may be certified, but since 1960 payments have been restricted to the following estimated or actual dressed carcase weights:—

|                     | 27th March, 1961<br>to 28th May, 1961 | On and after<br>29th May, 1961 |
|---------------------|---------------------------------------|--------------------------------|
| Lambs               | 55 lbs.                               | 55 lbs.                        |
| Hoggets             | 70 „                                  | 65 „                           |
| Other Clean Sheep   | 70 „                                  | 65 „                           |

There are no quality premiums for fat sheep and lambs and quality differences are normally reflected in realised market prices. In general there is a market preference for the lighter weight animals, but when fattening off grass it is often more profitable to produce 45-48 lb. lamb (d.c.w.) than the lighter 32-36 lb. lamb (d.c.w.).

As in the case of fat cattle, the guaranteed price for sheep is broken down to a seasonal scale of weekly prices, with the highest levels in late March and early April and the lowest in the period mid June to mid November. The rate is also subject to a stabilising adjustment so that the average return to producers in any week does not differ from the standard price for that week by more than 2d. a lb. either way.

**Pigs.** Clean pigs, weighing not less than 90 lb. live weight (60 lb. dead weight) are eligible for guaranteed prices. There is a maximum weight of 280 lb. live weight (210 lb. dead weight) beyond which no guaranteed payments are made. The guaranteed prices are linked to a feed costs formula and in 1961/62 so long as the standard ration was 24/7d. per cwt., the standard price for fat pigs was 43/7d. per score dead weight. For every 1d. per cent. movement up or down in the price of the ration, the standard price is changed by a penny per score. The composition of the standard ration is:—

| | | |
|---|---|---|
| feed wheat . . . . | 20 | per cent. |
| barley meal . . | 40 | ,, ,, |
| feed oats . . . | 10 | ,, ,, |
| maize meal . . | 10 | ,, ,, |
| wheat offals . . | 10 | ,, ,, |
| white fish meal . . | 5 | ,, ,, |
| extracted soya bean meal . | 5 | ,, ,, |

There are no seasonal variations in the guaranteed price for fat pigs but the price is subject to stabilising adjustments to ensure that the total return, *i.e.* market price plus guarantee payment, does not vary in any week by more than 2s. 0d. below and 2s. 6d. above the guaranteed price.

The marketing of pigs is complicated by the fact that there are two main outlets, one for fresh pork and the other for bacon. Most bacon pigs are bought by the Fatstock Marketing Corporation on a grade and dead weight basis, whereas most of the pork pigs are sold in the open market to butchers on a live weight basis. Guaranteed prices for bacon pigs provide for quality premiums based on back fat measurement and length of carcase. These premiums are payable on carcases within the weight range of 7 score to 8 score 5 lb. dead weight.

In recent years the two markets for fat pigs have tended to show considerable variations in price differentials. The general effect has been to encourage bacon producers to divert supplies to the pork market and thus denude the curing industry. Frequent switches of supplies of pigs from one market to another, is not very satisfactory, either for the farmer or the curer. In 1961, therefore, the Government introduced a flexible guarantee system for pigs in order to limit these fluctuations. The guaranteed price is adjusted automatically at quarterly intervals by reference to a forecast of certifications in a 12 month period, *i.e.* the number of pigs likely to receive the guarantee payment in that period. Adjustments are made in accordance with the following scale:—

| Forecast level of certifications | Adjustment to the basic guaranteed price |
|---|---|
| Less than 9·75 million . . . . . | an increase of 1s. 6d. |
| 9·75 million or more but less than 10 million . | an increase of 1s. 0d. |
| 10 million or more but less than 10·3 million . | an increase of 6d. |
| 10·3 million or more but less than 10·8 million. | basic guaranteed price |
| 10·8 million or more but less than 11 million . | a reduction of 6d. |
| 11 million or more but less than 11·25 million . | a reduction of 1s. 0d. |
| 11·25 million or more . . . . . | a reduction of 1s. 6d. |

## THE MARKETING OF LIVE STOCK PRODUCTS

**Milk.**—Milk is marketed through the Marketing Boards—one for England and Wales, one each for the three Scottish areas and one for Northern Ireland. These Boards purchase all milk produced for sale by producers (except that sold by producer retailers). Price guarantees are made to the Marketing Boards and not to individual producers. They relate to standard quantities and not to unlimited production, as in the case of most other guarantee commodities. There are two levels of guarantee—one for liquid milk and another for manufacturing milk. The manufacturing price guarantee is based on an estimate of the average realised price it will make during the year. Any excess or deficiency in the average price actually realised by manufacturing milk is shared by the Board on a 50/50 basis. In recent years approximately 80 per cent. of milk produced has been sold for liquid consumption, but in some seasons of high production the liquid proportion has been considerably lower and the excess, over the standard quantity, has been diverted to the cheaper manufacturing market. In these circumstances the average price paid to producers, or the pool price has been lower.

Each Board is free to fix its prices to producers in accordance with the circumstances ruling at the time. Thus the Milk Marketing Board for England and Wales varies its price to producers according to region, season and quality. The greatest variations are seasonal and in 1960/61 the May/June price was 2s. 1½d. per gal. whilst that for the months of December/March was 3s. 4½d.

There are also premiums for milk from attested herds of 2d. per gal. and a deduction of 4d. per gal. for non-T.T. milk. Milk from the Channel Island and Devon herds attracts special premiums varying from 10d. per gal. in the autumn down to 4d. per gal. in the summer.

**Eggs.**—The guaranteed price for eggs is paid through the Egg Marketing Board and is based on the difference between the standard price and the current market price of eggs. As in the case of pigs the standard price is related to the ruling price of a standard feed mixture, which has the following composition:—

|                          |   |   |    |           |
|--------------------------|---|---|----|-----------|
| feed wheat               | . | . | 20 | per cent. |
| feed barley              | . | . | 10 | ,, ,,     |
| feed oats .              | . | . | 20 | ,, ,,     |
| maize                    | . | . | 15 | ,, ,,     |
| wheat offals             | . | . | 20 | ,, ,,     |
| white fish meal          |   | . | 5  | ,, ,,     |
| extracted soya bean meal |   |   | 10 | ,, ,,     |

Each variation of 7d. per cwt. in the cost of this standard ration, above or below 26s. 5d. per cwt., influences the standard price of eggs by $\frac{1}{2}$d. per dozen.

Although producers may sell their eggs direct to consumers, they must sell through approved packing stations to obtain the guaranteed price. All producers with more than 50 head of poultry must register with the Board.

All eggs sold through the packing stations are graded according to size, cleanliness and internal condition and the price per dozen varies accordingly. As in the case of milk there is also an appreciable seasonal variation.

**Wool.**—The price guarantee for wool is made to the British Wool Marketing Board. This is an average price per lb. for wool (other than skin wool) produced in the United Kingdom and tendered to the Board. The guarantee is implemented in accordance with the provisions of an agreement between the Government and the Board. The Board operates a stabilisation fund, which started in May 1950. This ensures that 90 per cent. of any surplus of the realised price for wool, over the guaranteed price, is paid into the fund to meet deficiencies in other years. At five-yearly intervals any credit balance in excess of £5 million is made available to the Board, but any debit balance in excess of £3 million is written off. At fifteen-yearly intervals a full settlement of the account is made and a debit balance is written off, whilst a credit balance is taken out by the Board.

All wool producers with five or more sheep must register with the Board and their wool sold through authorised merchants, who grade and value the wool.

# APPENDIX

TABLE 1

## NUTRIENTS REMOVED FROM SOIL BY CROPS

*(Units of plant foods per acre per annum)*

| | Weight | Nitrogen (N) | Phosphoric Acid ($P_2O_5$) | Potash ($K_2O$) |
|---|---|---|---|---|
| Wheat . . | 23 cwt. | 45 | 19 | 13 |
| Barley . . | 21 „ | 37 | 17 | 10 |
| Oats . . | 19 „ | 41 | 15 | 10 |
| Beans . . | 17 „ | 78 | 24 | 24 |
| Hay . . . | 1½ tons | 49 | 12 | 51 |
| Clover . . | 2 „ | 102 | 25 | 83 |
| Cabbages . | 25 „ | 168 | 58 | 55 |
| Turnips . . | 15 „ | 56 | 20 | 96 |
| Swedes . . | 15 „ | 75 | 18 | 68 |
| Mangels . . | 22 „ | 87 | 34 | 222 |
| Potatoes . . | 8 „ | 47 | 29 | 102 |

*Note.*—In the above table, the straw, tops, and haulms are left out of account.

## COMPOSITION AND NUTRITIVE VALUE OF SOME COMMON FEEDING STUFFS

The tables of some common feeding stuffs on pages 784-792 are extracted from Bulletin No. 48 (fifteenth edition) " Rations for Livestock," Ministry of Agriculture, Fisheries and Food, to to whom grateful acknowledgment is made. Permission to reproduce has been obtained from the Controller of H. M. Stationery Office.

The figures on pages 784-792 Section A are based on digestibility trials carried out with ruminants and include figures for protein and starch equivalents which should be of help in working out rations. Column (12) V requires some explanation. The figures denote the percentages that the true starch equivalents bear in relation to the calculated starch equivalents. Take, for example, wheat broad bran with V = 77, the computed starch equivalent for that food has been multiplied by ·77 in order to arrive at its production value.

Section B p. 790 relates to pigs, for which more limited digestibility trials are available.

Section C (pp. 791-792) deals with the mineral composition of some common feeding stuffs. The table shows the wide variation in the mineral content of feeding stuffs; and so indirectly draws attention to the importance of mineral balance in rations especially for more productive live stock.

It should be noted that the figures in the tables are averages. Individual samples of feeding stuffs may be lower in nutritive value through higher moisture content or say reduced protein content, *e.g.* barley may vary between 7 per cent. and 11 per cent. crude protein. Any substantial variation of that nature should be taken into account in the making up of a ration, especially if that particular feeding stuff constitutes a substantial proportion of the whole ration.

TABLE 2

COMPOSITION AND NUTRITIVE VALUE OF SOME COMMON FEEDING STUFFS

| Section A | Composition per cent. as shown by Chemical Analysis | | | | | | | Digestible Nutrients per cent. | | | | | Calculated from Digestible Nutrients | |
|---|---|---|---|---|---|---|---|---|---|---|---|---|---|---|
| | (1) Dry Matter | (2) Crude Protein | (3) Oil (Ether Extract) | (4) Crude Fibre | (5) Carbohydrate (Nitrogen-free Extractives) | (6) Ash | (7) True Protein | (8) Digestible Crude Protein | (9) Digestible Oil (Digestible Ether Extract) | (10) Digestible Fibre | (11) Dig. Carbohydrate (Dig. Nitrogen-free Extractives) | (12) V | (13) Starch Equivalent | (14) Protein Equivalent |
| *Roots* | | | | | | | | | | | | | | |
| Kohlrabi | 12.7 | 2.0 | 0.1 | 1.4 | 8.2 | 1.0 | 1.6 | 0.7 | .. | 0.6 | 7.4 | 90 | 8.3 | 0.5 |
| Mangels, white fleshed globe | 10.7 | 1.0 | 0.1 | 0.7 | 8.2 | 0.7 | 0.4 | 0.7 | .. | 0.3 | 7.5 | 70 | 5.5 | 0.4 |
| Mangels, intermediate | 12.0 | 1.0 | 0.1 | 0.7 | 9.4 | 0.8 | 0.4 | 0.7 | .. | 0.3 | 8.5 | 70 | 6.2 | 0.4 |
| Mangels, yellow fleshed globe or tankard | 13.2 | 1.2 | 0.1 | 0.8 | 10.2 | 0.9 | 0.6 | 0.7 | .. | -0.3 | 9.4 | 70 | 6.8 | 0.4 |
| Mangels, long red | 13.1 | 1.0 | 0.1 | 0.8 | 10.3 | 0.9 | 0.4 | 0.7 | .. | 0.3 | 9.5 | 70 | 6.8 | 0.4 |
| Potatoes | 23.8 | 2.1 | 0.1 | 0.9 | 19.7 | 1.0 | 1.6 | 1.1 | .. | .. | 17.7 | 100 | 18.5 | 0.8 |
| Sugar beet | 23.4 | 1.1 | 0.1 | 1.1 | 20.4 | 0.7 | 0.6 | 0.8 | .. | 0.4 | 19.3 | 75 | 15.0 | 0.5 |
| Swede turnip | 11.5 | 1.3 | 0.2 | 1.2 | 8.1 | 0.7 | 0.5 | 1.1 | .. | 0.8 | 7.5 | 85 | 7.3 | 0.7 |
| Turnip | 8.5 | 1.0 | 0.2 | 0.9 | 5.7 | 0.7 | 0.6 | 0.6 | .. | 0.3 | 5.2 | 77 | 4.4 | 0.4 |
| *Green Foods—other than Grasses and Clovers* | | | | | | | | | | | | | | |
| Cabbage, drumhead | 11.0 | 1.5 | 0.4 | 2.0 | 5.9 | 1.2 | 1.1 | 1.1 | 0.2 | 1.4 | 4.6 | 94 | 6.6 | 0.9 |
| Cabbage, open leaved | 15.3 | 2.5 | 0.7 | 2.4 | 8.1 | 1.6 | 1.9 | 1.8 | 0.4 | 1.7 | 6.5 | 94 | 9.5 | 1.5 |
| Kale, thousandhead | 16.0 | 2.2 | 0.4 | 3.2 | 8.5 | 1.7 | 1.7 | 1.7 | 0.2 | 1.8 | 7.6 | 92 | 10.0 | 1.5 |
| Kale, marrowstem unthimmed | 16.0 | 2.2 | 0.5 | 2.5 | 6.9 | 1.9 | 1.6 | 1.7 | 0.3 | 1.6 | 6.1 | 93 | 9.1 | 1.4 |
| Kale, marrowstem singled | 14.0 | 2.1 | 0.3 | 2.5 | 7.3 | 1.8 | 1.5 | 1.6 | 0.2 | 1.5 | 6.5 | 93 | 9.0 | 1.3 |
| Kale, marrowstem dried | 88.0 | 13.3 | 2.1 | 15.1 | 48.4 | 9.1 | .. | .. | .. | .. | .. | .. | .. | .. |
| Mustard | 15.0 | 2.9 | 0.4 | 2.9 | 7.4 | 1.4 | 2.3 | 1.9 | 0.2 | 1.5 | 5.0 | 94 | 7.5 | 1.0 |
| Rape | 14.0 | 2.8 | 0.8 | 3.5 | 5.6 | 1.3 | 2.1 | 2.0 | 0.5 | 1.9 | 3.8 | 90 | 7.2 | 1.6 |
| Sugar beet tops | 16.2 | 2.0 | 0.5 | 1.6 | 8.7 | 3.4 | 1.5 | 1.4 | 0.3 | 1.1 | 7.2 | 84 | 8.6 | 1.1 |
| Oats in flower | 23.2 | 1.9 | 0.6 | 8.5 | 10.4 | 1.8 | 1.7 | 1.4 | 0.4 | 4.9 | 6.5 | 75 | 10.0 | 1.3 |
| Rye | 23.4 | 3.0 | 0.9 | 7.5 | 10.3 | 1.7 | 2.3 | 2.1 | 0.5 | 4.9 | 7.0 | 80 | 11.3 | 1.7 |

| Grasses, Clovers and other Legumes | | | | | | | | | | | | | | See digestible crude protein figures |
|---|---|---|---|---|---|---|---|---|---|---|---|---|---|---|
| Pasture grass, close grazing:— | | | | | | | | | | | | | | |
| Non-rotational | 20·0 | 5·3 | 1·1 | 2·6 | 8·9 | 2·1 | 4·6 | 4·5 | 0·7 | 2·1 | 7·8 | 95 | 14·7 | 4·1 |
| Rotational, with 3 weekly intervals | 20·0 | 4·5 | 1·3 | 3·1 | 9·3 | 1·8 | 4·0 | 3·7 | 0·8 | 2·5 | 8·0 | 94 | 14·6 | 3·4 |
| Rotational, with monthly intervals | 20·0 | 3·5 | 1·0 | 4·5 | 9·2 | 1·8 | 3·2 | 2·6 | 0·5 | 3·7 | 7·6 | 91 | 13·4 | 2·4 |
| Pasture grass, extensive grazing: | | | | | | | | | | | | | | |
| Spring value, running off in summer | 20·0 | 3·5 | 0·8 | 4·0 | 9·7 | 2·0 | 2·7 | 2·5 | 0·4 | 2·6 | 7·3 | 91 | 11·2 | 2·1 |
| Winter (free growth July-December) | 20·0 | 3·1 | 0·6 | 4·4 | 10·3 | 1·6 | 2·6 | 2·0 | 0·1 | 2·6 | 7·9 | 90 | 11·4 | 1·7 |
| Ryegrass, Italian | 25·0 | 3·4 | 1·0 | 6·2 | 11·6 | 2·8 | 2·6 | 2·1 | 0·5 | 3·6 | 7·7 | 85 | 11·4 | 1·7 |
| Red clover, beginning to flower | 19·0 | 3·4 | 0·7 | 5·2 | 8·1 | 1·6 | 2·6 | 2·5 | 0·5 | 3·0 | 6·3 | 86 | 10·2 | 2·1 |
| White clover, beginning to flower | 18·5 | 4·4 | 0·8 | 4·3 | 6·9 | 2·1 | 3·5 | 2·8 | 0·5 | 2·6 | 4·7 | 88 | 8·8 | 2·3 |
| Lucerne in early flower | 24·0 | 4·1 | 0·4 | 7·2 | 9·9 | 2·4 | 3·0 | 3·1 | 0·1 | 3·2 | 6·6 | 80 | 10·3 | 2·5 |
| Sainfoin early flower | 22·5 | 4·4 | 0·6 | 4·7 | 11·4 | 1·4 | 3·7 | 3·2 | 0·4 | 2·1 | 8·9 | 89 | 13·1 | 2·8 |
| Trefoil | 20·0 | 3·5 | 0·8 | 5·7 | 8·4 | 1·6 | 2·7 | 2·4 | 0·4 | 2·8 | 5·9 | 83 | 9·1 | 2·0 |
| Vetches in flower | 17·5 | 3·2 | 0·5 | 5·1 | 7·2 | 1·5 | 2·4 | 2·2 | 0·3 | 2·3 | 4·9 | 83 | 7·5 | 1·8 |
| Vetches full flower with oats | 29·0 | 3·0 | 0·9 | 8·1 | 14·7 | 2·3 | … | … | … | … | … | … | … | … |
| *Silages* | | | | | | | | | | | | | | |
| Grass, first quality | 20·0 | 3·6 | 1·0 | 4·1 | 9·3 | 2·0 | 2·0 | 2·6 | 0·6 | 2·9 | 7·0 | … | 12·2 | … |
| Grass, second quality | 22·5 | 3·2 | 0·8 | 6·1 | 10·4 | 2·0 | 1·8 | 2·2 | 0·5 | 4·0 | 6·8 | … | 11·6 | … |
| Grass, hay maturity | 25·0 | 2·6 | 1·0 | 8·4 | 10·5 | 2·5 | 1·8 | 1·8 | 0·5 | 4·9 | 6·1 | … | 10·2 | … |
| Lucerne | 25·0 | 4·2 | 2·1 | 7·4 | 8·8 | 2·5 | 3·1 | 2·8 | 1·0 | 3·1 | 6·1 | … | 11·1 | … |
| Maize | 20·0 | 1·7 | 0·9 | 6·2 | 9·7 | 1·5 | 1·3 | 0·9 | 0·4 | 3·5 | 6·7 | … | 9·3 | … |
| Marrowstem kale | 20·0 | 2·5 | 0·6 | 4·7 | 9·1 | 3·1 | 1·9 | 1·9 | … | 3·5 | 7·7 | … | 11·6 | … |
| Pea haulms and pods (canning industry) | 25·0 | 3·7 | 1·5 | 6·4 | 9·1 | 4·3 | 1·8 | 2·1 | 1·4 | 3·6 | 6·3 | … | 12·3 | … |
| Pea pods | 27·5 | 3·5 | 1·0 | 8·4 | 12·8 | 1·8 | 1·6 | 2·3 | 0·9 | 5·5 | 9·8 | … | 15·9 | … |
| Sugar beet tops | 20·0 | 2·1 | 0·6 | 3·0 | 7·9 | 6·4 | 1·0 | 1·3 | 0·3 | 2·2 | 6·3 | … | 8·3 | … |
| Vetches and oats | 25·0 | 3·1 | 1·1 | 7·3 | 11·5 | 2·0 | 2·1 | 2·0 | 0·8 | 4·2 | 8·0 | … | 11·7 | … |

COMPOSITION AND NUTRITIVE VALUE OF SOME COMMON FEEDING STUFFS—*continued*

| Section A | Composition per cent. as shown by Chemical Analysis | | | | | | | Digestible Nutrients per cent. | | | | | Calculated from Digestible Nutrients | |
|---|---|---|---|---|---|---|---|---|---|---|---|---|---|---|
| | Dry Matter (1) | Crude Protein (2) | Oil (Ether Extract) (3) | Crude Fibre (4) | Carbohydrate (Nitrogen-free Extractives) (5) | Ash (6) | True Protein (7) | Digestible Crude Protein (8) | Digestible Oil (Digestible Ether Extract) (9) | Digestible Fibre (10) | Dig. Carbohydrate (Dig. Nitrogen-free Extractives) (11) | V (12) | Starch Equivalent (13) | Protein Equivalent (14) |
| *Hays* | | | | | | | | | | | | | | |
| Clover, red, poor | 85·0 | 11·1 | 2·1 | 28·9 | 37·8 | 5·1 | 9·4 | 5·7 | 1·0 | 11·6 | 24·6 | … | 30·1 | 4·8 |
| Clover, red, good | 85·0 | 13·7 | 3·0 | 24·4 | 37·8 | 6·1 | 10·7 | 8·7 | 1·7 | 11·5 | 26·5 | … | 38·9 | 7·1 |
| Clover, red, very good | 85·0 | 15·6 | 3·3 | 22·6 | 36·4 | 7·1 | 11·8 | 10·9 | 2·1 | 11·2 | 27·3 | … | 43·3 | 9·0 |
| Lucerne, before flowering | 85·0 | 16·4 | 2·4 | 27·3 | 31·5 | 7·4 | 12·4 | 12·2 | 1·1 | 11·4 | 21·4 | … | 32·4 | 10·2 |
| Lucerne, in full flower | 85·0 | 14·5 | 2·6 | 30·0 | 29·7 | 8·2 | 10·9 | 9·9 | 1·2 | 13·4 | 18·4 | … | 27·5 | 8·1 |
| Lucerne, in half flower, very good quality | 85·0 | 19·1 | 1·1 | 25·7 | 31·0 | 8·1 | 15·0 | 14·1 | … | 12·3 | 20·6 | … | 37·4 | 12·0 |
| Meadow hay, excellent | 85·0 | 13·7 | 3·0 | 19·5 | 41·0 | 7·8 | 10·9 | 9·3 | 1·5 | 12·9 | 30·4 | … | 49 | 7·9 |
| Meadow hay, very good | 85·0 | 10·5 | 3·4 | 22·0 | 41·5 | 7·6 | 9·0 | 6·3 | 1·7 | 13·2 | 27·3 | … | 42 | 5·5 |
| Meadow hay, good | 85·0 | 8·5 | 2·5 | 25·5 | 41·7 | 6·8 | 7·1 | 4·8 | 1·3 | 14·0 | 25·0 | … | 36 | 4·1 |
| Meadow hay, medium | 85·0 | 8·2 | 2·0 | 28·1 | 40·1 | 6·6 | 7·2 | 4·1 | 1·0 | 15·5 | 22·9 | … | 32 | 3·6 |
| Meadow hay, poor | 85·0 | 7·6 | 1·6 | 30·4 | 38·9 | 6·5 | 6·7 | 3·4 | 0·7 | 15·2 | 21·4 | … | 27 | 2·9 |
| Meadow hay, very poor | 85·0 | 6·4 | 1·5 | 33·0 | 38·3 | 5·8 | 5·5 | 2·9 | 0·6 | 15·5 | 19·2 | … | 22 | 2·4 |
| Oats, milk stage | 85·0 | 8·0 | 2·6 | 27·5 | 40·2 | 6·7 | … | 4·4 | 1·6 | 14·3 | 22·6 | … | 33 | 4·4 |
| Sainfoin, in flower | 85·0 | 13·4 | 2·6 | 28·5 | 33·1 | 7·4 | 11·3 | 9·8 | 1·6 | 12·0 | 25·8 | … | 38 | 8·7 |
| Trefoil | 85·0 | 15·6 | 3·4 | 24·8 | 33·6 | 7·6 | 12·3 | 11·9 | 1·6 | 10·9 | 23·5 | … | 37 | 10·2 |
| Seeds hay, ryegrass and clover | 85·0 | 11·9 | 2·8 | 27·2 | 36·9 | 6·2 | 9·3 | 6·1 | 1·2 | 13·0 | 21·7 | … | 30 | 4·8 |
| Seeds hay, good quality | 85·0 | 13·0 | 2·3 | 23·1 | 37·8 | 8·8 | 11·5 | 7·8 | 1·3 | 13·0 | 25·5 | … | 40 | 7·0 |
| Vetches and Oats, vetches in flower | 85·0 | 11·7 | 3·3 | 24·5 | 36·8 | 8·7 | 9·4 | 6·6 | 1·7 | 12·4 | 23·6 | … | 34 | 5·4 |
| *Straws* | | | | | | | | | | | | | | |
| Barley, spring | 86·0 | 3·3 | 1·8 | 33·9 | 42·4 | 4·6 | 3·1 | 0·8 | 0·6 | 18·3 | 22·5 | … | 23 | 0·7 |
| Beans, including pods | 86·0 | 4·5 | 0·8 | 43·1 | 33·0 | 4·6 | 3·6 | 2·2 | 0·5 | 18·7 | 22·0 | … | 19 | 1·7 |
| Clover, red | 84·0 | 9·1 | 1·8 | 44·6 | 22·8 | 5·7 | 8·2 | 4·0 | 0·6 | 16·4 | 11·1 | … | 7 | 3·5 |
| Oats, spring | 88·0 | 2·9 | 1·9 | 33·9 | 42·4 | 4·9 | 2·7 | 1·0 | 0·6 | 18·3 | 19·4 | … | 20 | 0·9 |
| Oats, winter | 86·0 | 1·9 | 1·5 | 34·6 | 43·1 | 4·9 | 1·7 | 0·6 | 0·5 | 19·7 | 19·8 | … | 21 | 0·5 |
| Rye, winter | 86·0 | 3·1 | 1·4 | 40·0 | 37·6 | 3·9 | 2·9 | 0·6 | 0·7 | 20·4 | 15·3 | … | 14 | 0·5 |

| | | | | | | | | | | | | | | |
|---|---|---|---|---|---|---|---|---|---|---|---|---|---|---|
| Wheat, spring | 86·0 | 2·9 | 1·3 | 35·9 | 39·8 | 6·1 | … | 0·1 | 0·4 | 18·0 | 14·7 | … | 13 | 0·1 |
| Wheat, winter | 86·0 | 2·1 | 1·3 | 36·6 | 40·7 | 5·3 | … | 0·1 | 0·4 | 18·3 | 15·0 | … | 13 | 0·1 |
| *Cereals and Legume Grains* | | | | | | | | | | | | | | |
| Barley | 85·0 | 9·0 | 1·5 | 4·5 | 67·4 | 2·6 | 8·5 | 6·8 | 1·2 | 2·5 | 61·7 | 98 | 71·0 | 6·5 |
| Maize | 87·0 | 9·9 | 4·4 | 2·2 | 69·2 | 1·3 | 9·4 | 7·9 | 2·7 | 0·8 | 63·7 | 100 | 77·6 | 7·6 |
| Oats | 87·0 | 10·4 | 4·8 | 10·3 | 58·4 | 3·1 | 9·5 | 8·0 | 4·5 | 2·6 | 44·9 | 95 | 59·6 | 7·6 |
| Rye | 87·0 | 11·6 | 1·7 | 1·9 | 69·8 | 2·0 | 10·7 | 9·6 | 1·1 | 1·0 | 64·2 | 95 | 72·0 | 9·1 |
| Wheat | 87·0 | 12·2 | 1·9 | 1·9 | 69·3 | 1·7 | 11·0 | 10·3 | 1·2 | 0·9 | 63·8 | 95 | 72·0 | 9·6 |
| Beans | 86·0 | 25·5 | 1·5 | 7·1 | 48·7 | 3·2 | 24·7 | 20·2 | 1·2 | 4·1 | 44·3 | 96 | 66·0 | 19·8 |
| Peas | 86·0 | 22·5 | 1·6 | 5·4 | 53·7 | 2·8 | 20·0 | 19·4 | 1·0 | 2·5 | 49·9 | 98 | 69·0 | 18·1 |
| Vetches | 87·0 | 26·1 | 1·7 | 6·0 | 50·0 | 3·2 | 23·2 | 23·0 | 1·5 | 3·9 | 46·0 | 97 | 69·8 | 21·5 |
| *Oil Cakes and Meals* | | | | | | | | | | | | | | |
| Coconut cake | 90·0 | 21·2 | 7·3 | 11·4 | 44·2 | 5·9 | 19·7 | 16·6 | 7·1 | 7·2 | 36·6 | 100 | 75·1 | 15·8 |
| Coconut cake meal | 89·0 | 19·6 | 6·7 | 13·6 | 42·7 | 6·4 | 19·2 | 15·4 | 6·5 | 8·6 | 35·5 | 100 | 73·9 | 15·2 |
| Cotton cake, Bombay | 88·0 | 20·3 | 4·8 | 21·8 | 35·3 | 5·8 | 19·5 | 15·6 | 4·5 | 4·4 | 19·0 | 84 | 40·1 | 15·2 |
| Cotton cake, Brazilian | 89·0 | 27·1 | 5·4 | 24·9 | 27·1 | 4·5 | 22·2 | 20·8 | 5·0 | 5·2 | 14·7 | 84 | 42·0 | 20·2 |
| Cotton cake, Egyptian | 88·0 | 23·2 | 5·0 | 21·3 | 32·7 | 5·8 | 22·2 | 17·8 | 4·6 | 4·5 | 17·7 | 84 | 41·6 | 17·3 |
| Cotton cake, decorticated | 90·0 | 41·1 | 8·0 | 7·8 | 26·4 | 6·7 | 39·6 | 35·3 | 7·5 | 2·2 | 17·7 | 97 | 68·3 | 34·5 |
| Cotton cake, semi-decorticated | 90·0 | 38·3 | 6·2 | 12·9 | 26·7 | 5·9 | 35·3 | 32·9 | 5·8 | 3·5 | 17·6 | 95 | 59·9 | 31·4 |
| Ground nut cake, decorticated | 90·0 | 45·4 | 6·0 | 6·5 | 26·4 | 5·7 | 42·5 | 40·5 | 5·4 | 0·5 | 22·4 | 98 | 69·7 | 39·0 |
| Ground nut cake, undecorticated | 90·0 | 30·0 | 9·1 | 23·0 | 21·9 | 5·7 | 29·4 | 27·8 | 8·2 | 2·6 | 18·5 | 86 | 57·0 | 27·3 |
| Ground nut meal, decorticated extracted | 90·0 | 49·7 | 0·7 | 7·9 | 26·0 | 5·7 | 45·7 | 44·2 | 0·6 | 0·6 | 22·1 | 98 | 60·6 | 42·2 |
| Linseed cake, English made | 89·0 | 29·6 | 9·5 | 9·1 | 35·6 | 5·2 | 28·2 | 25·4 | 8·7 | 4·5 | 28·6 | 97 | 74·2 | 24·7 |
| Linseed cake, foreign | 90·0 | 31·9 | 6·9 | 9·4 | 36·2 | 5·6 | 27·7 | 27·4 | 6·4 | 4·7 | 29·0 | 97 | 68·7 | 25·3 |
| Linseed meal, extracted | 88·0 | 35·6 | 3·1 | 9·0 | 33·8 | 6·5 | 34·8 | 30·7 | 2·8 | 4·5 | 27·1 | 96 | 63·6 | 30·3 |

COMPOSITION AND NUTRITIVE VALUE OF SOME COMMON FEEDING STUFFS—continued

| Section A | Composition per cent. as shown by Chemical Analysis | | | | | | | Digestible Nutrients per cent. | | | | Calculated from Digestible Nutrients | | |
|---|---|---|---|---|---|---|---|---|---|---|---|---|---|---|
| | Dry Matter (1) | Crude Protein (2) | Oil (Ether Extract) (3) | Crude Fibre (4) | Carbohydrate (Nitrogen-free Extractives) (5) | Ash (6) | True Protein (7) | Digestible Crude Protein (8) | Digestible Oil (Digestible Ether Extract) (9) | Digestible Fibre (10) | Dig. Carbohydrate (Dig. Nitrogen-free Extractives) (11) | V (12) | Starch Equivalent (13) | Protein Equivalent (14) |
| Maize germ meal . . | 89·0 | 13·0 | 12·5 | 4·1 | 55·8 | 3·6 | 12·8 | 10·4 | 11·5 | 2·5 | 46·9 | 97 | 84·2 | 10·3 |
| Maize, flaked . . | 89·0 | 9·8 | 4·3 | 1·5 | 72·5 | 0·9 | 9·4 | 9·4 | 2·0 | 0·5 | 70·4 | 100 | 84·0 | 9·2 |
| Palm kernel cake . | 89·0 | 19·2 | 6·0 | 13·4 | 46·5 | 3·9 | 18·1 | 17·5 | 5·3 | 5·1 | 39·4 | 100 | 73·2 | 16·9 |
| Palm kernel meal, extracted | 90·0 | 20·4 | 0·9 | 15·0 | 49·7 | 4·0 | 19·6 | 18·4 | 0·8 | 7·5 | 43·7 | 100 | 69·6 | 18·0 |
| Soya bean cake . | 89·0 | 44·9 | 5·8 | 5·3 | 27·4 | 5·6 | 40·9 | 40·4 | 5·3 | 3·8 | 21·1 | 97 | 71·7 | 38·4 |
| Soya bean meal, extracted | 89·0 | 44·8 | 1·5 | 5·1 | 32·1 | 5·5 | 40·8 | 40·4 | 1·4 | 3·6 | 24·8 | 97 | 64·2 | 38·4 |
| *Feeding stuffs of Animal Origin* | | | | | | | | | | | | | | |
| Blood meal . . | 86·0 | 81·0 | 0·8 | ... | 1·5 | 2·7 | 71·9 | 72·7 | 0·8 | ... | ... | 100 | 61·3 | 68·1 |
| Fish meal, white . | 87·0 | 61·0 | 3·5 | ... | 1·5 | 21·0 | 57·0 | 55·0 | 3·3 | ... | 1·2 | 100 | 58·9 | 53·0 |
| Meat and bone meal . | 90·3 | 50·3 | 15·0 | ... | 1·0 | 24·0 | 40·3 | 39·2 | 14·3 | ... | ... | 100 | 67·8 | 34·2 |
| Feeding meat meal, high fat | 90·5 | 60·0 | 11·0 | ... | 0·5 | 19·0 | 46·0 | 56·4 | 9·8 | ... | 0·5 | 100 | 72·3 | 49·4 |
| Feeding meat meal, low fat | 93·0 | 66·7 | 2·9 | ... | 4·0 | 19·4 | 51·5 | 58·6 | 2·4 | ... | 3·9 | 100 | 59·6 | 51·0 |
| Milk, cows, whole . | 12·8 | 3·4 | 3·9 | ... | 4·8 | 0·7 | 3·4 | 3·2 | 3·9 | ... | 4·8 | 100 | 17·1 | 3·2 |
| Milk, separated . | 9·4 | 3·5 | 0·1 | ... | 5·0 | 0·8 | 3·5 | 3·3 | 0·1 | ... | 5·0 | 100 | 8·3 | 3·3 |
| Milk, skimmed, shallow set | 10·0 | 3·5 | 0·7 | ... | 5·0 | 0·8 | 3·5 | 3·3 | 0·7 | ... | 5·0 | 100 | 9·8 | 3·3 |
| Milk, whey . | 6·6 | 0·7 | 0·2 | ... | 2·7 | 0·7 | 0·7 | 0·6 | 0·2 | ... | 5·0 | 100 | 6·1 | 0·6 |
| Colostrum, first drawn . | 25·5 | 17·6 | 4·2 | ... | 2·7 | 1·0 | ... | ... | ... | ... | ... | ... | ... | ... |
| Dried whole milk . | 95·8 | 25·5 | 26·5 | ... | 37·4 | 6·4 | ... | ... | ... | ... | ... | ... | ... | ... |
| Dried separated milk . | 89·7 | 32·8 | 1·5 | ... | 47·9 | 7·5 | ... | ... | ... | ... | ... | ... | ... | ... |

*By-products*

| | | | | | | | | | | | | | | |
|---|---|---|---|---|---|---|---|---|---|---|---|---|---|---|
| Barley, brewers' grains, fresh | 32.4 | 7.5 | 2.8 | 6.1 | 14.6 | 1.4 | 7.2 | 5.5 | 2.4 | 2.4 | 9.1 | 86 | 18.4 | 5.3 |
| Barley, brewers' grains, dried | 89.7 | 18.3 | 6.4 | 15.2 | 45.9 | 3.9 | 17.4 | 13.0 | 5.6 | 7.3 | 27.6 | 84 | 48.3 | 12.5 |
| Barley, distillers' grains, fresh | 26.2 | 8.4 | 3.0 | 3.6 | 10.4 | 0.8 | 8.0 | 6.2 | 2.6 | 1.7 | 6.4 | 86 | 16.2 | 6.0 |
| Barley, distillers' grains, dried | 92.0 | 27.7 | 11.6 | 10.1 | 40.8 | 1.8 | 26.8 | 19.6 | 10.2 | 4.8 | 25.3 | 84 | 57.2 | 19.1 |
| Barley, malt culms | 90.0 | 24.4 | 2.0 | 14.0 | 42.4 | 7.2 | 16.5 | 19.9 | 1.5 | 12.7 | 30.9 | 75 | 43.4 | 15.9 |
| Maize bran | 88.2 | 8.4 | 4.2 | 11.7 | 62.0 | 1.9 | 7.7 | 5.5 | 3.6 | 3.9 | 53.4 | 95 | 67.0 | 5.1 |
| Maize, gluten feed | 89.6 | 23.5 | 3.4 | 3.5 | 56.7 | 2.5 | 21.9 | 20.0 | 2.7 | 2.5 | 49.3 | 100 | 75.6 | 19.2 |
| Maize, gluten meal | 90.0 | 35.5 | 4.7 | 2.1 | 47.5 | 1.1 | 35.2 | 30.6 | 4.4 | ... | 42.6 | 100 | 77.6 | 16.2 |
| Oat bran (from preparation of oatmeal) | 90.5 | 8.0 | 3.6 | 21.9 | 51.0 | 6.0 | 7.6 | 4.0 | 2.0 | 8.1 | 35.6 | 88 | 45.5 | 3.8 |
| Oatmeal | 91.8 | 16.0 | 6.7 | 1.6 | 65.5 | 2.0 | 14.5 | 12.0 | 5.4 | 0.8 | 48.0 | 99 | 71.1 | 11.2 |
| Sugar beet pulp, wet | 15.0 | 1.6 | 0.1 | 3.1 | 9.6 | 0.6 | 1.6 | 1.0 | ... | 2.8 | 8.7 | 94 | 11.7 | 1.0 |
| Sugar beet pulp, dried and molassed | 90.0 | 10.8 | 0.4 | 15.1 | 58.2 | 5.5 | 7.5 | 6.3 | ... | 13.5 | 53.0 | 81 | 58.3 | 4.6 |
| Wheat feeds— | | | | | | | | | | | | | | |
| Finest grade, fine middlings or sharps | 86.7 | 17.0 | 4.2 | 2.3 | 60.8 | 2.4 | 16.0 | 12.6 | 3.7 | ... | 51.1 | 97 | 67.0 | 12.1 |
| Second grade, coarse middlings | 86.0 | 15.9 | 4.5 | 6.0 | 55.9 | 3.7 | 14.4 | 11.6 | 3.9 | 1.4 | 45.9 | 86 | 56.5 | 10.8 |
| Broad bran | 87.0 | 14.7 | 4.0 | 10.3 | 52.1 | 5.9 | 12.7 | 11.0 | 2.8 | 2.2 | 36.9 | 77 | 42.6 | 10.0 |

## COMPOSITION AND NUTRITIVE VALUE OF SOME COMMON FEEDING STUFFS

| Section B (Pigs) | Composition per cent. as shown by Chemical Analysis | | | | | | Digestible Nutrients per cent. | | | | Calculated from Dig. Nutrients |
|---|---|---|---|---|---|---|---|---|---|---|---|
| | Dry Matter (1) | Crude Protein (2) | Oil (Ether Extract) (3) | Crude Fibre (4) | Carbohydrate (Nitrogen-free Extractives) (5) | Ash (6) | Crude Protein (7) | Digestible Oil (Ether Extractives) (8) | Digestible Fibre (9) | Dig. Carbohydrate (Nitrogen-free Extractives) (10) | Per 100 lb. Total Digestible Nutrients (11) |
| *Cereals* | | | | | | | | | | | |
| Barley meal | 86·0 | 10·5 | 1·5 | 4·8 | 66·6 | 2·6 | 8·6 | 1·2 | 0·5 | 59·1 | 70·9 |
| Maize meal, fed dry | 87·0 | 9·6 | 4·4 | 2·0 | 69·4 | 1·6 | 7·5 | 2·8 | 0·5 | 63·5 | 77·8 |
| Maize, flaked | 89·0 | 10·4 | 4·4 | 1·5 | 71·6 | 1·1 | 9·9 | 2·7 | 0·5 | 69·5 | 86·0 |
| Oats, farm ground | 87·0 | 11·2 | 4·7 | 10·0 | 58·2 | 2·9 | 9·6 | 4·1 | ... | 43·2 | 62·0 |
| Oats, crushed | 87·0 | 9·7 | 4·8 | 11·1 | 58·2 | 3·2 | 6·7 | 3·1 | ... | 38·3 | 52·0 |
| *Grass* | | | | | | | | | | | |
| Pasture, closely grazed | 20·0 | 5·2 | 0·8 | 3·4 | 8·9 | 1·7 | 3·5 | ... | 1·9 | 6·4 | 11·8 |
| Pasture, rotational grazed | 20·0 | 3·4 | 0·6 | 3·9 | 10·5 | 1·6 | 1·9 | ... | 2·1 | 7·3 | 11·3 |
| *Oil cakes and meals* | | | | | | | | | | | |
| Ground nut meal, decorticated, extracted | 88·0 | 53·8 | 0·6 | 5·2 | 22·5 | 5·9 | 50·0 | 0·3 | 3·6 | 19·1 | 73·4 |
| Palm kernel meal, extracted | 90·0 | 19·0 | 2·0 | 16·0 | 49·0 | 4·0 | 11·4 | 0·5 | 5·8 | 37·6 | 55·9 |
| Soya bean meal, extracted | 88·7 | 44·7 | 1·5 | 5·1 | 31·9 | 5·5 | 38·4 | 1·3 | 3·0 | 28·3 | 72·6 |
| *By-products* | | | | | | | | | | | |
| Lucerne meal | 91·4 | 20·0 | 4·7 | 22·7 | 34·8 | 9·2 | 11·7 | 1·4 | 7·4 | 24·5 | 46·8 |
| Potato meal | 88·0 | 8·6 | 0·5 | 2·0 | 73·4 | 3·5 | 3·4 | 0·2 | 1·3 | 70·7 | 75·7 |
| Swill— | | | | | | | | | | | |
| urban, winter | 25·0 | 3·7 | 3·0 | 1·4 | 14·5 | 2·4 | 2·3 | 2·3 | 0·8 | 13·9 | 22·2 |
| urban, summer | 25·0 | 4·1 | 3·1 | 2·4 | 12·4 | 3·0 | 2·7 | 2·5 | 0·9 | 10·9 | 20·1 |
| Whale meat meal, high protein, low ash | 94·4 | 87·7 | 3·4 | ... | 1·2 | 2·1 | 76·9 | 3·3 | ... | 1·1 | 85·4 |
| *Fine millers' offals } 85 per cent. | 87·0 | 14·1 | 4·3 | 10·3 | 53·4 | 4·9 | 9·0 | 2·7 | 1·6 | 34·7 | 51·4 |
| Coarse millers' offals } extractions | 87·0 | 12·3 | 3·9 | 13·4 | 51·4 | 6·0 | 6·7 | 1·8 | 1·7 | 28·7 | 41·2 |

* Wheat diluted with 10 per cent. barley before milling.

TABLE 4

# MINERAL COMPOSITION OF SOME COMMON FEEDING STUFFS

| Section C | Total Ash per cent. | Lime (CaO) per cent. | Phosphoric Acid ($P_2O_5$) per cent. | Potash ($K_2O$) per cent. | Chlorine (Cl) per cent. |
|---|---|---|---|---|---|
| *Roots and Green Forage Crops* | | | | | |
| Mangels  .   . | 0·9 | 0·02 | 0·09 | 0·45 | 0·16 |
| Potatoes  .   . | 1·0 | 0·03 | 0·18 | 0·60 | 0·04 |
| Swedes  .   . | 0·7 | 0·08 | 0·08 | 0·30 | 0·04 |
| Cabbage  .   . | 1·2 | 0·20 | 0·15 | 0·40 | 0·02 |
| Kale, thousandhead | 1·7 | 0·39 | 0·13 | 0·52 | 0·16 |
| Kale, marrowstem . | 1·9 | 0·43 | 0·12 | 0·55 | 0·21 |
| Sugar beet tops  . | 3·4 | 0·34 | 0·11 | 0·58 | 0·36 |
| *Pasture and Hays* | | | | | |
| Pasture grass (rotational grazed) | 2·0 | 0·28 | 0·16 | 0·60 | 0·19 |
| Lucerne, early flower | 2·4 | 0·96 | 0·12 | 0·43 | 0·08 |
| Lucerne meal  . | 9·2 | 2·73 | 0·78 | 1·82 | 0·55 |
| Pea haulm and pod silage | 4·1 | 0·54 | 0·16 | 0·40 | 0·11 |
| Meadow hay, good | 6·8 | 1·00 | 0·50 | 1·60 | 0·37 |
| Red clover hay  . | 7·0 | 1·60 | 0·39 | 2·20 | 0·24 |
| Seeds hay  .   . | 6·3 | 2·00 | 0·60 | 1·80 | 0·30 |
| Lucerne hay, half flower | 8·0 | 2·74 | 0·51 | 1·52 | 0·34 |
| *Straws* | | | | | |
| Oats  .   .   . | 4·9 | 0·36 | 0·18 | 1·50 | 0·30 |
| Wheat .   .   . | 5·3 | 0·29 | 0·13 | 0·80 | 0·20 |
| *Cereals, Leguminous Seeds and By-products* | | | | | |
| Barley  .   . | 2·6 | 0·07 | 0·84 | 0·57 | 0·12 |
| Maize  .   .   . | 1·3 | 0·02 | 0·82 | 0·40 | 0·07 |
| Oats  .   .   . | 3·1 | 0·14 | 0·81 | 0·55 | 0·07 |
| Wheat .   .   . | 1·7 | 0·05 | 0·86 | 0·60 | 0·08 |
| Beans  .   .   . | 3·2 | 0·18 | 0·88 | 1·28 | 0·03 |
| Peas  .   .   . | 2·8 | 0·10 | 0·90 | 1·00 | 0·04 |
| Bran  .   .   . | 5·8 | 0·20 | 2·80 | 1·50 | 0·09 |
| Middlings  .   . | 3·7 | 0·13 | 1·50 | 1·40 | 0·07 |
| Brewers' grains, dried | 3·9 | 0·40 | 1·60 | 0·20 | 0·06 |
| Maize meal, de-germed | 0·9 | 0·02 | 0·39 | 0·33 | 0·03 |
| Maize germ meal  . | 3·6 | 0·10 | 0·90 | 1·30 | 0·03 |
| Maize gluten feed | 2·5 | 0·10 | 0·70 | 0·20 | ... |
| *Oil Cakes and Meals* | | | | | |
| Coconut cake.  . | 5·6 | 0·16 | 1·27 | 2·41 | 0·65 |
| Cotton cake, un-decorticated | 5·8 | 0·30 | 2·50 | 1·60 | 0·05 |
| Ground nut cake, undecorticated | 5·7 | 0·20 | 1·00 | 1·00 | ... |
| Ground nut cake, decorticated | 5·8 | 0·20 | 1·30 | 1·50 | 0·03 |
| Linseed cake  . | 5·2 | 0·51 | 1·70 | 1·30 | 0·09 |
| Palm kernel cake  . | 3·8 | 0·30 | 1·10 | 0·50 | 0·16 |
| Soya bean cake  . | 5·4 | 0·30 | 2·00 | 1·80 | 0·03 |

TABLE 4 (*cont.*)

## MINERAL COMPOSITION OF SOME COMMON FEEDING STUFFS

| Section C | Total Ash per cent. | Lime (CaO) per cent. | Phosphoric Acid ($P_2O_5$) per cent. | Potash ($K_2O$) per cent. | Chlorine (Cl) per cent. |
|---|---|---|---|---|---|
| *Animal Products* | | | | | |
| Fish meal, white . | 22·0 | 10·0 | 9·00 | 1·20 | 1·00 |
| Meat meal . . | 19·0 | 8·00 | 7·20 | 0·70 | 1·20 |
| Meat and bone meal | 24·0 | 10·50 | 9·30 | 0·80 | 1·40 |
| Milk, whole . | 0·8 | 0·17 | 0·20 | 0·20 | 0·10 |
| Milk, separated . | 0·8 | 0·15 | 0·20 | 0·20 | 0·07 |
| *Miscellaneous* | | | | | |
| Sugar beet pulp, molassed | 5·5 | 1·20 | 0·17 | 1·34 | 0·48 |
| Swill, urban . . | 2·4 | 0·23 | 0·18 | ... | 0·19 |

TABLE 5

## APPROXIMATE LIVE WEIGHTS (LB.) OF COMMERCIAL ANIMALS

*Live weights show great variations according to breed and feeding and the following figures should be taken only as a general guide*

CATTLE

(1) *Young Stock*

| Age in Months | Beef Steer (full growth with fattening) | Beef Steer (full growth without fattening) | Smaller Dairy Type (Heifer) |
|---|---|---|---|
| 0 | 80 | 80 | 70 |
| 3 | 200 | 170 | 150 |
| 6 | 400 | 350 | 220 |
| 9 | 560 | 480 | 290 |
| 12 | 700 | 600 | 360 |
| 15 | 830 | 720 | 430 |
| 18 | 950 | 840 | 510 |
| 21 | 1080 | 950 | 580 |
| 24 | 1200 | 1060 | 660 |
| 27 | ... | 1170 | 750 |
| 30 | ... | ... | 850 |

(2) *Mature Animals in breeding condition*

| Cows | | | Bulls | | |
|---|---|---|---|---|---|
| Smaller Dairy Breeds | Larger Dairy Breeds | Average Beef Breeds | Smaller Dairy Breeds | Larger Dairy Breeds | Average Beef Breeds |
| 1000 | 1250 | 1350 | 1250 | 1600 | 1800 |

## TABLE 5 (cont.)

### SHEEP

#### (1) Young Stock

| Age in Months | Large Lowland (for sale as Lambs) | Large Lowland (for sale as Tegs) | Medium Breeds and Cross-breds (for sale as Tegs) | Small Upland Breeds |
|---|---|---|---|---|
| 0 | 10 | 10 | 8 | 5 |
| 1 | 30 | 25 | 18 | 12 |
| 2 | 50 | 41 | 32 | 20 |
| 3 | 70 | 58 | 45 | 28 |
| 4 | 90 | 75 | 57 | 38 |
| 5 | ... | 90 | 67 | 46 |
| 6 | ... | 105 | 76 | 53 |
| 7 | ... | 120 | 86 | 62 |
| 8 | ... | ... | 95 | 70 |
| 9 | ... | ... | 104 | 80 |
| 12 | ... | ... | ... | 100 |

#### (2) Mature Sheep, in breeding condition

| | EWES | | | RAMS | |
|---|---|---|---|---|---|
| Small Upland Breeds | Medium Breeds and Crosses | Large Lowland Breeds | Small Upland Breeds | Medium Breeds and Crosses | Large Lowland Breeds |
| 110 | 150 | 200 | 150 | 220 | 280 |

### PIGS

#### (1) Young Stock

| Age in Months | Pork Type | Bacon Type | Young Breeding Stock |
|---|---|---|---|
| 0 | 3 | 3 | 3 |
| 1 | 14 | 14 | 14 |
| 2 | 32 | 32 | 32 |
| 3 | 55 | 50 | 42 |
| 4 | 85 | 80 | 67 |
| 5 | 120 | 115 | 97 |
| 6 | ... | 155 | 130 |
| 7 | ... | 200 | 165 |
| 8 | ... | 245 | 200 |
| 9 | ... | ... | 230 |
| 12 | ... | ... | 280 |

#### (2) Mature Pigs, in breeding condition

| SOWS | | BOARS | |
|---|---|---|---|
| Small Breeds | Large Breeds | Small Breeds | Large Breeds |
| 350 | 450 | 450 | 600 |

TABLE 5 (*cont.*)

HORSES

| Age in Months | Draft Colt |
|:---:|:---:|
| 0 | 200 |
| 3 | 500 |
| 6 | 700 |
| 12 | 900 |
| 18 | 1150 |
| 24 | 1300 |
| 30 | 1400 |

*Mature Horses, in breeding condition*

| Farm Horses | | | Draft Stallions |
|:---:|:---:|:---:|:---:|
| Small | Medium | Large | |
| 1200 | 1400 | 1700 | 1900 |

## DENTITION OF LIVE STOCK

The following table shows the number of permanent teeth of farm live stock.

TABLE 6

TYPES OF TEETH

| | Incisors | Canines | Molars |
|:---|:---:|:---:|:---:|
| **Horses** | | | |
| Upper jaws | 6 | 2 | 12, 13 or 14 |
| Lower jaws | 6 | 2 | 12, 13 or 14 |
| **Cattle** | | | |
| Upper jaws | 0 | 0 | 12 |
| Lower jaws | 8 | 0 | 12 |
| **Sheep** | | | |
| Upper jaws | 0 | 0 | 12 |
| Lower jaws | 8 | 0 | 12 |
| **Pigs** | | | |
| Upper jaws | 6 | 2 | 14 |
| Lower jaws | 6 | 2 | 14 |

There is a fairly wide variation in the ages within each species when the different permanent teeth appear and are fully up, *e.g.* between breeds, between strains within a breed, and according to planes of nutrition and managemen conditions. Live stock bred from early maturing strains and raised on high planes of nutrition cut their permanent teeth at younger ages than those of late maturing strains, especially if reared on low planes of nutrition.

In spite of these variations, the appearance of the teeth are often sought as an aid in assessing the age of live stock, more particularly cattle, sheep and pigs. The following notes give some rough indication of the relationship between development of permanent teeth and age.

Horses are comparatively long lived and the wearing of the permanent incisors can give a useful guide as to age.

With cattle of the earlier maturing sorts reared on a high plane of nutrition, a guide is:—

| Appearance of teeth | Age |
| --- | --- |
| Central permanent incisors cut | more than 1 year 6 months |
| Central permanent incisors fully up | more than 1 year 9 months |
| Second permanent incisors fully up | more than 2 years 3 months |
| Third permanent incisors cut | more than 2 years 8 months |
| Fourth permanent incisors fully up and anterior molars showing signs of wear | more than 3 years |

In sheep, the corresponding details are:—

| Appearance of teeth | Age |
| --- | --- |
| Central permanent incisors cut | more than 10 months |
| Central permanent incisors fully up | more than 1 year |
| Second permanent incisors cut | more than 1 year 7 months |
| Third permanent incisors fully up | more than 2 years |
| Central permanent incisors fully up and showing marks of wear | more than 3 years |

With pigs well reared, a rough guide is:—

| Appearance of teeth | Age |
| --- | --- |
| Central permanent incisors cut | more than 6 months |
| Permanent tusks half-up | more than 9 months |
| Central permanent incisors well up and any of the first three molars showing | more than 1 year |
| Lateral temporary incisors shed and permanent incisors appearing in their place | more than 1 year 3 months |

# INDEX

2 D

PRINTED IN GREAT BRITAIN BY
OLIVER AND BOYD LTD
EDINBURGH